JOB HUNTER'S
SOURCEBOOK

ISSN 1053-1874

A GALE CAREER INFORMATION GUIDE

JOB HUNTER'S SOURCEBOOK

Where to find employment leads and other job search resources

TWELFTH EDITION
Volume 2

Sources of Job Hunting Information
by Occupations

Occupations L-Z
Entries 6742-13361

Joseph Palmisano, Project Editor

GALE
CENGAGE Learning

Detroit • New York • San Francisco • New Haven, Conn • Waterville, Maine • London

GALE
CENGAGE Learning·

Job Hunter's Sourcebook, 12th Edition

Product Management: Jerry Moore

Project Editor: Joseph Palmisano

Editorial Support Services: Scott Flaugher

Composition and Electronic Prepress: Gary Leach

Manufacturing: Rita Wimberley

Gale, Cengage Learning
27500 Drake Rd.
Farmington Hills, MI 48331-3535

ISBN-13: 978-1-4144-9026-7 (set)
ISBN-10: 1-4144-9026-7 (set)
ISBN-13: 978-1-4144-9027-4 (vol. 1)
ISBN-10: 1-4144-9027-5 (vol. 1)
ISBN-13: 978-1-4144-9028-1 (vol. 2)
ISBN-10: 1-4144-9028-3 (vol. 2)
ISBN-13: 978-1-4144-9029-8 (vol. 3)
ISBN-10: 1-4144-9029-1 (vol . 3)

ISSN 1053-1874

Printed in the United States of America
1 2 3 4 5   17 16 15 14 13

Contents

"The person who gets hired is not necessarily the one who can do that job best; but, the one who knows the most about how to get hired."

Richard Bolles
What Color Is Your Parachute?

Job hunting is often described as a campaign, a system, a strategic process. According to Joan Moore, principal of The Arbor Consulting Group, Inc. in Plymouth, Michigan, "Launching a thorough job search can be a full-time job in itself. It requires as much energy as you would put into any other major project—and it requires a creative mix of approaches to ensure its success."

Job Hunting Is Increasingly Complex

Today's competitive job market has become increasingly complex, requiring new and resourceful approaches to landing a position. The help-wanted ads are no longer the surest route to employment. In fact, most estimates indicate that only a small percentage of all jobs are found through the classified sections of local newspapers.

Although approaches vary among individual job seekers and the levels of jobs sought, a thorough job search today should involve the use of a wide variety of resources. Professional associations, library research, executive search firms, college placement offices, direct application to employers, professional journals, and networking with colleagues and friends are all approaches commonly in use. Job hotlines and resume referral services may be elements of the search as well. High-tech components might include the use of resume databases, and electronic bulletin boards that list job openings.

Job Hunters Are Changing

Just as the methods of job seeking have changed, so have the job hunters themselves. As Joyce Slayton Mitchell notes in College to Career, "Today, the average young person can look forward to six or seven different jobs, six or seven mini-careers, that will make up his or her lifetime of work." Lifelong commitment to one employer is no longer the norm; profes-

sionals seeking to change companies, workers re-entering the job market after a period of absence, and people exploring new career options are also represented in significant numbers in the job seeking pool. And in a time of significant corporate change, restructuring, divestiture, and downsizing, many job seekers are in the market unexpectedly. These include a growing number of white-collar workers who find themselves competing against other professionals in a shrinking market.

Help for Job Hunters

As the job market has become more competitive and complex, job seekers have increasingly looked for job search assistance. The rapid growth in the number of outplacement firms and employment agencies during the last 30 years reflects the perceived need for comprehensive help. Similarly, the library has become an increasingly important and valuable resource in the job hunt. In fact, some librarians report that their most frequently asked reference questions pertain to job seeking. In response to this need, many libraries have developed extensive collections of career and job-hunting publications, periodicals that list job openings, and directories of employers. Some libraries have developed centralized collections of career information, complemented by such offerings as resume preparation software, career planning databases, and interviewing skills videotapes.

Valuable Guide for Job Seekers

Job Hunter's Sourcebook (JHS) was designed to assist those planning job search strategies. Any job hunter—the student looking for an internship, the recent graduate, the executive hoping to relocate—will find *JHS* an important first step in the job search process because it identifies and organizes employment leads quickly and comprehensively. Best of all, *JHS* provides all the information a job hunter needs to turn a local public library into a customized employment agency, available free-of-charge. *Library Journal* and the New York Public Library concurred, and gave the first edition of this work their annual outstanding reference awards.

Job Hunter's Sourcebook (JHS) is a comprehensive guide to sources of information on employment leads and other job search resources. It streamlines the job-seeking process by identifying and organizing the wide array of publications, organizations, audio-visual and electronic resources, and other job hunting tools.

JHS completes much of the research needed to begin a job search, with in-depth coverage of information sources for more than 200 specific professional and vocational occupations. Listings of resources on more than 30 essential topics of interest to job hunters complement the profiles on specific occupations, providing the job seeker with leads to all the information needed to design a complete job search strategy.

Job Hunter's Sourcebook can be used to:

Find a job. *JHS* is designed for use by job seekers at all levels—from those seeking a first job, to executives on the move, to those in transition. Each individual may select from the wide range of resources presented to develop a customized job campaign.

Use career resources more effectively. As library research becomes an increasingly important component in the job hunting process, librarians are providing more information and support to job seekers. *JHS* helps users go directly to the most appropriate library material by providing comprehensive lists of job hunting resources on high-interest professional and vocational occupations.

Build a better career resources collection. Librarians, career counselors, outplacement firms, spouse relocation services, job referral agencies, and others who advise job seekers can use *JHS* to start or expand their collections of career and job hunting materials.

Comprehensive Coverage and Convenient Arrangement

The job search resources in *JHS* are conveniently arranged into three volumes, which are followed by a master index:

Volumes One and Two: Sources of Job-Hunting Information by Professions and Occupations—identifies information sources on employment opportunities for 249 specific types of jobs. A "List of Profiled Professions and Oc-

cupations" lists hundreds of alternate, popular, synonymous, and related job titles and links them to the jobs profiled in *JHS*, providing quick access to information sources on specific occupations or fields of interest by all their variant names—from accountant to aircraft mechanic and sports official to stockbroker. Each profile contains complete contact information and lists a variety of sources of job-opportunity information organized into eight easy-to-use categories:

1. Sources of Help-Wanted Ads
2. Placement and Job Referral Services
3. Employer Directories and Networking Lists
4. Handbooks and Manuals
5. Employment Agencies and Search Firms
6. Online Job Sources and Services
7. Tradeshows
8. Other Sources, including internships and resources such as job hotlines

Volume Three: Sources of Essential Job-Hunting Information—features such employment topics as:

- Interviewing Skills
- Employment Issues for Disabled Workers
- Electronic Job Search Information
- Working at Home
- Opportunities for Freelance Workers and Independent Contractors
- Opportunities for Temporary Workers

Each category includes:

- Reference Works
- Newspapers, Magazines, and Journals
- Audio/Visual Resources
- Online and Database Services
- Software
- Other Sources, such as special associations, job hunting kits, and organizers

The information sources listed under each topic are arranged by type of resource and include complete contact information.

Index to Information Sources—comprehensively lists all of the publications, organizations, electronic resources, and other sources of job hunting information contained in *JHS*.

Please consult the User's Guide for more information about the arrangement, content, and indexing of the information sources cited in *JHS*.

JHS Profiles High-Interest Professions and Occupations

JHS catalogs job hunting resources for more than 200 professional, technical, and trade occupations, carefully selected to provide a broad cross-section of occupations of interest to today's job seekers. The majority are profiled in the Department of Labor's *Occupational Outlook Handbook (OOH)*, a leading career resource containing detailed descriptions of professional and vocational occupations. Most of the professions cited in *OOH* are also included in *JHS*, as are representative vocational occupations selected from those listed in *OOH*. To round out this list, additional occupations were included on the basis of Bureau of Labor Statistics data projecting them as high-growth positions.

Coverage of Employment Alternatives and Trends

In addition to focusing on such "how-to" topics as resume writing and interviewing, the "Sources of Essential Job-Hunting Information" offers resources for non-traditional work options and diverse segments of the work force. Working part-time, at home, and in your own business are featured chapters, as are opportunities for minorities, older workers, women, disabled workers, and gay and lesbian job seekers. A chapter covering sources of electronic job search information is included, as well as a category titled, "Online Job Sources and Services." This category lists Internet websites related to specific job profiles.

New to this Edition

The twelfth edition is a complete revision of the previous *JHS*, incorporating thousands of updates to organization and publication data. This edition also features 5 new career profiles, including environmental scientists and specialists, instructional coordinators, and pharmacy technicians.

Method of Compilation

JHS contains citations compiled from direct contact with a wide range of associations and organizations, from dozens of publisher catalogs and other secondary sources, and from selected information from other Gale databases. While many resources cited in *JHS* contain career planning information, their usefulness in the job hunting process was the primary factor in their selection. Their annotations are tailored to support that function.

Comments and Suggestions Are Welcome

Libraries, associations, employment agencies, executive search firms, referral services, publishers, database producers, and other organizations involved in helping job seekers find opportunities or companies find candidates are encouraged to submit information about their activities and products for use in future editions of *JHS*. Comments and suggestions for improving this guide are also welcome. Please contact:

Project Editor
Job Hunter's Sourcebook
Gale, Cengage Learning
27500 Drake Rd.
Farmington Hills, MI 48331-3535
Phone: (248) 699-4253
Fax: (248) 699-8075
URL: gale.cengage.com

Job Hunter's Sourcebook (JHS) is divided into three volumes:

- Volumes One and Two: Sources of Job-Hunting Information by Professions and Occupations
- Volume Three: Sources of Essential Job-Hunting Information

Access to entries is facilitated by a "List of Profiled Professions and Occupations" and an "Index to Information Sources." Users should consult each section to benefit fully from the information in *JHS*.

Master List of Profiled Professions and Occupations

A "List of Profiled Professions and Occupations" alphabetically lists the job titles used to identify the professions and occupations appearing in Volumes One and Two of *JHS*, as well as alternate, popular, synonymous, and related job titles and names, and occupational specialties contained within job titles. Citations include "See" references to the appropriate occupational profiles and their beginning page numbers.

JHS is designed to meet the needs of job seekers at all levels of experience in a wide range of fields. Managers as well as entry-level job hunters will find information sources that will facilitate their career-specific searches. In addition, information on professions and occupations related to those profiled will be found.

All Career Levels. The title assigned to each profile identifies its occupational field or subject area; these titles are not meant to indicate the level of positions for which information is provided. Information systems managers, for example, will find highly useful information in the "Computer Programmers" and "Computer Systems Analysts" profiles, while financial analysts will benefit from information in the "Financial Managers" profile. The "General Managers and Top Executives" profile, on the other hand, is broad in nature and useful to any management-level search; it does not focus upon a specific profession or occupation.

Other Occupations. Job seekers not finding their specific career fields listed in this guide will discover that related profiles yield valuable sources of information. For example, legal secretaries will find relevant information about employment agencies serving the legal profession and about prospective employers in the "Legal Assistants" and "Law-

yers" profiles. An individual interested in finding a position in radio advertising sales might look to the entries in the broadcasting- and sales-related profiles to find appropriate resources. Career changers, too, can use *JHS* profiles to identify new professions to which their previously acquired skills would be transferable.

Volumes One and Two: Sources of Job-Hunting Information by Professions and Occupations

These volumes feature profiles of job-hunting information for 249 specific careers. Profiles are listed alphabetically by profession or occupation. Each profile contains up to eight categories of information sources, as described below. Within each category, entries are arranged in alphabetical order by name or title. Entries are numbered sequentially, beginning with the first entry in the first profile. All resources listed are included in each relevant profile (and in Volume Three chapters, as appropriate) providing a complete selection of information sources in each occupational profile.

Sources of Help-Wanted Ads. Includes professional journals, industry periodicals, association newsletters, placement bulletins, and online services. In most cases, periodicals that focus on a specific field are cited here; general periodical sources such as the *National Business Employment Weekly* are listed in Volume 3 under "Help-Wanted Ads." Publications specific to an industry will be found in all profiles related to that industry. Candidates in some occupational areas, such as word processing, are usually recruited from the local marketplace and therefore are not as likely to find openings through a professional publication. Profiles for these occupations may contain fewer ad sources as job hunters are better served by local newspapers and periodicals. Entries include: the source's title and the name, address, and phone number of its publisher or producer; publication frequency; subscription rate; description of contents; toll-free or additional phone numbers; and fax numbers, when applicable. Source titles appear in italics.

Placement and Job Referral Services. Various services designed to match job seekers with opportunities are included in this category. Primarily offered by professional associations, these services range from job banks to placement services to employment clearinghouses, operating on the national and local levels. Entries include: the association's or organization's name, address, and phone number; its membership, activities, and services; toll-free or additionall phone numbers; and fax numbers. E-mail and website addresses are provided, when available.

Employer Directories and Networking Lists. Covers directories and rankings of companies, membership rosters from professional associations, and other lists of organizations or groups that can be used to target prospective employers and identify potential contacts for networking purposes. In some cases, Who's Who titles are included where these can provide a source of contact information in a specialized field. General directories of companies such as Standard and Poor's Register of Corporations, Directors, and Executives are cited in Volume Three in the "Identifying Prospective Employers" profile. Entries include: the title and name, address, and phone number of the publisher or distributor; publication date or frequency; price; description of contents; arrangement; indexes; toll-free or additional phone numbers; and fax numbers, when available. Directory titles appear in italics.

Handbooks and Manuals. This category notes books, pamphlets, brochures, and other published materials that provide guidance and insight to the job-hunting process in a particular occupational field. Entries include: the title and name, address, and phone number of its publisher or distributor; editor's or author's name; publication date or frequency; price; number of pages; description of contents; toll-free or additional phone numbers; and fax numbers, when known. Publication titles appear in italics.

Employment Agencies and Search Firms. Features firms used by companies to recruit candidates for positions and, at times, by individuals to pursue openings. The following firms are covered:

1. Employment agencies, which are generally geared toward filling openings at entry- to mid-levels in the local job market. Candidates sometimes pay a fee for using their services. When possible, *JHS* lists agencies where the employer pays the fee.

2. Executive search firms, which are paid by the hiring organization to recruit professional and managerial candidates, usually for higher-level openings and from a regional or national market. Executive search firms are of two types: contingency, where the firm is paid only if it fills the position, and retainer, where the firm is compensated to undertake a recruiting assignment, regardless of whether or not that firm actually fills the opening. The majority of the search firms cited in *JHS* are contingency firms. Although executive search firms work for the hiring organization and contact candidates only when recruiting for a specific position, most will accept unsolicited resumes, and some may accept phone calls.

3. Temporary employment agencies, which also are included in some profiles because they can be a way to identify and obtain regular employment.

For the most part, each profile lists firms that typically service that career. Firms specializing in a particular industry are included in all profiles relevant to that industry. *JHS* covers a mix of large and small firms. Major national search firms, which are quite broad in scope, are listed only under the "General Managers and Top Executives" profile. Some occupations are not served by employment agencies or search firms (fire fighter, for example); therefore, there are no entries for this category in such profiles. Entries include: the firm's name, address, and phone number; whether it's an employment agency, executive search firm, or temporary agency; descriptive information, as appropriate; toll-free and additional phone numbers; and fax numbers, when applicable.

Online Job Sources and Services. Publicly available electronic databases, including websites that facilitate matching job hunters with openings are cited. Many are tailored to specific occupations. Entries include: the name of the product or service; the name, address, and phone number of the distributor or producer; price; special formats or arrangements; descriptive information; toll-free or additional phone numbers; and fax numbers, when applicable. For websites, URL is included along with descriptive information.

Tradeshows. Covers exhibitions and tradeshows held in the United States. Entries include: the name of the tradeshow; the name of the sponsoring organization; contact information for the sponsoring organization, including address, phone number, toll-free or additional phone numbers, fax number, email address, and URL; types of exhibits; and dates and location, when available.

Other Sources. This category comprises a variety of resources available to the job seeker in a specific field: job hotlines providing 24-hour recordings of openings; lists of internships, fellowships, and apprenticeships; bibliographies of job-hunting materials; video and audio cassettes; and salary surveys to be used as a guide when discussing compensation. Professional associations of significance or those that provide job hunting assistance (but not full placement services) are also included here. Because of the trend toward entrepreneurship, this section offers information sources on being one's own boss in a given field as well. Resources on job and career alternatives are provided for certain professions (such as educators), as is information on working abroad.

Entries for associations and organizations include: name, address, and phone number; the membership, activities, and services of associations; toll-free or additional phone numbers; and fax numbers. E-mail and website addresses are provided, when available. Entries for other resources include: title of the publication or name of the product or service; the name, address, and phone number of its publisher, distributor, or producer; editor's or author's name; pubication date or frequency; price; special formats or arrangements; descriptive information; hotline, toll-free, or additional phone phone numbers; and fax numbers, when available. Publication, videocassette, and audiocassette titles appear in italics.

Volume Three: Sources of Essential Job-Hunting Information

This volume presents 33 profiles on topics of interest to any job hunter, such as resume writing or interviewing, as well as those of specialized interest, such as working at home (see "List of Profiled Professions and Occupations" for the complete list). Profiles are arranged alphabetically by topic and contain up to six categories of information, as listed below. Within each category, citations are organized alphabetically by name or title. Entries are also numbered sequentially, continuing the number sequence from Volumes One and Two. The publications, periodicals, and other sources listed are fully cited in all relevant chapters (and in occupational profiles, as appropriate), providing the reader with a complete selection of resources in single, convenient location.

Reference Works. Includes handbooks and manuals, directories, pamphlets, and other published sources of information. Entries include: the title and name, address, and phone number of its publisher or distributor; editor's or author's name; publication date or frequency; price; number of pages; description of contents; toll-free or additional phone numbers; and fax numbers, when known. Publication titles appear in italics.

Newspapers, Magazines, and Journals. Lists items published on a serial basis. Entries include: the title and name, address, and phone number of its publisher or distributor; frequency; price; description of contents; toll-free or additional phone numbers; and fax numbers, when known. Publication titles appear in italics.

Audio/Visual Resources. Features audiocassettes, videocassettes, and filmstrips. Entries include: the title and name, address, and phone number of its distributor or producer; date; price; special formats; descriptive information; toll-free or additional phone numbers; and fax numbers, when applicable. Videocassette and audiocassette titles appear in italics.

Online and Database Services. Publicly available electronic databases, including websites that facilitate matching job hunters with openings are cited. Entries include: the name of the product or service; the name, address, and phone number of the distributor or producer; price; special formats or arrangements; descriptive information; toll-free or additional phone numbers; and fax numbers, when applicable. For websites: the online address (URL) is included along with descriptive information.

Software. This category notes software programs designed to help with various aspects of job hunting, such as resume preparation. Entries include: the name of the product or service; the name, address, and phone number of the distributor or producer; price; special formats or arrangements; hardware compatibility, if relevant; descriptive information; toll-free or additional phone numbers; and fax numbers, when applicable.

Other Sources. Varied resources such as special associations and organizations and job-hunting bibliographies, kits, and organizers are covered in this section. Citations for journal and newspaper articles are provided if a topic is relatively new. Entries include: the title of the publication or name of the organization, product, or service; the name, address, and phone number of the organization, publisher, distributor, or producer; editor's or author's name; publication date or frequency; price; special formats or arrangements; descriptive information; toll-free or additional phone numbers; and fax numbers, when applicable. Publication titles appear in italics. For article citations: the article title, publication date, and journal or newspaper title, as well as a description of the article.

Index to Information Sources

JHS provides a comprehensive Index to Information Sources that lists all publications, periodicals, associations, organizations, firms, online and database services, and other resources cited in Volumes One, Two, and Three. Entries are arranged alphabetically and are referenced by their entry numbers. Titles of publications, audiocassettes, and videocassettes appear in italics.

List of Profiled Professions and Occupations

This list outlines references to occupations and professions by job titles, alternate names contained within job titles, popular names, and synonymous and related names. Beginning page numbers for each occupation's profile are provided. Titles of profiles appear in boldface.

Sources of Help-Wanted Ads

6742 ■ American Nurseryman
American Nurseryman Publishing Co.
223 W Jackson Blvd., Ste. 500
Chicago, IL 60606-6904
Ph: (312)427-7339
Fax: (312)427-7346
Fr: 800-621-5727
E-mail: editors@amerinursery.com
URL: http://www.amerinursery.com/

Semimonthly. $48.00/year for individuals; $80.00/year for other countries; $84.00/year for Canada. Trade magazine containing information on commercial horticulture: nursery, landscape and garden center management.

6743 ■ Arboriculture Consultant
American Society of Consulting Arborists
9707 Key West Ave., Ste. 100
Rockville, MD 20850
Ph: (301)947-0483
Fax: (301)990-9771
E-mail: asca@mgmtsol.com
URL: http://www.asca-consultants.org

Description: Quarterly. Contains information on trees.

6744 ■ Architectural Record
McGraw-Hill Inc.
PO Box 182604
Columbus, OH 43218
Ph: (614)430-4000
Fax: (614)759-3749
Fr: 877-833-5524
URL: http://archrecord.construction.com

Monthly. $49.00/year for individuals; $59.00/year for Canada; $109.00/year for other countries. Magazine focusing on architecture.

6745 ■ Fabric Architecture
Industrial Fabrics Association International
1801 County Rd. B W
Roseville, MN 55113
Ph: (651)222-2508
Fax: (651)631-9334
Fr: 800-225-4324
URL: http://fabricarchitecturemag.com/

Bimonthly. $39.00/year for two years; $49.00/year for two years, Canada and Mexico; $69.00/year for two years, international. Magazine specializing in interior and exterior design ideas and technical information for architectural fabric applications in architecture and the landscape.

6746 ■ LAND
American Society of Landscape Architects
636 Eye St., NW
Washington, DC 20001-3736
Ph: (202)898-2444
Fax: (202)898-1185

Fr: 888-999-2752
E-mail: info@asla.org
URL: http://www.asla.org
Description: Biweekly. Carries news and monitors developments in landscape architecture, environmental design, and related fields. Focuses on public policy, education, and other areas affecting landscape architecture.

6747 ■ Landscape Architecture
American Society of Landscape Architects
636 Eye St. NW
Washington, DC 20001-3736
Ph: (202)898-2444
Fax: (202)898-1185
Fr: 888-999-2752
URL: http://archives.asla.org/nonmembers/lam.html

Monthly. $59.00/year for nonmembers; $99.00/year for other countries; $118.00/year for two years; $198.00/year for other countries, 2 years. Professional magazine covering land planning and design.

6748 ■ Landscape Construction
Moose River Media
374 Emerson Falls Rd.
St. Johnsbury, VT 05819
Fax: (802)748-1866
Fr: 800-422-7147
URL: http://www.lcmmagazine.com/

Monthly. Magazine featuring landscaping.

6749 ■ The Landscape Contractor
Illinois Landscape Contractor Association
2625 Butterfield Rd., Ste. 204-W
Oak Brook, IL 60523
Ph: (630)472-2851
Fax: (630)472-3150
URL: http://www.ilca.net/publications.aspx

Monthly. $75.00/year for individuals; $150.00/year for out of state. Magazine for the landscape trade.

6750 ■ Landscape Management
Questex Media Group
275 Grove St., 2-130
Newton, MA 02466
Ph: (617)219-8300
Fax: (617)219-8310
Fr: 888-552-4346
E-mail: landscapemanagement@halldata.com
URL: http://www.landscapemanagement.net/
 landscape/

$46.00/year for individuals, domestic; $69.00/year for Canada and Mexico; $89.00/year for other countries. Magazine for professionals in landscape, grounds management and lawn care, construction, and maintenance.

6751 ■ Landscape Superintendent and Maintenance Professional
Landscape Communications Inc.
14771 Plaza Dr., Ste. M
Tustin, CA 92780

Ph: (714)979-5276
URL: http://www.landscapeonline.com/contact/
 contact_mag.php?pub=l
Free to qualified subscribers. Magazine for landscape professionals.

6752 ■ Nursery News
Cenflo Inc.
PO Box 44040
Rio Rancho, NM 87174
Ph: (505)771-8841
Fax: (505)892-0986
Fr: 800-732-4581
URL: http://www.cenflo.com/nurserynews.html

Monthly. $20.00/year for individuals; $36.00/year for two years; $125.00/year for other countries. Trade newspaper (tabloid) for nursery industry.

6753 ■ PLANET News
Professional Landcare Network
950 Herndon Pkwy., Ste. 450
Herndon, VA 20170
Ph: (703)736-9666
Fax: (703)736-9668
Fr: 800-395-2522
URL: http://www.landcarenetwork.org

Description: Monthly. Features articles on technical, business, legislation and safety in the field of lawn care. Includes calendar of events, new member companies, and association news.

6754 ■ Qualified Remodeler Magazine
Cygnus Business Media
1233 Janesville Ave.
Fort Atkinson, WI 53538
Ph: (920)563-6388
Fax: (920)563-1702
Fr: 800-547-7377
URL: http://www.qualifiedremodeler.com

Monthly. Magazine for remodeling contractor/distributors.

6755 ■ Remodeling
Hanley-Wood L.L.C.
1 Thomas Cir. NW, Ste. 600
Washington, DC 20005-5803
Ph: (202)452-0800
Fax: (202)785-1974
E-mail: rm@omeda.com
URL: http://www.remodeling.hw.net

$25.00/year for individuals; $40.00/year for individuals, Canadian residents; $192.00/year for individuals, international residents. Trade magazine for the professional remodeling industry.

Employer Directories and Networking Lists

6756 ■ American Society of Landscape Architects—Members' Handbook
American Society of Landscape Architects
636 Eye St. NW
Washington, DC 20001-3736

Ph: (202)898-2444
Fax: (202)898-1185
Fr: 888-999-2752
URL: http://www.asla.org

Annual, November. $195.00 for individuals. Covers: 11,000 member landscape architects and affiliates. Entries include: Name, address, phone, chapter, membership category, year joined, type of practice. Arrangement: Alphabetical. Indexes: Geographical.

6757 ■ New York State Nursery/Landscape Association—Directory
New York State Nursery/Landscape Assoc. Inc.
PO Box 3293
Syracuse, NY 13220-3293
Fax: (518)694-4431
Fr: 877-210-4518
URL: http://www.nysnla.com

Annual, January. Covers: Over 800 member nursery, landscape, gardening, and lawn maintenance firms in New York. Entries include: Company name, address, phone, name. Arrangement: Alphabetical.

6758 ■ ProFile—The Architects Sourcebook
Reed Construction Data
30 Technology Pkwy. S, Ste. 100
Norcross, GA 30092
Ph: (770)417-4000
Fax: (770)417-4002
Fr: 800-424-3996
E-mail: profile@reedbusiness.com
URL: http://www.reedfirstsource.com

Annual. Covers: more than 27,000 architectural firms. Entries include: For firms—Firm name, address, phone, fax, year established, key staff and their primary responsibilities (for design, specification, etc.), number of staff personnel by discipline, types of work, geographical area served, projects. "ProFile" is an expanded version of, and replaces, the "Firm Directory." Arrangement: Firms are geographical. Indexes: Firm name, key individuals, specialization by category, consultants. Firm name, key individuals, specialization by category, consultants.

HANDBOOKS AND MANUALS

6759 ■ Becoming a Landscape Architect: A Guide to Careers in Design
Wiley
111 River St.
Hoboken, NJ 07030
Ph: (201)748-6000
Fax: (201)748-6088
E-mail: info@wiley.com
URL: http://as.wiley.com/WileyCDA/Section/index.html

Kelleann Foster. 2009. $39.95 (paper). 368 pages. Covers landscape architect need-to-know: from education and training, design specialties, and work settings to preparing an effective portfolio and finding a job in residential, ecological, commercial, and parks design.

6760 ■ Careers in Focus: Landscaping & Horticulture
Ferguson Publishing
132 W 31st St., 17th Fl.
New York, NY 10001
Fr: 800-322-8755
E-mail: custserv@factsonfile.com
URL: http://factsonfile.infobasepublishing.com

2008. $32.95. 192 pages. Covers jobs profiled in detail, including the nature of the job, earnings, prospects for employment, what kind of training and skills it requires and sources for further information.

6761 ■ Careers for Health Nuts and Others Who Like to Stay Fit
The McGraw-Hill Companies
PO Box 182604
Columbus, OH 43272
Fax: (614)759-3749

Fr: 877-883-5524
E-mail: customer.service@mcgraw-hill.com
URL: http://www.mhprofessional.com

Blythe Camenson. Second edition. $13.95 (paper). 208 pages.

6762 ■ Careers in Horticulture and Botany
The McGraw-Hill Companies
PO Box 182604
Columbus, OH 43272
Fax: (614)759-3749
Fr: 877-883-5524
E-mail: customer.service@mcgraw-hill.com
URL: http://www.mhprofessional.com/product.php?isbn=0071467734

Jerry Garner. 2006. 16.95 (paper). 192 pages. Includes bibliographical references.

6763 ■ Opportunities in Landscape Architecture, Botanical Gardens, and Arboreta Careers
The McGraw-Hill Companies
PO Box 182604
Columbus, OH 43272
Fax: (614)759-3749
Fr: 877-883-5524
E-mail: customer.service@mcgraw-hill.com
URL: http://www.mcgraw-hill.com

Blythe Cameron. 2007. $13.95 (paper). 160 pages. Includes bibliography.

6764 ■ Professional Practice for Landscape Architects
Elsevier
11830 Westline Industrial Dr.
St. Louis, MO 63146
Ph: (314)453-7010
Fax: (314)453-7095
Fr: 800-545-2522
E-mail: usbkinfo@elsevier.com
URL: http://www.elsevier.com

Tennant, Garmory, and Winsch. Second edition, 2007. $37.95 (paper). 312 pages.

6765 ■ Senior Landscape Architect
National Learning Corporation
212 Michael Dr.
Syosset, NY 11791
Fr: 800-632-8888
URL: http://www.passbooks.com

2009. $39.95 (paper). Serves as an exam preparation guide for senior landscape architects.

EMPLOYMENT AGENCIES AND SEARCH FIRMS

6766 ■ Claremont-Branan, Inc.
1298 Rockbridge Rd., Ste. B
Stone Mountain, GA 30087
Fr: 800-875-1292
URL: http://cbisearch.com

Employment agency. Executive search firm.

6767 ■ Precision Executive Search
977 E Schuylkill Rd., Ste. 201
Pottstown, PA 19465
Ph: (610)704-4942
E-mail: mbarcus@precision-recruiters.com
URL: http://precision-recruiters.com

Executive search firm specializing in the civil engineering, surveying, planning, and landscape architecture industries.

ONLINE JOB SOURCES AND SERVICES

6768 ■ American Society of Landscape Architects JobLink
E-mail: membership@asla.org
URL: http://www.asla.org

Description: A job-search site of the American Society of Landscape Architects. Fee: Resume postings cost $100 (nonmembers) for a two-month listing. Job postings cost $600 (nonmembers) or $300 (members) for a one-month listing.

6769 ■ Land8Lounge.com
URL: http://land8lounge.com

Description: Works as the central gathering place for landscape architects all over the world. Features a landscape architecture job board.

TRADESHOWS

6770 ■ American Society of Golf Course Architects Annual Meeting
American Society of Golf Course Architects
125 N Executive Dr., Ste. 302
Brookfield, WI 53005
Ph: (262)786-5960
Fax: (262)786-5919
URL: http://www.asgca.org

Annual. Serves as an event for interaction, innovation and education relating to golf course architecture in the United States.

6771 ■ American Society of Landscape Architects Annual Meeting and Expo
American Society of Landscape Architects
636 Eye St. N.W.
Washington, DC 20001-3736
Ph: (202)898-2444
Fax: (202)898-1185
Fr: 800-999-2752
E-mail: info@asla.org
URL: http://www.asla.org

Annual. Primary Exhibits: Irrigation supplies, outdoor lighting, park and playground equipment, paving and ground cover, street and park furniture, landscape maintenance equipment, computer hardware and software, architectural finishing materials, construction materials, historic preservation services, surveying and mapping equipment, and related equipment, supplies, and services. Dates and Locations: 2012 Sep 28 - Oct 01; Phoenix, AZ; Phoenix Convention Center; 2013 Nov 15-18; Boston, MA; Boston Convention and Exhibition Center; 2014 Nov 21-24; Denver, CO; Colorado Convention Center; 2015 Nov 06-09; Chicago, IL; McCormick Place.

6772 ■ Association of Professional Landscape Designers Annual Conference
Association of Professional Landscape Designers
4305 N 6th St., Ste. A
Harrisburg, PA 17110
Ph: (717)238-9780
Fax: (717)238-9985
URL: http://www.apld.com

Annual. Offers attendees an opportunity to network with fellow designers and to have garden tours.

OTHER SOURCES

6773 ■ American Nursery and Landscape Association (ANLA)
1200 G St., NW
Ste. 800
Washington, DC 20005
Ph: (202)789-2900
Fax: (202)789-1893
E-mail: cbeirne@anla.org
URL: http://www.anla.org

Description: Vertical organization of wholesale growers; landscape firms; garden centers; mail order nurseries; suppliers. Promotes the industry and its products. Offers management and consulting services and public relations programs. Provides government representation and bank card plan for members. Maintains hall of fame.

6774 ■ American Public Gardens Association (APGA)
351 Longwood Rd.
Kennett Square, PA 19348-1807
Ph: (610)708-3010
Fax: (610)444-3594
E-mail: dstark@publicgardens.org
URL: http://www.publicgardens.org
Description: Directors and staffs of botanical gardens, arboreta, institutions maintaining or conducting horticultural courses, and others. Seeks to serve North American public gardens and horticultural organizations by promoting professional development through its publications and meetings, advocating the interests of public gardens in political, corporate, foundation, and community arenas, and encouraging gardens to adhere to professional standards in their programs and operations.

6775 ■ American Society of Landscape Architects (ASLA)
636 Eye St. NW
Washington, DC 20001-3736
Ph: (202)898-2444
Fax: (202)898-1185
Fr: 888-999-ASLA
E-mail: nsomerville@asla.org
URL: http://www.asla.org
Description: Professional society of landscape architects. Promotes the advancement of education and skill in the art of landscape architecture as an instrument in service to the public welfare. Seeks to strengthen existing and proposed university programs in landscape architecture. Offers counsel to new and emerging programs; encourages state registration of landscape architects. Sponsors annual educational exhibit. Offers placement service; conducts specialized education and research.

6776 ■ Environmental Design Research Association
1760 Old Meadow Rd., Ste. 500
McLean, VA 22102
Ph: (703)506-2895
Fax: (703)506-3266
E-mail: edra@edra.org
URL: http://www.edra.org
Description: Promotes the advancement and dissemination of environmental design research. Improves understanding of the interrelationships between people and their natural surroundings and creates environments that are responsive to human needs.

6777 ■ International Society of Arboriculture (ISA)
PO Box 3129
Champaign, IL 61826-3129
Ph: (217)355-9411
Fax: (217)355-9516
Fr: 888-472-8733
E-mail: isa@isa-arbor.com
URL: http://www.isa-arbor.com
Description: Individuals engaged in commercial, municipal, and utility arboriculture; city, state, and national government employees; municipal and commercial arborists; others interested in shade tree welfare. Disseminates information on the care and preservation of shade and ornamental trees. Supports research projects at educational institutions.

6778 ■ Landscape Architecture Foundation (LAF)
818 18th St. NW, Ste. 810
Washington, DC 20006
Ph: (202)331-7070
Fax: (202)331-7079
E-mail: bdeutsch@lafoundation.org
URL: http://www.lafoundation.org
Description: Serves as an education and research vehicle for the landscape architecture profession in the U.S. Combines the capabilities of landscape architects, interests of environmentalists, and needs of agencies and resource foundations. Provides for the preparation and dissemination of educational and scientific information through publications, exhibits, lectures, and seminars. Solicits and expends gifts, legacies, and grants. Established an endowment fund for professorships at colleges and universities. Sponsors California Landscape Architectural Student Scholarship Fund. Conducts a study of the profession to establish goals in terms of education, research needs, practice, and formulation of public policy.

6779 ■ Organization of Women Architects and Design Professionals
PO Box 10078
Berkeley, CA 94709
E-mail: info@owa-usa.org
URL: http://owa-usa.org
Description: Comprised of architects, interior designers, landscape architects, planners, lighting designers, graphic designers, photographers, artists, writers, educators and students. Strives to improve the professional standing of women in architecture and design-related fields. Advocates young women and students entering design related fields through mentoring, education, and employment opportunities.

6780 ■ Society of Iranian Architects and Planners (SIAP)
PO Box 643066
Los Angeles, CA 90064
E-mail: abdiziai@gmail.com
URL: http://siap.org
Description: Represents Iranian graduates in the field of architecture, planning, interior design and landscape architecture. Promotes cultural, scientific and professional aspects in the field architecture and encourages members to develop and advance their skills and abilities in the profession. Provides members with a means of communication for coordination of mutual professional and cultural relationships with similar Iranian organizations around the globe.

SOURCES OF HELP-WANTED ADS

6781 ■ American City and County
Penton Media Inc.
9800 Metcalf Ave.
Overland Park, KS 66212
Ph: (913)341-1300
Fax: (913)967-1898
URL: http://americancityandcounty.com

Monthly. Municipal and county administration magazine.

6782 ■ American Nurseryman
American Nurseryman Publishing Co.
223 W Jackson Blvd., Ste. 500
Chicago, IL 60606-6904
Ph: (312)427-7339
Fax: (312)427-7346
Fr: 800-621-5727
E-mail: editors@amerinursery.com
URL: http://www.amerinursery.com/

Semimonthly. $48.00/year for individuals; $80.00/year for other countries; $84.00/year for Canada. Trade magazine containing information on commercial horticulture: nursery, landscape and garden center management.

6783 ■ Grower Talks
Ball Publishing
622 Town Rd.
PO Box 1660
West Chicago, IL 60186
Ph: (630)231-3675
Fax: (630)231-5254
Fr: 888-888-0013
URL: http://www.ballpublishing.com/GrowerTalks/default.aspx

Monthly. $35.00/year for U.S. and Canada; $99.00/year for other countries; free to qualified subscribers. Trade magazine covering issues for commercial greenhouse growers with a focus on North American production.

6784 ■ Landscape Construction
Moose River Media
374 Emerson Falls Rd.
St. Johnsbury, VT 05819
Fax: (802)748-1866
Fr: 800-422-7147
URL: http://www.lcmmagazine.com/

Monthly. Magazine featuring landscaping.

6785 ■ The Landscape Contractor
Illinois Landscape Contractor Association
2625 Butterfield Rd., Ste. 204-W
Oak Brook, IL 60523
Ph: (630)472-2851
Fax: (630)472-3150
URL: http://www.ilca.net/publications.aspx

Monthly. $75.00/year for individuals; $150.00/year for out of state. Magazine for the landscape trade.

6786 ■ Landscape Management
Questex Media Group
275 Grove St., 2-130
Newton, MA 02466
Ph: (617)219-8300
Fax: (617)219-8310
Fr: 888-552-4346
E-mail: landscapemanagement@halldata.com
URL: http://www.landscapemanagement.net/landscape/

$46.00/year for individuals, domestic; $69.00/year for Canada and Mexico; $89.00/year for other countries. Magazine for professionals in landscape, grounds management and lawn care, construction, and maintenance.

6787 ■ Landscape Superintendent and Maintenance Professional
Landscape Communications Inc.
14771 Plaza Dr., Ste. M
Tustin, CA 92780
Ph: (714)979-5276
URL: http://www.landscapeonline.com/contact/contact_mag.php?pub=l

Free to qualified subscribers. Magazine for landscape professionals.

6788 ■ Lawn & Landscape Magazine
G.I.E. Media, MC
4020 Kinross Lakes Pkwy., Ste. 201
Richfield, OH 44286
Ph: (330)523-5400
Fax: (330)659-0823
Fr: 800-456-0707
URL: http://www.lawnandlandscape.com

Monthly. $15.00/year for U.S., Canada, and Mexico; $35.00/year for individuals; $100.00/year for other countries, South America/Europe. Business management magazine for lawn and landscape contracting professionals.

6789 ■ The Municipality
League of Wisconsin Municipalities
122 W Washington Ave., Ste. 300
Madison, WI 53703-2715
Ph: (608)267-2380
Fax: (608)267-0645
Fr: 800-991-5502
URL: http://www.lwm-info.org/

Monthly. Magazine for officials of Wisconsin's local municipal governments.

6790 ■ NRPA Career Center
National Recreation and Park Association, Professional Services Div.
22377 Belmont Ridge Rd.
Ashburn, VA 20148
Ph: (703)858-0784
Fax: (703)858-0794

Fr: 800-626-6772
E-mail: customerservice@nrpa.org
URL: http://www.nrpa.org

Description: Provides listings of employment opportunities in the park, recreation, and leisure services field.

6791 ■ Nursery Management and Production
GIE Media, Inc.
4020 Kinross Lakes Pky., Ste. 201
Richfield, OH 44286
Fax: (330)659-0823
Fr: 800-456-0707
URL: http://www.nurserymanagementonline.com/

Monthly. Trade journal covering nursery growing, landscape distribution and landscaping.

6792 ■ Nursery News
Cenflo Inc.
PO Box 44040
Rio Rancho, NM 87174
Ph: (505)771-8841
Fax: (505)892-0986
Fr: 800-732-4581
URL: http://www.cenflo.com/nurserynews.html

Monthly. $20.00/year for individuals; $36.00/year for two years; $125.00/year for other countries. Trade newspaper (tabloid) for nursery industry.

6793 ■ Pro
Cygnus Business Media
1233 Janesville Ave.
Fort Atkinson, WI 53538
Ph: (920)563-6388
Fax: (920)563-1702
Fr: 800-547-7377
URL: http://www.promagazine.com

Magazine for landscape service firms.

6794 ■ Western City
League of California Cities
1400 K St., 4th Fl.
Sacramento, CA 95814
Ph: (916)658-8200
Fax: (916)658-8240
Fr: 800-262-1801
URL: http://www.westerncity.com

Monthly. $39.00/year for individuals; $63.00/year for two years; $52.00/year for other countries; $26.50/year for students. Municipal interest magazine.

6795 ■ Yard and Garden
Cygnus Business Media
1233 Janesville Ave.
Fort Atkinson, WI 53538
Ph: (920)563-6388
Fax: (920)563-1702
Fr: 800-547-7377
URL: http://www.cygnusexpos.com/PropertyPub.cfm?PropertyID=117

Yard and garden magazine featuring product news and retailer success stories.

EMPLOYER DIRECTORIES AND NETWORKING LISTS

6796 ■ *New York State Nursery/Landscape Association—Directory*
New York State Nursery/Landscape Assoc. Inc.
PO Box 3293
Syracuse, NY 13220-3293
Fax: (518)694-4431
Fr: 877-210-4518
URL: http://www.nysnla.com

Annual, January. Covers: Over 800 member nursery, landscape, gardening, and lawn maintenance firms in New York. Entries include: Company name, address, phone, name. Arrangement: Alphabetical.

6797 ■ *Who's Who in Landscape Contracting*
Professional Landcare Network
950 Herndon Pkwy., Ste. 450
Herndon, VA 20170-5528
Ph: (703)736-9666
Fax: (703)736-9668
Fr: 800-395-2522
E-mail: advertising@landcarenetwork.org
URL: http://www.landcarenetwork.org

Annual, winter. Covers: 2,500 member exterior and interior landscape contractors, related suppliers, affiliates, state associations, students, and student chapters. Entries include: Company name, address, phone, fax, Web site, e-mail, and names of key personnel, specialties. Arrangement: Alphabetical. Indexes: Interior contractor location, exterior contractor location, personal name.

HANDBOOKS AND MANUALS

6798 ■ *Careers in Horticulture and Botany*
The McGraw-Hill Companies
PO Box 182604
Columbus, OH 43272
Fax: (614)759-3749
Fr: 877-883-5524
E-mail: customer.service@mcgraw-hill.com
URL: http://www.mhprofessional.com/
   product.php?isbn=0071467734

Jerry Garner. 2006. 16.95 (paper). 192 pages. Includes bibliographical references.

6799 ■ *Opportunities in Landscape Architecture, Botanical Gardens, and Arboreta Careers*
The McGraw-Hill Companies
PO Box 182604
Columbus, OH 43272
Fax: (614)759-3749
Fr: 877-883-5524
E-mail: customer.service@mcgraw-hill.com
URL: http://www.mcgraw-hill.com

Blythe Cameron. 2007. $13.95 (paper). 160 pages. Includes bibliography.

TRADESHOWS

6800 ■ Association of Professional Landscape Designers Annual Conference
Association of Professional Landscape Designers
4305 N 6th St., Ste. A
Harrisburg, PA 17110
Ph: (717)238-9780

Fax: (717)238-9985
URL: http://www.apld.com

Annual. Offers attendees an opportunity to network with fellow designers and to have garden tours.

6801 ■ Green Industry and Equipment Expo
PLANET, The Professional Landcare Network
950 Herndon Parkway, Ste. 450
Herndon, VA 20170
Ph: (703)736-9666
Fax: (703)736-9668
Fr: 800-395-2522
URL: http://www.landcarenetwork.org

Annual. Primary Exhibits: Lawn care equipment, supplies, and services, including fertilizers, weed control materials, insurance information, and power equipment. Dates and Locations: 2012 Oct 25-27; 2013 Oct 24-26; 2014 Oct 23-25.

6802 ■ Mid-Atlantic Nursery Trade Show
The Mid-Atlantic Nursery Trade Show, Inc. MANTS
PO Box 818
Brooklandville, MD 21022
Ph: (410)296-6959
Fax: (410)296-8288
Fr: 800-431-0066
E-mail: info@mants.com
URL: http://www.mants.com

Annual. Primary Exhibits: Equipment, supplies, and services relating to all aspects of nursery, landscaping, and garden center businesses. Dates and Locations: 2013 Jan 09-11; Baltimore, MD; Baltimore Convention Center.

6803 ■ National Hardware Show & Lawn and Garden World
Reed Exhibitions North American Headquarters
383 Main Ave.
Norwalk, CT 06851
Ph: (203)840-4800
Fax: (203)840-5805
E-mail: inquiry@reedexpo.com
URL: http://www.reedexpo.com

Annual. Primary Exhibits: Exhibits relating to home, lawn, and garden tools and supplies. Dates and Locations: 2012 May 01-03; Las Vegas, NV; Las Vegas Convention Center.

6804 ■ Utah Green Industry Conference and Trade Show
Utah Nursery and Landscape Association
c/o Diane Jones
PO Box 526314
Salt Lake City, UT 84152
Ph: (801)484-4426
Fax: (801)463-0026
E-mail: utgreen1@aol.com
URL: http://www.utahgreen.org

Annual. Primary Exhibits: Exhibits relating to landscape maintenance and the green industry.

OTHER SOURCES

6805 ■ American Nursery and Landscape Association (ANLA)
1200 G St., NW
Ste. 800
Washington, DC 20005
Ph: (202)789-2900
Fax: (202)789-1893
E-mail: cbeirne@anla.org
URL: http://www.anla.org

Description: Vertical organization of wholesale growers; landscape firms; garden centers; mail order nurseries; suppliers. Promotes the industry and its products. Offers management and consulting services and public relations programs. Provides government

representation and bank card plan for members. Maintains hall of fame.

6806 ■ American Public Gardens Association (APGA)
351 Longwood Rd.
Kennett Square, PA 19348-1807
Ph: (610)708-3010
Fax: (610)444-3594
E-mail: dstark@publicgardens.org
URL: http://www.publicgardens.org

Description: Directors and staffs of botanical gardens, arboreta, institutions maintaining or conducting horticultural courses, and others. Seeks to serve North American public gardens and horticultural organizations by promoting professional development through its publications and meetings, advocating the interests of public gardens in political, corporate, foundation, and community arenas, and encouraging gardens to adhere to professional standards in their programs and operations.

6807 ■ International Society of Arboriculture (ISA)
PO Box 3129
Champaign, IL 61826-3129
Ph: (217)355-9411
Fax: (217)355-9516
Fr: 888-472-8733
E-mail: isa@isa-arbor.com
URL: http://www.isa-arbor.com

Description: Individuals engaged in commercial, municipal, and utility arboriculture; city, state, and national government employees; municipal and commercial arborists; others interested in shade tree welfare. Disseminates information on the care and preservation of shade and ornamental trees. Supports research projects at educational institutions.

6808 ■ Professional Grounds Management Society (PGMS)
720 Light St.
Baltimore, MD 21230-3816
Ph: (410)223-2861
Fax: (410)752-8295
Fr: 800-609-7467
E-mail: pgms@assnhqtrs.com
URL: http://www.pgms.org

Description: Professional society of grounds managers of large institutions of all sorts and independent landscape contractors. Establishes grounds management as a profession; secures opportunities for professional advancement of well-qualified grounds managers; acquaints the public with "the distinction between competent ground managers, equipped through practical experience and systematic study, and self-styled 'maintenance' personnel, lacking these essentials". Sponsors contests. Conducts research and surveys; sponsors certification program for professional grounds managers and grounds keepers. Takes action with the legislative and executive branches of government on issues affecting grounds managers; keeps members informed on matters affecting the profession.

6809 ■ Professional Landcare Network (PLANET)
950 Herndon Pkwy., Ste. 450
Herndon, VA 20170
Ph: (703)736-9666
Fax: (703)736-9668
Fr: 800-395-2522
E-mail: info@landcarenetwork.org
URL: http://www.landcarenetwork.org

Description: Landscape contractors. Works to represent, lead and unify the interior and exterior landscape industry by working together on a national basis; addressing environmental and legislative issues; and creating increased opportunities in business. Provides forum to encourage members' profitability, personal growth and professional advancement.

SOURCES OF HELP-WANTED ADS

6810 ▪ ACJS Today
Academy of Criminal Justice Sciences (ACJS)
PO Box 960
Greenbelt, MD 20768-0960
Ph: (301)446-6300
Fax: (301)446-2819
Fr: 800-757-2257
E-mail: info@acjs.org
URL: http://www.acjs.org/
Description: Four issues/year. Circulation is 2,000. Contains criminal justice information.

6811 ▪ American City and County
Penton Media Inc.
9800 Metcalf Ave.
Overland Park, KS 66212
Ph: (913)341-1300
Fax: (913)967-1898
URL: http://americancityandcounty.com
Monthly. Municipal and county administration magazine.

6812 ▪ American Society of Crime Laboratory Directors
139A Technology Dr.
Garner, NC 27529
Ph: (919)773-2044
Fax: (919)861-9930
URL: http://www.ascld.org
Description: Nonprofit professional society dedicated to providing excellence in forensic science analysis through leadership in the management of forensic science. The purpose of the organization is to foster professional interests; assist the development of laboratory management principles and techniques; acquire, preserve and disseminate forensic based information; maintain and improve communications among crime laboratory directors; and to promote, encourage and maintain the highest standards of practice in the field.

6813 ▪ CopCareer.com
1051 E. Hillsdale Blvd.
Foster City, CA 94404
Fax: (650)350-1423
URL: http://www.copcareer.com
Online job posting site for law enforcement professionals, including border patrol agents.

6814 ▪ Criminal Justice Studies
Routledge Journals
270 Madison Ave.
New York, NY 10016-0601
Ph: (212)216-7800
Fax: (212)563-2269
URL: http://www.tandf.co.uk/journals/titles/1478601x.html
Quarterly. $388.00/year for institutions, print + on-line; $375.00/year for institutions, online only; $123.00/year for individuals, print only. Peer-reviewed journal covering articles on criminal justice and criminological issues.

6815 ▪ D & O Advisor
American Lawyer Media L.P.
120 Broadway, 5th Fl.
New York, NY 10271
Ph: (212)457-9400
Fax: (646)417-7705
Fr: 800-603-6571
URL: http://www.alm.com
Quarterly. Magazine that offers advice and perspective on corporate oversight responsibilities for directors and officers.

6816 ▪ Executive Legal Adviser
Incisive Media
120 Broadway, 5th Fl.
New York, NY 10271
Ph: (212)457-9400
Fax: (646)417-7705
URL: http://www.executivelegaladviser.com
Bimonthly. Free to qualified subscribers. Magazine that offers legal advice for corporate executives.

6817 ▪ Homeland Response
Penton Media Inc.
249 W 17th St.
New York, NY 10011
Ph: (212)204-4200
URL: http://www.respondersafetyonline.com/
Bimonthly. Magazine covering homeland security.

6818 ▪ Institute of Justice and International Studies
Central Missouri State University
PO Box 800
Warrensburg, MO 64093
Ph: (660)543-4111
Fax: (660)543-8517
Fr: 877-729-8266
E-mail: cjinst@ucmo.edu
URL: http://www.ucmo.edu/cjinst/Journal.html
Irregular. Free. Journal that publishes reports on international crime including corrections, media coverage, public policy, counter terrorism, and civil liberties.

6819 ▪ Journal of the American Criminal Justice Association
American Criminal Justice Association
PO Box 601047
Sacramento, CA 95860-1047
Ph: (916)484-6553
Fax: (916)488-2227
URL: http://www.acjalae.org/journal1.html
Semiannual. Journal covering issues in criminal justice.

6820 ▪ Journal of Empirical Legal Studies
John Wiley & Sons Inc.
350 Main St., Commerce Pl.
Malden, MA 02148-5089
Ph: (781)388-8200
Fax: (781)388-8210
URL: http://www.wiley.com/bw/journal.asp?ref=1740-1453&site=1
Quarterly. $508.00/year for institutions, U.S. print & online; $441.00/year for institutions, U.S. print or on-line; $388.00/year for institutions, other countries, print & online; $337.00/year for institutions, other countries, print or online. Journal focusing on law and law-related fields, including civil justice, corporate law, criminal justice, domestic relations, economics, finance, health care, political science, psychology, public policy, securities regulation, and sociology.

6821 ▪ Journal of Health and Life Sciences Law
American Health Lawyers Association
1620 Eye St. NW, 6th Fl.
Washington, DC 20006-4010
Ph: (202)833-1100
Fax: (202)833-1105
URL: http://www.healthlawyers.org
Quarterly. $149.00/year for individuals. Professional journal covering healthcare issues and cases and their impact on the health care arena.

6822 ▪ Law Enforcement Technology
Cygnus Business Media
1233 Janesville Ave.
Fort Atkinson, WI 53538
Ph: (920)563-6388
Fax: (920)563-1702
Fr: 800-547-7377
URL: http://www.officer.com/magazine
Monthly. Free. Magazine for police technology and management.

6823 ▪ Law Officers Magazine
Elsevier Science Inc.
360 Park Ave. S
New York, NY 10010-1710
Ph: (212)989-5800
Fax: (212)633-3990
Fr: 888-437-4636
URL: http://www.elsevier.com/wps/find/journaldescription.cws_home
$70.00/year for institutions, other countries; $70.00/year for other countries; $70.00/year for students, other countries; $39.00/year for students; $60.00/year for institutions, Canada; $60.00/year for Canada. Journal for the professional law enforcement officer.

6824 ▪ Law and Order
Hendon Publishing
130 N Waukegan Rd., Ste. 202
Deerfield, IL 60015-5652
Ph: (847)444-3300
Fax: (847)444-3333

Fr: 800-843-9764
E-mail: law&ordermag@halldata.com
URL: http://www.hendonpub.com/publications/
lawandorder/

Monthly. $22.00/year for individuals. Law enforcement trade magazine.

6825 ■ The Municipality
League of Wisconsin Municipalities
122 W Washington Ave., Ste. 300
Madison, WI 53703-2715
Ph: (608)267-2380
Fax: (608)267-0645
Fr: 800-991-5502
URL: http://www.lwm-info.org/

Monthly. Magazine for officials of Wisconsin's local municipal governments.

6826 ■ Police & Security News
Days Communications
1208 Juniper St.
Quakertown, PA 18951-1520
Ph: (215)538-1240
Fax: (215)538-1208
E-mail: advertising@policeandsecuritynews.com
URL: http://policeandsecuritynews.com

Bimonthly. $18.00/year for by mail; $75.00/year for other countries, mail. Tabloid for the law enforcement and private security industries. Includes articles on training, new products, and new technology.

6827 ■ Western City
League of California Cities
1400 K St., 4th Fl.
Sacramento, CA 95814
Ph: (916)658-8200
Fax: (916)658-8240
Fr: 800-262-1801
URL: http://www.westerncity.com

Monthly. $39.00/year for individuals; $63.00/year for two years; $52.00/year for other countries; $26.50/year for students. Municipal interest magazine.

EMPLOYER DIRECTORIES AND NETWORKING LISTS

6828 ■ Association of Former Agents of the U.S. Secret Service—Membership Directory
Association of Former Agents of the U.S. Secret Service
525 SW 5th St., Ste. A
Des Moines, IA 50309-4501
Ph: (515)282-8192
Fax: (515)282-9117
URL: http://www.oldstar.org

Annual, March. Entries include: Name, home address. Arrangement: Alphabetical.

6829 ■ Career Opportunities in Law Enforcement, Security, and Protective Services
Facts On File Inc.
132 W 31st St., 17th Fl.
New York, NY 10001
Ph: (212)967-8800
Fax: 800-678-3633
Fr: 800-322-8755
URL: http://www.infobasepublishing.com

Latest edition 2nd; Published October, 2005. $49.50 for individuals. Covers: More than 77 profiles, in a diverse range of occupations, including law enforcement, physical security, computer security, emergency services, fire protection, and air travel safety.

6830 ■ Careers in Focus—Public Safety
Facts On File Inc.
132 W 31st St., 17th Fl.
New York, NY 10001
Ph: (212)967-8800
Fax: 800-678-3633

Fr: 800-322-8755
URL: http://www.infobasepublishing.com

Latest edition 3rd; Published August, 2007. $32.95 for individuals. Covers: An overview of public safety, followed by a selection of jobs profiled in detail, including the nature of the job, earnings, prospects for employment, what kind of training and skills it requires, and sources for further information.

6831 ■ International Association of Chiefs of Police Membership Directory
International Association of Chiefs of Police
515 N Washington St.
Alexandria, VA 22314
Ph: (703)836-6767
Fax: (703)836-4543
Fr: 800-843-4227
URL: http://www.theiacp.org/members/directory.htm

Annual, October. Covers: 20,000 members in command and administrative positions in federal, state, and local law enforcement and related fields; includes county police and sheriffs; international, national, and regional law enforcement agencies and related organizations. Entries include: For officers—Name, title, name of law enforcement agency, address, phone. For agencies and organizations—Name, address, names and titles of key personnel, publications. Arrangement: Geographical and alphabetical.

6832 ■ National Directory of Law Enforcement Administrators, Correctional Institutions & Related Agencies
National Public Safety Information Bureau
601 Main St.
PO Box 365
Stevens Point, WI 54481-2617
Ph: (715)345-2772
Fax: (715)345-7288
Fr: 800-647-7579
URL: http://www.safetysource.com

Annual, Latest edition 44th, Published 2008. $149.00 for individuals; $189.00. Covers: Police departments, sheriffs, coroners, criminal prosecutors, child support agencies, state law enforcement and criminal investigation agencies; federal criminal investigation and related agencies; state and federal correctional institutions; campus law enforcement departments; County jails, airport and harbor police, Bureau of Indian Affairs officials, plus new homeland security section. Entries include: Name, address, phone, fax, names and titles of key personnel, number of officers, population served. Arrangement: Separate geographical sections for police chiefs, coroners, sheriffs, prosecutors, prisons and state criminal investigation agencies; also separate sections for federal agencies and miscellaneous law enforcement and related agencies. Indexes: Departments.

HANDBOOKS AND MANUALS

6833 ■ Becoming a Police Officer: An Insider's Guide to a Career in Law Enforcement
iUniverse, Inc.
1663 Liberty Dr.
Bloomington, IN 47403
Fax: (812)355-4085
Fr: 800-288-4677
URL: http://www.iuniverse.com

Barry M. Baker. 2006. $12.95. 112 pages. Presents an examination of police work that is directed toward young people who are contemplating a career as a police officer. Describes the self-satisfaction that can be found in police work while identifying its pitfalls and how to avoid them. Covers topics a newly trained police officer must appreciate and master to ensure success and safety.

6834 ■ Careers for Legal Eagles and Other Law-and-Order Types
The McGraw-Hill Companies
PO Box 182604
Columbus, OH 43272

Fax: (614)759-3749
Fr: 877-883-5524
E-mail: customer.service@mcgraw-hill.com
URL: http://www.mhprofessional.com/
product.php?isbn=0071466207

Blythe Camenson. Second edition, 2005. $13.95 (paper). 176 pages.

6835 ■ Careers for Mystery Buffs and Other Snoops and Sleuths
The McGraw-Hill Companies
PO Box 182604
Columbus, OH 43272
Fax: (614)759-3749
Fr: 877-883-5524
E-mail: customer.service@mcgraw-hill.com
URL: http://www.mhprofessional.com

Blythe Camenson. Second edition. $14.95 (hardback). 160 pages.

6836 ■ The Everything Guide to Careers in Law Enforcement
Adams Media
4700 E Galbraith Rd.
Cincinnati, OH 45236
URL: http://www.adamsmediastore.com

Paul D. Bagley. 2011. $14.95 (paper). 304 pages. Covers all aspects of job options available in the field of law enforcement. Provides information on the application, hiring and training process.

6837 ■ FBI Careers, Third Edition
JIST Publishing
875 Montreal Way
St. Paul, MN 55102
Fax: 800-547-8329
Fr: 800-648-5478
E-mail: info@jist.com
URL: http://www.jist.com

Thomas H. Ackerman. 2010. $19.95. 368 pages. Guide to handling the FBI's rigorous selection process; reveals what it takes to succeed in landing a job. Useful for special agents as well as professional support personnel.

6838 ■ Ferguson Career Coach: Managing Your Career in Law Enforcement
Facts On File
132 W 31st St., 17th Fl.
New York, NY 10001
Fax: 800-678-3633
Fr: 800-322-8755
E-mail: custserv@factsonfile.com
URL: http://factsonfile.infobasepublishing.com

Shelly Field. 2008. $39.95 (hardcover). 288 pages. Provides readers with practical insight on a wide range of jobs in law enforcement including police work, corrections and rehabilitation, loss prevention, risk management, and security. Offers a wealth of industry secrets, tips, and basic advice from professionals for students who dream of a career in law enforcement or protective services.

6839 ■ Legally Green: Careers in Environmental Law
Crabtree Publishing Company
350 5th Ave., 59th Fl.
PMB 59051
New York, NY 10118
Ph: (212)496-5040
Fax: 800-355-7166
Fr: 800-387-7650
URL: http://www.crabtreebooks.com

Susan Down. 2012. $31.93. 64 pages (hardcover). Features careers in environmental law. Includes job information for public service and governmental agencies and environmental non-governmental organizations as well as attorneys and legal support staff for law firms that offer services related to environmental law.

EMPLOYMENT AGENCIES AND SEARCH FIRMS

6840 ■ Ferrari Search Group
200 East End Ave., Ste. 5N
New York, NY 10128
Ph: (212)289-5099
Fax: (716)386-2367
E-mail: contactus@ferrarisearchgroup.com
URL: http://www.ferrarisearchgroup.com
Executive search firm.

ONLINE JOB SOURCES AND SERVICES

6841 ■ ClearedConnections.com
URL: http://www.clearedconnections.com

Online resource lists jobs for those security-cleared professionals including counterintelligence specialists.

6842 ■ CriminalJusticeUSA.com
URL: http://www.criminaljusticeusa.com

Description: Provides a detailed description of a career in Corrections. Links to the top ten colleges for careers in criminal justice fields.

6843 ■ JobCop.com
URL: http://www.jobcop.com

Description: Lists job openings and career development opportunities in police and law enforcement. Sorts jobs according to department/bureau and state.

6844 ■ LawEnforcementCrossing.com
URL: http://www.lawenforcementcrossing.com

Description: Provides employment opportunities for law enforcement officers.

6845 ■ New Law Enforcement Jobs
URL: http://www.newlawenforcementjobs.com

Description: Provides a listing of companies with available law enforcement jobs in all specialties.

6846 ■ Officer.com
URL: http://www.officer.com

Description: Offers news, forums, chat rooms, online directories, and job listings.

6847 ■ PoliceEmployment.com
URL: http://www.policeemployment.com

Description: Online job information center for a variety of careers in federal, state, and local law enforcement. Offers career information and answers questions about obtaining a law enforcement job.

6848 ■ PoliceJobsInfo.com
E-mail: admin@policejobsinfo.com
URL: http://www.policejobsinfo.com

Description: Offers free information on law enforcement careers as well as agency links, job search sites, job recruitment telephone numbers, sample written entrance tests, and more.

6849 ■ PoliceMag.com
URL: http://www.policemag.com

Description: Offers articles and news in the law enforcement field. Helps officers of all ranks do their jobs more efficiently, professionally, and safely. Includes job listings and forums for discussion.

6850 ■ PoliceOne.com
URL: http://www.policeone.com

Description: Provides police officers and law enforcement professionals information and resources. Includes news, videos, products, training, jobs and career resources, awards and grants.

6851 ■ USADefenseIndustryJobs.com
E-mail: resumes@defensecareers.com
URL: http://usadefenseindustryjobs.com

Provides an online job search for intelligence positions with the American defense industry.

TRADESHOWS

6852 ■ Annual National Association of Women Law Enforcement Executives Conference
National Association of Women Law Enforcement Executives
160 Lawrenceville-Pennington Rd., Ste. 16-115
Lawrenceville, NJ 08648
Ph: (973)975-6146
Fax: (973)265-1410
E-mail: info@nawlee.com
URL: http://www.nawlee.com

Annual. Provides learning and information sharing opportunities for law enforcement professionals. Includes leadership workshops, mentoring sessions, awards and receptions. 2012 August 1-5; Austin, TX; Omni Hotel.

6853 ■ HAPCOA National Training Conference
Hispanic American Police Command Officers Association
PO Box 767
Cibolo, TX 78108
Ph: (210)641-1305
Fax: (210)641-1304
E-mail: villareal@hapcoa.org
URL: http://www.hapcoa.com

Annual. Features presentations, workshops, and training sessions about current and emerging topics which affect law enforcement and criminal justice. Includes exhibits and career fair. 2012 October 7-11; Long Beach, CA; Hilton Hotel.

6854 ■ International Association of Chiefs of Police Annual Conference
International Association of Chiefs of Police
515 N. Washington St.
Alexandria, VA 22314-2357
Ph: (703)836-6767
Fax: (703)836-4543
Fr: 800-THE-IACP
URL: http://www.theiacp.org

Annual. Primary Exhibits: Law enforcement equipment, supplies, and services. Dates and Locations: 2012 Sep 29 - Oct 03; San Diego, CA; San Diego Convention Center.

6855 ■ International Association of Crime Analysts Annual Training Conference
9218 Metcalf Ave., Ste. 364
Overland Park, KS 66212
Fr: 800-609-3419
E-mail: iaca@iaca.net
URL: http://www.iaca.net

Annual. Focuses on training in the areas of analysis and law enforcement and offers the IACA Certification Exam. 2012 September 10-13; Henderson, NV; The Ravella.

6856 ■ Michigan Association of Chiefs of Police Mid-Winter Conference
Michigan Association of Chiefs of Police
2133 University Park Dr., Ste. 200
Okemos, MI 48864-3975
Ph: (517)349-9420
Fax: (517)349-5823
E-mail: info@michiganpolicechiefs.org
URL: http://www.michiganpolicechiefs.org

Annual. Primary Exhibits: Law enforcement equipment, supplies, and services.

6857 ■ National Sheriffs' Association Annual Conference
National Sheriff Association
1450 Duke St.
Alexandria, VA 22314-3490
Ph: (703)836-7827
Fax: (703)838-5349
Fr: 800-424-7827
E-mail: nsamail@sheriffs.org
URL: http://www.sheriffs.org

Annual. Primary Exhibits: Exhibits of interest to local law enforcement professionals. Dates and Locations: 2012 Jun 16-20; Nashville, TN; 2013 Jun 22-26; Charlotte, NC; 2014 Jun 20-25; Forth Worth, TX.

6858 ■ WIFLE Annual Leadership Training Conference
Women in Federal Law Enforcement
2200 Wilson Blvd., Ste. 102
PMB-204
Arlington, VA 22201
Ph: (301)805-2180
Fax: (301)560-8836
Fr: 877-850-8302
E-mail: wifle@comcast.net
URL: http://www.wifle.org

Annual. Fosters awareness of the value that women bring to law enforcement. Features workshops for the development of women's involvement in federal law enforcement.

OTHER SOURCES

6859 ■ AFCEA Intelligence
4400 Fair Lakes Ct.
Fairfax, VA 22033-3899
Ph: (703)631-6219
Fax: (703)631-6133
URL: http://www.afcea.org/mission/intel

As part of the AFCEA International, the Association was established in 1981 to enhance outreach to the U.S. Intelligence Community and to support intelligence professionals in the government, military and private sector.

6860 ■ American Association of Police Polygraphers
PO Box 657
Waynesville, OH 45068
Ph: (937)728-7827
Fax: (937)488-1046
Fr: 888-743-5479
URL: http://www.policepolygraph.org

Description: Encourages the application and utilization of accepted polygraph techniques among law enforcement organizations. Develops standards of proficiency in the polygraph profession by fostering scientific training and research through advanced study and progressive techniques. Provides an opportunity and forum for the exchange of information regarding polygraph experiences, studies, and research.

6861 ■ American Board of Criminalistics (ABC)
PO Box 1358
Palmetto, FL 34220
E-mail: abcregistrar@verizon.net
URL: http://www.criminalistics.com

Description: Regional and national organizations of forensic scientists and criminalists. Offers certificates of Professional Competency in Criminalistics as well as in specialty disciplines of forensic biology, drug chemistry, fire debris analysis, and various areas of trace evidence examination. Works to establish professional standards and promote growth within the industry. Answers questions regarding the certification process.

6862 ■ American Federation of Police and Concerned Citizens (AFP&CC)
6350 Horizon Dr.
Titusville, FL 32780
Ph: (321)264-0911
E-mail: policeinfo@aphf.org
URL: http://www.afp-cc.org

Description: Governmental and private law enforcement officers (paid, part-time, or volunteer) united for the prevention of crime and the apprehension of criminals. Offers death benefits and training programs to members and police survivors. Sponsors American Police Academy. Maintains hall of fame. Conducts workshops.

6863 ■ American Society of Crime Laboratory Directors
139A Technology Dr.
Garner, NC 27529
Ph: (919)773-2044
Fax: (919)861-9930
URL: http://www.ascld.org

Description: Nonprofit professional society dedicated to providing excellence in forensic science analysis through leadership in the management of forensic science. The purpose of the organization is to foster professional interests; assist the development of laboratory management principles and techniques; acquire, preserve and disseminate forensic based information; maintain and improve communications among crime laboratory directors; and to promote, encourage and maintain the highest standards of practice in the field.

6864 ■ American Society of Criminology (ASC)
1314 Kinnear Rd., Ste. 212
Columbus, OH 43212-1156
Ph: (614)292-9207
Fax: (614)292-6767
E-mail: asc@asc41.com
URL: http://www.asc41.com

Description: Represents professional and academic criminologists, students of criminology in accredited universities, psychiatrists, psychologists, and sociologists. Develops criminology as a science and academic discipline. Aids in the construction of criminological curricula in accredited universities. Upgrades the practitioner in criminological fields (police, prisons, probation, parole, delinquency workers). Conducts research programs and sponsors three student paper competitions. Provides placement service at annual convention.

6865 ■ Central Valley Crime and Intelligence Analysts Association
c/o Kim Miller
PO Box 20756
Bakersfield, CA 93390
Ph: (661)391-7466
E-mail: info@cvciaa.org
URL: http://cvciaa.org

Works to enhance crime and intelligence analysis as a tool in law enforcement.

6866 ■ Federal Criminal Investigators Association (FCIA)
PO Box 23400
Washington, DC 20026
Ph: (630)969-8537
Fr: 800-403-3374
E-mail: fcianat@aol.com
URL: http://www.fedcia.org

Description: Serves as professional fraternal organization dedicated to the advancement of federal law enforcement officers and the citizens they serve. Aims to ensure law enforcement professionals have the tools and support network to meet the challenges of future criminal investigations while becoming more community oriented. Intends to pursue mission by promoting professionalism, enhancing the image of federal officers, fostering cooperation among all law enforcement professionals, providing a fraternal environment for the advancement of the membership

and community. Helps charitable programs and organizations.

6867 ■ Federal Flight Deck Officers Association (FFDOA)
PO Box 20024
Washington, DC 20041
Fax: (214)594-7345
E-mail: membership@ffdoa.org
URL: http://www.ffdoa.org

Description: Represents pilot volunteers who are screened, trained, and deputized as Federal Law Enforcement Officers. Offers benefits to members such as: insurance and legal counsel, discounts on training and equipment, and a forum to discuss operational issues. Provides a unified voice to Congress and the parent agency, TSA/OLE/FAMS, on issues relevant to improving flight operations.

6868 ■ Hispanic American Police Command Officers Association
PO Box 767
Cibolo, TX 78108
Ph: (210)641-1305
Fax: (210)641-1304
E-mail: achapa@hapcoa.org
URL: http://www.hapcoa.com

Description: Addresses the concerns of Hispanic Americans in professional law enforcement and criminal justice system. Offers professional development opportunities to members through training and educational programs.

6869 ■ International Association of Campus Law Enforcement Administrators (IACLEA)
342 N Main St.
West Hartford, CT 06117-2507
Ph: (860)586-7517
Fax: (860)586-7550
E-mail: info@iaclea.org
URL: http://www.iaclea.org

Description: Advances public safety for educational institutions by providing educational resources, advocacy, and professional development. Promotes professional ideals and standards in the administration of campus security/public safety/law enforcement. Works to make campus security/public safety/law enforcement an integral part of the educational community.

6870 ■ International Association of Computer Investigative Specialists (IACIS)
PO Box 2411
Leesburg, VA 20177
Ph: (304)915-0555
Fr: 888-884-2247
E-mail: secretary@cops.org
URL: http://www.iacis.com

Description: Provides education and certification of law enforcement professionals in the field of computer forensic science. Creates and establishes procedures, trains personnel, and certifies forensic examiners in the recovery of evidence from computer systems. Offers professional training in the seizure and processing computer systems. Provides an opportunity to network with other law enforcement officers trained in computer forensics, and to share and learn from others.

6871 ■ International Association of Crime Analysts
9218 Metcalf Ave., Ste. 364
Overland Park, KS 66212
Fr: 800-609-3419
E-mail: iaca@iaca.net
URL: http://www.iaca.net

Crime analysts, intelligence analysts, police officers of all ranks, educators and students.

6872 ■ International Association of Law Enforcement Intelligence Analysts
PO Box 13857
Richmond, VA 23225

Fax: (804)565-2059
E-mail: admin@ialeia.org
URL: http://www.ialeia.org

Promotes the development and enhancement of law enforcement intelligence analysts.

6873 ■ International Police Work Dog Association (IPWDA)
PO Box 7455
Greenwood, IN 46142
Ph: (317)882-9191
E-mail: ipwda1@yahoo.com
URL: http://www.ipwda.org

Description: Aims to unite and assist all law enforcement agencies in the training and continued progress of all police work dogs. Seeks to establish a working standard for all police work dogs, handlers, and trainers through an accreditation program. Promotes the image of the police work dog.

6874 ■ Law Enforcement and Emergency Services Video Association (LEVA)
PO Box 547
Midlothian, TX 76065
Ph: (469)285-9435
Fax: (469)533-3659
E-mail: president@leva.org
URL: http://www.leva.org

Description: Serves as a key resource to the global public safety community by focusing on the needs of video production and forensic imaging disciplines. Provides opportunities for professional development through quality training and informational exchange. Offers forensic video analysis training to law enforcement professionals.

6875 ■ National Association of Black Law Enforcement Officers (NABLEO)
PO Box 1182
Newark, NJ 07102
Ph: (401)465-9152
E-mail: memberships@nableo.org
URL: http://blackcops.net

Description: Seeks to address the concerns and issues of law enforcement officers of color throughout the United States and the communities they serve. Provides community-based solutions to policing issues that affect communities of color. Supports the efforts and continued development of law enforcement officers seeking to make a difference in promoting true justice for the communities they serve.

6876 ■ National Association of Investigative Specialists (NAIS)
PO Box 82148
Austin, TX 78708
Ph: (512)719-3595
Fax: (512)719-3594
E-mail: rthomas007@aol.com
URL: http://www.pimall.com/nais/dir.menu.html

Description: Private investigators, automobile repossessors, bounty hunters, and law enforcement officers. Promotes professionalism and provides for information exchange among private investigators. Lobbies for investigative regulations. Offers training programs and issues certificates of completion. Sponsors charitable programs; compiles statistics; maintains speakers' bureau and placement service. Operates Investigators' Hall of Fame of Private Investigators. Offers seminars on cassette tape.

6877 ■ National Association of Professional Canine Handlers (NAPCH)
3441 Filbert St.
Wayne, MI 48184
Ph: (734)506-8690
Fax: (734)641-9508
URL: http://napch.org

Description: Promotes excellence among police/ private working K-9s for the security and well-being of society. Seeks to enhance the image and improve the capabilities of all working dogs and handlers. Conducts training for members.

6878 ■ National Association of Traffic Accident Reconstructionists and Investigators (NATARI)
PO Box 2588
West Chester, PA 19382
Ph: (610)696-1919
E-mail: natari@natari.org
URL: http://www.natari.org

Description: Represents engineers, attorneys, police officers, private investigators, medical examiners, and other individuals involved in the analysis of motor vehicle traffic accidents. Gathers and disseminates information on techniques and equipment of potential use to members; reviews literature in the field. Participating Organization of the Accreditation Commission for Traffic Accident Reconstruction.

6879 ■ National Association of Women Law Enforcement Executives
160 Lawrenceville-Pennington Rd., Ste. 16-115
Lawrenceville, NJ 08648
Ph: (973)975-6146
Fax: (973)265-1410
E-mail: info@nawlee.com
URL: http://www.nawlee.com

Description: Serves the interests of women law enforcement executives and those who aspire to be executives in law enforcement. Promotes the ideals and principles of women executives in law enforcement. Conducts training seminars to train and educate women executives in law enforcement. Provides a forum for the exchange of information concerning law enforcement.

6880 ■ National Center for Women and Policing
433 S Beverly Dr.
Beverly Hills, CA 90212
Ph: (310)556-2526
Fax: (310)556-2509
E-mail: womencops@feminist.org
URL: http://www.womenandpolicing.org

Description: Strives to increase the number of women at all ranks of law enforcement. Educates policy makers, the media, and the public about the impact of increasing the representation of women in policing. Provides members with opportunities to network with women leaders in law enforcement throughout the country.

6881 ■ National Citizens Police Academy Association (NCPAA)
701 W Sample St.
South Bend, IN 46601
Ph: (574)235-9402
Fr: 800-324-1820
E-mail: rpowers@nationalcpaa.org
URL: http://www.nationalcpaa.org

Description: Fosters the professional development of information, instruction, guidance, and assistance to public safety agencies and citizens involved or interested in the Citizens Police Academy concept. Offers a Citizen Police Academy certification course for law enforcement officers. Keeps members informed of current trends and new developments pertaining to law enforcement Citizen Police Academy programs.

6882 ■ National Law Enforcement Associates
PO Box 3342
New York, NY 10008
E-mail: info@nationallaw.org
URL: http://www.nlea.us

Description: Facilitates cooperation among members of the law enforcement and private security communities. Furthers the preservation of, and adherence to, the Constitution of the United States. Provides educational opportunities and conducts training in the fields of law enforcement and security.

6883 ■ National Organization of Black Law Enforcement Executives (NOBLE)
4609-F Pinecrest Office Park Dr.
Alexandria, VA 22312-1442
Ph: (703)658-1529
Fax: (703)658-9479
URL: http://www.noblenational.org

Description: Represents law enforcement executives above the rank of lieutenant; police educators; academy directors; interested individuals and organizations. Provides a platform from which the concerns and opinions of minority law enforcement executives and command-level officers can be expressed. Facilitates the exchange of programmatic information among minority law enforcement executives. Aims to eliminate racism in the field of criminal justice and to increased cooperation from criminal justice agencies. Encourages coordination between law enforcement agencies and the community to prevent and abate crime and its causes. Conducts research and training and offers technical assistance in crime victim assistance, community oriented policing, domestic violence, use of deadly force, reduction of fear of crime, airport security assessment, and minority recruitment. Offers internships; operates speakers' bureau.

6884 ■ National Police Canine Association (NPCA)
PO Box 538
Waddell, AZ 85355
Ph: (713)562-7371
Fr: 877-362-1219
E-mail: info@npca.net
URL: http://www.npca.net

Description: Works as a resource for the professional development of canine teams and administrators. Works to achieve advancements and improvements in the area of law enforcement. Provides regional and national canine training seminars across the United States.

6885 ■ Nine Lives Associates (NLA)
Executive Protection Institute
16 Penn Pl., Ste. 1570
New York, NY 10001
Ph: (212)268-4555
Fax: (212)563-4783
Fr: 800-947-5827
E-mail: info@personalprotection.com
URL: http://www.personalprotection.com/nla.cfm

Description: Law enforcement, correctional, military, and security professionals who have been granted Personal Protection Specialist Certification through completion of the protective services program offered by the Executive Protection Institute; conducts research; EPI programs emphasize personal survival skills and techniques for the protection of others. Provides professional recognition for qualified individuals engaged in executive protection assignments. Maintains placement service. Operates speakers' bureau; compiles statistics.

6886 ■ Park Law Enforcement Association
4397 McCullough St.
Port Charlotte, FL 33948-9490
E-mail: nielsen4397@comcast.net
URL: http://myparkranger.org

Description: Represents park law enforcement professionals. Facilitates the exchange of information between park law enforcement personnel and other park and recreation professionals. Offers continuing education and technical assistance to persons working in park law enforcement.

6887 ■ Professional Law Enforcement Association
PO Box 1197
Troy, MI 48099
Fax: (248)641-8857

Fr: 800-367-4321
E-mail: info@plea.net
URL: http://www.plea.net

Description: Provides services to the men and women of law enforcement. Offers legal defense, job listings, and other benefit products to all members.

6888 ■ Reserve Police Officers Association (RPOA)
89 Rockland Ave.
Yonkers, NY 10705
Fr: 800-326-9416
URL: http://www.reservepolice.org

Description: Creates public awareness and support of the existence and contributions of reserve and auxiliary law enforcement programs. Provides training opportunities to reserve, auxiliary, and special law enforcement officers. Serves as a contact point and clearing house for information on reserve and auxiliary law enforcement programs.

6889 ■ Society of Asian Federal Officers (SOAFO)
PO Box 2978
New York, NY 10008
Ph: (212)436-1655
E-mail: soafo@yahoo.com
URL: http://www.soafo.org

Description: Represents law enforcement professionals including special agents, criminal investigators, inspectors, auditors, analysts, and attorneys from every branch of the Federal government. Promotes law enforcement as a premier occupation. Seeks to enhance hiring and employment opportunities of qualified applicants for Federal law enforcement positions from entry level to management. Fosters comradery and leadership among its members.

6890 ■ Society of Professional Investigators (SPI)
233 Broadway, Ste. 2201
New York, NY 10279
Ph: (646)584-9081
URL: http://spionline.info

Description: Persons with at least 5 years' investigative experience for an official federal, state, or local government agency or for a quasi-official agency formed for law enforcement or related activities. Seeks to advance knowledge of the science and technology of professional investigation, law enforcement, and police science; maintains high standards and ethics; promotes efficiency of investigators in the services they perform.

6891 ■ Student Association on Terrorism and Security Analysis
402 MacNaughton Hall
Syracuse, NY 13244-1030
E-mail: satsa@maxwell.syr.edu
URL: http://satsa.us

Dedicated to the critical analysis of terrorism, counterterrorism policy, and national and international security issues.

6892 ■ Women in Federal Law Enforcement
2200 Wilson Blvd., Ste. 102 PMB-204
Arlington, VA 22201
Ph: (301)805-2180
Fax: (301)560-8836
Fr: 877-850-8302
E-mail: wifle@comcast.net
URL: http://www.wifle.org

Description: Aims to achieve gender equity in federal law enforcement. Promotes gender equity through its leadership education center that provides training, research, scholarships, awards, and networking opportunities in partnership with law enforcement agencies, members and supportive sponsors. Helps agencies to recruit, develop better retention rates, and provide training to help promote women in federal law enforcement.

Sources of Help-Wanted Ads

6893 ■ Annual Review of Law and Social Science
Annual Reviews Inc.
4139 El Camino Way
Palo Alto, CA 94306
Ph: (650)493-4400
Fax: (650)424-0910
Fr: 800-523-8635
URL: http://www.annualreviews.org/journal/lawsocsci

Annual. $80.00/year for individuals, print & online; $242.00/year for institutions, print & online; $202.00/year for institutions, print only; $202.00/year for institutions, online only. Journal covering current issues in law and the social sciences.

6894 ■ Berkeley Business Law Journal
University of California, Boalt Hall School of Law
215 Boalt Hall
Berkeley, CA 94720-7200
Ph: (510)643-1741
URL: http://www.boalt.org/bblj

Semiannual. $45.00/year for individuals; $65.00/year for elsewhere. Journal that aims to create innovative business law-oriented commentary created by professors, professionals, and students.

6895 ■ BNA's Corporate Counsel Weekly
Bureau of National Affairs Inc.
1801 S Bell St.
Arlington, VA 22202
Fax: 800-253-0332
Fr: 800-372-1033
E-mail: customercare@bna.com
URL: http://www.bna.com/corporate-counsel-weekly-p6006

Description: Weekly. Covers law that affects business, including corporate law, securities law, antitrust law, and employment law. Carries brief reports of court cases, looks at government regulation of trade and the environment, and focuses each week on a topic of current importance. Includes texts of regulatory material and practitioner analysis.

6896 ■ Boston Bar Journal
Boston Bar Association
16 Beacon St.
Boston, MA 02108
Ph: (617)742-0615
Fax: (617)523-0127
URL: http://www.bostonbar.org/pub/bbj/index.htm

Journal for lawyers on important matters of legal interest.

6897 ■ California Lawyer
Daily Journal Corp.
915 E 1st St.
Los Angeles, CA 90012
Ph: (213)229-5300

Fax: (213)229-5481
URL: http://www.dailyjournal.com
Monthly. $95.00/year for individuals. Law magazine.

6898 ■ Chicago Lawyer
Law Bulletin Publishing Co.
415 N State St.
Chicago, IL 60610
Ph: (312)644-7800
E-mail: ryates@lbpc.com
URL: http://www.chicagolawyermagazine.com/Home.aspx

Monthly. $60.00/year for individuals; $96.00/year for two years. Legal magazine (Tabloid).

6899 ■ Columbia Journal of Law and Social Problems
Columbia Law School
435 W 116th St.
New York, NY 10027-7237
Ph: (212)854-2640
E-mail: jlsp@law.columbia.edu
URL: http://www.columbia.edu/cu/jlsp/

$40.00/year for individuals; $45.00/year for other countries; $17.50/year for single issue. Journal covering economic, sociological and political laws.

6900 ■ Cornerstone
National Legal Aid & Defender Association
1140 Connecticut Ave. NW, Ste. 900
Washington, DC 20036
Ph: (202)452-0620
Fax: (202)872-1031
E-mail: info@nlada.org
URL: http://www.nlada100years.org

Description: Three issues/year. Monitors current issues affecting legal aid attorneys and public defenders. Recurring features include job listings, conference and training updates, news of research, book reviews, and news of members.

6901 ■ Criminal Justice Studies
Routledge Journals
270 Madison Ave.
New York, NY 10016-0601
Ph: (212)216-7800
Fax: (212)563-2269
URL: http://www.tandf.co.uk/journals/titles/1478601x.html

Quarterly. $388.00/year for institutions, print + online; $375.00/year for institutions, online only; $123.00/year for individuals, print only. Peer-reviewed journal covering articles on criminal justice and criminological issues.

6902 ■ D & O Advisor
American Lawyer Media L.P.
120 Broadway, 5th Fl.
New York, NY 10271
Ph: (212)457-9400
Fax: (646)417-7705

Fr: 800-603-6571
URL: http://www.alm.com
Quarterly. Magazine that offers advice and perspective on corporate oversight responsibilities for directors and officers.

6903 ■ Executive Legal Adviser
Incisive Media
120 Broadway, 5th Fl.
New York, NY 10271
Ph: (212)457-9400
Fax: (646)417-7705
URL: http://www.executivelegaladviser.com

Bimonthly. Free to qualified subscribers. Magazine that offers legal advice for corporate executives.

6904 ■ Global Jurist Frontiers
Berkeley Electronic Press
2809 Telegraph Ave., Ste. 202
Berkeley, CA 94705-1167
Ph: (510)665-1200
Fax: (510)665-1201
URL: http://www.bepress.com/gj/frontiers/

Annual. $645.00/year corporate; $215.00/year academic. Journal that publishes papers on new issues of comparative law, law and economics, international law, law and development, and legal anthropology.

6905 ■ Houston Law Review
University of Houston
4800 Calhoun Rd.
Houston, TX 77004
Ph: (713)743-2255
E-mail: inquiry@houstonlawreview.org
URL: http://www.houstonlawreview.org/

Quarterly. $35.00/year for individuals. Journal focusing on current issues in law. Publishes contributions from academicians, practicing lawyers, and other scholars, and selected Law Review students.

6906 ■ Institute of Justice and International Studies
Central Missouri State University
PO Box 800
Warrensburg, MO 64093
Ph: (660)543-4111
Fax: (660)543-8517
Fr: 877-729-8266
E-mail: cjinst@ucmo.edu
URL: http://www.ucmo.edu/cjinst/Journal.html

Irregular. Free. Journal that publishes reports on international crime including corrections, media coverage, public policy, counter terrorism, and civil liberties.

6907 ■ Ius Gentium
University of Baltimore
1415 Maryland Ave.
Baltimore, MD 21201-5779
Ph: (410)837-4468

Fax: (410)837-4450

URL: http://law.ubalt.edu/template.cfm?page=615

Annual. $69.95/year for individuals. Journal that facilitates analysis and the exchange of ideas about contemporary legal issues from a comparative perspective.

6908 ■ Job Announcements

National Center for State Courts
300 Newport Ave.
Williamsburg, VA 23185
Ph: (757)259-1525
Fax: (757)220-0449
Fr: 800-616-6164
URL: http://www.ncsc.org

Description: Semimonthly. Provides lists of court-related job openings in the United States and its territories.

6909 ■ Journal of the American Criminal Justice Association

American Criminal Justice Association
PO Box 601047
Sacramento, CA 95860-1047
Ph: (916)484-6553
Fax: (916)488-2227
URL: http://www.acjalae.org/journal1.html

Semiannual. Journal covering issues in criminal justice.

6910 ■ Journal of Empirical Legal Studies

John Wiley & Sons Inc.
350 Main St., Commerce Pl.
Malden, MA 02148-5089
Ph: (781)388-8200
Fax: (781)388-8210
URL: http://www.wiley.com/bw/journal.asp?ref=1740-1453&site=1

Quarterly. $508.00/year for institutions, U.S. print & online; $441.00/year for institutions, U.S. print or online; $388.00/year for institutions, other countries, print & online; $337.00/year for institutions, other countries, print or online. Journal focusing on law and law-related fields, including civil justice, corporate law, criminal justice, domestic relations, economics, finance, health care, political science, psychology, public policy, securities regulation, and sociology.

6911 ■ Journal of Health and Life Sciences Law

American Health Lawyers Association
1620 Eye St. NW, 6th Fl.
Washington, DC 20006-4010
Ph: (202)833-1100
Fax: (202)833-1105
URL: http://www.healthlawyers.org

Quarterly. $149.00/year for individuals. Professional journal covering healthcare issues and cases and their impact on the health care arena.

6912 ■ Journal of the Missouri Bar

The Missouri Bar
326 Monroe St.
PO Box 119
Jefferson City, MO 65102-0119
Ph: (573)635-4128
Fax: (573)635-2811
URL: http://www.mobar.org/7b2e21b5-eb97-4f01-91da-1ff2beb5bb45.as

Bimonthly. Magazine featuring short, practical articles on legal subjects for practicing attorneys.

6913 ■ The Journal of Taxation

RIA Group
195 Broadway
New York, NY 10007-3100
Fr: 800-431-9025
URL: http://ria.thomson.com/estore/detail.aspx?ID=JTAX

Monthly. $390.00/year for individuals, print; $565.00/year for individuals, online/print bundle; $440.00/year for individuals, online. Journal for sophisticated tax practitioners.

6914 ■ Kentucky Bench & Bar Magazine

Kentucky Bar Association
514 W Main St.
Frankfort, KY 40601-1883
Ph: (502)564-3795
Fax: (502)564-3225

Bimonthly. $20.00/year for individuals. Kentucky law magazine.

6915 ■ Law Officers Magazine

Elsevier Science Inc.
360 Park Ave. S
New York, NY 10010-1710
Ph: (212)989-5800
Fax: (212)633-3990
Fr: 888-437-4636
URL: http://www.elsevier.com/wps/find/journaldescription.cws_home

$70.00/year for institutions, other countries; $70.00/year for other countries; $70.00/year for students, other countries; $39.00/year for students; $60.00/year for institutions, Canada; $60.00/year for Canada. Journal for the professional law enforcement officer.

6916 ■ Legal Affairs

Legal Affairs
254 Elm St.
New Haven, CT 06511
Ph: (203)789-1510
URL: http://legalaffairs.org/mediakit/LegalAffairsMediaKit.pdf

Bimonthly. $39.95/year for institutions, Canada. Publication that presents critical essays about current issues in law.

6917 ■ Legal Times

American Lawyer Media L.P.
1730 M St. NW, Ste. 802
Washington, DC 20036
Ph: (202)457-0686
Fax: (202)785-4539
Fr: 800-933-4317
URL: http://www.law.com/jsp/nlj/legaltimes/advertise.jsp

Weekly. $299.00/year for individuals, print & online. Legal publication covering law and lobbying in the nation's capitol.

6918 ■ Los Angeles Lawyer

Los Angeles County Bar Association
1055 W 7th St., Ste. 2700
PO Box 55020
Los Angeles, CA 90017-2577
Ph: (213)627-2727
Fax: (213)833-6717
URL: http://www.lacba.org/showpage.cfm?pageid=40

Monthly. $28.00/year for nonmembers; $4.00/year for single issue, plus handling; for Included in membership. Magazine featuring scholarly legal articles.

6919 ■ Massachusetts Lawyers Weekly

Lawyers Weekly Publications
10 Milk St., Ste. 1000
Boston, MA 02111
Ph: (617)451-7300
Fr: 800-451-9998
URL: http://www.masslaw.com

Weekly. $350.00/year for individuals; $210.00/year for individuals, 6 months; $665.00/year for two years. Newspaper (tabloid) reporting Massachusetts legal news.

6920 ■ Michigan Bar Journal

State Bar of Michigan
306 Townsend St.
Lansing, MI 48933-2012
Ph: (517)346-6300
Fax: (517)482-6248
Fr: 800-968-1442
URL: http://www.michbar.org/publications/bar_journal.cfm

Monthly. $60.00/year for nonmembers; $70.00/year for other countries, members. Legal magazine.

6921 ■ The National Law Journal

The New York Law Journal
120 Broadway, 5th Fl.
New York, NY 10271-1101
Ph: (212)457-9545
Fax: (866)305-3058
URL: http://www.law.com/jsp/nlj/index.jsp

Weekly. $299.00/year for individuals. Tabloid focusing on the practice of law and trends in law.

6922 ■ New Jersey Law Journal

New Jersey Law Journal
238 Mulberry St.
PO Box 20081
Newark, NJ 07101-6081
Ph: (973)642-0075
Fax: (973)642-0920
URL: http://www.law.com/jsp/nj/index.jsp?slreturn=1&hbxlogin=1

Weekly. $219.00/year for individuals. Journal containing digests of court opinions, notes, and orders to the bar from New Jersey Supreme Court and federal district court. Includes news articles on legal topics and commentary by legal specialists.

6923 ■ The Recorder

American Lawyer Media L.P.
120 Broadway
New York, NY 10271
Ph: (212)457-9400
URL: http://www.law.com/jsp/ca/index.jsp

Daily (morn.). $369.00/year for individuals, print and online. Legal newspaper.

6924 ■ Texas Bar Journal

State Bar of Texas
1414 Colorado St.
PO Box 12487
Austin, TX 78701-1627
Ph: (512)427-1463
Fax: (512)427-4100
Fr: 800-204-2222
URL: http://www.texasbar.com/AM/Template.cfm?Section=Texas_Bar_Jo

Monthly. $12.00/year for individuals; $15.00/year for other countries; $2.50/year for single issue. Legal news journal for the legal profession.

6925 ■ The Washington Lawyer

The District of Columbia Bar
1101 K St. NW, Ste. 200
Washington, DC 20005-4210
Ph: (202)737-4700
Fax: (202)626-3471
Fr: 877-333-2227
URL: http://www.dcbar.org/for_lawyers/resources/publications/inde

Forum for articles and news items for the Washington legal community.

6926 ■ Wisconsin Lawyer

State Bar of Wisconsin
PO Box 7158
Madison, WI 53707-7158
Ph: (608)257-3838
Fax: (608)257-5502
Fr: 800-728-7788
E-mail: wislawyer@wisbar.org
URL: http://www.wisbar.org/wislawmag

Monthly. $35.00/year for members; $53.00/year for nonmembers; $3.50/year for single issue. Official monthly publication of the State Bar of Wisconsin.

PLACEMENT AND JOB REFERRAL SERVICES

6927 ■ BCG Attorney Search

202 S Lake Ave., Unit 250
Pasadena, CA 91101

Ph: (213)895-7300
Fax: (213)895-7306
Fr: 800-298-6440
E-mail: jobs@bcgsearch.com
URL: http://www.bcgsearch.com

Represents legal professionals in the United States. Serves as a placement firm for associates and partners in law firms.

EMPLOYER DIRECTORIES AND NETWORKING LISTS

6928 ■ *The American Bar*
Forster Long Inc.
12160 N Abrams Rd., No. 516
Dallas, TX 75243
Ph: (214)838-5745
Fax: (214)838-5754
Fr: 800-328-5091
URL: http://www.forster-long.com

Annual, latest edition 2010. $495.00 for individuals; $75.00 for individuals. Covers: Lists top law firms in the United States and 100 other countries with individual attorney biographies; selected state administrative offices. Entries include: Firm name, type of practice, address, phone, names, educational data, and memberships of partners and associates. State offices' listings include address, phone. Arrangement: Geographical, alphabetical, separate sections for Canadian, Mexican and international lawyers. Indexes: Personal name; firm name and location; practice areas.

6929 ■ *American Bar Association—Directory*
American Bar Association
321 N Clark St.
Chicago, IL 60654-7598
Ph: (312)988-5000
Fax: (312)988-5568
Fr: 800-285-2221

Annual, October. $14.95. Covers: Approximately 7,500 lawyers active in the affairs of the Association, including officers, members of Boards of Governors and House of Delegates, section officers and council members, committee leaders, headquarters staff, state and local bars, affiliated and other legal organizations. Entries include: Section, council, or other unit name; names, addresses, and phone numbers of officers or chairpersons and members. Arrangement: Classified by position in ABA. Indexes: Alphabetical, Geographical committee.

6930 ■ *American Lawyers Quarterly*
The American Lawyers Co.
853 Westpoint Pky., Ste. 710
Cleveland, OH 44145-1532
Ph: (440)871-8700
Fax: (440)871-9997
Fr: 800-843-4000
URL: http://www.alqlist.com

Quarterly, January and July; monthly supplements. Covers: Law firms that specialize in debt collections, creditors' rights, and bankruptcy. Arrangement: Geographical.

6931 ■ *AttorneyHunter.com*
MegaHunter, Inc.
1705 2nd Ave., 3rd Fl., Ste. 314
Rock Island, IL 61201
Ph: (309)793-1051
Fax: (309)283-1257
Fr: (866)529-7732
URL: http://attorneyhunter.com

Provides a list of attorneys organized by practice area. Provides resources on advertising and listing of legal firms, searching for lawyers, information about hiring a lawyer, a legal dictionary and other legal resources.

6932 ■ *Best Lawyers in America*
Woodward/White Inc.
129 1st Ave. SW
Aiken, SC 29801
Ph: (803)648-0300
Fax: (803)641-4794
URL: http://www.bestlawyers.com

Biennial, Latest edition 2011; New edition expected 2012. $225.00. Covers: Approximately 15,000 attorneys selected as 'the best' in their specialties by a survey of their peers. Entries include: Individual or firm name, address, phone, and subspecialties of interest. Arrangement: Geographical, then classified by legal specialty. Indexes: Name index.

6933 ■ *Career Ideas for Teens in Law and Public Safety*
Facts On File Inc.
132 W 31st St., 17th Fl.
New York, NY 10001
Ph: (212)967-8800
Fax: 800-678-3633
Fr: 800-322-8755
URL: http://www.infobasepublishing.com

Published August, 2005. Covers: A multitude of career possibilities based on a teenager's specific interests and skills and links his/her talents to a wide variety of actual professions.

6934 ■ *Career Opportunities in Law and the Legal Industry*
Facts On File Inc.
132 W 31st St., 17th Fl.
New York, NY 10001
Ph: (212)967-8800
Fax: 800-678-3633
Fr: 800-322-8755
URL: http://factsonfile.infobasepublishing.com/

Latest edition 2nd; Published March, 2007. $49.50 for individuals. Publication includes: Lists of industry associations and organizations, educational institutions, and Web sites related to the legal industry. Principal content of publication is information on careers in the legal field. Indexes: Alphabetical.

6935 ■ *Careers in Focus—Law*
Facts On File Inc.
132 W 31st St., 17th Fl.
New York, NY 10001
Ph: (212)967-8800
Fax: 800-678-3633
Fr: 800-322-8755
URL: http://www.infobasepublishing.com

Latest edition 3rd; Published February, 2009. $32.95 for individuals. Covers: An overview of law, followed by a selection of jobs profiled in detail, including the nature of the job, earnings, prospects for employment, what kind of training and skills it requires, and sources for further information.

6936 ■ *Executor's Handbook*
Facts On File Inc.
132 W 31st St., 17th Fl.
New York, NY 10001
Ph: (212)967-8800
Fax: 800-678-3633
Fr: 800-322-8755
URL: http://www.infobasepublishing.com

Latest edition 3rd; June 1, 2007. $39.50 for individuals. Covers: Guides for nonprofessional estate executors, providing clear explanations of the most arcane aspects of estate law, including the responsibilities associated with being an executor, understanding the provisions of a will, managing or liquidating assets, dealing with beneficiaries and creditors, handling income and death taxes, resolving family issues and situations, and dispersal of non-monetary items.

6937 ■ *International Law and Practice—Leadership Directory*
International Law and Practice Section
740 15th St. NW
Washington, DC 20005-1019

Ph: (202)662-1000
URL: http://www.abanet.org

Annual, Latest edition 2010-2011. Covers: Over 300 member lawyers, academics, law students, and international associates in leadership positions in the section. Entries include: Name, address, phone, fax and e-mail address.

6938 ■ *Law and Legal Information Directory*
Gale
PO Box 6904
Florence, KY 41022-6904
Fr: 800-354-9706
URL: http://www.gale.cengage.com

Annual, Latest edition 24th; April, 2012. $716.00 for individuals. Covers: More than 21,000 national and international organizations, bar associations, federal and highest state courts, federal regulatory agencies, law schools, firms and organizations offering continuing legal education, paralegal education, sources of scholarships and grants, awards and prizes, special libraries, information systems and services, research centers, publishers of legal periodicals, books, and audiovisual materials, lawyer referral services, legal aid offices, public defender offices, legislature manuals and registers, small claims courts, corporation departments of state, state law enforcement agencies, state agencies, including disciplinary agencies, and state bar requirements. Entries include: All entries include institution or firm name, address, phone; many include names and titles of key personnel and, when pertinent, descriptive annotations. Contents based in part on information selected from several other Gale directories. Arrangement: Classified by type of organization, activity, service, etc. Indexes: Individual sections have special indexes as required.

6939 ■ *Lawyers' List*
Commercial Publishing Company Inc.
8706 Commerce Dr.
PO Box 2430
Easton, MD 21601
Ph: (410)820-8089
Fax: (410)820-4474
Fr: 800-824-9911
URL: http://www.thelawyerslist.com/about.shtml

Annual, latest edition 97th. Covers: about 2,500 lawyers in general, corporate, trial, patent, trademark, and copywrite practices internationally. Entries include: Firm name, address, phone, fax, e-mail, website, areas of practice, branch offices, names of representative clients, names of partners and associates. A general law list. Arrangement: Geographical.

6940 ■ *Lawyer's Register International by Specialties and Fields of Law Including a Directory of Corporate Counsel*
Lawyer's Register Publishing Co.
4555 Renaissance Pkwy., Ste. 101
Cleveland, OH 44128
URL: http://www.lawyersregister.com

Annual. Covers: corporate legal staffs worldwide; legal firms; independent practicing attorneys each identified as a specialist in one or more fields of law. Entries include: In corporate section—Corporation, subsidiary, and department names; address, phone, fax; names and titles of legal staff, law schools attended, specialties. In fields of law sections—Name, address, phone, fax, specialties (identified by Standard Industrial Classification (SIC) codes), personal data. A general international/corporate law list. Arrangement: Separate sections for specializing lawyers and their firms and corporate counsel. Indexes: Lawyers and firms by areas, corporations, more indexes.

6941 ■ *The Legal Directory*
Philadelphia Bar Association
1101 Market St., 11th Fl.
Philadelphia, PA 19107
Ph: (215)238-6300

Fax: (215)238-1159
URL: http://www.thelegaldirectory.org

Latest edition 2011. Covers: 18,000 attorneys and more than 1,600 law firms. Entries include: Name, address, area of concentration, phone and fax numbers, e-mail and website address.

6942 ■ Martindale-Hubbell Bar Register of Preeminent Lawyers

Martindale-Hubbell Inc.
121 Chanlon Rd.
New Providence, NJ 07974
Ph: (908)464-6800
Fax: (908)771-8704
Fr: 800-526-4902
URL: http://www.martindale.com

Annual. $195.00 for individuals. Covers: Over 8,900 of today's most skilled attorneys and law partnerships and firms. Entries include: Firm name, telephone, fax, e-mail, URL, members, associate clients, and name and title of contact. Arrangement: Geographical.

6943 ■ Martindale-Hubbell Law Directory

Martindale-Hubbell Inc.
121 Chanlon Rd.
New Providence, NJ 07974
Ph: (908)464-6800
Fax: (908)771-8704
Fr: 800-526-4902
URL: http://www.martindale.com

Annual, April. $1,065.00 for individuals. Covers: Lawyers and law firms in the United States, its possessions, and Canada, plus leading law firms worldwide; includes a biographical section by firm, and a separate list of patent lawyers, attorneys in government service, in-house counsel, and services, suppliers, and consultants to the legal profession. Entries include: For non-subscribing lawyers—Name, year of birth and of first admission to bar, code indicating college and law school attended and first degree, firm name (or other affiliation, if any) and relationship to firm, whether practicing other than as individual or in partnership. For subscribing lawyers—Above information plus complete address, phone, fax, e-mail and URL, type of practice, clients, plus additional personal details (education, certifications, etc.). A general law list. Arrangement: Geographical. Indexes: Alphabetical, area of practice.

6944 ■ MCBA Attorney Directory

Maricopa County Bar Association
303 E Palm Ln.
Phoenix, AZ 85004
Ph: (602)257-4200
Fax: (602)257-8601
URL: http://www.maricopabar.org

Latest edition 2004. Covers: More than 9,000 attorneys, MCBA boards, divisions, sections and bylaws, lawyer referral service and volunteer lawyers information, federal, state and county offices, court rosters.

6945 ■ NALP Directory of Legal Employers

National Association for Law Placement
1220 19th St. NW, Ste. 401
Washington, DC 20036-2405
Ph: (202)835-1001
Fax: (202)835-1112
E-mail: info@nalp.org
URL: http://www.nalp.org

Annual. 2011. $85.00. Features information on more than 1,500 legal employers. Includes indexes by location and practice area keyword.

6946 ■ National Directory of Prosecuting Attorneys

National District Attorneys Association
44 Canal Center Plz., Ste. 110
Alexandria, VA 22314
Ph: (703)549-9222

Fax: (703)836-3195
E-mail: cathy.yates@ndaa-apri.org
URL: http://www.ndaa.org/publications/ndaa/index.html

Biennial, latest edition 2007. $35.00 for members; $50.00 for nonmembers. Covers: About 2,800 elected or appointed local prosecuting attorneys. Entries include: Name, address, phone, jurisdiction, fax, email. Arrangement: Geographical. Indexes: Alphabetical.

6947 ■ NLADA Directory of Legal Aid and Defender Offices in the United States and Territories

National Legal Aid & Defender Association
1140 Connecticut Ave. NW, Ste. 900
Washington, DC 20036
Ph: (202)452-0620
URL: http://www.nlada.org/Member_Svcs/Publications/Directory/

Biennial, latest edition 2009-2010. $95.00 for nonmembers; $35.00 for individuals; $55.00 for individuals; $95.00 for nonmembers. Covers: Approximately 3,000 civil legal aid and indigent defense organizations in the United States; includes programs for specific groups such as prisoners, senior citizens, the disabled, etc. Entries include: Agency name, address, phone, director's name. Arrangement: Geographical. Indexes: Type of service.

6948 ■ USBD—United States Bar Directory

Attorneys National Clearing House Co.
PO Box 142828
Gainesville, FL 32614-2828
Ph: (352)336-3344
Fax: (866)859-2624
Fr: (866)860-2624
E-mail: usbd@usbardirectory.com
URL: http://www.usbardirectory.com

Annual, January. Covers: Over 3,000 general and specialized practice attorneys employed through correspondence (letter, phone, fax or e-mail). Entries include: Firm name, address, phone, preferred fields of practice, fax, email, Web site. Arrangement: Geographical.

6949 ■ Vault Guide to the Top 100 Law Firms

Vault.com Inc.
150 W 22nd St., 5th Fl.
New York, NY 10011
Ph: (212)366-4212
Fax: (212)366-6117
Fr: 888-562-8285
URL: http://www.vault.com/wps/portal/usa/store/bookdetail?item_no

Latest edition 13th; 2010. $39.95 for individuals; $33.96 for members. Covers: Top 100 law firms in the U.S. Entries include: Name, address, phone, fax, website, branch office location, major practice areas, salary information, notable perks, and rankings. Also includes a list of 60 legal recruiter firms, diversity programs, and pro bono programs.

6950 ■ Vault Guide to the Top Boston & Northeast Law Firms

Vault.com Inc.
150 W 22nd St., 5th Fl.
New York, NY 10011
Ph: (212)366-4212
Fax: (212)366-6117
Fr: 888-562-8285
URL: http://www.vault.com

Latest edition 4th; Published March, 2009. $29.95 for individuals; $25.95 for members. Covers: Law firms in Boston and Northeast region. Entries include: Company name, contact person, address, location, phone, statistics, and email.

6951 ■ Vault Guide to the Top Chicago & Midwest Law Firms

Vault.com Inc.
150 W 22nd St., 5th Fl.
New York, NY 10011
Ph: (212)366-4212

Fax: (212)366-6117
Fr: 888-562-8285
URL: http://www.vault.com

Latest edition March, 2007. $29.95 for individuals; $29.95 for members. Covers: Law firms in Chicago and Midwest region. Entries include: Company name, contact person, address, location, zip code, phone, statistics and email address.

6952 ■ Vault Guide to the Top Government and Non-Profit Legal Employers

Vault.com Inc.
150 W 22nd St., 5th Fl.
New York, NY 10011
Ph: (212)366-4212
Fax: (212)366-6117
Fr: 888-562-8285
URL: http://www.vault.com

$29.95 for individuals; $29.95 for members. Covers: 50 profiles of top legal employers in the United States. Entries include: Company name, contact person, address, location, phone and fax numbers, email, statistics, internship, compensations and hiring information.

6953 ■ Vault Guide to the Top Mid-Atlantic Law Firms

Vault.com Inc.
150 W 22nd St., 5th Fl.
New York, NY 10011
Ph: (212)366-4212
Fax: (212)366-6117
Fr: 888-562-8285
URL: http://www.vault.com

Latest edition February, 2008. $29.95 for individuals; $29.95 for members. Covers: Law firms in the Mid-Atlantic region. Entries include: Company name, contact person, address, phone and fax numbers, location, statistics and email address.

6954 ■ Vault Guide to the Top New York Law Firms

Vault.com Inc.
150 W 22nd St., 5th Fl.
New York, NY 10011
Ph: (212)366-4212
Fax: (212)366-6117
Fr: 888-562-8285
URL: http://www.vault.com

Latest edition 2009; 4th. $29.95 for individuals; $29.95 for members. Covers: Law firms in New York. Entries include: Company name, contact person, address, location, phone and fax numbers, statistics and email address.

6955 ■ Vault Guide to the Top Northern California Law Firms

Vault.com Inc.
150 W 22nd St., 5th Fl.
New York, NY 10011
Ph: (212)366-4212
Fax: (212)366-6117
Fr: 888-562-8285
URL: http://www.vault.com

Latest edition November, 2008. $29.95 for individuals; $29.95 for members. Covers: 81 leading law firms in Northern California legal markets. Entries include: Company name, contact person, address, location, statistics and email address.

6956 ■ Vault Guide to the Top Northwest & Great Plains Law Firms

Vault.com Inc.
150 W 22nd St., 5th Fl.
New York, NY 10011
Ph: (212)366-4212
Fax: (212)366-6117
Fr: 888-562-8285
URL: http://www.vault.com

Latest edition February, 2008. $29.95 for individuals; $29.95 for members. Covers: Law firms in the Northwest and Great Plains regions in the United States. Entries include: Company name, contact person, address, location, phone and fax numbers, statistics and email address.

6957 ■ Vault Guide to the Top Southeastern Law Firms
Vault.com Inc.
150 W 22nd St., 5th Fl.
New York, NY 10011
Ph: (212)366-4212
Fax: (212)366-6117
Fr: 888-562-8285
URL: http://www.vault.com

Latest edition May, 2006. $29.95 for individuals; $29.95 for members. Covers: 60 law firms in Southern-eastern legal markets including Miami, Atlanta and Charlotte. Entries include: Company name, contact person, address, location, phone and fax numbers, statistics and email address.

6958 ■ Vault Guide to the Top Texas & Southwest Law Firms
Vault.com Inc.
150 W 22nd St., 5th Fl.
New York, NY 10011
Ph: (212)366-4212
Fax: (212)366-6117
Fr: 888-562-8285
URL: http://www.vault.com

Latest edition March, 2007. $29.95 for individuals; $29.95 for members. Covers: 100 law firms in Texas and Southwest region. Entries include: Company name, contact person, address, location, phone, zip code, statistics, job offers and email.

6959 ■ Vault Guide to the Top Washington, D.C. Law Firms
Vault.com Inc.
150 W 22nd St., 5th Fl.
New York, NY 10011
Ph: (212)366-4212
Fax: (212)366-6117
Fr: 888-562-8285
URL: http://www.vault.com

Latest edition June, 2008. $29.95 for individuals; $29.95 for members. Covers: 50 law firms in Washington, DC. Entries include: Company name, contact person, address, phone and fax numbers, location, statistics and email address.

6960 ■ Who's Who in American Law
Marquis Who's Who L.L.C.
300 Connell Dr., Ste. 2000
Berkeley Heights, NJ 07922
Ph: (908)673-1000
Fax: (908)673-1189
Fr: 800-473-7020
E-mail: law@marquiswhoswho.com
URL: http://www.marquiswhoswho.com

Biennial, Latest edition 17th; 2011-2012. $365.00 for individuals. Covers: Over 19,000 lawyers, judges, law school deans and professors, and other legal professionals. Entries include: Name, home and office addresses, place and date of birth, educational background, career history, civic positions, professional memberships, publications, awards, special achievements. Arrangement: Alphabetical. Indexes: Fields of practice, professional area.

6961 ■ Wright-Holmes Law List
Wright-Holmes Inc.
45 Kensico Dr., 2nd Fl.
Mount Kisco, NY 10549
Ph: (914)241-3297
Fax: (914)241-3326
Fr: 800-258-5597
URL: http://www.collectioncenter.com/

Annual, April. Free. Covers: Over 1,400 law firms throughout the U.S., Canada and 35 other countries. Entries include: Firm name, address, phone. A commercial law list. Arrangement: Geographical.

HANDBOOKS AND MANUALS

6962 ■ Careers in Animal Law
American Bar Association
321 N Clark St.
Chicago, IL 60654
Ph: (312)988-5000
URL: http://apps.americanbar.org

Yolanda Eisenstein. 2011. $54.95. 160 pages (paperback). Contains an overview of the field from a practicing animal lawyer and professor of animal law. Includes information on how to be a successful animal law career with firms of all types and sizes like government agencies, major corporations, or nonprofit organizations.

6963 ■ Careers for Legal Eagles and Other Law-and-Order Types
The McGraw-Hill Companies
PO Box 182604
Columbus, OH 43272
Fax: (614)759-3749
Fr: 877-883-5524
E-mail: customer.service@mcgraw-hill.com
URL: http://www.mhprofessional.com/
    product.php?isbn=0071466207

Blythe Camenson. Second edition, 2005. $13.95 (paper). 176 pages.

6964 ■ Careers for Mystery Buffs and Other Snoops and Sleuths
The McGraw-Hill Companies
PO Box 182604
Columbus, OH 43272
Fax: (614)759-3749
Fr: 877-883-5524
E-mail: customer.service@mcgraw-hill.com
URL: http://www.mhprofessional.com

Blythe Camenson. Second edition. $14.95 (hardback). 160 pages.

6965 ■ Careers in Tax Law: Perspectives on the Tax Profession and What It Holds for You
American Bar Association
321 N Clark St.
Chicago, IL 60654
Ph: (312)988-5000
URL: http://apps.americanbar.org

John Gamino, Robb A. Longman and Matthew R. Sontag. 2009. $70.00. 308 pages (paperback). Serves as a guide for those considering or beginning a career in tax law. Contains perspectives, knowledge and experiences from 75 tax professionals.

6966 ■ Cleveland's Swimming Lessons for Baby Sharks: The Essential Guide to Thriving as a New Lawyer
West
610 Opperman Dr.
Eagan, MN 55123
Ph: (651)687-7000
URL: http://store.westlaw.com

Grover E. Cleveland. 2010. $30.00 (softbound). Provides practical, useful information that recent graduates need to survive their first year of law practice. Includes real-life examples with bulleted tips.

6967 ■ Future Performance: Your Guide to a Successful Career in Law
Aspatore Books
22 Thomson Pl.
Boston, MA 02210
Fax: (617)249-0219
URL: http://www.aspatore.com

Mona Mehta Stone. 2009. $40.00 (paper). 200 pages. Provides attorneys with a guide on how to excel professionally and get the most out of each stage of their careers. Offers invaluable insights about each phase of a lawyer's career, including life at law firms, government jobs and in-house positions.

6968 ■ Great Jobs for Liberal Arts Majors
The McGraw-Hill Companies
PO Box 182604
Columbus, OH 43272
Fax: (614)759-3749
Fr: 877-883-5524
E-mail: customer.service@mcgraw-hill.com
URL: http://www.mhprofessional.com/
    product.php?isbn=0071482148

Blythe Camenson. Second edition, 2007. $16.95 (paper). 192 pages.

6969 ■ The Happy Lawyer: Making a Good Life in the Law
Oxford University Press
198 Madison Ave.
New York, NY 10016
Ph: (212)726-6000
Fax: (919)677-1303
Fr: 800-445-9714
E-mail: custserv.us@oup.com
URL: http://www.oup.com/us

Nancy Levit and Douglas O. Linder. 2010. $19.95 (hardback). 304 pages. Offers an in-depth discussion of the causes of dissatisfaction among lawyers. Provides practical solutions to overcome professional unhappiness and achieve satisfaction.

6970 ■ Job Placement Strategies for Paralegals
Delmar Cengage Learning
5 Maxwell Dr.
Clifton Park, NY 12065
Fr: 800-648-7450
URL: http://www.delmarlearning.com/about/
    contact.aspx

Margaret E. Pickard. 2008. $48.95. Offers tools and strategies that can help paralegal students and professionals prepare a professional resume and cover letters as well as find job opportunities in the private and public sectors. Includes salary and detailed resume worksheets. Prepares job hunters for the job interview by providing practical advice including how to prepare, how to bring and what to wear.

6971 ■ Job Quest for Lawyers: The Essential Guide to Finding and Landing the Job You Want
American Bar Association
321 N Clark St.
Chicago, IL 60654
Ph: (312)988-5000
Fr: 800-285-2221
URL: http://www.americanbar.org/aba.html

Sheila Nielsen. 2011. $49.95 (paper). 160 pages. Provides guidelines for effective networking in order to enhance the job search of lawyers.

6972 ■ Landing a Federal Legal Job: Finding Success in the U.S. Government Job Market
American Bar Association
321 N Clark St.
Chicago, IL 60654
Ph: (312)988-5000
URL: http://apps.americanbar.org

Richard L. Hermann. 2011. $69.95. 552 pages (paperback). Contains U.S. government's legal employment opportunities.

6973 ■ Law School 101: How to Succeed in Your First Year of Law School and Beyond
Sphinx Publishing
1935 Brookdale Rd., Ste. 139
Naperville, IL 60563
Ph: (630)961-3900
Fax: (630)961-2168
Fr: 800-727-8866
URL: http://www.sphinxlegal.com/products/law-
    school-101-4.html

R. Stephanie Good. June 2009. $18.99

6974 ■ *Lawyer's Desk Book*
Aspen Publishers
76 Ninth Ave., 7th Fl.
New York, NY 10011
Ph: (212)771-0600
Fax: 800-561-4845
Fr: 800-638-8437
URL: http://www.aspenpublishers.com

Dana Shilling. First edition, supplementary. 2010.
$180.00. 1,860 pages.

**6975 ■ *The Lawyer's Guide to Finding
Success in Any Job Market***
Kaplan Publishing
395 Hudson St.
New York, NY 10014
Ph: (212)492-5800
URL: http://store.kaptest.com

Richard L. Hermann. 2009. $19.99. 288 pages
(paperback). Focuses on the job-search process for
attorneys who have been recently displaced and
gives detailed outlook on the current job scene.

**6976 ■ *The Legal Job Interview: Winning the
Law-Related Job in Today's Market***
Kaplan Publishing
1 Liberty Plz., 22nd Fl.
New York, NY 10006
Fax: (212)313-4800
E-mail: tim.brazier@kaplan.com
URL: http://www.kaptest.com

Cliff Ennico. 2008. $16.95. Helps legal professionals
learn the process and strategies of a typical interview,
what's different about legal job interviewers, things to
do before scheduling and arriving at the interview,
and the dos and don'ts of maximizing the chance of
getting the offered job.

**6977 ■ *Legally Green: Careers in
Environmental Law***
Crabtree Publishing Company
350 5th Ave., 59th Fl.
PMB 59051
New York, NY 10118
Ph: (212)496-5040
Fax: 800-355-7166
Fr: 800-387-7650
URL: http://www.crabtreebooks.com

Susan Down. 2012. $31.93. 64 pages (hardcover).
Features careers in environmental law. Includes job
information for public service and governmental agencies and environmental non-governmental organizations as well as attorneys and legal support staff for
law firms that offer services related to environmental
law.

6978 ■ *Letters to a Young Lawyer*
Basic Books
387 Park Ave. S., 12th Fl.
New York, NY 10016
Ph: (212)340-8100
URL: http://www.perseusbooksgroup.com/basic/

Alan Dershowitz. 2005. $14.95. 226 pages.

**6979 ■ *The Opportunity Maker: Strategies
for Inspiring Your Legal Career Through
Creative Networking and Business
Development***
West
610 Opperman Dr.
Eagan, MN 55123
Ph: (651)687-7000
URL: http://store.westlaw.com

Ari Kaplan. 2008. $26 (paper). 224 pages. Helps in
business development and empowering a legal
career from law school through partnership. Provides
techniques for defining personal brand, leveraging
creativity, and maximizing success. Offers perspectives on issues ranging from networking, mentoring,
and blogging to hosting a television show, starting a
charity, and getting published; also features a chapter
that addresses strategies for connecting with people

and establishing meaningful professional
relationships.

**6980 ■ *Real-Resumes for Legal and
Paralegal Jobs***
PREP Publishing
1110 1/2 Hay St., Ste. C
Fayetteville, NC 28305
Ph: (910)483-6611
Fax: (910)483-2439
E-mail: preppub@aol.com
URL: http://www.prep-pub.com/Bookstore/legal.htm

Anne McKinney. $16.95 (paper). 192 pages. Real-
Resumes Series.

6981 ■ *Resumes for Law Careers*
The McGraw-Hill Companies
PO Box 182604
Columbus, OH 43272
Fax: (614)759-3749
Fr: 877-883-5524
E-mail: customer.service@mcgraw-hill.com
URL: http://www.mhprofessional.com/
  product.php?isbn=0071482202

Third edition, 2007. $12.95 (paper). 144 pages.

6982 ■ *Should You Really Be a Lawyer?*
LawyerAvenue Press
4701 SW Admiral Way
PMB 278
Seattle, WA 98116
Ph: (206)229-9754
Fax: (206)319-4475
E-mail: info@lawyeravenue.com
URL: http://www.lawyeravenue.com

Deborah Schneider. 2010. $25.00 (paper). 276
pages. Serves as a guide for people who are considering a career in law. Offers advice on the decision
making process of entering or remaining in law
school.

6983 ■ *Vault Guide to Careers in Litigation*
Vault.com
132 W 31st St., 15th Fl.
New York, NY 10001
Ph: (212)366-4212
Fax: (212)366-6117
URL: http://www.vault.com

Kristin Nichols, Neeraja Viswanathan. 2009. $29.95
(paper). 162 pages.

EMPLOYMENT AGENCIES AND SEARCH FIRMS

6984 ■ Abelson Legal Search
1600 Market St., Ste. 505
Philadelphia, PA 19103
Ph: (215)561-3010
Fax: (215)561-3001
E-mail: abelson@abelsonlegalsearch.com
URL: http://www.abelsonlegalsearch.com

Provides attorneys, paralegals and legal professionals in all specialty areas to law firms, corporations
and financial institutions.

6985 ■ Access Staffing
360 Lexington Ave., 8th Fl.
New York, NY 10017
Ph: (212)687-5440
Fax: (212)557-2544
URL: http://www.accessstaffingco.com

Serves as a staffing firm covering accounting/
financial, advertising, bilingual Japanese, creative,
event planning, fashion/retail, healthcare/ human
services, human resources, information technology,
insurance, legal, light industrial and office support.

6986 ■ Assigned Counsel
950 W Valley Rd., Ste. 2600
Wayne, PA 19087
Ph: (610)964-8300

Fax: (610)964-2730
E-mail: info@assignedcounsel.com
URL: http://www.assignedcounsel.com

Description: Provides corporations, law firms and
other organizations with attorneys on temporary,
temp-to-perm or direct hire basis.

6987 ■ Attorney Recruiting Specialists
2031 Middle Rd.
Oneida, NY 13421
Ph: (315)363-1987
URL: http://www.attorneyrecruitingspecialists.com

Serves as a recruitment and placement agency for
attorneys who specialize in patent law.

6988 ■ Attorney Resources, Inc.
750 N St. Paul, Ste. 540
Dallas, TX 75201
Ph: (214)922-8050
E-mail: tlb@attorneyresource.com
URL: http://www.attorneyresource.com

Employment agency. Offices in Austin, Dallas, Fort
Worth, Houston and Tulsa, OK. Provides staffing assistance on regular or temporary basis.

6989 ■ A.W. Rush and Co.
230 Park Ave., Ste. 1000
New York, NY 10169
Ph: (212)551-3670
URL: http://www.awrush.com

Specializes in placing attorneys in all practice areas
including litigation, corporate, bankruptcy and restructuring, intellectual property, information technology,
real estate, healthcare, T and E, tax, regulatory, 40
Act, ERISA employment and labor.

**6990 ■ Beverly Hills Bar Association
Personnel Service**
300 S Beverly Dr., Ste. 201
Beverly Hills, CA 90212-4805
Ph: (310)601-2422
Fax: (310)601-2423
URL: http://www.bhba.org

Employment agency.

6991 ■ Career Advocates International
1539 Ave. A
Katy, TX 77493
Ph: (281)395-9848
Fax: (281)524-3949
URL: http://www.careeradvocates.org

Provides permanent placement and temporary staffing for executive and staff level positions. Specializes
in multiple niches including: sales and marketing, accounting and financial services, banking, communications, human resources, chemicals, oil and gas, medical and dental, legal, information technology, energy,
technology, engineering, manufacturing, construction,
and light industrial.

6992 ■ Coleman/Nourian
Two Penn Center, Ste. 1010
15th & JFK Blvd.
Philadelphia, PA 19102
Ph: (215)864-2700
Fax: (215)864-2709
E-mail: search@cnlegalsearch.com
URL: http://www.cnlegalsearch.com

Legal executive search firm.

6993 ■ Davidson Staffing
2302 Martin Ste. 150
Irvine, CA 92612
Ph: (949)955-3114
URL: http://www.davidsonstaffing.com

Provides full service staffing and recruiting solutions
for four core divisions namely: attorney staffing,
corporate administrative staff, legal support staff and
legal IT professionals.

6994 ■ Early Cochran & Olson LLC
1 E Wacker Dr., Ste. 2510
Chicago, IL 60601
Ph: (312)595-4200
Fax: (312)595-4209
E-mail: info@ecollc.com
URL: http://www.ecollc.com

Executive search firm focused specifically on the legal field.

6995 ■ ESQ Recruiting
1870 The Exchange SE, Ste. 100
Atlanta, GA 30339
Fr: 877-806-7215
E-mail: infoga@esqrecruiting.com
URL: http://www.esqrecruiting.com

Description: Legal recruiting firm that specializes in the placement of in-house attorneys for companies in the U.S. and around the world.

6996 ■ Exclusively Legal
2355 Northside Dr., Ste. 140
San Diego, CA 92108
Ph: (619)683-8501
Fr: 800-388-1178
E-mail: sandiego@exclusivelylegal.com
URL: http://www.exclusivelylegal.com

Description: Provides specialized staffing services to law firms and corporate legal departments.

6997 ■ Fergus Partnership Consulting Inc.
14 Wall St., Ste. 3C
New York, NY 10005
Ph: (212)767-1775
Fax: (212)346-7606
E-mail: ny@ferguslex.com
URL: http://www.ferguslex.com

An executive search firm for lawyers. Over 15 years of experience with prestigious law firms worldwide. Experienced in international business and finance.

6998 ■ Filcro Legal Staffing
521 Fifth Ave.
New York, NY 10175
Ph: (212)599-0909
Fax: (212)599-4772
E-mail: shannon@filcro.com
URL: http://www.filcro.com/page3.html

Serves as a legal recruitment firm specializing in the identification of legal support and legal administrative staff.

6999 ■ Garrison & Sisson
655 15th St., NW, Ste. 820
Washington, DC 20005
Ph: (202)429-5630
Fax: (202)659-2028
E-mail: gs@g-s.com
URL: http://www.g-s.com

Exists as a boutique attorney recruiting firm specializing in placement of former practicing attorneys in law firms and corporate legal departments.

7000 ■ Gibson Arnold & Associates Inc.
1111 Washington Ave., Ste. 220
Golden, CO 80401
Ph: (303)273-9420
Fax: (303)273-9420
Fr: 888-324-9420
E-mail: golden@gibsonarnold.com
URL: http://www.gibsonarnold.com

Supplies attorneys, paralegals, legal secretaries, support personnel and production clerks to major law firms and corporate legal departments nationwide on either a temporary or regular employment basis. Also maintains a full-time placement division. Assists law firms and corporations with staffing any in-house needs. Other services include assistance in law firm mergers, assistance in lateral partner moves and managing document review projects.

7001 ■ Greene-Levin-Snyder
150 E 58th St., 16th Fl.
New York, NY 10155
Ph: (212)752-5200
Fax: (212)752-8245
E-mail: search@glslsg.com
URL: http://www.glslsg.com

Places partners, associates, general counsel, and a broad spectrum of in-house attorneys, as well as compliance and regulatory professionals.

7002 ■ Houser Martin Morris
110th Ave. NE, 110 Atrium Pl., Ste. 580
Bellevue, WA 98004
Ph: (425)453-2700
Fax: (425)453-8726
E-mail: info@houser.com
URL: http://www.houser.com

Focus is in the areas of retained executive search, professional and technical recruiting. Areas of specialization include software engineering, sales and marketing, information technology, legal, human resources, accounting and finance, manufacturing, factory automation, and engineering.

7003 ■ Interquest Inc.
98 Cuttermill Rd., Ste. 337S
Great Neck, NY 11021-3006
Ph: (516)482-2330
Fax: (516)482-2114

Offers retained executive search and other consulting services for the legal profession, with primary focus being general counsel searches for corporations, law firm members and lateral movement of partners for law firms.

7004 ■ Karen Dexter & Associates Inc.
2012 Chestnut Ave. N, Ste. 29
Wilmette, IL 60091-1512
Ph: (847)853-9500
Fax: (847)256-7108

Training and development consultant offering interpersonal skills training and one on one performance counseling for employees of large organizations. Industries served: advertising, banking and finance, consumer products, entertainment, food and beverage, healthcare, legal profession, manufacturing, government agencies, publishing and broadcasting.

7005 ■ Keystone Attorney Placement
2421 W Pratt Blvd., Ste. 307
Chicago, IL 60645
Fax: 888-212-3204
Fr: 888-212-0242
E-mail: info@keystone-attorneys.com
URL: http://www.keystone-attorneys.com

Specializes in the recruitment and placement of lateral law firm associates nationwide.

7006 ■ The Klausner Group
60 E 42nd St., Ste. 3517
New York, NY 10165
Ph: (212)557-5800
Fax: (212)557-3833
Fr: 800-272-4615
E-mail: chassenbein@klausnergroup.com
URL: http://www.klausnergroup.com

Serves as a legal placement firm that focuses solely on the permanent placement of attorneys in companies and law firms throughout the country. Employs recruiters with an expertise of the market in a given practice area.

7007 ■ Kruza Legal Search
1845 Walnut St., Ste. 855
Philadelphia, PA 19103
Ph: (215)981-5455
Fax: (215)981-0662
E-mail: info@kruza.com
URL: http://www.kruza.com

Specializes in connecting law firms and corporate legal departments with attorneys, paralegals and administrative support staff.

7008 ■ LateralAttorneys.com
3575 Piedmont Rd. NE, Bldg. 15, Ste. 900
Atlanta, GA 30305
Ph: (404)221-9990
Fax: (404)221-9998
E-mail: jobs@partners-group.com
URL: http://www.lateralattorneys.com

Specialized search for the legal profession. Offers recruitment and placement of attorneys and paralegals.

7009 ■ Law Firm Staff
202 S Lake Ave., Ste. 250
Pasadena, CA 91101
Fr: 800-298-6440
E-mail: jobs@lawfirmstaff.com
URL: http://www.lawfirmstaff.com

Description: Provides both temporary and direct hire placement solutions for law firms and corporations seeking attorneys, paralegals, legal secretaries, and other administrative personnel crucial to the running of a successful law practice.

7010 ■ Law Resources
1140 Connecticut Ave. NW, Ste. 675
Washington, DC 20036
Ph: (202)371-1270
Fax: (202)371-0979
E-mail: apply@lawresources.com
URL: http://www.lawresources.com

Description: Exists as a legal placement firm seeking qualified and experienced legal and support staff, whether for short-term, long-term, temp-to-perm or permanent hire.

7011 ■ Legal Placement Services, Inc.
6737 W Washington St., Ste. 2390
West Allis, WI 53214
Ph: (414)276-6689
Fax: (414)276-1418
E-mail: info@ps-companies.com
URL: http://www.ps-companies.com/legal-placement-services

Employment agency. Periodically fills temporary placements, as well.

7012 ■ Major Legal Services
1301 E 9th St., Ste. 1414
Cleveland, OH 44114
Ph: (216)579-9782
Fax: (216)579-1662
Fr: 800-808-3097
URL: http://www.lawplacement.com

Description: Provides contract and permanent staffing needs of law firms and corporate legal departments.

7013 ■ Major, Lindsey, and Africa
7301 Parkway Dr. S
Hanover, MD 21076
Fax: (410)694-5172
Fr: 877-482-1010
E-mail: hr@mlaglobal.com
URL: http://www.mhaglobal.com

Executive search firm. Affiliate offices in Atlanta, GA, Chicago, IL, and New York, NY.

7014 ■ McCormack Schreiber Legal Search
303 W Madison St., Ste. 2150
Chicago, IL 60606
Ph: (312)377-2000
Fax: (312)377-2001
Fr: (866)819-4091
E-mail: info@thelawrecruiters.com
URL: http://www.thelawrecruiters.com

Exists as an attorney search firm that specializes in the permanent placement of associates, partners and practice groups at large, midsize and boutique law firms, and in-house counsel of all levels at regional, national and international corporations. Participates in acquisitions and transfers of practice groups and law firm mergers.

7015 ■ Momentum Legal
2630 Exposition Blvd., Ste. 119-B
Austin, TX 78703
Ph: (512)524-4241
E-mail: jane@momentumlegal.com
URL: http://www.momentumlegal.com

Executive search firm specializing in permanent search and temporary legal staffing solutions within law firms and corporations across the country. Focuses on creating opportunities and building long term relationships with attorneys, law firms and corporate legal departments.

7016 ■ MS Legal Search
2415 W Alabama St., Ste. 214
Houston, TX 77098
Ph: (713)807-8500
E-mail: ms@mslegalsearch.com
URL: http://www.mslegalsearch.com

Offers permanent attorney placement services to corporations and law firms.

7017 ■ Pat Taylor and Associates
1101 17th St. NW, Ste. 707
Washington, DC 20036
Ph: (202)466-5622
Fax: (202)466-5630
E-mail: pat@pattaylor.com
URL: http://www.pattaylor.com

Specializes in temporary and permanent placement of attorneys, paralegals, and law clerks.

7018 ■ Pittleman and Associates
336 E 43rd St.
New York, NY 10017
Ph: (212)370-9600
Fax: (212)370-9608
URL: http://pittlemanassociates.com

Legal recruiting firm specializing in placing attorneys in permanent jobs in law firms, corporations, investment banks, management consulting firms, and other organizations.

7019 ■ Post and Arneson
2657 Windmill Pkwy., Ste. 669
Henderson, NV 89074
Ph: (702)689-4663
Fax: 877-504-2015
Fr: 800-555-1024
E-mail: amandaj@counselscout.com
URL: http://counselscout.com

Specializes in the nationwide placement of all levels of attorneys in law firms and corporations. Places associates and partners in law firms ranging from boutique firms to large international firms.

7020 ■ Prescott Legal Search
3900 Essex Ln., Ste. 1110
Houston, TX 77027
Ph: (713)439-0911
Fax: (713)439-1317
URL: http://www.prescottlegal.com

Serves as a legal search firm providing law professionals for law firms and corporations.

7021 ■ Recruiting Partners
3494 Camino Tassajara Rd., No. 404
Danville, CA 94506
Ph: (925)964-0249
E-mail: info@recruitingpartners.com
URL: http://www.recruitingpartners.com

Description: Serves as an executive and technical recruiting firm that specializes in accounting, legal, information technology, engineering, executive management and technical writing.

7022 ■ Robert Half Legal
2884 Sand Hill Rd.
Menlo Park, CA 94025
Fr: 800-870-8367
URL: http://www.roberthalflegal.com

Description: Provides legal professionals on a

project and full-time basis. Specializes in the placement of attorneys, paralegals and legal support personnel for law firms and corporate legal departments.

7023 ■ Seltzer Fontaine Beckwith
2999 Overland Ave., Ste. 120
Los Angeles, CA 90064
Ph: (310)839-6000
Fax: (310)839-4408
E-mail: info@sfbsearch.com
URL: http://www.sfbsearch.com

Serves as a legal search firm specializing in the placement of lawyers with law firms, corporations, and non-profits in California and nationally. Provides counseling regarding career development strategies, resume drafting, and interviewing skills and consulting regarding diversity issues and other trends in the profession.

7024 ■ Synectics for Management Decisions Inc.
1901 N Moore St., Ste. 900
Arlington, VA 22209-1717
Ph: (703)528-2772
Fax: (703)528-2857
E-mail: info@smdi.com
URL: http://www.smdi.com

Organizational analysis and development consulting firm specializing in economic and international expertise, executive search, management information systems, data processing, training, economic expertise to legal profession, business brokerage, mergers and acquisitions, and leasing services. Serves private industries as well as government agencies.

7025 ■ T. Palmer Recruiters
One Center Plz., Ste. 220
Boston, MA 02108
Ph: (978)764-3819
Fax: (617)227-6886
URL: http://www.tpalmerrecruiters.com

Provides national recruitment services for corporations and law firms with a particular focus on intellectual property/patent law. Offers placements in a variety of industries including chemical, biotechnology, medical device, healthcare, telecommunications, information technology and clean technology.

7026 ■ Weiss & Associates
2422 Sweetwater Cc Place Dr.
PO Box 915656
Apopka, FL 32712
Ph: (407)774-1212
Fax: (407)774-0084
E-mail: weisslawstrategy@aol.com

Executive and legal search consultants and recruiters for major law firms and multinational corporations throughout North America and Europe. Special expertise with tax attorneys and key tax executives in addition to experienced partners with significant portable business. Also specializes in mergers and outplacement services.

7027 ■ Westwood Law Consultants
PO Box 1731
Beverly Hills, CA 90213
E-mail: westwoodlc@aol.com
URL: http://www.westwoodlc.com

Specializes in the nationwide recruiting of intellectual property lawyers who have acquired prior engineering, scientific or technical education and experience in addition to their legal expertise.

ONLINE JOB SOURCES AND SERVICES

7028 ■ AttorneyJobs.com
URL: http://attorneyjobs.com

Description: Provides a database of current attorney and law-related job opportunities, contract opportuni-

ties, and practice development options. Offers advice and assistance to lawyers in all employment sectors, at all levels of experience, and in all stages of their careers.

7029 ■ Counsel.net
URL: http://counsel.net

Description: Provides employment resources for the legal industry such as chatboards, legal jobs, classified ads, legal forums, practice areas, attorney marketing and more.

7030 ■ EmpLawyerNet.com
2331 Westwood Blvd., No. 331
Los Angeles, CA 90064
Fr: 800-270-2688
E-mail: membership@emplawyernet.com
URL: http://www.emplawyernet.com

Description: Career resource site for lawyers. Contains career information, resume posting and job board search, along with links to CLE events, online bookstores, and recruiter directories. Fee: Limited access permitted with free basic membership. Premier membership is $125/year or $14.95/month and includes free CLE courses, e-mail alerts, networking opportunities and personal career advice.

7031 ■ GetEntryLevelAttorneyJobs.com
URL: http://www.getentrylevelattorneyjobs.com

Description: Provides online job search for entry level attorney professionals.

7032 ■ Goinhouse.com
E-mail: info@goinhouse.com
URL: http://www.goinhouse.com

Description: Specializes in in-house legal positions. Features jobs ranging from general counsel to corporate and in-house counsel positions.

7033 ■ Headhunt.com: The Counsel Network
URL: http://www.thecounselnetwork.com

Description: Job search and career resource site for attorneys. Search for jobs, post profile, contact recruiters and consultants, download PDF career guides, and more. Registration is free.

7034 ■ iHireLegal.com
URL: http://www.ihirelegal.com

Description: Serves as an online resource of job postings, internet job boards and classified ads in the legal industry. Include features such as free summary resume blast, free salary data, email notification of jobs, live telephone customer support and more.

7035 ■ Law.com: Law Jobs
URL: http://www.lawjobs.com

Description: Visitors can post job openings for attorneys, legal support staff and temporary workers. Also resources for legal recruiters and temporary staffing agencies.

7036 ■ LawGuru.com
URL: http://www.lawguru.com

Description: Offers a legal bulletin board with an archive of questions and answers, links, job listings, legal news, chat, and FAQs.

7037 ■ LawInfo Career Center
Fr: 800-397-3743
URL: http://jobs.lawinfo.com

Description: Offers employment sites in the legal community including resources for both job seekers and employers.

7038 ■ Lawjobs.com
URL: http://www.lawjobs.com

Description: Features a career center that provides latest news and hiring trends, salary information, career advancement articles, career advice, surveys and more. Provides a job database categorized according to specific positions in the legal profession industry.

7039 ■ Lawmatch.com
URL: http://lawmatch.com

Description: Provides resume and job posting for legal staffing positions. Offers web-based recruitment tools and methodologies to job seekers and employers.

7040 ■ Lawyers Weekly
URL: http://lawyersweeklyclassifieds.com

Description: Provides legal employment opportunities on the web. Maintains job listings from law firms, legal recruiters and corporate legal departments throughout the country, with new listings posted weekly.

7041 ■ Legal Authority
URL: http://www.legalauthority.com

Description: Serves as a portal for legal employment opportunities. Maintains a legal employer database that is updated 24 hours a day.

7042 ■ LegalStaff.com
URL: http://www.legalstaff.com

Description: Provides list of legal and law-related jobs. Offers free searches, job agent feature, and the opportunity to post qualifications for employers to review.

7043 ■ Vault.com
132 W 31st St., 15th Fl.
New York, NY 10001
Ph: (212)366-4212
Fax: (212)366-6117
E-mail: publicity@vault.com
URL: http://www.vault.com

Description: Job board website with searches emphasizing jobs in legal, business, consulting and finance fields of practice. Contains online profile posting, resume review, company research, salary calculators and relocation tools.

TRADESHOWS

7044 ■ Academy of Legal Studies in Business Annual Conference
Academy of Legal Studies in Business
c/o Constance E. Bagley, Pres.
Yale School of Management
135 Prospect St.
PO Box 208200
New Haven, CT 06520
Ph: (203)432-8398
E-mail: connie.bagley@yale.edu
URL: http://alsb.roundtablelive.org

Annual. Provides opportunities for legal studies educators and others to network and meet with colleagues. Defines and advances legal studies in business and management education. 2012 August 7-11; Kansas, MO; Kansas City Intercontinental.

7045 ■ American Association of Attorney-Certified Public Accountants Annual Meeting and Educational Conference
American Association of Attorney-Certified Public Accountants
3921 Old Lee Hwy., Ste. No. 71A
Fairfax, VA 22030
Ph: (703)352-8064
Fax: (703)352-8073
Fr: 888-288-9272
URL: http://netforum.avectra.com/eWeb/
StartPage.aspx?Site=AAA-CPA

Annual. Primary Exhibits: Exhibits for persons licensed both as attorneys and CPAs.

7046 ■ American Association for Justice Convention/Exposition
American Association for Justice
777 6th St., N.W., Ste. 200
Washington, DC 20001
Ph: (202)965-3500
Fax: (202)625-7313
Fr: 800-424-2725
E-mail: info@atlahq.org
URL: http://www.atlanet.org

Annual. Primary Exhibits: Legal product/service providers, including computer animation videos, computer software/hardware, demonstrative evidence products, expert witness services and marketing firms, as well as high-end consumer gifts, online services, structured settlement services, litigation support, legal publishing. Dates and Locations: 2012 Feb 11-15; Phoenix, AZ; Arizona Biltmore Resort and Spa.

7047 ■ American Society of International Law Meeting
American Society of International Law
2223 Massachusetts Ave., N.W.
Washington, DC 20008
Ph: (202)939-6000
Fax: (202)797-7133
E-mail: services@asil.org
URL: http://www.asil.org

Annual. Primary Exhibits: Scholars, practitioners, government officials, political scientists, and specialists in subjects; international law publications and services. Dates and Locations: 2012 Mar 28-31; Washington, DC.

7048 ■ Association of American Law Schools Annual Meeting
Association of American Law Schools
1201 Connecticut Ave. N.W., Ste. 800
Washington, DC 20036-2717
Ph: (202)296-8851
Fax: (202)296-8869
E-mail: aals@aals.org
URL: http://www.aals.org

Annual. Primary Exhibits: Law books, personal computers and hardware and software, video equipment, and communication technology. Dates and Locations: 2013 Jan 04-08; New Orleans, LA; 2015 Jan 02-06.

7049 ■ Association for Continuing Legal Education Meeting
Association for Continuing Legal Education
PO Box 4646
Austin, TX 78765
Ph: (512)453-4340
Fax: (512)451-2911
E-mail: aclea@aclea.org
URL: http://www.aclea.org

Primary Exhibits: Legal education information and services. Dates and Locations: 2012 Jan 28-31; New Orleans, LA; The Astor Crowne Plaza.

7050 ■ Federal Bar Association Convention
Federal Bar Association
1220 N. Fillmore St., Ste. 444
Arlington, VA 22201
Ph: (571)481-9100
Fax: (571)481-9090
E-mail: fba@fedbar.org
URL: http://www.fedbar.org

Annual. Primary Exhibits: Legal publications, computer software, and insurance information.

7051 ■ Florida Bar Annual Convention
The Florida Bar
651 E Jefferson St.
Tallahassee, FL 32399-2300
Ph: (850)561-5600
E-mail: flabarwm@flabar.org
URL: http://www.floridabar.org/tfb/flabarwe.nsf

Annual. Primary Exhibits: Publications, office equipment, computers, insurance, and information on

investment services and overnight carriers. Dates and Locations: 2013 Jun 20-23; Kissimmee, FL; Gaylord Palms Hotel & Convention Center.

7052 ■ National Association of Hearing Officials Annual Conference
National Association of Hearing Officials
PO Box 4999
Midlothian, VA 23112
URL: http://www.naho.org

Annual. Provides participants with a wide choice of seminars at each training segment that will meet certification requirements. Provides a rich learning experience in the classroom and offers many opportunities for networking during conferences.

7053 ■ National Association for Law Placement Annual Education Conference
National Association for Law Placement
1220 19th St. N.W., Ste. 401
Washington, DC 20036-2405
Ph: (202)835-1001
Fax: (202)835-1112
E-mail: info@nalp.org
URL: http://www.nalp.org

Annual. Primary Exhibits: Exhibits relating to recruitment and placement of lawyers. Dates and Locations: 2012 Apr 18-21; Austin, TX; Hilton Austin; 2013 Apr 24-27; Tampa, FL; Greater Tampa Convention Center; 2014 Apr 09-12; Seattle, WA; Washington State Convention & Trade Center; 2015 Apr 22-25; Chicago, IL; Sheraton Chicago Hotel & Towers.

7054 ■ National Association of Legal Search Consultants Conference
National Association of Legal Search Consultants
1525 N Park Dr., Ste. 102
Weston, FL 33326
Ph: (954)349-8081
Fax: (954)349-1979
Fr: (866)902-6587
E-mail: info@nalsc.org
URL: http://www.nalsc.org

Annual. Offers legal search professionals the opportunity to network within the industry.

7055 ■ National Association of State Judicial Educators Annual Conference
National Association of State Judicial Educators
c/o Judith M. Anderson, Pres.
Administrative Office of the Courts
PO Box 41170
Olympia, WA 98504
Ph: (360)705-5231
Fax: (360)956-5700
E-mail: judith.anderson@courts.wa.gov
URL: http://nasje.org

Annual. Gives judicial educators the tools to develop effective and exciting education programs in their states. Includes educational sessions, demonstrations of model programs, technology showcase, regional meetings, leadership convocation, opportunities to network and more.

7056 ■ National Association of Women Judges Annual Conference
National Association of Women Judges
1341 Connecticut Ave. NW, Ste. 4.2
Washington, DC 20036-1834
Ph: (202)393-0222
Fax: (202)393-0125
E-mail: nawj@nawj.org
URL: http://www.nawj.org

Annual. Features panels and speeches addressing issues relevant to the judicial system and the role of women in facing new challenges. 2012 November 7-12; Miami, FL; Eden Roc Renaissance Miami Beach.

7057 ■ National Bar Association Annual Convention & Exhibits
National Bar Association
1225 11th St., N.W.
Washington, DC 20001

Ph: (202)842-3900
Fax: (202)289-6170
URL: http://www.nationalbar.org

Annual. Primary Exhibits: Computers and legal software; office products; accounting services; financial planners, temporary employment agencies; legal publications; travel agencies; luggage and leather goods; fine arts and jewelry. Dates and Locations: 2012 Jul 14-19; Las Vegas, NV; Caesars Palace.

7058 ■ National Council of Juvenile and Family Court Judges Annual Conference

National Council of Juvenile and Family Court Judges
PO Box 8970
Reno, NV 89507
Ph: (775)784-6012
Fax: (775)784-6628
E-mail: staff@ncjfcj.org
URL: http://www.ncjfcj.org

Annual. Covers discussions focusing on juvenile and family law topics including custody and visitation, divorce, child abuse and neglect, domestic violence, juvenile delinquency, and substance abuse.

7059 ■ National LGBT Bar Association Annual Career Fair & Conference

National LGBT Bar Association
1301 K St. NW, Ste. 1100 East Tower
Washington, DC 20005-3823
Ph: (202)637-7661
E-mail: info@lgbtbar.org
URL: http://www.lgbtbar.org

Annual. Features activities and events such as career services and job search strategies for law students, individual career counseling, various workshops, transgender appreciation activities, and more.

7060 ■ State Bar of California Annual Meeting

State Bar of California
180 Howard St.
San Francisco, CA 94105
Ph: (415)538-2000
Fax: (415)538-2247
E-mail: feedback@calbar.ca.gov
URL: http://www.calbar.ca.gov

Annual. Primary Exhibits: Publications, computers, timekeeping equipment, and office equipment.

7061 ■ State Bar of Michigan Annual Meeting

State Bar of Michigan
306 Townsend St.
Lansing, MI 48933-2012
Ph: (517)346-6300
Fax: (517)482-6248
Fr: 800-968-1442
E-mail: csharlow@mail.michbar.org
URL: http://www.michbar.org

Annual. Primary Exhibits: Law books, encyclopedias, telephones, stationery, legal newspapers, computers, and office equipment.

OTHER SOURCES

7062 ■ American Academy of Adoption Attorneys (AAAA)

PO Box 33053
Washington, DC 20033
Ph: (202)832-2222
Fax: (251)432-9706
E-mail: info@adoptionattorneys.org
URL: http://www.adoptionattorneys.org

Description: Attorneys who practice or have otherwise distinguished themselves in the field of adoption law. Promotes the reform of adoption laws and disseminating information on ethical adoption practices. Offers educational and charitable programs and a speakers' bureau.

7063 ■ American Academy of Matrimonial Lawyers (AAML)

150 N Michigan Ave., Ste. 1420
Chicago, IL 60601
Ph: (312)263-6477
Fax: (312)263-7682
E-mail: office@aaml.org
URL: http://www.aaml.org

Description: Represents board certified attorneys specializing in the field of matrimonial and family law. Seeks to encourage the study, improve the practice, elevate the standards, and advance the cause of matrimonial law in an effort to preserve the welfare of the family and society. Conducts legal institutes. Sponsors advanced mandatory continuing legal education program.

7064 ■ American Association for Justice (AAJ)

777 6th St. NW, Ste. 200
Washington, DC 20001
Ph: (202)965-3500
Fax: (202)298-6849
Fr: 800-424-2725
E-mail: membership@justice.org
URL: http://www.justice.org

Description: Represents lawyers, judges, law professors, paralegals, and students engaged in civil plaintiff or criminal defense advocacy. Advances jurisprudence and the law as a profession; encouraging mutual support and cooperation among members of the bar; advancing the cause of persons seeking redress for damages against person or property; training in advocacy; upholding and improving the adversary system and trial by jury. Holds year-round educational programs. Sponsors environmental law essay contest; student trial by jury program; public interest programs; and National Student Trial Advocacy Competition. Conducts research on insurance, product liability, premises liability, environmental torts, and medical malpractice.

7065 ■ American Association of Nurse Attorneys (TAANA)

PO Box 14218
Lenexa, KS 66285-4218
Fax: (913)895-4652
Fr: 877-538-2262
E-mail: taana_executive_office@goamp.com
URL: http://www.taana.org

Description: Nurse attorneys, nurses in law school, and attorneys in nursing school. Aims to inform the public on matters of nursing, health care and law. Facilitates communication and information sharing between professional groups; establishes an employment network; assists new and potential nurse attorneys; develops the profession; promotes the image of nurse attorneys as experts and consultants in nursing and law. Maintains educational foundation.

7066 ■ American Bar Association (ABA)

321 N Clark St.
Chicago, IL 60610
Ph: (312)988-5000
Fr: 800-285-2221
E-mail: service@americanbar.org
URL: http://www.abanet.org

Description: Attorneys in good standing of the bar of any state. Conducts research and educational projects and activities to: encourage professional improvement; provide public services; improve the administration of civil and criminal justice; increase the availability of legal services to the public. Sponsors Law Day USA. Administers numerous standing and special committees such as Committee on Soviet and East European Law, providing seminars and newsletters. Operates 25 sections, including Criminal Justice, Economics of Law Practice, and Family Law. Sponsors essay competitions. Maintains library.

7067 ■ American Board of Professional Liability Attorneys (ABPLA)

4355 Cobb Pkwy., Ste. J-208
Atlanta, GA 30339

Ph: (404)989-7663
URL: http://www.abpla.org

Description: Accredited by the American Bar Association to certify Attorneys in the areas of medical, legal or accounting professional. Liability litigation attorneys who have satisfied requirements of litigation experience and who have passed the written liability examination. Promotes and improves ethical and technical standards of advocacy and litigation practice in professional liability litigation; establishes basic standards for training, qualification, and recognition of specialists; fosters efficient administration of justice. Provides graduated training program for licensed attorneys desiring certification as specialists in the field. Offers placement service; compiles statistics. Maintains file of abstracts and program transcripts.

7068 ■ American Board of Trial Advocates (ABOTA)

2001 Bryan St., Ste. 3000
Dallas, TX 75201-3078
Ph: (214)871-7523
Fax: (214)871-6025
Fr: 800-932-2682
E-mail: briant@abota.org
URL: http://www.abota.org

Description: Civil trial plaintiff and defense attorneys. Seeks to preserve the jury system. Promotes the 7th Amendment. Fosters improvement in the ethical and technical standards of practice in the field of advocacy. Elevates the standards of integrity, honor and courtesy in the legal profession. Aids in further education and training of trial lawyers. Works for the preservation of the jury system. Improves the methods of procedure of the present trial court system.

7069 ■ American Catholic Lawyers Association (ACLA)

U.S. Highway Rt. 46, Ste. 7
PO Box 10092
Fairfield, NJ 07004
Ph: (973)244-9895
Fax: (973)244-9897
E-mail: info@acla-inc.org
URL: http://www.americancatholiclawyers.org

Description: Represents individuals dedicated to the free legal defense of and the rights of Catholics in America. Seeks to establish the "Social Kingship of Christ", and uphold the Divine prerogatives and moral law. Provides free legal services on behalf of Catholics needing legal defense in matters of faith and conscience.

7070 ■ American College of Environmental Lawyers (ACOEL)

1300 SW 5th Ave., Ste. 2300
Portland, OR 97201-5630
Ph: (207)774-1200
Fax: (207)774-1127
E-mail: jthaler@bernsteinshur.com
URL: http://www.acoel.org

Description: Represents the interests of lawyers who practice in the field of environmental law. Maintains and improves the ethical practice of environmental law, the administration of justice, and the development of environmental law at both the state and federal level.

7071 ■ American College of Trial Lawyers (ACTL)

19900 MacArthur Blvd., Ste. 530
Irvine, CA 92612
Ph: (949)752-1801
Fax: (949)752-1674
E-mail: nationaloffice@actl.com
URL: http://www.actl.com

Description: Maintains and improves the standards of trial practice, the administration of justice and the ethics of the profession. Brings together members of the profession who are qualified and who, by reason of probity and ability, will contribute to the accomplishments and good fellowship of the College.

7072 ■ American Employment Law Council (AELC)
4800 Hampden Ln., 7th Fl.
Bethesda, MD 20814
Ph: (301)951-9326
Fax: (301)654-7354
E-mail: info@aelc-law.org
URL: http://aelc-law.com

Description: Represents labor and employment attorneys practicing on the management side. Seeks to encourage and promote the standards of professional competence and responsibility in the field of labor and employment law. Provides a forum for discussion and exchange of information among employment attorneys.

7073 ■ American Foreign Law Association (AFLA)
Simpson Thatcher and Bartlett LLP
425 Lexington Ave.
New York, NY 10017-3954
E-mail: jkerr@stblaw.com
URL: http://www.afla-law.org

Description: Represents attorneys, jurists, and law professors concerned with issues in international, comparative, and foreign law. Maintains non-governmental organization status with the United Nations. Conducts research. Sponsors educational programs, monthly luncheon programs, and International Law Weekend.

7074 ■ American Health Lawyers Association (AHLA)
1620 Eye St. NW, 6th Fl.
Washington, DC 20006-4010
Ph: (202)833-1100
Fax: (202)833-1105
E-mail: pleibold@healthlawyers.org
URL: http://www.healthlawyers.org

Description: Focuses on the legal issues in the healthcare field. Provides resources to address the issues facing its active members who practice in law firms, government, in-house settings, and academia and who represent the entire spectrum of the health industry: physicians, hospitals and health systems, health maintenance organizations, health insurers, managed care companies, nursing facilities, home care providers, and consumers.

7075 ■ American Immigration Lawyers Association (AILA)
1331 G St. NW, Ste. 300
Washington, DC 20005-3142
Ph: (202)216-2400
Fax: (202)783-7853
E-mail: executive@aila.org
URL: http://www.aila.org

Description: Lawyers specializing in the field of immigration and nationality law. Fosters and promotes the administration of justice with particular reference to the immigration and nationality laws of the United States.

7076 ■ American Intellectual Property Law Association (AIPLA)
241 18th St. S, Ste. 700
Arlington, VA 22202
Ph: (703)415-0780
Fax: (703)415-0786
E-mail: aipla@aipla.org
URL: http://www.aipla.org

Description: Voluntary bar association of lawyers practicing in the fields of patents, trademarks, copyrights, and trade secrets. Aids in the operation and improvement of U.S. patent, trademark, and copyright systems, including the laws by which they are governed and rules and regulations under which federal agencies administer those laws. Sponsors moot court and legal writing competitions.

7077 ■ American Law Institute (ALI)
4025 Chestnut St.
Philadelphia, PA 19104-3099

Ph: (215)243-1600
Fax: (215)243-1636
Fr: 800-253-6397
E-mail: ali@ali.org
URL: http://www.ali.org

Description: Judges, law teachers, and lawyers. Promotes the clarification and simplification of the law and its better adaptation to social needs by continuing work on the Restatement of the Law, model and uniform codes, and model statutes. Conducts a program of continuing legal education jointly with the American Bar Association called "ALI-ABA".

7078 ■ Association of American Law Schools (AALS)
1201 Connecticut Ave. NW, Ste. 800
Washington, DC 20036-2717
Ph: (202)296-8851
Fax: (202)296-8869
E-mail: aals@aals.org
URL: http://www.aals.org

Description: Law schools association. Seeks to improve the legal profession through legal education. Interacts for law professors with state and federal government, other legal education and professional associations, and other national higher education and learned society organizations. Compiles statistics; sponsors teacher placement service. Presents professional development programs.

7079 ■ Association of Corporate Counsel
1025 Connecticut Ave. NW, Ste. 200
Washington, DC 20036
Ph: (202)293-4103
Fax: (202)293-4701
URL: http://www.acc.com

Description: Consists of attorneys who practice in the legal departments of corporations and other private sector organizations. Promotes the common interests of its members, contributes to their continuing education, seeks to improve understanding of the role of in-house attorneys, and encourages advancements in the standards of corporate legal practice. Connects its members to each other and to the people and resources necessary for their personal and professional growth.

7080 ■ Association of Defense Trial Attorneys (ADTA)
4135 Topsail Trail
New Port Richey, FL 34652
Ph: (727)859-0350
E-mail: gwalker@handarendall.com
URL: http://www.adtalaw.com

Description: Trial lawyers who have over five years' experience in the preparation and trial of insurance cases and the handling of insurance matters, and who possess the knowledge, skill, and facilities to provide insurance companies and self-insurers a legal service of the highest standard. Maintains current biographical data on each member.

7081 ■ Association of Family and Conciliation Courts (AFCC)
6525 Grand Teton Plz.
Madison, WI 53719
Ph: (608)664-3750
Fax: (608)664-3751
E-mail: afcc@afccnet.org
URL: http://www.afccnet.org

Description: Judges, counselors, family court personnel, attorneys, mediators, researchers, and teachers concerned with the resolution of family disputes as they affect children. Proposes to develop and improve the practice of dispute resolution procedure as a complement to judicial procedures. Aims to strengthen the family unit and minimize family strife by improving the process of marriage, family, and divorce counseling; and to provide an interdisciplinary forum for the exchange of ideas, for the creation of new approaches to child custody matters and solutions to problems of family discord. Collaborates with the National Council of Juvenile and

Family Court Judges, National Judicial College, the National Center for State Courts, the American Bar Association and several universities, law schools, and state organizations responsible for providing ongoing training for attorneys, judges, and family therapists. Conducts research and offers technical assistance and training to courts, legal associations, judicial organizations, and behavioral science professionals.

7082 ■ Association of Muslim American Lawyers (AMAL)
Woolworth Bldg., Ste. 801
233 Broadway
New York, NY 10279-0815
E-mail: info@theamal.org
URL: http://theassociationofmuslimamericanlawyers.law.officelive.com/default.a

Description: Seeks to assist the Muslim American community's exercise of legal rights through education. Encourages entry of Muslim Americans into the legal profession. Promotes high standards of professionalism, integrity, and honor among members.

7083 ■ Association of Patent Law Firms (APLF)
2125 Center Ave., Ste. 406
Fort Lee, NJ 07024
Ph: (201)403-0927
E-mail: admin@aplf.org
URL: http://www.aplf.org

Description: Represents independent specialty law firms that devote a majority of their practice to patent, trademark and copyright law. Provides expert patent litigation support, portfolio strategy advice and protection against copyright and trademark theft. Strives to ensure excellence in intellectual property law practice.

7084 ■ Center for American and International Law
5201 Democracy Dr.
Plano, TX 75024-3561
Ph: (972)244-3400
Fax: (972)244-3401
Fr: 800-409-1090
E-mail: cail@cailaw.org
URL: http://www.cailaw.org

Description: Provides continuing legal and law enforcement education, focusing primarily on continuing education programs for lawyers and management training programs for law enforcement officials.

7085 ■ Center for Environmental Science Advocacy and Reliability (CESAR)
1990 3rd St., Ste. 400
Sacramento, CA 95811
Ph: (916)341-7407
Fax: (916)341-7410
E-mail: info@bestscience.org
URL: http://bestscience.org

Description: Seeks to ensure the efficient and effective enforcement of the Endangered Species Act (ESA). Provides members and the public with educational information about ESA and its applications. Encourages scientific rigor in implementing environmental statutes.

7086 ■ Croatian American Bar Association (CABA)
6 Papette Cir.
Ladera Ranch, CA 92694
Ph: (949)274-5360
E-mail: marko@croatianamericanbar.com
URL: http://www.croatianamericanbar.com

Description: Promotes the advancement of lawyers and law students of Croatian heritage in the legal profession. Provides a forum for professional networking, support, and exchange of ideas among its members. Supports the provision of legal services to the Croatian-American community. Fosters camaraderie among its members.

7087 ■ Decalogue Society of Lawyers (DSL)
39 S LaSalle St., Ste. 410
Chicago, IL 60603
Ph: (312)263-6493
Fax: (312)263-6512
E-mail: decaloguesociety@gmail.com
URL: http://decaloguesociety.org

Description: Represents lawyers of the Jewish faith. Seeks to promote and cultivate social and professional relations among members of the legal profession. Conducts a forum on topics of general and Jewish interest. Maintains placement service to help members find employment and office facilities.

7088 ■ Education Law Association (ELA)
300 College Park
Dayton, OH 45469-0528
Ph: (937)229-3589
Fax: (937)229-3845
E-mail: ela@educationlaw.org
URL: http://www.educationlaw.org

Description: School attorneys, law professors, professors of education, school administrators, teachers, and school board members. Works for exchange of information on law school; seeks to stimulate research and publication in the field.

7089 ■ Employment Law Alliance (ELA)
727 Sansome St.
San Francisco, CA 94111
Ph: (415)835-9011
Fax: (415)834-0443
E-mail: shirschfeld@employmentlawalliance.com
URL: http://www.employmentlawalliance.com

Description: Represents lawyers working for independent law firms throughout the world. Aims to help prevent employment and labor problems from arising. Works to ensure legal compliance around the globe.

7090 ■ Equal Justice Works
2120 L St. NW, Ste. 450
Washington, DC 20037-1541
Ph: (202)466-3686
E-mail: dstern@equaljusticeworks.org
URL: http://www.equaljusticeworks.org

Description: Works to surmount barriers to equal justice that affect millions of low-income individuals and families. Engaged in organizing, training, and supporting public service-minded law students and creates summer and postgraduate public interest jobs.

7091 ■ Federation of Defense and Corporate Counsel (FDCC)
11812 N 56th St.
Tampa, FL 33617
Ph: (813)983-0022
Fax: (813)988-5837
E-mail: mstreeper@thefederation.org
URL: http://www.thefederation.org

Description: Professional society of attorneys actively engaged in the legal aspects of the insurance industry; insurance company executives; corporate counsel involved in the defense of claims. Conducts research through Federation of Defense and Corporate Counsel Foundation. Sponsors annual essay competition for students at accredited law colleges. Maintains 36 law sections and committees. Conducts seminars and educational sessions.

7092 ■ First Amendment Lawyers Association (FALA)
123 W Madison St., Ste. 1300
Chicago, IL 60602
Ph: (312)236-0606
Fax: (312)236-9264
E-mail: wgiampietro@wpglawyers.com
URL: http://firstamendmentlawyers.org

Description: Lawyers who support and defend cases involving the First Amendment to the U.S. Constitution (i.e., freedom of religion, freedom of speech and the press, freedom to peaceably assemble, and

freedom to petition the government for a redress of grievances).

7093 ■ Food and Drug Law Institute (FDLI)
1155 15th St. NW, Ste. 800
Washington, DC 20005
Ph: (202)371-1420
Fax: (202)371-0649
Fr: 800-956-6293
E-mail: comments@fdli.org
URL: http://www.fdli.org

Description: Provides forum regarding laws, regulations and policies related to drugs, medical devices, and other health care technologies.

7094 ■ Human Rights Advocates (HRA)
PO Box 5675
Berkeley, CA 94705
E-mail: info@humanrightsadvocates.org
URL: http://www.humanrightsadvocates.org

Description: International human rights lawyers and professionals. Objectives are to provide education about the application of human rights law and to promote this body of law domestically and internationally. Organizes public conferences, lectures, and seminars; submits amicus curiae briefs. Maintains library of current United Nations documents and materials on human rights organizations; has consultative status with ECOSOC.

7095 ■ Institute of Judicial Administration (IJA)
New York University School of Law
Wilf Hall
139 MacDougal St., Rm. 116
New York, NY 10012
Ph: (212)998-6149
Fax: (212)995-4657
E-mail: torrey.whitman@nyu.edu
URL: http://www.law.nyu.edu/centers/judicial/index.htm

Description: Lawyers, judges, and laypersons with an interest in judicial administration. Promotes judicial, procedural, and administrative improvements in the courts; encourages dialogue among the bench, bar, and academy. Furthers empirical research on improving the understanding of the justice system. Offers educational programs for appellate and trial judges.

7096 ■ Inter-American Bar Association (IABA)
1211 Connecticut Ave. NW, Ste. 202
Washington, DC 20036
Ph: (202)466-5944
Fax: (202)466-5946
E-mail: iaba@iaba.org
URL: http://www.iaba.org

Description: National, regional, and special associations of attorneys; individual lawyers. Purposes are to: advance the science of jurisprudence, and in particular, the study of comparative law; promote uniformity in commercial legislation; further the knowledge of laws of Western Hemisphere countries; propagate justificative administration through the creation and maintenance of independent judicial systems; protect and defend civil, human, and political rights of individuals; uphold the honor of the legal profession; encourage geniality and brotherhood among members.

7097 ■ International Academy of Trial Lawyers (IATL)
5841 Cedar Lake Rd., Ste. 204
Minneapolis, MN 55416-5657
Ph: (952)546-2364
Fax: (952)545-6073
Fr: (866)823-2443
E-mail: iatl@llmsi.com
URL: http://www.iatl.net

Description: Represents the interests of attorneys who have been practicing for a minimum of 12 years and who are principally engaged in trial and appellate practice. Maintains museum-type Lincoln Library,

including old and rare books. Operates charitable program.

7098 ■ International Amusement and Leisure Defense Association (IALDA)
PO Box 4563
Louisville, KY 40204
Ph: (502)473-0956
Fax: (502)473-7352
E-mail: info@ialda.org
URL: http://www.ialda.org

Description: Promotes and protects the interests of the amusement and leisure industries. Encourages members to exchange information, share experiences and develop litigation strategies regarding the amusement and leisure industry. Serves as a clearinghouse for speakers and authors on industry-specific topics.

7099 ■ International Municipal Lawyers Association (IMLA)
7910 Woodmont Ave., Ste. 1440
Bethesda, MD 20814
Ph: (202)466-5424
Fax: (202)785-0152
E-mail: info@imla.org
URL: http://www.imla.org

Description: Seeks to promote and advance the development of local government law and. Serves as a clearinghouse of local law materials; collects and disseminates information; assists government agencies to prepare for litigation and develop new local laws; provides legal research and writing services; offers continuing legal education opportunities; conducts research programs.

7100 ■ International Society of Barristers (ISOB)
University of Michigan Law School
802 Legal Research Bldg.
Ann Arbor, MI 48109-1215
Ph: (734)763-0165
Fax: (734)764-8309
E-mail: info@internationalsocietyofbarristers.org
URL: http://www.internationalsocietyofbarristers.org

Description: Encourages the continuation of advocacy under the adversary system. Seeks young lawyers to enter advocacy and preserves the right of trial by jury.

7101 ■ International Technology Law Association (ITechLaw)
401 Edgewater Pl., Ste. 600
Wakefield, MA 01880
Ph: (781)876-8877
Fax: (781)224-1239
E-mail: office@itechlaw.org
URL: http://www.itechlaw.org

Description: Lawyers, law students, and others interested in legal problems related to computer-communications technology. Aids in: contracting for computer-communications goods and services; perfecting and protecting proprietary rights chiefly in software; and taxing computer-communications goods, services, and transactions, and liability for acquisition and use of computer-communications goods and services. Provides specialized educational programs; and offers limited placement service. Holds Annual Computer Law Update.

7102 ■ Iranian American Bar Association (IABA)
51855 MacArthur Blvd. NW, No. 624
Washington, DC 20016
Ph: (202)828-1217
Fax: (202)857-9799
E-mail: info@iaba.us
URL: http://www.iaba.us

Description: Works to educate and inform the Iranian American community about legal issues of interest. Seeks to ensure that the American public at large, Iranian American representatives and other government officials are fully and accurately informed on legal matters of interest and concern to the Iranian

American community. Promotes the social, economic, professional and educational advancement of the Iranian American community. Strives to publicize and promote the achievements of Iranian American lawyers and other legal professionals.

7103 ■ Lithuanian-American Bar Association (LABAS)
221 N Main St., Ste. 300
Ann Arbor, MI 48104
Ph: (734)222-0088
Fax: (734)769-2196
E-mail: pas@patstreeter.com
URL: http://javadvokatai.org

Description: Organizes, sponsors, and supports educational programs promoting the highest standards in legal scholarship and its application. Advances an understanding of the legal system of the United States of America in the Republic of Lithuania, and of the legal system of the Republic of Lithuania in the United States of America. Promotes a harmonious and productive relationship between the United States of America and the Republic of Lithuania.

7104 ■ Media Law Resource Center (MLRC)
North Tower, 20th Fl.
520 Eighth Ave.
New York, NY 10018
Ph: (212)337-0200
Fax: (212)337-9893
E-mail: medialaw@medialaw.org
URL: http://www.medialaw.org

Description: Provides support for media defendants in libel and privacy cases, including development of statistical and empirical data, assistance in locating expert witnesses or consultants, and help in coordinating amicus curiae briefs by supporting organizations. Maintains a brief, pleading, and information bank; collects and disseminates information on pending libel and privacy cases for use in legal defense against claims. Serves as a liaison with media organizations, attorneys, and other groups working to advance the defense of libel and privacy claims. Prepares bulletins and reports on current developments and cases, legal theories, privileges, and defenses. Compiles statistics on the incidence and cost of libel and privacy litigation. Provides employment for law student interns. Conducts educational and training workshops and programs; has established fellowship program in libel law.

7105 ■ Minority Corporate Counsel Association (MCCA)
1111 Pennsylvania Ave. NW
Washington, DC 20004
Ph: (202)739-5901
Fax: (202)739-5999
E-mail: info@mcca.com
URL: http://www.mcca.com

Description: Advocates for the expanded hiring, retention, and promotion of minority attorneys in corporate law departments and the law firms that serve them. Collects and disseminates information about diversity in the legal profession. Creates effective professional skills development programs for minority attorneys.

7106 ■ NALS, The Association for Legal Professionals
8159 E 41st St.
Tulsa, OK 74145
Ph: (918)582-5188
Fax: (918)582-5907
E-mail: info@nals.org
URL: http://www.nals.org

Description: Consists of members who represent every area of the industry from paralegals and legal assistants to legal administrators and office managers. Aims to enhance the careers of legal secretaries. Offers professional development by providing continuing legal education, certifications, information, and training.

7107 ■ National Association of Appellate Court Attorneys (NAACA)
University of Richmond Law School
28 Westhampton Way
University of Richmond, VA 23173
Ph: (804)289-8204
Fax: (804)289-8992
E-mail: mdonaghy@richmond.edu
URL: http://www.naacaonline.org

Description: Comprised of attorneys employed by state and federal appellate courts across the country. Aims to provide educational, networking and professional development opportunities for staff attorneys, judges' law clerks and other attorneys employed by appellate courts.

7108 ■ National Association of College and University Attorneys (NACUA)
1 Dupont Cir., Ste. 620
Washington, DC 20036
Ph: (202)833-8390
Fax: (202)296-8379
E-mail: nacua@nacua.org
URL: http://www.nacua.org

Description: Represents attorneys from U.S. and Canadian campuses, colleges and universities. Compiles and distributes legal decisions, opinions, and other writings and information on legal problems affecting colleges and universities.

7109 ■ National Association of Criminal Defense Lawyers (NACDL)
1660 L St. NW, 12th Fl.
Washington, DC 20036
Ph: (202)872-8600
Fax: (202)872-8690
E-mail: assist@nacdl.org
URL: http://www.nacdl.org

Description: Advances the mission of the nation's criminal defense lawyers to ensure justice and due process for persons accused of crime or other misconduct. A professional bar association that includes private criminal defense lawyers, public defenders, law professors, active military defense counsel and judges committed to preserving fairness within America's criminal justice system.

7110 ■ National Association of Hearing Officials
PO Box 4999
Midlothian, VA 23112
URL: http://www.naho.org

Description: Consists of individuals involved in administrative hearings. Works to improve the administrative hearing process and thereby benefit hearing officials, their employing agencies, and the individuals they serve. Provides training, continuing education, a national forum for discussion of issues, and leadership concerning administrative hearings.

7111 ■ National Association for Law Placement (NALP)
1220 19th St. NW, Ste. 401
Washington, DC 20036-2405
Ph: (202)835-1001
Fax: (202)835-1112
E-mail: info@nalp.org
URL: http://www.nalp.org

Description: Brings together law schools, legal employers, and bar associations to share information, research, and professional development opportunities. Works to facilitate legal career counseling and planning, recruitment and retention, and the professional development of law students and lawyers. Aims to cultivate ethical practices and fairness in legal career counseling and planning, recruitment, employment, and professional development; to promote the full range of legal career opportunities and to foster access to legal public interest and public sector employment; and to advocate for diversity in the legal profession and in the membership.

7112 ■ National Association of Legal Investigators (NALI)
235 N Pine St.
Lansing, MI 48933
Ph: (517)702-9835
Fax: (517)372-1501
Fr: (866)520-6254
E-mail: pjaeb@heartlandinfo.com
URL: http://www.nalionline.org

Description: Legal investigators, both independent and law firm staff, who specialize in investigation of personal injury matters for the plaintiff and criminal defense. Promotes professionalization of the legal investigator, accomplished by seminars and a professional certification program. Provides nationwide network of contact among members. Compiles statistics.

7113 ■ National Association of Minority and Women Owned Law Firms (NAMWOLF)
735 N Water St., Ste. 1205
Milwaukee, WI 53202
Ph: (414)277-1139
Fax: (414)831-2285
E-mail: contact@namwolf.org
URL: http://www.namwolf.org

Description: Encourages women and minorities to pursue careers in the legal profession and fosters the formation of minority and women-owned law firms. Urges major corporations and public entities to utilize the services of minority and women-owned law firms. Assists its members in developing strategic alliances, coalitions, and affiliations with corporations, in-house counsel, and other legal trade associations. Strives to ensure the long-term survival of minority and women-owned law firms.

7114 ■ National Association of State Judicial Educators
c/o Judith M. Anderson, Pres.
Administrative Office of the Courts
PO Box 41170
Olympia, WA 98504
Ph: (360)705-5231
Fax: (360)956-5700
E-mail: judith.anderson@courts.wa.gov
URL: http://news.nasje.org

Description: Strives to improve the justice system through judicial branch education. Furthers the professional education, growth and experience of state judicial educators.

7115 ■ National Association of Traffic Accident Reconstructionists and Investigators (NATARI)
PO Box 2588
West Chester, PA 19382
Ph: (610)696-1919
E-mail: natari@natari.org
URL: http://www.natari.org

Description: Represents engineers, attorneys, police officers, private investigators, medical examiners, and other individuals involved in the analysis of motor vehicle traffic accidents. Gathers and disseminates information on techniques and equipment of potential use to members; reviews literature in the field. Participating Organization of the Accreditation Commission for Traffic Accident Reconstruction.

7116 ■ National Association of Women Lawyers (NAWL)
American Bar Center, MS 15.2
321 N Clark St.
Chicago, IL 60654
Ph: (312)988-6186
Fax: (312)988-5100
E-mail: nawl@nawl.org
URL: http://www.nawl.org

Description: Purpose: Membership is open to any person who is a member in good standing of the bar of any state or U.S. territory, any non-U.S. legal professional (attorney or judge), any prospective attorney currently attending law school, and any state or local bar or law school association with compatible objectives. Men are welcome and encouraged to join.

7117 ■ National Bar Association (NBA)
1225 11th St. NW
Washington, DC 20001
Ph: (202)842-3900
Fax: (202)289-6170
E-mail: dsheltonjd@aol.com
URL: http://www.nationalbar.org

Description: Professional association of minority (predominantly African-American) attorneys, members of the judiciary, law students, and law faculty. Represents the interests of members and the communities they serve. Offers continuing legal education programs. Maintains hall of fame.

7118 ■ National Black Law Students Association (NBLSA)
1225 11th St. NW
Washington, DC 20001-4217
Ph: (202)618-2572
E-mail: info@nblsa.org
URL: http://www.nblsa.org

Description: Aims to serve the needs and goals of black law students and "effectuate change" in the legal community. Includes chapters or affiliates in six different countries including the Bahamas, Nigeria, and South Africa. Conducts sessions comprising a program of prominent speakers, seminars, case study analyses, and small group discussions covering concerns, problems, issues, and opportunities in academic administration.

7119 ■ National Council of Juvenile and Family Court Judges
PO Box 8970
Reno, NV 89507
Ph: (775)784-6012
Fax: (775)784-6628
E-mail: staff@ncjfcj.org
URL: http://www.ncjfcj.org

Description: Serves as a group of judges dedicated to improving the effectiveness of the nation's juvenile courts. Works to improve courts and systems practice and raise awareness of the core issues that touch the lives of many of the nation's children and families. Provides training, technical assistance, and research to help the nation's courts, judges and staff.

7120 ■ National Criminal Justice Association (NCJA)
720 7th St. NW, 3rd Fl.
Washington, DC 20001
Ph: (202)628-8550
Fax: (202)448-1723
E-mail: info@ncja.org
URL: http://www.ncja.org

Description: State, tribal and local criminal justice planners, police chiefs, judges, prosecutors, defenders, corrections officials, educators, researchers, and elected officials. Promotes innovation in the criminal justice system through the focused coordination of law enforcement, the courts, corrections, and juvenile justice. Seeks to: focus attention on national issues and developments related to the control of crime; determine and effectively express the states' and tribes' collective views on pending legislative and administrative action encompassing criminal and juvenile justice; improve the states' and tribes' administration of their criminal and juvenile justice responsibilities through the development and dissemination of information to and among justice administrators and policy makers. Conducts technical assistance and training programs.

7121 ■ National District Attorneys Association (NDAA)
44 Canal Center Plz., Ste. 110
Alexandria, VA 22314
Ph: (703)549-9222
Fax: (703)836-3195
E-mail: cyates@ndaa.org
URL: http://www.ndaa.org

Description: Elected/appointed prosecuting at-torneys; associate members are assistant prosecuting attorneys, investigators, paralegals, and other prosecution office staff. Dedicated in providing information and a national forum for prosecuting attorneys. Seeks to serve prosecuting attorneys and to improve and facilitate the administration of justice in the U.S. Provides educational and informational services, technical assistance and research in areas such as vehicular crimes, juvenile justice, guns prosecution, community prosecution, DNA forensics, white collar crime, drug prosecution and child abuse prosecution through the American Prosecutors Research Institute. Prepares amicus curiae briefs.

7122 ■ National Employment Lawyers Association (NELA)
417 Montgomery St., 4th Fl.
San Francisco, CA 94104
Ph: (415)296-7629
Fax: (415)677-9445
E-mail: nelahq@nelahq.org
URL: http://www.nela.org

Description: Attorneys who represent individual employees in cases involving employment discrimination, wrongful termination, benefits, and other employment-related matters. Promotes the professional development of members through networking, publications, technical assistance, and education. Supports the workplace rights of individual employees via lobbying and other activities. Maintains informational bank of pleadings and briefs; does not operate a lawyer referral service. Conducts regional seminars; conducts educational programs.

7123 ■ National Lawyers Association (NLA)
44 Cook St., Ste. 100
Denver, CO 80206
Ph: (303)398-7030
Fax: (303)398-7001
E-mail: nla@nla.org
URL: http://www.nla.org

Description: Seeks to improve the image of the legal profession. Aims to advance legal institutions and respect for the law, and to educate the public on such matters. Provide services, benefits, technology, education, guidance and professional assistance to its members.

7124 ■ National Lawyers Guild (NLG)
132 Nassau St., Rm. 922
New York, NY 10038
Ph: (212)679-5100
Fax: (212)679-2811
E-mail: director@nlg.org
URL: http://www.nlg.org

Description: Lawyers, law students, legal workers, and jailhouse lawyers dedicated to seek economic justice, social equality, and the right to political dissent. Serves as national center for progressive legal work providing training programs to both members and nonmembers. Sponsors skills seminars in different areas of law. Maintains speakers' bureau and offers legal referrals.

7125 ■ National LGBT Bar Association
1301 K St. NW, Ste. 1100, East Tower
Washington, DC 20005-3823
Ph: (202)637-7661
E-mail: info@lgbtbar.org
URL: http://www.lgbtbar.org

Description: Serves as a group of lawyers, judges and other legal professionals, law students, activists, and affiliate lesbians, gay, bisexual, transgender legal organizations. Promotes justice in and through the legal profession for the LGBT community in all its diversity.

7126 ■ National Organization of Bar Counsel (NOBC)
110 E Main St.
Madison, WI 53703
Ph: (608)267-8915

Fax: (608)267-1959
E-mail: bill.weigel@wicourts.gov
URL: http://www.nobc.org

Description: Attorneys for bar associations and disciplinary agencies in the U.S. and Canada who are professionally involved in representing their associations in all legal matters, with emphasis on matters of professional misconduct by lawyers. Participates in interpreting and prosecuting professional ethics, investigating unauthorized practice of law, and initiating improved legislation.

7127 ■ Personal Injury Lawyers Marketing and Management Association (PILMMA)
607 Briarwood Dr., Ste. 4
Myrtle Beach, SC 29572
Fax: (866)859-8126
Fr: 800-497-1890
E-mail: info@pilmma.org
URL: http://www.pilmma.org

Description: Represents personal injury lawyers and disability attorneys. Provides members with the necessary tools, information and education to help grow and manage a successful contingency-based injury and disability law practice. Seeks to fulfill the marketing and management needs of members by granting access to sources of credible information and educational events.

7128 ■ Puerto Rican Legal Defense and Education Fund (PRLDEF)
99 Hudson St., 14th Fl.
New York, NY 10013-2815
Ph: (212)219-3360
Fax: (212)431-4276
Fr: 800-328-2322
URL: http://www.prldef.org

Description: Seeks to secure, promote and protect the civil and human rights of the Puerto Rican and wider Latino community. (Three divisions, Legal, Policy and Education, carry out the core program areas - Civil and Human Rights, Civic Engagement and Empowerment, Civil Society and Culture and Equitable Educational Opportunities -the pursuit of a legal career for Puerto Ricans and other minorities via its LSAT prep course, Law Day and other programs).

7129 ■ Serbian Bar Association of America (SBAA)
20 S Clark, Ste. 700
Chicago, IL 60603
Ph: (312)782-8500
E-mail: apavich@monicopavich.com
URL: http://www.serbbar.org

Description: Provides resource assistance to, and promotes the best interests of, the Serbian American community. Acts as a vehicle for making unified public pronouncements to represent and advocate the vital interests of the Serbian American community as a whole with respect to current social, political, economic, legal and other matters of vital concern. Serves as a national network of communication among members of the Serbian American legal community for purposes of networking, exchange of ideas, client referrals and career placement opportunities.

7130 ■ Society of Ethical Attorneys at Law (SEAL)
PO Box 5993
San Antonio, TX 78201
Ph: (210)785-0935
Fax: (210)785-9254
E-mail: info@societyofethicalattorneys.org
URL: http://www.societyofethicalattorneys.org

Description: Aims to restore the public integrity of all lawyers. Seeks to advance the positive public image of attorneys and the profession of practicing law. Promotes honesty, clarity and integrity in the practice of law and in attorney relations with tribunals, clients, potential clients and the public.

7131 ■ Society of Trust and Estate Practitioners USA (STEP USA)
40 E 84th St., Ste. 5D
New York, NY 10028
Ph: (212)737-3690
Fax: (917)206-4306
E-mail: step@step.org
URL: http://www.step.org

Description: Aims to bring together all practitioners in the field of trusts and estates. Raises the public profile of trust and estate work as a profession in its own right. Advances knowledge and learning in trusts, estates and allied subjects. Encourages and promotes the study of trusts and estate practice. Provides education, training, representation and networking for its members.

7132 ■ Swedish-American Bar Association (SABA)
5020 Campus Dr.
Newport Beach, CA 92660
Ph: (949)706-9111
Fax: (949)706-9155
Fr: 888-656-5824
E-mail: mikael@koltailaw.com
URL: http://www.saba-advokat.com

Description: Represents Swedish speaking attorneys in the United States. Provides sources of Swedish speaking professional legal services for Swedish-American businesses. Facilitates communication and collaboration among members.

7133 ■ Taiwanese American Lawyers Association (TALA)
3333 S Brea Canyon Rd., Ste. 213
Diamond Bar, CA 91765
Ph: (909)468-4650
Fax: (909)468-5020
E-mail: tonymlu@yahoo.com
URL: http://www.tala-ca.org

Description: Represents Taiwanese attorneys practicing law in the United States. Works to provide a forum for professional exchange and to serve the Taiwanese community in the United States. Raises the awareness and knowledge of U.S. laws, legal system and individual rights.

7134 ■ Total Practice Management Association (TPMA)
25 E Washington St., Ste. 510
Chicago, IL 60602
Ph: (312)496-6074

Fr: (866)200-5744
E-mail: info@totalattorneys.com
URL: http://www.totalattorneys.com

Description: Focuses on the advancement of attorneys, paralegals and other legal support staff. Offers solo practitioners and small law firms the tools, training and network needed to collaborate with peers, connect with experts and find better work-life balance. Coordinates workshops and conferences, educational resources, legal tools, affinity partnerships and community forums.

7135 ■ Transportation Lawyers Association (TLA)
PO Box 15122
Lenexa, KS 66285-5122
Ph: (913)895-4615
Fax: (913)895-4652
E-mail: tla-info@goamp.com
URL: http://www.translaw.org

Description: Attorneys representing transportation interests throughout the U.S. and Canada. Assists members in the practice of transportation law through exchange of ideas, education, and participation in rule-making proceedings. Cosponsors annual Transportation Law Institute.

SOURCES OF HELP-WANTED ADS

7136 ■ Annual Review of Law and Social Science
Annual Reviews Inc.
4139 El Camino Way
Palo Alto, CA 94306
Ph: (650)493-4400
Fax: (650)424-0910
Fr: 800-523-8635
URL: http://www.annualreviews.org/journal/lawsocsci

Annual. $80.00/year for individuals, print & online; $242.00/year for institutions, print & online; $202.00/year for institutions, print only; $202.00/year for institutions, online only. Journal covering current issues in law and the social sciences.

7137 ■ Berkeley Business Law Journal
University of California, Boalt Hall School of Law
215 Boalt Hall
Berkeley, CA 94720-7200
Ph: (510)643-1741
URL: http://www.boalt.org/bblj

Semiannual. $45.00/year for individuals; $65.00/year for elsewhere. Journal that aims to create innovative business law-oriented commentary created by professors, professionals, and students.

7138 ■ Boston Bar Journal
Boston Bar Association
16 Beacon St.
Boston, MA 02108
Ph: (617)742-0615
Fax: (617)523-0127
URL: http://www.bostonbar.org/pub/bbj/index.htm

Journal for lawyers on important matters of legal interest.

7139 ■ California Lawyer
Daily Journal Corp.
915 E 1st St.
Los Angeles, CA 90012
Ph: (213)229-5300
Fax: (213)229-5481
URL: http://www.dailyjournal.com

Monthly. $95.00/year for individuals. Law magazine.

7140 ■ Chicago Lawyer
Law Bulletin Publishing Co.
415 N State St.
Chicago, IL 60610
Ph: (312)644-7800
E-mail: ryates@lbpc.com
URL: http://www.chicagolawyermagazine.com/
Home.aspx

Monthly. $60.00/year for individuals; $96.00/year for two years. Legal magazine (Tabloid).

7141 ■ Columbia Journal of Law and Social Problems
Columbia Law School
435 W 116th St.
New York, NY 10027-7237
Ph: (212)854-2640
E-mail: jlsp@law.columbia.edu
URL: http://www.columbia.edu/cu/jlsp/

$40.00/year for individuals; $45.00/year for other countries; $17.50/year for single issue. Journal covering economic, sociological and political laws.

7142 ■ Cornerstone
National Legal Aid & Defender Association
1140 Connecticut Ave. NW, Ste. 900
Washington, DC 20036
Ph: (202)452-0620
Fax: (202)872-1031
E-mail: info@nlada.org
URL: http://www.nlada100years.org

Description: Three issues/year. Monitors current issues affecting legal aid attorneys and public defenders. Recurring features include job listings, conference and training updates, news of research, book reviews, and news of members.

7143 ■ Criminal Justice Studies
Routledge Journals
270 Madison Ave.
New York, NY 10016-0601
Ph: (212)216-7800
Fax: (212)563-2269
URL: http://www.tandf.co.uk/journals/titles/
1478601x.html

Quarterly. $388.00/year for institutions, print + online; $375.00/year for institutions, online only; $123.00/year for individuals, print only. Peer-reviewed journal covering articles on criminal justice and criminological issues.

7144 ■ D & O Advisor
American Lawyer Media L.P.
120 Broadway, 5th Fl.
New York, NY 10271
Ph: (212)457-9400
Fax: (646)417-7705
Fr: 800-603-6571
URL: http://www.alm.com

Quarterly. Magazine that offers advice and perspective on corporate oversight responsibilities for directors and officers.

7145 ■ Executive Legal Adviser
Incisive Media
120 Broadway, 5th Fl.
New York, NY 10271
Ph: (212)457-9400
Fax: (646)417-7705
URL: http://www.executivelegaladviser.com

Bimonthly. Free to qualified subscribers. Magazine that offers legal advice for corporate executives.

7146 ■ Global Jurist Frontiers
Berkeley Electronic Press
2809 Telegraph Ave., Ste. 202
Berkeley, CA 94705-1167
Ph: (510)665-1200
Fax: (510)665-1201
URL: http://www.bepress.com/gj/frontiers/

Annual. $645.00/year corporate; $215.00/year academic. Journal that publishes papers on new issues of comparative law, law and economics, international law, law and development, and legal anthropology.

7147 ■ Houston Law Review
University of Houston
4800 Calhoun Rd.
Houston, TX 77004
Ph: (713)743-2255
E-mail: inquiry@houstonlawreview.org
URL: http://www.houstonlawreview.org/

Quarterly. $35.00/year for individuals. Journal focusing on current issues in law. Publishes contributions from academicians, practicing lawyers, and other scholars, and selected Law Review students.

7148 ■ Institute of Justice and International Studies
Central Missouri State University
PO Box 800
Warrensburg, MO 64093
Ph: (660)543-4111
Fax: (660)543-8517
Fr: 877-729-8266
E-mail: cjinst@ucmo.edu
URL: http://www.ucmo.edu/cjinst/Journal.html

Irregular. Free. Journal that publishes reports on international crime including corrections, media coverage, public policy, counter terrorism, and civil liberties.

7149 ■ Ius Gentium
University of Baltimore
1415 Maryland Ave.
Baltimore, MD 21201-5779
Ph: (410)837-4468
Fax: (410)837-4450
URL: http://law.ubalt.edu/template.cfm?page=615

Annual. $69.95/year for individuals. Journal that facilitates analysis and the exchange of ideas about contemporary legal issues from a comparative perspective.

7150 ■ Job Announcements
National Center for State Courts
300 Newport Ave.
Williamsburg, VA 23185
Ph: (757)259-1525
Fax: (757)220-0449
Fr: 800-616-6164
URL: http://www.ncsc.org

Description: Semimonthly. Provides lists of court-related job openings in the United States and its territories.

7151 ■ Journal of the American Criminal Justice Association
American Criminal Justice Association
PO Box 601047
Sacramento, CA 95860-1047
Ph: (916)484-6553
Fax: (916)488-2227
URL: http://www.acjalae.org/journal1.html

Semiannual. Journal covering issues in criminal justice.

7152 ■ Journal of Empirical Legal Studies
John Wiley & Sons Inc.
350 Main St., Commerce Pl.
Malden, MA 02148-5089
Ph: (781)388-8200
Fax: (781)388-8210
URL: http://www.wiley.com/bw/journal.asp?ref=1740-1453&site=1

Quarterly. $508.00/year for institutions, U.S. print & online; $441.00/year for institutions, U.S. print or online; $388.00/year for institutions, other countries, print & online; $337.00/year for institutions, other countries, print or online. Journal focusing on law and law-related fields, including civil justice, corporate law, criminal justice, domestic relations, economics, finance, health care, political science, psychology, public policy, securities regulation, and sociology.

7153 ■ Journal of Health and Life Sciences Law
American Health Lawyers Association
1620 Eye St. NW, 6th Fl.
Washington, DC 20006-4010
Ph: (202)833-1100
Fax: (202)833-1105
URL: http://www.healthlawyers.org

Quarterly. $149.00/year for individuals. Professional journal covering healthcare issues and cases and their impact on the health care arena.

7154 ■ Journal of the Missouri Bar
The Missouri Bar
326 Monroe St.
PO Box 119
Jefferson City, MO 65102-0119
Ph: (573)635-4128
Fax: (573)635-2811
URL: http://www.mobar.org/7b2e21b5-eb97-4f01-91da-1ff2beb5bb45.as

Bimonthly. Magazine featuring short, practical articles on legal subjects for practicing attorneys.

7155 ■ The Journal of Taxation
RIA Group
195 Broadway
New York, NY 10007-3100
Fr: 800-431-9025
URL: http://ria.thomson.com/estore/detail.aspx?ID=JTAX

Monthly. $390.00/year for individuals, print; $565.00/year for individuals, online/print bundle; $440.00/year for individuals, online. Journal for sophisticated tax practitioners.

7156 ■ Kentucky Bench & Bar Magazine
Kentucky Bar Association
514 W Main St.
Frankfort, KY 40601-1883
Ph: (502)564-3795
Fax: (502)564-3225

Bimonthly. $20.00/year for individuals. Kentucky law magazine.

7157 ■ Law Officers Magazine
Elsevier Science Inc.
360 Park Ave. S
New York, NY 10010-1710
Ph: (212)989-5800
Fax: (212)633-3990

Fr: 888-437-4636
URL: http://www.elsevier.com/wps/find/journaldescription.cws_home

$70.00/year for institutions, other countries; $70.00/year for other countries; $70.00/year for students, other countries; $39.00/year for students; $60.00/year for institutions, Canada; $60.00/year for Canada. Journal for the professional law enforcement officer.

7158 ■ Legal Affairs
Legal Affairs
254 Elm St.
New Haven, CT 06511
Ph: (203)789-1510
URL: http://legalaffairs.org/mediakit/LegalAffairsMediaKit.pdf

Bimonthly. $39.95/year for institutions, Canada. Publication that presents critical essays about current issues in law.

7159 ■ The Legal Investigator
National Association of Legal Investigators Inc.
235 N Pine St.
Lansing, MI 48933
Ph: (517)702-9835
Fax: (517)372-1501
Fr: (866)520-6254
E-mail: info@nalionline.org
URL: http://www.nalionline.org/publications.htm

Description: Six issues/year. Focuses on concerns of the legal investigator, especially on professionalization of the career through a certification program. Discusses issues and legal developments relating to the investigation of personal injury matters for the plaintiff and criminal defense.

7160 ■ Legal Times
American Lawyer Media L.P.
1730 M St. NW, Ste. 802
Washington, DC 20036
Ph: (202)457-0686
Fax: (202)785-4539
Fr: 800-933-4317
URL: http://www.law.com/jsp/nlj/legaltimes/advertise.jsp

Weekly. $299.00/year for individuals, print & online. Legal publication covering law and lobbying in the nation's capitol.

7161 ■ Los Angeles Lawyer
Los Angeles County Bar Association
1055 W 7th St., Ste. 2700
PO Box 55020
Los Angeles, CA 90017-2577
Ph: (213)627-2727
Fax: (213)833-6717
URL: http://www.lacba.org/showpage.cfm?pageid=40

Monthly. $28.00/year for nonmembers; $4.00/year for single issue, plus handling; for Included in membership. Magazine featuring scholarly legal articles.

7162 ■ Michigan Bar Journal
State Bar of Michigan
306 Townsend St.
Lansing, MI 48933-2012
Ph: (517)346-6300
Fax: (517)482-6248
Fr: 800-968-1442
URL: http://www.michbar.org/publications/bar_journal.cfm

Monthly. $60.00/year for nonmembers; $70.00/year for other countries, members. Legal magazine.

7163 ■ The National Law Journal
The New York Law Journal
120 Broadway, 5th Fl.
New York, NY 10271-1101
Ph: (212)457-9545
Fax: (866)305-3058
URL: http://www.law.com/jsp/nlj/index.jsp

Weekly. $299.00/year for individuals. Tabloid focusing on the practice of law and trends in law.

7164 ■ National Paralegal Reporter
National Federation of Paralegal Associations Inc.
PO Box 2016
Edmonds, WA 98020
Ph: (425)967-0045
Fax: (425)771-9588
E-mail: info@paralegals.org
URL: http://www.paralegals.org

Description: Bimonthly. $33 per year. Focuses on issues of concern to the paralegal profession such as responsibility and ethics, new developments in the field, and educational opportunities. Promotes the recognition and advancement of paralegals and provides information on programs and help offered by paralegal associations. Reports regional NFPA news and news of paralegal associations throughout the U.S. Recurring features include book reviews, news of research, and President's Column.

7165 ■ New Jersey Law Journal
New Jersey Law Journal
238 Mulberry St.
PO Box 20081
Newark, NJ 07101-6081
Ph: (973)642-0075
Fax: (973)642-0920
URL: http://www.law.com/jsp/nj/index.jsp?slreturn=1&hbxlogin=1

Weekly. $219.00/year for individuals. Journal containing digests of court opinions, notes, and orders to the bar from New Jersey Supreme Court and federal district court. Includes news articles on legal topics and commentary by legal specialists.

7166 ■ The Recorder
American Lawyer Media L.P.
120 Broadway
New York, NY 10271
Ph: (212)457-9400
URL: http://www.law.com/jsp/ca/index.jsp

Daily (morn.). $369.00/year for individuals, print and online. Legal newspaper.

7167 ■ The Washington Lawyer
The District of Columbia Bar
1101 K St. NW, Ste. 200
Washington, DC 20005-4210
Ph: (202)737-4700
Fax: (202)626-3471
Fr: 877-333-2227
URL: http://www.dcbar.org/for_lawyers/resources/publications/inde

Forum for articles and news items for the Washington legal community.

7168 ■ Wisconsin Lawyer
State Bar of Wisconsin
PO Box 7158
Madison, WI 53707-7158
Ph: (608)257-3838
Fax: (608)257-5502
Fr: 800-728-7788
E-mail: wislawyer@wisbar.org
URL: http://www.wisbar.org/wislawmag/

Monthly. $35.00/year for members; $53.00/year for nonmembers; $3.50/year for single issue. Official monthly publication of the State Bar of Wisconsin.

EMPLOYER DIRECTORIES AND NETWORKING LISTS

7169 ■ American Bar Association—Directory
American Bar Association
321 N Clark St.
Chicago, IL 60654-7598
Ph: (312)988-5000
Fax: (312)988-5568
Fr: 800-285-2221

Annual, October. $14.95. Covers: Approximately 7,500 lawyers active in the affairs of the Association, including officers, members of Boards of Governors and House of Delegates, section officers and council members, committee leaders, headquarters staff, state and local bars, affiliated and other legal organizations. Entries include: Section, council, or other unit name; names, addresses, and phone numbers of officers or chairpersons and members. Arrangement: Classified by position in ABA. Indexes: Alphabetical, Geographical committee.

7170 ■ American Lawyers Quarterly
The American Lawyers Co.
853 Westpoint Pky., Ste. 710
Cleveland, OH 44145-1532
Ph: (440)871-8700
Fax: (440)871-9997
Fr: 800-843-4000
URL: http://www.alqlist.com

Quarterly, January and July; monthly supplements. Covers: Law firms that specialize in debt collections, creditors' rights, and bankruptcy. Arrangement: Geographical.

7171 ■ Career Opportunities in Law and the Legal Industry
Facts On File Inc.
132 W 31st St., 17th Fl.
New York, NY 10001
Ph: (212)967-8800
Fax: 800-678-3633
Fr: 800-322-8755
URL: http://factsonfile.infobasepublishing.com/

Latest edition 2nd; Published March, 2007. $49.50 for individuals. Publication includes: Lists of industry associations and organizations, educational institutions, and Web sites related to the legal industry. Principal content of publication is information on careers in the legal field. Indexes: Alphabetical.

7172 ■ Law and Legal Information Directory
Gale
PO Box 6904
Florence, KY 41022-6904
Fr: 800-354-9706
URL: http://www.gale.cengage.com

Annual, Latest edition 24th; April, 2012. $716.00 for individuals. Covers: More than 21,000 national and international organizations, bar associations, federal and highest state courts, federal regulatory agencies, law schools, firms and organizations offering continuing legal education, paralegal education, sources of scholarships and grants, awards and prizes, special libraries, information systems and services, research centers, publishers of legal periodicals, books, and audiovisual materials, lawyer referral services, legal aid offices, public defender offices, legislature manuals and registers, small claims courts, corporation departments of state, state law enforcement agencies, state agencies, including disciplinary agencies, and state bar requirements. Entries include: All entries include institution or firm name, address, phone; many include names and titles of key personnel and, when pertinent, descriptive annotations. Contents based in part on information selected from several other Gale directories. Arrangement: Classified by type of organization, activity, service, etc. Indexes: Individual sections have special indexes as required.

7173 ■ Lawyer's Register International by Specialties and Fields of Law Including a Directory of Corporate Counsel
Lawyer's Register Publishing Co.
4555 Renaissance Pkwy., Ste. 101
Cleveland, OH 44128
URL: http://www.lawyersregister.com

Annual. Covers: corporate legal staffs worldwide; legal firms; independent practicing attorneys each identified as a specialist in one or more fields of law. Entries include: In corporate section—Corporation, subsidiary, and department names; address, phone, fax; names and titles of legal staff, law schools attended, specialties. In fields of law sections—Name, address, phone, fax, specialties (identified by Standard Industrial Classification (SIC) codes), personal

data. A general international/corporate law list. Arrangement: Separate sections for specializing lawyers and their firms and corporate counsel. Indexes: Lawyers and firms by areas, corporations, more indexes.

7174 ■ Martindale-Hubbell Law Directory
Martindale-Hubbell Inc.
121 Chanlon Rd.
New Providence, NJ 07974
Ph: (908)464-6800
Fax: (908)771-8704
Fr: 800-526-4902
URL: http://www.martindale.com

Annual, April. $1,065.00 for individuals. Covers: Lawyers and law firms in the United States, its possessions, and Canada, plus leading law firms worldwide; includes a biographical section by firm, and a separate list of patent lawyers, attorneys in government service, in-house counsel, and services, suppliers, and consultants to the legal profession. Entries include: For non-subscribing lawyers—Name, year of birth and of first admission to bar, code indicating college and law school attended and first degree, firm name (or other affiliation, if any) and relationship to firm, whether practicing other than as individual or in partnership. For subscribing lawyers—Above information plus complete address, phone, fax, e-mail and URL, type of practice, clients, plus additional personal details (education, certifications, etc.). A general law list. Arrangement: Geographical. Indexes: Alphabetical, area of practice.

7175 ■ NLADA Directory of Legal Aid and Defender Offices in the United States and Territories
National Legal Aid & Defender Association
1140 Connecticut Ave. NW, Ste. 900
Washington, DC 20036
Ph: (202)452-0620
URL: http://www.nlada.org/Member_Svcs/
    Publications/Directory/

Biennial, latest edition 2009-2010. $95.00 for nonmembers; $35.00 for individuals; $55.00 for individuals; $95.00 for nonmembers. Covers: Approximately 3,000 civil legal aid and indigent defense organizations in the United States; includes programs for specific groups such as prisoners, senior citizens, the disabled, etc. Entries include: Agency name, address, phone, director's name. Arrangement: Geographical. Indexes: Type of service.

7176 ■ USBD—United States Bar Directory
Attorneys National Clearing House Co.
PO Box 142828
Gainesville, FL 32614-2828
Ph: (352)336-3344
Fax: (866)859-2624
Fr: (866)860-2624
E-mail: usbd@usbardirectory.com
URL: http://www.usbardirectory.com

Annual, January. Covers: Over 3,000 general and specialized practice attorneys employed through correspondence (letter, phone, fax or e-mail). Entries include: Firm name, address, phone, preferred fields of practice, fax, email, Web site. Arrangement: Geographical.

7177 ■ Who's Who in American Law
Marquis Who's Who L.L.C.
300 Connell Dr., Ste. 2000
Berkeley Heights, NJ 07922
Ph: (908)673-1000
Fax: (908)673-1189
Fr: 800-473-7020
E-mail: law@marquiswhoswho.com
URL: http://www.marquiswhoswho.com

Biennial, Latest edition 17th; 2011-2012. $365.00 for individuals. Covers: Over 19,000 lawyers, judges, law school deans and professors, and other legal professionals. Entries include: Name, home and office addresses, place and date of birth, educational background, career history, civic positions, professional memberships, publications, awards, special

achievements. Arrangement: Alphabetical. Indexes: Fields of practice, professional area.

7178 ■ Wright-Holmes Law List
Wright-Holmes Inc.
45 Kensico Dr., 2nd Fl.
Mount Kisco, NY 10549
Ph: (914)241-3297
Fax: (914)241-3326
Fr: 800-258-5597
URL: http://www.collectioncenter.com/

Annual, April. Free. Covers: Over 1,400 law firms throughout the U.S., Canada and 35 other countries. Entries include: Firm name, address, phone. A commercial law list. Arrangement: Geographical.

HANDBOOKS AND MANUALS

7179 ■ Basic Administrative Law for Paralegals
Aspen Publishers Inc.
76 Ninth Ave., 7th Fl.
New York, NY 10011
Ph: (212)771-0600
Fax: (212)771-0885
Fr: 800-234-1660
URL: http://www.aspenpublishers.com/

Anne Adams. Fourth edition, 2009. $89.95. 384 pages. Explore the basics of Administrative Law.

7180 ■ Becoming a Paralegal
LearningExpress, LLC
2 Rector St., 26th Fl.
New York, NY 10006
Fr: 800-295-9556
E-mail: customerservice@learningexpressllc.com
URL: http://www.learningexpressllc.com

LearningExpress Editors. 2010. $16.95 (paper). 216 pages. Covers all aspects involved in paralegal work. Includes opportunities and trends in paralegal careers and up-to-date salary and education information.

7181 ■ Careers for Legal Eagles and Other Law-and-Order Types
The McGraw-Hill Companies
PO Box 182604
Columbus, OH 43272
Fax: (614)759-3749
Fr: 877-883-5524
E-mail: customer.service@mcgraw-hill.com
URL: http://www.mhprofessional.com/
    product.php?isbn=0071466207

Blythe Camenson. Second edition, 2005. $13.95 (paper). 176 pages.

7182 ■ Introduction to Paralegalism: Perspectives, Problems, & Skills
Cengage Learning
PO Box 6904
Florence, KY 41022
Fax: 800-487-8488
Fr: 800-354-9706
URL: http://www.cengage.com

William P. Statsky. Seventh Edition, 2009. $168.95. 912 pages.

7183 ■ Job Placement Strategies for Paralegals
Delmar Cengage Learning
5 Maxwell Dr.
Clifton Park, NY 12065
Fr: 800-648-7450
URL: http://www.delmarlearning.com/about/
    contact.aspx

Margaret E. Pickard. 2008. $48.95. Offers tools and strategies that can help paralegal students and professionals prepare a professional resume and cover letters as well as find job opportunities in the private and public sectors. Includes salary and detailed resume worksheets. Prepares job hunters for the job interview by providing practical advice including how to prepare, how to bring and what to wear.

7184 ■ The Legal Job Interview: Winning the Law-Related Job in Today's Market

Kaplan Publishing
1 Liberty Plz., 22nd Fl.
New York, NY 10006
Fax: (212)313-4800
E-mail: tim.brazier@kaplan.com
URL: http://www.kaptest.com

Cliff Ennico. 2008. $16.95. Helps legal professionals learn the process and strategies of a typical interview, what's different about legal job interviewers, things to do before scheduling and arriving at the interview, and the dos and don'ts of maximizing the chance of getting the offered job.

7185 ■ Opportunities in Paralegal Careers

The McGraw-Hill Companies
PO Box 182604
Columbus, OH 43272
Fax: (614)759-3749
Fr: 877-883-5524
E-mail: customer.service@mcgraw-hill.com
URL: http://www.mhprofessional.com/
    product.php?isbn=0071466258

Alice Fins. 2005. $13.95 (paper). 160 pages. Defines job opportunities and provides advice about identifying and obtaining positions. Includes bibliography and illustrations.

7186 ■ Paralegal Career for Dummies

For Dummies
111 River St.
Hoboken, NJ 07030
Ph: (201)748-6000
Fax: (201)748-6088
E-mail: info@wiley.com
URL: http://www.dummies.com/Section/id-
    322438.html

Scott Hatch and Lisa Hatch. 2006. $24.99. 384 pages. Comprehensive guide to becoming a paralegal; includes CD-ROM with forms.

7187 ■ Paralegal Career Starter

LearningExpress, LLC
Two Rector St., 26th Fl.
New York, NY 10006
Fax: (212)995-5512
Fr: 800-295-9556
E-mail: customerservice@learningexpressllc.com
URL: http://www.learningexpressllc.com

LearningExpress Editors. Third Updated edition, 2006. $15.95. 208 pages.

7188 ■ The Paralegal Internship Manual

Prentice Hall PTR
One Lake St.
Upper Saddle River, NJ 07458
URL: http://www.pearsonhighered.com

Deborah Orlik. 2006. $26.67.

7189 ■ Paralegal Practice and Procedure

Prentice Hall Press
c/o Penguin Group (USA)
375 Hudson St.
New York, NY 10014-3657
Ph: (212)366-2000
Fax: (212)366-2933
E-mail: ecommerce@us.penguingroup.com
URL: http://us.penguingroup.com

Deborah E. Larbalestrier and Linda Spagnola. 2009. $50.00 (paper). 640 pages. Covers topics for every aspect of a paralegal's job. Includes detailed information on practice and procedures for working in specialty law firms.

7190 ■ A Paralegal Primer

The Center for Legal Studies
523 Park Point Dr., Ste. 320
Golden, CO 80401
Ph: (303)273-9777

Fax: (303)271-1777
Fr: 800-522-7737
E-mail: info@legalstudies.com
URL: http://www.legalstudies.com

Scott A. Hatch. Third edition, 2006. $25.00 (paper). 182 pages.

7191 ■ The Paralegal Professional

Prentice Hall
1 Lake St.
Upper Saddle River, NJ 07458
URL: http://www.pearsonhighered.com

Thomas F. Goldman and Henry R. Cheeseman. 2010. $168.33 (paper). 912 pages. Covers topics on all aspects of the paralegal profession. Contains chapter opening vignettes, critical perspectives, advice from the field and chapter exercises. Provides an overview of the most common individual legal areas of practice.

7192 ■ A Practical Introduction to Paralegal Studies: Strategies for Success

Aspen Publishers Inc.
76 Ninth Ave., 7th Fl.
New York, NY 10011
Ph: (212)771-0600
Fax: (212)771-0885
URL: http://www.aspenpublishers.com

Deborah E. Bouchoux. 2008. $110.95. 480 pages.

7193 ■ The Professional Paralegal: A Guide to Finding a Job and Career Success

Prentice Hall
One Lake St.
Upper Saddle River, NJ 07458
URL: http://www.pearsonhighered.com

Charlsye Smith Diaz and Vicki Voisin. 2012. $61.33 (paper). 240 pages. Covers topics on how to prepare for and build a paralegal career. Discusses the dynamics of working in the legal environment and offers strategies for working collaboratively with attorneys.

7194 ■ The Professional Paralegal Workbook

Cengage Learning
PO Box 6904
Florence, KY 41022
Fax: 800-487-8488
Fr: 800-354-9706
E-mail: esales@cengage.com
URL: http://www.cengage.com

Elizabeth Angus. 2007. $32.95. 144 pages. Workbook for paralegals covering criminal, tort, and contract law.

7195 ■ Real-Resumes for Legal and Paralegal Jobs

PREP Publishing
1110 1/2 Hay St., Ste. C
Fayetteville, NC 28305
Ph: (910)483-6611
Fax: (910)483-2439
E-mail: preppub@aol.com
URL: http://www.prep-pub.com/Bookstore/legal.htm

Anne McKinney. $16.95 (paper). 192 pages. Real-Resumes Series.

EMPLOYMENT AGENCIES AND SEARCH FIRMS

7196 ■ Abelson Legal Search

1600 Market St., Ste. 505
Philadelphia, PA 19103
Ph: (215)561-3010
Fax: (215)561-3001
E-mail: abelson@abelsonlegalsearch.com
URL: http://www.abelsonlegalsearch.com

Provides attorneys, paralegals and legal professionals in all specialty areas to law firms, corporations and financial institutions.

7197 ■ Access Staffing

360 Lexington Ave., 8th Fl.
New York, NY 10017
Ph: (212)687-5440
Fax: (212)557-2544
URL: http://www.accessstaffingco.com

Serves as a staffing firm covering accounting/ financial, advertising, bilingual Japanese, creative, event planning, fashion/retail, healthcare/ human services, human resources, information technology, insurance, legal, light industrial and office support.

7198 ■ Attorney Resources, Inc.

750 N St. Paul, Ste. 540
Dallas, TX 75201
Ph: (214)922-8050
E-mail: tlb@attorneyresource.com
URL: http://www.attorneyresource.com

Employment agency. Offices in Austin, Dallas, Fort Worth, Houston and Tulsa, OK. Provides staffing assistance on regular or temporary basis.

7199 ■ Beverly Hills Bar Association Personnel Service

300 S Beverly Dr., Ste. 201
Beverly Hills, CA 90212-4805
Ph: (310)601-2422
Fax: (310)601-2423
URL: http://www.bhba.org

Employment agency.

7200 ■ Coleman/Nourian

Two Penn Center, Ste. 1010
15th & JFK Blvd.
Philadelphia, PA 19102
Ph: (215)864-2700
Fax: (215)864-2709
E-mail: search@cnlegalsearch.com
URL: http://www.cnlegalsearch.com

Legal executive search firm.

7201 ■ Cook Associates Inc.

212 W Kinzie St.
Chicago, IL 60610
Ph: (312)329-0900
Fax: (312)329-1528
E-mail: info@cookassociates.com
URL: http://www.cookassociates.com

Management and executive recruiting specialists offering a commitment to clients to find the best candidates and to find those candidates as efficiently as possible. Approach provides a flexible and effective structure that serves the special needs of both large and small companies. Serves the following industries: industrial, equipment manufacturer, food processing, graphic arts, chemical process, retailing, mechanical products, healthcare services, financial and professional services, legal, consumer products, construction and engineering, packaging, pulp and paper.

7202 ■ Davidson Staffing

2302 Martin Ste. 150
Irvine, CA 92612
Ph: (949)955-3114
URL: http://www.davidsonstaffing.com

Provides full service staffing and recruiting solutions for four core divisions namely: attorney staffing, corporate administrative staff, legal support staff and legal IT professionals.

7203 ■ Early Cochran & Olson LLC

1 E Wacker Dr., Ste. 2510
Chicago, IL 60601
Ph: (312)595-4200
Fax: (312)595-4209
E-mail: info@ecollc.com
URL: http://www.ecollc.com

Executive search firm focused specifically on the legal field.

7204 ■ Exclusively Legal
2355 Northside Dr., Ste. 140
San Diego, CA 92108
Ph: (619)683-8501
Fr: 800-388-1178
E-mail: sandiego@exclusivelylegal.com
URL: http://www.exclusivelylegal.com

Description: Provides specialized staffing services to law firms and corporate legal departments.

7205 ■ Filcro Legal Staffing
521 Fifth Ave.
New York, NY 10175
Ph: (212)599-0909
Fax: (212)599-4772
E-mail: shannon@filcro.com
URL: http://www.filcro.com/page3.html

Serves as a legal recruitment firm specializing in the identification of legal support and legal administrative staff.

7206 ■ Gibson Arnold & Associates Inc.
1111 Washington Ave., Ste. 220
Golden, CO 80401
Ph: (303)273-9420
Fax: (303)273-9424
Fr: 888-324-9420
E-mail: golden@gibsonarnold.com
URL: http://www.gibsonarnold.com

Supplies attorneys, paralegals, legal secretaries, support personnel and production clerks to major law firms and corporate legal departments nationwide on either a temporary or regular employment basis. Also maintains a full-time placement division. Assists law firms and corporations with staffing any in-house needs. Other services include assistance in law firm mergers, assistance in lateral partner moves and managing document review projects.

7207 ■ Kruza Legal Search
1845 Walnut St., Ste. 855
Philadelphia, PA 19103
Ph: (215)981-5455
Fax: (215)981-0662
E-mail: info@kruza.com
URL: http://www.kruza.com

Specializes in connecting law firms and corporate legal departments with attorneys, paralegals and administrative support staff.

7208 ■ LateralAttorneys.com
3575 Piedmont Rd. NE, Bldg. 15, Ste. 900
Atlanta, GA 30305
Ph: (404)221-9990
Fax: (404)221-9998
E-mail: jobs@partners-group.com
URL: http://www.lateralattorneys.com

Specialized search for the legal profession. Offers recruitment and placement of attorneys and paralegals.

7209 ■ Law Resources
1140 Connecticut Ave. NW, Ste. 675
Washington, DC 20036
Ph: (202)371-1270
Fax: (202)371-0979
E-mail: apply@lawresources.com
URL: http://www.lawresources.com

Description: Exists as a legal placement firm seeking qualified and experienced legal and support staff, whether for short-term, long-term, temp-to-perm or permanent hire.

7210 ■ Legal Placement Services, Inc.
6737 W Washington St., Ste. 2390
West Allis, WI 53214
Ph: (414)276-6689
Fax: (414)276-1418
E-mail: info@ps-companies.com
URL: http://www.ps-companies.com/legal-placement-services

Employment agency. Periodically fills temporary placements, as well.

7211 ■ Major Legal Services
1301 E 9th St., Ste. 1414
Cleveland, OH 44114
Ph: (216)579-9782
Fax: (216)579-1662
Fr: 800-808-3097
URL: http://www.lawplacement.com

Description: Provides contract and permanent staffing needs of law firms and corporate legal departments.

7212 ■ Momentum Legal
2630 Exposition Blvd., Ste. 119-B
Austin, TX 78703
Ph: (512)524-4241
E-mail: jane@momentumlegal.com
URL: http://www.momentumlegal.com

Executive search firm specializing in permanent search and temporary legal staffing solutions within law firms and corporations across the country. Focuses on creating opportunities and building long term relationships with attorneys, law firms and corporate legal departments.

7213 ■ Pat Taylor and Associates
1101 17th St. NW, Ste. 707
Washington, DC 20036
Ph: (202)466-5622
Fax: (202)466-5630
E-mail: pat@pattaylor.com
URL: http://www.pattaylor.com

Specializes in temporary and permanent placement of attorneys, paralegals, and law clerks.

7214 ■ Prescott Legal Search
3900 Essex Ln., Ste. 1110
Houston, TX 77027
Ph: (713)439-0911
Fax: (713)439-1317
URL: http://www.prescottlegal.com

Serves as a legal search firm providing law professionals for law firms and corporations.

7215 ■ Robert Half Legal
2884 Sand Hill Rd.
Menlo Park, CA 94025
Fr: 800-870-8367
URL: http://www.roberthalflegal.com

Description: Provides legal professionals on a project and full-time basis. Specializes in the placement of attorneys, paralegals and legal support personnel for law firms and corporate legal departments.

7216 ■ Synectics for Management Decisions Inc.
1901 N Moore St., Ste. 900
Arlington, VA 22209-1717
Ph: (703)528-2772
Fax: (703)528-2857
E-mail: info@smdi.com
URL: http://www.smdi.com

Organizational analysis and development consulting firm specializing in economic and international expertise, executive search, management information systems, data processing, training, economic expertise to legal profession, business brokerage, mergers and acquisitions, and leasing services. Serves private industries as well as government agencies.

ONLINE JOB SOURCES AND SERVICES

7217 ■ EmpLawyerNet.com
2331 Westwood Blvd., No. 331
Los Angeles, CA 90064
Fr: 800-270-2688
E-mail: membership@emplawyernet.com
URL: http://www.emplawyernet.com

Description: Career resource site for lawyers. Contains career information, resume posting and job board search, along with links to CLE events, online bookstores, and recruiter directories. Fee: Limited access permitted with free basic membership. Premier membership is $125/year or $14.95/month and includes free CLE courses, e-mail alerts, networking opportunities and personal career advice.

7218 ■ iHireLegal.com
URL: http://www.ihirelegal.com

Description: Serves as an online resource of job postings, internet job boards and classified ads in the legal industry. Include features such as free summary resume blast, free salary data, email notification of jobs, live telephone customer support and more.

7219 ■ Law.com: Law Jobs
URL: http://www.lawjobs.com

Description: Visitors can post job openings for attorneys, legal support staff and temporary workers. Also resources for legal recruiters and temporary staffing agencies.

7220 ■ LawGuru.com
URL: http://www.lawguru.com

Description: Offers a legal bulletin board with an archive of questions and answers, links, job listings, legal news, chat, and FAQs.

7221 ■ LawInfo Career Center
Fr: 800-397-3743
URL: http://jobs.lawinfo.com

Description: Offers employment sites in the legal community including resources for both job seekers and employers.

7222 ■ Lawjobs.com
URL: http://www.lawjobs.com

Description: Features a career center that provides latest news and hiring trends, salary information, career advancement articles, career advice, surveys and more. Provides a job database categorized according to specific positions in the legal profession industry.

7223 ■ Lawmatch.com
URL: http://lawmatch.com

Description: Provides resume and job posting for legal staffing positions. Offers web-based recruitment tools and methodologies to job seekers and employers.

7224 ■ LegalStaff.com
URL: http://www.legalstaff.com

Description: Provides list of legal and law-related jobs. Offers free searches, job agent feature, and the opportunity to post qualifications for employers to review.

7225 ■ ParalegalJobFinder.com
URL: http://www.paralegaljobfinder.com

Description: Serves as an online career site that provides paralegal jobs, careers and employment. Caters to both job seekers and employers with its free job database where companies that are seeking to hire paralegals, paralegal positions, law assistants and other industry related positions post jobs daily on the network.

7226 ■ ParalegalJobs.com
URL: http://www.paralegaljobs.com

Description: Offers paralegal job postings and resumes.

TRADESHOWS

7227 ■ Academy of Legal Studies in Business Annual Conference
Academy of Legal Studies in Business
c/o Constance E. Bagley, Pres.
Yale School of Management
135 Prospect St.
PO Box 208200
New Haven, CT 06520

Ph: (203)432-8398
E-mail: connie.bagley@yale.edu
URL: http://alsb.roundtablelive.org

Annual. Provides opportunities for legal studies educators and others to network and meet with colleagues. Defines and advances legal studies in business and management education. 2012 August 7-11; Kansas, MO; Kansas City Intercontinental.

7228 ■ American Association for Paralegal Education Convention
American Association for Paralegal Education
19 Mantua Rd.
Mount Royal, NJ 08061
Ph: (856)423-2829
Fax: (856)423-3420
E-mail: info@aafpe.org
URL: http://www.aafpe.org/

Annual. Primary Exhibits: Computer hardware and software; paralegal publications and educational materials; related supplies. Dates and Locations: 2012 Oct 10-13; Savannah, GA; Hyatt Regency Savannah on the Historic Riverfront; 2013 Nov 06-09; Phoenix, AZ; 2014 Oct 15-18; Summerlin, NV; 2015 Oct 21-24; Milwaukee, WI.

7229 ■ NALS Annual Education Conference & National Forum
NALS, The Association for Legal Professionals
8159 E 41st St.
Tulsa, OK 74145
Ph: (918)582-5188
Fax: (918)582-5907
E-mail: info@nals.org
URL: http://www.nals.org

Annual. Features courses on a wide variety of legal and management topics taught by experts in the profession. 2012 October 18-21; Portland, OR; Sheraton Portland Airport Hotel.

7230 ■ National Conference on Bankruptcy Clerks - Annual Conference
National Conference on Bankruptcy Clerks
c/o Ken Hirz, Pres.
Northern District of Ohio
201 Superior Ave.
Cleveland, OH 44114
Ph: (216)615-4340
URL: http://ncbc.memberclicks.net

Annual. Offers speakers, educational classes and sessions, social activities, a vendor fair, and an information sharing fair. 2012 August 7-10; San Francisco, CA; City by the Bay.

OTHER SOURCES

7231 ■ International Technology Law Association (ITechLaw)
401 Edgewater Pl., Ste. 600
Wakefield, MA 01880
Ph: (781)876-8877
Fax: (781)224-1239
E-mail: office@itechlaw.org
URL: http://www.itechlaw.org

Description: Lawyers, law students, and others interested in legal problems related to computer-communications technology. Aids in: contracting for computer-communications goods and services; perfecting and protecting proprietary rights chiefly in software; and taxing computer-communications goods, services, and transactions, and liability for acquisition and use of computer-communications goods and services. Provides specialized educational programs; and offers limited placement service. Holds Annual Computer Law Update.

7232 ■ Legal Marketing Association
401 N Michigan Ave., Ste. 2200
Chicago, IL 60611-6610
Ph: (312)321-6898

Fax: (312)673-6894
E-mail: membersupport@legalmarketing.org
URL: http://www.legalmarketing.org

Description: Provides information on a variety of legal marketing issues so that professionals may grow professionally as well as personally. Maintains a job bank for marketing and related service professionals.

7233 ■ Legal Secretaries International
2302 Fannin St., Ste. 500
Houston, TX 77002-9136
Ph: (713)651-2933
Fax: (713)651-2908
E-mail: info@legalsecretaries.org
URL: http://www.legalsecretaries.org

Description: Consists of individuals who are presently or formerly employed or interested in the legal secretarial profession. Responds to the educational and networking needs of legal secretaries as an affordable means of increasing knowledge, skills and networking opportunities.

7234 ■ Media Law Resource Center (MLRC)
North Tower, 20th Fl.
520 Eighth Ave.
New York, NY 10018
Ph: (212)337-0200
Fax: (212)337-9893
E-mail: medialaw@medialaw.org
URL: http://www.medialaw.org

Description: Provides support for media defendants in libel and privacy cases, including development of statistical and empirical data, assistance in locating expert witnesses or consultants, and help in coordinating amicus curiae briefs by supporting organizations. Maintains a brief, pleading, and information bank; collects and disseminates information on pending libel and privacy cases for use in legal defense against claims. Serves as a liaison with media organizations, attorneys, and other groups working to advance the defense of libel and privacy claims. Prepares bulletins and reports on current developments and cases, legal theories, privileges, and defenses. Compiles statistics on the incidence and cost of libel and privacy litigation. Provides employment for law student interns. Conducts educational and training workshops and programs; has established fellowship program in libel law.

7235 ■ NALS, The Association for Legal Professionals
8159 E 41st St.
Tulsa, OK 74145
Ph: (918)582-5188
Fax: (918)582-5907
E-mail: info@nals.org
URL: http://www.nals.org

Description: Consists of members who represent every area of the industry from paralegals and legal assistants to legal administrators and office managers. Aims to enhance the careers of legal secretaries. Offers professional development by providing continuing legal education, certifications, information, and training.

7236 ■ National Association of Legal Assistants (NALA)
1516 S Boston, Ste. 200
Tulsa, OK 74119
Ph: (918)587-6828
Fax: (918)582-6772
E-mail: nalanet@nala.org
URL: http://www.nala.org

Description: Professional paralegals employed for over six months; graduates or students of legal assistant training programs; attorneys. Members subscribe to and are bound by the NALA Code of Ethics and Professional Responsibility. Cooperates with local, state, and national bar associations in setting standards and guidelines for legal assistants. Promotes the profession and attempts to broaden public understanding of the function of the legal assistant. Offers continuing education for legal as-

sistants both nationwide and statewide, and professional certification on a national basis to members and nonmembers who meet certain criteria.

7237 ■ National Association of Legal Investigators (NALI)
235 N Pine St.
Lansing, MI 48933
Ph: (517)702-9835
Fax: (517)372-1501
Fr: (866)520-6254
E-mail: pjaeb@heartlandinfo.com
URL: http://www.nalionline.org

Description: Legal investigators, both independent and law firm staff, who specialize in investigation of personal injury matters for the plaintiff and criminal defense. Promotes professionalization of the legal investigator, accomplished by seminars and a professional certification program. Provides nationwide network of contact among members. Compiles statistics.

7238 ■ National Federation of Paralegal Associations (NFPA)
PO Box 2016
Edmonds, WA 98020
Ph: (425)967-0045
Fax: (425)771-9588
E-mail: info@paralegals.org
URL: http://www.paralegals.org

Description: State and local paralegal associations and other organizations supporting the goals of the federation; individual paralegals. Works to serve as a national voice of the paralegal profession; to advance, foster, and promote the paralegal concept; to monitor and participate in developments in the paralegal profession; to maintain a nationwide communications network among paralegal associations and other members of the legal community. Provides a resource center of books, publications, and literature of the field. Monitors activities of local, state, and national bar associations and legislative bodies; presents testimony on matters affecting the profession. Developed PACE exam for Registered Paralegal credentials.

7239 ■ National Paralegal Association (NPA)
Box 406
Solebury, PA 18963
Ph: (215)297-8333
Fax: (215)297-8358
E-mail: admin@nationalparalegal.org
URL: http://www.nationalparalegal.org

Description: Paralegals, paralegal students, educators, supervisors, paralegal schools, administrators, law librarians, law clinics, and attorneys. Advances the paralegal profession by promoting recognition, economic benefits, and high standards. Registers paralegals; maintains speakers' bureau, job bank, and placement service; offers resume preparation assistance. Offers free job bank nationally. Sponsors commercial exhibits. Operates mail order bookstore and gift shop. Compiles statistics. Develops promotion and public relations, insurance, certification, and computer bank programs. Compiles and maintains for rental the largest list of paralegals nationwide.

7240 ■ Total Practice Management Association (TPMA)
25 E Washington St., Ste. 510
Chicago, IL 60602
Ph: (312)496-6074
Fr: (866)200-5744
E-mail: info@totalattorneys.com
URL: http://www.totalattorneys.com

Description: Focuses on the advancement of attorneys, paralegals and other legal support staff. Offers solo practitioners and small law firms the tools, training and network needed to collaborate with peers, connect with experts and find better work-life balance. Coordinates workshops and conferences, educational resources, legal tools, affinity partnerships and community forums.

Sources of Help-Wanted Ads

7241 ■ *American Theological Library Association Newsletter*
American Theological Library Association
300 S Wacker Dr., Ste. 2100
Chicago, IL 60606-6701
Ph: (312)454-5100
Fax: (312)454-5505
Fr: 888-665-2852
E-mail: newsletter@atla.com
URL: http://www.atla.com/Members/benefits/
newsletter/Pages/default.aspx

Description: Monthly. Presents news of interest to library professionals at theological schools. Recurring features include notices of publications available and job listings. Also available via e-mail.

7242 ■ *Base Line*
Map and Geography Round Table
c/o Danielle M. Alderson
American Library Association
50 E Huron St.
Chicago, IL 60611-2788
Ph: (312)280-3213
Fax: (312)944-6131
E-mail: dponton@ala.org
URL: http://www.ala.org/magirt

Description: Bimonthly. Provides current information on cartographic materials, publications of interest to map and geography librarians, related government activities, and map librarianship. Recurring features include conference and meeting information, news of research, job listings, and columns by the Division chair and the editor.

7243 ■ *Book Marks*
South Dakota Library Association
28363 472nd Ave.
Worthing, SD 57077
Ph: (605)372-0235
Fax: (605)274-5447
E-mail: bookmarkssd@gmail.com
URL: http://www.sdlibraryassociation.org

Description: Quarterly. Carries news by and for South Dakota public, school, academic, and special libraries. Discusses statewide library issues, reviews South Dakota books, and advises members of continuing education opportunities. Recurring features include columns, a calendar of events, news from libraries, and job listings.

7244 ■ *Change*
Heldref Publications
325 Chestnut St., Ste. 800
Philadelphia, PA 19106
Ph: (215)625-8900
Fr: 800-354-1420
E-mail: ch@heldref.org
URL: http://www.heldref.org/change.php

Bimonthly. $52.00/year for individuals, print only;

$39.00/year for institutions, print only; $64.00/year for individuals, print and online; $207.00/year for institutions, print and online. Magazine dealing with contemporary issues in higher learning.

7245 ■ *Children and Libraries*
American Library Association
50 E Huron St.
Chicago, IL 60611-2729
Ph: (312)280-4223
Fax: (312)280-4380
Fr: 800-545-2433
URL: http://www.ala.org/ala/mgrps/divs/alsc/
compubs/childrenlib/i

for Included in membership; $50.00/year for other countries; $40.00/year for nonmembers. Journal that focuses on the continuing education of librarians working with children.

7246 ■ *The Chronicle of Higher Education*
The Chronicle of Higher Education
1255 23rd St. NW, 7th Fl.
Washington, DC 20037-1125
Ph: (202)466-1000
Fax: (202)452-1033
Fr: 800-728-2803
URL: http://chronicle.com

Weekly. $82.50/year for individuals, 43 issues; $45.00/year for individuals, 21 issues; $140.00/year for individuals, 86 issues. Higher education magazine (tabloid).

7247 ■ *Computers in Libraries*
Information Today Inc.
143 Old Marlton Pike
Medford, NJ 08055-8750
Ph: (609)654-6266
Fax: (609)654-4309
Fr: 800-300-9868
URL: http://www.infotoday.com/cilmag/default.shtml

$99.95/year for individuals, computers in libraries; $188.00/year for individuals, 2 years, U.S.; $288.00/year for individuals, 3 year, U.S.; $118.00/year for Canada and Mexico; $131.00/year for individuals, outside North America; $69.95/year for individuals; $132.00/year for two years; $201.00/year for individuals, 3 years; $88.00/year for Canada and Mexico; $101.00/year for individuals, outside North America. Library science magazine that provides complete coverage of the news and issues in the rapidly evolving field of library information technology.

7248 ■ *Information Technology Management*
Idea Group Publishing
701 E Chocolate Ave., Ste. 200
Hershey, PA 17033-1240
Ph: (717)533-8845
Fax: (717)533-8661
Fr: (866)342-6657
E-mail: cust@igi-global.com
URL: http://www.igi-pub.com/journals

Description: 2/year. Discusses cybrary networks,

library practices, information access, and new technology product releases. Recurring features include letters to the editor, interviews, news of research, a calendar of events, news of educational opportunities, and book reviews.

7249 ■ *Information Today*
Information Today Inc.
143 Old Marlton Pike
Medford, NJ 08055-8750
Ph: (609)654-6266
Fax: (609)654-4309
Fr: 800-300-9868
URL: http://www.infotoday.com

$87.50/year for individuals; $115.00/year for Canada and Mexico; $165.00/year for two years; $126.00/year for individuals, outside North America. User and producer magazine (tabloid) covering electronic and optical information services.

7250 ■ *Intercom*
District of Columbia Library Association
Box 14177
Benjamin Franklin Station
Washington, DC 20044
Ph: (202)872-1112
URL: http://www.dcla.org/

Description: Eleven issues/year (monthly with July/August combined). Deals with libraries and librarians in the Washington D.C., area. Recurring features include a calendar of events, reports of meetings, job listings, and notices of publications available.

7251 ■ *Journal of Access Services*
Routledge Journals
270 Madison Ave.
New York, NY 10016-0601
Ph: (212)216-7800
Fax: (212)563-2269
URL: http://www.tandf.co.uk/journals/WJAS

Quarterly. $77.00/year for individuals, online only; $82.00/year for individuals, print + online; $210.00/year for institutions, online only; $233.00/year for institutions, print + online. Journal focusing on the basic business of providing library users with access to information, and helping librarians stay up to date on continuing education and professional development in the field of access services.

7252 ■ *Journal of Classification*
Springer-Verlag New York Inc.
233 Spring St.
New York, NY 10013-1578
Ph: (212)460-1500
Fax: (212)460-1575
Fr: 800-777-4643
URL: http://www.springer.com/statistics/
statistical+theory+and+me

Semiannual. $447.00/year for institutions, print or online; $536.00/year for institutions, print & enchanced access. Journal of the Classification Society of North America.

7253 ■ *Journal of Interlibrary Loan, Document Delivery & Electronic Reserve*

Routledge Journals
270 Madison Ave.
New York, NY 10016-0601
Ph: (212)216-7800
Fax: (212)563-2269
URL: http://www.informaworld.com/smpp/
 title~content=t792306877

$100.00/year for individuals, online only; $108.00/year for individuals, print + online; $396.00/year for institutions, online only; $440.00/year for institutions, print + online. Journal focusing on a broad spectrum of library and information center functions that rely heavily on interlibrary loan, document delivery, and electronic reserve.

7254 ■ *Law Librarians' Bulletin Board*

Legal Information Services
PO Box 31425
Charlotte, NC 28231
Ph: (980)333-3049
Fax: (704)541-6817
E-mail: info@legalinformationservices.com
URL: http://www.legalinformationservices.com/
 Publications/librarians-newsletter.php

Description: 8/year. Tracks current events in law librarianship. Recurring features include job listings.

7255 ■ *Library Journal*

Media Source Inc
7858 Industrial Pkwy.
Plain City, OH 43064
Ph: (614)873-7635
Fr: (866)207-0310
E-mail: ljinfo@mediasourceinc.com
URL: http://www.libraryjournal.com

$157.99/year for individuals; $199.99/year for Canada and Mexico; $259.99/year for other countries. Library management and book selection journal.

7256 ■ *MAHD Bulletin*

Museums, Arts, and Humanities Div., Special Libraries Assn.
331 S Patrick St.
Alexandria, VA 22314-3501
Ph: (703)647-4900
Fax: (703)647-4901
E-mail: membership@sla.org
URL: http://units.sla.org/division/dmah

Description: Four issues/year. Discusses pertinent events, issues, and publications concerning special libraries. Recurring features include interviews, news of research, a calendar of events, reports of meetings, news of educational opportunities, book reviews, notices of publications available, and a column titled On My Mind.

7257 ■ *MLA Newsletter*

Music Library Association
8551 Research Way, Ste. 180
Middleton, WI 53562
Ph: (608)836-5825
Fax: (608)831-8200
E-mail: mla@areditions.com
URL: http://www.musiclibraryassoc.org

Description: Quarterly. Serves as an information exchange among music librarians. Published to keep members abreast of events, ideas, and trends related to music librarianship. Presents Association committee and round table updates, chapter news, and listings of music-related articles appearing in non-music journals. Recurring features include notices of publications available, a calendar of events, news of members, and columns titled The President Reports and Placement Service News.

7258 ■ *The Outrider*

Wyoming State Library
2800 Central Ave.
Cheyenne, WY 82002
Ph: (307)777-6333
Fax: (307)777-6289
URL: http://will.state.wy.us/slpub/outrider/index.html

Description: Biennial. Provides news about the activities of the Wyoming State Library, its board, other tax-supported libraries in the state, the American Library Association, and the library field in general. Recurring features include job listings, meetings, workshops, and other events; personnel news; reports on consultant activities and acquisitions news; and columns titled News Briefs, Around the State.

7259 ■ *The Reference Librarian*

Routledge Journals
270 Madison Ave.
New York, NY 10016-0601
Ph: (212)216-7800
Fax: (212)563-2269
URL: http://www.tandf.co.uk/journals/WREF

Quarterly. $241.00/year for individuals, online only; $258.00/year for individuals, print + online; $1,016.00/year for institutions, online only; $1,129.00/year for institutions, print + online. Journal for librarians and students, providing information on the changing field of reference librarianship.

7260 ■ *School Library Journal*

Media Source Inc
7858 Industrial Pkwy.
Plain City, OH 43064
Ph: (614)873-7635
Fr: (866)207-0310
E-mail: slj@reedbusiness.com
URL: http://www.schoollibraryjournal.com/

Monthly. $136.99/year for individuals; $199.99/year for Canada; $259.99/year for other countries. A new Canadian Web site launched with the blessing of Microsoft Chairman Bill Gates is using games and cartoons to teach kids about the evils of online predators.

7261 ■ *TEST Engineering & Management*

The Mattingley Publishing Company Inc.
3756 Grand Ave., Ste. 205
Oakland, CA 94610-1545
Ph: (510)839-0909
Fax: (510)839-2950
E-mail: testmag@testmagazine.biz
URL: http://www.testmagazine.biz/

$60.00/year for individuals; $70.00/year for other countries. Trade publication that covers physical and mechanical testing and environmental simulation; edited for test engineering professionals.

EMPLOYER DIRECTORIES AND NETWORKING LISTS

7262 ■ *American Library Directory*

Information Today Inc.
143 Old Marlton Pike
Medford, NJ 08055-8750
Ph: (609)654-6266
Fax: (609)654-4309
Fr: 800-300-9868
URL: http://books.infotoday.com

Annual, latest edition 64th; 2011-2012. $329.00 for individuals; $296.10 for individuals. Covers: Over 36,000 U.S. and Canadian academic, public, county, provincial, and regional libraries; library systems; medical, law, and other special libraries; and libraries for the blind and physically handicapped. Separate section lists over 350 library networks and consortia and 220 accredited and unaccredited library school programs. Entries include: For libraries—Name, supporting or affiliated institution or firm name, address, phone, fax, electronic mail address, Standard Address Number (SANs), names of librarian and department heads, income, collection size, special collections, computer hardware, automated functions, and type of catalog. For library systems—Name, location. For library schools—Name, address, phone, fax, electronic mail address, director, type of training and degrees, admission requirements, tuition, faculty size. For networks and consortia—Name, address, phone, names of affiliates, name of director, function. Ar-

rangement: Geographical. Indexes: Institution name. Library Services & Suppliers index.

7263 ■ *The Basic Business Library*

Greenwood Publishing Group Inc.
88 Post Rd. W
PO Box 5007
Westport, CT 06881
Ph: (203)226-3571
Fax: (203)222-1502
Fr: 800-225-5800
URL: http://www.abc-clio.com/
 product.aspx?id=64414

Latest edition 4th. $78.95 for single issue. Publication includes: Publisher's Web site as part of each entry. Principal content of publication is list of 210 entries of suggested resources for business libraries, as well as essays on business references sources and services. Indexes: Alphabetical.

7264 ■ *Career Opportunities in Library and Information Science*

Facts On File Inc.
132 W 31st St., 17th Fl.
New York, NY 10001
Ph: (212)967-8800
Fax: 800-678-3633
Fr: 800-322-8755
URL: http://www.infobasepublishing.com

Published July, 2009. $49.50 for individuals. Covers: More than 85 different jobs typically held by librarians, including academic, government, K-12, outside the library, public, and special.

7265 ■ *Directory of Federal Libraries*

Oryx Press
88 Post Rd. W
PO Box 5007
Westport, CT 06881
Fax: (203)222-1502
URL: http://www.greenwood.com/catalog/
 OXDFL3.aspx

Irregular, Latest edition 3rd. $138.95 for individuals; $95.95 for individuals. Covers: nearly 3,000 libraries serving branches of the federal government. Entries include: Library name, type, address, phone, fax, e-mail, telnet, and websites, name of administrator and selected staff, special collections, database services available, depository status for documents from the Government Printing Office or other organizations, involvement with cooperative library organizations, electronic mail or cataloging networks, whether accessible to the public. Arrangement: Classified by federal establishment. Indexes: Library type, subject, geographical, alphabetical index of libraries by name.

7266 ■ *Directory of Public School Systems in the U.S.*

American Association for Employment in Education
3040 Riverside Dr., Ste. 117
Columbus, OH 43221
Ph: (614)485-1111
Fax: (360)244-7802
E-mail: office@aaee.org
URL: http://www.aaee.org/

Annual, Winter; latest edition 2004-2005 edition. $55.00 for members; $80.00 for nonmembers. Covers: About 14,000 public school systems in the United States and their administrative personnel. Entries include: System name, address, phone, website address, name and title of personnel administrator, levels taught and approx. Student population. Arrangement: Geographical by state.

7267 ■ *Directory of Special Libraries and Information Centers*

Gale
PO Box 6904
Florence, KY 41022-6904
Fr: 800-354-9706
URL: http://www.gale.cengage.com

Annual, Latest edition 39th; April, 2011. $1533.00 for individuals; $920.00 for individuals. Covers: Over

34,800 special libraries, information centers, documentation centers, etc.; about 500 networks and consortia; major special libraries abroad also included. Volume 1 part 3 contains 6 other appendices (besides networks and consortia): Regional and Subregional Libraries for the Blind & Physically Handicapped, Patent & Trademark Depository Libraries, Regional Government Depository Libraries, United Nations Depository Libraries, World Bank Depository Libraries, and European Community Depository Libraries. Entries include: Library name, address, phone, fax, e-mail address; contact; year founded; sponsoring organization; special collections; subject interests; names and titles of staff; services (copying, online searches); size of collection; subscriptions; computerized services and automated operations; Internet home page address; publications; special catalogs; special indexes. For consortia and networks—Name, address, phone, contact. Other appendices have varying amounts of directory information. Contents of Volume 1 are available in "Subject Directory of Special Libraries and Information Centers". Arrangement: Libraries are alphabetical by name of sponsoring organization or institution; consortia and networks are geographical. Indexes: Subject. Geographic and personnel indexes constitute volume 2.

7268 ■ Guide to Employment Sources in the Library & Information Professions

Office for Human Resource Development and Recruitment
50 E Huron St.
Chicago, IL 60611
Ph: (312)280-2428
Fax: (312)280-3256
Fr: 800-545-2433
E-mail: customerservice@ala.org
URL: http://www.ala.org

Annual, Latest edition 2009. Covers: Library job sources, such as specialized and state and regional library associations, state library agencies, federal library agencies, and overseas exchange programs. Entries include: Library, company, or organization name, address, phone; contact name, description of services, publications, etc. This is a reprint of a segment of the "Bowker Annual of Library and Book Trade Information," described separately. Arrangement: Classified by type of source.

7269 ■ Handbook of Private Schools

Porter Sargent Publishers Inc.
11 Beacon St., Ste. 1400
Boston, MA 02108-3099
Ph: (617)523-1670
Fax: (617)523-1021
Fr: 800-342-7470
URL: http://www.portersargent.com

Annual, latest edition 92nd, 2011-2012. $99.00 for individuals. Covers: More than 1,700 elementary and secondary boarding and day schools in the United States. Entries include: School name, address, phone, fax, E-mail, URL, type of school (boarding or day), sex and age range, names and titles of administrators, grades offered, academic orientation, curriculum, new admissions yearly, tests required for admission, enrollment and faculty, graduate record, number of alumni, tuition and scholarship figures, summer session, plant evaluation and endowment, date of establishment, calendar, association membership, description of school's offerings and history, test score averages, uniform requirements, geographical, and demographic date. Arrangement: Geographical. Indexes: Alphabetical by school name, cross indexed by state, region, grade range, sexes accepted, school features and enrollment.

7270 ■ Higher Education Directory

Higher Education Publications Inc.
1801 Robert Fulton Dr., Ste. 340
Reston, VA 20191
Ph: (571)313-0478
Fax: (571)313-0526
Fr: 888-349-7715
URL: http://www.hepinc.com

Annual, latest edition 2011. $75.00 for individuals. Covers: Over 4,364 degree granting colleges and universities accredited by approved agencies recognized by the U.S. Secretary of Education and by the Council of Higher Education Accreditation (CHEA); 103 systems offices; over 550 related associations and state government agencies; recognized accrediting agencies. Entries include: For institutions—Name, address, congressional district, phone, fax, year established; Carnegie classification; enrollment; type of student body; religious or other affiliation; undergraduate tuition and fees; type of academic calendar; highest degree offered; accreditations; IRS status; names, titles and job classification codes for academic and administrative officers. For associations and state agencies—Name, address, phone, name of chief executive officer. Same content and coverage as the base volume of the Department of Education's publication "Directory of Postsecondary Institutions" . Arrangement: Geographical, alphabetical by state. Indexes: Administrator name (with phone and e-mail addresses), accreditation, FICE numbers, college or university name.

7271 ■ Independent Schools Association of the Southwest—Membership List

Independent Schools Association of the Southwest
Energy Sq., 505 N Big Spring St., Ste. 406
Midland, TX 79701
Ph: (432)684-9550
Fax: (432)684-9401
Fr: 800-688-5007
URL: http://www.isasw.org

Annual, August. Covers: Over 84 schools located in Arizona, Kansas, Louisiana, Mexico, New Mexico, Oklahoma, and Texas enrolling over 38,000 students. Entries include: School name, address, phone, chief administrative officer, structure, and enrollment. Arrangement: Geographical. Indexes: Alphabetical.

7272 ■ MDR's School Directories

Market Data Retrieval
6 Armstrong Rd., Ste. 301
Shelton, CT 06484-4722
Ph: (203)926-4800
Fax: (203)926-1826
Fr: 800-333-8802
URL: http://www.schooldata.com/mdrdir.asp

Annual, Latest edition 2008-2009. Covers: Over 90,000 public, 8,000 Catholic, and 15,000 other private schools (grades K-12) in the United States; over 15,000 school district offices, and 76,000 school librarians; and 27,000 media specialists, 33,000 technology coordinators. Includes names of over 165,000 school district administrators and staff members in county and state education administration. Entries include: District name and address; telephone and fax number; number of schools; number of teachers in the district; district enrollment; special Ed students; limited-English proficient students; minority percentage by race, college bound students; expenditures per student for instructional materials; poverty level; title 1 dollars; site-based management; district open/close dates; construction indicator; technologies and quantities; district-level administrators, *new superintendents shaded*; school name and address—new public shaded; telephone and fax number; principal *new principal shaded*; librarian, media specialist and technology coordinator; grade span; special programs and school type; student enrollment; technologies and quantities (instructional computer brand noting predominant brand); Multi-Media Computers; Internet connection or access; Tech Sophistication Index. Arrangement: Geographical. Indexes: District County; District Personnel; Principal; New Public Schools and Key Personnel; District and School Telephone; District URLs.

7273 ■ Midwest Archives Conference—Membership Directory

Midwest Archives Conference
4440 PGA Blvd., Ste. 600
Palm Beach Gardens, FL 33410
URL: http://www.midwestarchives.org

Annual. Covers: More than 1,150 individual and institutional members, largely librarians, archivists, records managers, manuscripts curators, historians, and museum and historical society personnel; about 25 archival associations in the Midwest. Entries include: For institutions—Name of archives, parent organization, address, phone. For individuals—Name, title, business address, phone. Arrangement: Separate alphabetical sections for individuals and institutions.

7274 ■ Patterson's American Education

Educational Directories Inc.
1025 W Wise Rd., Ste. 101
PO Box 68097
Schaumburg, IL 60168-0097
Ph: (847)891-1250
Fax: (847)891-0945
Fr: 800-357-6183
URL: http://www.ediusa.com

Annual, Latest edition 2012, vol. 108. $97.00 for individuals. Covers: Over 11,000 school districts in the United States; more than 34,000 public, private, and Catholic high schools, middle schools, and junior high schools; Approximately 300 parochial superintendents; 400 state department of education personnel. Entries include: For school districts and schools—District and superintendent Name, address, phone, fax, grade ranges, enrollment, school names, addresses, phone numbers, grade ranges, enrollment, names of principals. For postsecondary schools—School name, address, phone number, URL, e-mail, names of administrator or director of admissions. For private and Catholic high schools—name, address, phone, fax, enrollment, grades offered, name of principal. Postsecondary institutions are covered in 'Patterson's Schools Classified'. Arrangement: Geographical by state, then alphabetical by city.

7275 ■ Patterson's Schools Classified

Educational Directories Inc.
1025 W Wise Rd., Ste. 101
PO Box 68097
Schaumburg, IL 60168-0097
Ph: (847)891-1250
Fax: (847)891-0945
Fr: 800-357-6183
URL: http://www.ediusa.com

Annual, Latest edition 2010, volume 60. $23.00 for individuals. Covers: Over 6,000 accredited colleges, universities, community colleges, junior colleges, career schools and teaching hospitals. Entries include: School name, address, phone, URL, e-mail, name of administrator or admissions officer, description, professional accreditation (where applicable). Updated from previous year's edition of 'Patterson's American Education'. Arrangement: Classified by area of study, then geographical by state. Indexes: Alphabetical by name.

7276 ■ Requirements for Certification of Teachers, Counselors, Librarians, Administrators for Elementary and Secondary Schools

University of Chicago Press
Journals Division
1427 E 60th St.
Chicago, IL 60637-2954
Ph: (773)702-7636
Fax: (773)702-9756
URL: http://www.press.uchicago.edu

Annual, Latest edition 74th. $53.00. Publication includes: List of state and local departments of education. Entries include: Office name, address, phone. Principal content of publication is summaries of each state's teaching and administrative certification requirements. Arrangement: Geographical.

HANDBOOKS AND MANUALS

7277 ■ Careers in Focus: Library & Information Science

Ferguson Publishing
132 W 31st St., 17th Fl.
New York, NY 10001

Fr: 800-322-8755
E-mail: custserv@factsonfile.com
URL: http://factsonfile.infobasepublishing.com

2006. $32.95. 212 pages. Covers an overview of library and information science, followed by a selection of jobs profiled in detail, including the nature of the job, earnings, prospects for employment, what kind of training and skills it requires and sources for further information.

7278 ■ Careers in Health Care

The McGraw-Hill Companies
PO Box 182604
Columbus, OH 43272
Fax: (614)759-3749
Fr: 877-883-5524
E-mail: customer.service@mcgraw-hill.com
URL: http://www.mhprofessional.com/
product.php?isbn=0071466533

Barbara M. Swanson. Fifth edition, 2005. $19.95 (paper). 192 pages. Describes job duties, work settings, salaries, licensing and certification requirements, educational preparation, and future outlook. Gives ideas on how to secure a job.

7279 ■ Careers in Music Librarianship II: Traditions and Transitions

Scarecrow Press, Inc.
4501 Forbes Blvd., Ste. 200
Lanham, MD 20706-4310
Ph: (301)459-3366
Fax: (301)429-5748
Fr: 800-462-6420
URL: http://rowman.com/Scarecrow

Paula Elliot and Linda Blair. 2004. $37 (paper). 168 pages. Explores music librarianship.

7280 ■ Great Jobs for History Majors

The McGraw-Hill Companies
PO Box 182604
Columbus, OH 43272
Fax: (614)759-3749
Fr: 877-883-5524
E-mail: customer.service@mcgraw-hill.com
URL: http://www.mhprofessional.com

Julie DeGalan and Stephen Lambert. 2007. $16.95 (paper). 192 pages.

7281 ■ Hiring, Training, and Supervising Library Shelvers

ALA Editions
c/o American Library Association
50 E Huron St.
Chicago, IL 60611
Fax: (312)280-5275
Fr: 800-545-2433
URL: http://www.ala.org

Patricia Tunstall. 2010. $50.00 (softcover). 120 pages. Provides advice and information on hiring, testing, training and retaining library shelvers. Includes: templates for signs advertising employment; screening tests; interview questions; and employee assessments.

7282 ■ How to Stay Afloat in the Academic Library Job Pool

ALA Editions
c/o American Library Association
50 E Huron St.
Chicago, IL 60611
Fax: (312)280-5275
Fr: 800-545-2433
URL: http://www.ala.org

Teresa Neely. 2011. $40.00 (softcover). 152 pages. Provides information for jobseekers interested in a career in an academic library. Features advice on: the job search process, assembling application essentials, and winning over the job's search committee. Includes tips on interviews.

7283 ■ A Librarian's Guide to an Uncertain Job Market

ALA Editions
c/o American Library Association
50 E Huron St.
Chicago, IL 60611-2729
Fax: (312)280-5275
Fr: 800-545-2433
URL: http://www.ala.org

Jeannette Woodward. 2011. $45.00 (softcover). 112 pages. Helps librarians plan ahead for changes in employment, gain versatile skills and adjust career goals, and search for job opportunities in non-library settings.

7284 ■ New Challenges Facing Academic Librarians Today: Electronic Journals, Archival Digitization, Document Delivery, Etc.

Edwin Mellen Press
PO Box 450
Lewiston, NY 14092-0450
Ph: (716)754-2266
Fax: (716)754-4056
URL: http://www.mellenpress.com/
mellenpress.cfm?bookid=6547&pc=9

Jean Caswell, Paul G. Haschak, and Dayne Sherman. $119.95. 304 pages. Collection of essays by individuals offering scholarship in library science, information science, and higher education.

7285 ■ The New Graduate Experience: Post-MLS Residency Programs and Early Career Librarianship

Libraries Unlimited
130 Cremona Dr.
Santa Barbara, CA 93117
Fax: (866)270-3856
Fr: 800-368-6868
URL: http://www.abc-clio.com

Megan Zoe Perez and Cindy Ann Gruwell. 2010. $55.00. 219 pages (paperback). Serves as a guide for program managers, recent graduates and early career librarians, and students of library and information science. Contains 20 authors representing 13 different residency programs, variety of useful materials, and bibliographic reference lists.

7286 ■ The NextGen Librarian's Survival Guide

Information Today Inc.
143 Old Marlton Pike
Medford, NJ 08055-8750
Ph: (609)654-6266
Fax: (609)654-4309
Fr: 800-300-9868
E-mail: custserv@infotoday.com
URL: http://books.infotoday.com/books/
NextGenLib.shtml

Rachel Singer Gordon. 2006. $29.50. 224 pages.

7287 ■ Opportunities in Library and Information Science Careers

The McGraw-Hill Companies
PO Box 182604
Columbus, OH 43272
Fax: (614)759-3749
Fr: 877-883-5524
E-mail: customer.service@mcgraw-hill.com
URL: http://www.mhprofessional.com/
product.php?isbn=007154531X

Kathleen de la Pena McCook. 2008. $14.95 (paper). 160 pages. A guide to planning for and seeking opportunities in this changing field. Includes bibliography and illustrations.

7288 ■ Pre- and Post-Retirement Tips for Librarians

American Library Association
50 E Huron St.
Chicago, IL 60611
Fr: 800-545-2433
URL: http://www.alastore.ala.org

Carol Smallwood. 2012. $47.00 (softcover). 256 pages. Offers insight, inspiration and tips for librarians who are considering retirement or those already retired. Includes topics on pros and cons of early retirement, taking second careers and other post-retirement activities and concerns.

7289 ■ Principal Librarian

National Learning Corporation
212 Michael Dr.
Syosset, NY 11791
Fr: 800-632-8888
URL: http://www.passbooks.com

2009. $34.95 (paper). Serves as an exam preparation guide for principal librarians.

7290 ■ So You Want To Be a Librarian

Library Juice Press
PO Box 3320
Duluth, MN 55803
Ph: (218)260-6115
E-mail: inquiries@libraryjuicepress.com
URL: http://libraryjuicepress.com

Lauren Pressley. 2009. $15.00 (paper). Serves as a valuable resource for anyone who wants to pursue a career in librarianship.

7291 ■ What They Don't Teach You in Library School

ALA Editions
c/o American Library Association
50 E Huron St.
Chicago, IL 60611
Fax: (312)280-5275
Fr: 800-545-2433
URL: http://www.ala.org

Elisabeth Doucett. 2010. $50.00 (softcover). 160 pages. Serves as guide for new librarians. Covers library topics relevant to the day-to-day job, such as management, administration and marketing. Shows how librarians can further their careers through practical business and organizational skills.

7292 ■ Writing and Publishing: The Librarian's Handbook

ALA Editions
c/o American Library Association
50 E Huron St.
Chicago, IL 60611
Fax: (312)280-5275
Fr: 800-545-2433
URL: http://www.ala.org

Carol Smallwood. 2010. $65.00 (softcover). 199 pages. Serves as reference tool for librarians interested in an alternate career in writing and publishing. Covers fiction, poetry, children's books and magazines, personal blogging, self-publishing, and other topics.

EMPLOYMENT AGENCIES AND SEARCH FIRMS

7293 ■ Brattle Temps

50 Congress St., Ste. 935
Boston, MA 02109-4008
Ph: (617)523-4600
Fax: (617)523-3939
E-mail: temps@brattletemps.com

Personnel consulting firm specializes in providing temporary consultants. Skill areas available include: computer operators, secretaries, editors, librarians, graphic artists, and marketing professionals. Industries served: universities, publishing, engineering, manufacturing, and government agencies.

7294 ■ C. Berger Group Inc.

327 E Gundersen Dr.
PO Box 274
Carol Stream, IL 60188
Ph: (630)653-1115
Fax: (630)653-1691

Fr: 800-382-4222
E-mail: cberger@cberger.com
URL: http://www.cberger.com

Provides consultation in library services and information and knowledge management. The firm staffs and directs projects which range from organizing, inventorying and cataloging special collections and files to installing custom PC databases. Personnel services include executive search for information specialists and supplying temporary and contract librarians, support staff and loose leaf filers on demand. Serves corporate, not for profit and academic libraries as well as government agencies.

7295 ■ Gossage Sager Associates
4545 Wornall, Ste. 805
Kansas City, MO 64111
Ph: (816)531-2468
E-mail: danbradbury@gossagesager.com
URL: http://www.gossagesager.com

Firm provides executive recruiting for public libraries, college and university libraries, corporate libraries, nonprofit libraries, information centers, archives, records management, and other information handling organizations. Offers additional expertise in library management consulting, emphasizing planning, personnel and labor relations and management and systems evaluation. Other areas of specialization include: records management consultation for corporations and nonprofit organizations and computer systems consultation for libraries, corporate and nonprofit records management and other information handling systems. Serves private industries as well as government agencies.

Online Job Sources and Services

7296 ■ American Library Association Education and Employment
50 E Huron
Chicago, IL 60611
Fr: 800-545-2433
URL: http://www.ala.org/ala/educationcareers/
employment/index.cfm

Description: Contains links to monthly job and career leads lists posted in American Libraries and College & Research Libraries NewsNet and other sources, as well as a Conference Placement Service and accreditation information.

7297 ■ Library and Information Technology Association Job Listing
E-mail: lita@ala.org
URL: http://www.ftrf.org/ala/mgrps/divs/lita/
professional/jobs/index.cfm

Description: Contains weekly postings of available library jobs. Searchable by region.

7298 ■ Library Job Postings on the Internet
E-mail: sarah@libraryjobpostings.org
URL: http://www.libraryjobpostings.org

Description: Employers may post library position announcements. Also contains links to around 250 library employment sites and links to library-related e-mail lists. Positions are searchable by region and type of library.

7299 ■ LibraryCrossing.com
URL: http://www.librarycrossing.com

Description: Provides job listings and other resources related to library employment opportunities.

7300 ■ LIScareer.com
URL: http://www.liscareer.com

Description: Offers career development resources for librarians, information professionals, students and those considering a career in library and information science. Includes practical advice contributed by information professionals, links to online resources and information about print resources.

7301 ■ LISJobs.com
URL: http://www.lisjobs.com

Description: Provides career information for librarians and information professionals. Offers more resources beyond job hunting such as career development resources that are intended to help clients continue to grow as professionals.

Tradeshows

7302 ■ American Association of Law Libraries Meeting
American Association of Law Libraries
105 W. Adams St., Ste. 3300
Chicago, IL 60603
Ph: (312)939-4764
Fax: (312)431-1097
E-mail: events@aall.org
URL: http://www.aallnet.org/

Annual. Primary Exhibits: Library equipment, supplies, and services, including computer hardware and software/publishers of legal materials/information. Dates and Locations: 2012 Jul 21-24; Boston, MA; Hynes Veterans Memorial Convention Center; 2013 Jul 13-16; Seattle, WA; Washington State Convention & Trade Center; 2014 Jul 12-15; San Antonio, TX; Henry B. Gonzalez Convention Center; 2015 Jul 18-21; Philadelphia, PA; Pennsylvania Convention Center; 2016 Jul 16-19; Chicago, IL; Hyatt Regency.

7303 ■ American Association of School Librarians National Conference and Exhibition
American Association of School Librarians
50 E. Huron St.
Chicago, IL 60611
Fr: 800-545-2433
E-mail: library@ala.org
URL: http://www.ala.org

Biennial. Primary Exhibits: Equipment, supplies, and services for school library media centers, including print and nonprint materials and other equipment.

7304 ■ American Library Association Annual Conference
American Library Association
50 E. Huron St.
Chicago, IL 60611-2795
Fax: (312)440-9374
Fr: 800-545-2433
E-mail: ala@ala.org
URL: http://www.ala.org

Annual. Primary Exhibits: Books, periodicals, reference works, audio-visual equipment, films, data processing services, computer hardware and software, library equipment and supplies. Dates and Locations: 2012 Jun 21-26; Anaheim, CA; 2013 Jun 27-02; Chicago, IL; 2014 Jun 26 - Jul 01; Las Vegas, NV; 2015 Jun 25-30; San Francisco, CA; 2016 Jun 23-28; Orlando, FL.

7305 ■ American Library Association Mid-Winter Meeting
American Library Association
50 E. Huron St.
Chicago, IL 60611-2795
Fax: (312)440-9374
Fr: 800-545-2433
E-mail: ala@ala.org
URL: http://www.ala.org

Annual. Primary Exhibits: Books, periodicals, reference works, audio-visual equipment, films, data processing services, computer hardware and software, library equipment and supplies. Dates and Locations: 2013 Jan 25-29; Seattle, WA; 2014 Jan 24-28; Philadelphia, PA; 2015 Jan 23-27; Chicago, IL; 2016 Jan 22-26; Boston, MA.

7306 ■ Arkansas Library Association Annual Conference
Arkansas Library Association
PO Box 958
Benton, AR 72018-0958

Ph: (501)860-7585
Fax: (501)776-9709
E-mail: arlib2@sbcglobal.net
URL: http://www.arlib.org

Annual. Primary Exhibits: Products related to libraries.

7307 ■ Art Libraries Society of North America Conference
Art Libraries Society of North America
7044 S 13th St.
Oak Creek, WI 53154
Ph: (414)768-8000
Fax: (414)768-8001
Fr: 800-817-0621
URL: http://www.arlisna.org

Annual. 2013 April 25-29; Pasadena, CA. Provides networking opportunities for attendees.

7308 ■ Association of College and Research Libraries National Conference
Association of College and Research Libraries
50 E. Huron St.
Chicago, IL 60611-2795
Ph: (312)280-2523
Fax: (312)280-2520
Fr: 800-545-2433
E-mail: acrl@ala.org
URL: http://www.ala.org/acrl

Biennial. Primary Exhibits: Books, computers, Web products, furniture, journals, and audiovisual publications; library materials, equipment, supplies, and services.

7309 ■ California Library Association Annual Conference
California Library Association
2471 Flores St.
San Mateo, CA 94403
Ph: (650)376-0886
Fax: (650)539-2341
E-mail: info@cla-net.org
URL: http://www.cla-net.org

Annual. Primary Exhibits: Publications and library equipment, supplies, and services.

7310 ■ Catholic Library Association Convention
Catholic Library Association
205 W. Monroe St., Ste. 314
Chicago, IL 60606-5061
Ph: (312)739-1776
E-mail: cla@cathla.org
URL: http://www.cathla.org

Annual. Primary Exhibits: Exhibits relating to Catholic libraries and their specialized problems and the writing, publishing, and distribution of Catholic literature. Dates and Locations: 2012 Apr 11-13; Boston, MA.

7311 ■ Church and Synagogue Library Association Conference
Church and Synagogue Library Association
2920 S.W. Dolph Ct., Ste. 3A
Portland, OR 97219-4055
Ph: (503)244-6919
Fax: (503)977-3734
Fr: 800-542-2752
E-mail: csla@worldaccessnet.com
URL: http://cslainfo.org

Annual. Primary Exhibits: Books, media, and library equipment, supplies, and services. Dates and Locations: 2012 Jul 29-31; Springfield, IL.

7312 ■ Colorado Association Library Conference
Colorado Association of Libraries
3030 W. 81st Ave.
Westminster, CO 80031
Ph: (303)463-6400
Fax: (303)458-0002
E-mail: cal@cal-webs.org
URL: http://www.cal-webs.org

Annual. Primary Exhibits: Print and non-print media, bibliographic services, computer products and services, furniture and facilities products, and database and reference services, space planners, architects and more. Dates and Locations: 2012 Oct 18-20; Keystone, CO.

7313 ■ Computers in Libraries
Information Today, Inc.
143 Old Marlton Pike
Medford, NJ 08055-8750
Ph: (609)654-6266
Fax: (609)654-4309
Fr: 800-300-9868
E-mail: custserv@infotoday.com
URL: http://www.infotoday.com

Annual. Primary Exhibits: Computer hardware, software, CD-ROMS, and related equipment, supplies, and services for use in libraries. Dates and Locations: 2012 Mar 21-23; Washington, DC; Hilton Washington.

7314 ■ Florida Library Association Annual Conference and Trade Show
Florida Library Association
PO Box 1571
164 N.W. Madison St., Ste. 104
Lake City, FL 32056-1571
Ph: (386)438-5795
Fax: (386)438-5796
E-mail: fla.admin@comcast.net
URL: http://www.flalib.org

Annual. Primary Exhibits: Library equipment, books, binding information, and furniture. Dates and Locations: 2012 Apr 18-20; Orlando, FL; Wyndham Orlando Resort.

7315 ■ Illinois School Library Media Association Conference
Illinois School Library Media Association
PO Box 598
Canton, IL 61520
Ph: (309)649-0911
Fax: (309)649-0916
E-mail: islma@islma.org
URL: http://www.islma.org

Annual. Primary Exhibits: Equipment, supplies, and services for elementary and secondary school library media specialists interested in the general improvement and extension of services for children and young people. Dates and Locations: 2012 Nov 08-10; Arlington Heights, IL; Sheraton Chicago Northwest.

7316 ■ International Association of Aquatic and Marine Science Libraries and Information Centers Conference
International Association of Aquatic and Marine Science Libraries and Information Centers
Hatfield Marine Science Ctr.
Oregon State Univ.
2030 S. Marine Science Dr.
Newport, OR 97365
E-mail: janet.webster@oregonstate.edu
URL: http://www.iamslic.org

Annual. Primary Exhibits: Equipment, supplies, and services for marine-related libraries and information centers. Dates and Locations: 2012 Aug 26-30; Anchorage, AK.

7317 ■ Internet Librarian International
Information Today, Inc.
143 Old Marlton Pike
Medford, NJ 08055-8750
Ph: (609)654-6266
Fax: (609)654-4309
Fr: 800-300-9868
E-mail: custserv@infotoday.com
URL: http://www.infotoday.com

Annual. Primary Exhibits: Internet librarians equipment, supplies, and services.

7318 ■ Iowa Library Association Annual Conference
Iowa Library Association
525 SW 5th St., Ste. A
Des Moines, IA 50309

Ph: (515)273-5322
Fax: (515)309-4576
Fr: 800-452-5507
E-mail: admin@iowalibraryassociation.org
URL: http://www.iowalibraryassociation.org

Annual. Primary Exhibits: Equipment, supplies, and services for libraries.

7319 ■ Medical Library Association Annual Meeting
Medical Library Association
65 E. Wacker Pl., Ste. 1900
Chicago, IL 60601-7246
Ph: (312)419-9094
Fax: (312)419-8950
E-mail: info@mlahq.org
URL: http://www.mlanet.org

Annual. Primary Exhibits: Computers, security equipment, audiovisual equipment, office equipment, publications, library suppliers, and computer vendors. Dates and Locations: 2012 May 18-23; Seattle, WA.

7320 ■ Mountain Plains Library Association Annual Conference
Mountain Plains Library Association
USD Library
414 E. Clark St.
University of South Dakota
Vermillion, SD 57069
Ph: (605)677-6082
Fax: (605)677-5488
URL: http://www.usd.edu

Annual. Primary Exhibits: Publications and library equipment, supplies, and services. Dates and Locations: 2012 Oct 17-19; 2013 Sep 25-27; Sioux Falls, SD.

7321 ■ New England Library Association Annual Conference
New England Library Association
31 Connor Ln.
Wilton, NH 03086
Ph: (603)654-3533
Fax: (603)654-3526
E-mail: executivemanager@nela1.org
URL: http://www.nelib.org

Annual. Primary Exhibits: Books, media, supplies, furniture, equipment, hardware, software and services used by libraries.

7322 ■ New York Library Association Conference
New York Library Association
6021 State Farm Rd.
Guilderland, NY 12084
Ph: (518)432-6952
Fax: (518)427-1697
Fr: 800-252-6952
E-mail: info@nyla.org
URL: http://www.nyla.org

Annual. Primary Exhibits: New products and services of interest to the library community. Dates and Locations: 2012 Nov 07-10; Saratoga Springs, NY; 2013 Sep 25-28; Niagara Falls, NY.

7323 ■ North Carolina Library Association Conference
MW Bell Library
PO Box 309
Jamestown, NC 27282-0309
Ph: (336)334-4822
Fax: (336)841-4350

Biennial. Primary Exhibits: Library-related equipment, supplies, and services.

7324 ■ Pacific Northwest Library Association Conference and Exhibition
Pacific Northwest Library Association
629 Dock St.
Ketchikan, AK 99901
Ph: (907)225-0370

Fax: (907)225-0153
E-mail: charg@firstcitylibraries.org
URL: http://www.pnla.org

Annual. Primary Exhibits: Library supplies and services.

7325 ■ Public Library Association National Conference
Public Library Association
50 E. Huron St.
Chicago, IL 60611
Ph: (312)280-5752
Fax: (312)280-5029
Fr: 800-545-2433
E-mail: pla@ala.org
URL: http://www.pla.org

Biennial. Primary Exhibits: Books, software & hardware and other equipment, supplies, and services for libraries. Dates and Locations: 2012 Mar 13-17; Philadelphia, PA.

7326 ■ Southeastern Library Association Biennial Conference
Southeastern Library Association
Administrative Services
PO Box 950
Rex, GA 30273
Ph: (678)466-4334
Fax: (678)466-4349
URL: http://selaonline.org/

Biennial. Primary Exhibits: Reps of libraries, furnishings, supplies, services, publishers, and binders, jobbers, computer and networking systems, security, and film systems.

7327 ■ Special Libraries Association Information Revolution
Special Libraries Association
331 S. Patrick St.
Alexandria, VA 22314-3501
Ph: (703)647-4900
Fax: (703)647-4901
E-mail: sla@sla.org
URL: http://www.sla.org

Annual. Primary Exhibits: Library equipment, supplies, and services, including computers and software, Database information.

7328 ■ Texas Library Association Conference
Texas Library Association
3355 Bee Cave Rd., Ste. 401
Austin, TX 78746-6763
Ph: (512)328-1518
Fax: (512)328-8852
Fr: 800-580-2852
E-mail: tla@txla.org
URL: http://www.txla.org

Annual. Primary Exhibits: Library equipment, supplies, and services, including bookbinding materials, library shelving and furniture, computers, books, audiovisual materials, small press publications, automation, hardware, software, and telecommunications.

7329 ■ Wisconsin Library Association Annual Conference
Wisconsin Library Association
4610 S. Biltmore Ln.
Madison, WI 53718
Ph: (608)245-3640
Fax: (608)245-3646
E-mail: wla@scls.lib.wi.us
URL: http://www.wla.lib.wi.us

Annual. Primary Exhibits: Library equipment, supplies, and services, including books. Dates and Locations: 2012 Oct 23-26; La Crosse, WI; Radisson Hotel & La Crosse Center; 2013 Oct 22-25; Green Bay, WI; KI Convention Center and Hotel Sierra.

OTHER SOURCES

7330 ■ African Studies Association (ASA)
Rutgers University, Livingston Campus
54 Joyce Kilmer Ave.
Piscataway, NJ 08854-8045
Ph: (848)445-8173
Fax: (732)445-1366
E-mail: karen.jenkins@africanstudies.org
URL: http://www.africanstudies.org

Description: Persons specializing in teaching, writing, or research on Africa including political scientists, historians, geographers, anthropologists, economists, librarians, linguists, and government officials; persons who are studying African subjects; institutional members are universities, libraries, government agencies, and others interested in receiving information about Africa. Seeks to foster communication and to stimulate research among scholars on Africa. Sponsors placement service; conducts panels and discussion groups; presents exhibits and films.

7331 ■ American Association of Law Libraries (AALL)
105 W Adams St., Ste. 3300
Chicago, IL 60603
Ph: (312)939-4764
Fax: (312)431-1097
E-mail: support@aall.org
URL: http://www.aallnet.org

Description: Librarians who serve the legal profession in the courts, bar associations, law societies, law schools, private law firms, federal, state, and county governments, and business; associate members are legal publishers and other interested persons. Seeks to advance the profession of law librarianship. Conducts continuing professional development programs for members; maintains placement service.

7332 ■ American Library Association (ALA)
50 E Huron St.
Chicago, IL 60611
Ph: (312)944-6780
Fax: (312)440-9374
Fr: 800-545-2433
E-mail: ala@ala.org
URL: http://www.ala.org

Description: Librarians, libraries, trustees, friends of libraries, and others interested in the responsibilities of libraries in the educational, social, and cultural needs of society. Promotes and improves library service and librarianship. Establishes standards of service, support, education, and welfare for libraries and library personnel; promotes the adoption of such standards in libraries of all kinds; safeguards the professional status of librarians; encourages the recruiting of competent personnel for professional careers in librarianship; promotes popular understanding and public acceptance of the value of library service and librarianship. Works in liaison with federal agencies to initiate the enactment and administration of legislation that will extend library services. Offers placement services.

7333 ■ American Society for Information Science and Technology (ASIS&T)
1320 Fenwick Ln., Ste. 510
Silver Spring, MD 20910
Ph: (301)495-0900
Fax: (301)495-0810
E-mail: asis@asis.org
URL: http://www.asis.org

Description: Information specialists, scientists, librarians, administrators, social scientists, and others interested in the use, organization, storage, retrieval, evaluation, and dissemination of recorded specialized information. Seeks to improve the information transfer process through research, development, application, and education. Provides a forum for the discussion, publication, and critical analysis of work dealing with the theory, practice, research, and development of elements involved in communication

of information. Members are engaged in a variety of activities and specialties including classification and coding systems, automatic and associative indexing, machine translation of languages, special librarianship and library systems analysis, and copyright issues. Sponsors National Auxiliary Publications Service, which provides reproduction services and a central depository for all types of information. Maintains placement service. Sponsors numerous special interest groups. Conducts continuing education programs and professional development workshops.

7334 ■ Art Libraries Society of North America
7044 S 13th St.
Oak Creek, WI 53154
Ph: (414)768-8000
Fax: (414)768-8001
Fr: 800-817-0621
URL: http://www.arlisna.org

Description: Consists of architecture and art librarians, visual resources professionals, artists, curators, educators, publishers, students, and others interested in visual arts information. Promotes the advancement of art library and information professionals. Collaborates with other professional and educational organizations through participation in international forums.

7335 ■ Asian Pacific American Librarians Association (APALA)
Loyola Law School
William M. Rains Library
919 Albany St.
Los Angeles, CA 90015
Ph: (213)736-1431
Fax: (213)487-2204
E-mail: florante.ibanez@lls.edu
URL: http://www.apalaweb.org

Description: Librarians and information specialists of Asian Pacific descent working in the U.S.; interested persons. Provides a forum for discussing problems and concerns; supports and encourages library services to Asian Pacific communities; recruits and supports Asian Pacific Americans in the library and information science professions. Offers placement service; compiles statistics. Conducts fundraising for scholarships.

7336 ■ Association of Christian Librarians
PO Box 4
Cedarville, OH 45314
Ph: (937)766-2255
Fax: (937)766-5499
E-mail: info@acl.org
URL: http://www.acl.org

Description: Seeks to empower evangelical librarians through professional development, scholarship and spiritual encouragement for service in higher education.

7337 ■ Association of College and Research Libraries (ACRL)
50 E Huron St.
Chicago, IL 60611-2795
Ph: (312)280-2523
Fax: (312)280-2520
Fr: 800-545-2433
E-mail: acrl@ala.org
URL: http://www.ala.org/ala/mgrps/divs/acrl/index.cfm

Description: A division of the American Library Association. Academic and research librarians seeking to improve the quality of service in academic libraries; promotes the professional and career development of academic and research librarians; represent the interests and support the programs of academic and research libraries. Operates placement services; sponsors specialized education and research grants and programs; gathers, compiles, and disseminates statistics. Establishes and adopts standards; maintains publishing program; offers professional development courses.

7338 ■ Association of Jewish Libraries (AJL)
PO Box 1118
Teaneck, NJ 07666-1118
Ph: (212)725-5359
E-mail: ajlibs@osu.edu
URL: http://www.jewishlibraries.org

Description: Devoted to the educational, informational, and networking needs of librarians responsible for collections of Judaica and to the promotion of Judaic librarianship.

7339 ■ Association for Library and Information Science Education (ALISE)
65 E Wacker Pl., Ste. 1900
Chicago, IL 60601-7246
Ph: (312)795-0996
Fax: (312)419-8950
E-mail: contact@alise.org
URL: http://www.alise.org

Description: Graduate schools offering degree programs in library science and their faculties. Seeks to: promote excellence in education for library and information science as a means of increasing the effectiveness of library and information services; provide a forum for the active interchange of ideas and information among library educators; promote research related to teaching and to library and information science; formulate and promulgate positions on matters related to library education. Offers employment program at annual conference.

7340 ■ Association of Research Libraries
21 Dupont Cir. NW, Ste. 800
Washington, DC 20036
Ph: (202)296-2296
Fax: (202)872-0884
E-mail: webmgr@arl.org
URL: http://www.arl.org

Description: Represents the interests of libraries in North American research institutions. Provides leadership in public and information policy to the scholarly and higher education communities. Serves as a forum for the exchange of ideas and as an agent for collective action.

7341 ■ Association of Seventh-Day Adventist Librarians (ASDAL)
Loma Linda University
11072 Anderson St.
Loma Linda, CA 92350-1704
E-mail: lcurtis@llu.edu
URL: http://www.asdal.org

Description: Librarians belonging to the Seventh-Day Adventist church. Aims to: enhance communication among members; serve as a forum for discussion of mutual problems and professional concerns; promote librarianship and library services to Seventh-Day Adventist institutions. Sponsors D. Glenn Hilts Scholarship for graduate studies. Maintains placement service. Compiles statistics.

7342 ■ Health Science Communications Association (HeSCA)
39 Wedgewood Dr., Ste. A
Jewett City, CT 06351-2420
Ph: (860)376-5915
Fax: (860)376-6621
E-mail: hescaone@sbcglobal.net
URL: http://www.hesca.org

Description: Represents media managers, graphic artists, biomedical librarians, producers, faculty members of health science and veterinary medicine schools, health professional organizations, and industry representatives. Acts as a clearinghouse for information used by professionals engaged in health science communications. Coordinates Media Festivals Program that recognizes outstanding media productions in the health sciences. Offers placement service.

7343 ■ Music Library Association (MLA)
8551 Research Way, Ste. 180
Middleton, WI 53562-3567
Ph: (608)836-5825

Fax: (608)831-8200
E-mail: mla@areditions.com
URL: http://www.musiclibraryassoc.org
Description: Promotes the establishment, growth, and use of music libraries and collection of music, musical instruments, musical literature, and audiovisual aids. Maintains placement service.

7344 ■ North American Serials Interest Group (NASIG)
PMB 305
1902 Ridge Rd.
West Seneca, NY 14224
E-mail: info@nasig.org
URL: http://www.nasig.org

Description: Promotes communication, information exchange, and continuing education about serials and the broader issues of scholarly communication. Represents librarians; subscription vendors; publishers; serial automation vendors; serials binders; library science educators; others involved in serials management. Purpose: Promotes educational and social networking among members.

7345 ■ Special Libraries Association (SLA)
331 S Patrick St.
Alexandria, VA 22314-3501
Ph: (703)647-4900
Fax: (703)647-4901
E-mail: janice@sla.org
URL: http://www.sla.org

Description: International association of information professionals who work in specialized information environments such as business, research, government, universities, newspapers, museums, and institutions. Seeks to advance the leadership role of information professionals through learning, networking and advocacy. Offers consulting services to organizations that wish to establish or expand a library or information services. Conducts strategic learning and development courses, public relations, and government relations programs. Provides employment services. Operates knowledge exchange on topics pertaining to the development and management of special libraries.

SOURCES OF HELP-WANTED ADS

7346 ■ Base Line
Map and Geography Round Table
c/o Danielle M. Alderson
American Library Association
50 E Huron St.
Chicago, IL 60611-2788
Ph: (312)280-3213
Fax: (312)944-6131
E-mail: dponton@ala.org
URL: http://www.ala.org/magirt

Description: Bimonthly. Provides current information on cartographic materials, publications of interest to map and geography librarians, related government activities, and map librarianship. Recurring features include conference and meeting information, news of research, job listings, and columns by the Division chair and the editor.

7347 ■ Book Marks
South Dakota Library Association
28363 472nd Ave.
Worthing, SD 57077
Ph: (605)372-0235
Fax: (605)274-5447
E-mail: bookmarkssd@gmail.com
URL: http://www.sdlibraryassociation.org

Description: Quarterly. Carries news by and for South Dakota public, school, academic, and special libraries. Discusses statewide library issues, reviews South Dakota books, and advises members of continuing education opportunities. Recurring features include columns, a calendar of events, news from libraries, and job listings.

7348 ■ Children and Libraries
American Library Association
50 E Huron St.
Chicago, IL 60611-2729
Ph: (312)280-4223
Fax: (312)280-4380
Fr: 800-545-2433
URL: http://www.ala.org/ala/mgrps/divs/alsc/
   compubs/childrenlib/i

for Included in membership; $50.00/year for other countries; $40.00/year for nonmembers. Journal that focuses on the continuing education of librarians working with children.

7349 ■ Computers in Libraries
Information Today Inc.
143 Old Marlton Pike
Medford, NJ 08055-8750
Ph: (609)654-6266
Fax: (609)654-4309
Fr: 800-300-9868
URL: http://www.infotoday.com/cilmag/default.shtml

$99.95/year for individuals, computers in libraries; $188.00/year for individuals, 2 years, U.S.; $288.00/ year for individuals, 3 year, U.S.; $118.00/year for Canada and Mexico; $131.00/year for individuals, outside North America; $69.95/year for individuals; $132.00/year for two years; $201.00/year for individuals, 3 years; $88.00/year for Canada and Mexico; $101.00/year for individuals, outside North America. Library science magazine that provides complete coverage of the news and issues in the rapidly evolving field of library information technology.

7350 ■ Information Technology Management
Idea Group Publishing
701 E Chocolate Ave., Ste. 200
Hershey, PA 17033-1240
Ph: (717)533-8845
Fax: (717)533-8661
Fr: (866)342-6657
E-mail: cust@igi-global.com
URL: http://www.igi-pub.com/journals

Description: 2/year. Discusses cybrary networks, library practices, information access, and new technology product releases. Recurring features include letters to the editor, interviews, news of research, a calendar of events, news of educational opportunities, and book reviews.

7351 ■ Information Today
Information Today Inc.
143 Old Marlton Pike
Medford, NJ 08055-8750
Ph: (609)654-6266
Fax: (609)654-4309
Fr: 800-300-9868
URL: http://www.infotoday.com

$87.50/year for individuals; $115.00/year for Canada and Mexico; $165.00/year for two years; $126.00/ year for individuals, outside North America. User and producer magazine (tabloid) covering electronic and optical information services.

7352 ■ Intercom
District of Columbia Library Association
Box 14177
Benjamin Franklin Station
Washington, DC 20044
Ph: (202)872-1112
URL: http://www.dcla.org/

Description: Eleven issues/year (monthly with July/ August combined). Deals with libraries and librarians in the Washington D.C., area. Recurring features include a calendar of events, reports of meetings, job listings, and notices of publications available.

7353 ■ Journal of Access Services
Routledge Journals
270 Madison Ave.
New York, NY 10016-0601
Ph: (212)216-7800
Fax: (212)563-2269
URL: http://www.tandf.co.uk/journals/WJAS

Quarterly. $77.00/year for individuals, online only; $82.00/year for individuals, print + online; $210.00/ year for institutions, online only; $233.00/year for institutions, print + online. Journal focusing on the basic business of providing library users with access to information, and helping librarians stay up to date on continuing education and professional development in the field of access services.

7354 ■ Journal of Classification
Springer-Verlag New York Inc.
233 Spring St.
New York, NY 10013-1578
Ph: (212)460-1500
Fax: (212)460-1575
Fr: 800-777-4643
URL: http://www.springer.com/statistics/
   statistical+theory+and+me

Semiannual. $447.00/year for institutions, print or online; $536.00/year for institutions, print & enchanced access. Journal of the Classification Society of North America.

7355 ■ Journal of Interlibrary Loan,
   Document Delivery & Electronic Reserve
Routledge Journals
270 Madison Ave.
New York, NY 10016-0601
Ph: (212)216-7800
Fax: (212)563-2269
URL: http://www.informaworld.com/smpp/
   title~content=t792306877

$100.00/year for individuals, online only; $108.00/ year for individuals, print + online; $396.00/year for institutions, online only; $440.00/year for institutions, print + online. Journal focusing on a broad spectrum of library and information center functions that rely heavily on interlibrary loan, document delivery, and electronic reserve.

7356 ■ Law Librarians' Bulletin Board
Legal Information Services
PO Box 31425
Charlotte, NC 28231
Ph: (980)333-3049
Fax: (704)541-6817
E-mail: info@legalinformationservices.com
URL: http://www.legalinformationservices.com/
   Publications/librarians-newsletter.php

Description: 8/year. Tracks current events in law librarianship. Recurring features include job listings.

7357 ■ Library Journal
Media Source Inc
7858 Industrial Pkwy.
Plain City, OH 43064
Ph: (614)873-7635
Fr: (866)207-0310
E-mail: ljinfo@mediasourceinc.com
URL: http://www.libraryjournal.com

$157.99/year for individuals; $199.99/year for Canada and Mexico; $259.99/year for other countries. Library management and book selection journal.

7358 ■ *The Outrider*
Wyoming State Library
2800 Central Ave.
Cheyenne, WY 82002
Ph: (307)777-6333
Fax: (307)777-6289
URL: http://will.state.wy.us/slpub/outrider/index.html

Description: Biennial. Provides news about the activities of the Wyoming State Library, its board, other tax-supported libraries in the state, the American Library Association, and the library field in general. Recurring features include job listings, meetings, workshops, and other events; personnel news; reports on consultant activities and acquisitions news; and columns titled News Briefs, Around the State.

7359 ■ *School Library Journal*
Media Source Inc
7858 Industrial Pkwy.
Plain City, OH 43064
Ph: (614)873-7635
Fr: (866)207-0310
E-mail: slj@reedbusiness.com
URL: http://www.schoollibraryjournal.com/

Monthly. $136.99/year for individuals; $199.99/year for Canada; $259.99/year for other countries. A new Canadian Web site launched with the blessing of Microsoft Chairman Bill Gates is using games and cartoons to teach kids about the evils of online predators.

EMPLOYER DIRECTORIES AND NETWORKING LISTS

7360 ■ *American Library Directory*
Information Today Inc.
143 Old Marlton Pike
Medford, NJ 08055-8750
Ph: (609)654-6266
Fax: (609)654-4309
Fr: 800-300-9868
URL: http://books.infotoday.com

Annual, latest edition 64th; 2011-2012. $329.00 for individuals; $296.10 for individuals. Covers: Over 36,000 U.S. and Canadian academic, public, county, provincial, and regional libraries; library systems; medical, law, and other special libraries; and libraries for the blind and physically handicapped. Separate section lists over 350 library networks and consortia and 220 accredited and unaccredited library school programs. Entries include: For libraries—Name, supporting or affiliated institution or firm name, address, phone, fax, electronic mail address, Standard Address Number (SANs), names of librarian and department heads, income, collection size, special collections, computer hardware, automated functions, and type of catalog. For library systems—Name, location. For library schools—Name, address, phone, fax, electronic mail address, director, type of training and degrees, admission requirements, tuition, faculty size. For networks and consortia—Name, address, phone, names of affiliates, name of director, function. Arrangement: Geographical. Indexes: Institution name. Library Services & Suppliers index.

7361 ■ *The Basic Business Library*
Greenwood Publishing Group Inc.
88 Post Rd. W
PO Box 5007
Westport, CT 06881
Ph: (203)226-3571
Fax: (203)222-1502
Fr: 800-225-5800
URL: http://www.abc-clio.com/
product.aspx?id=64414

Latest edition 4th. $78.95 for single issue. Publication includes: Publisher's Web site as part of each entry. Principal content of publication is list of 210 entries of suggested resources for business libraries, as well as essays on business references sources and services. Indexes: Alphabetical.

7362 ■ *Directory of Federal Libraries*
Oryx Press
88 Post Rd. W
PO Box 5007
Westport, CT 06881
Fax: (203)222-1502
URL: http://www.greenwood.com/catalog/
OXDFL3.aspx

Irregular, Latest edition 3rd. $138.95 for individuals; $95.95 for individuals. Covers: nearly 3,000 libraries serving branches of the federal government. Entries include: Library name, type, address, phone, fax, e-mail, telnet, and websites, name of administrator and selected staff, special collections, database services available, depository status for documents from the Government Printing Office or other organizations, involvement with cooperative library organizations, electronic mail or cataloging networks, whether accessible to the public. Arrangement: Classified by federal establishment. Indexes: Library type, subject, geographical, alphabetical index of libraries by name.

7363 ■ *Directory of Public School Systems in the U.S.*
American Association for Employment in Education
3040 Riverside Dr., Ste. 117
Columbus, OH 43221
Ph: (614)485-1111
Fax: (360)244-7802
E-mail: office@aaee.org
URL: http://www.aaee.org/

Annual, Winter; latest edition 2004-2005 edition. $55.00 for members; $80.00 for nonmembers. Covers: About 14,000 public school systems in the United States and their administrative personnel. Entries include: System name, address, phone, website address, name and title of personnel administrator, levels taught and approx. Student population. Arrangement: Geographical by state.

7364 ■ *Directory of Special Libraries and Information Centers*
Gale
PO Box 6904
Florence, KY 41022-6904
Fr: 800-354-9706
URL: http://www.gale.cengage.com

Annual, Latest edition 39th; April, 2011. $1533.00 for individuals; $920.00 for individuals. Covers: Over 34,800 special libraries, information centers, documentation centers, etc.; about 500 networks and consortia; major special libraries abroad also included. Volume 1 part 3 contains 6 other appendices (besides networks and consortia): Regional and Subregional Libraries for the Blind & Physically Handicapped, Patent & Trademark Depository Libraries, Regional Government Depository Libraries, United Nations Depository Libraries, World Bank Depository Libraries, and European Community Depository Libraries. Entries include: Library name, address, phone, fax, e-mail address; contact; year founded; sponsoring organization; special collections; subject interests; names and titles of staff; services (copying, online searches); size of collection; subscriptions; computerized services and automated operations; Internet home page address; publications; special catalogs; special indexes. For consortia and networks—Name, address, phone, contact. Other appendices have varying amounts of directory information. Contents of Volume 1 are available in "Subject Directory of Special Libraries and Information Centers". Arrangement: Libraries are alphabetical by name of sponsoring organization or institution; consortia and networks are geographical. Indexes: Subject. Geographic and personnel indexes constitute volume 2.

7365 ■ *Guide to Employment Sources in the Library & Information Professions*
Office for Human Resource Development and Recruitment
50 E Huron St.
Chicago, IL 60611

Ph: (312)280-2428
Fax: (312)280-3256
Fr: 800-545-2433
E-mail: customerservice@ala.org
URL: http://www.ala.org

Annual, Latest edition 2009. Covers: Library job sources, such as specialized and state and regional library associations, state library agencies, federal library agencies, and overseas exchange programs. Entries include: Library, company, or organization name, address, phone; contact name, description of services, publications, etc. This is a reprint of a segment of the "Bowker Annual of Library and Book Trade Information," described separately. Arrangement: Classified by type of source.

7366 ■ *Higher Education Directory*
Higher Education Publications Inc.
1801 Robert Fulton Dr., Ste. 340
Reston, VA 20191
Ph: (571)313-0478
Fax: (571)313-0526
Fr: 888-349-7715
URL: http://www.hepinc.com

Annual, latest edition 2011. $75.00 for individuals. Covers: Over 4,364 degree granting colleges and universities accredited by approved agencies recognized by the U.S. Secretary of Education and by the Council of Higher Education Accreditation (CHEA); 103 systems offices; over 550 related associations and state government agencies; recognized accrediting agencies. Entries include: For institutions—Name, address, congressional district, phone, fax, year established; Carnegie classification; enrollment; type of student body; religious or other affiliation; undergraduate tuition and fees; type of academic calendar; highest degree offered; accreditations; IRS status; names, titles and job classification codes for academic and administrative officers. For associations and state agencies—Name, address, phone, name of chief executive officer. Same content and coverage as the base volume of the Department of Education's publication "Directory of Postsecondary Institutions" . Arrangement: Geographical, alphabetical by state. Indexes: Administrator name (with phone and e-mail addresses), accreditation, FICE numbers, college or university name.

7367 ■ *Midwest Archives Conference—Membership Directory*
Midwest Archives Conference
4440 PGA Blvd., Ste. 600
Palm Beach Gardens, FL 33410
URL: http://www.midwestarchives.org

Annual. Covers: More than 1,150 individual and institutional members, largely librarians, archivists, records managers, manuscripts curators, historians, and museum and historical society personnel; about 25 archival associations in the Midwest. Entries include: For institutions—Name of archives, parent organization, address, phone. For individuals—Name, title, business address, phone. Arrangement: Separate alphabetical sections for individuals and institutions.

7368 ■ *Patterson's American Education*
Educational Directories Inc.
1025 W Wise Rd., Ste. 101
PO Box 68097
Schaumburg, IL 60168-0097
Ph: (847)891-1250
Fax: (847)891-0945
Fr: 800-357-6183
URL: http://www.ediusa.com

Annual, Latest edition 2012, vol. 108. $97.00 for individuals. Covers: Over 11,000 school districts in the United States; more than 34,000 public, private, and Catholic high schools, middle schools, and junior high schools; Approximately 300 parochial superintendents; 400 state department of education personnel. Entries include: For school districts and schools—District and superintendent Name, address, phone, fax, grade ranges, enrollment, school names, addresses, phone numbers, grade ranges, enrollment, names of principals. For postsecondary schools—School name, address, phone number, URL, e-mail, names of administrator or director of admissions. For private and Catholic high schools—name, address, phone, fax, enrollment, grades offered, name of principal. Postsecondary institutions are covered in 'Patterson's Schools Classified'. Arrangement: Geographical by state, then alphabetical by city.

7369 ■ *Patterson's Schools Classified*
Educational Directories Inc.
1025 W Wise Rd., Ste. 101
PO Box 68097
Schaumburg, IL 60168-0097
Ph: (847)891-1250
Fax: (847)891-0945
Fr: 800-357-6183
URL: http://www.ediusa.com

Annual, Latest edition 2010, volume 60. $23.00 for individuals. Covers: Over 6,000 accredited colleges, universities, community colleges, junior colleges, career schools and teaching hospitals. Entries include: School name, address, phone, URL, e-mail, name of administrator or admissions officer, description, professional accreditation (where applicable). Updated from previous year's edition of 'Patterson's American Education'. Arrangement: Classified by area of study, then geographical by state. Indexes: Alphabetical by name.

7370 ■ *Requirements for Certification of Teachers, Counselors, Librarians, Administrators for Elementary and Secondary Schools*
University of Chicago Press
Journals Division
1427 E 60th St.
Chicago, IL 60637-2954
Ph: (773)702-7636
Fax: (773)702-9756
URL: http://www.press.uchicago.edu

Annual, Latest edition 74th. $53.00. Publication includes: List of state and local departments of education. Entries include: Office name, address, phone. Principal content of publication is summaries of each state's teaching and administrative certification requirements. Arrangement: Geographical.

HANDBOOKS AND MANUALS

7371 ■ *Opportunities in Library and Information Science Careers*
The McGraw-Hill Companies
PO Box 182604
Columbus, OH 43272
Fax: (614)759-3749
Fr: 877-883-5524
E-mail: customer.service@mcgraw-hill.com
URL: http://www.mhprofessional.com/product.php?isbn=007154531X

Kathleen de la Pena McCook. 2008. $14.95 (paper). 160 pages. A guide to planning for and seeking opportunities in this changing field. Includes bibliography and illustrations.

EMPLOYMENT AGENCIES AND SEARCH FIRMS

7372 ■ Gossage Sager Associates
4545 Wornall, Ste. 805
Kansas City, MO 64111
Ph: (816)531-2468
E-mail: danbradbury@gossagesager.com
URL: http://www.gossagesager.com

Firm provides executive recruiting for public libraries, college and university libraries, corporate libraries, nonprofit libraries, information centers, archives, records management, and other information handling organizations. Offers additional expertise in library

management consulting, emphasizing planning, personnel and labor relations and management and systems evaluation. Other areas of specialization include: records management consultation for corporations and nonprofit organizations and computer systems consultation for libraries, corporate and nonprofit records management and other information handling systems. Serves private industries as well as government agencies.

ONLINE JOB SOURCES AND SERVICES

7373 ■ Library and Information Technology Association Job Listing
E-mail: lita@ala.org
URL: http://www.ftrf.org/ala/mgrps/divs/lita/professional/jobs/index.cfm
Description: Contains weekly postings of available library jobs. Searchable by region.

7374 ■ Library Job Postings on the Internet
E-mail: sarah@libraryjobpostings.org
URL: http://www.libraryjobpostings.org
Description: Employers may post library position announcements. Also contains links to around 250 library employment sites and links to library-related e-mail lists. Positions are searchable by region and type of library.

7375 ■ LibraryCrossing.com
URL: http://www.librarycrossing.com
Description: Provides job listings and other resources related to library employment opportunities.

7376 ■ LIScareer.com
URL: http://www.liscareer.com
Description: Offers career development resources for librarians, information professionals, students and those considering a career in library and information science. Includes practical advice contributed by information professionals, links to online resources and information about print resources.

7377 ■ LISJobs.com
URL: http://www.lisjobs.com
Description: Provides career information for librarians and information professionals. Offers more resources beyond job hunting such as career development resources that are intended to help clients continue to grow as professionals.

TRADESHOWS

7378 ■ Computers in Libraries
Information Today, Inc.
143 Old Marlton Pike
Medford, NJ 08055-8750
Ph: (609)654-6266
Fax: (609)654-4309
Fr: 800-300-9868
E-mail: custserv@infotoday.com
URL: http://www.infotoday.com

Annual. Primary Exhibits: Computer hardware, software, CD-ROMS, and related equipment, supplies, and services for use in libraries. Dates and Locations: 2012 Mar 21-23; Washington, DC; Hilton Washington.

7379 ■ Illinois School Library Media Association Conference
Illinois School Library Media Association
PO Box 598
Canton, IL 61520
Ph: (309)649-0911
Fax: (309)649-0916
E-mail: islma@islma.org
URL: http://www.islma.org

Annual. Primary Exhibits: Equipment, supplies, and services for elementary and secondary school library

media specialists interested in the general improvement and extension of services for children and young people. Dates and Locations: 2012 Nov 08-10; Arlington Heights, IL; Sheraton Chicago Northwest.

7380 ■ Public Library Association National Conference
Public Library Association
50 E. Huron St.
Chicago, IL 60611
Ph: (312)280-5752
Fax: (312)280-5029
Fr: 800-545-2433
E-mail: pla@ala.org
URL: http://www.pla.org

Biennial. Primary Exhibits: Books, software & hardware and other equipment, supplies, and services for libraries. Dates and Locations: 2012 Mar 13-17; Philadelphia, PA.

7381 ■ Special Libraries Association Information Revolution
Special Libraries Association
331 S. Patrick St.
Alexandria, VA 22314-3501
Ph: (703)647-4900
Fax: (703)647-4901
E-mail: sla@sla.org
URL: http://www.sla.org

Annual. Primary Exhibits: Library equipment, supplies, and services, including computers and software, Database information.

OTHER SOURCES

7382 ■ American Library Association (ALA)
50 E Huron St.
Chicago, IL 60611
Ph: (312)944-6780
Fax: (312)440-9374
Fr: 800-545-2433
E-mail: ala@ala.org
URL: http://www.ala.org

Description: Librarians, libraries, trustees, friends of libraries, and others interested in the responsibilities of libraries in the educational, social, and cultural needs of society. Promotes and improves library service and librarianship. Establishes standards of service, support, education, and welfare for libraries and library personnel; promotes the adoption of such standards in libraries of all kinds; safeguards the professional status of librarians; encourages the recruiting of competent personnel for professional careers in librarianship; promotes popular understanding and public acceptance of the value of library service and librarianship. Works in liaison with federal agencies to initiate the enactment and administration of legislation that will extend library services. Offers placement services.

7383 ■ American Society for Information Science and Technology (ASIS&T)
1320 Fenwick Ln., Ste. 510
Silver Spring, MD 20910
Ph: (301)495-0900
Fax: (301)495-0810
E-mail: asis@asis.org
URL: http://www.asis.org

Description: Information specialists, scientists, librarians, administrators, social scientists, and others interested in the use, organization, storage, retrieval, evaluation, and dissemination of recorded specialized information. Seeks to improve the information transfer process through research, development, application, and education. Provides a forum for the discussion, publication, and critical analysis of work dealing with the theory, practice, research, and development of elements involved in communication of information. Members are engaged in a variety of activities and specialties including classification and coding systems, automatic and associative indexing, machine translation of languages, special librarianship and library systems analysis, and copyright issues. Sponsors National Auxiliary Publications Service, which provides reproduction services and a central depository for all types of information. Maintains placement service. Sponsors numerous special interest groups. Conducts continuing education programs and professional development workshops.

7384 ■ Association of Christian Librarians
PO Box 4
Cedarville, OH 45314
Ph: (937)766-2255
Fax: (937)766-5499
E-mail: info@acl.org
URL: http://www.acl.org

Description: Seeks to empower evangelical librarians through professional development, scholarship and spiritual encouragement for service in higher education.

7385 ■ Association of College and Research Libraries (ACRL)
50 E Huron St.
Chicago, IL 60611-2795
Ph: (312)280-2523
Fax: (312)280-2520
Fr: 800-545-2433
E-mail: acrl@ala.org
URL: http://www.ala.org/ala/mgrps/divs/acrl/index.cfm

Description: A division of the American Library Association. Academic and research librarians seeking to improve the quality of service in academic libraries; promotes the professional and career development of academic and research librarians; represent the interests and support the programs of academic and research libraries. Operates placement services; sponsors specialized education and research grants and programs; gathers, compiles, and disseminates statistics. Establishes and adopts standards; maintains publishing program; offers professional development courses.

7386 ■ Association of Jewish Libraries (AJL)
PO Box 1118
Teaneck, NJ 07666-1118
Ph: (212)725-5359
E-mail: ajlibs@osu.edu
URL: http://www.jewishlibraries.org

Description: Devoted to the educational, informational, and networking needs of librarians responsible for collections of Judaica and to the promotion of Judaic librarianship.

7387 ■ Association of Research Libraries
21 Dupont Cir. NW, Ste. 800
Washington, DC 20036
Ph: (202)296-2296
Fax: (202)872-0884
E-mail: webmgr@arl.org
URL: http://www.arl.org

Description: Represents the interests of libraries in North American research institutions. Provides leadership in public and information policy to the scholarly and higher education communities. Serves as a forum for the exchange of ideas and as an agent for collective action.

7388 ■ Council on Library-Media Technicians (COLT)
28262 Chardon Rd.
PMB 168
Willoughby Hills, OH 44092-2793
Ph: (202)231-3836
Fax: (202)231-3838
E-mail: jmhite0@dia.mil
URL: http://colt.ucr.edu

Description: Persons involved in two-year associate degree programs for the training of library technical assistants (professional-support workers) and graduates of programs employed as library/media technical assistants (B.A. degree holders without M.L.S. degree). Membership includes junior college deans, librarians, curriculum directors, professors, employers, special libraries, university libraries, library schools, publishers, and library technical assistants. Provides a channel of communication among the institutions and personnel that have developed such training programs; attempts to standardize curriculum offerings; develops educational standards; conducts research on graduates of the programs; represents the interests of library technical assistants and support staff. The council's concerns also include development of clear job descriptions and criteria for employment of technicians and dissemination of information to the public and to prospective students. Sponsors workshops for support staff in areas such as management, supervisory skills, interpersonal communication, business writing, and media center management. Maintains speakers' bureau. Develops a program for certification of library media technicians and a continuing education program for library support staff.

7389 ■ Music Library Association (MLA)
8551 Research Way, Ste. 180
Middleton, WI 53562-3567
Ph: (608)836-5825
Fax: (608)831-8200
E-mail: mla@areditions.com
URL: http://www.musiclibraryassoc.org

Description: Promotes the establishment, growth, and use of music libraries and collection of music, musical instruments, musical literature, and audiovisual aids. Maintains placement service.

7390 ■ North American Serials Interest Group (NASIG)
PMB 305
1902 Ridge Rd.
West Seneca, NY 14224
E-mail: info@nasig.org
URL: http://www.nasig.org

Description: Promotes communication, information exchange, and continuing education about serials and the broader issues of scholarly communication. Represents librarians; subscription vendors; publishers; serial automation vendors; serials binders; library science educators; others involved in serials management. Purpose: Promotes educational and social networking among members.

7391 ■ Special Libraries Association (SLA)
331 S Patrick St.
Alexandria, VA 22314-3501
Ph: (703)647-4900
Fax: (703)647-4901
E-mail: janice@sla.org
URL: http://www.sla.org

Description: International association of information professionals who work in specialized information environments such as business, research, government, universities, newspapers, museums, and institutions. Seeks to advance the leadership role of information professionals through learning, networking and advocacy. Offers consulting services to organizations that wish to establish or expand a library or information services. Conducts strategic learning and development courses, public relations, and government relations programs. Provides employment services. Operates knowledge exchange on topics pertaining to the development and management of special libraries.

SOURCES OF HELP-WANTED ADS

7392 ■ AANA Journal
AANA Publishing Inc.
222 S Prospect Ave.
Park Ridge, IL 60068-4001
Ph: (847)692-7050
Fax: (847)692-6968
URL: http://www.aana.com/
Resources.aspx?id=5324&linkidentifier=id

Bimonthly. Nursing and anesthesia journal.

7393 ■ AAOHN Journal
SLACK Incorporated
6900 Grove Rd.
Thorofare, NJ 08086-9447
Ph: (856)848-1000
Fax: (856)848-6091
E-mail: aaohn@slackinc.com
URL: http://www.slackjournals.com/aaohn

Monthly. $115.00/year for individuals; $230.00/year for individuals, two years; $345.00/year for individuals, three years; $259.00/year for institutions; $518.00/year for institutions, two years; $777.00/year for institutions, three years; $29.00/year for single issue. Official journal of the American Association of Occupational Health Nurses.

7394 ■ AAOHN News
American Association of Occupational Health Nurses Inc.
7794 Grow Dr.
Pensacola, FL 32514
Ph: (850)474-6963
Fax: (850)484-8762
Fr: 800-241-8014
E-mail: aaohn@dancyamc.com
URL: http://www.aaohn.org/membership/corporate-partnerships.html

Description: Quarterly. Covers Association events as well as trends and legislation affecting occupational and environmental health nursing. Recurring features include news of research, a calendar of events, reports of meetings, news of educational opportunities, job listings, notices of publications available, resources for career-building, briefs on governmental issues concerning occupational and environment health, and a President's column.

7395 ■ ADVANCE for LPNs
Merion Publications Inc.
2900 Horizon Dr.
PO Box 61556
King of Prussia, PA 19406-0956
Ph: (610)278-1400
Fr: 800-355-5627
URL: http://lpn.advanceweb.com/

Biweekly. Free to qualified subscribers. Magazine for licensed practical nurses covering clinical information and job opportunities.

7396 ■ ADVANCE for Nurse Practitioners
Merion Publications Inc.
2900 Horizon Dr.
PO Box 61556
King of Prussia, PA 19406-0956
Ph: (610)278-1400
Fr: 800-355-5627
URL: http://nurse-practitioners-and-physician-assistants.advancew

Monthly. Free to qualified subscribers. For practicing nurse practitioner students with senior status.

7397 ■ Advances in Neonatal Care
National Association of Neonatal Nurses
4700 W Lake Ave.
Glenview, IL 60025
Ph: (847)375-3660
Fax: (866)927-5321
Fr: 800-451-3795
E-mail: info@nann.org
URL: http://www.nann.org

Bimonthly. $100.99/year for individuals in the U.S.; $236/year for institutions in the U.S.; $169.22/year for international individuals; $319.22/year for international institutions. Contains research and clinical practice articles. Features various job opportunities in the field.

7398 ■ Advances in Nursing Science (ANS)
Lippincott Williams & Wilkins
530 Walnut St.
Philadelphia, PA 19106-3619
Ph: (215)521-8300
Fax: (215)521-8902
Fr: 800-638-3030
URL: http://www.lww.com/product/?0161-9268

Quarterly. $114.99/year for individuals; $432.00/year for institutions; $68.49/year for individuals, in-training; $219.73/year for other countries; $561.73/year for institutions, other countries. Academic medical journal focusing on nursing research and education.

7399 ■ American Family Physician
American Academy of Family Physicians
11400 Tomahawk Creek Pky.
PO Box 11210
Leawood, KS 66211-2680
Ph: (913)906-6000
Fax: (913)906-6075
Fr: 800-274-2237
E-mail: afpedit@aafp.org
URL: http://www.aafp.org/online/en/home/publications/journals/afp

Semimonthly. $101.00/year for individuals, healthcare professionals; $164.00/year for Canada, healthcare professionals; $227.00/year for other countries, healthcare professionals; $173.00/year for individuals, physicians and other individuals; $240.00/year for Canada, physicians and other individuals; $299.00/year for other countries, physicians and other individuals; $236.00/year for institutions; $299.00/year for institutions, Canada; $362.00/year

for institutions, other countries. Peer-reviewed clinical journal for family physicians and others in primary care. Review articles detail the latest diagnostic and therapeutic techniques in the medical field. Department features in each issue include 'Tips from other Journals,' CME credit opportunities and course calendar.

7400 ■ American Journal of Nursing
American Journal of Nursing
c/o Lippincott, Williams & Wilkins
2 Commerce Sq., 2001 Market St.
Philadelphia, PA 19103
Ph: (215)521-8300
Fax: (215)521-8902
URL: http://www.nursingcenter.com

Monthly. $51.00/year for individuals; $425.00/year for institutions; $129.00/year for other countries; $465.00/year for institutions, other countries. Peer-reviewed journal promoting excellence in nursing and health care.

7401 ■ The American Nurse
American Nurses Association
8515 Georgia Ave., Ste. 400
Silver Spring, MD 20910
Ph: (301)628-5000
Fax: (301)628-5001
Fr: 800-274-4262
E-mail: adsales@ana.org
URL: http://nursingworld.org/tan/

Monthly. $20.00/year for individuals, practicing nurses; $10.00/year for students. Newspaper (tabloid) for the nursing profession.

7402 ■ Cancer Nursing
Lippincott Williams & Wilkins
530 Walnut St.
Philadelphia, PA 19106-3619
Ph: (215)521-8300
Fax: (215)521-8902
Fr: 800-638-3030
E-mail: editor@gator.net
URL: http://journals.lww.com/cancernursingonline/pages/default.as

Bimonthly. $109.99/year for individuals; $378.00/year for institutions; $63.99/year for individuals, in-training; $203.22/year for other countries; $518.22/year for institutions, other countries. Medical journal covering problems arising in the care and support of cancer patients.

7403 ■ Clinical Nurse Specialist
Lippincott Williams & Wilkins
530 Walnut St.
Philadelphia, PA 19106-3619
Ph: (215)521-8300
Fax: (215)521-8902
Fr: 800-638-3030
E-mail: jasfulto@iupui.edu
URL: http://journals.lww.com/cns-journal/pages/default.aspx

Bimonthly. $104.99/year for individuals; $356.00/year for institutions; $63.99/year for individuals, in-training; $218.22/year for other countries; $535.22/year for institutions, other countries. Nursing journal.

7404 ■ Critical Care Nurse
Critical Care Nurse
101 Columbia
Aliso Viejo, CA 92656
Ph: (949)362-2000
Fax: (949)362-2020
Fr: 800-899-2226
URL: http://ccn.aacnjournals.org

Bimonthly. Included in membership; $265.00/year for institutions, print & online. Nursing journal.

7405 ■ Dialysis & Transplantation
John Wiley & Sons Inc.
111 River St.
Hoboken, NJ 07030-5773
Ph: (201)748-6000
Fax: (201)748-6088
Fr: 800-825-7550
URL: http://onlinelibrary.wiley.com/journal/10.1002/(ISSN)1932-69

Monthly. $128.00/year for U.S. and other countries, institution; print only; $65.00/year for institutions, print only; $82.00/year for institutions, print only. Multidisciplinary, peer-reviewed journal on clinical applications in dialysis, transplantation and nephrology for renal-care team.

7406 ■ EndoNurse
Virgo Publishing Inc.
PO Box 40079
Phoenix, AZ 85067-0079
Ph: (480)990-1101
Fax: (480)990-0819
URL: http://endonurse.com/

Bimonthly. $40.00/year for individuals; $60.00/year for Canada; $70.00/year for other countries. Magazine covering endoscopic nursing.

7407 ■ Heart and Lung
Mosby
1600 John F. Kennedy Blvd., Ste. 1800
Philadelphia, PA 19103-2899
Ph: (215)239-3275
Fax: (215)239-3286
URL: http://www.elsevier.com/wps/find/journaldescription.cws_home

Bimonthly. $103.00/year for individuals; $445.00/year for institutions; $524.00/year for institutions, other countries; $153.00/year for other countries. Journal offering articles prepared by nurse and physician members of the critical care team, recognizing the nurse's role in the care and management of major organ-system conditions in critically ill patients.

7408 ■ Home Healthcare Nurse
Lippincott Williams & Wilkins
530 Walnut St.
Philadelphia, PA 19106-3619
Ph: (215)521-8300
Fax: (215)521-8902
Fr: 800-638-3030
URL: http://journals.lww.com/homehealthcarenurseonline/pages/defa

$62.14/year for individuals; $324.00/year for institutions; $156.11/year for other countries; $481.11/year for institutions, other countries; $40.99/year for individuals, in-training. Magazine for the practicing professional nurse working in the home health, community health, and public health areas.

7409 ■ HomeCare Magazine
Penton Media
249 W 17th St.
New York, NY 10011-5390
Ph: (212)204-4200
URL: http://homecaremag.com/

Monthly. Free, in US; $135.00/year for Canada; $150.00/year for two years, Canada; $250.00/year

for other countries; $250.00/year for two years, other countries. Magazine serving home medical equipment suppliers, including independent and chain centers specializing in home care, pharmacies or chain drug stores with home care products, and joint-ventured hospital home health care businesses. Contains industry news and new product launches and marketing strategies.

7410 ■ Hospitals & Health Networks
Health Forum L.L.C.
155 N Wacker Dr., Ste. 400
Chicago, IL 60606
Ph: (312)893-6800
Fax: (312)422-4500
Fr: 800-821-2039
URL: http://www.hhnmag.com

Weekly. Free. Publication covering the health care industry.

7411 ■ The IHS Primary Care Provider
Indian Health Service
The Reyes Bldg.
801 Thompson Ave., Ste. 400
Rockville, MD 20852-1627
Ph: (301)443-1011
URL: http://www.ihs.gov/provider

Monthly. Journal for health care professionals, physicians, nurses, pharmacists, dentists, and dietitians.

7412 ■ Imprint
National Student Nurses' Association Inc.
45 Main St., Ste. 606
Brooklyn, NY 11201
Ph: (718)210-0705
Fax: (718)797-1186
E-mail: nsna@nsna.org
URL: http://www.nsna.org/Publications.aspx

$18.00/year for individuals; $30.00/year for other countries; $36.00/year for institutions. Magazine for nursing students, focusing on issues and trends in nursing.

7413 ■ Intensive and Critical Care Nursing
Mosby Inc.
11830 Westline Industrial Dr.
St. Louis, MO 63146-3326
Ph: (314)872-8370
Fax: (314)432-1380
Fr: 800-325-4177
URL: http://www.elsevier.com/wps/find/journaldescription.cws_home

Bimonthly. $114.00/year for individuals, for all countries except Europe, Japan & Iran; $501.00/year for institutions, for all countries except Europe, Japan & Iran; $124.00/year for individuals, for European countries and Iran; $565.00/year for institutions, for European countries and Iran. Journal for nurses in intensive and critical care nursing.

7414 ■ International Journal of Nursing Education Scholarship
Berkeley Electronic Press
2809 Telegraph Ave., Ste. 202
Berkeley, CA 94705-1167
Ph: (510)665-1200
Fax: (510)665-1201
URL: http://www.bepress.com/ijnes

Annual. $525.00/year corporate; $175.00/year academic. Journal that publishes original papers on nursing education issues and research.

7415 ■ International Journal of Nursing Practice
John Wiley & Sons Inc.
350 Main St., Commerce Pl.
Malden, MA 02148-5089
Ph: (781)388-8200
Fax: (781)388-8210
URL: http://www.wiley.com/bw/journal.asp?ref=1322-7114

Bimonthly. $146.00/year for individuals, print and online; $1,053.00/year for institutions, print and online;

$916.00/year for institutions, print or online; $651.00/year for institutions, other countries, print and online; $566.00/year for institutions, other countries, print or online; $850.00/year for institutions, print and premium online, Australia/New Zealand; $739.00/year for institutions, print or online, Australia/New Zealand. Journal publishing articles about advances the international understanding and development of nursing, both as a profession and as an academic discipline.

7416 ■ International Journal of Orthopaedic and Trauma Nursing
Mosby Inc.
11830 Westline Industrial Dr.
St. Louis, MO 63146-3326
Ph: (314)872-8370
Fax: (314)432-1380
Fr: 800-325-4177
URL: http://www.elsevier.com/wps/find/journaldescription.cws_home

Quarterly. $106.00/year for individuals, for all countries except Europe, Japan and Iran; $409.00/year for institutions, for all countries except Europe, Japan and Iran. Journal for orthopaedic nurses.

7417 ■ International Nursing Review
John Wiley & Sons Inc.
350 Main St., Commerce Pl.
Malden, MA 02148-5089
Ph: (781)388-8200
Fax: (781)388-8210
URL: http://www.wiley.com/bw/journal.asp?ref=0020-8132

Quarterly. $63.00/year for individuals, UK & non Euro zone; print + online; $71.00/year for U.S. and other countries, members; $223.00/year for institutions, print + online; $202.00/year for institutions, print or online; $118.00/year for individuals, print + online; $431.00/year for institutions, print + online; $374.00/year for institutions, print or online; $95.00/year for individuals, print + online; $295.00/year for institutions, print + online; $256.00/year for institutions, print or online. Journal focusing on current concerns and issues of modern day nursing and health care from an international perspective.

7418 ■ Journal of Addictions Nursing
Informa Healthcare
52 Vanderbilt Ave., 7th Fl.
New York, NY 10017-3846
Ph: (212)520-2777
URL: http://informahealthcare.com/journal/jan

$342.00/year for institutions; $556.00/year for institutions; $444.00/year for institutions. Journal for nursing addiction professionals.

7419 ■ Journal of Clinical Nursing
John Wiley & Sons Inc.
350 Main St., Commerce Pl.
Malden, MA 02148-5089
Ph: (781)388-8200
Fax: (781)388-8210
E-mail: jcn@oxon.blackwellpublishing.com
URL: http://www.wiley.com/bw/journal.asp?ref=0962-1067

Monthly. $381.00/year for individuals, print and online; $208.00/year for students, print and online; $2,428.00/year for institutions, print and online; $2,111.00/year for institutions, print or online; $312.00/year for individuals, print and online; $167.00/year for students, print and online; $1,315.00/year for institutions, other countries, print and online; $1,143.00/year for institutions, other countries, print or online. Peer-reviewed scientific journal that seeks to promote the development and exchange of knowledge that is directly relevant to spheres of nursing and midwifery practice.

7420 ■ The Journal of Continuing Education in Nursing
SLACK Incorporated
6900 Grove Rd.
Thorofare, NJ 08086-9447

Ph: (856)848-1000
Fax: (856)848-6091
E-mail: jcen@slackinc.com
URL: http://www.slackjournals.com/jcen

Monthly. $124.00/year for individuals; $248.00/year for two years; $29.00/year for single issue; $355.00/year for institutions. Peer-reviewed journal for nurses involved in planning and implementing educational programs for the practitioner and others in patient care.

7421 ■ Journal of the Dermatology Nurses' Association
Dermatology Nurses' Association
15000 Commerce Pkwy., Ste. C
Mount Laurel, NJ 08054
Fax: (856)439-0525
Fr: 800-454-4362
E-mail: dna@dnanurse.org
URL: http://www.dnanurse.org

Bimonthly. Features clinical snapshots, patient perspective pieces, a product review section, a legal forum, health policy and advocacy articles, nursing research studies, and rotating topical columns on a variety of dermatology nursing related issues. Contains product and recruitment/placement advertising.

7422 ■ Journal of Emergency Nursing
Mosby
1600 John F. Kennedy Blvd., Ste. 1800
Philadelphia, PA 19103-2899
Ph: (215)239-3275
Fax: (215)239-3286
URL: http://www.elsevier.com/wps/find/
    journaleditorialboard.cws_h

Bimonthly. $96.00/year for individuals; $380.00/year for institutions; $121.00/year for other countries; $408.00/year for institutions, other countries. Journal containing peer-reviewed articles on clinical aspects of emergency care by, and for, emergency nurses. Presents information about professional, political, administrative, and educational aspects of emergency nursing and nursing in general.

7423 ■ Journal of Gerontological Nursing
SLACK Incorporated
6900 Grove Rd.
Thorofare, NJ 08086-9447
Ph: (856)848-1000
Fax: (856)848-6091
E-mail: jgn@slackinc.com
URL: http://www.slackjournals.com/jgn

Monthly. $95.00/year for individuals; $190.00/year for two years; $315.00/year for institutions; $630.00/year for institutions, two years; $29.00/year for single issue. Gerontological nursing journal.

7424 ■ Journal of Infusion Nursing
Infusion Nurses Society
315 Norwood Park S
Norwood, MA 02062
Ph: (781)440-9408
Fax: (781)440-9409
Fr: 800-694-0298
E-mail: ins@ins1.org
URL: http://www.ins1.org

Bimonthly. Features new research, clinical reviews, case studies, and professional development information relevant to the practice of infusion therapy. Also features product, recruitment, and classified advertisements.

7425 ■ Journal of Nursing Administration (JONA)
Lippincott Williams & Wilkins
530 Walnut St.
Philadelphia, PA 19106-3619
Ph: (215)521-8300
Fax: (215)521-8902
Fr: 800-638-3030
E-mail: jonaeditor@aol.com
URL: http://journals.lww.com/jonajournal/pages/
    default.aspx

$126.99/year for individuals; $69.99/year for individuals, in-training; $261.10/year for other countries; $544.00/year for institutions; $74.63/year for individuals, in-training; $690.70/year for institutions, other countries. Journal covering developments and advances in nursing administration and management.

7426 ■ Journal of Nursing Scholarship
John Wiley & Sons Inc.
350 Main St., Commerce Pl.
Malden, MA 02148-5089
Ph: (781)388-8200
Fax: (781)388-8210
URL: http://www.wiley.com/bw/journal.asp?ref=1527-
    6546&site=1

Quarterly. $63.00/year for individuals, print & online; $263.00/year for institutions, print & online; $228.00/year for institutions, print, online; $73.00/year for individuals, print & online; $191.00/year for institutions, other countries, print & online; $243.00/year for institutions, print & online; $49.00/year for individuals, print & online. Peer-reviewed journal covering nursing.

7427 ■ Journal of Obstetric, Gynecologic and Neonatal Nursing (JOGNN)
John Wiley & Sons Inc.
350 Main St., Commerce Pl.
Malden, MA 02148-5089
Ph: (781)388-8200
Fax: (781)388-8210
URL: http://www.wiley.com/bw/journal.asp?ref=0884-
    2175&site=1

Bimonthly. $121.00/year for individuals, print & online; $1,117.00/year for institutions, print & online; $971.00/year for institutions, online only; $102.00/year for individuals, print & online; $788.00/year for institutions, print & online; $685.00/year for institutions, online only; $68.00/year for individuals, print & online; $621.00/year for institutions, print & online; $540.00/year for institutions, online only. Journal covering trends, policies, and research. Official publication of the Association of Women's Health, Obstetric, and Neonatal Nurses (AWHONN).

7428 ■ Journal of Pediatric Health Care
Mosby
1600 John F. Kennedy Blvd., Ste. 1800
Philadelphia, PA 19103-2899
Ph: (215)239-3275
Fax: (215)239-3286
URL: http://www.elsevier.com/wps/find/
    journaldescription.cws_home

Bimonthly. $141.00/year for other countries; $347.00/year for institutions, other countries; $302.00/year for institutions; $100.00/year for individuals. Official publication of the National Association of Pediatric Nurse Practitioners. Provides current information on pediatric clinical topics as well as research studies, health policy, and legislative issues applicable to pediatric clinical practice.

7429 ■ Journal of PeriAnesthesia Nursing
Mosby Inc.
11830 Westline Industrial Dr.
St. Louis, MO 63146-3326
Ph: (314)872-8370
Fax: (314)432-1380
Fr: 800-325-4177
URL: http://www.elsevier.com/wps/find/
    journaldescription.cws_home

Bimonthly. $454.00/year for institutions; $134.00/year for individuals; $328.00/year for institutions; $298.00/year for individuals. Peer-reviewed journal publishing research for a primary audience that includes nurses in perianesthesia settings, including ambulatory surgery, preadmission testing, postanesthesia (Phases I, II, and III) care, and pain management. Journal providing forum for sharing professional knowledge and experience relating to management, ethics, legislation, research, and other aspects of perianesthesia nursing.

7430 ■ Journal of Practical Nursing
National Association for Practical Nurse Education and Service Inc.
1940 Duke St., Ste. 200
Alexandria, VA 22313
Ph: (703)933-1003
Fax: (703)940-4089
URL: http://www.napnes.org/jpn/jpn_
    subscriptions.html

Quarterly. $25.00/year for individuals, print; $75.00/year for other countries, print. Journal providing information on licensed practical nursing for LPNs, PN educators, and students.

7431 ■ Journal of Psychosocial Nursing and Mental Health Services
SLACK Incorporated
6900 Grove Rd.
Thorofare, NJ 08086-9447
Ph: (856)848-1000
Fax: (856)848-6091
E-mail: jpn@slackinc.com
URL: http://www.slackjournals.com/jpn

Monthly. $95.00/year for individuals; $190.00/year for individuals, two years; $315.00/year for institutions; $630.00/year for institutions, two years; $29.00/year for single issue. Peer-reviewed journal presenting original, peer-reviewed articles on psychiatric/mental health nursing.

7432 ■ Journal of Radiology Nursing
Mosby Inc.
11830 Westline Industrial Dr.
St. Louis, MO 63146-3326
Ph: (314)872-8370
Fax: (314)432-1380
Fr: 800-325-4177
URL: http://www.radiologynursing.org

Quarterly. $80.00/year for individuals, U.S.; $152.00/year for institutions, U.S.; $121.00/year for individuals, International; $202.00/year for institutions, International. Journal publishing articles about patient care in the diagnostic and therapeutic imaging environments.

7433 ■ Journal for Specialists in Pediatric Nursing
John Wiley & Sons Inc.
350 Main St., Commerce Pl.
Malden, MA 02148-5089
Ph: (781)388-8200
Fax: (781)388-8210
URL: http://www.wiley.com/bw/journal.asp?ref=1539-
    0136&site=1

Quarterly. $88.00/year for individuals, U.S. print and online; $221.00/year for institutions, U.S. print and online; $192.00/year for institutions, U.S. print or online; $92.00/year for individuals, print and online; $155.00/year for institutions, print and online; $134.00/year for institutions, print or online. Peer-reviewed journal focusing on nurses who specialize in the care of children and families.

7434 ■ LPN2009
Lippincott Williams & Wilkins
530 Walnut St.
Philadelphia, PA 19106-3619
Ph: (215)521-8300
Fax: (215)521-8902
Fr: 800-638-3030
URL: http://www.lww.com/product/?1553-0582

Bimonthly. $149.96/year for institutions; $29.96/year for individuals; $22.75/year for individuals, in-training; $75.96/year for other countries; $214.96/year for institutions, other countries. Peer-reviewed journal that focuses on bedside care skills for practical nurses.

7435 ■ McKnight's Long-Term Care News
McKnight's Long-Term Care News
1 Northfield Plz., Ste. 521
Northfield, IL 60093-1216
Ph: (847)784-8706
Fax: (847)784-9346

Fr: 800-558-1703
URL: http://www.mcknightsonline.com/home

$60.00/year for individuals; $108.00/year for two years; $75.00/year for Canada; $135.00/year for Canada, two years; $75.00/year for other countries; $135.00/year for other countries, two years. Professional magazine.

7436 ■ MCN, The American Journal of Maternal/Child Nursing
Lippincott Williams & Wilkins
530 Walnut St.
Philadelphia, PA 19106-3619
Ph: (215)521-8300
Fax: (215)521-8902
Fr: 800-638-3030
URL: http://journals.lww.com/mcnjournal/pages/default.aspx

Bimonthly. $63.99/year for individuals; $300.00/year for institutions; $149.22/year for other countries; $421.22/year for institutions, other countries; $42.43/year for individuals, in-training. Peer-reviewed journal focusing on maternal/child nursing and health.

7437 ■ Military Medicine
AMSUS - The Society of the Federal Health Agencies
9320 Old Georgetown Rd.
Bethesda, MD 20814
Ph: (301)897-8800
Fax: (301)503-5446
Fr: 800-761-9320
URL: http://www.amsus.org/index.php/journal

Monthly. $170.00/year for individuals, print and online; $225.00/year for other countries. Journal for professional personnel affiliated with the Federal medical services.

7438 ■ Modern Healthcare
Crain Communications Inc.
360 N Michigan Ave.
Chicago, IL 60601
Ph: (312)649-5200
E-mail: subs@crain.com
URL: http://www.modernhealthcare.com

Weekly. $164.00/year for individuals; $255.00/year for Canada; $218.00/year for other countries. Weekly business news magazine for healthcare management.

7439 ■ NANN Central
National Association of Neonatal Nurses
4700 W Lake Ave.
Glenview, IL 60025-1485
Ph: (847)375-3660
Fax: (866)927-5321
Fr: 800-451-3795
E-mail: info@nann.org
URL: http://www.nann.org

Three times a year. Features association news, announcements, and meeting information along with the latest information, educational, and employment opportunities and products related to the care of neonatal patients.

7440 ■ Neonatal Network
The Academy of Neonatal Nursing
1425 N McDowell Blvd., Ste. 105
Petaluma, CA 94954
Ph: (707)795-2168
Fax: (707)569-0786
E-mail: editorial@neonatalnetwork.com
URL: http://www.academyonline.org

Bimonthly. Contains the latest information on neonatal nursing practice. Features articles on current developments in neonatal care.

7441 ■ Nephrology Nursing Journal
American Nephrology Nurses' Association
East Holly Ave.
PO Box 56
Pitman, NJ 08071-0056
Ph: (856)256-2320

Fax: (856)589-7463
Fr: 888-600-2662
URL: http://www.annanurse.org/cgi-bin/WebObjects/ANNANurse.woa/wa

Bimonthly. $42.00/year for individuals; $69.00/year for institutions; $15.00/year for single issue; $72.00/year for other countries; $99.00/year for institutions, other countries; $20.00/year for single issue, other countries. Nursing journal.

7442 ■ Newborn and Infant Nursing Reviews
Elsevier Inc.
1600 John F. Kennedy Blvd., Ste. 1800
Philadelphia, PA 19103
Ph: (215)239-3900
Fax: (215)238-7883
URL: http://www.elsevier.com

Quarterly. $275/year for institution; $99/year individual. Provides a comprehensive overview of newborn, infant, and neonatal nursing and all its practice settings. Contains product print advertising, recruitment, and classified print advertising.

7443 ■ Nurse Education in Practice
Mosby Inc.
11830 Westline Industrial Dr.
St. Louis, MO 63146-3326
Ph: (314)872-8370
Fax: (314)432-1380
Fr: 800-325-4177
URL: http://www.elsevier.com/wps/find/journaldescription.cws_home

Bimonthly. $105.00/year for individuals, for all countries except Europe, Japan & Iran; $399.00/year for institutions, for all countries except Europe, Japan & Iran. Journal enabling lecturers and practitioners to both share and disseminate evidence that demonstrates the actual practice of education as it is experienced in the realities of their respective work environments.

7444 ■ Nurse Leader
Mosby Inc.
11830 Westline Industrial Dr.
St. Louis, MO 63146-3326
Ph: (314)872-8370
Fax: (314)432-1380
Fr: 800-325-4177
URL: http://www.nurseleader.com

$73.00/year for individuals; $185.00/year for institutions; $297.00/year for institutions, other countries; $122.00/year for other countries. Journal publishing articles on the vision, skills, and tools needed by nurses currently aspiring to leadership positions.

7445 ■ The Nurse Practitioner
Lippincott Williams & Wilkins
530 Walnut St.
Philadelphia, PA 19106-3619
Ph: (215)521-8300
Fax: (215)521-8902
Fr: 800-638-3030
E-mail: npedit@wolterskluwer.com
URL: http://journals.lww.com/tnpj/pages/default.aspx

Monthly. $86.76/year for individuals; $401.76/year for institutions; $52.72/year for U.S., in-training; $176.49/year for other countries, individual; $620.49/year for institutions. Magazine presenting clinical information to nurses in advanced primary care practice. Also covers legal, business, economic, ethical, research, and pharmaceutical issues.

7446 ■ Nursing Clinics of North America
Mosby Inc.
11830 Westline Industrial Dr.
St. Louis, MO 63146-3326
Ph: (314)872-8370
Fax: (314)432-1380
Fr: 800-325-4177
URL: http://www.elsevier.com/wps/find/journaldescription.cws_home

Quarterly. $135.00/year for individuals; $343.00/year for institutions; $74.00/year for students; $197.00/

year for Canada; $419.00/year for institutions, Canada; $121.00/year for students, Canada. Journal publishing articles by experts in the field provide current, practical information geared to the active nurse.

7447 ■ Nursing Education Perspectives
National League for Nursing
61 Broadway, 33rd Fl.
New York, NY 10006-2701
Ph: (212)363-5555
Fax: (212)812-0393
Fr: 800-669-1656
URL: http://www.nln.org/nlnjournal/index.htm

Bimonthly. $40.00/year for individuals; $90.00/year for nonmembers; $110.00/year for Canada, nonmembers; $120.00/year for other countries, nonmember; $152.00/year for institutions; $172.00/year for libraries; $182.00/year for other countries, libraries. Professional journal for nurses. Includes articles on health policy, social and economic issues affecting health care, and nursing education and practice.

7448 ■ Nursing Management
Lippincott Williams & Wilkins
530 Walnut St.
Philadelphia, PA 19106-3621
Ph: (215)521-8300
Fax: (215)521-8902
URL: http://journals.lww.com/nursingmanagement/pages/default.aspx

Monthly. $76.76/year for individuals; $371.76/year for institutions; $168.49/year for other countries; $518.49/year for institutions, other countries. Magazine focusing on nursing management.

7449 ■ Nursing Outlook
Mosby Inc.
10801 Executive Center Dr., Ste. 509
Little Rock, AR 72211
Ph: (501)223-5165
Fax: (501)223-0519
URL: http://journals.elsevierhealth.com/periodicals/ymno

Bimonthly. $133.00/year for Canada; $84.00/year for individuals; $133.00/year for individuals, Mexico; $133.00/year for other countries. Official journal of the American Academy of Nursing, reporting on trends and issues in nursing.

7450 ■ Pediatric Nursing
Jannetti Publications Inc.
East Holly Ave., Box 56
Pitman, NJ 08071-0056
Ph: (856)256-2300
URL: http://www.pediatricnursing.net

Bimonthly. $47.00/year for individuals; $80.00/year for two years; $72.00/year for institutions; $125.00/year for institutions, 2 years; $77.00/year for other countries; $140.00/year for other countries, 2 years; $102.00/year for institutions, other countries; $185.00/year for institutions, other countries, 2 years; $15.00/year for single issue, current issue; $15.00/year for single issue, back future issue. Professional nursing magazine.

7451 ■ Provider
American Health Care Association
1201 L St. NW
Washington, DC 20005
Ph: (202)842-4444
Fax: (202)842-3860
E-mail: sales@ahca.org
URL: http://www.providermagazine.com

Monthly. $48.00/year for U.S.; $61.00/year for Canada and Mexico; $85.00/year for other countries; free to qualified subscribers. Provider Magazine.

7452 ■ Rehabilitation Nursing
Rehabilitation Nursing
4700 W Lake Ave.
Glenview, IL 60025
Ph: (847)375-4710

Fax: (847)375-6481
Fr: 800-229-7530
E-mail: info@rehabnurse.org
URL: http://awebsource.com/clients/arn/ws_resource/
    public_index.p

Bimonthly. $120.00/year for individuals, regular;
$150.00/year for individuals, premium; $195.00/year
for other countries, regular; $240.00/year for other
countries, premium; $175.00/year for institutions,
regular (USA); $220.00/year for institutions, premium
(USA); $195.00/year for institutions, regular
(international); $240.00/year for institutions, premium
(international). Magazine focusing on rehabilitation
nursing involving clinical practice, research, education, and administration.

7453 ■ Research in Nursing & Health
John Wiley & Sons Inc.
111 River St.
Hoboken, NJ 07030-5773
Ph: (201)748-6000
Fax: (201)748-6088
Fr: 800-825-7550
URL: http://onlinelibrary.wiley.com/journal/10.1002/
    (ISSN)1098-24

Bimonthly. $164.00/year for U.S., Canada, and
Mexico, print only; $206.00/year for other countries,
print only; $1,483.00/year for institutions, print only;
$1,567.00/year for institutions, Canada and Mexico,
print only; $1,609.00/year for institutions, other
countries, print only. Peer-reviewed journal publishing
wide range of research and theory that will inform the
practice of nursing and other health disciplines.

7454 ■ Seminars in Oncology Nursing
Mosby Inc.
11830 Westline Industrial Dr.
St. Louis, MO 63146-3326
Ph: (314)872-8370
Fax: (314)432-1380
Fr: 800-325-4177
URL: http://www.nursingoncology.com

Quarterly. $105.00/year for individuals; $298.00/year
for institutions; $212.00/year for individuals, Interna-
tional; $402.00/year for institutions, other countries.
Journal publishing material to disseminate knowledge
in the complex field of cancer nursing.

**7455 ■ Supporting Innovations in
    Gerontological Nursing**
National Gerontological Nursing Association
3493 Lansdowne Dr., Ste. 2
Lexington, KY 40517
Ph: (859)977-7453
Fax: (859)271-0607
Fr: 800-723-0560
E-mail: info@ngna.org
URL: http://www.ngna.org

Bimonthly. Provides updates on NGNA's activities as
well as other information of interest to gerontological
nurses. Features job opportunities in the field.

7456 ■ Teaching and Learning in Nursing
Elsevier Science Inc.
360 Park Ave. S
New York, NY 10010-1710
Ph: (212)989-5800
Fax: (212)633-3990
Fr: 888-437-4636
URL: http://www.elsevier.com/wps/find/
    journaldescription.cws_home

Quarterly. $232.00/year for institutions, other coun-
tries; $134.00/year for other countries; $160.00/year
for institutions; $91.00/year for individuals. Journal
devoted to associate degree nursing education and
practice.

7457 ■ World Journal of AIDS
Scientific Research Publishing
PO Box 54821
Irvine, CA 92619-4821
E-mail: wja@scirp.org
URL: http://www.scirp.org/journal/wja/

Quarterly. $156.00/year for individuals. Peer-reviewed
journal publishing articles on research data and
education in all aspects of HIV and AIDS.

7458 ■ World Journal of Vaccines
Scientific Research Publishing
PO Box 54821
Irvine, CA 92619-4821
E-mail: wjv@scirp.org
URL: http://www.scirp.org/journal/wjv/

Quarterly. $156.00/year for individuals. Peer-reviewed
journal publishing articles on the latest advancements
in vaccine.

**7459 ■ Worldviews on Evidence-Based
    Nursing**
John Wiley & Sons Inc.
350 Main St., Commerce Pl.
Malden, MA 02148-5089
Ph: (781)388-8200
Fax: (781)388-8210
URL: http://www.wiley.com/bw/journal.asp?ref=1545-
    102X

Quarterly. $149.00/year for individuals, print and on-
line; $142.00/year for individuals, online only;
$450.00/year for institutions, print and online;
$391.00/year for institutions, print or online; $161.00/
year for individuals, print and online; $154.00/year for
individuals, online only. Peer-reviewed journal that offers research, policy and practice, education and
management for nursing.

EMPLOYER DIRECTORIES AND
NETWORKING LISTS

**7460 ■ Crain's List—Chicago's Largest
    Hospitals**
Crain Communications Inc.
360 N Michigan Ave.
Chicago, IL 60601
Ph: (312)649-5200
URL: http://www.chicagobusiness.com/section/lists

Published November, 2010. $25.00 for individuals;
$45.00 for individuals. Covers: 25 hospitals in
Chicago area ranked by net patient revenues. Entries
include: Name, address, phone number, fax, web address, corporate e-mail, hospital administrator,
network affiliation, 2009 net patient revenue, percentage change from 2008, 2009 net profits, percentage
change from 2008, inpatient days, available beds,
daily occupancy rate, number of hospital employees
as of December 31, 2009, fiscal year end, Chairman,
President, CEO, Chief Financial Officer, Human
Resources Manager, Media Relations/Public Relations Director, and Hospital Administrator.

7461 ■ Directory of Hospital Personnel
Grey House Publishing
4919 Rte. 22
PO Box 56
Amenia, NY 12501
Ph: (518)789-8700
Fax: (518)789-0556
Fr: 800-562-2139
URL: http://www.greyhouse.com/hospital_
    personnel.htm

Annual, Latest edition 2011. $325.00 for individuals.
Covers: 200,000 executives at 6,000 U.S. Hospitals.
Entries include: Name of hospital, address, phone,
number of beds, type and JCAHO status of hospital,
names and titles of key department heads and staff,
medical and nursing school affiliations; number of
residents, interns, and nursing students. Arrangement: Geographical. Indexes: Hospital name, personnel, hospital size.

7462 ■ Hospital Blue Book
Billian Publishing Inc. and Trans World Publishing
Inc.
2100 River Edge Pky.
Atlanta, GA 30328

Ph: (770)955-5656
Fax: (770)952-0669
Fr: 800-800-5668
E-mail: blu-book@billian.com
URL: http://www.billianshealthdata.com/Products/
    bluebook.html

Annual, Latest edition 2010. $575.00 for individuals;
$575.00 for individuals. Covers: More than 6,500
hospitals; some listings also appear in a separate
southern edition of this publication. Entries include:
Name of hospital, accreditation, mailing address,
phone, fax, number of beds, type of facility (nonprofit,
general, state, etc.); list of administrative personnel
and chiefs of medical services, with specific titles. Arrangement: Geographical.

**7463 ■ How to Survive and Maybe Even
    Love Nursing School!**
F.A. Davis Co.
1915 Arch St.
Philadelphia, PA 19103
Ph: (215)568-2270
Fax: (215)568-5065
Fr: 800-523-4049
URL: http://www.fadavis.com

Latest edition 3rd. $28.95 for individuals. Publication
includes: List of resources for nursing students such
as Web sites and organizations. Principal content of
publication is information about succeeding in nursing school.

**7464 ■ Medical and Health Information
    Directory**
Gale
PO Box 6904
Florence, KY 41022-6904
Fr: 800-354-9706
URL: http://www.gale.cengage.com

Annual, Latest edition April 2011. $1190.00 for
individuals; $501.00 for individuals. Covers: In volume
1, more than 33,000 medical and health oriented associations, organizations, institutions, and government agencies, including health maintenance organizations (HMOs), preferred provider organizations
(PPOs), insurance companies, pharmaceutical
companies, research centers, and medical and allied
health schools. In Volume 2, over 20,000 medical
book publishers; medical periodicals, directories,
audiovisual producers and services, medical libraries
and information centers, electronic resources, and
health-related internet search engines. In Volume 3,
more than 40,500 clinics, treatment centers, care
programs, and counseling/diagnostic services for 34
subject areas. Entries include: Institution, service, or
firm name, address, phone, fax, email and URL;
many include names of key personnel and, when
pertinent, descriptive annotation. Volume 3 was
formerly listed separately as Health Services
Directory. Arrangement: Classified by organization
activity, service, etc. Indexes: Each volume has a
complete alphabetical name and keyword index.

**7465 ■ Peterson's Guide to Nursing
    Programs**
Peterson's
Princeton Pike Corporate Ctr.
2000 Lenox Dr.
PO Box 67005
Lawrenceville, NJ 08648
Ph: (609)896-1800
Fax: (609)896-4531
Fr: 800-338-3282
URL: http://www.petersons.com/

Annual, Latest edition 2009. $18.48 for individuals.
Covers: Over 700 institutions offering approximately
3,600 accredited nursing programs in the U.S. and
Canada. Entries include: Academic information,
extracurricular issues, costs, financial aid.

7466 ■ Saunders Student Nurse Planners
W.B. Saunders Company
c/o Elsevier
30 Corporate Dr., 4th Fl.
Burlington, MA 01803

Ph: (781)313-4700
Fax: (781)313-4880
URL: http://www.elsevier.com

Latest edition 7th. $19.95 for individuals. Covers: nursing orientation. Publication includes: telephone and address directory.

HANDBOOKS AND MANUALS

7467 ■ 101 Careers in Nursing
Springer-Verlag New York, Inc.
11 W 42nd St., 15th Fl.
New York, NY 10036
Ph: (212)431-4370
Fax: (212)941-7842
Fr: 877-687-7476
URL: http://www.springerpub.com/product/
9780826102713

Jeanne M. Novotny, Doris T. Lippman, Nicole K. Sanders, Joyce J. Fitzpatrick. June 2006. $18.00 (paper). Illustrated. 240 pages.

7468 ■ Career Opportunities in Health Care (Career Opportunities)
Facts On File Inc.
132 W 31st St., 17th Fl.
New York, NY 10001-2006
Fax: 800-678-3633
Fr: 800-322-8755
E-mail: custserv@factsonfile.com
URL: http://www.infobasepublishing.com

Shelly Field. 2007. Third Edition. $49.50. 304 pages. Part of the Career Opportunities Series.

7469 ■ Careers in Health Care
The McGraw-Hill Companies
PO Box 182604
Columbus, OH 43272
Fax: (614)759-3749
Fr: 877-883-5524
E-mail: customer.service@mcgraw-hill.com
URL: http://www.mhprofessional.com/
product.php?isbn=0071466533

Barbara M. Swanson. Fifth edition, 2005. $19.95 (paper). 192 pages. Describes job duties, work settings, salaries, licensing and certification requirements, educational preparation, and future outlook. Gives ideas on how to secure a job.

7470 ■ Comprehensive Review of Practical Nursing for NCLEX-PN
Mosby
3251 Riverport Lane
Maryland Heights, MO 63043
Ph: (314)872-8370
Fax: (314)432-1280
Fr: 800-325-4177
URL: http://www.elsevier.com

Mary O. Eyles, editor. Fifteenth edition, 2008. $39.95 (paper). 736 pages. With more than 3,600 review questions, this useful study tool covers essential nursing content from all core clinical areas.

7471 ■ Core Curriculum for the Licensed Practical/Vocational Hospice and Palliative Nurse
Kendall/Hunt Publishing Company
4050 Westmark Dr.
Dubuque, IA 52004
Ph: (563)589-1000
Fax: (563)589-1046
Fr: 800-228-0810
E-mail: orders@kendallhunt.com
URL: http://www.kendallhunt.com

Hospice & Palliative Nurses Association. 2010. $60.00. 250 pages.

7472 ■ Developing Your Career in Nursing
Sage Publications, Inc.
2455 Teller Rd.
Thousand Oaks, CA 91320-2218

Fax: 800-583-2665
Fr: 800-818-7243
E-mail: info@sagepub.com
URL: http://www.sagepub.com/books/Book226518

Robert Newell, editor. $37.95. 184 pages.

7473 ■ Expert Resumes for Health Care Careers
Jist Works
875 Montreal Way
St. Paul, MN 55102
Fr: 800-648-5478
E-mail: educate@emcp.com
URL: http://www.jist.com

Wendy S. Enelow and Louise M. Kursmark. 2010. $16.95. 288 pages.

7474 ■ Health Careers Today
Elsevier
11830 Westline Industrial Dr.
St. Louis, MO 63146
Ph: (314)453-7010
Fax: (314)453-7095
Fr: 800-545-2522
E-mail: usbkinfo@elsevier.com
URL: http://www.elsevier.com

Gerdin, Judith. Fourth edition. 2007. $74.95. 496 pages. Covers more than 45 health careers. Discusses the roles and responsibilities of various occupations and provides a solid foundation in the skills needed for all health careers.

7475 ■ Introduction to the Health Professions
Jones & Bartlett Learning, LLC
PO Box 417289
Boston, MA 02241-7289
Ph: (978)443-5000
Fax: (978)443-8000
Fr: 800-832-0034
E-mail: info@jblearning.com
URL: http://www.jblearning.com

Peggy S. Stanfield, Y. H. Hui and Nanna Cross. 2012. $93.95. 502 pages. Sixth edition. Provides current coverage of all major health professions. Outlines health-related careers, a review of the U.S. healthcare delivery system, managed care, and impact of new technology on healthcare services.

7476 ■ LPN-to-RN Bridge: Transitions to Advance Your Career
Jones & Bartlett Learning
5 Wall St.
Burlington, MA 01803
Ph: (978)443-5000
Fax: (978)443-8000
Fr: 800-832-0034
E-mail: info@jblearning.com
URL: http://www.jblearning.com

Allison J. Terry. 2012. $46.95. 300 pages. Serves as a resource for students who have previously acquired training as a licensed practical nurse and are currently pursuing a degree as a registered nurse. Includes preparation for licensure examination.

7477 ■ Mosby's Review Questions for NCLEX-RN
Mosby
11830 Westline Industrial Dr.
St. Louis, MO 63146
Ph: (314)872-8370
Fax: (314)432-1280
Fr: 800-325-4177
URL: http://www.us.elsevierhealth.com/
product.jsp?isbn=9780323047241

Dolores F. Saxton, Patricia M. Nugent, Phyllis K. Pelikan, and Judith S. Green. Sixth edition, 2011. $46.95 (paper). 576 pages.

7478 ■ Mosby's Tour Guide to Nursing School: A Student's Road Survival Guide
Mosby
11830 Westline Industrial Dr.
St. Louis, MO 63146
Ph: (314)872-8370
Fax: (314)432-1280
Fr: 800-325-4177
URL: http://www.elsevier.com

Melodie Chenevert. Sixth edition, 2011. $29.95 (paper). 240 pages.

7479 ■ The Nursing Experience: Trends, Challenges & Transitions
The McGraw-Hill Companies
PO Box 182604
Columbus, OH 43272
Fax: (614)759-3749
Fr: 877-883-5524
E-mail: customer.service@mcgraw-hill.com
URL: http://www.mhprofessional.com

Lucille A. Joel and L.Y. Kelly. Fifth edition, 2006. $44.95 (paper). 792 pages.

7480 ■ Nursing Today: Transition and Trends
W. B. Saunders Co.
6277 Sea Harbor Dr.
Orlando, FL 32887
Ph: (407)345-2000
Fr: 800-545-2522
URL: http://www.elsevier.com

JoAnn Zerwekh and Jo C. Claborn, editors. Sixth edition, 2009. $52.95 (paper). 640 pages.

7481 ■ Opportunities in Child Care Careers
The McGraw-Hill Companies
PO Box 182604
Columbus, OH 43272
Fax: (614)759-3749
Fr: 877-883-5524
E-mail: customer.service@mcgraw-hill.com
URL: http://www.mhprofessional.com/
product.php?isbn=0071467661

Renee Wittenberg. 2006. $13.95 (paper). 160 pages. Discusses various job opportunities and how to secure a position. Illustrated.

7482 ■ Opportunities in Health and Medical Careers
The McGraw-Hill Companies
PO Box 182604
Columbus, OH 43272
Fax: (614)759-3749
Fr: 877-883-5524
E-mail: customer.service@mcgraw-hill.com
URL: http://www.mhprofessional.com/
product.php?isbn=0071437274

I. Donald Snook, Jr. and Leo D'Orazio. 2004. $14.95 (paper). 157 pages. Covers the full range of medical and health occupations. Illustrated.

7483 ■ Opportunities in Physician Assistant Careers
The McGraw-Hill Companies
PO Box 182604
Columbus, OH 43272
Fax: (614)759-3749
Fr: 877-883-5524
E-mail: customer.service@mcgraw-hill.com
URL: http://www.mhprofessional.com/
product.php?isbn=0071400613

Terence J. Sacks. $15.95. 160 pages.

7484 ■ Plunkett's Health Care Industry Almanac 2012
Plunkett Research, Ltd.
PO Drawer 541737
Houston, TX 77254-1737
Ph: (713)932-0000
Fax: (713)932-7080
E-mail: customersupport@plunkettresearch.com
URL: http://www.plunkettresearch.com

Jack W. Plunkett. 2011. $299.99. 717 pages. Features in-depth profiles of leading companies, associations and professional societies in the healthcare field. Covers major issues and trends, market forecasts and industry statistics.

7485 ■ *Resumes for Nursing Careers*
The McGraw-Hill Companies
PO Box 182604
Columbus, OH 43272
Fax: (614)759-3749
Fr: 877-883-5524
E-mail: customer.service@mcgraw-hill.com
URL: http://www.mhprofessional.com/
  product.php?isbn=0071509860
2007. $11.95 (paper). 144 pages.

7486 ■ *Your Career in Nursing: Get the Most Out of Your Nursing Career Today and Tomorrow*
Kaplan Publishing
1 Liberty Plaza, 24th Fl.
New York, NY 10006
Ph: (212)618-2405
Fax: (212)618-2499
Fr: 800-527-4836
URL: http://www.kaplanpublishing.com
Annette Vallano. Fifth edition. $17.00. Illustrated. 384 Pages. Vocational guide.

EMPLOYMENT AGENCIES AND SEARCH FIRMS

7487 ■ Access Staffing
360 Lexington Ave., 8th Fl.
New York, NY 10017
Ph: (212)687-5440
Fax: (212)557-2544
URL: http://www.accessstaffingco.com
Serves as a staffing firm covering accounting/financial, advertising, bilingual Japanese, creative, event planning, fashion/retail, healthcare/ human services, human resources, information technology, insurance, legal, light industrial and office support.

7488 ■ Actuary Resources
115 N Castle Heights Ave., Ste. 202
Lebanon, TN 37087-2768
Ph: (615)360-5171
Fax: (615)360-5173
E-mail: info@actuaryresources.org
URL: http://www.actuaryresources.org
Provides staffing services to several different types of industries. Offers a free screening service to clients.

7489 ■ Axis Medical Staffing
100 W Harrison St., Ste. 550
Seattle, WA 98119
Ph: (206)285-6300
Fax: (206)285-6302
Fr: 888-299-AXIS
E-mail: hr@axismedicalstaffing.com
URL: http://www.axismedicalstaffing.com
Description: Focuses on recruiting medical professionals and matching their requirements to the needs of facilities. Provides quality medical staffing for facilities nationwide. Specializes in per diem staffing, local/national travel assignments and direct hire full-time placements for nursing/nursing aides, radiological technologists and business services.

7490 ■ CompHealth
PO Box 713100
Salt Lake City, UT 84171-3100
Ph: (801)930-3000
Fax: (801)930-4517
Fr: 800-453-3030
E-mail: info@comphealth.com
URL: http://www.comphealth.com
Provides healthcare staffing and recruiting services covering certified registered nurse anesthetist, do-

simetrist, imaging and radiation therapy, laboratory technology, medical physicist, nurse practitioner, nursing, pharmacy, physician, physician assistant, rehab therapy and respiratory therapy.

7491 ■ CoreMedical Group
2 Keewaydin Dr.
Salem, NH 03079
Ph: (603)893-4515
Fax: (603)893-8442
Fr: 800-995-2673
E-mail: info@coremedicalgroup.com
URL: http://www.coremedicalgroup.com
Provides career resources and staffing solutions for nursing jobs, travel nurses and permanent nursing assignments.

7492 ■ Cross Country TravCorps
6551 Park of Commerce Blvd.
Boca Raton, FL 33487-8247
Fax: (561)998-8533
Fr: 800-530-6125
E-mail: sms@cctc.com
URL: http://www.crosscountrytravcorps.com/cctc/
Places traveling nurses in assignments nationwide.

7493 ■ Diversified Staffing Group, Inc.
85 Newbury St.
Boston, MA 02116
Ph: (617)259-1001
Fax: (617)259-1009
Fr: 877-229-1118
E-mail: info@dsgworld.com
URL: http://www.dsgworld.com/main.htm
Description: Serves as an executive search firm for nursing professionals.

7494 ■ Harper Associates
31000 NW Hwy., Ste. 240
Farmington Hills, MI 48334
Ph: (248)932-1170
Fax: (248)932-1214
E-mail: info@harperjobs.com
URL: http://www.harperjobs.com
Executive search firm and employment agency.

7495 ■ MedPro Healthcare Staffing
1580 Sawgrass Corporate Pkwy., Ste. 100
Sunrise, FL 33323
Ph: (954)739-4247
Fax: 800-370-0755
Fr: 800-886-8108
E-mail: medprogeneralinquiries@medprostaffing.com
URL: http://www.medprostaffing.com
Provides temporary and contract staffing services to healthcare facilities.

7496 ■ Nursing Technomics
814 Sunset Hollow Rd.
West Chester, PA 19380-1848
Ph: (610)436-4551
Fax: (610)436-0255
Administrative nursing consultants offer expertise in the design and implementation of customized software applications for departments of nursing, organizational design and implementation and executive nurse search. Also specializes in department staffing, scheduling and nurse recruitment. Serves private industries as well as government agencies.

7497 ■ Preferred Healthcare Staffing
9089 Clairemont Mesa Blvd., No. 200
San Diego, CA 92123
Fr: 800-787-6787
E-mail: staffing@preferredregistry.com
URL: http://preferredregistry.com
Description: Specializes in placing registered nurses on travel nursing assignments.

7498 ■ Professional Placement Associates, Inc.
287 Bowman Ave.
Purchase, NY 10577-2517

Ph: (914)251-1000
Fax: (914)251-1055
E-mail: careers@ppasearch.com
URL: http://www.ppasearch.com
Executive search firm specializing in the health and medical field.

7499 ■ Stat Group, LLC
PO Box 1674
Owensboro, KY 42302-1674
Ph: (270)663-8020
Fax: 877-998-9940
Fr: 877-998-9930
E-mail: info@statgroupllc.com
URL: http://www.statgroupllc.com
Description: Serves as a healthcare staffing firm which provides healthcare facilities with a workforce pool. Attracts and retains medical professionals to assist healthcare facilities throughout the United States.

7500 ■ Team Placement Service, Inc.
1414 Prince St., Ste. 202
Alexandria, VA 22314
Ph: (703)820-8618
Fax: (703)820-3368
Fr: 800-495-6767
E-mail: 4jobs@teamplace.com
URL: http://www.teamplace.com
Full-service personnel consultants provide placement for healthcare staff, physician and dentist, private practice, and hospitals. Conduct interviews, tests, and reference checks to select the top 20% of applicants. Survey applicants' skill levels, provide backup information on each candidate, select compatible candidates for consideration, and insure the hiring process minimizes potential legal liability. Industries served: healthcare and government agencies providing medical, dental, biotech, laboratory, hospitals, and physician search.

7501 ■ Whitaker Medical
1200 Enclave Pkwy., Ste. 200
Houston, TX 77077
Ph: (281)870-1000
Fax: (866)513-0183
Fr: 800-444-5628
URL: http://www.whitakermedical.com
Exists as a healthcare recruitment firm that provides staffing solutions for healthcare professionals and facilities across the nation.

ONLINE JOB SOURCES AND SERVICES

7502 ■ Health Care Job Store
395 South End Ave., Ste. 15-D
New York, NY 10280
Ph: (561)630-5201
E-mail: jobs@healthcarejobstore.com
URL: http://www.healthcarejobstore.com
Description: Job sites include every job title in the healthcare industry, every healthcare industry and every geographic location in the U.S.

7503 ■ Health Care Recruitment Online
E-mail: info@healthcarerecruitment.com
URL: http://healthcarerecruitment.com
Description: Helps seekers find healthcare positions through on-line postings with national staffing companies and hospital partners. Main files include: Featured Employers, Job Search, Immediate Openings, Relocating, Career Management, State boards, and more.

7504 ■ HealthcareCrossing.com
URL: http://www.healthcarecrossing.com
Description: Provides a collection of health care jobs, hospitals and medical jobs, nursing jobs and healthcare employment. Includes a variety of employers in the health care business.

7505 ■ HealthCareerWeb.com
URL: http://www.healthcareerweb.com

Description: Advertises jobs for healthcare professionals. Main files include: Jobs, Employers, Resumes, Jobwire. Relocation tools and career guidance resources available.

7506 ■ HEALTHeCAREERS Network
Fr: 888-884-8242
E-mail: info@healthecareers.com
URL: http://www.healthecareers.com

Description: Career search site for jobs in all health care specialties; educational resources; visa and licensing information for relocation; interesting articles; relocation tools; links to professional organizations and general resources.

7507 ■ HireNursing.com
URL: http://www.hirenursing.com

Description: Provides job opportunities for professional nurses. Features career tools, educational resources, networking, and industry news.

7508 ■ Hospital Jobs OnLine
E-mail: support@hospitaljobsonline.com
URL: http://www.hospitaljobsonline.com

Description: Serves as a niche healthcare job board designed exclusively for hospitals, healthcare companies, and healthcare job seekers.

7509 ■ JobsInLTC.com
URL: http://www.jobsinltc.com

Description: Serves as a job board for long-term care jobs for nursing home administrators, assisted living staff, directors of nursing, MDS coordinators, and other related fields.

7510 ■ Lippincott's NursingCenter.com
URL: http://www.nursingcenter.com

Description: Helps spread clinical information to nurses in rural areas who would otherwise not have access to the latest journals and technology. Provides access to job openings as well as upcoming clinical expos and job fairs.

7511 ■ Locate Nurse Jobs
URL: http://www.locatenursejobs.com

Description: Serves as an online job search and employee recruiting resource. Provides opportunities for nurses in a wide range of health care settings from hospitals to home health care.

7512 ■ LPNJobsHelp.com
URL: http://www.lpnjobshelp.com

Description: Features job listings for licensed practical nurses. Includes information pertaining to the profession of licensed practical nursing.

7513 ■ MedExplorer.com
E-mail: medmaster@medexplorer.com
URL: http://www.medexplorer.com

Description: Employment postings make up one module of this general medical site. Other sections contain: Newsletter, Classifieds, and Discussion Forum.

7514 ■ Monster Healthcare
URL: http://healthcare.monster.com

Description: Delivers nationwide access to healthcare recruiting. Employers can post job listings or ads. Job seekers can post and code resumes, and search over 150,000 healthcare job listings, healthcare career advice columns, career resources information, and member employer profiles and services.

7515 ■ nurse-recruiter.com
URL: http://www.nurse-recruiter.com

Description: Serves as a resource of jobs for the nursing and allied health fields.

7516 ■ NurseJobsLink.com
URL: http://www.nursejobslink.com

Description: Provides job opportunities for nursing professionals.

7517 ■ NurseJungle.com
URL: http://www.nursejungle.com

Description: Serves as career center for nurses, providing resume posting, job search and career development resources. Provides job postings for employers in the nursing community.

7518 ■ NursePath.com
URL: http://www.nursepath.com

Description: Serves as a clearinghouse for those seeking nursing positions. Contains job postings by specialty in critical care, education, emergency, gerontology, and psychiatry.

7519 ■ Nurses123.com
URL: http://www.nurses123.com

Description: Offers nursing job information through its listing of job opportunities nationwide. Helps nurses search for work, research healthcare organizations and access career-related resources.

7520 ■ Nurses.info
URL: http://www.nurses.info

Description: Provides healthcare information for the professional development of nurses and health professionals. Provides links to a range of educational and vocational information, conferences, journals and other nursing related resources.

7521 ■ NursesRX.com
12400 High Bluff Dr.
Huntersville, NC 28078
Fax: 877-744-9052
Fr: 800-733-9354
E-mail: info@nursesrx.com
URL: http://www.nursesrx.com

Description: Job board site for travel nursing. In addition to traditional travel nursing, Nurses RX provides staffing possibilities from temporary-to-permanent, traditional permanent placement, staffing/recruitment outsourcing, new graduate internship programs, and a full Canadian Placement Division.

7522 ■ NurseZone.com
URL: http://www.nursezone.com

Description: Aims to provide nurses with professional and personal development information and opportunities. Provides student nurses, new graduates, and experienced nurses with the resources needed to succeed in the profession.

7523 ■ Nursing-Jobs.us
URL: http://www.nursing-jobs.us

Description: Features permanent, per diem, or travel nursing jobs. Partners with hospitals, travel nurse companies and recruitment agencies to assist job seekers in the nursing industry.

7524 ■ NursingCrossing.com
URL: http://www.nursingcrossing.com

Description: Provides job listings and other resources related to nursing employment opportunities.

7525 ■ ProHealthJobs.com
Ph: (484)443-8545
Fax: (484)443-8549
E-mail: info@prohealthjobs.com
URL: http://prohealthjobs.com/jobboard

Description: Career resources site for the medical and health care field. Lists professional opportunities, product information, continuing education and open positions.

7526 ■ United Search Associates: Health Network USA
PO Box 342
Vinita, OK 74301
Ph: (918)323-4165
E-mail: jobs@hnusa.com
URL: http://homepage.mac.com/hnusa

Description: Visitors may explore healthcare positions, submit an electronic resume, or advertise with the site.

TRADESHOWS

7527 ■ American Academy of Ambulatory Care Nursing Annual Conference
American Academy of Ambulatory Care Nursing
East Holly Ave., Box 56
Pitman, NJ 08071-0056
Fr: 800-262-6877
E-mail: aaacn@ajj.com
URL: http://www.aaacn.org

Annual. Includes speakers presenting the latest information on topics pertinent and timely to ambulatory care nursing. 2013 April 23-25; Las Vegas, NV; Las Vegas Hilton.

7528 ■ APHON Annual Conference and Exhibit
Association of Pediatric Hematology/Oncology Nurses
4700 W Lake Ave.
Glenview, IL 60025
Ph: (847)375-4724
Fax: (847)375-6478
E-mail: info@aphon.org
URL: http://www.aphon.org

Annual. Includes exhibits of pharmaceutical products, medical equipment, blood services, educational materials, training programs, publications, support services, therapeutic products, and recruitment services. 2012 October 4-6; Pittsburgh, PA; David L. Lawrence Convention Center.

7529 ■ Conference of the National Association of Pediatric Nurse Associates and Practitioners
National Association of Pediatric Nurse Associates and Practitioners
20 Brace Rd., Ste. 200
Cherry Hill, NJ 08034-2634
Ph: (856)857-9700
Fax: (856)857-1600
Fr: 877-662-7627
E-mail: info@napnap.org
URL: http://www.napnap.org

Annual. Primary Exhibits: Equipment, supplies, and services for pediatric, school, and family nurse practitioners. Dates and Locations: 2012 Mar 28-31; San Antonio, TX.

7530 ■ DNA Annual Convention
Dermatology Nurses' Association
15000 Commerce Pkwy., Ste. C
Mount Laurel, NJ 08054
Fax: (856)439-0525
Fr: 800-454-4362
E-mail: dna@dnanurse.org
URL: http://www.dnanurse.org

Annual. Includes exhibits of new technologies, products and services, supplies, and equipment in the field of dermatology nursing. 2013 April 4-7; New Orleans, LA; Sheraton New Orleans Hotel.

7531 ■ Emergency Nurses Association Annual Meeting
Emergency Nurses Association
915 Lee St.
Des Plaines, IL 60016-6569
Fr: 800-900-9659
URL: http://www.ena.org

Annual. Primary Exhibits: Exhibits relating to emergency room care.

7532 ■ INS Annual Meeting and Industrial Exhibition

Infusion Nurses Society
315 Norwood Park S
Norwood, MA 02062
Ph: (781)440-9408
Fax: (781)440-9409
Fr: 800-694-0298
E-mail: ins@ins1.org
URL: http://www.ins1.org

Annual. Includes exhibits of homecare and infusion services, dialysis products, infusion medications and solutions, injection products, pharmacy services, specimen management products, medical devices, and other services used in infusion therapy.

7533 ■ International Society of Psychiatric-Mental Health Nurses Annual Conference

International Society of Psychiatric - Mental Health Nurses
2424 American Ln.
Madison, WI 53704-3102
Ph: (608)443-2463
Fax: (608)443-2474
Fr: (866)330-7227
E-mail: info@ispn-psych.org
URL: http://www.ispn-psych.org

Annual. Primary Exhibits: Psychiatric nursing equipment, supplies, and services.

7534 ■ NADONA's Conference

National Association Directors of Nursing Administration
Reed Hartman Tower
11353 Reed Hartman Hwy., Ste. 210
Cincinnati, OH 45241
Ph: (513)791-3679
Fax: (513)791-3699
Fr: 800-222-0539
URL: http://www.nadona.org

Annual. Discusses new topics in the field and features exhibits of new technology, products, and services. 2012 July 21-25; Nashville, TN; Gaylord Opryland Resort.

7535 ■ NANN Annual Educational Conference

National Association of Neonatal Nurses
4700 W Lake Ave.
Glenview, IL 60025-1485
Ph: (847)375-3660
Fax: (866)927-5321
Fr: 800-451-3795
E-mail: info@nann.org
URL: http://www.nann.org

Annual. Includes exhibits of the latest products and services. Provides opportunities for neonatal nurses to network and interact with each other. 2012 October 17-20; Palm Springs, CA; Palm Springs Convention Center and Renaissance Hotel.

7536 ■ National Advanced Practice Neonatal Nurses Conference

The Academy of Neonatal Nursing
1425 N McDowell Blvd., Ste. 105
Petaluma, CA 94954
Ph: (707)568-2168
Fax: (707)569-0786
URL: http://www.academyonline.org

Annual. Includes exhibits to promote advancement of the organization's service opportunities, strategic educational developments, and product innovations relevant in today's neonatal and mother-baby specialty health care markets.

7537 ■ National Association of Orthopedic Nurses Annual Congress

Smith, Bucklin and Associates, Inc. (Chicago, Illinois)
401 N Michigan Ave.
Chicago, IL 60611-4267
Ph: (312)321-6610
Fax: (312)673-6670
Fr: 800-289-NAON
E-mail: info@smithbucklin.com
URL: http://www.smithbucklin.com

Annual. Primary Exhibits: Pharmaceuticals, medical equipment, medical instruments, and publications.

7538 ■ National Federation of Licensed Practical Nurses Annual Convention

National Federation of Licensed Practical Nurses
111 W Main St., Ste. 100
Garner, NC 27529
Ph: (919)779-0046
Fax: (919)779-5642
E-mail: nflpn@mgmt4u.com
URL: http://www.nflpn.org

Annual. Offers continuing education to keep LPNs current and updated in their profession.

7539 ■ National Student Nurses' Association Convention

National Student Nurse Association
45 Main St., Ste. 606
Brooklyn, NY 11201
Ph: (718)210-0705
Fax: (718)797-1186
E-mail: nsna@nsna.org
URL: http://www.nsna.org

Annual. Primary Exhibits: Equipment, supplies, and services for the student nurse. Dates and Locations: 2012 Apr 11-15; Pittsburgh, PA; David L. Lawrence Convention Center.

7540 ■ North Carolina Nurses Association Convention

North Carolina Nurses Association
103 Enterprise St.
PO Box 12025
Raleigh, NC 27607
Ph: (919)821-4250
Fax: (919)829-5807
Fr: 800-626-2153
E-mail: rns@ncnurses.org
URL: http://www.ncnurses.org

Annual. Primary Exhibits: Nursing equipment, supplies, and services, books.

7541 ■ Oncology Nursing Society Meeting

Oncology Nursing Society
125 Enterprise Dr.
Pittsburgh, PA 15275-1214
Ph: (412)859-6100
Fax: (412)859-6162
Fr: 877-369-5497
E-mail: customer.service@ons.org
URL: http://www.ons.org

Annual. Primary Exhibits: Oncology nursing equipment, supplies, and services.

OTHER SOURCES

7542 ■ Academy of Medical-Surgical Nurses

East Holly Ave.
Box 56
Pitman, NJ 08071
Ph: (856)256-2422
Fax: (856)589-7463
Fr: (866)877-2676
E-mail: amsn@ajj.com
URL: http://www.amsn.org

Description: Represents registered, licensed practical, licensed vocational nurses, clinical nurse specialists, nurse practitioners, educators, researchers, administrators, and students. Promotes standards of nursing practice and facilitates the implementation of

practice guidelines. Provides education programs for members, fosters scholarly activities and disseminates new ideas for all areas of adult health/medical-surgical nursing.

7543 ■ Academy of Medical-Surgical Nurses Annual Convention

Academy of Medical-Surgical Nurses
East Holly Ave.
Box 56
Pitman, NJ 08071
Fr: (866)877-2676
E-mail: amsn@ajj.com
URL: http://www.amsn.org

Annual. Includes exhibits of various products, technologies, and publications specific to medical-surgical nursing care and services. 2012 October 4-7; Salt Lake City, UT; Salt Palace Convention Center.

7544 ■ American Academy of Ambulatory Care Nursing

PO Box 56
Pitman, NJ 08071-0056
Fr: 800-262-6877
E-mail: aaacn@ajj.com
URL: http://www.aaacn.org

Description: Comprised of nurses and other professionals interested in ambulatory care and telehealth nursing. Serves as a voice for ambulatory care nurses across the continuum of health care delivery. Provides education to ambulatory care professionals through conference, audio-conferences, and newsletter.

7545 ■ American Academy of Medical Esthetic Professionals (AAMEP)

2000 S Andrews Ave.
Fort Lauderdale, FL 33316
Ph: (954)463-5594
Fax: (954)463-4459
E-mail: sashas@bellsouth.net
URL: http://www.amen-usa.org

Description: Promotes the highest standard of practice in medical esthetic nursing. Enhances the professional growth of medical esthetic nurses. Provides education, certification, scientific inquiry and research. Facilitates the dissemination of current information, technical skills, and expertise relating to medical esthetic nursing.

7546 ■ American Association for Long Term Care Nursing

PO Box 62956
Cincinnati, OH 45262-0956
Fax: (513)791-1477
Fr: 888-458-2687
E-mail: charlotte@ltcnursing.org
URL: http://ltcnursing.org

Description: Represents the interests of long-term care nurses and other professionals who wish to achieve excellence in the specialty of long-tem care nursing. Provides educational resources that bridge current practices with managerial and clinical activities.

7547 ■ American Association of Managed Care Nurses

4435 Waterfront Dr., Ste. 101
Glen Allen, VA 23060
Ph: (804)747-9698
Fax: (804)747-5316
E-mail: phulcher@aamcn.org
URL: http://www.aamcn.org

Description: Comprised of managed health care professionals, including registered nurses, licensed practical nurses, and nurse practitioners. Seeks to enhance the abilities of members to meet the future needs of the managed health care profession through education. Establishes standards for managed care nursing practice and formulates public policies regarding managed health care delivery.

7548 ■ American Association of Occupational Health Nurses (AAOHN)
7794 Grow Dr.
Pensacola, FL 32514
Ph: (850)474-6963
Fax: (850)484-8762
Fr: 800-241-8014
E-mail: aaohn@aaohn.org
URL: http://www.aaohn.org

Description: Represents registered professional nurses employed by business and industrial firms; nurse educators, nurse editors, nurse writers, and others interested in occupational health nursing. Promotes and sets standards for the profession. Provides and approves continuing education; maintains governmental affairs program; offers placement service.

7549 ■ American Health Care Association (AHCA)
1201 L St. NW
Washington, DC 20005
Ph: (202)842-4444
Fax: (202)842-3860
E-mail: hr@ahca.org
URL: http://www.ahcancal.org/Pages/Default.aspx

Description: Federation of state associations of long-term health care facilities. Promotes standards for professionals in long-term health care delivery and quality care for patients and residents in a safe environment. Focuses on issues of availability, quality, affordability, and fair payment. Operates as liaison with governmental agencies, Congress, and professional associations. Compiles statistics.

7550 ■ American Holistic Nurses Association
323 N San Francisco St., Ste. 201
Flagstaff, AZ 86001
Ph: (928)526-2196
Fax: (928)526-2752
Fr: 800-278-2462
E-mail: info@ahna.org
URL: http://www.ahna.org

Description: Comprised of nurses and other holistic healthcare professionals. Advances the profession of holistic nursing by providing continuing education, helping to improve the health care workplace through the incorporation of the concepts of holistic nursing, and educating professionals and the public about holistic nursing and integrative health care. Promotes research and scholarship in the field of holistic nursing.

7551 ■ American Hospital Association (AHA)
155 N Wacker Dr.
Chicago, IL 60606
Ph: (312)422-3000
Fax: (312)422-4796
E-mail: rich@aha.org
URL: http://www.aha.org

Description: Represents health care provider organizations. Seeks to advance the health of individuals and communities. Leads, represents, and serves health care provider organizations that are accountable to the community and committed to health improvement.

7552 ■ American Organization of Nurse Executives (AONE)
325 Seventh St. NW
Liberty Pl.
Washington, DC 20004
Ph: (202)626-2240
Fax: (202)638-5499
E-mail: aone@aha.org
URL: http://www.aone.org

Description: Provides leadership, professional development, advocacy, and research to advance nursing practice and patient care, promote nursing leadership and excellence, and shape healthcare public policy. Supports and enhances the management, leadership, educational, and professional development of nursing leaders. Offers placement

service through Career Development and Referral Center.

7553 ■ American Psychiatric Nurses Association
1555 Wilson Blvd., Ste. 530
Arlington, VA 22209
Ph: (703)243-2443
Fax: (703)243-3390
Fr: (866)243-2443
E-mail: ncroce@apna.org
URL: http://www.apna.org

Description: Represents psychiatric nurses who are at all levels of education from basic to doctoral and work in a variety of settings including inpatient, outpatient, research, education, administration, clinical, private practice, military, and forensic.

7554 ■ American Public Health Association (APHA)
800 I St. NW
Washington, DC 20001
Ph: (202)777-2742
Fax: (202)777-2534
E-mail: comments@apha.org
URL: http://www.apha.org

Description: Professional organization of physicians, nurses, educators, academicians, environmentalists, epidemiologists, new professionals, social workers, health administrators, optometrists, podiatrists, pharmacists, dentists, nutritionists, health planners, other community and mental health specialists, and interested consumers. Seeks to protect and promote personal, mental, and environmental health. Services include: promulgation of standards; establishment of uniform practices and procedures; development of the etiology of communicable diseases; research in public health; exploration of medical care programs and their relationships to public health. Sponsors job placement service.

7555 ■ American School Health Association (ASHA)
4340 East West Hwy., Ste. 403
Bethesda, MD 20814
Ph: (301)652-8072
Fax: (301)652-8077
Fr: 800-445-2742
E-mail: info@ashaweb.org
URL: http://www.ashaweb.org

Description: School physicians, school nurses, counselors, nutritionists, psychologists, social workers, administrators, school health coordinators, health educators, and physical educators working in schools, professional preparation programs, public health, and community-based organizations. Promotes coordinated school health programs that include health education, health services, a healthful school environment, physical education, nutrition services, and psycho-social health services offered in schools collaboratively with families and other members of the community. Offers professional reference materials and professional development opportunities. Conducts pilot programs that inform materials development, provides technical assistance to school professionals, advocates for school health.

7556 ■ Association of Operating Room Nurses
2170 S Parker Rd., Ste. 400
Denver, CO 80231
Ph: (303)755-6304
Fax: (303)750-3212
Fr: 800-755-2676
E-mail: custsvc@aorn.org
URL: http://www.aorn.org

Description: Represents registered professional nurses, individuals pursuing education leading to eligibility to sit for the registered nurse licensing exam, and registered professional nurses who are retired from the health care industry. Aims to promote safety and optimal outcomes for patients undergoing operative and other invasive procedures by providing practice support and professional development op-

portunities to perioperative nurses. Advocates for excellence in perioperative practice and healthcare.

7557 ■ Association of Pediatric Hematology/Oncology Nurses
4700 W Lake Ave.
Glenview, IL 60025-1485
Ph: (847)375-4724
Fax: (847)375-6478
E-mail: info@aphon.org
URL: http://www.aphon.org

Description: Represents pediatric hematology/oncology nurses and other pediatric hematology/oncology healthcare professionals. Promotes optimal nursing care for children, adolescents, and young adults with cancer and blood disorders and their families. Provides leadership and expertise to pediatric hematology/oncology nurses.

7558 ■ Association for Radiologic and Imaging Nursing
7794 Grow Dr.
Pensacola, FL 32514
Ph: (850)474-7292
Fax: (850)484-8762
Fr: (866)486-2762
E-mail: arin@dancyamc.com
URL: http://www.arinursing.org

Description: Represents nurses who practice in the diagnostic, neuro/cardiovascular, interventional, ultrasonography, computerized tomography, nuclear medicine, magnetic resonance, and radiation oncology. Fosters the professional growth of nurses who advance the standard of care in the imaging environment.

7559 ■ Association of Staff Physician Recruiters (ASPR)
1000 Westgate Dr., Ste. 252
St. Paul, MN 55114
Ph: (651)290-7475
Fax: (651)290-2266
Fr: 800-830-2777
E-mail: admin@aspr.org
URL: http://www.aspr.org

Description: Recruits physicians and other healthcare providers to staff hospitals, clinics and managed care organizations where the members are employed. Sponsors educational programs and meetings on various recruitment issues.

7560 ■ Association of Women's Health, Obstetric and Neonatal Nurses
2000 L St. NW, Ste. 740
Washington, DC 20036
Ph: (202)261-2400
Fax: (202)728-0575
Fr: 800-673-8499
E-mail: customerservice@awhonn.org
URL: http://www.awhonn.org

Description: Seeks to improve and promote the health of women and newborns and to strengthen the nursing profession through the delivery of superior advocacy, research, education, and other professional and clinical resources to nurses and other health care professionals.

7561 ■ Council of International Neonatal Nurses
94 Lyall Ter.
Boston, MA 02132
Ph: (405)684-1476
E-mail: info@coinnurses.org
URL: http://www.coinnurses.org

Description: Represents nurses who specialize in the care of newborn infants and their families. Promotes high standards in neonatal nursing practice and care. Creates guidelines for neonatal nursing issues.

7562 ■ Dermatology Nurses' Association
15000 Commerce Pkwy., Ste. C
Mount Laurel, NJ 08054

Fax: (856)439-0525
Fr: 800-454-4362
E-mail: dna@dnanurse.org
URL: http://www.dnanurse.org

Description: Represents registered nurses, nurse practitioners, licensed practical nurses or licensed vocational nurses, medical assistants, and other associate members. Focuses on providing quality care through sharing of knowledge and expertise. Promotes excellence in dermatologic care.

7563 ■ Infusion Nurses Society

315 Norwood Park S
Norwood, MA 02062
Ph: (781)440-9408
Fax: (781)440-9409
Fr: 800-694-0298
E-mail: ins@ins1.org
URL: http://www.ins1.org

Description: Represents infusion nurses, home infusion therapists, health-system pharmacists, and all other healthcare professionals involved in or interested in the specialty practice or application of infusion therapy. Aims to advance the delivery of quality therapy to patients, enhance the specialty through standards of practice and professional ethics, and promote research and education in the infusion nursing field. Offers educational meetings, professional development opportunities, publications, printed and multimedia resources, and access to a national network of infusion experts.

7564 ■ International Palestinian Cardiac Relief Organization (IPCRO)

PO Box 1926
Kent, OH 44240
Ph: (330)678-2645
Fax: (330)678-2661
E-mail: pcrf1@pcrf.net
URL: http://www.pcrf.net/?page_id=529

Description: Seeks to provide medical and humanitarian assistance to people in the Middle East. Sends volunteer teams of doctors and nurses to provide expert surgical treatment for sick children as well as training for local staff. Helps local institutions in the Middle East get the resources to further their medical services for poor and needy patients throughout the region.

7565 ■ National Alliance of Wound Care

5464 N Port Washington Rd., No. 134
Glendale, WI 53217
Fax: 800-352-8339
Fr: 877-922-6292
E-mail: information@nawccb.org
URL: http://www.nawccb.org

Description: Represents the interests of wound care certified professionals. Provides resources and support to advance professional recognition of members.

7566 ■ National Association of Bariatric Nurses (NABN)

East Carolina University
College of Nursing
2111 Health Sciences Bldg.
Greenville, NC 27858
Ph: (252)744-6379
Fax: (252)744-6387
E-mail: nabn@bariatricnurses.org
URL: http://www.bariatricnurses.org

Description: Represents nursing and allied health professionals interested in learning and sharing knowledge about the care, treatment and intervention of health-related problems caused by obesity. Seeks to advance the health and quality of life of individuals and families experiencing obesity. Works to promote best practices of holistic nursing care for bariatric patients and their families.

7567 ■ National Association Directors of Nursing Administration

Reed Hartman Tower
11353 Reed Hartman Hwy., Ste. 210
Cincinnati, OH 45241
Ph: (513)791-3679
Fax: (513)791-3699
Fr: 800-222-0539
URL: http://www.nadona.org

Description: Represents the interests of nurses and administrators in long term care. Promotes ethical principles and practices within the long term care continuum. Advocates for the benefit of directors of nursing, assistant directors of nursing, and registered nurses in long term care. Supports and promotes quality of care for individuals who are receiving long-term care.

7568 ■ National Association of Neonatal Nurses

4700 W Lake Ave.
Glenview, IL 60025
Ph: (847)375-3660
Fax: (866)927-5321
Fr: 800-451-3795
E-mail: info@nann.org
URL: http://www.nann.org

Description: Represents registered neonatal nurse practitioners and registered nurses who support neonatal nursing. Aims to address the educational and practice needs within the evolving specialty of neonatal nursing. Provides educational programs, research and translation, advocacy, and membership engagement.

7569 ■ National Association of Pediatric Nurse Practitioners (NAPNAP)

20 Brace Rd., Ste. 200
Cherry Hill, NJ 08034-2634
Ph: (856)857-9700
Fax: (856)857-1600
Fr: 877-662-7627
E-mail: info@napnap.org
URL: http://www.napnap.org

Description: Pediatric, school, and family nurse practitioners and interested persons. Seeks to improve the quality of infant, child, and adolescent health care by making health care services accessible and providing a forum for continuing education of members. Facilitates and supports legislation designed to promote the role of pediatric nurse practitioners; promotes salary ranges commensurate with practitioners' responsibilities; facilitates exchange of information between prospective employers and job seekers in the field. Supports research programs; compiles statistics.

7570 ■ National Association for Practical Nurse Education and Service (NAPNES)

1940 Duke St., Ste. 200
Alexandria, VA 22314
Ph: (703)933-1003
Fax: (703)940-4089
E-mail: napnes@napnes.org
URL: http://www.napnes.org

Description: Licensed practical/vocational nurses, registered nurses, physicians, hospital and nursing home administrators, and interested others. Provides consultation service to advise schools wishing to develop a practical/vocational nursing program on facilities, equipment, policies, curriculum, and staffing. Promotes recruitment of students through preparation and distribution of recruitment materials. Sponsors seminars for directors and instructors in schools of practical/vocational nursing and continuing education programs for LPNs/LVNs; approves continuing education programs and awards contact hours; holds national certification courses in post licensure specialties such as pharmacology, long term care and gerontics.

7571 ■ National Black Nurses Association

8630 Fenton St., Ste. 330
Silver Spring, MD 20910
Ph: (301)589-3200
Fax: (301)589-3223
E-mail: contact@nbna.org
URL: http://www.nbna.org

Description: Consists of registered nurses, licensed vocational/practical nurses, nursing students, and retired nurses. Facilitates the professional development and career advancement of nurses. Serves as a forum for collective action by African American nurses to investigate, define, and determine the health care needs of African Americans.

7572 ■ National Federation of Licensed Practical Nurses (NFLPN)

111 W Main St., Ste. 100
Garner, NC 27529
Ph: (919)779-0046
Fax: (919)779-5642
E-mail: nflpn@mgmt4u.com
URL: http://www.nflpn.org

Description: Federation of state associations of licensed practical and vocational nurses. Aims to: preserve and foster the ideal of comprehensive nursing care for the ill and aged; improve standards of practice; secure recognition and effective utilization of LPNs; further continued improvement in the education of LPNs. Acts as clearinghouse for information on practical nursing and cooperates with other groups concerned with better patient care. Maintains loan program.

7573 ■ National Gerontological Nursing Association

3493 Landowne Dr., Ste. 2
Lexington, KY 40517
Ph: (859)977-7453
Fax: (859)271--060
Fr: 800-723-0560
E-mail: info@ngna.org
URL: http://www.ngna.org

Description: Dedicated to the clinical care of older adults across diverse care settings. Represents the interests of clinicians, educators, and researchers with vastly different educational preparation, clinical roles, and interests in practice issues.

7574 ■ National League for Nursing (NLN)

61 Broadway, 33rd Fl.
New York, NY 10006
Ph: (212)363-5555
Fax: (212)812-0391
Fr: 800-669-1656
E-mail: generalinfo@nln.org
URL: http://www.nln.org

Description: Champions the pursuit of quality nursing education. A professional association of nursing faculty, education agencies, health care agencies, allied/public agencies, and public members whose mission is to advance quality nursing education that prepares the nursing workforce to meet the needs of diverse populations in an ever-changing health care environment. Serves as the primary source of information about every type of nursing education program, from the LVN and LPN to the EdD and PhD. There are 20 affiliated constituent leagues that provide a local forum for members. The National League for Nursing Accrediting Commission is an independent corporate affiliate of the NLN, responsible for providing accreditation services to all levels of nursing education.

7575 ■ National Rural Health Association (NRHA)

Administrative Office
521 E 63rd St.
Kansas City, MO 64110-3329
Ph: (816)756-3140
Fax: (816)756-3144
E-mail: mail@nrharural.org
URL: http://www.ruralhealthweb.org

Description: Administrators, physicians, nurses, physician assistants, health planners, academicians, and others interested or involved in rural health care. Creates a better understanding of health care problems unique to rural areas; utilizes a collective approach in finding positive solutions; articulates and represents the health care needs of rural America; supplies current information to rural health care providers; serves as a liaison between rural health care programs throughout the country. Offers continuing education credits for medical, dental, nursing, and management courses.

7576 ■ Visiting Nurse Associations of America (VNAA)
900 19th St. NW, Ste. 200
Washington, DC 20006

Ph: (202)384-1420
Fax: (202)384-1444
Fr: 888-866-8773
E-mail: vnaa@vnaa.org
URL: http://www.vnaa.org

Description: Home health care agencies. Develops competitive strength among community-based nonprofit visiting nurse organizations; works to strengthen business resources and economic programs through contracting, marketing, governmental affairs and publications.

7577 ■ American Banker
Banking Group
1 State Street Plz., 27th Fl.
New York, NY 10004-1483
Ph: (212)803-8200
Fax: (212)843-9600
Fr: 800-221-1809
URL: http://www.americanbanker.com

Daily. $995.00/year for individuals. Newspaper for senior executives in banking and other financial services industries. Coverage includes trends, analysis, and statistics of the legislative scene in Washington; finance; mortgages; technology; small business; and regional banking.

7578 ■ Mortgage Banking Magazine
Mortgage Bankers Association of America
1717 Rhode Island Ave., NW, Ste. 400
Washington, DC 20036
Ph: (202)557-2700
Fax: (202)721-0245
Fr: 800-793-MBAA
URL: http://www.mortgagebankingmagazine.com

Monthly. $65.00/year for members; $75.00/year for nonmembers; $90.00/year for other countries. Magazine of the real estate finance industry.

7579 ■ National Mortgage News
SourceMedia Inc.
1 State St. Plz., 27th Fl.
New York, NY 10004-1561
Ph: (212)803-8200
Fax: (646)264-6828
URL: http://www.nationalmortgagenews.com

Weekly. Newspaper for mortgage lenders and investment bankers.

7580 ■ Northwestern Financial Review
NFR Communications Inc.
7400 Metro Blvd., Ste. 217
Minneapolis, MN 55439
Ph: (952)835-2275
URL: http://www.northwesternfinancialreview.com

$99.00/year for individuals. Trade publication covering commercial banking.

7581 ■ Servicing Management
Zackin Publications Inc.
PO Box 2180
Waterbury, CT 06722
Ph: (203)262-4670
Fax: (203)262-4680
Fr: 800-325-6745
URL: http://www.sm-online.com/sm

Monthly. $48.00/year for individuals; $72.00/year for two years. Trade magazine for mortgage professionals involved with mortgage loan servicing .

7582 ■ U.S. Banker
SourceMedia Inc.
1 State St. Plz., 27th Fl.
New York, NY 10004-1561
Ph: (212)803-8200
Fax: (646)264-6828
URL: http://www.americanbanker.com/usb.html

Monthly. $109.00/year for individuals; $139.00/year for individuals, Canada; $139.00/year for individuals, outside North America; $179.00/year for two years; $239.00/year for two years, Canada; $239.00/year for two years, outside North America. Magazine serving the financial services industry.

EMPLOYER DIRECTORIES AND NETWORKING LISTS

7583 ■ The Bank Directory
Accuity Inc.
4709 Golf Rd.
Skokie, IL 60076
Ph: (847)676-9600
Fax: (847)933-8101
Fr: 800-321-3373
URL: http://store.accuitysolutions.com/order.html

Semiannual, June and December. $1,195.00 for individuals. Covers: In five volumes, about 11,000 banks and 50,000 branches of United States banks, and 60,000 foreign banks and branches engaged in foreign banking; Federal Reserve system and other United States government and state government banking agencies; 500 largest North American and International commercial banks; paper and automated clearinghouses. Volumes 1 and 2 contain North American listings; volumes 3 and 4, international listings (also cited as "M Thomson International Bank Directory"); volume 5, Worldwide Correspondents Guide containing key correspondent data to facilitate funds transfer. Entries include: For domestic banks—Bank name, address, phone, telex, cable, date established, routing number, charter type, bank holding company affiliation, memberships in Federal Reserve System and other banking organizations, principal officers by function performed, principal correspondent banks, and key financial data (deposits, etc.). For international banks—Bank name, address, phone, fax, telex, cable, SWIFT address, transit or sort codes within home country, ownership, financial data, names and titles of key personnel, branch locations. For branches—Bank name, address, phone, charter type, ownership and other details comparable to domestic bank listings. Arrangement: Geographical. Indexes: Alphabetical, geographical.

7584 ■ Corporate Finance Sourcebook
LexisNexis Group
9443 Springboro Pike
Dayton, OH 45342
Fr: 888-285-3947
E-mail: nrpsales@marquiswhoswho.com
URL: http://www.financesourcebook.com

Annual, Latest edition 2010. $695.00 for individuals; $556.00 for individuals. Covers: Securities research analysts; major private lenders; investment banking firms; commercial banks; United States-based foreign banks; commercial finance firms; leasing companies; foreign investment bankers in the United States; pension managers; banks that offer master trusts; cash managers; business insurance brokers; business real estate specialists; lists about 3,500 firms; 14,500 key financial experts. Entries include: All entries include firm name, address, phone, e-mail, and names and titles of officers, contacts, or specialists in corporate finance. Additional details are given as appropriate, including names of major clients, number of companies served, services, total assets, branch locations, years in business. Arrangement: Classified by line of business and then alphabetized within that line of business. Indexes: Firm name, personnel name, geographical.

7585 ■ North American Financial Institutions Directory
Accuity Inc.
4709 Golf Rd.
Skokie, IL 60076
Ph: (847)676-9600
Fax: (847)933-8101
Fr: 800-321-3373
URL: http://store.accuitysolutions.com/order.html

Semiannual, January and July. $955.00 for individuals. Covers: 15,000 banks and their branches; over 2,000 head offices, and 15,500 branches of savings and loan associations; over 5,500 credit unions with assets over $5 million; Federal Reserve System and other U.S. government and state government banking agencies; bank holding, commercial finance, and leasing companies; coverage includes the United States, Canada, Mexico, and Central America. Entries include: Bank name, address, phone, fax, telex, principal officers and directors, date established, financial data, association memberships, attorney or counsel, correspondent banks, out-of-town branch, holding company affiliation, ABA transit number and routing symbol, MICR number with check digit, credit card(s) issued, trust powers, current par value and dividend of common stock, kind of charter. Arrangement: Geographical. Indexes: Alphabetical.

7586 ■ Who's Who in Finance and Business
Marquis Who's Who L.L.C.
300 Connell Dr., Ste. 2000
Berkeley Heights, NJ 07922
Ph: (908)673-1000
Fax: (908)673-1189
Fr: 800-473-7020
E-mail: finance@marquiswhoswho.com
URL: http://www.marquiswhoswho.com

Biennial, latest edition 37th; 2009-2010. $349.00 for individuals. Covers: Over 24,000 individuals. Entries include: Name, home and office addresses, personal, career, and family data; civic and political activities; memberships, publications, awards. Arrangement: Alphabetical.

HANDBOOKS AND MANUALS

7587 ■ *Loan Officer Exam Secrets Study Guide*
Mometrix Media, LLC
3827 Phelan Blvd., No. 179
Beaumont, TX 77707
Fr: 800-673-8175
URL: http://www.mo-media.com

2011. $39.99. Helps test takers ace the loan officer exam. Includes specific content areas, study tips and essential skills needed in preparation for the exam.

7588 ■ *Opportunities in Financial Careers*
The McGraw-Hill Companies
PO Box 182604
Columbus, OH 43272
Fax: (614)759-3749
Fr: 877-883-5524
E-mail: customer.service@mcgraw-hill.com
URL: http://www.mhprofessional.com/
   product.php?isbn=0071442502

Michael Sumichrast and Martin A. Sumichrast. 2004. $13.95 (paper). 160 pages. A guide to planning for and seeking opportunities in this challenging field.

EMPLOYMENT AGENCIES AND SEARCH FIRMS

7589 ■ Financial Professionals
4100 Spring Valley Rd., Ste. 250
Dallas, TX 75244
Ph: (972)991-8999
Fax: (972)702-0776
E-mail: rita@fpstaff.net
URL: http://www.fpstaff.net

Executive search consultants with additional offices in Forth Worth and Houston.

7590 ■ KForce
Fr: 877-4KF-ORCE
URL: http://www.kforce.com

Executive search firm. More than 41 locations throughout the United States and two in the Philippines.

7591 ■ ManpowerGroup
100 Manpower Pl.
Milwaukee, WI 53212
Ph: (414)961-1000
Fax: (414)906-7822
URL: http://us.manpower.com

Specializes in a wide range of employment services including permanent placement, recruitment process outsourcing, managed service programs, outplacement and human resources consulting. Provides companies with workforce solutions that help them increase productivity and improve efficiency.

ONLINE JOB SOURCES AND SERVICES

7592 ■ BankingCareers.com
URL: http://www.bankingcareers.com

Description: Provides lists of jobs and products to bankers in the banking and finance community.

7593 ■ FinancialServicesCrossing.com
URL: http://www.financialservicescrossing.com

Description: Offers a collection of top financial services job openings carefully researched by analysts. Provides instant access to a comprehensive pool of listings in the industry of financial services.

7594 ■ JobsForLoanOfficers.com
URL: http://jobsforloanofficers.com

Description: Serves the mortgage, real estate, financial services, insurance, title, and related industries. Provides tips, training, and advice to mortgage, real estate, and related professionals.

7595 ■ loanofficerjobs.net
URL: http://www.loanofficerjobs.net

Description: Features employment opportunities for loan officers.

OTHER SOURCES

7596 ■ American Bankers Association (ABA)
1120 Connecticut Ave. NW
Washington, DC 20036
Ph: (202)663-5564
Fax: (202)663-7543
Fr: 800-226-5377
E-mail: custserv@aba.com
URL: http://www.aba.com

Description: Members are principally commercial banks and trust companies; combined assets of members represent approximately 90% of the U.S. banking industry; approximately 94% of members are community banks with less than $500 million in assets. Seeks to enhance the role of commercial bankers as preeminent providers of financial services through communications, research, legal action, lobbying of federal legislative and regulatory bodies, and education and training programs. Serves as spokesperson for the banking industry; facilitates exchange of information among members. Maintains the American Institute of Banking, an industry-sponsored adult education program. Conducts educational and training programs for bank employees and officers through a wide range of banking schools and national conferences. Maintains liaison with federal bank regulators; lobbies Congress on issues affecting commercial banks; testifies before congressional committees; represents members in U.S. postal rate proceedings. Serves as secretariat of the International Monetary Conference and the Financial Institutions Committee for the American National Standards Institute. Files briefs and lawsuits in major court cases affecting the industry. Conducts teleconferences with state banking associations on such issues as regulatory compliance; works to build consensus and coordinate activities of leading bank and financial service trade groups. Provides services to members including: public advocacy; news media contact; insurance program providing directors and officers with liability coverage, financial institution bond, and trust errors and omissions coverage; research service operated through ABA Center for Banking Information; fingerprint set processing in conjunction with the Federal Bureau of Investigation; discounts on operational and income-producing projects through the Corporation for American Banking. Conducts conferences, forums, and workshops covering subjects such as small business, consumer credit, agricultural and community banking, trust management, bank operations, and automation. Sponsors ABA Educational Foundation and the Personal Economics Program, which educates schoolchildren and the community on banking, economics, and personal finance.

7597 ■ Bank Administration Institute (BAI)
115 S LaSalle St., Ste. 3300
Chicago, IL 60603
Ph: (312)683-2464
Fax: (312)683-2373
Fr: 800-224-9889
E-mail: info@bai.org
URL: http://www.bai.org

Description: Works to improve the competitive position of banking companies through strategic research and educational offerings.

7598 ■ Community Development Bankers Association (CDBA)
1801 K St. NW, Ste. M-100
Washington, DC 20006
Ph: (202)689-8935
E-mail: info@cdbanks.org
URL: http://www.cdbanks.org

Description: Represents the interests of the community development bank sector. Educates policy makers on how to deliver credit and financial services to low and moderate income communities.

7599 ■ Financial Managers Society (FMS)
100 W Monroe St., Ste. 1700
Chicago, IL 60603-1907
Ph: (312)578-1300
Fax: (312)578-1308
Fr: 800-275-4367
E-mail: info@fmsinc.org
URL: http://www.fmsinc.org

Description: Works for the needs of finance and accounting professionals from banks, thrifts and credit unions. Offers career-enhancing education, specialized publications, national leadership opportunities and worldwide connections with other industry professionals.

7600 ■ National Association of Mortgage Processors (NAMP)
1250 Connecticut Ave. NW, Ste. 200
Washington, DC 20036
Ph: (202)261-6505
Fax: (202)318-0655
Fr: 800-977-1197
E-mail: contact@mortgageprocessor.org
URL: http://www.mortgageprocessor.org

Description: Represents mortgage processors. Assists contract loan processors as well as in-house mortgage loan processors in all aspects of their businesses. Offers services such as training classes, blog cafe, community discussion, certification programs and download library.

7601 ■ National Bankers Association (NBA)
1513 P St. NW
Washington, DC 20005
Ph: (202)588-5432
Fax: (202)588-5443
E-mail: mgrant@nationalbankers.org
URL: http://www.nationalbankers.org

Description: Minority banking institutions owned by minority individuals and institutions. Serves as an advocate for the minority banking industry. Organizes banking services, government relations, marketing, scholarship, and technical assistance programs. Offers placement services; compiles statistics.

7602 ■ Risk Management Association
1801 Market St., Ste. 300
Philadelphia, PA 19103-1628
Ph: (215)446-4000
Fax: (215)446-4101
Fr: 800-677-7621
E-mail: member@rmahq.org
URL: http://www.rmahq.org/RMA

Description: Commercial and savings banks, and savings and loan, and other financial services companies. Conducts research and professional development activities in areas of loan administration, asset management, and commercial lending and credit to increase professionalism.

Logisticians

SOURCES OF HELP-WANTED ADS

7603 ■ Inbound Logistics
Thomas Publishing Company
5 Penn Plz.
New York, NY 10001
Ph: (212)695-0500
Fax: (212)290-7362
E-mail: contact@thomaspublishing.com
URL: http://www.thomaspublishing.com

Monthly. Free. Provides today's business logistics managers with the information they need to speed cycle times, reduce inventories, and use logistics expertise to get closer to their markets and customers.

7604 ■ International Journal of Information Systems and Supply Chain Management
IGI Global
701 E Chocolate Ave.
Hershey, PA 17033
Ph: (717)533-8845
Fax: (717)533-8661
Fr: (866)342-6657
URL: http://www.igi-global.com/Bookstore/
    TitleDetails.aspx?Titlel

Quarterly. $595.00/year for institutions, print or online; $210.00/year for individuals, print; $860.00/year for institutions, print and online. Peer-reviewed journal covering information systems and technology in supply chain management.

7605 ■ Journal of Business Logistics
Council of Supply Chain Management Professionals
333 E Butterfield Rd., Ste. 140
Lombard, IL 60148
Ph: (630)574-0985
Fax: (630)574-0989
E-mail: cscmpadmin@cscmp.org
URL: http://cscmp.org

Semiannual. $49.95/member; $74.95/non-member. Provides a forum for the dissemination of thoughts, research, and practices within the logistics and supply chain arenas. Features articles in subject areas which have significant current impact on thought and practice in logistics and supply chain management.

7606 ■ The Journal of Commerce
UBM Global Trade
2 Penn Plz. E
Newark, NJ 07105
Ph: (973)776-8660
Fr: 877-675-4761
E-mail: joc@halldata.com
URL: http://www.joc.com

Weekly. Contains information that will help international logistics executives plan their global supply chain and manage their day-to-day international logistics and shipping needs. Features career opportunities for job seekers in the field of transportation and logistics.

7607 ■ Logistics Today
Penton Media
1300 E 9th St.
Cleveland, OH 44114-1503
Ph: (216)696-7000
Fax: (216)696-1752
URL: http://www.penton.com

Semi-monthly. Free. Features topics from three areas within the logistics industry: technology/supply chain solutions, transportation and global logistics. Complements the LogisticsToday.com.

7608 ■ Reverse Logistics Magazine
Reverse Logistics Association
441 W Main St., Ste. D
Lehi, UT 84043
Ph: (801)331-8949
Fax: (801)206-0090
Fr: (866)801-6332
E-mail: info@rltinc.com
URL: http://www.reverselogisticsassociation.org

Bimonthly. $18.00/year (United States); $35.00/year (Canada); $70.00/year (international). Provides information pertaining to the various areas of reverse logistics including returns management, refurbishment, field service, and warranty management.

EMPLOYER DIRECTORIES AND NETWORKING LISTS

7609 ■ CSCMP Executive Recruiter Directory
Council of Supply Chain Management Professionals
333 E Butterfield Rd., Ste. 140
Lombard, IL 60148
Ph: (630)574-0985
Fax: (630)574-0989
E-mail: cscmpadmin@cscmp.org
URL: http://cscmp.org/career/recruiter.asp

Directory of executive recruiting firms that are active in all functions of the supply chain management discipline. Published primarily to assist CSCMP members in hiring supply chain management professionals or those looking for new positions.

HANDBOOKS AND MANUALS

7610 ■ Career Opportunities in Transportation
Facts On File
132 W 31st St., 17th Fl.
New York, NY 10001
Fax: 800-678-3633
Fr: 800-322-8755
E-mail: custserv@factsonfile.com
URL: http://factsonfile.infobasepublishing.com

Richard A. McDavid and Susan Echaore-McDavid. 2009. $49.50 (hardcover). 392 pages. Examines careers that the transportation industry has to offer.

Features more than 100 job profiles in ground, air, rail, maritime, pipeline and other areas of transportation. Offers an introduction that guides readers through the history of the modern transportation industry. Contains appendixes that include information on commercial driver's license, education and training resources, professional associations, web resources and more.

7611 ■ Shipping and Receiving in Plain English - A Best Practices Guide
Transportation and Logistics Council
120 Main St.
Huntington, NY 11743
Ph: (631)549-8988
Fax: (631)549-8962
E-mail: tlc@transportlaw.com
URL: http://www.tlcouncil.org

George Carl Pezold. 2010. $87.50. 160 pages. Includes tips and suggestions for practices as well as references to other available information and resources. Contains information about shipping and receiving procedures. Contains appendices with relevant statutes, regulations, forms, NMFC rules, lists of service providers, and other materials. May be used as a primer for newcomers in the transportation and logistics area, as a refresher and guide for experienced professionals, and as a reference for developing in-house company policies and procedures.

7612 ■ Supply Chain Excellence
AMACOM Publishing
c/o American Management Association
1601 Broadway
New York, NY 10019-7434
Ph: (212)586-8100
Fax: (518)891-0368
Fr: 800-714-6395
E-mail: pubs_cust_serv@amanet.org
URL: http://www.amacombooks.org

Peter Bolstorff and Robert Rosenbaum. 2011. $45.00 (hardback). 304 pages. Gives professionals implementing new supply chain projects a step-by-step guide to adopting methodologies developed by the Supply Chain Council (SCC). Shows readers how they can: align strategy, material, workflow, and information; conduct analysis to define business opportunity; establish the metrics that will determine the project's level of success; and gain internal support by educating employees and executives.

7613 ■ Transportation and Logistics - Q&A in Plain English
Transportation and Logistics Council
120 Main St.
Huntington, NY 11743
Ph: (631)549-8988
Fax: (631)549-8962
E-mail: tlc@transportlaw.com
URL: http://www.tlcouncil.org

George Carl Pezold and Raymond A. Selvaggio. 2010. $80.00. Serves as a teaching aid for students and newcomers to the transportation and logistics field. Contains compilations of questions from shippers, carriers, and logistics professionals, with answers provided by the authors.

EMPLOYMENT AGENCIES AND SEARCH FIRMS

7614 ■ Centennial, Inc.
8044 Montgomery Rd., Ste. 260
Cincinnati, OH 45236
Ph: (513)366-3760
Fax: (513)366-3761
E-mail: info@centennialinc.com
URL: http://www.centennialinc.com

Serves as an executive search firm specializing in the areas of executive and general management, accounting and finance, human resources, information technology, manufacturing, engineering, marketing and advertising, not-for-profit, sales and business development, and supply chain and logistics. Performs executive coaching as well as career coaching for clients.

7615 ■ Crabtree and Eller, LLC
558 E Castle Pines Pkwy., Ste. B4-169
Castle Rock, CO 80108
Ph: (303)814-5878
E-mail: results@crabtreeandeller.com
URL: http://crabtreeandeller.com

Search firm dedicated to the transportation, distribution, and logistics industry.

7616 ■ JP Canon Associates
225 Broadway, Ste. 3602
New York, NY 10007
Ph: (212)233-3131
Fax: (212)233-0457
Fr: 888-233-3131
E-mail: mailbox@jpcanon.com
URL: http://www.jpcanon.com

Specializes in the recruitment and placement of supply chain management professionals.

7617 ■ McMillan Associates
4969 Alamanda Dr.
Melbourne, FL 32940
Ph: (321)254-4423
E-mail: jmcmillan@mcmillanassoc.com
URL: http://www.mcmillanassoc.com

Executive recruiting firm that specializes in all areas of the supply chain including materials management, purchasing, and logistics.

7618 ■ MCR Agency, LLC
226 N Nova Rd., No. 388
Ormond Beach, FL 32174
Fax: (510)405-2023
Fr: 800-510-0916
E-mail: mcrsoft@fdn.com
URL: http://www.logisticspersonnel.com

Assists shippers and carriers in finding qualified transportation and logistics personnel. Offers confidential search capability and industry knowledge.

7619 ■ MGRM associates, ltd.
558 Columbine Ave.
Lisle, IL 60532
Ph: (630)724-9458
Fax: (630)724-9459
E-mail: logrecruiter@mgrmassociates.com
URL: http://www.mgrmassociates.com

Executive placement firm focused exclusively to the field of logistics including: supply chain management, transportation, distribution, warehousing, fulfillment, procurement, and the related technologies.

7620 ■ Palladian International, LLC
105-A Lew Dewitt Blvd., Ste. 197
Waynesboro, VA 22980

Fr: (866)766-8447
E-mail: palladian@palladianinternational.com
URL: http://www.palladianinternational.com

Acts as an executive recruiting firm that specializes in manufacturing and engineering, distribution and logistics, and former military officers. Offers free guides in resume writing, interview preparation, and resume benchmarking surveys.

7621 ■ Robins Consulting
15950 N Dallas Pkwy., Ste. 400
Dallas, TX 75248
Ph: (214)432-8288
Fax: (214)722-1466
E-mail: craig@robinsconsulting.com
URL: http://www.robinsconsulting.com

Provides executive recruiting for the transportation, logistics, and supply chain industries. Offers jobs from middle management to executive level positions, truckload (TL), less-than-truckload (LTL), intermodal, flatbed, container, and tanker companies.

7622 ■ Search Group
6102 Seven Lakes W
Seven Lakes, NC 27376
Ph: (910)687-0064
Fax: (910)687-0067
E-mail: results@theesearchgroup.com
URL: http://search-one.com

Partners with clients in need of executive, managerial, IT, engineering, and sales positions supporting materials handling, logistics, and supply chain management.

7623 ■ Shey-Harding Associates
PO Box 67
Seal Beach, CA 90740
Ph: (562)799-8854
Fax: (562)799-6174
E-mail: info@shey-harding.com
URL: http://www.shey-harding.com

Executive recruiting/human resource consulting firm specializing in domestic and international transportation, supply chain, logistics, and related industries. Provides middle management to executive level placements.

7624 ■ Wise Executive Resources
3667-C Evergreen Pkwy.
PO Box 969
Evergreen, CO 80437-0969
Ph: (303)679-3590
E-mail: talent@wiseexecutiveresources.com
URL: http://www.wiseexecutiveresources.com

Executive search, staffing, and consulting firm. Specializes in the placement of professionals in transportation, logistics, and supply chain services. Provides staffing services for regional, national, and global organizations that are furnishing transportation, logistics, and information systems to supply chain owners.

ONLINE JOB SOURCES AND SERVICES

7625 ■ Careers in Supply Chain Management
URL: http://www.careersinsupplychain.org

Description: Provides information about the supply chain industry, the importance of supply chain management, impacts of careers in the supply chain, and education options. Features links to supply chain publications, government agencies, and national organizations that serve the supply chain profession.

7626 ■ Logistics Online
E-mail: info@logisticsonline.com
URL: http://www.logisticsonline.com

Description: Provides logistics industry career channels with information that is tailored to an individual's career goals. Features career resources such as continuing education, franchise opportunities, search articles and blogs, and resource center.

7627 ■ LogisticsCareers.net
URL: http://www.logisticscareers.net

Description: Career community for the logistics industry. Lists job openings for logistics specialists. Features research in the transportation and logistics employment market and a career articles section written and frequented by industry professionals.

7628 ■ LogisticsCoordinator.com
URL: http://www.logisticscoordinator.com

Description: Serves as a clearinghouse for professionals seeking positions as logistics coordinators. Provides access to resumes and other career resources.

7629 ■ LogisticsCrossing.com
URL: http://www.logisticscrossing.com

Description: Serves as a clearinghouse for those seeking positions in the logistics industry.

7630 ■ LogisticsIndustryJobs.com
URL: http://logisticsindustryjobs.com

Description: Provides employment opportunities for logistics professionals. Offers recruitment assistance as well as resume writing and searching services.

7631 ■ LogJobs
E-mail: info@logjobs.com
URL: http://www.logjobs.com

Description: Provides logistics recruitment services to employers, recruiters, and job seekers in the supply chain and logistics fields.

7632 ■ New Logistics Jobs
URL: http://www.newlogisticsjobs.com

Description: Provides an online listing of companies with available logistics jobs in all specialties.

7633 ■ TransportationAndLogistics.net
URL: http://transportationandlogistics.net

Description: Serves as a transportation and logistics career search and professional networking community. Provides access to books, magazines, articles, and continuing education. Helps individual to find a new job, post and search resumes, and access to other career resources.

TRADESHOWS

7634 ■ Annual Meeting and TransComp Exhibition
National Industrial Transportation League
1700 N Moore St., Ste. 1900
Arlington, VA 22209
Ph: (703)524-5011
Fax: (703)524-5017
E-mail: info@nitl.org
URL: http://www.nitl.org

Annual. Showcases the latest innovations in information technology applications and management tools for transportation and distribution operations. 2012 November 10-14; Anaheim, CA; 2013 November 16-20; Houston, TX; 2014 November 15-19; Fort Lauderdale, FL; 2015 November 14-18; Anaheim, CA; 2016 November 12-16; Houston, TX.

7635 ■ Material Handling & Logistics Conference
Dematic Group
2855 S James Dr.
New Berlin, WI 53151
Ph: (262)860-7000
Fax: (262)860-7010
Fr: 800-424-7365
URL: http://www.dematic.com

Annual. Features classes, workshops, roundtables, and panel discussions that address supply chain strategies, trends, and thought leadership.

7636 ■ ProMat
Material Handling Industry of America
8720 Red Oak Blvd., Ste. 201
Charlotte, NC 28217
Ph: (704)676-1190
Fax: (704)676-1199
Fr: 800-345-1815
E-mail: customerservice@promatshow.com
URL: http://www.mhia.org

Features the latest manufacturing and distribution innovations, trends, and technologies. Showcases the products and services of over 700 material handling and logistics providers. 2013 January 21-24; Chicago, IL; McCormick Place South.

7637 ■ Warehousing Education and Research Council Annual Conference
Warehousing Education and Research Council
1100 Jorie Blvd., Ste. 170
Oak Brook, IL 60523-4413
Ph: (630)990-0001
Fax: (630)990-0256
E-mail: wercoffice@werc.org
URL: http://www.werc.org

Annual. Provides educational programs that cater to the needs of warehouse and distribution management professionals. Provides networking opportunities.

OTHER SOURCES

7638 ■ American Society of Transportation and Logistics
PO Box 3363
Warrenton, VA 20188
Ph: (202)580-7270
Fax: (202)962-3939
E-mail: info@astl.org
URL: http://www.astl.org

Description: Consists of shippers, carriers, educators, consultants, and third-party logistics individuals who promote professionalism and continuing education in the field of transportation logistics.

7639 ■ APICS: The Association for Operations Management
8430 W Bryn Mawr Ave., Ste. 1000
Chicago, IL 60631
Ph: (773)867-1777
Fax: (773)639-3000
Fr: 800-444-2742
E-mail: service@apics.org
URL: http://www.apics.org

Description: Represents academic professionals, students, enterprises, and professionals committed to building excellence in operations management. Aims to provide knowledge in operations management including production, inventory, supply chain, materials management, purchasing, and logistics. Provides

training, certifications, resources, and a worldwide network of industry professionals.

7640 ■ Council of Supply Chain Management Professionals
333 E Butterfield Rd., Ste. 140
Lombard, IL 60148
Ph: (630)574-0985
Fax: (630)574-0989
E-mail: cscmpadmin@cscmp.org
URL: http://cscmp.org

Description: Consists of supply chain management professionals. Provides leadership in developing, defining, understanding, and enhancing the logistics and supply chain management profession. Provides opportunities for supply chain professionals to communicate in order to develop and improve supply chain management skills. Creates awareness of the significance of supply chain to business and to the economy.

7641 ■ International Warehouse Logistics Association
2800 S River Rd., Ste. 260
Des Plaines, IL 60018
Ph: (847)813-4699
Fax: (847)813-0115
E-mail: email@iwla.com
URL: http://www.iwla.com

Description: Promotes the growth and success of public and contract warehousing and related logistics services. Provides members with educational resources and information on the latest industry trends and practices.

7642 ■ Logistics Officer Association
PO Box 2264
Arlington, VA 22202
Ph: (703)568-5651
Fax: (703)740-8379
E-mail: infoofficer@loanational.org
URL: http://www.loanational.org

Description: Represents the interests of military officers and civilians in logistics fields. Aims to enhance the mission of the United States Air Force and the Department of Defense (DoD) through concerted efforts to promote quality logistics, professional development of logistics officers, and an open forum for leadership, management, and technical interchange. Conducts conferences that provide opportunities for the mentorship and professional development of logistics professionals.

7643 ■ National Industrial Transportation League
1700 N Moore St., Ste. 1900
Arlington, VA 22209
Ph: (703)524-5011
Fax: (703)524-5017
E-mail: info@nitl.org
URL: http://www.nitl.org

Description: Serves as the voice of the freight transportation industry. Develops and formulates freight policies over all transportation modes. Provides educational forums which allow members to take advantage of the latest opportunities and trends in the industry.

7644 ■ Reverse Logistics Association
441 W Main St., Ste. D
Lehi, UT 84043
Ph: (801)331-8949
Fax: (801)206-0090
Fr: (866)801-6332
E-mail: info@rltinc.com
URL: http://www.reverselogisticsassociation.org

Description: Educates and informs reverse logistics professionals around the world. Serves manufacturers and retailers by offering updates on market trends, mergers and acquisitions, and potential outsourcing opportunities to 3PSPs.

7645 ■ Supply Chain Council
12320 Barker Cypress Rd., Ste. 600
PMB 321
Cypress, TX 77429-8329
Ph: (202)962-0440
Fax: (202)540-9027
E-mail: info@supply-chain.org
URL: http://supply-chain.org

Description: Represents the interests of practitioners from different industries including manufacturers, services, distributors, and retailers. Educates organizations on the use and application of the Supply Chair Operations Reference (SCOR) model.

7646 ■ Transportation and Logistics Council
120 Main St.
Huntington, NY 11743
Ph: (631)549-8988
Fax: (631)549-8962
URL: http://www.tlcouncil.org

Description: Represents all segments of the transportation community: shippers, carriers, third party logistics providers, brokers, freight forwarders, and other service providers. Provides education and representation in issues relating to the transportation of goods.

7647 ■ Warehousing Education and Research Council
1100 Jorie Blvd., Ste. 170
Oak Brook, IL 60523
Ph: (630)990-0001
Fax: (630)990-0256
E-mail: wercoffice@werc.org
URL: http://www.werc.org

Description: Represents distribution and warehousing professionals who lead, direct, and manage the efficient flow of information, materials, and finished goods throughout the supply chain. Promotes professional development through education, peer-to-peer idea exchange, and networking.

SOURCES OF HELP-WANTED ADS

7648 ■ *Academy of Management Journal*
Academy of Management
235 Elm Rd.
PO Box 3020
Briarcliff Manor, NY 10510-8020
Ph: (914)923-2607
Fax: (914)923-2615
URL: http://journals.aomonline.org/amj/

Bimonthly. Professional journal covering management.

7649 ■ *Academy of Management Learning & Education*
Academy of Management
235 Elm Rd.
PO Box 3020
Briarcliff Manor, NY 10510-8020
Ph: (914)923-2607
Fax: (914)923-2615
URL: http://journals.aomonline.org/amle

Quarterly. $85.00/year for individuals, print; $130.00/year for individuals, print & online; $125.00/year for libraries, print; $170.00/year for libraries, print and online; $105.00/year for other countries, print; $150.00/year for other countries, print & online; $195.00/year for other countries, print, corporate library; $235.00/year for other countries, print & online, corporate library. Journal covering management issues for professionals.

7650 ■ *Business Performance Management*
Penton Media Inc.
249 W 17th St.
New York, NY 10011
Ph: (212)204-4200
URL: http://www.bpmmag.net/

Free to qualified subscribers. Magazine for business managers. Covers organizing, automating, and analyzing of business methodologies and processes.

7651 ■ *CXO*
IDG Communications Inc.
3 Speen St.
Framingham, MA 01701
Ph: (508)875-5000
URL: http://www.idg.com/www/IDGProducts.nsf/0/
  022796185EED5984852

Monthly. Magazine providing technology information for chief officers and managers.

7652 ■ *D & O Advisor*
American Lawyer Media L.P.
120 Broadway, 5th Fl.
New York, NY 10271
Ph: (212)457-9400
Fax: (646)417-7705
Fr: 800-603-6571
URL: http://www.alm.com

Quarterly. Magazine that offers advice and perspective on corporate oversight responsibilities for directors and officers.

7653 ■ *E Journal of Organizational Learning and Leadership*
WeLEAD Inc.
PO Box 202
Litchfield, OH 44253
Fr: 877-778-5494
URL: http://www.leadingtoday.org/weleadinlearning/

Semiannual. Free. Online academic journal about organizational leadership.

7654 ■ *Event Management*
Cognizant Communications Corp.
3 Hartsdale Rd.
Elmsford, NY 10523-3701
Ph: (914)592-7720
Fax: (914)592-8981
URL: http://www.cognizantcommunication.com/
  journal-titles/event-

Quarterly. $445.00/year for institutions, online only; $525.00/year for institutions, online & hard copy; $52.00/year for individuals, professional; $50.00/year for members, online & hard copy; $65.00/year for single issue. Peer-reviewed journal covering research and analytic needs of a rapidly growing profession focused on events.

7655 ■ *Executive Legal Adviser*
Incisive Media
120 Broadway, 5th Fl.
New York, NY 10271
Ph: (212)457-9400
Fax: (646)417-7705
URL: http://www.executivelegaladviser.com

Bimonthly. Free to qualified subscribers. Magazine that offers legal advice for corporate executives.

7656 ■ *Fleet Maintenance*
Cygnus Business Media Inc.
3 Huntington Quadrangle, Ste. 301 N
Melville, NY 11747
Ph: (631)845-2700
Fax: (631)845-7109
Fr: 800-308-6397
URL: http://www.fleetmag.com

Business tabloid magazine offering a chapterized curriculum of technical, regulatory and managerial information designed to help maintenance managers, directors and supervisors better perform their jobs and reduce their overall cost-per-mile.

7657 ■ *Forbes*
Forbes Magazine
60 5th Ave.
New York, NY 10011
Ph: (212)366-8900
Fr: 800-295-0893
URL: http://www.forbes.com

Biweekly. $19.99/year for individuals; $22.25/year for

Canada. Magazine reporting on industry, business and finance management.

7658 ■ *Forrester*
Forrester Research Inc.
400 Technology Sq.
Cambridge, MA 02139
Ph: (617)613-5730
Fr: (866)367-7378
URL: http://www.forrester.com/mag

Free. Journal that aims to provide ideas and advice that is relevant to today's CEOs.

7659 ■ *International Journal of Business Research*
International Academy of Business and Economics
PO Box 2536
Ceres, CA 95307
Ph: (702)560-0653
Fax: (702)508-9166
URL: http://www.iabe.eu/domains/iabeX/
  journal.aspx?journalid=12

Peer-reviewed journal publishing theoretical, conceptual, and applied research on topics related to research, practice and teaching in all areas of business, management, and marketing.

7660 ■ *Journal of Academic Leadership*
Academic Leadership
600 Park St.
Rarick Hall 219
Hays, KS 67601-4099
Ph: (785)628-4547
URL: http://www.academicleadership.org/

Journal focusing on the leadership issues in the academic world.

7661 ■ *Journal of Business and Psychology*
Springer-Verlag New York Inc.
233 Spring St.
New York, NY 10013-1578
Ph: (212)460-1500
Fax: (212)460-1575
Fr: 800-777-4643
URL: http://www.springer.com/psychology/
  community+%26+environment

$904.00/year for institutions, print or online; $1,085.00/year for institutions, print & enchanced access. Journal covering all aspects of psychology that apply to the business segment. Includes topics such as personnel selection and training, organizational assessment and development, risk management and loss control, marketing and consumer behavior research.

7662 ■ *Journal of International Business Strategy*
International Academy of Business and Economics
PO Box 2536
Ceres, CA 95307
Ph: (702)560-0653

Fax: (702)508-9166
URL: http://www.iabe.eu/domains/iabeX/
journal.aspx?journalid=7

Peer-reviewed journal publishing theoretical, conceptual, and applied research on topics related to
strategy in international business.

7663 ■ Management Research
M.E. Sharpe Inc.
80 Business Pk. Dr.
Armonk, NY 10504
Ph: (914)273-1800
Fax: (914)273-2106
Fr: 800-541-6563
URL: http://www.mesharpe.com/mall/
results1.asp?ACR=JMR

$75.00/year for individuals; $399.00/year for institutions; $87.00/year for other countries; $441.00/year
for institutions, other countries. International journal
dedicated to advancing the understanding of management in private and public sector organizations
through empirical investigation and theoretical
analysis. Attempts to promote an international
dialogue between researchers, improve the understanding of the nature of management in different
settings, and achieve a reasonable transfer of
research results to management practice in several
contexts. Receptive to research across a broad range
of management topics such as human resource
management, organizational behavior, organizational
theory, and strategic management. While not regional
in nature, articles dealing with Iberoamerican issues
are particularly welcomed.

7664 ■ Organization Management Journal
Eastern Academy of Management
c/o Vicki Fairbanks Taylor, VP
John I. Grove College of Business
45 Keefer Way
Mechanicsburg, PA 17011
Ph: (518)762-4651
Fax: (518)736-1716
E-mail: omj@palgrave.com
URL: http://www1.wnec.edu/omj

Free to qualified subscribers. Refereed, online journal
focusing on organization management issues.

**7665 ■ Public Performance and Management
Review**
M.E. Sharpe Inc.
80 Business Pk. Dr.
Armonk, NY 10504
Ph: (914)273-1800
Fax: (914)273-2106
Fr: 800-541-6563
URL: http://www.mesharpe.com/mall/
results1.asp?ACR=pmr

Quarterly. $95.00/year for individuals; $528.00/year
for institutions; $111.00/year for other countries;
$560.00/year for institutions, other countries. Journal
addressing a broad range of factors influencing the
performance of public and nonprofit organizations
and agencies. Aims to facilitate the development of
innovative techniques and encourage a wider application of those already established; stimulate
research and critical thinking about the relationship
between public and private management theories;
present integrated analyses of theories, concepts,
strategies and techniques dealing with productivity,
measurement and related questions of performance
improvement; and provide a forum for practitioner-
academic exchange. Continuing themes include
managing for productivity, measuring and evaluating
performance, improving budget strategies, managing
human resources, building partnerships, and applying new technologies.

7666 ■ Supply Chain Management Review
Reed Business Information
360 Park Ave. S
New York, NY 10010-1710
Ph: (646)746-6400
URL: http://www.scmr.com

$199.00/year for individuals; $199.00/year for

Canada; $337.00/year for other countries. Publication
covering business and management.

7667 ■ T+D Magazine
American Society for Training & Development
1640 King St.
PO Box 1443
Alexandria, VA 22313-2043
Ph: (703)683-8100
Fax: (703)683-1523
Fr: 800-628-2783
URL: http://www.astd.org/content/publications/

Monthly. $89.00/year for members; $150.00/year for
nonmembers, outside US; for Included in membership; $300.00/year for institutions. Magazine on train-
ing and development.

EMPLOYER DIRECTORIES AND NETWORKING LISTS

**7668 ■ Consultants and Consulting
Organizations Directory**
Gale
PO Box 6904
Florence, KY 41022-6904
Fr: 800-354-9706
URL: http://www.gale.cengage.com

Annual, New edition expected 37th; February, 2012.
$1,392.00 for individuals. Covers: Over 26,000 firms,
individuals, and organizations active in consulting.
Entries include: Individual or organization name, address, phone, fax, e-mail, URL, specialties, founding
date, branch offices, names and titles of key personnel, number of employees, financial data, publications, seminars and workshops. Arrangement: By
broad subject categories. Indexes: Subject, geographical, organization name.

7669 ■ D & B Consultants Directory
Dun & Bradstreet Corp.
103 JFK Pky.
Short Hills, NJ 07078
Ph: (973)921-5500
Fr: 800-234-3867
URL: http://www.dnb.com

Annual, Latest edition September, 2008. Covers: Top
30,000 U.S. consulting firms in more than 200 areas
of specialization. Entries include: Firm name, address, phone, sales, number of employees, year
established, description of service, other locations,
names and titles of key personnel, reference to parent company, D&B DUNS number, trade name,
consulting activity, owned companies clientele, territory served, number of accounts, stock exchange
symbol and indicator for publicly owned companies.
Arrangement: Complete consultants profiles appear
in the consultants alphabetical section. Companies
are cross-referenced geographically and by activity.
Indexes: All companies with a primary or secondary
Standard Industrial Classification (SIC) code of 8748
"Business Consulting Services," as well as those
companies whose type of business description
includes the word "consult." All companies must have
a phone number and be either a headquarters or
single location.

**7670 ■ Directory of Certified Business
Counselors**
Institute of Certified Business Counselors
18831 Willamette Dr.
West Linn, OR 97068
Fax: (503)292-8237
Fr: 877-422-2674
URL: http://www.i-cbc.org/directory_alphabetical.htm

Irregular, updated as necessary. Covers: 160 member
counselors, brokers, and attorneys qualified to act as
advisors for persons with business problems. Entries
include: Name, address, phone, business specialty.
Arrangement: Alphabetical.

**7671 ■ Harvard Business School Guide to
Careers in Management Consulting**
Harvard Business School Publishing
60 Harvard Way
Boston, MA 02163
Ph: (617)783-7400
Fax: (617)783-7489
Fr: 888-500-1016
URL: http://www.hbsp.harvard.edu

$10.83 for individuals. Publication includes: Well-
known consulting firms, a mailing list of recruiting
contacts, and a selective bibliography of relevant
books and directories compiled by the Harvard Business School.

**7672 ■ Professional and Technical
Consultants Association—Directory of
Consultants**
Professional and Technical Consultants Association
PO Box 2261
Santa Clara, CA 95055
Ph: (408)971-5902
Fax: (866)746-1053
Fr: 800-747-2822
URL: http://www.patca.org

Annual, January; Latest edition 2009-2010. Covers:
More than 350 consultants involved in computer
technology, management, marketing, manufacturing,
engineering, etc. Entries include: Individual or firm
name, address, phone, specialties, degrees held. Arrangement: Alphabetical. Indexes: Specialty,
geographical.

HANDBOOKS AND MANUALS

7673 ■ Associate Management Analyst
National Learning Corporation
212 Michael Dr.
Syosset, NY 11791
Fr: 800-632-8888
URL: http://www.passbooks.com

2009. $34.95 (paper). Serves as an exam prepara-
tion guide for associate management analysts.

**7674 ■ FabJob Guide to Become a
Management Consultant**
FabJob Inc.
4616 - 25th Ave. NE, No. 224
Seattle, WA 98105
Ph: (403)949-4980
Fr: 888-322-5621
URL: http://www.fabjob.com/consultjsb.asp

Jennie S. Bev. $14.97(e-book). 165 pages. Offers
information for anyone who wants to become a
management consultant. Includes insider tips and
expert advice from 15 leading management consultants and several best-selling management authors.

7675 ■ How to Make it Big as a Consultant
AMACOM Publishing
c/o American Management Association
1601 Broadway
New York, NY 10019-7434
Ph: (212)586-8100
Fr: 800-714-6395
E-mail: pubs_cust_serv@amanet.org
URL: http://www.amacombooks.org

William A. Cohen. 2009. $18.95 (paper). 332 pages.
Features advice on every aspect of starting up and
maintaining a consulting career. Helps readers: get a
handle on the legal, tax, and insurance issues
involved in setting up and running the business;
understand what clients really need; create the
structure for an assignment; market the business;
and solve problems using the Harvard Case Study
Method.

**7676 ■ An Insider's Guide to Building a
Successful Consulting Practice**
AMACOM Publishing
c/o American Management Association
1601 Broadway
New York, NY 10019-7420

Fax: (212)903-8083
Fr: 800-250-5308
URL: http://www.amacombooks.org

Bruce L. Katcher and Adam Snyder. 2010. $18.95 (paper). Offers ways to make a smooth transition from employee to independent consultant. Features real stories from successful independent consultants in diverse industries.

EMPLOYMENT AGENCIES AND SEARCH FIRMS

7677 ■ A-L Associates Inc.
60 E 42nd St., Ste. 1534
New York, NY 10036
Ph: (212)878-9000
URL: http://www.alassociatesltd.com

Executive search firm.

7678 ■ Allerton Heneghan & O'Neill
1415 W 22nd St., Tower Fl.
Oak Brook, IL 60523
Ph: (630)645-2294
Fax: (630)645-2298
E-mail: info@ahosearch.com
URL: http://www.ahosearch.com

Executive search firm.

7679 ■ Baker Montgomery
One Magnificent Mile, Ste. 1815
980 N Michigan Ave.
Chicago, IL 60611
Ph: (312)397-8808
Fax: (312)397-9631
E-mail: contact@bakermontgomery.com
URL: http://www.bakermontgomery.com

Executive search firm.

7680 ■ BeechTree Partners LLC
875 N Michigan Ave., Ste. 3100
Chicago, IL 60611
Ph: (312)794-7808
E-mail: brad@beechtreepartners.com
URL: http://www.beechtreepartners.com

Executive search firm.

7681 ■ Callan Associates Ltd.
1211 W 22nd St., Ste. 821
Oak Brook, IL 60523
Ph: (630)574-9300
Fax: (630)574-3099
E-mail: info@callanassociates.com
URL: http://www.callanassociates.com

Executive search firm.

7682 ■ Chandler Group
4165 Shoreline Dr., Ste. 220
Spring Park, MN 55384
Ph: (952)471-3000
Fax: (952)471-3021
E-mail: resumes@chandgroup.com
URL: http://www.chandgroup.com

Executive search firm.

7683 ■ Charles Aris, Inc.
300 N Greene St., Ste. 1800
Greensboro, NC 27401
Ph: (336)378-1818
Fax: (336)378-0129
E-mail: info@charlesaris.com
URL: http://www.charlesaris.com

Provides executive search and placement services in the areas of consumer packaged goods, retail, strategy/business development, global life sciences, healthcare, chemicals, textiles/apparel, private equity, and business services.

7684 ■ Charleston Partners
2 Bellevue Ave.
Rumson, NJ 07760

Ph: (732)842-5015
E-mail: info@charlestonpartners.com
URL: http://www.charlestonpartners.com/human-capital-partners.html

Executive search firm concentrated on human resource services.

7685 ■ Consulting Resource Group
1100 5th Ave. S, Ste. 201
Naples, FL 34102
Ph: (678)623-5403
Fax: (678)623-5403
E-mail: mailbox@careersinconsulting.com
URL: http://www.careersinconsulting.com

Description: Exists as an executive search and recruiting services firm focusing exclusively on the recruitment and placement of management consulting and technology consulting professionals nationwide.

7686 ■ DNPitchon Associates
60 W Ridgewood Ave.
Ridgewood, NJ 07450
Ph: (201)612-8350
E-mail: info@dnpitchon.com
URL: http://www.dnpitchon.com

Executive search firm.

7687 ■ DuVall & Associates
4203 Costa Salada
San Clemente, CA 92673
Ph: (949)488-8790
Fax: (949)488-8793
E-mail: karen@ducall.com
URL: http://www.duvall.com

Executive search firm specializing in management team placement.

7688 ■ The Executive Source Inc.
55 5th Ave., 19th Fl.
New York, NY 10003
Ph: (212)691-5505
Fax: (212)691-9839
E-mail: tes1@executivesource.com
URL: http://executivesource.com

Executive search firm.

7689 ■ Explore Company
5 Rokeby Court
Kensington, MD 20895
Ph: (301)933-8008
E-mail: resumes@explorecompany.com
URL: http://www.explorecompany.com

Executive search firm.

7690 ■ Heidrick and Struggles, Inc.
233 S Wacker Dr., Ste. 4200
Sears Tower
Chicago, IL 60606-6303
Ph: (312)496-1200
URL: http://www.heidrick.com

Executive search firm. International organization with a variety of affiliate offices.

7691 ■ Kenmore Executives Inc.
PO Box 66
Boca Raton, FL 33429
Ph: (561)392-0700
Fax: (561)750-0818
E-mail: inquires@kenmoreexecutives.com
URL: http://www.kenmoreexecutives.com

Executive search firm that works with consultants in a variety of fields.

7692 ■ Korn/Ferry International
1900 Ave. of the Stars, Ste. 2600
Los Angeles, CA 90067
Ph: (310)552-1834
URL: http://www.kornferry.com

Executive search firm. International organization with a variety of affiliate offices.

7693 ■ Protocol Agency Inc.
27001 Agoura Rd., Ste. 210
Calabasas, CA 91301
Fr: 877-371-0069
E-mail: corp@protocolexec.com
URL: http://www.protocolagency.com

Executive search firm focusing on a variety of placements.

7694 ■ Ronald Dukes Associates LLC
20 N Wacker, Ste. 2010
Chicago, IL 60606
Ph: (312)357-2895
Fax: (312)357-2897
E-mail: ron@rdukesassociates.com
URL: http://www.rdukesassociates.com

Executive search firm focused on the industrial and automotive industries.

7695 ■ Russell Reynolds Associates, Inc.
200 Park Ave., Ste. 2300
New York, NY 10166-0002
Ph: (212)351-2000
E-mail: hcamericas@russellreynolds.com
URL: http://www.russellreynolds.com

Executive search firm. Affiliate offices across the country and abroad.

7696 ■ Valerie Fredrickson & Company
800 Menlo Ave., Ste. 220
Menlo Park, CA 94025
Ph: (650)614-0220
E-mail: recruiting@vfandco.com
URL: http://www.vfandco.com

Executive search firm.

ONLINE JOB SOURCES AND SERVICES

7697 ■ BusinessAnalystCrossing.com
URL: http://www.businessanalystcrossing.com

Description: Offers business analyst job listings. Includes entry level business analyst, technical and business analyst jobs.

7698 ■ ConsultingCrossing.com
URL: http://www.consultingcrossing.com

Description: Provides job listings and other resources related to consulting employment opportunities.

TRADESHOWS

7699 ■ Association of Career Management Consulting Firms International Annual Conference
Association of Career Management Consulting Firms International
204 E St., NE
Washington, DC 20002
Ph: (202)547-6344
Fax: (202)547-6348
E-mail: acf@acfinternational.org
URL: http://www.aocfi.org

Annual. Primary Exhibits: Exhibits relating for outplacement consultants, who counsel and assist in job searching, as well as educate about the techniques and practices of choosing a career.

7700 ■ Organization Development Network Conference
Organization Development Network
401 N. Michigan Ave., Ste. 2200
Chicago, IL 60611
Ph: (312)321-5136
Fax: (312)673-6836
E-mail: odnetwork@odnetwork.org
URL: http://www.odnetwork.org

Annual. Primary Exhibits: Exhibits related to organization development.

OTHER SOURCES

**7701 ■ Alliance of Meeting Management
Companies (AMMC)**
PO Box 1857
West Jefferson, NC 28694
Ph: (336)846-7270
Fax: (336)246-5291
E-mail: info@ammc.org
URL: http://ammc.org

Description: Represents professional and experienced independent meeting professionals. Fosters the interests of those business entities primarily engaged in providing meeting management and consultation services. Seeks to promote the success of business owners in the meeting industry through marketing, networking and education.

**7702 ■ Association of Business Process
Management Professionals (ABPMP)**
47 W Polk St., Ste. 100-279
Chicago, IL 60605-2085
E-mail: president@abpmp.org
URL: http://www.abpmp.org

Description: Fosters the advancement of business process management concepts and its practices. Seeks to develop a common body of knowledge in business process management. Provides educational and networking activities for the continuing education of its members and their professional colleagues.

**7703 ■ Association of Management
Consulting Firms (AMCF)**
370 Lexington Ave., Ste. 2209
New York, NY 10017
Ph: (212)262-3055
Fax: (212)262-3054
E-mail: info@amcf.org
URL: http://www.amcf.org/amcf

Description: Trade association for consulting organizations that provide a broad range of managerial services to commercial, industrial, governmental, and other organizations and individuals. Seeks to unite management-consulting firms in order to develop and improve professional standards and practice in the field. Offers information and referral services on management consultants; administers public relations program. Conducts research. Monitors regulatory environment.

**7704 ■ International Society for Organization
Development**
11234 Walnut Ridge Rd.
Chesterland, OH 44026
Ph: (440)729-7419
Fax: (440)729-9319
E-mail: info@theisod.org
URL: http://www.theisod.org

Description: Professionals, students, and individuals interested in organization development. Disseminates information on and promotes a better understanding of organization development worldwide. Conducts specialized education programs. Develops the International O.D. Code of Ethics and a competency test for individuals wishing to qualify as a Registered Organization Development Consultant and a statement on the knowledge and skill necessary to be competent in organization development and criteria for the accreditation of OD/OB academic programs. Maintains job and consultant information service. Sponsors International Registry of Organization Development Professionals and Research/Study Team on Nonviolent Large Systems Change. Maintains 18 committees including an International Advisory Board.

**7705 ■ National Society of Certified
Healthcare Business Consultants
(NSCHBC)**
12100 Sunset Hills Rd., Ste. 130
Reston, VA 20190
Ph: (703)234-4099

Fax: (703)435-4390
E-mail: info@nschbc.org
URL: http://www.nschbc.org/index.cfm

Description: Advances the profession of healthcare business consultants through education, certification and professional interaction. Provides education and training to assist members in fulfilling the requirements of certification.

**7706 ■ Organization Development Network
(ODN)**
401 N Michigan Ave., Ste. 2200
Chicago, IL 60611
Ph: (312)321-5136
Fax: (973)763-7488
URL: http://www.odnetwork.org

Description: Represents practitioners, academics, managers and students employed or interested in organization development. Works to enhance and provide opportunities for colleagueship and professional development.

**7707 ■ Professional and Technical
Consultants Association (PATCA)**
PO Box 2261
Santa Clara, CA 95055
Ph: (408)971-5902
Fax: (866)746-1053
Fr: 800-74-PATCA
E-mail: info@patca.org
URL: http://www.patca.org

Description: Represents Independent consultants active in the support of business, industry, and government. Serves as a referral service to aid independent consultants in marketing their services as well as to assist those seeking their services.

SOURCES OF HELP-WANTED ADS

7708 ■ Beauty Store Business
Creative Age Publications Inc.
7628 Densmore Ave.
Van Nuys, CA 91406-2042
Ph: (818)782-7328
Fax: (818)782-7450
Fr: 800-442-5667
URL: http://www.beautystorebusiness.com/

Monthly. Business magazine for beauty industry professionals and beauty store owners.

7709 ■ Global Cosmetic Industry
Allured Publishing Corp.
336 Gundersen Dr., Ste. A
Carol Stream, IL 60188-2403
Ph: (630)653-2155
Fax: (630)653-2192
URL: http://www.gcimagazine.com/

Monthly. Free to qualified subscribers, U.S. and Canada; $98.00/year for other countries; $176.00/year for two years, other countries. Trade publication covering the cosmetics industry worldwide.

7710 ■ Modern Salon
Vance Publishing Corp.
400 Knightsbridge Pky.
Lincolnshire, IL 60069
Ph: (847)634-2600
Fax: (847)634-4379
URL: http://www.modernsalon.com/

Monthly. Magazine focusing on hairstyling salons for men and women.

7711 ■ Nailpro
Creative Age Publications Inc.
7628 Densmore Ave.
Van Nuys, CA 91406-2042
Ph: (818)782-7328
Fax: (818)782-7450
Fr: 800-442-5667
E-mail: nailpro@creativeage.com
URL: http://www.nailpro.com

Monthly. Salon owners and nail technicians read Nailpro for continuing education in techniques and services, marketing and management tips, product information and industry news.

7712 ■ Soap and Cosmetics
Chemical Week Associates
2 Grand Central Tower
140 E 45th St., 40th Fl.
New York, NY 10017
Ph: (212)884-9528

Fax: (212)883-9514
URL: http://www.chemweek.com/verticals/sc/
Monthly. $225.97/year for individuals, print + online; $259.97/year for Canada, print + online; $629.00/year for other countries, print + online. Trade publication covering the cosmetics industry.

7713 ■ Spa 20/20
Virgo Publishing Inc.
PO Box 40079
Phoenix, AZ 85067-0079
Ph: (480)990-1101
Fax: (480)990-0819
URL: http://www.spa20-20.com
Bimonthly. $14.00/year for individuals, in U.S.; $26.00/year for Canada; $82.00/year for elsewhere. Magazine covering the spa industry, including skin care, cosmetics, and sunless tanning.

HANDBOOKS AND MANUALS

7714 ■ Nails Career Handbook
Cyndy Drummey
3520 Challenger St.
Torrance, CA 90503
Ph: (310)533-2400
Fax: (310)533-2507
E-mail: cyndy.drummey@bobit.com
URL: http://www.nailsmag.com
2009. $8.00. Provides resources to help start a career in nail art and/or manicuring including passing the state exam, preparing a resume, building business, honing one's skills, salon violations and sanitation rules, and tips on expanding one's horizons.

ONLINE JOB SOURCES AND SERVICES

7715 ■ Nail Technician Jobs
URL: http://www.nailtechjobs.org
Description: Contains current employment opportunities for nail technicians. Offers job postings for employers and recruiters.

7716 ■ NailTechnicianJobs.org
URL: http://nailtechnicianjobs.org
Description: Features job sites, company career pages and associations for nail technician jobs.

TRADESHOWS

7717 ■ American Association of Cosmetology Schools Annual Conference - AACS Annual Convention & Expo
American Association of Cosmetology Schools
15825 N. 71st St., Ste. 100
Scottsdale, AZ 85254-1521

Ph: (480)281-0431
Fax: (480)905-0993
Fr: 800-831-1086
E-mail: dilsah@beautyschools.org
URL: http://www.beautyschools.org

Annual. Primary Exhibits: Beauty supplies and products, and cosmetology services.

7718 ■ American Electrology Association Annual Convention
American Electrology Association
PO Box 687
Bodega Bay, CA 94923
Ph: (707)875-9135
E-mail: infoaea@electrology.com
URL: http://www.electrology.com

Annual. Primary Exhibits: Electrology equipment, supplies, and services.

7719 ■ International Beauty Show, New York
Advanstar Communications
641 Lexington Ave., 8th Fl.
New York, NY 10022
Ph: (212)951-6600
Fax: (212)951-6793
E-mail: info@advanstar.com
URL: http://www.advanstar.com

Annual. Primary Exhibits: Beauty and health related equipment, supplies, and services.

7720 ■ Midwest Beauty Show
Chicago Cosmetologists Inc.
401 N. Michigan Ave.
Chicago, IL 60611
Ph: (312)321-6809
Fax: (312)245-1080
Fr: 800-648-2505
E-mail: info@americasbeautyshow.com
URL: http://www.isnow.com

Annual. Primary Exhibits: Goods and services for the beauty trade. Dates and Locations: 2012 Mar 03-05; Chicago, IL; McCormick Place.

7721 ■ National Beauty Show - HAIRWORLD
National Cosmetology Association
15825 N. 71st St., Ste. 100
Scottsdale, AZ 85254
Ph: (480)281-0424
Fax: (480)905-0708
Fr: 800-468-2274
E-mail: info@probeauty.org
URL: http://www.probeauty.org/nca/

Annual. Primary Exhibits: Hair products, cosmetics, and jewelry.

Manufacturer's Sales Representatives

Sources of Help-Wanted Ads

7722 ■ AATCC Review
American Association of Textile Chemists and Colorists
1 Davis Dr.
PO Box 12215
Research Triangle Park, NC 27709-2215
Ph: (919)549-8141
Fax: (919)549-8933
URL: http://www.aatcc.org/media/index.htm

Monthly. $200.00/year for nonmembers; $55.00/year for members; $26.00/year for single issue, within U.S.; $36.00/year for single issue, outside U.S. Magazine focusing on dyeing, finishing of fibers and fabrics.

7723 ■ Agency Sales Magazine
Manufacturers' Agents National Association
16 A Journey, Ste. 200
Aliso Viejo, CA 92656-3317
Ph: (949)859-4040
Fax: (949)855-2973
Fr: 877-626-2776
URL: http://www.manaonline.org/html/agency_sales_magazine.html

Monthly. $79.00/year for individuals; $89.00/year for Canada; $102.00/year for other countries. Magazine for manufacturers' agents and manufacturers. Includes tax developments and tips, management aids for manufacturers and agents, legal bulletins, trend-identifying market data, classified ads.

7724 ■ Apparel
Edgell Communications Inc.
4 Middlebury Blvd., Ste. 1
Randolph, NJ 07869-1121
Ph: (973)607-1300
Fax: (973)252-9020
E-mail: apparelmag@halldata.com
URL: http://www.apparelmag.com

Monthly. $69.00/year for U.S.; $85.00/year for Canada; $190.00/year for other countries, by airmail. Trade magazine on sewn-products industry management and manufacturing. Reports on industry trends, technology, new products, etc.

7725 ■ BedTimes
International Sleep Products Association
501 Wythe St.
Alexandria, VA 22314-1917
Ph: (703)683-8371
Fax: (703)683-4503
E-mail: bedtimes@sleepproducts.org
URL: http://www.sleepproducts.org/bedtimes/

Monthly. $50.00/year for U.S.; $90.00/year for U.S., 2 years; $65.00/year for other countries; $110.00/year for other countries, 2 years; free for ISPA members. Trade magazine covering trends and developments in the mattress bedding industry.

7726 ■ Beverage World
Beverage World
200 E Randolph St., 7th Fl.
Chicago, IL 60601
Ph: (646)708-7300
Fax: (646)708-7399
Fr: (866)890-8541
URL: http://www.beverageworld.com

Monthly. $99.00/year for individuals. Trade magazine for corporate, marketing, distribution, production, and purchasing top and middle management in the multi-product beverage industry.

7727 ■ BtoB Magazine
Crain Communications Inc.
360 N Michigan Ave.
Chicago, IL 60601
Ph: (312)649-5200
URL: http://www.btobonline.com

Monthly. $59.00/year for individuals; $69.00/year for Canada; $89.00/year for other countries. Trade magazine on business-to-business marketing news, strategy, and tactics.

7728 ■ Chemical Market Reporter
Schnell Publishing Company Inc.
360 Park Ave. S
12th Fl.
New York, NY 10010
Ph: (212)791-4200
Fax: (212)791-4321
URL: http://www.icis.com/v2/magazine/home.aspx

Weekly (Mon.). International tabloid newspaper for the chemical process industries. Includes analytical reports on developments in the chemical marketplace, plant expansions, new technology, corporate mergers, finance, current chemical prices, and regulatory matters.

7729 ■ Concrete Products
Mining Media Inc.
8751 E Hampden Ave., Ste. B-1
Denver, CO 80231
Ph: (303)283-0640
Fax: (303)283-0641
E-mail: dmarsh@prismb2b.com
URL: http://concreteproducts.com

Monthly. Free, online; $96.00/year for other countries, print. Magazine on concrete products and ready-mixed concrete.

7730 ■ Cosmetics & Toiletries
Allured Publishing Corp.
336 Gundersen Dr., Ste. A
Carol Stream, IL 60188-2403
Ph: (630)653-2155
Fax: (630)653-2192
E-mail: lhince@allured.com
URL: http://www.cosmeticsandtoiletries.com

Monthly. $98.00/year for individuals; $137.00/year for Canada; $189.00/year for other countries; $169.00/year for two years; $231.00/year for Canada, two

years; $330.00/year for other countries, two years. Trade magazine on cosmetic and toiletries manufacturing with an emphasis on product research and development issues.

7731 ■ CRN
United business Media L.L.C
240 W 35th St.
New York, NY 10001
Ph: (516)562-5000
URL: http://www.crn.com

Weekly. Newspaper for value added resellers, retailers, and distributors in the computer market.

7732 ■ Dealernews
Advanstar Communications
6200 Canoga Ave., 2nd Fl.
Woodland Hills, CA 91367
Ph: (818)593-5000
Fax: (818)593-5020
Fr: 800-598-6008
URL: http://www.dealernews.com

Monthly. Magazine covering dealers of motorcycles, ATV/off-road vehicles, watercraft, other powersport vehicles, and related aftermarket and apparel products.

7733 ■ Electrical Wholesaling
Penton Media Inc.
9800 Metcalf Ave.
Overland Park, KS 66212
Ph: (913)341-1300
Fax: (913)967-1898
URL: http://ewweb.com

Monthly. Magazine focusing on electrical wholesaling for distributors of electrical supplies.

7734 ■ Feedstuffs
Miller Publishing Co.
12400 Whitewater Dr., Ste. 160
Minnetonka, MN 55343
Ph: (952)931-0211
Fax: (952)938-1832
Fr: 800-441-1410
URL: http://www.feedstuffs.com/ME2/Default.asp

Weekly. $144.00/year for individuals; $230.00/year for two years; $150.00/year for Canada; $235.00/year for individuals, Europe and Mid East; airmail; $280.00/year for other countries, Japan, Far E./Aus. airmail; $210.00/year for individuals, Mexico/Central/South America; $196.00/year for individuals, print & internet version; $334.00/year for two years, print & internet version; $202.00/year for Canada, print & internet version; $404.00/year for Canada, print & internet version, 2 years. Magazine serving the grain and feed industries and animal agriculture.

7735 ■ Furniture Today
Reed Business Information
360 Park Ave. S
New York, NY 10010

Ph: (646)746-6400
URL: http://www.furnituretoday.com/

$127.48/year for U.S. and Canada; $244.49/year for other countries. Furniture retailing and manufacturing magazine (tabloid).

7736 ■ Gases & Welding Distributor
Penton Media Inc.
249 W 17th St.
New York, NY 10011
Ph: (212)204-4200
URL: http://www.weldingmag.com

$72.00/year for individuals, international; $121.50/year for individuals, two years, international; free to qualified subscribers, in U.S. and Canada. Distributor magazine featuring industrial, medical, specialty gases and welding supplies.

7737 ■ Home Channel News
Lebhar-Friedman, Inc.
425 Park Ave.
New York, NY 10022
Ph: (212)756-5000
URL: http://www.homechannelnews.com

$189.00/year for individuals. Business tabloid serving home center/building material retailers.

7738 ■ Implement & Tractor
Farm Journal Media Inc.
1550 Northwest Hwy., Ste. 403
Park Ridge, IL 60068
E-mail: info@scissortailproductionsllc.com
URL: http://www.implementandtractor.com

Bimonthly. $38.00/year for U.S. and Canada; $98.00/year for other countries; $72.00/year for U.S. and Canada, 2 years; $175.00/year for two years, foreign. Magazine about agricultural equipment and machinery.

7739 ■ Industrial Distribution
Reed Business Information
360 Park Ave. S
New York, NY 10010-1710
Ph: (646)746-6400
URL: http://www.inddist.com

Monthly. $121.00/year for individuals; $145.00/year for Canada; $140.00/year for individuals, for Mexico; $280.00/year for other countries. Magazine covering industrial supplies marketing, management, sales, telecommunications, computers, inventory, and warehouse management.

7740 ■ Industrial Heating
Business News Publishing Co.
2401 W Big Beaver Rd., Ste. 700
Troy, MI 48084-3333
Ph: (248)362-3700
URL: http://www.industrialheating.com/
Monthly. Magazine.

7741 ■ Kitchen and Bath Business
Nielsen Business Media
770 Broadway
New York, NY 10003-9595
E-mail: kbb@mediabrains.com
URL: http://www.kitchen-bath.com/kbb/index.jsp

Monthly. $10.00/year for individuals, cover; $79.00/year for individuals, domestic; $94.00/year for Canada and Mexico; $139.00/year for other countries. Trade magazine on kitchen and bath remodeling and construction.

7742 ■ Laser Focus World
PennWell Corp.
98 Spit Brook Rd.
Nashua, NH 03062-5737
Ph: (603)891-0123
Fax: (603)891-9294
Fr: 800-225-0556
URL: http://www.optoiq.com/index/photonics-technologies-applicati
Monthly. $162.00/year for individuals; $216.00/year

for Canada; $60.00/year for individuals, digital distribution; $270.00/year for other countries. Magazine covering advances and applications in optoelectronics and photonics.

7743 ■ LDB Interior Textiles
E.W. Williams Publications Co.
2125 Center Ave., Ste. 305
Fort Lee, NJ 07024-5898
Ph: (201)592-7007
Fax: (201)592-7171
URL: http://www.ldbinteriortextiles.com

Monthly. $72.00/year for individuals; $125.00/year for Canada; $150.00/year for elsewhere, airmail; $100.00/year for two years; $7.00/year for single issue; $12.00/year for single issue, Canada; $18.00/year for single issue, elsewhere. Magazine for buyers of home fashions, including bed, bath and table linens, hard and soft window treatments, home fragrances, decorative pillows and home accessories, accent rugs, and decorative fabrics.

7744 ■ Managing Automation
Thomas Publishing Co.
5 Penn Plz.
New York, NY 10001
Ph: (212)695-0500
Fax: (212)290-7362
E-mail: contact@thomaspublishing.com
URL: http://www.managingautomation.com/maonline/

Monthly. $60.00/year for individuals; $75.00/year for Canada and Mexico; $125.00/year for other countries. Managing Automation covers advanced manufacturing technology including automation, integrated manufacturing, enterprise applications, and IT and e-business for the manufacturing enterprise.

7745 ■ Manufacturers Representatives of America-Newsline
Manufacturers Representatives of America
PO Box 150229
Arlington, TX 76015
Ph: (682)518-6008
Fax: (682)518-6476
E-mail: assnhqtrs@aol.com
URL: http://www.mra-reps.com/

Description: Monthly. Published for member independent manufacturers' representatives handling sanitary supplies and paper and plastic disposable products. Carries articles to help improve agent sales skills, market coverage, and customer service, and to help establish more effective agent/principal communications. Recurring features include news of members, a calendar of events, job listings, notices of publications available, news of educational opportunities, and a column titled President's Report.

7746 ■ Meat & Poultry
Sosland Publishing Co.
4800 Main St., Ste. 100
Kansas City, MO 64112-2504
Ph: (816)756-1000
Fax: (816)756-0494
Fr: 800-338-6201
URL: http://www.meatpoultry.com

Monthly. Free to qualified subscribers; $85.00/year for other countries, print; $165.00/year for other countries, print, airmail delivery. Magazine serving the meat and poultry processing, distributing, and wholesaling industries in the U.S. and Canada.

7747 ■ Med Ad News
UBM Canon
11444 W Olympic Blvd.
Los Angeles, CA 90064
Fax: (310)445-4200
URL: http://www.pharmalive.com/magazines/medad/

Monthly. $190.00/year for individuals. Pharmaceutical business and marketing magazine.

7748 ■ Milling & Baking News
Sosland Publishing Co.
4800 Main St., Ste. 100
Kansas City, MO 64112-2504
Ph: (816)756-1000
Fax: (816)756-0494
Fr: 800-338-6201
E-mail: mbncirc@sosland.com?subject=mbn
URL: http://www.bakingbusiness.com

Weekly (Tues.). $135.00/year for U.S. and Canada; $210.00/year for U.S. and Canada, 2 years; $290.00/year for U.S. and Canada, 3 years; $190.00/year for out of country; $320.00/year for out of country, 2 years; $455.00/year for out of country, 3 years. Trade magazine covering the grain-based food industries.

7749 ■ Modern Grocer
GC Publishing Company Inc.
744 Main St., Rte. 6A
PO Box 2010
Dennis, MA 02638
Ph: (508)385-7700
Fax: (508)385-0089
URL: http://www.gccomm.net/moderngrocer/index.asp

Monthly. $50.00/year for individuals. Magazine for food retailers, wholesalers, distributors, brokers, manufacturers, and packers in the metro New York and New Jersey marketing area.

7750 ■ Modern Plastics Worldwide
Canon Communications L.L.C.
11444 W Olympic Blvd., Ste. 900
Los Angeles, CA 90064
Ph: (310)445-4200
Fax: (310)445-4299
URL: http://www.modplas.com

Monthly. $59.00/year for individuals; $99.00/year for two years, U.S. and possessions; $110.00/year for Canada; $199.00/year for two years, for Canada; $150.00/year for other countries; $250.00/year for two years. Magazine for the plastics industry.

7751 ■ Money Making Opportunities
Success Publishing International
11071 Ventura Blvd.
Studio City, CA 91604
Ph: (818)980-9166
Fax: (818)980-7829
URL: http://www.moneymakingopps.com/

Free. Magazine Source for small business opportunity seekers.

7752 ■ Multi-Housing News
Multi-Housing News
370 Lexington Ave., Ste. 2100
New York, NY 10017
Ph: (212)977-0041

Monthly. $10.00/year for individuals, cover. Trade magazine (tabloid).

7753 ■ Packaging Digest
Canon Communications L.L.C.
11444 W Olympic Blvd., Ste. 900
Los Angeles, CA 90064
Ph: (310)445-4200
Fax: (310)445-4299
URL: http://www.packagingdigest.com/

Monthly. Business trade magazine for the packaging field.

7754 ■ Paperboard Packaging Worldwide
Questex Media Group
275 Grove St., 2-130
Newton, MA 02466
Ph: (617)219-8300
Fax: (617)219-8310
Fr: 888-552-4346
URL: http://www.packaging-online.com

Monthly. $30.00/year for individuals. Trade magazine for the corrugated container, folding carton, and rigid box converting industry.

7755 ■ *PMA Magazine*

PMA
3000 Picture Pl.
Jackson, MI 49201
Ph: (517)788-8100
Fax: (517)788-8371
Fr: 800-762-9287
URL: http://www.pmai.org/content.aspx?id=8110

Monthly. $50.00/year for individuals; $55.00/year for Canada; $70.00/year for out of country; $5.00/year for single issue; $90.00/year for two years; $100.00/year for two years, Canada; $130.00/year for two years, other countries. Trade magazine for photo/video dealers and photo finishers.

7756 ■ *RV Business*

TL Enterprises Inc.
2575 Vista Del Mar
Ventura, CA 93001
Ph: (805)667-4100
Fax: (805)667-4419
URL: http://www.rvbusiness.com

Monthly. Free. Magazine about the business of manufacturing, distributing, and selling travel trailers, conversion vehicles, and motorhomes and related parts, accessories, and services.

7757 ■ *Sales & Marketing Management*

Nielsen Business Media
770 Broadway
New York, NY 10003-9595
URL: http://www.salesandmarketing.com

Bimonthly. $48.00/year for individuals, print + online; $67.00/year for Canada, print + online; $146.00/year for other countries, print + online. Business magazine.

7758 ■ *Sporting Goods Dealer*

Bill Communications Inc.
1115 Northmeadow Pkwy.
Roswell, GA 30076
Ph: (770)569-1540
Fax: (770)569-5105
Fr: 800-241-9034
URL: http://www.sgdealer.com/sportinggoodsdealer/index.jsp

Bimonthly. Magazine which offers expert reporting on trends affecting team dealers and retailers who service schools, colleges, pro and local teams.

7759 ■ *Timber Harvesting*

Hatton-Brown Publishers Inc.
225 Hanrick St.
PO Box 2268
Montgomery, AL 36102
Ph: (334)834-1170
Fax: (334)834-4525
Fr: 800-669-5613
URL: http://www.timberharvesting.com/

Free to qualified subscribers. National magazine for the U.S. logging industry.

7760 ■ *Transmission Digest*

MD Publications Inc.
3057 E Cairo St.
PO Box 2210
Springfield, MO 65802
Ph: (417)866-3917
Fax: (417)866-2781
Fr: 800-274-7890
URL: http://www.transmissiondigest.com/

Monthly. Automotive transmission industry news.

7761 ■ *TWICE*

NewBay Media, LLC
28 E 28th St., 12th Fl.
New York, NY 10016
Ph: (212)378-0400
Fax: (917)281-4704
URL: http://www.twice.com

Free. Trade tabloid covering consumer electronics, appliance, and camera industries for retailers, manufacturers, and distributors.

7762 ■ *UAMR Confidential Bulletin*

United Association of Manufacturers' Representatives (UAMR)
PO Box 784
Branson, MO 65615
Ph: (417)779-1575
Fax: (417)779-1576
E-mail: info@uamr.com
URL: http://www.uamr.com

Description: Monthly. Covers product lines offered for representation in all fields. Provides details of the company and product, type of accounts to be serviced, and the areas open for representation. Subscription includes bulletin of lines for representatives, articles on rep business, and trade show listings.

7763 ■ *Undercar Digest*

MD Publications Inc.
3057 E Cairo St.
PO Box 2210
Springfield, MO 65802
Ph: (417)866-3917
Fax: (417)866-2781
Fr: 800-274-7890
URL: http://www.undercardigest.com/

Monthly. $49.00/year for individuals. Magazine for the undercar service and supply industry.

7764 ■ *Watch & Jewelry Review*

Golden Bell Press
2403 Champa St.
Denver, CO 80205
Ph: (303)296-1600
Fax: (303)295-2159
URL: http://www.goldenbellpress.com/Pages/front.html

$19.50/year for individuals; $35.00/year for two years; $60.00/year for other countries; $115.00/year for two years, other countries. Magazine on watches and clocks.

7765 ■ *Yard and Garden*

Cygnus Business Media
1233 Janesville Ave.
Fort Atkinson, WI 53538
Ph: (920)563-6388
Fax: (920)563-1702
Fr: 800-547-7377
URL: http://www.cygnusexpos.com/PropertyPub.cfm?PropertyID=117

Yard and garden magazine featuring product news and retailer success stories.

EMPLOYER DIRECTORIES AND NETWORKING LISTS

7766 ■ *American Hardware Manufacturers Association—Rep/Factory Contact Service Directory*

American Hardware Manufacturers Association
801 N Plz. Dr.
Schaumburg, IL 60173
Ph: (847)605-1025
Fax: (847)605-1030
URL: http://www.ahma.org

Annual, April. Covers: Over 280 manufacturer representatives in the hardware industry. Entries include: Firm name, address, number of years in business, number of salespeople, territory covered, manufacturers represented, products or service offered, type of accounts currently served, whether firm has a distribution network or warehouses, whether firm provides in-store service. Arrangement: Geographical. Indexes: Product line, firm name.

7767 ■ *American Wholesalers and Distributors Directory*

Gale
PO Box 6904
Florence, KY 41022-6904

Fr: 800-354-9706
URL: http://www.gale.cengage.com

Annual, Latest edition 22nd; April, 2011. $410.00 for individuals. Covers: Name and address, fax number, SIC code, principal product lines, total number of employees, estimated annual sales volume and principal officers' information of 27,000 large and small wholesalers and distributors in the U.S. and Puerto Rico. Arrangement: By broad subject from principal product line, by Standard Industrial Classification code (SIC index), by state and city (geographical index), and by company name (alphabetic index). Indexes: SIC, geographical, alphabetical.

7768 ■ *Bacon's Radio/TV/Cable Directory, Volume 1*

Cision US Inc.
332 S Michigan Ave., Ste. 900
Chicago, IL 60604
Ph: (312)363-9793
Fax: (312)922-9387
Fr: (866)639-5087
URL: http://us.cision.com

Annual, Latest edition 2012. $650.00 for individuals. Covers: over 13,500 radio and television stations, including college radio and public television stations, and cable companies. Entries include: For radio and television stations—Call letters, address, phone, names and titles of key personnel, programs, times broadcast, name of contact, network affiliation, frequency or channel number, target audience data. For cable companies—Name, address, phone, description of activities. Arrangement: Geographical.

7769 ■ *Career Ideas for Teens in Manufacturing*

Facts On File Inc.
132 W 31st St., 17th Fl.
New York, NY 10001
Ph: (212)967-8800
Fax: 800-678-3633
Fr: 800-322-8755
URL: http://www.infobasepublishing.com

Published August, 2005. $40.00 for individuals. Covers: A multitude of career possibilities based on a teenager's specific interests and skills and links his/her talents to a wide variety of actual professions.

7770 ■ *Careers in Focus—Manufacturing*

Facts On File Inc.
132 W 31st St., 17th Fl.
New York, NY 10001
Ph: (212)967-8800
Fax: 800-678-3633
Fr: 800-322-8755
URL: http://www.infobasepublishing.com

Latest edition 3rd; Published February, 2008. $32.95 for individuals. Covers: An overview of manufacturing, followed by a selection of jobs profiled in detail, including the nature of the job, earnings, prospects for employment, what kind of training and skills it requires, and sources for further information.

7771 ■ *Electrical Equipment Representatives Association—Membership Directory*

Electrical Equipment Representatives Association
638 W 39th St.
Kansas City, MO 64111
Ph: (816)561-5323
Fax: (816)561-1249
URL: http://www.eera.org

Continuous. Free. Covers: More than 105 manufacturers' representatives of electrical equipment companies. Entries include: Company name, address, phone, names and titles of key personnel. Arrangement: Alphabetical.

7772 ■ *Equipment Marketing and Distribution Association—Membership Directory*

Equipment Marketing & Distribution Association
PO Box 1347
Iowa City, IA 52244

Ph: (319)354-5156
Fax: (319)354-5157
URL: http://www.emda.net/directory.htm

Annual. Covers: 120 members; coverage includes Canada. Entries include: Company name, address, phone, name of principal executive, territory covered. Arrangement: Alphabetical.

7773 ■ Gift and Decorative Accessories Center Association—Directory
Gift and Decorative Accessories Center Association
360 Park Ave. S
New York, NY 10010
Ph: (646)746-6400
Fax: (646)746-7431
Fr: 800-309-3332
URL: http://www.giftsanddec.com

Continuous. Free. Covers: About 60 individuals who are giftware manufacturers' representatives in New England; also lists their manufacturers and suppliers. Entries include: For representatives—Name, address, phone, e-mail, manufacturers and products represented. Arrangement: Alphabetical.

7774 ■ The Locator—The Electronics Representatives Directory/Electronics Industry Calendar
Electronics Representatives Association
300 W Adams St., Ste. 617
Chicago, IL 60606
Ph: (312)527-3050
Fax: (312)527-3783
URL: http://www.era.org

Annual, October. Covers: 1,400 member and approximately 4,000 nonmember firms and 500 electronics industry trade shows; international coverage. Entries include: Firm name, address, phone; names of owners; facilities; states in territory; association divisional memberships; number of employees; branch offices' addresses, phone numbers, fax, and names of managers. Type of product handled is shown in separate tabulation at beginning of each chapter section. Arrangement: Geographical, by chapter. Indexes: Key personnel name, company.

7775 ■ Manufacturers' Agents National Association—Directory of Manufacturers' Sales Agencies
Manufacturers' Agents National Association
16 A Journey, Ste. 200
Aliso Viejo, CA 92656-3317
Ph: (949)859-4040
Fax: (949)855-2973
Fr: 877-626-2776
URL: http://www.manaonline.org

Online Directory. Covers: 4,000 independent agents and firms representing manufacturers and other businesses in specified territories on a commission basis, including consultants and associate member firms interested in the manufacturer/agency method of marketing. Entries include: For manufacturers—Company name, address, phone, fax, E-mail, URL, name of contact, product. For agencies—Agency name, address, phone, fax, E-mail, URL, name of contact, warehouse facilities, territory covered, number of field sales representatives, branch office location, year established, date of joining association. Arrangement: Separate alphabetical sections for manufacturers and agencies. Indexes: Geographic, target industries.

7776 ■ Manufacturers Representatives of America—Yearbook and Directory of Members
Manufacturers Representatives of America
PO Box 150229
Arlington, TX 76015
Ph: (682)518-6008
Fax: (682)518-6476
URL: http://www.mra-reps.com/lookup.asp

Annual, fall. Covers: Several hundred independent manufacturers' representatives in paper, plastic, packaging, and sanitary supplies. Entries include: Name, address, phone, distributors served, territory,

number of persons in sales, branch offices, products handled, marketing services provided, warehouse locations and facilities. Arrangement: Geographical. Indexes: Organization, personal name.

7777 ■ Thomas Register of American Manufacturers
Thomas Publishing Co.
5 Penn Plz.
New York, NY 10001
Ph: (212)695-0500
Fax: (212)290-7362
URL: http://www.thomasregister.com

Annual, January. More than 168,000 manufacturing firms are listed in this 34 volume set. Volumes 1-23 list the firms under 68,000 product headings. Thomas Register is enhanced with over 8,000 manufacturers' catalogs and is available in print, CD-ROM, DVD or online. Logistics Guide, a reference manual for freight and shipping sourcing. Arrangement: Volumes 1-23, classified by product or service; Volumes 24-26 alphabetical by company; Volumes 27-34 company catalogs alphabetical by company. Indexes: Product/service, brand/trade name (volume 22).

7778 ■ The Wholesaler—'The Wholesaling 100' Issue
TMB Publishing Inc.
1838 Techny Ct.
Northbrook, IL 60062
Ph: (847)564-1127
URL: http://www.plumbingengineer.com

Annual, July. $50.00 for individuals. Publication includes: Ranks 100 leading wholesalers of plumbing, heating, air conditioning, refrigeration equipment, and industrial pipe, valves and fittings. Entries include: Company name, address, phone, fax, names and titles of key personnel, number of employees, business breakdown (percentage). Arrangement: Ranked by sales.

HANDBOOKS AND MANUALS

7779 ■ Great Jobs for Business Majors
The McGraw-Hill Companies
PO Box 182604
Columbus, OH 43272
Fax: (614)759-3749
Fr: 877-883-5524
E-mail: customer.service@mcgraw-hill.com
URL: http://www.mhprofessional.com/
product.php?isbn=0071544836

Stephen Lambert. Third edition, 2008. $16.95 (paper). 240 pages.

7780 ■ Opportunities in Marketing Careers
The McGraw-Hill Companies
PO Box 182604
Columbus, OH 43272
Fax: (614)759-3749
Fr: 877-883-5524
E-mail: customer.service@mcgraw-hill.com
URL: http://www.mhprofessional.com/
product.php?isbn=0071448985

Margery Steinberg. 2005. $13.95 (paper). 176. Gives guidance on identifying and pursuing job opportunities. Illustrated.

EMPLOYMENT AGENCIES AND SEARCH FIRMS

7781 ■ Bender Executive Search
45 N Station Plaza, Ste. 315
Great Neck, NY 11021
Ph: (516)773-4300
Fax: (516)482-5355
E-mail: benderexec@aol.com
URL: http://www.benderexecutivesearch.com

Executive search firm.

7782 ■ The Caler Group
23337 Lago Mar Cir.
Boca Raton, FL 33433
Ph: (561)394-8045
Fax: (561)394-4645
URL: http://www.calergroup.com

Executive search firm.

7783 ■ Cizek Associates Inc.
2415 E Camelback Rd., Ste. 700
Phoenix, AZ 85016
Ph: (602)553-1066
Fax: (602)553-1166
E-mail: phx@cizekassociates.com
URL: http://www.cizekassociates.com

Executive search firm. Also maintains offices in Chicago and San Francisco.

7784 ■ Clarey Andrews & Klein Inc.
1347 Hillside Rd.
Northbrook, IL 60062
Ph: (847)498-2870
E-mail: cak@clarey-a-klein.com
URL: http://www.clarey-a-klein.com

Executive search firm.

7785 ■ The Dalley Hewitt Company
PO Box 19973
Atlanta, GA 30325
Ph: (404)992-5065
Fax: (404)355-6136
E-mail: rives@dalleyhewitt.com
URL: http://www.dalleyhewitt.com

Executive search firm.

7786 ■ DMR Global Inc.
10230 W Sample Rd.
Coral Springs, FL 33065
Ph: (954)796-5043
Fax: (954)796-5044
Fr: 888-796-0032
E-mail: rdaratany@dmrglobal.com
URL: http://www.dmrglobal.com

Executive search firm.

7787 ■ Egan & Associates Inc.
White House Ctr.
1784 Barton Ave., Ste. 10
West Bend, WI 53095
Ph: (262)335-0707
Fax: (262)335-0625
E-mail: info@eganassociates.com
URL: http://www.eganassociates.com

Executive search firm.

7788 ■ Executive Search International
1525 Centre St.
Newton, MA 02461-1200
Ph: (617)527-8787
E-mail: contactus@execsearchintl.com
URL: http://www.execsearchintl.com

Executive search firm.

7789 ■ Fairfield
Trump Tower
721 5th Ave.
New York, NY 10022-2523
Ph: (212)838-0220
E-mail: newyork@fairfield.ch
URL: http://www.fairfield.ch

Executive search firm specializing in retail and apparel manufacturing.

7790 ■ Highlander Search Inc.
1901 Lendew St., Ste. 9
PO Box 4163
Greensboro, NC 27408-7034
Ph: (336)333-9886
Fax: (336)574-8305
E-mail: jphighlander@mindspring.com

Conducts retained search of technical and staff level professionals. Contingency search services available.

Also provides counseling of salaried work force caught in RIF's, and job search and resume preparation. Instruction is offered on an individual basis. Industries served: manufacturing, automotive and furniture industry worldwide. Consulting services in organizational and human resource areas.

7791 ■ James Drury Partners
875 N Michigan Ave., Ste. 3805
Chicago, IL 60611
Ph: (312)654-6708
Fax: (312)654-6710
E-mail: resume@jdrurypartners.com
URL: http://www.jdrurypartners.com
Executive search firm.

7792 ■ National Register - USA
550 Polaris Pkwy., Ste. 530
Westerville, OH 43082
Ph: (614)890-1200
Fax: (614)890-1259
E-mail: sales@nrcols.com
URL: http://www.nrcols.com
Employment agency. Offices in Akron and Toledo, OH.

7793 ■ Sales Executives Inc.
33900 W 8 Mile Rd., Ste. 171
Farmington Hills, MI 48335
Ph: (248)615-0100
E-mail: dale@salesexecutives.com
URL: http://www.salesexecutives.com
Employment agency. Executive search firm.

7794 ■ SalesPositions.com
Heather Croft
Ste. 250
Egg Harbor Township, NY 08234
Ph: (609)407-4774
Fax: (609)939-0488
E-mail: sales@salespositions.com
URL: http://www.salespositions.com
Employment agency.

7795 ■ Wellington Executive Search
3162 Johnson Ferry Rd., Ste. 260
Marietta, GA 30062
Ph: (770)645-5799
Fax: (678)278-0928
E-mail: jobs@wellingtonsearch.com
URL: http://www.wellingtonsearch.com
Serves as an executive search firm covering sales representative, research and development, food scientists, and purchasing managers.

TRADESHOWS

7796 ■ Marketing Seminar Conference
Manufacturers Agents Association for the Foodservice Industry MAFSI
1199 Euclid Ave.
Atlanta, GA 30307
Ph: (404)214-9474
Fax: (404)522-0132
E-mail: info@mafsi.org
URL: http://www.mafsi.org
Annual. Primary Exhibits: Manufacturers' representative equipment, furnishings, and supplies for dealers and users.

OTHER SOURCES

7797 ■ American Wholesale Marketers Association (AWMA)
2750 Prosperity Ave., Ste. 530
Fairfax, VA 22031
Ph: (703)208-3358

Fax: (703)573-5738
Fr: 800-482-2962
E-mail: info@awmanet.org
URL: http://www.awmanet.org
Description: Represents the interests of distributors of convenience-related products. Its members include wholesalers, retailers, manufacturers, brokers and allied organizations from across the U.S. and abroad. Programs include strong legislative representation in Washington and a broad spectrum of targeted education, business and information services. Sponsors the country's largest show for candy and convenience related products in conjunction with its semi-annual convention.

7798 ■ Asian America MultiTechnology Association (AAMA)
3 W 37th Ave., Ste. 19
San Mateo, CA 94403-4470
Ph: (650)350-1124
E-mail: aama@aamasv.com
URL: http://www.aamasv.com
Description: Promotes the success of the Asia America region's technology enterprises. Through its diverse programs ranging from monthly Speakers Series to the Asia-Silicon Valley Technology Investment Conference. Provides a forum in which members can network, exchange ideas and share resources to promote and build one another's companies and careers, ultimately benefiting the larger Pacific Rim technological community.

7799 ■ Association of Independent Manufacturers'/Representatives (AIM/R)
16 A Journey, Ste. 200
Aliso Viejo, CA 92656
Ph: (949)859-2884
Fax: (949)855-2973
Fr: (866)729-0975
E-mail: info@aimr.net
URL: http://www.aimr.net
Description: Manufacturers' representative companies in the plumbing-heating-cooling-piping industry promoting the use of independent sales representatives. Conducts educational programs and establishes a code of ethics between members and customers.

7800 ■ Automotive Aftermarket Industry Association (AAIA)
7101 Wisconsin Ave., Ste. 1300
Bethesda, MD 20814-3415
Ph: (301)654-6664
Fax: (301)654-3299
E-mail: aaia@aftermarket.org
URL: http://www.aftermarket.org
Description: Automotive parts and accessories retailers, distributors, manufacturers, and manufacturers' representatives. Conducts research and compiles statistics. Conducts seminars and provides specialized education program.

7801 ■ Computing Technology Industry Association (CompTIA)
3500 Lacey Rd., Ste. 100
Downers Grove, IL 60515
Ph: (630)678-8300
Fax: (630)678-8384
E-mail: membership@comptia.org
URL: http://www.comptia.org
Description: Trade association of more than 19,000 companies and professional IT members in the rapidly converging computing and communications market. Has members in more than 89 countries and provides a unified voice for the industry in the areas of e-commerce standards, vendor-neutral certification, service metrics, public policy and workforce development. Serves as information clearinghouse and resource for the industry; sponsors educational programs.

7802 ■ Manufacturers' Agents National Association (MANA)
16 A Journey, Ste. 200
Aliso Viejo, CA 92656-3317
Ph: (949)859-4040
Fax: (949)855-2973
Fr: 877-626-2776
E-mail: mana@manaonline.org
URL: http://www.manaonline.org
Description: Manufacturers' agents in all fields representing two or more manufacturers on a commission basis; associate members are manufacturers and others interested in improving the agent-principal relationship. Maintains code of ethics and rules of business and professional conduct; issues model standard form of agreement.

7803 ■ National Association of Chain Drug Stores (NACDS)
413 N Lee St.
Alexandria, VA 22314
Ph: (703)549-3001
Fax: (703)683-1451
URL: http://www.nacds.org
Description: Represents the concerns of community pharmacies in Washington, in state capitals, and across the country. Members are more than 210 chain community pharmacy companies. Collectively, community pharmacy comprises the largest component of pharmacy practice with over 107,000 FTE pharmacists.

7804 ■ National Electrical Manufacturers Representatives Association (NEMRA)
28 Deer St., Ste. 302
Portsmouth, NH 03801
Ph: (914)524-8650
Fax: (914)524-8655
Fr: 800-446-3672
E-mail: nemra@nemra.org
URL: http://www.nemra.org
Description: Purpose: North American trade association dedicated to promoting continuing education, professionalism, and the use of independent manufacturers representatives in the electrical industry. Offers professional development programs in business management and sales training, and offers a proprietary computer system for independent electrical representatives. Sponsors educational programs; compiles statistics; and holds an annual networking conference for its representative members and their manufacturers.

7805 ■ National Marine Representatives Association (NMRA)
PO Box 360
Gurnee, IL 60031
Ph: (847)662-3167
Fax: (847)336-7126
E-mail: info@nmraonline.org
URL: http://www.nmraonline.org
Description: Works to serve the marine industry independent sales representatives and the manufacturers selling through representatives. Serves as industry voice, networking tool and information source promoting benefits of utilizing independent marine representatives for sales. Aims to assist manufacturers find the right marine sales reps for product lines.

7806 ■ Retail Industry Leaders Association
1700 N Moore St., Ste. 2250
Arlington, VA 22209
Ph: (703)841-2300
Fax: (703)841-1184
URL: http://www.rila.org
Description: Represents retailers, product manufacturers, and associate companies. Promotes consumer choice and economic freedom through public policy and industry operational excellence. Focuses on five core areas: supply chain, asset protection, finance, human resources, and enterprise issues. Provides educational and networking events that provide forums for sharing ideas and expertise among peers and industry experts.

SOURCES OF HELP-WANTED ADS

7807 ■ BtoB Magazine
Crain Communications Inc.
360 N Michigan Ave.
Chicago, IL 60601
Ph: (312)649-5200
URL: http://www.btobonline.com

Monthly. $59.00/year for individuals; $69.00/year for Canada; $89.00/year for other countries. Trade magazine on business-to-business marketing news, strategy, and tactics.

7808 ■ Direct Marketing Magazine
Hoke Communications Inc.
224 7th St.
Garden City, NY 11530
Ph: (516)746-6700
URL: http://www.directmarketingmag.com/

Monthly. $60.00/year for individuals; $6.00/year for single issue. Direct response advertising magazine.

7809 ■ DM News
DM News
114 W 26th St., 4th Fl.
New York, NY 10001
Ph: (646)638-6000
Fax: (646)638-6159
E-mail: inquiry@dmnews.com
URL: http://www.dmnews.com/

Weekly. $148.00/year for individuals; $198.00/year for Canada; $228.00/year for other countries; $265.00/year for two years; $355.00/year for Canada, 2 years; $395.00/year for other countries, 2 years. Tabloid newspaper for publishers, fund raisers, financial marketers, catalogers, package goods advertisers and their agencies, and other marketers who use direct mail, mail order advertising, catalogs, or other direct response media to sell their products or services.

7810 ■ Marketing News
American Marketing Association
311 S Wacker Dr., Ste. 5800
Chicago, IL 60606
Ph: (312)542-9000
Fax: (312)542-9001
Fr: 800-262-1150
URL: http://www.marketingpower.com/AboutAMA/
   Pages/AMA%20Publicati

$35.00/year for members; $100.00/year for nonmembers; $130.00/year for institutions, libraries and corporations; $3.00/year for single issue, individuals; $5.00/year for single issue, institutions; $140.00/year for institutions, other countries, extra for air delivery. Business magazine focusing on current marketing trends.

7811 ■ Quirk's Marketing Research Review
Quirk Enterprises Inc.
4662 Slater Rd.
Eagan, MN 55122
Ph: (651)379-6200
URL: http://www.quirks.com

Trade publication for the marketing research industry.

7812 ■ Sales & Marketing Management
Nielsen Business Media
770 Broadway
New York, NY 10003-9595
URL: http://www.salesandmarketing.com

Bimonthly. $48.00/year for individuals, print + online; $67.00/year for Canada, print + online; $146.00/year for other countries, print + online. Business magazine.

PLACEMENT AND JOB REFERRAL SERVICES

7813 ■ Morgan Search LLC
1424 Lincoln Blvd., Ste. A
Santa Monica, CA 90401
Ph: (310)393-3366
Fax: (310)458-1886
E-mail: info@morgansearch.com
URL: http://www.morgansearch.com

Placement firm for market research and brand communications professionals.

EMPLOYER DIRECTORIES AND NETWORKING LISTS

7814 ■ Bradford's International Directory of Marketing Research Agencies
Business Research Services Inc.
7720 Wisconsin Ave., Ste. 213
Bethesda, MD 20814
Ph: (301)229-5561
Fax: (301)229-6133
Fr: 800-845-8420
E-mail: verify@bradfordsdirectory.com
URL: http://www.bradfordsdirectory.com

Biennial, Latest edition 30th. $95.00 for individuals; $95.00 for individuals; $125.00 for individuals. Covers: Over 2,300 marketing research agencies worldwide. Includes domestic and international demographic data and professional association contacts. Entries include: Company name, address, phone, name and title of contact, date founded, number of employees, description of products or services, e-mail, URL. Arrangement: Geographical. Indexes: Alphabetical by company.

7815 ■ GreenBook Worldwide—Directory of Marketing Research Companies and Services
New York AMA Communication Services Inc.
116 E 27th St., 6th Fl.
New York, NY 10016

Ph: (212)849-2752
Fax: (212)202-7920
Fr: 800-792-9202
URL: http://www.greenbook.org

Annual, Latest edition 49th; 2011. $180.00; $15.00 for individuals; $38.00 for other countries. Covers: 1,600 marketing research companies worldwide (computer services, interviewing services, etc.) of marketing research needs; international coverage. Includes a list of computer programs for marketing research. Entries include: Company name, address, phone, name of principal executive, products and services, branch offices. Arrangement: Alphabetical. Indexes: Geographical, principal executive name, research services, market/industry served, computer program name, trademark/servicemarks.

7816 ■ MRA Blue Book Research Services Directory
Marketing Research Association
110 National Dr., 2nd Fl.
Glastonbury, CT 06033-1212
Ph: (860)682-1000
Fax: (866)512-1050
E-mail: bluebook@mra-net.org
URL: http://www.bluebook.org

Annual, latest edition 2012. $170.00 for nonmembers; $100.00 for members. Covers: Over 1,200 marketing research companies and field interviewing services. Entries include: Company name, address, phone, names of executives, services, facilities, special interviewing capabilities. Arrangement: Geographical; business type. Indexes: Geographic and by specialty.

7817 ■ Quirk's Marketing Research Review—Researcher SourceBook Issue
Quirk Enterprises Inc.
4662 Slater Rd.
Eagan, MN 55122
Ph: (651)379-6200
URL: http://www.quirks.com

Annual, Latest edition 2011-2012. $70.00 for individuals; $119.00 for individuals; $100.00 for individuals. Covers: About 7,100 organizations providing marketing research products and services. Entries include: Name, address, phone, fax, contact, research specialties, URL, e-mail. Arrangement: Geographical. Indexes: Personnel, industry specialization, research specialization, alphabetic.

HANDBOOKS AND MANUALS

7818 ■ Careers in Marketing
The McGraw-Hill Companies
PO Box 182604
Columbus, OH 43272
Fax: (614)759-3749
Fr: 877-883-5524
E-mail: customer.service@mcgraw-hill.com
URL: http://www.mhprofessional.com/
   product.php?isbn=0071493123

Leslie Stair. 2008. $16.95 (paper). 192 pages. Surveys career opportunities in marketing and related areas such as marketing research, product development, and sales promotion. Includes a description of the work, places of employment, employment outlook, trends, and salaries. Offers job hunting advice.

7819 ■ *Great Jobs for History Majors*
The McGraw-Hill Companies
PO Box 182604
Columbus, OH 43272
Fax: (614)759-3749
Fr: 877-883-5524
E-mail: customer.service@mcgraw-hill.com
URL: http://www.mhprofessional.com

Julie DeGalan and Stephen Lambert. 2007. $16.95 (paper). 192 pages.

7820 ■ *Marketing Research Tools and Techniques*
Oxford University Press
198 Madison Ave.
New York, NY 10016
Ph: (212)726-6000
URL: http://www.oup.com/us/

Nigel Bradley. 2010. $79.95 (paperback). 560 pages. 2nd edition. Provides insight into marketing research. Covers basic tools of marketing research, and evaluates techniques applicable to a specific research. Includes sample questionnaires and case studies in accompanying online resource centre.

7821 ■ *Opportunities in Direct Marketing*
The McGraw-Hill Companies
PO Box 182604
Columbus, OH 43272
Fax: (614)759-3749
Fr: 877-883-5524
E-mail: customer.service@mcgraw-hill.com
URL: http://www.mhprofessional.com/
   product.php?isbn=0071493085

Anne Basye. 2008. $14.95 (paper). 160 pages. Examines opportunities with direct marketers, catalog companies, direct marketing agencies, telemarketing firms, mailing list brokers, and database marketing companies. Describes how to prepare for a career in direct marketing and how to break into the field. Includes sources of short-term professional training.

7822 ■ *Opportunities in Marketing Careers*
The McGraw-Hill Companies
PO Box 182604
Columbus, OH 43272
Fax: (614)759-3749
Fr: 877-883-5524
E-mail: customer.service@mcgraw-hill.com
URL: http://www.mhprofessional.com/
   product.php?isbn=0071448985

Margery Steinberg. 2005. $13.95 (paper). 176. Gives guidance on identifying and pursuing job opportunities. Illustrated.

EMPLOYMENT AGENCIES AND SEARCH FIRMS

7823 ■ Analytic Recruiting, Inc.
144 E 44th St., 3rd Fl.
New York, NY 10017
Ph: (212)545-8511
E-mail: email@analyticrecruiting.com
URL: http://www.analyticrecruiting.com

Executive search firm.

7824 ■ Fristoe & Carleton
4589 Rockridge Way
Copley, OH 44321
Ph: (216)916-9331
E-mail: fc@adjob.com
URL: http://www.adjob.com

Description: Provides job placement services for candidates who have at least two years plus ad

agency, public relations, sales promotion, direct marketing or client-side marketing experience.

7825 ■ Marketing Pro Resources, Inc.
PO Box 1686
New York, NY 10021
Ph: (212)472-5310
Fax: (212)879-1206
E-mail: info@marketingproresources.com
URL: http://www.marketingproresources.com

Description: Provides professional staffing of temporary and permanent positions in marketing, communications, advertising, public relations, market research, analytics and more.

ONLINE JOB SOURCES AND SERVICES

7826 ■ Marketing Research Association - Career Center
URL: http://www.marketingresearch.org/career

Description: Offers current job openings and career guide in the field of marketing research. Allows employers to view resumes and post jobs.

7827 ■ MarketResearchCareers.com
URL: http://www.marketresearchcareers.com

Description: Focuses exclusively on the market research industry. Offers a comprehensive database of resumes and jobs dedicated to market research professionals. Provides online services to fill marketing research jobs with a selection of qualified professionals.

7828 ■ National Employment Minority Network
URL: http://www.nemnet.com

Description: Features different kinds of resources for the marketing research field. Maintains a listing of market research and market research related companies, as well as an employment board for interested job seekers.

7829 ■ ResearchInfo.com
URL: http://www.researchinfo.com

Description: Offers free market research and marketing research resources. Includes market research job listings.

7830 ■ ResearchingCrossing.com
URL: http://www.researchingcrossing.com

Description: Offers a collection of top research job openings; includes the lists of employer career pages, job websites, newspaper classifieds and recruitment sites.

OTHER SOURCES

7831 ■ Academy of Marketing Science (AMS)
PO Box 3072
Ruston, LA 71272
Ph: (318)257-2612
Fax: (318)257-4253
E-mail: ams@latech.edu
URL: http://www.ams-web.org

Description: Marketing academicians and practitioners; individuals interested in fostering education in marketing science. Aims to promote the advancement of knowledge and the furthering of professional standards in the field of marketing. Explores the special application areas of marketing science and its responsibilities as an economic, ethical, and social force; promotes research and the widespread dissemination of findings. Facilitates exchange of information and experience among members, and the transfer of marketing knowledge and technology to developing countries; promotes marketing science on an international level. Provides a forum for discussion and refinement of concepts, methods and applications, and the opportunity to publish papers in

the field. Assists member educators in the development of improved teaching methods, devices, directions, and materials. Offers guidance and direction in marketing practice and reviewer assistance on scholarly works. Contributes to the solution of marketing problems encountered by individual firms, industries, and society as a whole. Encourages members to utilize their marketing talents to the fullest through redirection, reassignment, and relocation. Sponsors competitions.

7832 ■ American Marketing Association (AMA)
311 S Wacker Dr., Ste. 5800
Chicago, IL 60606
Ph: (312)542-9000
Fax: (312)542-9001
Fr: 800-262-1150
E-mail: info@ama.org
URL: http://www.marketingpower.com

Description: Serves as a professional society of marketing and market research executives, sales and promotion managers, advertising specialists, academics, and others interested in marketing. Fosters research; sponsors seminars, conferences, and student marketing clubs; provides educational placement service and doctoral consortium.

7833 ■ Marketing Agencies Association Worldwide (MAA)
89 Woodland Cir.
Minneapolis, MN 55424
Ph: (952)922-0130
Fax: (760)437-4141
E-mail: keith.mccracken@maaw.org
URL: http://www.maaw.org

Description: Represents the interests of CEOs, presidents, managing directors and principals of top marketing services agencies. Provides opportunity for marketing professionals to meet with peers, raise company profile on both a national and a global platform, and influence the future of industry. Fosters networking through conferences.

7834 ■ Marketing Research Association (MRA)
110 National Dr., 2nd Fl.
Glastonbury, CT 06033-1212
Ph: (860)682-1000
Fax: (860)682-1050
E-mail: email@mra-net.org
URL: http://www.mra-net.org

Description: Companies and individuals involved in any area of opinion and marketing research, such as data collection, research, or as an end-user.

7835 ■ Mobile Compass
Discovery Research Group
6975 Union Park Ctr., Ste. 450
Midvale, UT 84047
Fr: 800-678-3748
URL: http://www.discoveryresearchgroup.com

Description: Serves as research tool that helps to effectively reach market research respondents who are increasingly difficult to identify.

7836 ■ Society for Marketing Professional Services (SMPS)
44 Canal Center Plz., Ste. 444
Alexandria, VA 22314
Ph: (703)549-6117
Fax: (703)549-2498
Fr: 800-292-7677
E-mail: info@smps.org
URL: http://www.smps.org

Description: Marketing employees of architectural, engineering, planning, interior design, landscape architectural, and construction management firms who are responsible for the new business development of their companies. Compiles statistics. Offers local and national educational programs; maintains certification program.

SOURCES OF HELP-WANTED ADS

7837 ■ Advertising Age
Crain Communications
711 Third Ave.
New York, NY 10017-4036
Ph: (212)210-0100
Fax: (212)210-0200
E-mail: rcrain@adage.com
URL: http://adage.com/index.php

Weekly. $99/year print, digital and online editions. Features news and intelligence on advertising, marketing and media. Contains job opportunities, editorial insights and exclusive analysis. Gives news in IT context to help readers understand ongoing and emerging trends.

7838 ■ Adweek
Nielsen Business Media
770 Broadway
New York, NY 10003-9595
URL: http://www.adweek.com/

Weekly. $299.00/year for individuals, print & online; $24.95/year for individuals, print & online per month; $19.95/year for individuals, online per month; $149.95/year for individuals, digital edition access. Advertising news magazine.

7839 ■ Adweek/New England
Adweek L.P.
100 Boylston St., Ste. 210
Boston, MA 02116
Fr: 800-641-2030
URL: http://www.adweek.com

Weekly. $299.00/year for individuals, print and online; $149.00/year for individuals, digital access only; $24.95/year for individuals, monthly, print + online; $19.95/year for individuals, monthly, online only. News magazine serving the advertising, marketing, and media industries in New England.

7840 ■ B2B MarketingTrends
Penton Media Inc.
249 W 17th St.
New York, NY 10011
Ph: (212)204-4200
URL: http://www.b2bmarketingtrends.com/pdfs/B2BMediaKit.pdf

Quarterly. Free to qualified subscribers. Magazine that covers business-to-business marketing.

7841 ■ BtoB Magazine
Crain Communications Inc.
360 N Michigan Ave.
Chicago, IL 60601
Ph: (312)649-5200
URL: http://www.btobonline.com

Monthly. $59.00/year for individuals; $69.00/year for Canada; $89.00/year for other countries. Trade magazine on business-to-business marketing news, strategy, and tactics.

7842 ■ The Counselor
Advertising Specialty Institute
4800 St. Rd.
Trevose, PA 19053
Ph: (215)953-4000
Fr: 800-546-1350
URL: http://www.asicentral.com/asp/open/news/counselor/index.asp

$75.00/year for individuals; $150.00/year for other countries. Magazine.

7843 ■ Creativity
Crain Communications Inc.
1155 Gratiot Ave.
Detroit, MI 48207-2997
Ph: (313)446-6000
URL: http://creativity-online.com/

Monthly. Magazine featuring insight and information for creative leaders involved in all aspects of advertising and design.

7844 ■ Direct Marketing Magazine
Hoke Communications Inc.
224 7th St.
Garden City, NY 11530
Ph: (516)746-6700
URL: http://www.directmarketingmag.com/

Monthly. $60.00/year for individuals; $6.00/year for single issue. Direct response advertising magazine.

7845 ■ DM News
DM News
114 W 26th St., 4th Fl.
New York, NY 10001
Ph: (646)638-6000
Fax: (646)638-6159
E-mail: inquiry@dmnews.com
URL: http://www.dmnews.com/

Weekly. $148.00/year for individuals; $198.00/year for Canada; $228.00/year for other countries; $265.00/year for two years; $355.00/year for Canada, 2 years; $395.00/year for other countries, 2 years. Tabloid newspaper for publishers, fund raisers, financial marketers, catalogers, package goods advertisers and their agencies, and other marketers who use direct mail, mail order advertising, catalogs, or other direct response media to sell their products or services.

7846 ■ Editor & Publisher
Editor & Publisher Magazine
17782 Cowan, Ste. A
Irvine, CA 92614
Ph: (949)660-6150
Fax: (949)660-6172
URL: http://www.editorandpublisher.com/

Weekly (Mon.). $65.00/year for individuals, print and online; $125.00/year for two years, print and online; $85.00/year for other countries; $49.00/year for individuals, digital only. Magazine focusing on newspaper journalism, advertising, printing equipment and interactive services.

7847 ■ Event Marketer
Red 7 Media Inc.
10 Norden Pl.
Norwalk, CT 06855
Ph: (203)854-6730
Fax: (203)854-6735
URL: http://www.eventmarketer.com

$45.00/year for individuals; $106.00/year for Canada and Mexico; $116.00/year for other countries. Magazine for brand-side event marketers and face-to-face media agency executives.

7848 ■ Foundations and Trends in Marketing
Now Publishers
PO Box 1024
Hanover, MA 02339-1001
Ph: (781)871-0245
URL: http://www.worldscinet.com/ftmkt/mkt/editorial.shtml

Weekly. $390.00/year for institutions, electronic; $450.00/year for institutions, combined; $390.00/year for institutions, electronic; $450.00/year for institutions, combined. Journal covering business to business marketing, Bayesian models, behavioral decision making, branding and brand equity, channel management, choice modeling, comparative market structure and competitive marketing strategy.

7849 ■ Franchising World
International Franchise Association
1501 K St. NW, Ste. 350
Washington, DC 20005
Ph: (202)628-8000
Fax: (202)628-0812
Fr: 800-543-1038
URL: http://www.franchise.org/

Monthly. $50.00/year for individuals. Trade magazine covering topics of interest to franchise company executives and the business world.

7850 ■ Marketing News
American Marketing Association
311 S Wacker Dr., Ste. 5800
Chicago, IL 60606
Ph: (312)542-9000
Fax: (312)542-9001
Fr: 800-262-1150
URL: http://www.marketingpower.com/AboutAMA/Pages/AMA%20Publicati

$35.00/year for members; $100.00/year for nonmembers; $130.00/year for institutions, libraries and corporations; $3.00/year for single issue, individuals; $5.00/year for single issue, institutions; $140.00/year for institutions, other countries, extra for air delivery. Business magazine focusing on current marketing trends.

7851 ■ Media Relations Report
Lawrence Ragan Communications Inc.
111 E Wacker Dr., Ste. 500
Chicago, IL 60601
Ph: (312)960-4100
Fax: (312)861-3592
Fr: 800-878-5331
E-mail: cservice@ragan.com
URL: http://www.ragan.com

Description: Monthly. Covers advertising and public relations media placement. Topics include placement opportunities, media news, pitching media campaigns, targeting ads, press releases, and others.

7852 ■ Media Week
Nielsen Business Media
770 Broadway
New York, NY 10003-9595
URL: http://www.mediaweek.com/mw/index.jsp

$24.95/year for individuals, monthly, print & online; $149.00/year for individuals, print & online; $19.95/year for individuals, monthly, online; $149.95/year individuals, digital edition. Weekly magazine covering the media decision-makers at the top 350 ad agencies and all top media buying services and client media departments in the U.S.

7853 ■ Multichannel Merchant
Penton Media Inc.
9800 Metcalf Ave.
Overland Park, KS 66212
Ph: (913)341-1300
Fax: (913)967-1898
URL: http://multichannelmerchant.com

Magazine for marketing and advertising professionals that covers print, web, and cross-channel marketing.

7854 ■ Package Design Magazine
ST Media Group International Inc.
11262 Cornell Park Dr.
Cincinnati, OH 45242
Ph: (513)421-2050
Fax: (513)421-5144
Fr: 800-421-1321
URL: http://www.packagedesignmag.com/

Free to qualified subscribers. Magazine that covers marketing and branding through package design.

7855 ■ Quirk's Marketing Research Review
Quirk Enterprises Inc.
4662 Slater Rd.
Eagan, MN 55122
Ph: (651)379-6200
URL: http://www.quirks.com

Trade publication for the marketing research industry.

7856 ■ Revenue
Montgomery Media International
55 New Montgomery St., Ste. 617
San Francisco, CA 94105
Ph: (415)371-8800
URL: http://www.revenuetoday.com/

Free to qualified subscribers. Magazine covering internet marketing strategies.

7857 ■ Sales & Marketing Management
Nielsen Business Media
770 Broadway
New York, NY 10003-9595
URL: http://www.salesandmarketing.com

Bimonthly. $48.00/year for individuals, print + online; $67.00/year for Canada, print + online; $146.00/year for other countries, print + online. Business magazine.

7858 ■ TelevisionWeek
Crain Communications Inc. (Detroit, Michigan)
1155 Gratiot Ave.
Detroit, MI 48207-2997
Ph: (313)446-6000
Fax: (313)567-7681
URL: http://www.tvweek.com/

Weekly. $119.00/year for individuals; $171.00/year for Canada, incl. GST; $309.00/year for other countries, airmail. Newspaper covering management, programming, cable and trends in the television and the media industry.

EMPLOYER DIRECTORIES AND NETWORKING LISTS

7859 ■ Adcrafter—Roster Issue
Adcraft Club of Detroit
3011 W Grand Blvd., Ste. 561
Detroit, MI 48202-3000
Ph: (313)872-7850
Fax: (313)872-7858
E-mail: cyoung@adcraft.org
URL: http://www.adcraft.org

Annual, Latest edition 2011. $30.00 for individuals. Covers: 3,000 executives of advertising agencies, advertising media, and advertising companies in the Detroit metropolitan area, and 500 out-of-state members. Entries include: Name, title, company name, office address and phone, business classification, membership code. Arrangement: Alphabetical and classified by line of business; identical information in both sections.

7860 ■ Advertiser & Agency Red Books Plus
LexisNexis Group
9443 Springboro Pike
Dayton, OH 45342
Fr: 888-285-3947
URL: http://www.redbooks.com

Quarterly, Latest edition January, 2007. $2,195.00 for individuals. CD-ROM. Covers 15,750 of the world's top advertisers, their products and what media they use, as well as 13,900 U.S. and international ad agencies and nearly 100,000 key executives worldwide in management, creative, and media positions. Entries include: For advertisers—Company name, job function/title, product/brand name, advertising expenditures by media. For personnel—Name and title.

7861 ■ Advertising Age—Advertising Agency Income Report Issue
Crain Communications Inc.
360 N Michigan Ave.
Chicago, IL 60601
Ph: (312)649-5200
URL: http://www.adage.com

Annual, April. $3.50. Publication includes: Ranked lists of about 650 U.S advertising agencies, 1,600 foreign agencies, the world's Top 50 advertising organizations, top media services companies in the U.S. and worldwide, top U.S. healthcare agencies, and multicultural agencies, which reported billings and gross income, or whose billings and gross incomes were ascertained through research.

7862 ■ The ADWEEK Directory
ADWEEK Magazines
770 Broadway, 7th Fl.
New York, NY 10003-9595
URL: http://www.adweek.com

Annual. $499.00 for individuals; $799.00 for individuals. Covers: Over 23,000 personal listings and it has information on more than 5,900 full-service advertising agencies, public relations firms, media buying services, direct marketing and related organizations. Entries include: Agency name, address, phone, fax/e-mail, URL; names and titles of key personnel; major accounts; Ultimate parent company; headquarters location; major subsidiaries and other operating units; year founded; number of employees; fee income; billings; percentage of billings by medium. Individual listings for each agency branch. Arrangement: Alphabetical. Indexes: Geographical; parent company, subsidiary, branch; ethnic specialties; organization, name changes, agencies opened/closed.

7863 ■ Agri Marketing—The Top 50
Doane Agricultural Services
77 Westport Plz., Ste. 250
St. Louis, MO 63146-4193
Ph: (314)569-2700
Fax: (314)569-1083
Fr: (866)647-0918
URL: http://www.doane.com

Annual, April or May. Publication includes: List of the top 50 U.S. and Canadian advertising agencies and public relations firms, chosen on the basis of agricultural business income. Entries include: Agency name, location, income for agricultural accounts in most recent year, branch offices, major clients served. Arrangement: Alphabetical.

7864 ■ American Marketing Association—The M Guide Services Directory
American Marketing Association
311 S Wacker Dr., Ste. 5800
Chicago, IL 60606
Ph: (312)542-9000
Fax: (312)542-9001
Fr: 800-262-1150
E-mail: lgil@ama.org
URL: http://www.marketingpower.com/_layouts/mguide/default.aspx

Annual, latest edition 2009. Covers: 26,500 individual members and about 1,000 paid listings for member research and service firms. Entries include: For individuals—Member name, position, home and office address, and phone numbers. For advertisers—Company name, address, phone, names of principal executives.

7865 ■ Black Book Photography
Black Book Marketing Group
740 Broadway, Ste. 202
New York, NY 10003
Ph: (212)979-6700
Fax: (212)673-4321
Fr: 800-841-1246
URL: http://www.BlackBook.com

Annual, Latest edition 2008. $60.00 for individuals. Publication includes: Over 19,000 art directors, creative directors, photographers and photographic services, design firms, advertising agencies, and other firms whose products or services are used in advertising.

7866 ■ Careers in Focus—Advertising & Marketing
Facts On File Inc.
132 W 31st St., 17th Fl.
New York, NY 10001
Ph: (212)967-8800
Fax: 800-678-3633
Fr: 800-322-8755
URL: http://www.infobasepublishing.com

Latest edition 2nd; Published January, 2009. $32.95 for individuals. Covers: An overview of advertising and marketing, followed by a selection of jobs profiled in detail, including the nature of the job, earnings, prospects for employment, what kind of training and skills it requires, and sources for further information.

7867 ■ Chicago Creative Directory
Chicago Creative Directory
4149 N Leamington Ave.
Chicago, IL 60601
Ph: (773)427-7777
Fax: (773)427-7771
URL: http://creativedir.com

Annual, March. Covers: Over 6,000 advertising agencies, photographers, sound studios, talent agencies, audiovisual services, and others offering creative and production services. Entries include: For most listings—Company name, address, phone, list of officers, description of services. For freelance listings—Name, talent, address, phone. Arrangement: Classified by specialty.

7868 ■ *Discovering Careers for Your Future—Advertising & Marketing*
Facts On File Inc.
132 W 31st St., 17th Fl.
New York, NY 10001
Ph: (212)967-8800
Fax: 800-678-3633
Fr: 800-322-8755
URL: http://factsonfile.infobasepublishing.com

Published 2005. $21.95 for individuals; $19.75 for libraries. Covers: Advertising account executives, buyers, composers, demographers, illustrators, public opinion researchers, telemarketers, and more; links career education to curriculum, helping children investigate the subjects they are interested in, and the careers those subjects might lead to.

7869 ■ *Fashion & Print Directory*
Peter Glenn Publications
235 SE 5th Ave., Ste. R
Delray Beach, FL 33483
Ph: (561)404-4685
Fax: (561)279-4672
Fr: 888-332-6700
URL: http://www.pgdirect.com/fpintro.asp

Annual, November; latest edition 47th. $39.95 for individuals. Covers: Advertising agencies, PR firms, marketing companies, 1,000 client brand companies and related services in the U.S. and Canada. Includes photographers, marketing agency, suppliers, sources of props and rentals, fashion houses, beauty services, locations. Entries include: Company name, address, phone; paid listings numbering 5,000 include description of products or services, key personnel. Arrangement: Classified by line of business.

7870 ■ *IAA Membership Directory*
International Advertising Association
521 5th Ave., Ste. 1807
New York, NY 10175
Ph: (212)557-1133
Fax: (212)983-0455
URL: http://www.iaaglobal.org

Annual. Free; $15.00 for individuals; $80.00 for individuals. Covers: The advertising industry, with emphasis on the value of advertising, freedom of commercial speech, and consumer choice.

7871 ■ *O'Dwyer's Directory of Public Relations Firms*
J.R. O'Dwyer Company Inc.
271 Madison Ave., No. 600
New York, NY 10016
Ph: (212)679-2471
Fax: (212)683-2750
Fr: (866)395-7710
E-mail: john@odwyerpr.com
URL: http://www.odwyerpr.com

Annual, Latest edition 2011. $95.00 for individuals. Covers: Over 1,600 public relations firms; international coverage. Entries include: Firm name, address, phone, principal executives, branch and overseas offices, billings, date founded, and 7,750 clients are cross-indexed. Arrangement: Geographical by country. Indexes: Specialty (beauty and fashions, finance/investor, etc.), geographical, client.

7872 ■ *PlanetInform's Global Directory for Major Communications Companies*
Business Information Agency, Inc.
1300 S Arlington Ridge Rd., Ste. 502
Arlington, VA 22202
Ph: (703)685-2776
Fax: (703)685-1851
URL: http://planetinform.com/html/prodCard.aspx?prodID=3646

Annual, January; Latest edition 11th. $199.00 for individuals; $249.00. Covers: 5,000 communication companies from 60 countries in North America, Europe, and Asia. Entries include: Company name, location, contact information, SIC codes, number of employees, type of business, year founded, legal status, and subsidiary indicators. Indexes: Alphabeti-

cally and Geographically by SIC code and by industrial activity.

7873 ■ *Plunkett's Advertising and Branding Industry Almanac*
Plunkett Research Ltd.
4102 Bellaire Blvd.
PO Box 541737
Houston, TX 77025-1004
Ph: (713)932-0000
Fax: (713)932-7080
URL: http://www.plunkettresearch.com

Latest edition 2011; New edition expected April 2012. $299.99 for individuals. Covers: Leading companies in advertising and marketing including the areas of media, direct mail, online advertising, branding, and image-crafting. Entries include: Name, address, phone, fax, and key executives. Also includes analysis and information on trends, technology, and statistics in the field.

7874 ■ *Process Buyer's Guide*
Runbeck Graphics, Inc.
2404 W 14 St., Ste. 110
Tempe, AZ 85281-6920
Ph: (602)437-1311
Fax: (602)437-1411
Fr: 888-333-1237
URL: http://www.southwestgraphics.net/index.php?v=about_us

Annual, Latest edition 2010. Covers: Companies that provide products and services useful for advertising, design, printing, interactive, public relation, and photography services.

7875 ■ *Public Relations Tactics—Member Services Directory—The Blue Book*
Public Relations Society of America
33 Maiden Ln., 11th Fl.
New York, NY 10038-5150
Ph: (212)460-1400
Fax: (212)995-0757
E-mail: 74224.1456@compuserve.com
URL: http://www.prsa.org

Annual, latest edition 2007. Covers: PRSA members—headquaters, staff contacts, and chapter, section, and district information. Entries include: Name, professional affiliation and title, address, phone, membership rank. Arrangement: Alphabetical. Indexes: Geographical, organizational.

7876 ■ *Quirk's Marketing Research Review—Researcher SourceBook Issue*
Quirk Enterprises Inc.
4662 Slater Rd.
Eagan, MN 55122
Ph: (651)379-6200
URL: http://www.quirks.com

Annual, Latest edition 2011-2012. $70.00 for individuals; $119.00 for individuals; $100.00 for individuals. Covers: About 7,100 organizations providing marketing research products and services. Entries include: Name, address, phone, fax, contact, research specialties, URL, e-mail. Arrangement: Geographical. Indexes: Personnel, industry specialization, research specialization, alphabetic.

7877 ■ *Society for Marketing Professional Services—Membership Directory*
Society for Marketing Professional Services
44 Canal Center Plz., Ste. 444
Alexandria, VA 22314
Ph: (703)549-6117
Fax: (703)549-2498
Fr: 800-292-7677
URL: http://www.smps.org

Latest edition 2009-2010. Covers: 7,000 marketing and business development professionals from architectural, engineering, planning, interior design, construction, and specialty consulting firms throughout U.S.

7878 ■ *Standard Directory of Advertising Agencies*
LexisNexis Group
9443 Springboro Pike
Dayton, OH 45342
Fr: 888-285-3947
URL: http://www.redbooks.com

Semiannual, Latest edition January, 2010. $1,399.00 for individuals. Covers: Nearly 10,800 advertising agencies. Entries include: Agency name, address, phone, e-mail, website, year founded, number of employees, association memberships, area of specialization, annual billing, breakdown of gross billings by media, clients, executives, special markets, and new agencies. Arrangement: Alphabetical. Indexes: Geographical (includes address), special market, agency responsibilities, and personnel.

7879 ■ *Standard Directory of International Advertisers and Agencies*
LexisNexis Group
9443 Springboro Pike
Dayton, OH 45342
Fr: 888-285-3947
URL: http://www.lexisnexis.com/

Annual, latest edition January, 2010. $1,299.00 for individuals. Covers: Nearly 14,000 advertiser companies and advertising agencies; international coverage. Entries include: Company name, address, phone, fax, telex, annual sales or billings, number of employees, Standard Industrial Classification (SIC) code, names and titles of key personnel, line of business, subsidiary and branch office names, address, phone, telex, key officers; advertiser companies include their advertising agency's name, address, and description of advertising budget and strategies; advertising agencies include names of client companies and their lines of business. Arrangement: Separate alphabetical and geographical sections for advertiser companies and advertising agencies. Indexes: Geographical, company name, personal name, trade name, SIC.

7880 ■ *Vault Guide to the Top Advertising & PR Employers*
Vault.com Inc.
150 W 22nd St., 5th Fl.
New York, NY 10011
Ph: (212)366-4212
Fax: (212)366-6117
Fr: 888-562-8285
URL: http://www.vault.com/wps/portal/usa/store/

Latest edition 2010. $19.95 for individuals; $19.95 for members. Covers: Advertising and PR agencies. Entries include: Name, address, phone, fax, website, and other branch office locations. Also includes employer type, name of chairman and CEO, key competitors, employment contact, recent company news, and information on the hiring process. Arrangement: Alphabetical by company name.

7881 ■ *The Workbook*
Scott & Daughters Publishing Inc.
6762 Lexington Ave.
Los Angeles, CA 90038
Ph: (323)856-0008
Fax: (323)856-4368
Fr: 800-547-2688
URL: http://www.workbook.com

Annual, Latest edition 2011. $60.00 for individuals; $30.00 for individuals; $35.00 for individuals. Covers: 55,000 advertising agencies, art directors, photographers, freelance illustrators and designers, artists' representatives, interactive designers, pre-press services, and other graphic arts services in the U.S. Entries include: Company or individual name, address, phone, specialty. National in scope. Arrangement: Classified by product or service.

HANDBOOKS AND MANUALS

7882 ■ *A Big Life in Advertising*
Alfred A. Knopf Incorporated
1745 Broadway
New York, NY 10019

Ph: (212)782-9000
Fax: (212)572-6066
Fr: 800-733-3000
URL: http://www.randomhouse.com

Mary Wells Lawrence. $26.00. 320 pages. Story of how Mary Wells Lawrence lived her life in advertising and helped shape her profession.

7883 ■ Career Opportunities in Advertising and Public Relations

Facts On File Inc.
132 W 31st St., 17th Fl.
New York, NY 10001
Fr: 800-322-8755
E-mail: custserv@factsonfile.com
URL: http://factsonfile.infobasepublishing.com

2005. $49.50. 336 pages. Provides detailed information on salary ranges, employment and advancement prospects and job duties. Reflects changes in the industry, new trends and current employment information.

7884 ■ Careers in Advertising

The McGraw-Hill Companies
PO Box 182604
Columbus, OH 43272
Fax: (614)759-3749
Fr: 877-883-5524
E-mail: customer.service@mcgraw-hill.com
URL: http://www.mhprofessional.com/
    product.php?isbn=0071430490

S. William Pattis. Third Edition, 2004. $15.95 (paper). 192 pages.

7885 ■ Careers in Communications

The McGraw-Hill Companies
PO Box 182604
Columbus, OH 43272
Fax: (614)759-3749
Fr: 877-883-5524
E-mail: customer.service@mcgraw-hill.com
URL: http://www.mhprofessional.com/
    product.php?isbn=0071454764

Shonan Noronha. Fourth edition, 2004. $15.95 (paper). 192 pages. Examines the fields of journalism, photography, radio, television, film, public relations, and advertising. Gives concrete details on job locations and how to secure a job. Suggests many resources for job hunting.

7886 ■ Careers in Marketing

The McGraw-Hill Companies
PO Box 182604
Columbus, OH 43272
Fax: (614)759-3749
Fr: 877-883-5524
E-mail: customer.service@mcgraw-hill.com
URL: http://www.mhprofessional.com/
    product.php?isbn=0071493123

Leslie Stair. 2008. $16.95 (paper). 192 pages. Surveys career opportunities in marketing and related areas such as marketing research, product development, and sales promotion. Includes a description of the work, places of employment, employment outlook, trends, and salaries. Offers job hunting advice.

7887 ■ FabJob Guide to Become an Advertising Copywriter

FabJob Inc.
4616 - 25th Ave. NE, No. 224
Seattle, WA 98105
Ph: (403)949-4980
Fr: 888-322-5621
URL: http://www.fabjob.com

Brooke J. Claussen. $14.97. 140 pages. Discusses key points on how to get started and how to succeed in the advertising industry.

7888 ■ Great Jobs for Business Majors

The McGraw-Hill Companies
PO Box 182604
Columbus, OH 43272
Fax: (614)759-3749

Fr: 877-883-5524
E-mail: customer.service@mcgraw-hill.com
URL: http://www.mhprofessional.com/
    product.php?isbn=0071544836

Stephen Lambert. Third edition, 2008. $16.95 (paper). 240 pages.

7889 ■ Great Jobs for English Majors

The McGraw-Hill Companies
PO Box 182604
Columbus, OH 43272
Fax: (614)759-3749
Fr: 877-883-5524
E-mail: customer.service@mcgraw-hill.com
URL: http://www.mhprofessional.com

Julie DeGalan and Stephen Lambert. Third edition, 2006. $15.95 (paper). 192 pages.

7890 ■ Great Jobs for Liberal Arts Majors

The McGraw-Hill Companies
PO Box 182604
Columbus, OH 43272
Fax: (614)759-3749
Fr: 877-883-5524
E-mail: customer.service@mcgraw-hill.com
URL: http://www.mhprofessional.com/
    product.php?isbn=0071482148

Blythe Camenson. Second edition, 2007. $16.95 (paper). 192 pages.

7891 ■ Opportunities in Direct Marketing

The McGraw-Hill Companies
PO Box 182604
Columbus, OH 43272
Fax: (614)759-3749
Fr: 877-883-5524
E-mail: customer.service@mcgraw-hill.com
URL: http://www.mhprofessional.com/
    product.php?isbn=0071493085

Anne Basye. 2008. $14.95 (paper). 160 pages. Examines opportunities with direct marketers, catalog companies, direct marketing agencies, telemarketing firms, mailing list brokers, and database marketing companies. Describes how to prepare for a career in direct marketing and how to break into the field. Includes sources of short-term professional training.

7892 ■ Opportunities in Marketing Careers

The McGraw-Hill Companies
PO Box 182604
Columbus, OH 43272
Fax: (614)759-3749
Fr: 877-883-5524
E-mail: customer.service@mcgraw-hill.com
URL: http://www.mhprofessional.com/
    product.php?isbn=0071448985

Margery Steinberg. 2005. $13.95 (paper). 176. Gives guidance on identifying and pursuing job opportunities. Illustrated.

7893 ■ Opportunities in Writing Careers

The McGraw-Hill Companies
PO Box 182604
Columbus, OH 43272
Fax: (614)759-3749
Fr: 877-883-5524
E-mail: customer.service@mcgraw-hill.com
URL: http://www.mhprofessional.com/
    product.php?isbn=0071458727

Elizabeth Foote-Smith. 2006. $13.95 (paper). 160 pages. Discusses opportunities in the print media, broadcasting, advertising or publishing. Business writing, public relations, and technical writing are among the careers covered. Contains bibliography and illustrations.

7894 ■ Sales and Marketing Resumes for $100,000 Careers

JIST Publishing
875 Montreal Way
St. Paul, MN 55102

Fr: 800-648-5478
E-mail: info@jist.com
URL: http://www.jist.com

Louise M. Kursmark. 2009. $19.95 (softcover). 352 pages. Provides advice on writing and polishing resumes and cover letters, managing the job search, and using strategies to land a $100,000 job.

EMPLOYMENT AGENCIES AND SEARCH FIRMS

7895 ■ Access Staffing

360 Lexington Ave., 8th Fl.
New York, NY 10017
Ph: (212)687-5440
Fax: (212)557-2544
URL: http://www.accessstaffingco.com

Serves as a staffing firm covering accounting/financial, advertising, bilingual Japanese, creative, event planning, fashion/retail, healthcare/ human services, human resources, information technology, insurance, legal, light industrial and office support.

7896 ■ Allen Associates

3805 Edwards Rd., Ste. 550
Cincinnati, OH 45209
Ph: (513)563-3040
E-mail: feedback@allensearch.com
URL: http://www.allensearch.com

Executive senior-level search firm.

7897 ■ Allen Austin

4543 Post Oak Place Dr., Ste. 217
Houston, TX 77027
Ph: (713)355-1900
Fax: (713)355-1901
E-mail: randrews@allenaustinsearch.com
URL: http://www.allenaustinsearch.com

Executive search firm. Branches in North Carolina and Dallas.

7898 ■ American Executive Management Inc.

30 Federal St.
Salem, MA 01970
E-mail: execsearch@americanexecutive.us
URL: http://www.americanexecutive.us

Executive search firm. Second location in Boston.

7899 ■ Apple and Associates

PO Box 996
Chapin, SC 29036
Ph: (803)932-2000
E-mail: info@appleassoc.com
URL: http://www.appleassoc.com

Provides staffing services to medical device, plastics, pharmaceutical and performance materials industries.

7900 ■ Barton Associates Inc.

4314 Yoakum Blvd.
Houston, TX 77006
Ph: (713)961-9111
Fax: (713)403-5574
E-mail: info@bartona.com
URL: http://www.bartona.com

Executive search firm. Affiliate in Houston, TX.

7901 ■ Bernhart Associates Executive Search, LLC

2068 Greenwood Dr.
Owatonna, MN 55060
Ph: (507)451-4270
E-mail: info@bernhart.com
URL: http://www.bernhart.com

Specializes in digital, multichannel direct marketing, data mining and customer relationship management recruitment. Conducts research on salary data.

7902 ■ Bert Davis Executive Search Inc.

425 Madison Ave.
New York, NY 10017

Ph: (212)838-4000
Fax: (212)935-3291
E-mail: info@bertdavis.com
URL: http://www.bertdavis.com

Executive search firm.

7903 ■ Blumenthal-Hart LLC
195 N Harbor Dr., Ste. 2902
Chicago, IL 60604-3413
Ph: (312)318-1930
Fax: (312)946-1928
E-mail: resumes@blumenthal-hart.com
URL: http://www.blumenthal-hart.com

Executive search firm.

7904 ■ The BOSS Group
4350 E West Hwy., Ste. 307
Bethesda, MD 20814
Ph: (301)656-6284
Fax: (301)656-9466
E-mail: questions@thebossgroup.com
URL: http://www.thebossgroup.com

Provides a venue where creative and marketing communications professionals come to find jobs and assignments, resources and industry connections and where clients find the talent and expertise to help them succeed. Provides human capital solutions for the creative industry.

7905 ■ Buffkin & Associates LLC
730 Cool Springs Blvd., Ste. 120
Franklin, TN 37067
Ph: (615)778-2142
E-mail: info@thebuffkingroup.com
URL: http://www.buffkinassociates.com/www

Executive search firm.

7906 ■ Byron Leonard International
99 Long Ct., Ste. 201
Thousand Oaks, CA 91360
Ph: (805)373-7500
Fax: (805)373-5531
E-mail: bli@bli-inc.com
URL: http://www.bli-inc.com

Executive search firm.

7907 ■ Canny, Bowen Inc.
400 Madison Ave., Rm. 11-D
New York, NY 10017
Ph: (212)949-6611
Fax: (212)949-5191
E-mail: main@cannybowen.com
URL: http://www.cannybowen.com

Executive search firm.

7908 ■ Cardinal Mark Inc.
17113 Minnetonka Blvd., Ste. 112
Minnetonka, MN 55345
Ph: (952)314-4636
Fax: (610)228-7390
E-mail: jimz@cardinalmark.com
URL: http://www.cardinalmark.com

Executive search firm concentrated on telecommunication industry.

7909 ■ Career Advocates International
1539 Ave. A
Katy, TX 77493
Ph: (281)395-9848
Fax: (281)574-3949
URL: http://www.careeradvocates.org

Provides permanent placement and temporary staffing for executive and staff level positions. Specializes in multiple niches including: sales and marketing, accounting and financial services, banking, communications, human resources, chemicals, oil and gas, medical and dental, legal, information technology, energy, technology, engineering, manufacturing, construction, and light industrial.

7910 ■ Centennial, Inc.
8044 Montgomery Rd., Ste. 260
Cincinnati, OH 45236
Ph: (513)366-3760
Fax: (513)366-3761
E-mail: info@centennialinc.com
URL: http://www.centennialinc.com

Serves as an executive search firm specializing in the areas of executive and general management, accounting and finance, human resources, information technology, manufacturing, engineering, marketing and advertising, not-for-profit, sales and business development, and supply chain and logistics. Performs executive coaching as well as career coaching for clients.

7911 ■ cFour Partners
100 Wilshire Blvd., Ste. 1840
Santa Monica, CA 90401
Ph: (310)471-5444
Fax: (310)388-0411
E-mail: info@cfour.com
URL: http://www.cfour.com/web/default.asp

Executive search firm.

7912 ■ Chaloner Associates
36 Milford St.
Boston, MA 02118
Ph: (617)451-5170
Fax: (617)451-8160
E-mail: info@chaloner.com
URL: http://www.chaloner.com

Executive search firm.

7913 ■ Charles Aris, Inc.
300 N Greene St., Ste. 1800
Greensboro, NC 27401
Ph: (336)378-1818
Fax: (336)378-0129
E-mail: info@charlesaris.com
URL: http://www.charlesaris.com

Provides executive search and placement services in the areas of consumer packaged goods, retail, strategy/business development, global life sciences, healthcare, chemicals, textiles/apparel, private equity, and business services.

7914 ■ Cheryl Alexander & Associates
8588 Shadow Creek Dr.
Maple Grove, MN 55311
Ph: (763)416-4570
E-mail: cheryl@cherylalexander.com
URL: http://www.cherylalexander.com

Executive search firm.

7915 ■ Cooper Staffing & Consulting, Inc.
730 Orchard Court
Atlanta, GA 30328
Ph: (770)522-8868
URL: http://www.cooperstaffing.com

Specializes in finding and placing sales, marketing, technical professionals and senior management for companies in the pharmaceutical, biotech, medical, and advertising sectors.

7916 ■ Corporate Moves Inc.
PO Box 1638
Williamsville, NY 14231-1638
Ph: (716)633-0234
Fax: (716)626-9147
E-mail: info@cmisearch.com
URL: http://www.corporatemovesinc.com

Executive search and recruitment specialist firm with emphasis on Sales, Marketing and Senior Management generally in the $70,000 and above income levels. Industries served: medical, biotech, scientific, pharmaceutical, industrial, business products.

7917 ■ Creative Group
18200 Von Karman Ave., Ste. 800
Irvine, CA 92612
Fr: 888-846-1668
URL: http://www.creativegroup.com

Description: Serves as an executive search firm specializing in placement of advertising, marketing, web and public relations professionals.

7918 ■ Creative Placement
13 N Main St.
Norwalk, CT 06854-2702
Ph: (203)838-7772
Fr: 800-521-4616
E-mail: kheine@creativeplacement.com
URL: http://www.creativeplacement.com

Description: Serves as an executive search firm for the creative industry. Provides placement for web, design, branding, packaging, advertising, and promotion.

7919 ■ DFBryant & Co
3701 Iron Horse Ct.
Leawood, KS 66224
Ph: (913)402-1701
E-mail: jobs1@dfbryant.com
URL: http://www.dfbryant.com

Description: Serves as executive search firm for advertising and marketing professionals to leading national advertising agencies and multi-national corporations.

7920 ■ The Dinerstein Group
45 Rockefeller Plaza, Ste. 2000
New York, NY 10111
Ph: (212)332-3224
URL: http://www.dinersteingroup.com

Executive search firm. Branch in Stamford, CT.

7921 ■ DLB Associates
265 Industrial Way, W
Eatontown, NJ 07724
Ph: (732)774-2000
Fax: (732)774-5000
E-mail: info@dlbassociates.com
URL: http://www.dlbassociates.com

Executive search firm.

7922 ■ DSML Executive Search
120 N La Salle St., Ste. 2600
Chicago, IL 60602
Ph: (312)268-6166
E-mail: contact@dsmlexecutivesearch.com
URL: http://www.dsmlexecutivesearch.com

Provides recruiting services for European companies doing business in the United States. Specializes in the recruitment of qualified personnel for sales, marketing and operational management positions.

7923 ■ Dussick Management Associates
White Birch Rd., Ste. 28
Madison, CT 06443
Ph: (203)245-9311
Fax: (203)245-1648
E-mail: vince@dussick.com
URL: http://www.dussick.com

Executive search firm.

7924 ■ The Enfield Company
3005 S Lamar Blvd., Ste. D109-172
Austin, TX 78704
Ph: (512)585-0876
URL: http://silverdevelopment.com

Executive search firm.

7925 ■ Epsen, Fuller & Associates LLC
1776 On The Green
67 Park Pl., E
Morristown, NJ 07960
Ph: (973)387-4900
Fax: (973)359-9928
E-mail: info@epsenfuller.com
URL: http://www.epsenfuller.com

Executive search firm.

7926 ■ The Esquire Staffing Group Ltd.
1 S Wacker Dr., Ste. 1616
Chicago, IL 60606-4616
Ph: (312)795-4300
URL: http://www.esquirestaffing.com

Employment agency. Fills permanent as well as temporary openings.

7927 ■ Fairfield
Trump Tower
721 5th Ave.
New York, NY 10022-2523
Ph: (212)838-0220
E-mail: newyork@fairfield.ch
URL: http://www.fairfield.ch

Executive search firm specializing in retail and apparel manufacturing.

7928 ■ Filcro Media Staffing
521 5th Ave., Fl. 18
New York, NY 10175
Ph: (212)599-0909
Fax: (212)599-1023
E-mail: mail@executivesearch.tv
URL: http://www.executivesearch.tv

Executive search firm for the entertainment industry.

7929 ■ FILTER, LLC
1505 Fifth Ave., Ste. 600
Seattle, WA 98101
Ph: (206)682-6005
Fax: (206)682-5830
Fr: 800-336-0809
URL: http://www.filterdigital.com

Serves as creative resources company that provides talent in web, marketing, and creative professions. Represents virtually every discipline: designers, copywriters, web architects, icon artists, illustrators, animators, and other specialized artistic and technological talents.

7930 ■ Food Management Search
235 State St., Ste. 326
Springfield, MA 01103
Ph: (413)732-2666
Fax: (413)732-6466
E-mail: recruiters@foodmanagementsearch.com
URL: http://foodmanagementsearch.com/index.cfm

Specializes in contingency recruiting projects exclusively in the food manufacturing and food service industries. Provides positions covering food production/manufacturing, supply chain, food service, sales and marketing.

7931 ■ Franchise Recruiters Ltd.
Lincolnshire Country Club
3500 Innsbruck
Crete, IL 60417
Ph: (708)757-5595
Fax: (708)758-8222
Fr: 800-334-6257
E-mail: franchise@att.net
URL: http://www.franchiserecruiters.com

Executive search firm. Second location in Toronto, Canada.

7932 ■ Generator Group
17933 NW Evergreen Pkwy., Ste. 240
Beaverton, OR 97006
Ph: (503)224-4811
URL: http://www.generatorgroup.net

Works as a talent management services firm that delivers executive search and talent management consulting to organizations in consumer products and retail, technology, and public transportation.

7933 ■ Gundersen Partners L.L.C.
30 Irving Pl., 2nd Fl.
New York, NY 10003
Ph: (212)677-7660
Fax: (212)358-0275
E-mail: esteffen@gpllc.com
URL: http://www.gundersenpartners.com

Management consulting firm provides the following: marketing consulting and executive search. Industries served: marketing, marketing services, consumer packaged goods, financial services, internet/high tech, sales promotion and advertising agencies.

7934 ■ Hager Executive Search
1483 Sutter St., Ste. 1003
San Francisco, CA 94109
Ph: (415)441-2234
E-mail: connect@hagerexecutivesearch.com
URL: http://www.hagerexecutivesearch.com

Specializes in executive and C level talent searches in marketing/branding, business development, sales and digital media across varied business sectors.

7935 ■ Hilleren & Associates
3800 American Blvd. W, Ste. 880
Minneapolis, MN 55431
Ph: (952)956-9090
Fax: (952)956-9009
E-mail: heather@hilleren.com
URL: http://www.hilleren.com

Provides executive search services in sales, marketing and management in the healthcare and pharmaceutical manufacturing industry.

7936 ■ Houser Martin Morris
110th Ave. NE, 110 Atrium Pl., Ste. 580
Bellevue, WA 98004
Ph: (425)453-2700
Fax: (425)453-8726
E-mail: info@houser.com
URL: http://www.houser.com

Focus is in the areas of retained executive search, professional and technical recruiting. Areas of specialization include software engineering, sales and marketing, information technology, legal, human resources, accounting and finance, manufacturing, factory automation, and engineering.

7937 ■ Howard-Sloan Professional Search Inc.
261 Madison Ave.
New York, NY 10016
Ph: (212)704-0444
Fr: 800-221-1326
E-mail: info@howardsloan.com
URL: http://www.howardsloan.com

Executive search firm.

7938 ■ Insperity, Inc.
19001 Crescent Springs Dr.
Kingwood, TX 77339-3802
Ph: (281)358-8986
Fr: 800-237-3170
E-mail: douglas.sharp@insperity.com
URL: http://www.insperity.com

Description: Serves as a full-service human resources department for small and medium-sized businesses throughout the United States. Provides client companies with benefits and services such as employment administration, government compliance, recruiting and selection, performance management, benefits management, employer liability management, training and development, and business services.

7939 ■ Intech Summit Group Inc.
3450 Bonita Rd., Ste. 203
Chula Vista, CA 91910
Ph: (619)862-2720
Fax: (619)862-2699
Fr: 800-750-8100
E-mail: isg@isgsearch.com
URL: http://www.isgsearch.com

Retained executive search and human resources consulting firm. Industries served: healthcare, MIS, sales and marketing, high tech, other consulting groups, human resources, and information systems.

7940 ■ Joy Reed Belt Search Consultants Inc.
PO Box 54410
Oklahoma City, OK 73154
Ph: (405)842-5155
Fax: (405)842-6357
E-mail: executiverecruiter@joyreedbelt.com
URL: http://www.joyreedbeltsearch.com

Executive search firm. Branch in Tulsa, OK.

7941 ■ JT Brady & Associates
10900 Perry Hwy. No. 12203
Wexford, PA 15090
Fax: (724)935-8059
E-mail: jack@jtbrady.net
URL: http://www.jtbrady.net

Executive search firm.

7942 ■ Judith Cushman & Associates
15600 NE 8th St., Ste. B1
Bellevue, WA 98008
Ph: (425)392-8660
Fax: (425)644-9043
E-mail: jcushman@jc-a.com
URL: http://www.jc-a.com

Executive search firm.

7943 ■ Karen Dexter & Associates Inc.
2012 Chestnut Ave. N, Ste. 29
Wilmette, IL 60091-1512
Ph: (847)853-9500
Fax: (847)256-7108

Training and development consultant offering interpersonal skills training and one on one performance counseling for employees of large organizations. Industries served: advertising, banking and finance, consumer products, entertainment, food and beverage, healthcare, legal profession, manufacturing, government agencies, publishing and broadcasting.

7944 ■ Lamay Associates
1465 Post Rd. E
Old Greenwich, CT 06870
Ph: (203)637-8440
Fax: (203)256-3594
E-mail: dmsearch_lamay@msn.com

Offers executive search and recruitment specializing in all areas of direct marketing-both to consumers, business-to-business, and non-profit development. Clients include advertising agencies, retailers, manufacturers of consumer goods, cataloguers, publishers, and Internet/e-commerce entities.

7945 ■ LandaJob Advertising Staffing Specialists
222 W Gregory Blvd., Ste. 304
Kansas City, MO 64114
Ph: (816)523-1881
Fax: (816)523-1876
Fr: 800-931-8806
E-mail: adstaff@landajobnow.com
URL: http://www.landajobnow.com

Personnel consultants and recruiters for advertising, marketing, and communications positions. Industries served: advertising, communications, marketing, graphic arts, printing and publishing.

7946 ■ Lynn Hazan & Associates
55 E Washington St., Ste. 715
Chicago, IL 60602
Ph: (312)863-5401
E-mail: lynn@lhazan.com
URL: http://www.lhazan.com

Description: Serves as an executive search and consulting firm specializing in Marketing and Communications placement. Focuses on national searches in communications, marketing and consulting, with a special emphasis on Chicago and the Midwest.

7947 ■ Marcom Choices Staffing
PO Box 620632
Woodside, CA 94062-0632

Ph: (650)851-9055
E-mail: marketingjobs@marcomchoices.com
URL: http://www.marcomchoices.com

Description: Executive search firm which specializes and excels in placing product marketing, sales and corporate communications professionals.

7948 ■ Marketing Pro Resources, Inc.
PO Box 1686
New York, NY 10021
Ph: (212)472-5310
Fax: (212)879-1206
E-mail: info@marketingproresources.com
URL: http://www.marketingproresources.com

Description: Provides professional staffing of temporary and permanent positions in marketing, communications, advertising, public relations, market research, analytics and more.

7949 ■ Max Brown
3208 Q St. NW
Washington, DC 20007
Ph: (202)338-2727
Fax: (202)338-3131
E-mail: maxbrown65@hotmail.com

Executive recruiter to the magazine and book publishing industries. Employment placements in all publishing disciplines, including operation and financial management, new product development, marketing, advertising sales, editorial, graphic design, production, manufacturing, circulation, distribution, corporate communications, promotion and administration. Secondary concentrations include management advising for publishers, providing the following services: marketing and product positioning for new and existing publications, market research and development, business planning and financial projections, publishing models, launch strategies and start-up operations and acquisitions and mergers counsel.

7950 ■ Melinda Holm & Associates
7630 Madison St.
Forest Park, IL 60130
Ph: (708)488-9701
Fax: (708)488-9702
E-mail: info@mhajobs.com
URL: http://www.melindaholm.com

Description: Covers both freelance and permanent placement needs in corporations and agencies. Specializes in marketing and advertising positions on all levels.

7951 ■ MJS Executive Search
2 Overhill Rd., Ste. 400
Scarsdale, NY 10583
Ph: (914)631-1774
Fax: (914)631-0435
E-mail: info@mjsearch.com
URL: http://www.mjsearch.com

Serves as a retained executive recruiting firm specializing in placing professionals in consumer goods, entertainment, media, social media, sports, marketing services and other industries.

7952 ■ Neil Frank & Company
PO Box 3570
Redondo Beach, CA 90277-1570
Ph: (310)543-1611
E-mail: neilnick@aol.com
URL: http://www.neilfrank.com

Executive search firm.

7953 ■ Normyle/Erstling Health Search Group
350 W Passaic St.
Rochelle Park, NJ 07662
Ph: (201)843-6009
Fax: (201)843-2060
E-mail: jobs@MedPharmSales.com
URL: http://www.healthcaresales.com

Firm performs executive search and recruitment of medical device and pharmaceutical sales and marketing professionals.

7954 ■ Paladin Recruiting and Staffing
1050 Crown Pointe Pkwy., Ste. 1750
Atlanta, GA 30338
Ph: (404)495-0900
Fax: (866)858-2484
Fr: 888-725-2346
E-mail: southeast@paladinstaff.com
URL: http://www.paladinstaff.com

Description: Serves as a professional staffing and recruitment firm dedicated to the marketing, creative and communications professions. Provides freelance, direct hire, temp-to-perm, and payrolling services. Provides services to clients within all major industries, across corporate, agency, and non-for-profit organizations.

7955 ■ Paxton Resources
50 Main St., Ste. 1000
White Plains, NY 10606
Ph: (914)941-7152
Fax: (914)923-4624
E-mail: xyz@paxtonresources.com
URL: http://www.paxtonresources.com

Description: Specializes in the recruitment and placement of HR, marketing communications, public relations and facilities management professionals.

7956 ■ Primary Group
2180 W State Rd. 434, Ste. 4160
Longwood, FL 32791-6160
Ph: (407)869-4111
Fax: (407)682-3321
URL: http://www.theprimarygroup.com

Exists as an executive search firm that recruits professionals from the spectrum of sales, marketing, management, operations, or any executive level.

7957 ■ Pro Advantage Executive Search
381 Park Ave. S, Ste. 1112
New York, NY 10016
Ph: (212)944-0222
Fax: (212)944-2666
E-mail: info@proadvantagejobs.com
URL: http://www.proadvantagejobs.com

Description: Executive recruiting and research firm specializes in financial services industries. Offers career opportunities in the field of accounting, internal auditing, finance, compliance, tax, operations, and marketing.

7958 ■ Profiles
217 N Charles St., 4th Fl.
Baltimore, MD 21201
Ph: (410)244-6400
Fax: (410)244-6406
URL: http://careerprofiles.com

Recruits professionals for freelance, temporary, and direct hire opportunities specializing in marketing, advertising, creative, web design, graphic design and communications.

7959 ■ Recruiting Partners
3494 Camino Tassajara Rd., No. 404
Danville, CA 94506
Ph: (925)964-0249
E-mail: info@recruitingpartners.com
URL: http://www.recruitingpartners.com

Description: Serves as an executive and technical recruiting firm that specializes in accounting, legal, information technology, engineering, executive management and technical writing.

7960 ■ Roberson & Co.
10751 Parfet St.
Broomfield, CO 80021
Ph: (303)410-6510
E-mail: roberson@recruiterpro.com
URL: http://www.recruiterpro.com

Professional and executive recruiting firm working the national and international marketplace. Special-izes in accounting, finance, data processing and information services, health care, environmental and mining, engineering, manufacturing, human resources, and sales and marketing.

7961 ■ Sales Executives Inc.
33900 W 8 Mile Rd., Ste. 171
Farmington Hills, MI 48335
Ph: (248)615-0100
E-mail: dale@salesexecutives.com
URL: http://www.salesexecutives.com

Employment agency. Executive search firm.

7962 ■ Scion Staffing
576 Sacramento St., 2nd Fl.
San Francisco, CA 94111
Ph: (415)392-7500
E-mail: info@scionstaffing.com
URL: http://scionstaffing.com

Serves as an executive search firm and temporary agency for professional candidates.

7963 ■ SOURCE Executive Search/Consulting
2209 Collier Parkway Ste. 304
Land O Lakes, FL 34639
Ph: (813)909-4434
Fr: (866)822-2330
E-mail: info@sourceexecutive.com
URL: http://www.sourceexecutive.com

Description: Specializes in the sourcing, recruitment, and placement of advertising and marketing, media, sales promotion, and public relations executives. Includes other services such as references, salary negotiation advice, and career counseling.

7964 ■ Spectrum Group, LLC
1919 Gallows Rd., Ste. 600
Vienna, VA 22182
Ph: (703)738-1200
Fax: (703)761-9477
E-mail: web@spectrumcareers.com
URL: http://www.spectrumcareers.com

Description: Serves as executive search firm for accounting and finance, information technology and sales and marketing industries.

7965 ■ Sports Group International
7317 Spyglass Way, Ste. 400
Raleigh, NC 27615
Ph: (919)855-0226
Fax: (919)855-0793
E-mail: sgisearch@aol.com
URL: http://www.sgisearch.com

Serves as an executive search firm for the sporting goods and recreational products industries. Specializes in the recruitment of senior and middle level managers who excel in sales, marketing, product design and development, and general management.

7966 ■ Starpoint Solutions, LLC
22 Cortlandt St., Fl. 14
New York, NY 10007
Ph: (212)962-1550
Fax: (212)962-7175
URL: http://www.starpoint.com

Description: Serves as a staffing agency that places candidates in both freelance and full-time positions at Chicago and New York's advertising agencies, interactive agencies, and design firms.

7967 ■ Talent Driven
888 Humphrey
Birmingham, MI 48009
Ph: (248)496-9600
URL: http://www.talentdriven.com

Description: Serves as an executive search firm specializing in the creative industry. Provides positions for executive director level management, account executives, art directors, copywriters, creative directors, information architects, strategists, flash developers, human resources, programmers, and project managers.

7968 ■ Techtronix Technical Search
4805 N 24th Pl.
PO Box 17713
Milwaukee, WI 53217-0173
Ph: (414)466-3100
Fax: (414)466-3598

Firm specializes in recruiting executives for the engineering, information systems, manufacturing, marketing, finance, and human resources industries. Industries include electronic, manufacturing and finance.

7969 ■ Toby Clark Associates Inc.
405 E 54th St., Ste. 6C
New York, NY 10022-5128
Ph: (212)752-5670
Fax: (212)752-5674

Executive recruiting firm specializing in marketing communications and public relations. Industries served: all.

7970 ■ Tyler & Co.
375 N Ridge Rd., Ste. 400
Atlanta, GA 30350-3299
Ph: (770)396-3939
Fax: (770)396-6693
Fr: 800-989-6789
E-mail: art@tylerandco.com
URL: http://www.tylerandco.com

Retained executive search for the healthcare, food, market research, manufacturing and insurance industries.

7971 ■ Wendell L. Johnson Associates Inc.
12 Grandview Dr., Ste. 1117
Danbury, CT 06811-4321
Ph: (203)743-4112
Fax: (203)778-5377

Executive search firm specializing in areas of workforce diversity, accounting/finance, human resources, marketing/sales, strategic planning, and MIS.

7972 ■ Witzig Group
PO Box 6053
Bloomington, IL 61702
Ph: (309)664-7755
E-mail: witzig@witzig.com
URL: http://www.witzig.com

Executive search firm specializing in advertising and marketing communications. Includes all functions of the various marketing disciplines such as direct marketing, promotions, public relations, and interactive.

7973 ■ Young & Thulin
555 Clover Ln.
Boulder, CO 80303
Ph: (303)499-7242
Fax: (303)499-6436
E-mail: bill@ytsearch.com

A retained executive search firm formed to serve local and international technology, communications, medical and media industries. Assists in strengthening clients' management team or acquiring new talent. Works with companies that have a sound business plan, a solid market, and realistic potential for growth.

7974 ■ Zachary & Sanders Inc.
24 Linden Ln.
PO Box 32
East Norwich, NY 11732
Ph: (516)922-5500
Fax: (516)922-2286
Fr: 800-540-7919
E-mail: zacharyserch@earthlink.net

Serves the printing, packaging, publishing, advertising, direct marketing industries.

ONLINE JOB SOURCES AND SERVICES

7975 ■ AccountManager.com
E-mail: info@careermarketplace.com
URL: http://www.accountmanager.com

Description: Features account manager jobs and products to the account management community.

7976 ■ Ad Age TalentWorks
URL: http://adage.com/section/talentworks/474

Description: Provides a database of advertising jobs and resources for both job seekers and employers. Includes a collection of news and analysis regarding goings-on in the world of advertising.

7977 ■ AdRecruiter.com
URL: http://www.adrecruiter.com

Description: Provides job opportunities for professionals in the marketing and advertising industry.

7978 ■ AdvertiseCareers.com
URL: http://www.advertisecareers.com

Description: Provides job opportunities for marketing professionals.

7979 ■ AdvertisingCrossing.com
URL: http://www.advertisingcrossing.com

Description: Offers job opportunities in the advertising fields, including jobs for executives, managers, assistants, and entry-level workers.

7980 ■ AdvertisingIndustryJobs.com
URL: http://www.advertisingindustryjobs.com

Description: Features job opportunities, resume searching and postings for advertising professionals.

7981 ■ LobbyingJobs.com
URL: http://www.lobbyingjobs.com

Description: Provides online recruitment and career opportunities for individuals looking for lobbying firm or lobbyist jobs.

7982 ■ Marketing Advertising Jobs
URL: http://www.marketingadvertisingjobs.com

Description: Serves as a clearinghouse for professionals seeking positions in the marketing and advertising fields.

7983 ■ Marketing Career Network
Fr: 888-491-8833
URL: http://www.marketingcareernetwork.com

Description: Online recruitment resource that aligns employers with professional marketing membership organizations. Brings together audiences from every marketing discipline and connects them through a single job board network.

7984 ■ Marketing Research Association - Career Center
URL: http://www.marketingresearch.org/career

Description: Offers current job openings and career guide in the field of marketing research. Allows employers to view resumes and post jobs.

7985 ■ Marketing Specialist Jobs
URL: http://www.marketingspecialistjobs.com

Description: Provides employment opportunities for marketing specialists and marketing professionals.

7986 ■ MarketingCrossing.com
URL: http://www.marketingcrossing.com

Description: Offers collection of marketing jobs, including marketing director, marketing analyst, marketing content writer, and associate brand manager positions. Features industry-specific articles relating to job searches and developments in the marketing industry.

7987 ■ MarketingHire.com
URL: http://www.marketinghire.com

Description: Provides users with access to marketing jobs, advertising jobs and public relations jobs from respected employers. Enables employers and recruiters to reach a highly targeted audience of qualified marketing, advertising, PR, research and sales professionals.

7988 ■ MarketingJobForce.com
URL: http://www.marketingjobforce.com

Description: Online destination for professionals looking to enhance their careers in marketing.

7989 ■ MarketingJobs.com
URL: http://www.marketingjobs.com

Description: Provides professional jobs across the United States in sales, marketing, and advertising. Includes jobs from entry to executive level.

7990 ■ MarketResearchCareers.com
URL: http://www.marketresearchcareers.com

Description: Focuses exclusively on the market research industry. Offers a comprehensive database of resumes and jobs dedicated to market research professionals. Provides online services to fill marketing research jobs with a selection of qualified professionals.

7991 ■ Media-Match.com
URL: http://www.media-match.com/usa

Description: Serves as an online database of TV and film professionals' resumes and availabilities. Provides an up-to-date television production jobs board and film production jobs board for new openings in the film and TV production business across the United States.

7992 ■ MediaBistro.com
URL: http://www.mediabistro.com

Description: Serves as a career resource for anyone who creates or works with content, or who is a non-creative professional working in a content/creative industry (including editors, writers, producers, graphic designers, book publishers, and others in industries including magazines, television, film, radio, newspapers, book publishing, online media, advertising, PR, and design). Provides opportunities to meet, share resources, become informed of job opportunities and interesting projects and news, improve career skills, and showcase one's work.

7993 ■ MediaJobMarket.com
URL: http://jobs.adweek.com

Description: Exists as a job search resource for finding advertising and media jobs.

7994 ■ MediaRecruiter.com
E-mail: art@mediarecruiter.com
URL: http://www.mediarecruiter.com

Description: Provides a listing of media positions nationwide, serving the advertising and communications industry. Specializes in the areas of employment that are associated with the media, including management, marketing, news, talent, research, promotion, co-op, traffic, engineering, production, technical, and sales support.

7995 ■ Mobile Marketing Joblist
URL: http://www.mobilemarketingjoblist.com

Description: Focuses on the mobile marketing, special event, seasonal marketing, experiential marketing and promotional marketing industries.

7996 ■ New Sales and Marketing Jobs
URL: http://www.newsalesandmarketingjobs.com

Description: Provides an online listing of companies with available sales and marketing jobs in all specialties.

7997 ■ Omni Search, Inc.
E-mail: omni@omnisearch.biz
URL: http://www.omnisearch.biz/opps.htm

Description: Job search engine for those in the sales and marketing positions in the pharmaceutical, medical and consumer industries.

7998 ■ PR Manager Jobs
URL: http://www.prmanagerjobs.org

Description: Serves as a job board that features employment opportunities for public relations managers.

7999 ■ PRCrossing.com
URL: http://www.prcrossing.com

Description: Provides a collection of public relations job openings from Fortune 500 and Fortune 1,000 companies.

8000 ■ PrintCareers.com
URL: http://www.printcareers.com

Description: Provides job opportunities for marketing, advertising and creative professionals.

8001 ■ PrintingMVP.com
URL: http://www.printingmvp.com

Description: Provides job opportunities for marketing, advertising and creative professionals.

8002 ■ PRJobForce.com
URL: http://www.prjobforce.com

Description: Provides resources for public relations professionals including job listings for careers in public relations as well as resume posting.

8003 ■ PRMVP.com
URL: http://www.prmvp.com

Description: Provides job opportunities for public relations professionals.

8004 ■ PromotionsCareers.com
URL: http://www.promotionscareers.com

Description: Provides job opportunities for marketing professionals.

8005 ■ PRRecruiter.com
URL: http://www.prrecruiter.com

Description: Provides online job search for marketing, advertising jobs and resources for both job seekers and employers.

8006 ■ PublishingMVP.com
URL: http://www.publishingmvp.com

Description: Provides job opportunities in the publishing arena of the marketing industry.

8007 ■ Talent Zoo
E-mail: support@talentzoo.com
URL: http://www.talentzoo.com

Description: Serves as a resource for advertising, marketing, digital and creative jobs.

TRADESHOWS

8008 ■ Association for Accounting Marketing Summit
Association for Accounting Marketing
15000 Commerce Pkwy., Ste. C
Mount Laurel, NJ 08054
Ph: (856)380-6850
Fax: (856)439-0525
E-mail: info@accountingmarketing.org
URL: http://www.accountingmarketing.org

Annual. Features current trends in accounting marketing. Provides opportunities to build relationships through networking among peers in the accounting marketing industry.

8009 ■ Association of Hispanic Advertising Agencies Conference
Association of Hispanic Advertising Agencies
8400 Westpark Dr., 2nd Fl.
McLean, VA 22102
Ph: (703)610-9014
Fax: (703)610-0227
E-mail: info@ahaa.org
URL: http://www.ahaa.org

Semiannual. Primary Exhibits: Exhibits relating to Hispanic marketing and advertising. Dates and Locations: 2012 May 02-04; Miami, FL.

8010 ■ Build Business. Take Action.
Society for Marketing Professional Services
123 N. Pitt St., Ste. 400
Alexandria, VA 22314
Ph: (703)549-6117
Fax: (703)549-2498
Fr: 800-292-7677
E-mail: info@smps.org
URL: http://www.smps.org

Annual. Primary Exhibits: New business development equipment, supplies, and services. Dates and Locations: 2013 Jul 11-13; San Francisco, CA; Hyatt Regency San Francisco.

8011 ■ Convention Sales Professionals International Conference
Convention Sales Professionals International
191 Clarksville Rd.
Princeton Junction, NJ 08550
Ph: (609)269-2461
Fax: (609)799-7032
E-mail: info@cspionline.org
URL: http://www.cspionline.org

Annual. Primary Exhibits: Management and marketing products and services, for convention centers and convention bureaus.

8012 ■ Direct Marketing Association Annual Conference & Exhibition
Direct Marketing Association
1120 Avenue of the Americas
New York, NY 10036-6700
Ph: (212)768-7277
Fax: (212)302-6714
Fr: 800-255-0006
E-mail: customerservice@the-dma.org
URL: http://www.the-dma.org

Annual. Primary Exhibits: Printers, list brokers, envelope manufacturers, telephone marketing companies, computers and other equipment, supplies, and services for direct marketing.

8013 ■ DMD New York Conference and Expo
Direct Marketing Association
1120 Avenue of the Americas
New York, NY 10036-6700
Ph: (212)768-7277
Fax: (212)302-6714
Fr: 800-255-0006
E-mail: customerservice@the-dma.org
URL: http://www.the-dma.org

Annual. Primary Exhibits: Providing information covering all aspects of marketing, including Internet, radio, phone, Internet, and mail. Dates and Locations: 2012 Oct 13-18; Las Vegas, NV; Mandalay Bay.

8014 ■ Eight Sheet Outdoor Advertising Association Annual Conference
Eight Sheet Outdoor Advertising Association
PO Box 2680
Bremerton, WA 98310-0344
Ph: (360)377-9867
Fax: (360)377-9870
Fr: 800-874-3387
E-mail: ddjesoaa@comcast.net
URL: http://www.esoaa.com

Annual. Primary Exhibits: Exhibits relating to outdoor advertising.

8015 ■ International Collegiate Conference
American Marketing Association
311 S. Wacker Dr., Ste. 5800
Chicago, IL 60606
Ph: (312)542-9000
Fax: (312)542-9001
Fr: 800-AMA-1150
URL: http://www.marketingpower.com

Annual. Primary Exhibits: Provides career development and chapter management information. Includes demonstrations of collegiate chapter activities.

8016 ■ Marketing and Advertising Global Network Annual Meeting
Marketing and Advertising Global Network
1017 Perry Hwy., Ste. 5
Pittsburgh, PA 15237
Ph: (412)366-6850
Fax: (412)366-6840
E-mail: cheri@magnetglobal.org
URL: http://www.magnetglobal.org

Annual. Primary Exhibits: Exhibits relating to marketing and advertising. Dates and Locations: 2012 Oct 13-16; Cleveland, OH; Ritz Carlton.

8017 ■ Marketing Research Conference
American Marketing Association
311 S. Wacker Dr., Ste. 5800
Chicago, IL 60606
Ph: (312)542-9000
Fax: (312)542-9001
Fr: 800-AMA-1150
URL: http://www.marketingpower.com

Annual. Primary Exhibits: Marketing research products and services.

8018 ■ National Center for Database Marketing
Cowles Event Management
11 River Bend Dr. South
PO Box 4232
Stamford, CT 06907
Ph: (203)358-3751

Primary Exhibits: Database marketing industry exhibition.

8019 ■ National Federation of Press Women Conference
National Federation of Press Women
PO Box 5556
Arlington, VA 22205
Fax: (703)237-9808
Fr: 800-780-2715
E-mail: presswomen@aol.com
URL: http://www.nfpw.org

Annual. Features speakers as well as other activities, workshops, resources, and networking opportunities.

8020 ■ Net.Finance
Worldwide Business Research
535 Fifth Ave.
New York, NY 10017
Ph: 888-482-6012
Fax: (646)200-7535
E-mail: info@wbresearch.com
URL: http://www.wbresearch.com

Annual. Primary Exhibits: Internet marketing, interactive marketing, mobile business, e-commerce, social media marketing. Dates and Locations: 2012 May 21-23; Chandler, AZ; Sheraton Wildhorse Pass.

8021 ■ Outdoor Advertising Association of America Out of Home Media Conference & Marketing Expo
Outdoor Advertising Association of America
1850 M St. N.W., Ste. 1040
Washington, DC 20036
Ph: (202)833-5566
Fax: (202)833-1522
E-mail: kklein@oaaa.org
URL: http://www.oaaa.org

Biennial. Primary Exhibits: Exhibits relating to outdoor advertising.

8022 ■ PPAI Expo
Promotional Products Association International
3125 Skyway Cir. N.
Irving, TX 75038-3526
Ph: (972)258-3100
Fax: (972)258-3003
Fr: 888-492-6890
E-mail: expo@ppa.org
URL: http://www.ppa.org

Annual. Primary Exhibits: Specialty advertising and business gifts.

8023 ■ Retail Marketing Conference
Dydacomp
11 D Commerce Way
Totowa, NJ 07512-1154
Ph: (973)237-9415
Fax: (973)237-9043
Fr: 800-858-3666
E-mail: info@dydacomp.com
URL: http://www.dydacomp.com/

Primary Exhibits: Marketing industry exhibition.

OTHER SOURCES

8024 ■ ABA Marketing Network (ABAMN)
1120 Connecticut Ave. NW
Washington, DC 20036
Ph: (202)663-5269
Fax: (202)828-5053
Fr: 800-BAN-KERS
E-mail: marketingnetwork@aba.com
URL: http://www.aba.com/MarketingNetwork/
default.htm

Description: Marketing and public relations executives for commercial and savings banks, credit unions, and savings and loans associations, and related groups such as advertising agencies and research firms. Provides marketing education, information, and services to the financial services industry. Conducts research; cosponsors summer sessions of fundamentals and advanced courses in marketing at the University of Colorado at Boulder; compiles statistics.

8025 ■ Academy of Marketing Science (AMS)
PO Box 3072
Ruston, LA 71272
Ph: (318)257-2612
Fax: (318)257-4253
E-mail: ams@latech.edu
URL: http://www.ams-web.org

Description: Marketing academicians and practitioners; individuals interested in fostering education in marketing science. Aims to promote the advancement of knowledge and the furthering of professional standards in the field of marketing. Explores the special application areas of marketing science and its responsibilities as an economic, ethical, and social force; promotes research and the widespread dissemination of findings. Facilitates exchange of information and experience among members, and the transfer of marketing knowledge and technology to developing countries; promotes marketing science on an international level. Provides a forum for discussion and refinement of concepts, methods and applications, and the opportunity to publish papers in the field. Assists member educators in the development of improved teaching methods, devices, directions, and materials. Offers guidance and direction in marketing practice and reviewer assistance on scholarly works. Contributes to the solution of marketing problems encountered by individual firms, industries, and society as a whole. Encourages members to utilize their marketing talents to the fullest through redirection, reassignment, and relocation. Sponsors competitions.

8026 ■ Accountants Motivational Marketing Organization (AMMO)
1 Country Club Exec. Park
Glen Carbon, IL 62034

Ph: (618)288-8795
E-mail: charles@tzinberg.com
URL: http://accountantsadvmarketing.com

Description: Represents professionals and practitioners in marketing and accounting. Fosters excellence in accounting practice and services. Promotes the marketing and sales programs of members.

8027 ■ Advertising Club of New York (ACNY)
235 Park Ave. S, 6th Fl.
New York, NY 10003-1450
Ph: (212)533-8080
Fax: (212)533-1929
E-mail: gina@theadvertisingclub.org
URL: http://www.theadvertisingclub.org

Description: Professionals in advertising, publishing, marketing and business. Sponsors educational and public service activities, promotional and public relations projects and talks by celebrities and advertising persons. Conducts annual advertising and marketing course, which offers classes in copywriting, special graphics, verbal communication, advertising production, sale promotion, marketing and management. Sponsors competitions and charitable programs.

8028 ■ Advertising Council (AC)
815 2nd Ave., 9th Fl.
New York, NY 10017
Ph: (212)922-1500
Fax: (212)922-1676
Fr: 800-933-7727
E-mail: info@adcouncil.org
URL: http://www.adcouncil.org

Description: Founded and supported by American business, media, and advertising sectors to conduct public service advertising campaigns. Encourages advertising media to contribute time and space and advertising agencies to supply creative talent and facilities to further timely national causes. Specific campaigns include: Drug Abuse Prevention; AIDS Prevention; Teen-Alcoholism; Child Abuse; Crime Prevention; Forest Fire Prevention.

8029 ■ Advertising and Marketing International Network (AMIN)
3587 Northshore Dr.
Wayzata, MN 55391
Ph: (952)457-1116
Fax: (952)471-7752
E-mail: jsundby@aminworldwide.com
URL: http://www.aminworldwide.com

Description: Comprised of cooperative worldwide network of non-competing independent advertising agencies organized to provide facilities and branch office services for affiliated agencies.

8030 ■ Advertising Production Club of New York (APC)
Euro RSCG Life, 7th Fl.
200 Madison Ave.
New York, NY 10016
Ph: (212)251-7295
Fax: (212)726-5057
E-mail: admin@apc-ny.org
URL: http://www.apc-ny.org

Description: Production and traffic department personnel from advertising agencies, corporate or retail advertising departments, and publishing companies; college level graphic arts educators. Meetings include educational programs on graphic arts procedures and plant tours. Maintains employment service for members.

8031 ■ Advertising Research Foundation (ARF)
432 Park Ave. S, 6th Fl.
New York, NY 10016-8013
Ph: (212)751-5656
E-mail: cassandra@thearf.org
URL: http://www.thearf.org

Description: Advertisers, advertising agencies, research organizations, associations, and the media are regular members of the foundation; colleges and

universities are associate members. Objectives are to: further scientific practices and promote greater effectiveness of advertising and marketing by means of objective and impartial research; develop new research methods and techniques; analyze and evaluate existing methods and techniques, and define proper applications; establish research standards, criteria, and reporting methods. Compiles statistics and conducts research programs.

8032 ■ Advertising Women of New York (AWNY)
25 W 45th St., Ste. 403
New York, NY 10036
Ph: (212)221-7969
Fax: (212)221-8296
E-mail: awny@awny.org
URL: http://www.awny.org

Description: Women in advertising and related industries that provides a forum for professional growth, serves as catalyst for enhancement and advancement of women; promotes philanthropic endeavors. Conducts events of interest and benefit to members and non-members involved in the industry. Membership concentrated in the metropolitan New York area.

8033 ■ American Academy of Advertising (AAA)
24710 Shaker Blvd.
Beachwood, OH 44122
Ph: (786)393-3333
Fr: (866)607-8512
E-mail: director@aaasite.org
URL: http://www.aaasite.org

Description: Serves as a professional organization for college and university teachers of advertising and for industry professionals who wish to contribute to the development of advertising education.

8034 ■ American Advertising Federation (AAF)
1101 Vermont Ave. NW, Ste. 500
Washington, DC 20005-6306
Ph: (202)898-0089
Fax: (202)898-0159
Fr: 800-999-2231
E-mail: aaf@aaf.org
URL: http://www.aaf.org

Description: Works to advance the business of advertising as a vital and essential part of the American economy and culture through government and public relations; professional development and recognition; community service, social responsibility and high standards; and benefits and services to members. Operates Advertising Hall of Fame, Hall of Achievement, and National Student Advertising Competition. Maintains speakers' bureau.

8035 ■ American Association of Advertising Agencies (AAAA)
405 Lexington Ave., 18th Fl.
New York, NY 10174-1801
Ph: (212)682-2500
Fax: (212)682-8391
E-mail: nhill@aaaa.org
URL: http://www.aaaa.org

Description: Fosters development of the advertising industry; assists member agencies to operate more efficiently and profitably. Sponsors member information and international services. Maintains 47 committees. Conducts government relations.

8036 ■ American Marketing Association (AMA)
311 S Wacker Dr., Ste. 5800
Chicago, IL 60606
Ph: (312)542-9000
Fax: (312)542-9001
Fr: 800-262-1150
E-mail: info@ama.org
URL: http://www.marketingpower.com

Description: Serves as a professional society of

marketing and market research executives, sales and promotion managers, advertising specialists, academics, and others interested in marketing. Fosters research; sponsors seminars, conferences, and student marketing clubs; provides educational placement service and doctoral consortium.

8037 ■ American Society of Association Executives (ASAE)

1575 I St. NW
Washington, DC 20005
Ph: (202)371-0940
Fax: (202)371-8315
Fr: 888-950-2723
E-mail: asaeservice@asaecenter.org
URL: http://www.asaecenter.org

Description: Professional society of paid executives of international, national, state, and local trade, professional, and philanthropic associations. Seeks to educate association executives on effective management, including: the proper objectives, functions, and activities of associations; the basic principles of association management; the legal aspects of association activity; policies relating to association management; efficient methods, procedures, and techniques of association management; the responsibilities and professional standards of association executives. Maintains information resource center. Conducts resume, guidance, and consultation services; compiles statistics in the form of reports, surveys, and studies; carries out research and education. Maintains ASAE Services Corporation to provide special services and ASAE Foundation to do future-oriented research and make grant awards. Offers executive search services and insurance programs. Provides CEO center for chief staff executives. Conducts Certified Association Executive (CAE) program.

8038 ■ American Wholesale Marketers Association (AWMA)

2750 Prosperity Ave., Ste. 530
Fairfax, VA 22031
Ph: (703)208-3358
Fax: (703)573-5738
Fr: 800-482-2962
E-mail: info@awmanet.org
URL: http://www.awmanet.org

Description: Represents the interests of distributors of convenience-related products. Its members include wholesalers, retailers, manufacturers, brokers and allied organizations from across the U.S. and abroad. Programs include strong legislative representation in Washington and a broad spectrum of targeted education, business and information services. Sponsors the country's largest show for candy and convenience related products in conjunction with its semi-annual convention.

8039 ■ Asian American Advertising Federation (3AF)

PO Box 69851
West Hollywood, CA 90069
Ph: (310)289-5500
Fax: (310)289-5501
E-mail: nsong@iwgroupinc.com
URL: http://www.3af.org

Description: Represents Asian American advertising agency principals, media, advertisers and strategic partners. Strives to sustain the growth of the Asian American advertising and marketing industry. Aims to further professionalism in the fields of advertising and marketing.

8040 ■ Association for Accounting Marketing

15000 Commerce Pkwy., Ste. C
Mount Laurel, NJ 08054
Ph: (856)380-6850
Fax: (856)439-0525
E-mail: info@accountingmarketing.org
URL: http://www.accountingmarketing.org

Description: Provides resources and support to CPA and consulting firm marketing and sales professionals, partners, firm administrators and representatives of businesses that offer products and services to the accounting industry. Promotes accounting marketing industry growth, development and education through a network of chapters. Conducts a national conference and trade show, educational seminars and industry awards. Develops partnerships with other accounting industry associations.

8041 ■ Association of Independent Commercial Producers (AICP)

3 W 18th St., 5th Fl.
New York, NY 10011
Ph: (212)929-3000
Fax: (212)929-3359
E-mail: mattm@aicp.com
URL: http://www.aicp.com

Description: Represents the interests of companies that specialize in producing television commercials for advertisers and agencies, and the businesses that furnish supplies and services to this industry. Serves as a collective voice for the industry before government and business councils, and in union negotiations; disseminates information; works to develop industry standards and tools; provides professional development; and markets American production.

8042 ■ Association of International Product Marketing Managers

2533 N Carson St., Ste. 1996
Carson City, NV 89706
Fax: (781)917-0188
Fr: 877-275-5500
E-mail: contact@aipmm.com
URL: http://www.aipmm.com

Description: Product managers, brand managers, product marketing managers and other individuals responsible for guiding organizations and clients through a constantly changing business landscape. Focuses on providing educational programs and standards of excellence necessary for a product or brand professional to achieve professional recognition. Provides training, education, certification and professional networking opportunities.

8043 ■ Association of National Advertisers (ANA)

708 3rd Ave., 33rd Fl.
New York, NY 10017-4270
Ph: (212)697-5950
Fax: (212)687-7310
E-mail: bliodice@ana.net
URL: http://www.ana.net

Description: Serves the needs of members by providing marketing and advertising industry leadership in traditional and e-marketing, legislative leadership, information resources, professional development and industry-wide networking. Maintains offices in New York City and Washington, DC.

8044 ■ Association for Women in Communications (AWC)

3337 Duke St.
Alexandria, VA 22314
Ph: (703)370-7436
Fax: (703)342-4311
E-mail: info@womcom.org
URL: http://www.womcom.org

Description: Professional association of journalism and communications.

8045 ■ Business Marketing Association (BMA)

1833 Centre Point Cir., Ste. 123
Naperville, IL 60563
Ph: (630)544-5054
Fax: (630)544-5055
E-mail: info@marketing.org
URL: http://www.marketing.org

Description: Business-to-business marketing and communications professionals working in business, industry and the professions. Develops and delivers benefits, services, information, skill enhancement, and networking opportunities to help members grow, develop, and succeed throughout business-to-business careers.

8046 ■ Cabletelevision Advertising Bureau (CAB)

830 Third Ave., 2nd Fl.
New York, NY 10022
Ph: (212)508-1200
Fax: (212)832-3268
E-mail: joleenm@cabletvadbureau.com
URL: http://www.thecab.tv

Description: Ad-supported cable networks. Provides marketing and advertising support to members and promotes the use of cable by advertisers and ad agencies locally, regionally, and nationally.

8047 ■ Direct Marketing Association (DMA)

1120 Avenue of the Americas
New York, NY 10036-6700
Ph: (212)768-7277
Fax: (212)302-6714
E-mail: presiden@the-dma.org
URL: http://www.the-dma.org

Description: Manufacturers, wholesalers, public utilities, retailers, mail order firms, publishers, schools, clubs, insurance companies, financial organizations, business equipment manufacturers, paper and envelope manufacturers, list brokers, compilers, managers, owners, computer service bureaus, advertising agencies, letter shops, research organizations, printers, lithographers, creators and producers of direct mail and direct response advertising. Studies consumer and business attitudes toward direct mail and related direct marketing statistics. Offers Mail Preference Service for consumers who wish to receive less mail advertising, Mail Order Action Line to help resolve difficulties with mail order purchases and Telephone Preference Service for people who wish to receive fewer telephone sales calls. Maintains hall of fame; offers placement service; compiles statistics. Sponsors several three-day Basic Direct Marketing Institutes, Advanced Direct Marketing Institutes and special interest seminars and workshops. Maintains Government Affairs office in Washington, DC. Operates Direct Marketing Educational Foundation.

8048 ■ Direct Marketing Educational Foundation (DMEF)

1120 Avenue of the Americas
New York, NY 10036-6700
Ph: (212)768-7277
Fax: (212)790-1561
E-mail: dmef@directworks.org
URL: http://www.the-dma.org/dmef

Description: Represents individuals, firms, and organizations interested in furthering college-level education in direct marketing. Functions as the collegiate arm of the direct marketing profession. Sponsors a summer internship, programs for students and professors, and campaign competition for students. Provides educational materials and course outlines to faculty members; arranges for speakers for college classes and clubs. Co-sponsors academic research competitions. Maintains hall of fame.

8049 ■ Hispanic Marketing and Communication Association (HMCA)

PO Box 565891
Miami, FL 33256-5891
Ph: (305)648-2848
E-mail: hmca@hmca.org
URL: http://www.hmca.org

Description: Represents individuals of diverse backgrounds with a common interest in the Hispanic market in the United States, Latin America and the Caribbean. Promotes excellence in Hispanic marketing. Encourages professional development. Provides opportunities to network among practitioners who practice or have an interest in the Hispanic Market.

8050 ■ Information Technology Services Marketing Association (ITSMA)

Lexington Office Park
420 Bedford St., Ste. 110
Lexington, MA 02420
Ph: (781)862-8500
Fax: (781)674-1366
E-mail: info@itsma.com
URL: http://www.itsma.com

Description: Supports marketing executives who market and sell technology-related services and solutions. Provides research, consulting and training to the world's leading technology, communications, and professional services providers. Facilitates peer sharing and networking opportunities among members.

8051 ■ Intermarket Agency Network (IAN)

5307 S 92nd St.
Hales Corners, WI 53130
Ph: (414)425-8800
Fax: (414)425-0021
E-mail: camg@greenrubio.com
URL: http://www.intermarketnetwork.com

Description: An active network of high-powered marketing/communications agencies in the United States, Canada, Central and South America, and Europe.

8052 ■ International Design Guild (IDG)

670 Commercial St.
Manchester, NH 03101
Fr: 800-205-4345
E-mail: info@design-guild.com
URL: http://www.design-guild.com

Description: Brings together interior designers to share and gain insight for business development and networking. Provides members with customizable marketing, merchandising, educational and operational tools. Aims to help members operate their businesses more profitably.

8053 ■ Mailing and Fulfillment Service Association (MFSA)

1421 Prince St., Ste. 410
Alexandria, VA 22314-2806
Ph: (703)836-9200
Fax: (703)548-8204
Fr: 800-333-6272
E-mail: mfsa-mail@mfsanet.org
URL: http://www.mfsanet.org

Description: Commercial direct mail producers, letter shops, mailing list houses, fulfillment operations, and advertising agencies. Conducts special interest group meetings. Offers specialized education; conducts research programs.

8054 ■ Marketing and Advertising Global Network (MAGNET)

1017 Perry Hwy., Ste. 5
Pittsburgh, PA 15237
Ph: (412)366-6850
Fax: (412)366-6840
E-mail: mxdirector@verizon.net
URL: http://www.magnetglobal.org

Description: Cooperative network of non-competing advertising, marketing, merchandising, and public relations agencies. Aims to bring about, through mutual cooperation, greater accomplishment and efficiency in the management of member advertising agencies. Other goals are: to raise standards of the advertising agency business through the exchange of information relative to agency management and all phases of advertising; to exchange information on all common problems, such as management, sales development, market studies, agency functions, and operations. Aims to inform the general public of current global marketing trends.

8055 ■ Marketing Agencies Association Worldwide (MAA)

89 Woodland Cir.
Minneapolis, MN 55424

Ph: (952)922-0130
Fax: (760)437-4141
E-mail: keith.mccracken@maaw.org
URL: http://www.maaw.org

Description: Represents the interests of CEOs, presidents, managing directors and principals of top marketing services agencies. Provides opportunity for marketing professionals to meet with peers, raise company profile on both a national and a global platform, and influence the future of industry. Fosters networking through conferences.

8056 ■ Marketing Research Association (MRA)

110 National Dr., 2nd Fl.
Glastonbury, CT 06033-1212
Ph: (860)682-1000
Fax: (860)682-1050
E-mail: email@mra-net.org
URL: http://www.mra-net.org

Description: Companies and individuals involved in any area of opinion and marketing research, such as data collection, research, or as an end-user.

8057 ■ Multi-Level Marketing International Association

119 Stanford Ct.
Irvine, CA 92612
Ph: (949)854-0484
Fax: (949)854-7687
E-mail: info@mlmia.com
URL: http://www.mlmia.com

Description: Represents the interest of direct sales/multi level/network marketing companies, supporters and distributors. Focuses its efforts specifically on the protection, support and promotion of the individual opportunities and entrepreneurial aspects of the network marketing/multi-level marketing/direct sales industry. Provides diversified member programs, services, seminars, publications, training, educational, informational assistance, and special benefits.

8058 ■ National Alliance of Market Developers (NAMD)

620 Sheridan Ave.
Plainfield, NJ 07060
Ph: (908)561-4062
E-mail: clyde@allenandpartners.com
URL: http://www.namdntl.org

Description: Professionals engaged in marketing, sales, sales promotion, advertising, or public relations who are concerned with the delivery of goods and services to the minority consumer market.

8059 ■ National Black Public Relations Society

14636 Runnymede St.
Van Nuys, CA 91405
Fax: 888-976-0005
Fr: 888-976-0005
URL: http://www.nbprs.org

Description: Serves the interests of black professionals in public relations, media relations, corporate communications, investor relations, government affairs, community relations, and related fields. Addresses the needs of members through programs and partnerships. Offers peer-to-peer support, mentorship, networking, job opportunities, internships, and career advancement.

8060 ■ National Federation of Press Women

PO Box 5556
Arlington, VA 22205
Fax: (703)237-9808
Fr: 800-780-2715
E-mail: presswomen@aol.com
URL: http://www.nfpw.org

Description: Serves as a group of professional women and men pursuing careers across the communications spectrum.

8061 ■ National Management Association (NMA)

2210 Arbor Blvd.
Dayton, OH 45439
Ph: (937)294-0421
Fax: (937)294-2374
E-mail: nma@nma1.org
URL: http://www.nma1.org

Description: Business and industrial management personnel; membership comes from supervisory level, with the remainder from middle management and above. Seeks to develop and recognize management as a profession and to promote the free enterprise system. Prepares chapter programs on basic management, management policy and practice, communications, human behavior, industrial relations, economics, political education, and liberal education. Maintains speakers' bureau and hall of fame. Maintains educational, charitable, and research programs. Sponsors charitable programs.

8062 ■ National School Public Relations Association (NSPRA)

15948 Derwood Rd.
Rockville, MD 20855-2123
Ph: (301)519-0496
Fax: (301)519-0494
E-mail: info@nspra.org
URL: http://www.nspra.org

Description: Represents school system public relations directors, school administrators, and others interested in furthering public understanding of the public schools. Has adopted standards for public relations professionals and programs and an accreditation program.

8063 ■ Outdoor Advertising Association of America (OAAA)

1850 M St. NW, Ste. 1040
Washington, DC 20036
Ph: (202)833-5566
Fax: (202)833-1522
E-mail: kklein@oaaa.org
URL: http://www.oaaa.org

Description: Firms owning, erecting, and maintaining standardized poster panels and painted display advertising facilities. Aims to provide leadership, services, and standards to promote, protect and advance the outdoor advertising industry.

8064 ■ PKF North American Network (PFK NA)

1745 N Brown Rd., Ste. 350
Lawrenceville, GA 30043
Ph: (770)279-4560
Fax: (770)279-4566
E-mail: tsnyder@pkfnan.org
URL: http://www.pkfna.org

Description: Independent certified public accounting firms practicing on a regional or local basis. Objectives are to: strengthen accounting practices; increase competency and quality of service; provide a practice management program; maintain technical competence in accounting principles and auditing standards; make available a reservoir of specialists who are immediately accessible to members; provide for the sharing of skills, knowledge and experience. Offers technical, marketing, and public relations support; promotes continuing professional education; facilitates networking. Conducts 4 staff development, 2 tax training, and 3 manager/partner training courses per year; operates committees and task forces.

8065 ■ Point-of-Purchase Advertising International (POPAI)

1600 Duke St., Ste. 610
Alexandria, VA 22314
Ph: (703)373-8800
Fax: (703)373-8801
URL: http://www.popai.com

Description: Producers and suppliers of point-of-purchase advertising signs and displays and national and regional advertisers and retailers interested in use and effectiveness of signs, displays and other point-of-purchase media. Conducts student education programs; maintains speakers' bureau.

8066 ■ PROMAXBDA

1522e Cloverfield Blvd.
Santa Monica, CA 90404
Ph: (310)788-7600
Fax: (310)788-7616
E-mail: jbv@promaxbda.org
URL: http://www.promaxbda.org

Description: Advertising, public relations, and promotion managers of cable, radio, and television stations, systems and networks; syndicators. Seeks to: advance the role and increase the effectiveness of promotion and marketing within the industry, related industries, and educational communities. Conducts workshops and weekly fax service for members. Operates employment service. Maintains speakers' bureau, hall of fame, and resource center with print, audio, and visual materials.

8067 ■ Promotion Marketing Association (PMA)

650 First Ave., Ste. 2-5W
New York, NY 10016
Ph: (212)420-1100
Fax: (212)533-7622
E-mail: pma@pmalink.org
URL: http://www.pmalink.org

Description: Fortune 500 marketer companies, promotion agencies, and companies using promotion programs; supplier members are manufacturers of package goods, cosmetics, and pharmaceuticals, consultants, and advertising agencies. Conducts surveys and studies of industry issues.

8068 ■ Promotional Products Association International (PPAI)

3125 Skyway Cir. N
Irving, TX 75038-3526
Ph: (972)252-0404
Fax: (972)258-3004
Fr: 888-426-7724
E-mail: membership@ppai.org
URL: http://www.ppai.org

Description: Suppliers and distributors of promo-tional products including incentives, imprinted ad specialties, premiums, and executive gifts. Promotes industry contacts in 60 countries. Holds executive development and sales training seminars. Conducts research and compiles statistics. Administers industry advertising and public relations program. Maintains speakers' bureau. Conducts trade shows, regional training, publishes educational resources.

8069 ■ Public Relations Society of America (PRSA)

33 Maiden Ln., 11th Fl.
New York, NY 10038-5150
Ph: (212)460-1400
Fax: (212)995-0757
E-mail: william.murray@prsa.org
URL: http://www.prsa.org

Description: Professional society of public relations practitioners in business and industry, counseling firms, government, associations, hospitals, schools, and nonprofit organizations. Conducts professional development programs. Maintains a Professional Resource Center. Offers accreditation program.

8070 ■ Retail Advertising and Marketing Association (RAMA)

325 7th St. NW, Ste. 1100
Washington, DC 20004-2818
Ph: (202)661-3052
Fax: (202)737-2849
E-mail: gattim@nrf.com
URL: http://www.rama-nrf.org

Description: Persons in retail sales promotion, advertising and marketing and persons serving retailers in promotional capacities. Elects one professional to the Retail Advertising Hall of Fame. Conducts research programs.

8071 ■ Society for Marketing Professional Services (SMPS)

44 Canal Center Plz., Ste. 444
Alexandria, VA 22314
Ph: (703)549-6117
Fax: (703)549-2498
Fr: 800-292-7677
E-mail: info@smps.org
URL: http://www.smps.org

Description: Marketing employees of architectural, engineering, planning, interior design, landscape architectural, and construction management firms who are responsible for the new business development of their companies. Compiles statistics. Offers local and national educational programs; maintains certification program.

8072 ■ Trade Show Exhibitors Association (TSEA)

2301 S Lake Shore Dr., Ste. 1005
Chicago, IL 60616
Ph: (312)842-8732
Fax: (312)842-8744
E-mail: membership@tsea.org
URL: http://www.tsea.org

Description: Exhibitors working to improve the effectiveness of trade shows as a marketing tool. Purposes are to promote the progress and development of trade show exhibiting; to collect and disseminate trade show information; conduct studies, surveys, and stated projects designed to improve trade shows; to foster good relations and communications with organizations representing others in the industry; to undertake other activities necessary to promote the welfare of member companies. Sponsors Exhibit Industry Education Foundation and professional exhibiting seminars; the forum series of educational programs on key issues affecting the industry. Maintains placement services; compiles statistics.

8073 ■ Transworld Advertising Agency Network (TAAN)

814 Watertown St.
Newton, MA 02465
Ph: (617)795-1706
Fax: (419)730-1706
E-mail: peterg@taan.org
URL: http://www.taan.org

Description: Independently owned advertising agencies that cooperate for exchange of management education and information, reciprocal service, and personal local contact. Allows members to seek aid of other members in campaign planning, creative services, merchandising, public relations, publicity, media, research, and test facilities. Conducts annual expertise audit.

8074 ■ *American Journal of Family Therapy*
Routledge Journals
270 Madison Ave.
New York, NY 10016-0601
Ph: (212)216-7800
Fax: (212)563-2269
URL: http://www.tandf.co.uk/journals/titles/
   01926187.asp

$200.00/year for institutions, print + online; $180.00/year for individuals, online only; $92.00/year for individuals, print only; $332.00/year for institutions, print + online; $299.00/year for institutions, online only; $155.00/year for individuals, print only; $264.00/year for institutions, print + online; $238.00/year for institutions, online only; $123.00/year for individuals, print only. Periodical covering the techniques for treating families, theory on normal and dysfunctional family relationships, research on sexuality and intimacy, the effects of traditional and alternative family styles, and community approaches to family intervention. Also includes family measurement techniques, family behavioral medicine and health, family law issues in family therapy practice, and continuing education and training.

8075 ■ *Family Relations*
National Council on Family Relations
1201 W River Pkwy., Ste. 200
Minneapolis, MN 55454-1115
Ph: (763)781-9331
Fax: (763)781-9348
Fr: 888-781-9331
URL: http://www.ncfr.org/journals/family_relations/
   home.asp

$136.00/year for individuals, print and online; $55.00/year for other countries, student, print and online; $165.00/year for individuals, Europe (euro zone); print and online; $82.00/year for students, Europe (euro zone); print and online; $110.00/year for other countries, print and online; $55.00/year for students, Europe, non-euro zone, print and online; $1,155.00/year for institutions, print + online; $1,004.00/year for institutions, print or online only; $1,119.00/year for institutions, other countries, print + online; $883.00/year for institutions, other countries, print + online. Publication for family practitioners and academics on relationships across the life cycle with implications for intervention, education and public policy.

8076 ■ *Family Studies Abstracts*
EBSCO Publishing Inc.
10 Estes St.
Ipswich, MA 01938
Ph: (978)356-6500
Fax: (978)356-6565
Fr: 800-653-2726
URL: http://www.ebscohost.com/
   thisTopic.php?marketID=1&topicID=95

Quarterly. $999.00/year for institutions, print only;

$215.00/year for individuals, print only; $275.00/year for single issue, institutional; $70.00/year for single issue, individual. Journal containing family studies abstracts.

8077 ■ *Family Therapy News*
American Association for Marriage and Family Therapy
112 S Alfred St.
Alexandria, VA 22314-3061
Ph: (703)838-9808
Fax: (703)838-9805
E-mail: central@aamft.org
URL: http://www.aamft.org

Description: Bimonthly. Provides broad coverage of news in the field of marital and family therapy. Reports legislative and other governmental and organizational developments affecting families. Recurring features include letters to the editor, interviews with leading therapists, information on workshops and conferences, and regional news.

8078 ■ *Journal of Counseling Psychology*
American Psychological Association
750 1st St. NE
Washington, DC 20002-4242
Ph: (202)336-5500
Fax: (202)336-5549
Fr: 800-374-2721
E-mail: journals@apa.org
URL: http://www.apa.org/pubs/journals/cou/
   index.aspx

Quarterly. $55.00/year for members, domestic; $77.00/year for members, foreign, surface; $89.00/year for members, foreign, air mail; $44.00/year for students, domestic; $66.00/year for students, foreign, surface; $78.00/year for students, foreign, air mail; $145.00/year for nonmembers, domestic; $172.00/year for nonmembers, foreign, surface; $183.00/year for nonmembers, foreign, air mail; $415.00/year for institutions, domestic. Journal presenting empirical studies about counseling processes and interventions, theoretical articles about counseling, and studies dealing with evaluation of counseling applications and programs.

8079 ■ *Journal of Divorce and Remarriage*
Routledge Journals
270 Madison Ave.
New York, NY 10016-0601
Ph: (212)216-7800
Fax: (212)563-2269
URL: http://www.tandf.co.uk/journals/WJDR

$158.00/year for individuals, online only; $171.00/year for individuals, print + online; $1,495.00/year for institutions, online only; $1,661.00/year for institutions, print + online. Journal covering all aspects of divorce, including pre-divorce marital and family treatment, marital separation and dissolution, children's responses to divorce and separation, single parenting, remarriage, and stepfamilies.

8080 ■ *Journal of Family Psychology*
American Psychological Association
750 1st St. NE
Washington, DC 20002-4242
Ph: (202)336-5500
Fax: (202)336-5549
Fr: 800-374-2721
E-mail: journals@apa.org
URL: http://www.apa.org/journals/fam.html

Bimonthly. $55.00/year for members, domestic; $78.00/year for members, surface; $97.00/year for members, airmail; $47.00/year for students, domestic; $70.00/year for students, foreign, surface; $89.00/year for students, foreign, air mail; $156.00/year for nonmembers, domestic; $187.00/year for nonmembers, surface, airmail; $202.00/year for nonmembers, airmail; $465.00/year for institutions, domestic. Journal reporting on theory, research, and clinical practice in family psychology; including articles on family and marital theory and concepts, research and evaluation, therapeutic frameworks and methods, and policies and legal matters concerning family and marriage.

8081 ■ *Journal of Family Psychotherapy*
Routledge Journals
270 Madison Ave.
New York, NY 10016-0601
Ph: (212)216-7800
Fax: (212)563-2269
URL: http://www.tandf.co.uk/journals/WJFP

Quarterly. $110.00/year for individuals, online only; $118.00/year for individuals, print + online; $624.00/year for institutions, online only; $693.00/year for institutions, print + online. Journal includes case studies, treatment reports, and strategies in clinical practice for psychotherapists.

8082 ■ *Journal of Family Social Work*
Routledge Journals
270 Madison Ave.
New York, NY 10016-0601
Ph: (212)216-7800
Fax: (212)563-2269
URL: http://www.tandf.co.uk/journals/WFSW

$133.00/year for individuals, online only; $141.00/year for individuals, print + online; $341.00/year for institutions, online only; $379.00/year for institutions, print + online. Journal serves as a forum for family practitioners, scholars, and educators in the field of social work.

8083 ■ *Journal of Feminist Family Therapy*
Routledge Journals
270 Madison Ave.
New York, NY 10016-0601
Ph: (212)216-7800
Fax: (212)563-2269
URL: http://www.tandf.co.uk/journals/WFFT

Quarterly. $110.00/year for individuals, online only; $118.00/year for individuals, print + online; $624.00/year for institutions, online only; $693.00/year for institutions, print + online. Journal exploring the relationship between feminist theory and family therapy practice and theory.

8084 ■ *Journal of Marital & Family Therapy*
American Association for Marriage and Family Therapy
112 S Alfred St.
Alexandria, VA 22314-3061
Ph: (703)838-9808
Fax: (703)838-9805
URL: http://www.aamft.org/

Quarterly. $81.00/year for individuals, print & online; $326.00/year for institutions, print & premium online; $296.00/year for institutions, online. Peer-reviewed journal for professional therapists. Covers clinical techniques, research, and theory of marital and family therapy.

8085 ■ *Journal of Marriage and Family*
National Council on Family Relations
1201 W River Pkwy., Ste. 200
Minneapolis, MN 55454-1115
Ph: (763)781-9331
Fax: (763)781-9348
Fr: 888-781-9331
URL: http://www.ncfr.org/jmf

Quarterly. Publication in the family field featuring original research and theory, research interpretation, and critical discussion related to marriage and the family.

8086 ■ *Marriage and Family Review*
Routledge Journals
270 Madison Ave.
New York, NY 10016-0601
Ph: (212)216-7800
Fax: (212)563-2269
URL: http://www.tandf.co.uk/journals/WMFR

$241.00/year for individuals, online only; $258.00/year for individuals, print + online; $1,522.00/year for institutions, online only; $1,691.00/year for institutions, print + online. Journal for socially oriented and clinically oriented marriage and family specialists in a broad range of research and applied disciplines.

8087 ■ *Monitor on Psychology*
American Psychological Association
750 1st St. NE
Washington, DC 20002-4242
Ph: (202)336-5500
Fax: (202)336-5549
Fr: 800-374-2721
E-mail: journals@apa.org
URL: http://www.apa.org/monitor/

$50.00/year for nonmembers; $99.00/year for individuals, foreign, surface freight; $126.00/year for individuals, foreign, air mail; $93.00/year for institutions; $190.00/year for institutions, surface freight; $217.00/year for institutions, air freight; $20.00/year for single issue. Magazine of the APA. Reports on the science, profession, and social responsibility of psychology, including latest legislative developments affecting mental health, education, and research support.

HANDBOOKS AND MANUALS

8088 ■ *101 Careers in Counseling*
Springer Publishing Company
11 W 42nd St., 15th Fl.
New York, NY 10036
Ph: (212)431-4370
Fax: (212)941-7842
Fr: 877-687-7476
URL: http://www.springerpub.com

Shannon Hodges. 2012. $25.00 (paper). 332 pages. Describes the many benefits of a counseling career and explores a wealth of opportunities in both traditional and non-traditional settings. Includes an overview, salary range, employment prospects, best

and most challenging aspects of the job, and educational and licensing requirements.

8089 ■ *Careers in Social and Rehabilitation Services*
The McGraw-Hill Companies
PO Box 182604
Columbus, OH 43272
Fax: (614)759-3749
Fr: 877-883-5524
E-mail: customer.service@mcgraw-hill.com
URL: http://www.mhprofessional.com/
    product.php?isbn=0071641955

Geraldine O. Garner. 2008. $16.95. 192 pages.

8090 ■ *Great Jobs for Liberal Arts Majors*
The McGraw-Hill Companies
PO Box 182604
Columbus, OH 43272
Fax: (614)759-3749
Fr: 877-883-5524
E-mail: customer.service@mcgraw-hill.com
URL: http://www.mhprofessional.com/
    product.php?isbn=0071482148

Blythe Camenson. Second edition, 2007. $16.95 (paper). 192 pages.

TRADESHOWS

8091 ■ American Counseling Association Conference and Exposition
American Counseling Association
5999 Stevenson Ave.
Alexandria, VA 22304-3300
Fax: 800-473-2329
Fr: 800-347-6647
E-mail: membership@counseling.org
URL: http://www.counseling.org

Annual. Primary Exhibits: Books, career development information, college selection, student financial aid, testing and measurement techniques, practice management companies, software, rehabilitation aids, and community agencies and private clinics specializing in substance abuse and mental health. Dates and Locations: 2012 Mar 21-25; San Francisco, CA.

8092 ■ Association for Counselor Education and Supervision National Conference
Association for Counselor Education and Supervision
5999 Stevenson Ave.
Alexandria, VA 22304
Ph: (703)212-2237
Fr: (866)815-2237
URL: http://www.acesonline.net

Annual. Primary Exhibits: Exhibits relating to the professional preparation of counselors.

OTHER SOURCES

8093 ■ Alliance for Children and Families
11700 W Lake Park Dr.
Milwaukee, WI 53224-3099
Ph: (414)359-1040
Fax: (414)359-1074
E-mail: severson@alliance1.org
URL: http://www.alliance1.org

Description: Membership organization of local agencies in thousands of communities providing family counseling, family life education, residential treatment, and family advocacy services, and other programs to help families with parent-child, marital, mental health, and other problems. Assists member agencies in developing capacity and maintaining high performance. Compiles statistics; conducts research. Maintains extensive files of unpublished materials from member agencies.

8094 ■ American Association for Marriage and Family Therapy (AAMFT)
112 S Alfred St.
Alexandria, VA 22314-3061
Ph: (703)838-9808
Fax: (703)838-9805
E-mail: central@aamft.org
URL: http://www.aamft.org

Description: Professional society of marriage and family therapists. Assumes a major role in developing and maintaining the highest standards of excellence in this field. Conducts 76 accredited training programs throughout the U.S. Sponsors educational and research programs.

8095 ■ American Psychological Association (APA)
750 First St. NE
Washington, DC 20002-4242
Ph: (202)336-5500
Fax: (202)336-6069
Fr: 800-374-2721
E-mail: president@apa.org
URL: http://www.apa.org

Description: Scientific and professional society of psychologists; students participate as affiliates. Advances psychology as a science, a profession, and as a means of promoting health, education and the human welfare.

8096 ■ Association of Family and Conciliation Courts (AFCC)
6525 Grand Teton Plz.
Madison, WI 53719
Ph: (608)664-3750
Fax: (608)664-3751
E-mail: afcc@afccnet.org
URL: http://www.afccnet.org

Description: Judges, counselors, family court personnel, attorneys, mediators, researchers, and teachers concerned with the resolution of family disputes as they affect children. Proposes to develop and improve the practice of dispute resolution procedure as a complement to judicial procedures. Aims to strengthen the family unit and minimize family strife by improving the process of marriage, family, and divorce counseling; and to provide an interdisciplinary forum for the exchange of ideas, for the creation of new approaches to child custody matters and solutions to problems of family discord. Collaborates with the National Council of Juvenile and Family Court Judges, National Judicial College, the National Center for State Courts, the American Bar Association and several universities, law schools, and state organizations responsible for providing ongoing training for attorneys, judges, and family therapists. Conducts research and offers technical assistance and training to courts, legal associations, judicial organizations, and behavioral science professionals.

8097 ■ International Association for Marriage and Family Counselors (IAMFC)
Texas A&M University - Corpus Christi
College of Education
6300 Ocean Dr.
Corpus Christi, TX 78412
Ph: (361)825-2307
Fr: 800-347-6647
E-mail: robert.smith@tamucc.edu
URL: http://www.counseling.org

Description: A division of the American Counseling Association. Individuals working in the areas of marriage counseling, marital therapy, divorce counseling, mediation, and family counseling and therapy; interested others. Promotes ethical practices in marriage and family counseling/therapy. Encourages research; provides a forum for dialogue on relevant issues; facilitates the exchange of information. Assists couples and families in coping with life challenges; works to ameliorate problems confronting families and married couples.

8098 ■ National Council on Family Relations (NCFR)
1201 W River Pkwy., Ste. 200
Minneapolis, MN 55454-1115
Ph: (763)781-9331
Fax: (763)781-9348
Fr: 888-781-9331
E-mail: info@ncfr.org
URL: http://www.ncfr.org
Description: Multidisciplinary group of family life professionals, including clergy, counselors, educators, home economists, lawyers, nurses, therapists, librarians, physicians, psychologists, social workers, sociologists, and researchers. Seeks to provide opportunities for members to plan and act together to advance marriage and family life through consultation, conferences, and the dissemination of information and research.

SOURCES OF HELP-WANTED ADS

8099 ■ *Acta Mathematica*
Springer-Verlag New York Inc.
233 Spring St.
New York, NY 10013-1578
Ph: (212)460-1500
Fax: (212)460-1575
Fr: 800-777-4643
URL: http://www.springer.com/math/journal/11511

$440.00/year for institutions, print or online; $528.00/ year for institutions, print & enchanced access. Journal for mathematics.

8100 ■ *Association for Women in Mathematics Newsletter*
Association for Women in Mathematics
11240 Waples Mill Rd., Ste. 200
Fairfax, VA 22030
Ph: (703)934-0163
Fax: (703)359-7562
E-mail: awm@awm-math.org
URL: http://www.awm-math.org/newsletter.html

Description: Six issues/year. Has a circulation of 3,500. $50/year for libraries, women's studies centers, and non-mathematics departments. Concerned with the progress of women in professional fields, particularly in mathematics and related careers. Recounts facets of the history of women in mathematics, discusses issues related to education, and highlights women being honored for studies and achievements. Recurring features include letters to the editor and a section on job openings.

8101 ■ *The Broadcast*
EYH Network
Mills College
5000 Macarthur Blvd.
Oakland, CA 94613
Ph: (510)430-2222
Fax: (510)430-2090
E-mail: msneyh@mills.edu
URL: http://www.expandingyourhorizons.org/news/ newsletters.php

Description: Quarterly. Carries news of the Network, which is interested in promoting the continuing development in mathematics and science of all people, with special emphasis on the needs of women. Recurring features include information on career education conferences, teacher education programs which encourage girls and women to pursue scientific careers, and news of resources available.

8102 ■ *Communications in Mathematical Analysis (CMA)*
Howard University Press
2225 Georgia Ave. NW, Ste. 718
Washington, DC 20059
Ph: (202)238-2518
Fax: (202)986-2005

Fr: 800-537-5487
E-mail: cma.math@gmail.com
URL: http://math-res-pub.org/cma

Semiannual. Peer-reviewed journal focusing on analysis and applications of mathematics.

8103 ■ *Electronic Research Announcements in Mathematical Sciences*
American Mathematical Society
201 Charles St.
Providence, RI 02904-2294
Ph: (401)455-4000
Fax: (401)331-3842
Fr: 800-321-4267
URL: http://www.math.psu.edu/era/

Free. Electronic journal publishing announcements of significant advances in all branches of mathematics.

8104 ■ *Employment Information in the Mathematical Sciences/Journal*
American Mathematical Society
201 Charles St.
Providence, RI 02904-2294
Ph: (401)455-4000
Fax: (401)331-3842
Fr: 800-321-4267
E-mail: reprint-permission@ams.org
URL: http://www.ams.org/profession/employment-services/eims/eims-home

Description: Six issues/year. Provides concise listings of open positions (1,400-1,500/yr.) suitable for mathematicians with education and experience at every level beyond the Bachelor's degree. Lists positions by state.

8105 ■ *Global Journal of Pure and Applied Mathematics (GJPAM)*
Howard University Press
2225 Georgia Ave. NW, Ste. 718
Washington, DC 20059
Ph: (202)238-2518
Fax: (202)986-2005
Fr: 800-537-5487
URL: http://www.ripublication.com/gjpam.htm

$580.00/year for institutions, print & online; $290.00/ year for individuals, print & online. Journal publishing research articles from pure and applied mathematics. Covers pure and applied aspects of all sub-disciplines of mathematical analysis.

8106 ■ *International Journal of Fluid Mechanics Research*
Begell House Inc.
50 Cross Hwy.
Redding, CT 06896
Ph: (203)938-1300
Fax: (203)938-1304
URL: http://www.begellhouse.com/journals/ 71cb29ca5b40f8f8

$1,811.00/year for institutions. Journal publishing articles on fluid mechanics.

8107 ■ *International Journal for Multiscale Computational Engineering*
Begell House Inc.
50 Cross Hwy.
Redding, CT 06896
Ph: (203)938-1300
Fax: (203)938-1304
URL: http://www.begellhouse.com/journals/ 61fd1b191cf7e96f

$1,245.00/year for institutions. Journal featuring the advancement of multiscale computational science and engineering.

8108 ■ *ISRN Signal Processing*
Hindawi Publishing Corporation
410 Park Ave., 15th Fl.
287 PMB
New York, NY 10022
E-mail: sp@isrn.com
URL: http://www.isrn.com/journals/sp

Peer-reviewed journal publishing information in all areas of signal processing.

8109 ■ *Journal of Applied Mathematics*
Hindawi Publishing Corp.
410 Park Ave., 15th Fl.
287 PMB
New York, NY 10022-4407
Fax: (215)893-4392
E-mail: jam@hindawi.com
URL: http://www.hindawi.com/journals/jam/

Annual. $295.00/year for individuals. Journal that publishes original Research papers and review articles in all areas of applied, computational, and industrial mathematics.

8110 ■ *Journal of Concrete and Applicable Mathematics*
Nova Science Publishers Inc.
400 Oser Ave., Ste. 1600
Hauppauge, NY 11788-3667
Ph: (631)231-7269
Fax: (631)231-8175
URL: http://www.msci.memphis.edu/~ganastss/ jcaam/

Quarterly. Peer-reviewed international journal that publishes high quality original research articles from all sub-areas of non-pure and/or applicable mathematics as well connections to other areas of mathematical sciences.

8111 ■ *Journal of Mathematics and the Arts*
Taylor & Francis Group Journals
325 Chestnut St., Ste. 800
Philadelphia, PA 19106-2608
Ph: (215)625-8900
Fax: (215)625-2940
Fr: 800-354-1420
URL: http://www.tandf.co.uk/journals/titles/ 17513472.asp

$418.00/year for institutions, print and online; $376.00/year for institutions, online only; $91.00/year for individuals, print. Peer-reviewed journal focusing on connections between mathematics and the arts.

8112 ■ *Journal of Mathematics and Statistics*
Science Publications
Vails Gate Heights Dr.
PO Box 879
Vails Gate, NY 12584-0879
URL: http://thescipub.com/jms.toc

Quarterly. Peer-reviewed scholarly journal covering all areas of mathematics and statistics.

8113 ■ *Journal of Signal and Information Processing*
Scientific Research Publishing
PO Box 54821
Irvine, CA 92619-4821
E-mail: jsip@scirp.org
URL: http://www.scirp.org/journal/jsip/

Quarterly. $156.00/year for individuals. Peer-reviewed journal publishing articles on the latest advancements in signal and information processing.

8114 ■ *Notices of the American Mathematical Society*
American Mathematical Society
201 Charles St.
Providence, RI 02904-2294
Ph: (401)455-4000
Fax: (401)331-3842
Fr: 800-321-4267
E-mail: notices@math.wustl.edu
URL: http://www.ams.org/notices

$488.00/year for nonmembers; free to members. Peer-reviewed AMS journal publishing programs, meeting reports, new publications, announcements, upcoming mathematical meetings, scientific development trends, computer software reviews, and federal funding reports.

EMPLOYER DIRECTORIES AND NETWORKING LISTS

8115 ■ *American Men and Women of Science*
Gale
PO Box 6904
Florence, KY 41022-6904
Fr: 800-354-9706
URL: http://www.gale.cengage.com

Biennial, even years; New edition expected 29th, June 2011. $1,368.00 for individuals. Covers: Over 135,000 U.S. and Canadian scientists active in the physical, biological, mathematical, computer science, and engineering fields; includes references to previous edition for deceased scientists and nonrespondents. Entries include: Name, address, education, personal and career data, memberships, honors and awards, research interest. Arrangement: Alphabetical. Indexes: Discipline (in separate volume).

8116 ■ *Assistantships and Graduate Fellowships in the Mathematical Sciences*
American Mathematical Society
201 Charles St.
Providence, RI 02904-2294
Ph: (401)455-4000
Fax: (401)331-3842
Fr: 800-321-4267
URL: http://www.ams.org

Annual, latest edition 2009. $23.00 for individuals; $18.00 for members. Publication includes: List of assistantship and graduate fellowship opportunities in math, statistics, computer science and related fields in about 270 colleges and universities in the United States and Canada; sources of fellowship information. Entries include: For assistantships and fellowships—Title, sponsoring organization name, web site address, address, name and title of contact; description of position, including stipend (if any), duties, deadline

for application; number and type of degrees awarded for previous year. For fellowship information sources—Name, address. Arrangement: Geographical. Indexes: Type of stipend.

8117 ■ *Careers in Focus—Mathematics and Physics*
Facts On File Inc.
132 W 31st St., 17th Fl.
New York, NY 10001
Ph: (212)967-8800
Fax: 800-678-3633
Fr: 800-322-8755
URL: http://www.infobasepublishing.com

Latest edition 2nd; Published March, 2008. $32.95 for individuals. Covers: An overview of mathematics and physics, followed by a selection of jobs profiled in detail, including the nature of the job, earnings, prospects for employment, what kind of training and skills it requires, and sources for further information.

8118 ■ *Discovering Careers for Your Future—Math*
Facts On File Inc.
132 W 31st St., 17th Fl.
New York, NY 10001
Ph: (212)967-8800
Fax: 800-678-3633
Fr: 800-322-8755
URL: http://factsonfile.infobasepublishing.com

Latest edition 2nd, 2008. $21.95 for individuals. Covers: Auditors, computer programmers, financial planners, and physicists; links career education to curriculum, helping children investigate the subjects they are interested in, and the careers those subjects might lead to.

8119 ■ *Employment Information in the Mathematical Sciences*
American Mathematical Society
201 Charles St.
Providence, RI 02904-2294
Ph: (401)455-4000
Fax: (401)331-3842
Fr: 800-321-4267
E-mail: eims-info@ams.org
URL: http://www.ams.org/profession/employment-services/eims/eims-

Five times a year. $190.00 for individuals; $114.00 for individuals. Covers: Colleges and universities with departments in the mathematical sciences, and nonacademic and foreign organizations with employment openings. Entries include: For departments—Name, address, name and title of contact; job title, job description, salary (if applicable). Arrangement: Classified as academic or nonacademic, then geographical.

8120 ■ *Facts On File Geometry Handbook*
Facts On File Inc.
132 W 31st St., 17th Fl.
New York, NY 10001
Ph: (212)967-8800
Fax: 800-678-3633
Fr: 800-322-8755
URL: http://www.infobasepublishing.com

Latest edition 2009. $40.00 for individuals. Publication includes: List of Web sites to consult for further information on geometry. Principal content of publication is over 3,000 terms covering Euclidean and non-Euclidean geometry as well as other overlapping mathematical branches. Indexes: Alphabetical.

8121 ■ *Mathematical Sciences Professional Directory*
American Mathematical Society
201 Charles St.
Providence, RI 02904-2294
Ph: (401)455-4000
Fax: (401)331-3842
Fr: 800-321-4267
URL: http://www.ams.org

Annual, latest edition 2010. $44.00 for institutions; $55.00 for individuals. Covers: 37 professional

organizations concerned with mathematics, government agencies, academic institutions with department in the mathematical sciences, nonacademic organizations, and individuals. Entries include: For professional organizations and government agencies—Name, address, names and titles of key personnel. For institutions—Name, address; name, title, and address of department chair. Arrangement: Classified by type of organization; institutions are then geographical; others, alphabetical. Indexes: University or college name.

HANDBOOKS AND MANUALS

8122 ■ *Great Jobs for Math Majors*
The McGraw-Hill Companies
PO Box 182604
Columbus, OH 43272
Fax: (614)759-3749
Fr: 877-883-5524
E-mail: customer.service@mcgraw-hill.com
URL: http://www.mhprofessional.com/product.php?isbn=0071448594

Stephen Lambert and Ruth J. DeCotis. Second edition, 2005. $15.95 (paper). 208 pages.

8123 ■ *Math for Soil Scientists*
Cengage Learning
PO Box 6904
Florence, KY 41022
Fax: 800-487-8488
Fr: 800-354-9706
E-mail: esales@cengage.com
URL: http://www.cengage.com

Mark S. Coyne and James A. Thompson. 2006. $39.95. 288 pages. Soil science students and practitioners are offered a review of basic mathematical operations in the field.

8124 ■ *Mathematician*
National Learning Corporation
212 Michael Dr.
Syosset, NY 11791
Fr: 800-632-8888
URL: http://www.passbooks.com

2009. $34.95 (paper). Serves as an exam preparation guide for mathematicians.

TRADESHOWS

8125 ■ *American Mathematical Association of Two-Year Colleges Conference*
American Mathematical Association of Two Year Colleges
5983 Macon Cove
Memphis, TN 38134
Ph: (901)333-6243
Fax: (901)333-6251
E-mail: amatyc@amatyc.org
URL: http://www.amatyc.org

Annual. Primary Exhibits: Exhibits relating to the improvement of mathematics education and mathematics-related experiences of students in two-year colleges or at the lower division level.

8126 ■ *Joint Mathematics Meetings*
American Mathematical Society
201 Charles St.
Providence, RI 02904-2294
Ph: (401)455-4000
Fax: (401)331-3842
Fr: 800-321-4AMS
E-mail: ams@ams.org
URL: http://www.ams.org

Annual. Primary Exhibits: Software and online systems, books, publishers, mathematical associations, insurance companies, math-related games, accessories, tee shirts, hardware. Dates and Locations: 2013 Jan 09-13; San Diego, CA; San Diego Convention Center.

OTHER SOURCES

8127 ■ American Geophysical Union (AGU)
2000 Florida Ave. NW
Washington, DC 20009-1277
Ph: (202)462-6900
Fax: (202)328-0566
Fr: 800-966-2481
E-mail: service@agu.org
URL: http://www.agu.org

Description: Individuals professionally associated with the field of geophysics; supporting institutional members are companies and other organizations whose work involves geophysics. Promotes the study of problems concerned with the figure and physics of the earth; initiates and coordinates research that depends upon national and international cooperation and provides for scientific discussion of research results. Sponsors placement service at semiannual meeting.

8128 ■ American Mathematical Society (AMS)
201 Charles St.
Providence, RI 02904-2213
Ph: (401)455-4000
Fax: (401)331-3842
Fr: 800-321-4AMS
E-mail: ams@ams.org
URL: http://www.ams.org

Description: Professional society of mathematicians and educators. Promotes the interests of mathematical scholarship and research. Holds institutes, seminars, short courses, and symposia to further mathematical research; awards prizes. Offers placement services; compiles statistics.

8129 ■ Association for International Practical Training (AIPT)
10400 Little Patuxent Pkwy., Ste. 250
Columbia, MD 21044-3519
Ph: (410)997-2200
Fax: (410)992-3924
E-mail: aipt@aipt.org
URL: http://www.aipt.org

Description: Providers worldwide of on-the-job training programs for students and professionals seeking international career development and life-changing experiences. Arranges workplace exchanges in hundreds of professional fields, bringing employers and trainees together from around the world. Client list ranges from small farming communities to Fortune 500 companies.

8130 ■ Institute of Mathematical Statistics (IMS)
PO Box 22718
Beachwood, OH 44122
Ph: (216)295-2340
Fax: (216)295-5661
Fr: 877-557-4674
E-mail: ims@imstat.org
URL: http://www.imstat.org

Description: Professional society of mathematicians and others interested in mathematical statistics and probability theory. Seeks to further research in mathematical statistics and probability.

8131 ■ Mathematical Association of America (MAA)
1529 18th St. NW
Washington, DC 20036-1358
Ph: (202)387-5200
Fax: (202)265-2384
Fr: 800-741-9415
E-mail: maahq@maa.org
URL: http://www.maa.org

Description: College mathematics teachers; individuals using mathematics as a tool in a business or profession. Sponsors annual high school mathematics contests and W.L. Putnam Competition for college students. Conducts faculty enhancement workshops and promotes the use of computers through classroom training. Offers college placement test program; operates speakers' bureau.

8132 ■ National Council of Teachers of Mathematics (NCTM)
1906 Association Dr.
Reston, VA 20191-1502
Ph: (703)620-9840
Fax: (703)476-2970
Fr: 800-235-7566
E-mail: nctm@nctm.org
URL: http://www.nctm.org

Description: Aims to improve teaching and learning of mathematics.

8133 ■ Society for Industrial and Applied Mathematics
3600 Market St., 6th Fl.
Philadelphia, PA 19104-2688
Ph: (215)382-9800
Fax: (215)386-7999
Fr: 800-447-SIAM
E-mail: service@siam.org
URL: http://www.siam.org

Description: Caters to academic, manufacturing, research and development, service and consulting organizations, government, and military organizations. Fosters the development of applied mathematical and computational methodologies needed in these various application areas. Builds cooperation between mathematics and the worlds of science and technology through publications and research.

SOURCES OF HELP-WANTED ADS

8134 ■ *Advanced Materials & Processes*
ASM International
9639 Kinsman Rd.
Novelty, OH 44073-0001
Ph: (440)338-5151
Fax: (440)338-4634
Fr: 800-336-5152
URL: http://www.asminternational.org/portal/site/
www/membership/b

Monthly. Magazine covering advances in metal, materials, testing technology and more.

8135 ■ *AIE Perspectives Newsmagazine*
American Institute of Engineers
4630 Appian Way, Ste. 206
El Sobrante, CA 94803-1875
Ph: (510)758-6240
Fax: (510)758-6240
URL: http://www.members-aie.org

Monthly. Professional magazine covering engineering.

8136 ■ *Applied Mechanics Transactions*
American Society of Mechanical Engineers
3 Park Ave.
New York, NY 10016-5990
Ph: (973)882-1170
Fr: 800-843-2763
URL: http://journaltool.asme.org/Content/
JournalDescriptions.cfm?

Quarterly. $60.00/year for members, print and online; $126.00/year for members, international; print and online; $51.00/year for members, online only; $629.00/year for nonmembers, U.S. and Canada; print and online; $563.00/year for nonmembers, international; print and online. Journal covering mechanical engineering.

8137 ■ *ASME News*
American Society of Mechanical Engineers
3 Park Ave.
New York, NY 10016-5990
Ph: (973)882-1170
Fr: 800-843-2763
E-mail: infocentral@asme.org
URL: http://www.asme.org/about-asme/press-
releases

Monthly. Engineering tabloid.

8138 ■ *Chemical Equipment*
Reed Business Information (New York, New York)
360 Park Ave. S
New York, NY 10010
Ph: (646)746-6400
Fax: (646)746-7431
Fr: 800-446-6551
URL: http://www.reedbusinessinteractive.com

Free for qualified professionals; $72.90/year for individuals, cover price. Tabloid on the chemical process industry.

8139 ■ *Consulting-Specifying Engineer*
CFE Media LLC
1111 W 22nd St., Ste. 250
Oak Brook, IL 60523
Ph: (630)571-4070
Fax: (630)214-4504
URL: http://www.csemag.com

The integrated engineering magazine of the building construction industry.

8140 ■ *Engineering*
Scientific Research Publishing
PO Box 54821
Irvine, CA 92619-4821
E-mail: eng@scirp.org
URL: http://www.scirp.org/journal/eng/

Monthly. $708.00/year for individuals. Peer-reviewed journal publishing articles on the latest advancements in engineering.

8141 ■ *Engineering Conferences International Symposium Series*
Berkeley Electronic Press
2809 Telegraph Ave., Ste. 202
Berkeley, CA 94705-1167
Ph: (510)665-1200
Fax: (510)665-1201
URL: http://services.bepress.com/eci/

Journal focusing on advance engineering science.

8142 ■ *ENR: Engineering News-Record*
McGraw-Hill Inc.
PO Box 182604
Columbus, OH 43218
Ph: (614)430-4000
Fax: (614)759-3749
Fr: 877-833-5524
URL: http://enr.construction.com/Default.asp

Weekly. $49.00/year for individuals, print; $89.00/year for Canada, print; $125.00/year for other countries, print. Magazine focusing on engineering and construction.

8143 ■ *Graduating Engineer & Computer Careers*
Career Recruitment Media
2 LAN Dr., Ste. 100
Westford, MA 01886
Ph: (978)692-5092
Fax: (978)692-4174
URL: http://www.graduatingengineer.com

Quarterly. $16.95/year for individuals. Magazine focusing on employment, education, and career development for entry-level engineers and computer scientists.

8144 ■ *High Technology Careers Magazine*
HTC
4701 Patrick Henry Dr., No. 1901
Santa Clara, CA 95054
Fax: (408)567-0242
URL: http://www.hightechcareers.com

Bimonthly. $29.00/year; $35.00/year for Canada; $85.00/year for out of country. Magazine (tabloid) containing employment opportunity information for the engineering and technical community.

8145 ■ *Hydraulics & Pneumatics*
Penton Media Inc.
249 W 17th St.
New York, NY 10011
Ph: (212)204-4200
URL: http://www.hydraulicspneumatics.com/
default.aspx

Monthly. $63.00/year for individuals; $90.00/year for two years. Magazine of hydraulic and pneumatic systems and engineering.

8146 ■ *InterJournal*
New England Complex Systems Institute
283 Main St., Ste. 319
Cambridge, MA 02142
Ph: (617)547-4100
Fax: (617)661-7711
URL: http://www.interjournal.org/

Journal covering the fields of science and engineering.

8147 ■ *ISRN Mechanical Engineering*
Hindawi Publishing Corporation
410 Park Ave., 15th Fl.
287 PMB
New York, NY 10022
E-mail: me@isrn.com
URL: http://www.isrn.com/journals/me

Peer-reviewed journal publishing research articles in all areas of mechanical engineering.

8148 ■ *Journal of Engineering Education*
American Society for Engineering Education
1818 N St. NW, Ste. 600
Washington, DC 20036-2479
Ph: (202)331-3500
Fax: (202)265-8504
URL: http://www.jee.org

Quarterly. $100.00/year for libraries, online; $160.00/year for other countries, library; $150.00/year for U.S., Canada, and Mexico, library; $160.00/year for other countries, library. Peer-reviewed journal covering scholarly research in engineering education.

8149 ■ *Journal of Women and Minorities in Science and Engineering*
Begell House Inc.
50 Cross Hwy.
Redding, CT 06896
Ph: (203)938-1300

Fax: (203)938-1304
URL: http://www.begellhouse.com/journals/
00551c876cc2f027

$248.00/year for institutions. Peer-reviewed journal featuring innovative ideas and programs for classroom teachers, scientific studies, and formulation of concepts related to the education, recruitment, and retention of under-represented groups in science and engineering.

8150 ■ *Machine Design*
Penton Media Inc.
249 W 17th St.
New York, NY 10011
Ph: (212)204-4200
URL: http://machinedesign.com/

Magazine on design engineering function.

8151 ■ *Mechanical Engineering*
American Society of Mechanical Engineers
3 Park Ave.
New York, NY 10016-5990
Ph: (973)882-1170
Fr: 800-843-2763
E-mail: memag@asme.org
URL: http://www.memagazine.org

Monthly. $25.00/year for single issue; $3.50/year for single issue, international surface. Mechanical Engineering featuring technical and industry related technological advancements and news.

8152 ■ *NSBE Magazine*
NSBE Publications
205 Daingerfield Rd.
Alexandria, VA 22314
Ph: (703)549-2207
Fax: (703)683-5312
URL: http://www.nsbe.org/News-Media/Magazines/
About-NSBE-Magazine

$20.00/year for individuals; $35.00/year for other countries; $15.00/year for students. Journal providing information on engineering careers, self-development, and cultural issues for recent graduates with technical majors.

8153 ■ *PE*
National Society of Professional Engineers
1420 King St.
Alexandria, VA 22314
Ph: (703)684-2800
Fax: (703)684-4875
URL: http://www.nspe.org/PEmagazine/index.html

Monthly. Magazine (tabloid) covering professional, legislative, and techology issues for an engineering audience.

8154 ■ *Plumbing Engineer*
TMB Publishing Inc.
1838 Techny Ct.
Northbrook, IL 60062
Ph: (847)564-1127
URL: http://www.plumbingengineer.com/

Monthly. Trade journal for consulting engineering, mechanical engineering, architecture, and contracting professionals.

8155 ■ *SPE Technical Journals*
Society of Petroleum Engineers (SPE)
830 S. Greenville Ave.
Allen, TX 75002
Ph: (972)952-9393
Fax: (972)952-9435
Fr: 800-456-6863

$80.00/year for members, print or online. Journal devoted to engineers and scientists.

8156 ■ *SWE, Magazine of the Society of Women Engineers*
Society of Women Engineers
120 S La Salle St., Ste. 1515
Chicago, IL 60603
Ph: (312)596-5223

Fr: 877-793-4636
URL: http://societyofwomenengineers.swe.org/
index.php

Quarterly. $30.00/year for nonmembers. Magazine for engineering students and for women and men working in the engineering and technology fields. Covers career guidance, continuing development and topical issues.

8157 ■ *WEPANEWS*
Women in Engineering Programs & Advocates Network
1901 E Asbury Ave., Ste. 220
Denver, CO 80208
Ph: (303)871-4643
Fax: (303)871-4628
E-mail: dmatt@wepan.org
URL: http://www.wepan.org

Description: 2/year. Seeks to provide greater access for women to careers in engineering. Includes news of graduate, undergraduate, freshmen, pre-college, and re-entry engineering programs for women. Recurring features include job listings, faculty, grant, and conference news, international engineering program news, action group news, notices of publications available, and a column titled Kudos.

8158 ■ *Woman Engineer*
Equal Opportunity Publications, Inc.
445 Broadhollow Rd., Ste. 425
Melville, NY 11747
Ph: (631)421-9421
Fax: (631)421-1352
E-mail: info@eop.com
URL: http://www.eop.com

Annual. Magazine that is offered at no charge to qualified female engineering, computer-science, and information-technology students and professionals seeking to find employment and advancement in their careers.

8159 ■ *World Journal of Mechanics*
Scientific Research Publishing
PO Box 54821
Irvine, CA 92619-4821
E-mail: wjm@scirp.org
URL: http://www.scirp.org/journal/wjm/

Quarterly. $156.00/year for individuals. Peer-reviewed journal publishing articles in the general field of mechanics.

EMPLOYER DIRECTORIES AND NETWORKING LISTS

8160 ■ *American Men and Women of Science*
Gale
PO Box 6904
Florence, KY 41022-6904
Fr: 800-354-9706
URL: http://www.gale.cengage.com

Biennial, even years; New edition expected 29th, June 2011. $1,368.00 for individuals. Covers: Over 135,000 U.S. and Canadian scientists active in the physical, biological, mathematical, computer science, and engineering fields; includes references to previous edition for deceased scientists and nonrespondents. Entries include: Name, address, education, personal and career data, memberships, honors and awards, research interest. Arrangement: Alphabetical. Indexes: Discipline (in separate volume).

8161 ■ *Career Opportunities in the Automotive Industry*
Facts On File Inc.
132 W 31st St., 17th Fl.
New York, NY 10001
Ph: (212)967-8800
Fax: 800-678-3633

Fr: 800-322-8755
URL: http://factsonfile.infobasepublishing.com

Published 2005. $49.50 for individuals. Covers: 70 jobs from pit crew mechanic to restoration expert, from mechanical engineer to parts distribution director, from RV specialist to exotic car museum director.

8162 ■ *Directory of Contract Staffing Firms*
C.E. Publications Inc.
PO Box 3006
Bothell, WA 98041-3006
Ph: (425)806-5200
Fax: (425)806-5585
URL: http://www.cjhunter.com/dcsf/overview.html

Annual. Covers: Nearly 1,300 contract firms actively engaged in the employment of engineering, IT/IS, and technical personnel for 'temporary' contract assignments throughout the world. Entries include: Company name, address, phone, name of contact, email, web address. Arrangement: Alphabetical. Indexes: Geographical.

8163 ■ *Indiana Society of Professional Engineers—Directory*
Indiana Society of Professional Engineers
PO Box 20806
Indianapolis, IN 46220
Ph: (317)255-2267
Fax: (317)255-2530
URL: http://www.indspe.org

Annual, fall. Covers: Member registered engineers, land surveyors, engineering students, and engineers in training. Entries include: Member name, address, phone, type of membership, business information, specialty. Arrangement: Alpha by chapter area.

8164 ■ *Mechanical Contractors Association of America—Membership Directory*
National Certified Pipe Welding Bureau
1385 Piccard Dr.
Rockville, MD 20850
Ph: (301)869-5800
Fax: (301)990-9690
Fr: 800-556-3653
E-mail: membership@mcaa.org
URL: http://www.mcaa.org/directory

Annual, December. Covers: About 600 mechanical contractors regularly engaged in the fabrication or erecting of piping systems, who employ certified pipe welders. Entries include: Firm name, address, phone, telex, fax, name of contact. Arrangement: By each chapter, then by firm name.

HANDBOOKS AND MANUALS

8165 ■ *Expert Resumes for Engineers*
JIST Publishing
875 Montreal Way
St. Paul, MN 55102
Fr: 800-648-5478
E-mail: educate@emcp.com
URL: http://www.jist.com

Louise M. Kursmark and Wendy S. Enelow. 2009. $16.95 (softcover). 272 pages. Features a collection of written resume samples for all types of engineers including civil, mechanical, industrial, electrical, electronics, computer, and more. Contains tips and strategies for writing engineering resumes and finding the best jobs.

8166 ■ *Great Jobs for Engineering Majors*
The McGraw-Hill Companies
PO Box 182604
Columbus, OH 43272
Fax: (614)759-3749
Fr: 877-883-5524
E-mail: customer.service@mcgraw-hill.com
URL: http://www.mhprofessional.com/
product.php?isbn=0071641963

Geraldine O. Garner. Second edition, 2008. $16.95. 192 pages. Covers all the career options open to students majoring in engineering.

8167 ■ *Principal Mechanical Engineer*
National Learning Corporation
212 Michael Dr.
Syosset, NY 11791
Fr: 800-632-8888
URL: http://www.passbooks.com

2009. $39.95 (paper). Serves as an exam preparation guide for principal mechanical engineers.

8168 ■ *Resumes for Scientific and Technical Careers*
The McGraw-Hill Companies
PO Box 182604
Columbus, OH 43272
Fax: (614)759-3749
Fr: 877-883-5524
E-mail: customer.service@mcgraw-hill.com
URL: http://www.mhprofessional.com/
product.php?isbn=0071482199

Third edition, 2007. $12.95 (paper). 144 pages. Provides resume advice for individuals interested in working in scientific and technical careers. Includes sample resumes and cover letters.

EMPLOYMENT AGENCIES AND SEARCH FIRMS

8169 ■ The Aspire Group
711 Boylston St.
Boston, MA 02116-2616
Fax: (617)500-7284
Fr: 800-487-2967
URL: http://www.bmanet.com/Aspire/index.html

Employment agency.

8170 ■ ATR Engineering
1230 Oakmead Pkwy.
Sunnyvale, CA 94085
Ph: (408)328-8000
Fax: (408)328-8001
Fr: 877-412-1100
E-mail: corporate@atr1.com
URL: http://www.atr-engineering.com

Description: Serves as an executive search firm specializing in the placement of engineering professionals in contract, contract-to-hire and full-time basis across all disciplines including design engineering, manufacturing engineering, hardware engineering, design engineering, electrical engineering and mechanical engineering.

8171 ■ Bell Oaks Co.
115 Perimeter Center Pl., Ste. 400
Atlanta, GA 30346
Ph: (678)287-2000
Fax: (678)287-2002
E-mail: info@belloaks.com
URL: http://www.belloaks.com

Personnel service firm.

8172 ■ The Bradbury Group Inc.
1200 E Cole St.
PO Box 667
Moundridge, KS 67107
Ph: (620)345-6394
Fax: (620)345-6381
Fr: 800-397-6394
URL: http://www.bradburygroup.net

Executive search firm.

8173 ■ Brown Venture Associates Inc.
5150 El Camino Real, Ste. B-30
Los Altos, CA 94022
Ph: (650)233-0205
E-mail: brown@bva.com
URL: http://www.bva.com

Executive search firm.

8174 ■ Claremont-Branan, Inc.
1298 Rockbridge Rd., Ste. B
Stone Mountain, GA 30087
Fr: 800-875-1292
URL: http://cbisearch.com

Employment agency. Executive search firm.

8175 ■ The Corporate Source Group Inc.
5420 Bay Center Dr., Ste. 105
Tampa, FL 33609
Ph: (813)286-4422
Fax: (978)475-6800
E-mail: inquiry@csg-search.com
URL: http://www.csg-search.com

Executive search firm branches in Boston, MA; Chicago, IL; Los Angeles, CA; New York, NY; Tampa, FL; Washington, DC.

8176 ■ The Coxe Group Inc.
1904 Third Ave., Ste. 229
Seattle, WA 98101-1194
Ph: (206)467-4040
Fax: (206)467-4038
E-mail: info@coxegroup.com
URL: http://www.coxegroup.com

Executive search firm.

8177 ■ Engineer One, Inc.
PO Box 23037
Knoxville, TN 37933
Fax: (865)691-0110
E-mail: engineerone@engineerone.com
URL: http://www.engineerone.com

Engineering employment service specializing in engineering and management in the chemical process, power utilities, manufacturing, mechanical, electrical, and electronic industries. Maintains an Information Technology Division that works nationwide across all industries. Also provides systems analysis consulting services specializing in VAX based systems.

8178 ■ ENTEGEE
70 Blanchard Rd., Ste. 102
Burlington, MA 01803
Fr: 800-368-3433
E-mail: corporate@entegee.com
URL: http://www.entegee.com

Specializes in recruiting experienced professionals in the engineering and technical industries. Features a searchable database of employment opportunities in the engineering and technical fields.

8179 ■ Executive Recruiters Agency
PO Box 21810
Little Rock, AR 72211
Ph: (501)224-7000
Fax: (501)224-8534
E-mail: jobs@execrecruit.com
URL: http://www.execrecruit.com

Personnel service firm.

8180 ■ Global Employment Solutions
10375 Park Meadows Dr., Ste. 375
Littleton, CO 80124
Ph: (303)216-9500
Fax: (303)216-9533
URL: http://www.gesnetwork.com

Employment agency.

8181 ■ Recruiting Partners
3494 Camino Tassajara Rd., No. 404
Danville, CA 94506
Ph: (925)964-0249
E-mail: info@recruitingpartners.com
URL: http://www.recruitingpartners.com

Description: Serves as an executive and technical recruiting firm that specializes in accounting, legal, information technology, engineering, executive management and technical writing.

8182 ■ Search Group
6102 Seven Lakes W
Seven Lakes, NC 27376
Ph: (910)687-0064
Fax: (910)687-0067
E-mail: results@theesearchgroup.com
URL: http://search-one.com

Partners with clients in need of executive, managerial, IT, engineering, and sales positions supporting materials handling, logistics, and supply chain management.

8183 ■ SPECTRA Associates
PO Box 688
Stevensville, MT 59870
Ph: (406)369-1188
E-mail: engineering@spectra-assoc.com
URL: http://www.spectra-assoc.com

Description: Serves as an executive search firm specializing in recruitment for engineering markets including companies involved with manufacturing, production and engineering.

8184 ■ Trambley The Recruiter
5325 Wyoming Blvd. NE, Ste. 200
Albuquerque, NM 87109-3132
Ph: (505)821-5440
Fax: (505)821-8509

Personnel consultancy firm recruits and places engineering professionals in specific areas of off-road equipment design and manufacturing. Industries served: construction, agricultural, lawn and garden, oil exploration and mining equipment manufacturing.

8185 ■ TRS Staffing Solutions USA
3 Polaris Way
Aliso Viejo, CA 92656
Ph: (949)349-3630
Fax: (949)349-7196
Fr: 800-248-8774
E-mail: info-av@trsstaffing.com
URL: http://www.trsstaffing.com/us

Specializes in engineering recruitment. Maintains a pool of experienced technical, engineering and professional services personnel.

ONLINE JOB SOURCES AND SERVICES

8186 ■ ConstructionJobs.com
URL: http://www.constructionjobs.com/index_eng.cfm

Description: Serves as an employment job board and resume database built exclusively for the construction, design, and building industries. Provides targeted candidate searches by geographic region, specific industries, job titles, education, and experience.

8187 ■ Engineering Classifieds
URL: http://www.engineeringclassifieds.com

Description: Serves as a career site for engineering professionals. Provides services including job search agents, resume creation and posting.

8188 ■ EngineerJobs.com
URL: http://www.engineerjobs.com

Description: Provides job opportunities for engineering professionals in the following disciplines: aerospace, agricultural, biomedical, chemical, civil, electrical, environmental, industrial, manufacturing, marine, materials, mechanical, mining, nuclear, petroleum, process, project, quality, sales, software, solar, systems, and structural.

8189 ■ Engineer.net
URL: http://www.engineer.net

Description: Provides engineering employment tools such as job search, job posting, and engineering resumes.

8190 ■ MechanicalEngineer.com
URL: http://www.mechanicalengineer.com

Description: Provides job listings, employment information and career resources for mechanical engineers.

8191 ■ MEP Jobs
URL: http://www.mepjobs.com

Description: Serves as a job board and resume bank for professionals in the mechanical, electrical, and plumbing industries.

8192 ■ PowerPlantPro.com
E-mail: support@powerplantpro.com
URL: http://www.powerplantpro.com/main/sendform/4/18/3472

Description: Dedicated to professionals in the power and energy industry. Features career advice and employer listings.

8193 ■ Spherion
2050 Spectrum Blvd.
Fort Lauderdale, FL 33309
Ph: (954)308-7600
Fr: 800-774-3746
E-mail: help@spherion.com
URL: http://www.spherion.com

Description: Recruitment firm specializing in accounting and finance, sales and marketing, interim executives, technology, engineering, retail and human resources.

8194 ■ ThinkEnergyGroup.com
E-mail: resumes@thinkjobs.com
URL: http://www.thinkenergygroup.com

Description: Serves as a job board for professionals looking for positions in engineering, power plant, energy, and technical fields. Contains advice and tips on interviews, job searching, resume writing, hiring, and management. Provides choices of work location, pay rates in the field of expertise and contract, temp-to-hire, and direct hiring options.

TRADESHOWS

8195 ■ American Society for Engineering Education Annual Conference and Exposition
American Society for Engineering Education
1818 N. St. N.W., Ste. 600
Washington, DC 20036-2479
Ph: (202)331-3500
Fax: (202)265-8504
E-mail: conferences@asee.org
URL: http://www.asee.org

Annual. Primary Exhibits: Publications, engineering supplies and equipment, computers, software, and research companies all products and services related to engineering education. Dates and Locations: 2012 Jun 10-13; San Antonio, TX.

OTHER SOURCES

8196 ■ Acoustical Society of America
2 Huntington Quadrangle, Ste. 1NO1
Melville, NY 11747-4502
Ph: (516)576-2360
Fax: (516)576-2377
E-mail: asa@aip.org
URL: http://acousticalsociety.org

Description: Represents members from various fields related to sound including physics, electrical, mechanical and aeronautical engineering, oceanography, biology, physiology, psychology, architecture, speech, noise and noise control, and music. Aims to increase and diffuse the knowledge of acoustics and its practical applications. Organizes meetings, provides reprints of out-of-print classic texts in acoustics, and translation books.

8197 ■ American Association of Engineering Societies (AAES)
1801 Alexander Bell Dr.
Reston, VA 20191
Ph: (202)296-2237
Fax: (202)296-1151
Fr: 888-400-2237
E-mail: dbateson@aaes.org
URL: http://www.aaes.org

Description: Coordinates the efforts of the member societies in the provision of reliable and objective information to the general public concerning issues which affect the engineering profession and the field of engineering as a whole; collects, analyzes, documents, and disseminates data which will inform the general public of the relationship between engineering and the national welfare; provides a forum for the engineering societies to exchange and discuss their views on matters of common interest; and represents the U.S. engineering community abroad through representation in WFEO and UPADI.

8198 ■ American Indian Science and Engineering Society (AISES)
PO Box 9828
Albuquerque, NM 87119-9828
Ph: (505)765-1052
Fax: (505)765-5608
E-mail: info@aises.org
URL: http://www.aises.org

Description: Represents American Indian and non-Indian students and professionals in science, technology, and engineering fields; corporations representing energy, mining, aerospace, electronic, and computer fields. Seeks to motivate and encourage students to pursue undergraduate and graduate studies in science, engineering, and technology. Sponsors science fairs in grade schools, teacher training workshops, summer math/science sessions for 8th-12th graders, professional chapters, and student chapters in colleges. Offers scholarships. Adult members serve as role models, advisers, and mentors for students. Operates placement service.

8199 ■ American Society of Mechanical Engineers (ASME)
3 Park Ave.
New York, NY 10016-5990
Ph: (973)882-1170
Fax: (973)882-1717
Fr: 800-843-2763
E-mail: infocentral@asme.org
URL: http://www.asme.org

Description: Technical society of mechanical engineers and students. Conducts research; develops boiler, pressure vessel, and power test codes. Develops safety codes and standards for equipment. Conducts short course programs, and Identifying Research Needs Program. Maintains 19 research committees and 38 divisions.

8200 ■ Association for International Practical Training (AIPT)
10400 Little Patuxent Pkwy., Ste. 250
Columbia, MD 21044-3519
Ph: (410)997-2200
Fax: (410)992-3924
E-mail: aipt@aipt.org
URL: http://www.aipt.org

Description: Providers worldwide of on-the-job training programs for students and professionals seeking international career development and life-changing experiences. Arranges workplace exchanges in hundreds of professional fields, bringing employers and trainees together from around the world. Client list ranges from small farming communities to Fortune 500 companies.

8201 ■ Chinese American Association of Engineering (CAAE)
PO Box 869
New York, NY 10268
Ph: (718)591-6012
URL: http://www.caae.org

Description: Serves as a bridge for cooperation between China and the United States in engineering and related fields. Provides assistance in setting up business or launching programs to advertise new techniques, products and equipment in both countries. Offers professional consultation and service to U.S. and China enterprises or individuals. Provides a forum for members to exchange and share professional experience.

8202 ■ Engineering Society of Detroit (ESD)
20700 Civic Center Dr., Ste. 450
Southfield, MI 48076
Ph: (248)353-0735
Fax: (248)353-0736
E-mail: esd@esd.org
URL: http://ww2.esd.org/home.htm

Description: Engineers from all disciplines; scientists and technologists. Conducts technical programs and engineering refresher courses; sponsors conferences and expositions. Maintains speakers' bureau; offers placement services; although based in Detroit, MI, society membership is international.

8203 ■ Intelligent Transportation Society of America
1100 17th St. NW, Ste. 1200
Washington, DC 20036
Ph: (202)484-4847
Fr: 800-374-8472
E-mail: info@itsa.org
URL: http://www.itsa.org

Description: Includes private corporations, public agencies, and academic institutions involved in the research, development, and design of intelligent transportation systems technologies that enhance safety, increase mobility, and sustain the environment.

8204 ■ International Society of Automation (ISA)
67 Alexander Dr.
PO Box 12277
Research Triangle Park, NC 27709
Ph: (919)549-8411
Fax: (919)549-8288
E-mail: info@isa.org
URL: http://www.isa.org

Description: Sets the standard for automation by helping over 30,000 worldwide members and other professionals solve difficult technical problems, while enhancing their leadership and personal career capabilities. Develops standards; certifies industry professionals; provides education and training; publishes books and technical articles; and hosts the largest conference and exhibition for automation professionals in the Western Hemisphere. Is the founding sponsor of The Automation Federation.

8205 ■ Korean-American Scientists and Engineers Association (KSEA)
1952 Gallows Rd., Ste. 300
Vienna, VA 22182
Ph: (703)748-1221
Fax: (703)748-1331
E-mail: sejong@ksea.org
URL: http://www.ksea.org

Description: Represents scientists and engineers holding single or advanced degrees. Promotes friendship and mutuality among Korean and American scientists and engineers; contributes to Korea's scientific, technological, industrial, and economic developments; strengthens the scientific, technological, and cultural bonds between Korea and the U.S. Sponsors symposium. Maintains speakers' bureau, placement service, and biographical archives. Compiles statistics.

8206 ■ National Action Council for Minorities in Engineering (NACME)
440 Hamilton Ave., Ste. 302
White Plains, NY 10601-1813
Ph: (914)539-4010

Fax: (914)539-4032
E-mail: info@nacme.org
URL: http://www.nacme.org

Description: Leads the national effort to increase access to careers in engineering and other science-based disciplines. Conducts research and public policy analysis, develops and operates national demonstration programs at precollege and university levels, and disseminates information through publications, conferences and electronic media. Serves as a privately funded source of scholarships for minority students in engineering.

8207 ■ National Society of Professional Engineers (NSPE)
1420 King St.
Alexandria, VA 22314-2794
Ph: (703)684-2800
Fax: (703)836-4875
Fr: 888-285-6773
E-mail: memserv@nspe.org
URL: http://www.nspe.org

Description: Represents professional engineers and engineers-in-training in all fields registered in ac-

cordance with the laws of states or territories of the U.S. or provinces of Canada; qualified graduate engineers, student members, and registered land surveyors. Is concerned with social, professional, ethical, and economic considerations of engineering as a profession; encompasses programs in public relations, employment practices, ethical considerations, education, and career guidance. Monitors legislative and regulatory actions of interest to the engineering profession.

8208 ■ Society of Hispanic Professional Engineers (SHPE)
13181 Crossroads Pkwy. N, Ste. 450
City of Industry, CA 91746-3496
Ph: (323)725-3970
Fax: (323)725-0316
E-mail: shpenational@shpe.org
URL: http://oneshpe.shpe.org/wps/portal/national

Description: Represents engineers, student engineers, and scientists. Aims to increase the number of Hispanic engineers by providing motivation and support to students. Sponsors competitions and educational programs. Maintains placement service and speakers' bureau; compiles statistics.

8209 ■ Society of Women Engineers (SWE)
203 N La Salle St., Ste. 1675
Chicago, IL 60601
Ph: (312)596-5223
Fax: (312)596-5252
Fr: 877-SWE-INFO
E-mail: hq@swe.org
URL: http://societyofwomenengineers.swe.org

Description: Educational and service organization representing both students and professional women in engineering and technical fields.

8210 ■ SPIE
PO Box 10
Bellingham, WA 98227-0010
Ph: (360)676-3290
Fax: (360)647-1445
Fr: 888-504-8171
E-mail: customerservice@spie.org
URL: http://www.spie.org

Description: Advances scientific research and engineering applications of optical, photonic, imaging and optoelectronic technologies through meetings, education programs and publications.

SOURCES OF HELP-WANTED ADS

8211 ■ American Journal of Emergency Medicine
Mosby Inc.
11830 Westline Industrial Dr.
St. Louis, MO 63146-3326
Ph: (314)872-8370
Fax: (314)432-1380
Fr: 800-325-4177
URL: http://www.elsevier.com/wps/find/
journaldescription.cws_home

$340.00/year for individuals; $529.00/year for institutions; $159.00/year for students; $523.00/year for other countries; $711.00/year for institutions, other countries; $261.00/year for students, other countries. Journal reporting on emergency medicine.

8212 ■ Annals of Medicine
Informa Healthcare
52 Vanderbilt Ave., 7th Fl.
New York, NY 10017-3846
Ph: (212)520-2777
URL: http://informahealthcare.com/ann

$595.00/year for institutions; $980.00/year for institutions; $780.00/year for institutions. Journal covering health science and medical education.

8213 ■ Clinical Medicine & Research
Marshfield Clinic
1000 N Oak Ave.
Marshfield, WI 54449
Ph: (715)387-5511
Fax: (715)389-3808
Fr: 800-782-8581
E-mail: clinmedres@mcrf.mfldclin.edu
URL: http://www.clinmedres.org/

Quarterly. Free within the U.S. Peer-reviewed journal that publishes scientific medical research that is relevant to a broad audience of medical researchers and healthcare professionals.

8214 ■ The CMA Today
American Association of Medical Assistants
20 N Wacker Dr., Ste. 1575
Chicago, IL 60606
Ph: (312)899-1500
Fax: (312)899-1259
URL: http://www.aama-ntl.org/cmatoday/about.aspx

Bimonthly. $30.00/year free to members; $60.00/year for nonmembers. Professional health journal.

8215 ■ CME Supplement to Emergency Medicine Clinics of North America
Elsevier Science Inc.
360 Park Ave. S
New York, NY 10010-1710
Ph: (212)989-5800
Fax: (212)633-3990

Fr: 888-437-4636
URL: http://www.elsevier.com/wps/find/
journaldescription.cws_home

$209.00/year for individuals. Journal covering emergency medicine clinics.

8216 ■ Discovery Medicine
Discovery Medicine
10 Gerard Ave., Ste. 201
Timonium, MD 21093
Ph: (410)773-9938
Fax: 888-833-0526
URL: http://www.discoverymedicine.com

Bimonthly. $599.00/year for institutions, digital edition; $99.95/year for individuals, digital edition. Online journal that publishes articles on diseases, biology, new diagnostics, and treatments for medical professionals.

8217 ■ Education & Treatment of Children
West Virginia University Press
139 Stansbury Hall
PO Box 6295
Morgantown, WV 26506
Ph: (304)293-8400
Fax: (304)293-6585
URL: http://www.educationandtreatmentofchildren.net

Quarterly. $85.00/year for institutions; $45.00/year for individuals; $100.00/year for institutions, elsewhere; $60.00/year for individuals, elsewhere. Periodical featuring information concerning the development of services for children and youth. Includes reports written for educators and other child care and mental health providers focused on teaching, training, and treatment effectiveness.

8218 ■ Genes and Nutrition
New Century Health Publishers L.L.C.
PO Box 175
Coppell, TX 75019
Fax: (940)565-8148
URL: http://www.newcenturyhealthpublishers.com/
genes_and_nutritio

Quarterly. $428.00/year for institutions; $228.00/year for individuals. International, interdisciplinary peer reviewed scientific journal for critical evaluation of research on the relationship between genetics & nutrition with the goal of improving human health.

8219 ■ Global Change, Peace & Security
Routledge
711 3 Ave., 8 Fl.
New York, NY 10016
Ph: (212)216-7800
Fax: (212)563-2269
Fr: 800-634-7064
URL: http://www.tandfonline.com/toc/cpar20/current

$160.00/year for institutions, print; $602.00/year for individuals, online only; $669.00/year for individuals, print & online. Journal promoting physical therapy and integration.

8220 ■ Hospitals & Health Networks
Health Forum L.L.C.
155 N Wacker Dr., Ste. 400
Chicago, IL 60606
Ph: (312)893-6800
Fax: (312)422-4500
Fr: 800-821-2039
URL: http://www.hhnmag.com

Weekly. Free. Publication covering the health care industry.

8221 ■ The IHS Primary Care Provider
Indian Health Service
The Reyes Bldg.
801 Thompson Ave., Ste. 400
Rockville, MD 20852-1627
Ph: (301)443-1011
URL: http://www.ihs.gov/provider

Monthly. Journal for health care professionals, physicians, nurses, pharmacists, dentists, and dietitians.

8222 ■ Injury
Mosby Inc.
11830 Westline Industrial Dr.
St. Louis, MO 63146-3326
Ph: (314)872-8370
Fax: (314)432-1380
Fr: 800-325-4177
URL: http://www.elsevier.com/wps/find/
journaldescription.cws_home

Monthly. $200.00/year for individuals, European countries and Iran; $224.00/year for individuals, all countries except Europe, Japan and Iran; $26,500.00/year for individuals; $1,381.00/year for institutions, European countries and Iran; $1,543.00/year for institutions, all Countries except Europe, Japan and Iran; $183,200.00/year for institutions. Journal publishing articles and research related to the treatment of injuries such as trauma systems and management; surgical procedures; epidemiological studies; surgery (of all tissues); resuscitation; biomechanics; rehabilitation; anaesthesia; radiology and wound management.

8223 ■ Intensive and Critical Care Nursing
Mosby Inc.
11830 Westline Industrial Dr.
St. Louis, MO 63146-3326
Ph: (314)872-8370
Fax: (314)432-1380
Fr: 800-325-4177
URL: http://www.elsevier.com/wps/find/
journaldescription.cws_home

Bimonthly. $114.00/year for individuals, for all countries except Europe, Japan & Iran; $501.00/year for institutions, for all countries except Europe, Japan & Iran; $124.00/year for individuals, for European countries and Iran; $565.00/year for institutions, for European countries and Iran. Journal for nurses in intensive and critical care nursing.

8224 ■ Journal of the American Society of Podiatric Medical Assistants
American Society of Podiatric Medical Assistants
1616 N 78th Ct.
Elmwood Park, IL 60707
Fr: 888-882-7762
URL: http://www.aspma.org

Quarterly. Included in membership. Professional journal covering issues in podiatry.

8225 ■ Journal of Health and Life Sciences Law
American Health Lawyers Association
1620 Eye St. NW, 6th Fl.
Washington, DC 20006-4010
Ph: (202)833-1100
Fax: (202)833-1105
URL: http://www.healthlawyers.org

Quarterly. $149.00/year for individuals. Professional journal covering healthcare issues and cases and their impact on the health care arena.

8226 ■ Journal of Hospital Medicine
John Wiley & Sons Inc.
111 River St.
Hoboken, NJ 07030-5773
Ph: (201)748-6000
Fax: (201)748-6088
Fr: 800-825-7550
URL: http://onlinelibrary.wiley.com/journal/10.1002/ (ISSN)1553-56

$827.00/year for U.S., Canada, and Mexico, print only; $827.00/year for institutions, other countries, print only. Journal on hospital medicine.

8227 ■ USA Body Psychotherapy Journal
United States Association for Body Psychotherapy
8639 B 16th St., Ste. 119
Silver Spring, MD 20910
Ph: (202)466-1619
E-mail: admin@usabp.org
URL: http://www.usabp.org/ displaycommon.cfm?an=4

Semiannual. Academic journal that seeks to support, promote and stimulate the exchange of ideas, scholarship and research within the field of body psychotherapy as well as an interdisciplinary exchange with related fields of clinical practice and inquiry.

8228 ■ World Journal of AIDS
Scientific Research Publishing
PO Box 54821
Irvine, CA 92619-4821
E-mail: wja@scirp.org
URL: http://www.scirp.org/journal/wja/

Quarterly. $156.00/year for individuals. Peer-reviewed journal publishing articles on research data and education in all aspects of HIV and AIDS.

8229 ■ Year Book of Critical Care Medicine
Elsevier Science Inc.
360 Park Ave. S
New York, NY 10010-1710
Ph: (212)989-5800
Fax: (212)633-3990
Fr: 888-437-4636
URL: http://www.elsevier.com/wps/find/ journaldescription.cws_home

Annual. $271.00/year for institutions, other countries; $197.00/year for other countries; $103.00/year for students, other countries; $250.00/year for institutions; $167.00/year for individuals; $81.00/year for students. Journal focused on treatment of severe sepsis and septic shock, echocardiography in the evaluation of hemo-dynamically unstable patients & mechanical ventilation of acute respiratory distress syndrome.

EMPLOYER DIRECTORIES AND NETWORKING LISTS

8230 ■ Crain's List—Chicago's Largest Hospitals
Crain Communications Inc.
360 N Michigan Ave.
Chicago, IL 60601
Ph: (312)649-5200
URL: http://www.chicagobusiness.com/section/lists

Published November, 2010. $25.00 for individuals; $45.00 for individuals. Covers: 25 hospitals in Chicago area ranked by net patient revenues. Entries include: Name, address, phone number, fax, web address, corporate e-mail, hospital administrator, network affiliation, 2009 net patient revenue, percentage change from 2008, 2009 net profits, percentage change from 2008, inpatient days, available beds, daily occupancy rate, number of hospital employees as of December 31, 2009, fiscal year end, Chairman, President, CEO, Chief Financial Officer, Human Resources Manager, Media Relations/Public Relations Director, and Hospital Administrator.

8231 ■ Hospital Blue Book
Billian Publishing Inc. and Trans World Publishing Inc.
2100 River Edge Pky.
Atlanta, GA 30328
Ph: (770)955-5656
Fax: (770)952-0669
Fr: 800-800-5668
E-mail: blu-book@billian.com
URL: http://www.billianshealthdata.com/Products/ bluebook.html

Annual, Latest edition 2010. $575.00 for individuals; $575.00 for individuals. Covers: More than 6,500 hospitals; some listings also appear in a separate southern edition of this publication. Entries include: Name of hospital, accreditation, mailing address, phone, fax, number of beds, type of facility (nonprofit, general, state, etc.); list of administrative personnel and chiefs of medical services, with specific titles. Arrangement: Geographical.

8232 ■ Medical and Health Information Directory
Gale
PO Box 6904
Florence, KY 41022-6904
Fr: 800-354-9706
URL: http://www.gale.cengage.com

Annual, Latest edition April 2011. $1190.00 for individuals; $501.00 for individuals. Covers: In volume 1, more than 33,000 medical and health oriented associations, organizations, institutions, and government agencies, including health maintenance organizations (HMOs), preferred provider organizations (PPOs), insurance companies, pharmaceutical companies, research centers, and medical and allied health schools. In Volume 2, over 20,000 medical book publishers; medical periodicals, directories, audiovisual producers and services, medical libraries and information centers, electronic resources, and health-related internet search engines. In Volume 3, more than 40,500 clinics, treatment centers, care programs, and counseling/diagnostic services for 34 subject areas. Entries include: Institution, service, or firm name, address, phone, fax, email and URL; many include names of key personnel and, when pertinent, descriptive annotation. Volume 3 was formerly listed separately as Health Services Directory. Arrangement: Classified by organization activity, service, etc. Indexes: Each volume has a complete alphabetical name and keyword index.

HANDBOOKS AND MANUALS

8233 ■ Careers in Health Care
The McGraw-Hill Companies
PO Box 182604
Columbus, OH 43272

Fax: (614)759-3749
Fr: 877-883-5524
E-mail: customer.service@mcgraw-hill.com
URL: http://www.mhprofessional.com/ product.php?isbn=0071466533

Barbara M. Swanson. Fifth edition, 2005. $19.95 (paper). 192 pages. Describes job duties, work settings, salaries, licensing and certification requirements, educational preparation, and future outlook. Gives ideas on how to secure a job.

8234 ■ Comprehensive Exam Review for the Medical Assistant
Prentice Hall PTR
1 Lake St.
Upper Saddle River, NJ 07458
Fr: 800-922-0579
URL: http://pearsonhighered.com

Robyn S. Gohsman. 2011. $88.07 (paper). 504 pages. Covers essential exam topics and presents valuable study hints and test-taking strategies. Contains practice questions and answers. Includes information about the medical assistant profession.

8235 ■ Delmar's Comprehensive Medical Assisting: Administrative and Clinical Competencies
Delmar, Cengage Learning
PO Box 6904
Florence, KY 41022
Fax: 800-487-8488
Fr: 800-354-9706
E-mail: esales@cengage.com
URL: http://www.cengage.com

Wilburta Q. Lindh, Marilyn Pooler, Carol D. Tamparo, and Barbara M. Dahl. 4th edition, 2010. $111.95. Illustrated. 1552 pages. Explores medical assisting.

8236 ■ Expert Resumes for Health Care Careers
Jist Works
875 Montreal Way
St. Paul, MN 55102
Fr: 800-648-5478
E-mail: educate@emcp.com
URL: http://www.jist.com

Wendy S. Enelow and Louise M. Kursmark. 2010. $16.95. 288 pages.

8237 ■ Exploring Health Care Careers, Second Edition
JIST Publishing
875 Montreal Way
St. Paul, MN 55102
Fax: 800-547-8329
Fr: 800-648-5478
E-mail: info@jist.com
URL: http://www.jist.com

2006. $125.00. 992 pages. Information about careers in the health industry, including education and certification requirements, earnings, and job outlook.

8238 ■ Health Care Job Explosion! High Growth Health Care Careers and Job Locator
Bookhaven Press LLC
249 Field Club Cir.
McKees Rocks, PA 15136
Ph: (412)494-6926
Fax: (412)494-5749
Fr: 800-782-7424
E-mail: bookhaven@aol.com
URL: http://www.bookhavenpress.com

Dennis V. Damp. Fourth edition, 2006. 320 pages. $19.95.

8239 ■ Health Careers Today
Elsevier
11830 Westline Industrial Dr.
St. Louis, MO 63146
Ph: (314)453-7010
Fax: (314)453-7095

Fr: 800-545-2522
E-mail: usbkinfo@elsevier.com
URL: http://www.elsevier.com

Gerdin, Judith. Fourth edition. 2007. $74.95. 496 pages. Covers more than 45 health careers. Discusses the roles and responsibilities of various occupations and provides a solid foundation in the skills needed for all health careers.

8240 ■ How To Get a Job in Health Care

Cengage Learning
PO Box 6904
Florence, KY 41022-6904
Fax: 800-487-8488
Fr: 800-354-9706
URL: http://www.cengage.com

Robert H. Zedlitz. 2012. $58.00. 144 pages (paperback). Serves as a preparatory reference tool for job seekers, includes job research, writing resumes, completing applications, and preparing for interviews.

8241 ■ Introduction to the Health Professions

Jones & Bartlett Learning, LLC
PO Box 417289
Boston, MA 02241-7289
Ph: (978)443-5000
Fax: (978)443-8000
Fr: 800-832-0034
E-mail: info@jblearning.com
URL: http://www.jblearning.com

Peggy S. Stanfield, Y. H. Hui and Nanna Cross. 2012. $93.95. 502 pages. Sixth edition. Provides current coverage of all major health professions. Outlines health-related careers, a review of the U.S. healthcare delivery system, managed care, and impact of new technology on healthcare services.

8242 ■ Medical Assisting: Administrative and Clinical Competencies

The McGraw-Hill Companies
PO Box 182604
Columbus, OH 43272
Fax: (614)759-3749
Fr: 877-883-5524
E-mail: customer.service@mcgraw-hill.com
URL: http://www.mcgraw-hill.com

Barbara Prickett-Ramutkowski. Second edition, 2004. $108.00. 1205 pages. Explores medical assisting and the competencies of it.

8243 ■ Opportunities in Health and Medical Careers

The McGraw-Hill Companies
PO Box 182604
Columbus, OH 43272
Fax: (614)759-3749
Fr: 877-883-5524
E-mail: customer.service@mcgraw-hill.com
URL: http://www.mhprofessional.com/
  product.php?isbn=0071437274

I. Donald Snook, Jr. and Leo D'Orazio. 2004. $14.95 (paper). 157 pages. Covers the full range of medical and health occupations. Illustrated.

8244 ■ Plunkett's Health Care Industry Almanac 2012

Plunkett Research, Ltd.
PO Drawer 541737
Houston, TX 77254-1737
Ph: (713)932-0000
Fax: (713)932-7080
E-mail: customersupport@plunkettresearch.com
URL: http://www.plunkettresearch.com

Jack W. Plunkett. 2011. $299.99. 717 pages. Features in-depth profiles of leading companies, associations and professional societies in the healthcare field. Covers major issues and trends, market forecasts and industry statistics.

8245 ■ Preparing to Pass the Medical Assisting Exam

Jones & Bartlett Learning
5 Wall St.
Burlington, MA 01803
Ph: (978)443-5000
Fax: (978)443-8000
Fr: 800-832-0034
E-mail: info@jblearning.com
URL: http://www.jblearning.com

Carlene Harrison and Valerie Weiss. 2011. $73.95 (paper). 319 pages. Serves as a review for medical assistants preparing to take the certified medical assisting exam. Contains up-to-date content reflective of the exam. Includes study tips, test-taking strategies, practice questions and answers.

8246 ■ Resumes for Health and Medical Careers

The McGraw-Hill Companies
PO Box 182604
Columbus, OH 43272
Fax: (614)759-3749
Fr: 877-883-5524
E-mail: customer.service@mcgraw-hill.com
URL: http://www.mhprofessional.com/
  product.php?isbn=0071545352

Third edition, 2008. $12.95 (paper). 144 pages.

8247 ■ Saunders Essentials of Medical Assisting

Saunders
c/o Elsevier Health
1600 John F. Kennedy Blvd., Ste. 1800
Philadelphia, PA 19103-2899
Ph: (215)239-3900
Fax: (215)239-3990
Fr: 800-523-1649
URL: http://www.us.elsevierhealth.com

Dianne M. Klieger. 2010. $89.95. 1248 pages. 2nd edition. Gives essential information needed to prepare for a career as a medical assistant. Contains up-to-date material on basic body systems and foundational concepts, plus full coverage of administrative and clinical procedures. Includes case studies and illustrations.

EMPLOYMENT AGENCIES AND SEARCH FIRMS

8248 ■ Actuary Resources

115 N Castle Heights Ave., Ste. 202
Lebanon, TN 37087-2768
Ph: (615)360-5171
Fax: (615)360-5173
E-mail: info@actuaryresources.org
URL: http://www.actuaryresources.org

Provides staffing services to several different types of industries. Offers a free screening service to clients.

8249 ■ Davis-Smith, Inc.

27656 Franklin Rd.
Southfield, MI 48034
Ph: (248)354-4100
Fax: (248)354-6702
E-mail: info@davissmith.com
URL: http://www.davissmith.com

Healthcare staffing agency. Executive search firm.

8250 ■ Harper Associates

31000 NW Hwy., Ste. 240
Farmington Hills, MI 48334
Ph: (248)932-1170
Fax: (248)932-1214
E-mail: info@harperjobs.com
URL: http://www.harperjobs.com

Executive search firm and employment agency.

8251 ■ Insperity, Inc.

19001 Crescent Springs Dr.
Kingwood, TX 77339-3802

Ph: (281)358-8986
Fr: 800-237-3170
E-mail: douglas.sharp@insperity.com
URL: http://www.insperity.com

Description: Serves as a full-service human resources department for small and medium-sized businesses throughout the United States. Provides client companies with benefits and services such as employment administration, government compliance, recruiting and selection, performance management, benefits management, employer liability management, training and development, and business services.

8252 ■ Professional Placement Associates, Inc.

287 Bowman Ave.
Purchase, NY 10577-2517
Ph: (914)251-1000
Fax: (914)251-1055
E-mail: careers@ppasearch.com
URL: http://www.ppasearch.com

Executive search firm specializing in the health and medical field.

ONLINE JOB SOURCES AND SERVICES

8253 ■ CareerVitals.com

URL: http://www.careervitals.com

Description: Serves as a job board for healthcare professionals in different specializations.

8254 ■ CertMedAssistant.com

URL: http://www.certmedassistant.com

Description: Offers medical assistant training options, certification avenues, job opportunities, and scope of practice for medical assistants. Encourages certification for all medical assistants.

8255 ■ HEALTHeCAREERS Network

Fr: 888-884-8242
E-mail: info@healthecareers.com
URL: http://www.healthecareers.com

Description: Career search site for jobs in all health care specialties; educational resources; visa and licensing information for relocation; interesting articles; relocation tools; links to professional organizations and general resources.

8256 ■ Hospital Jobs OnLine

E-mail: support@hospitaljobsonline.com
URL: http://www.hospitaljobsonline.com

Description: Serves as a niche healthcare job board designed exclusively for hospitals, healthcare companies, and healthcare job seekers.

8257 ■ Medical Assistant Jobs

URL: http://medicalassistant-jobs.net

Description: Features current listings for medical assistant jobs. Includes articles about certification, job description and salary information.

8258 ■ Medical Assistant Net

URL: http://www.medicalassistant.net

Description: Offers career direction and advice for medical assistant students and graduates including online learning resources and networking opportunities to assist professional growth.

8259 ■ Medjobsdata.com

URL: http://www.medjobsdata.com

Description: Helps jobseekers find a health profession from clinical to administrative.

8260 ■ ProHealthJobs.com

Ph: (484)443-8545
Fax: (484)443-8549
E-mail: info@prohealthjobs.com
URL: http://prohealthjobs.com/jobboard

Description: Career resources site for the medical

and health care field. Lists professional opportunities, product information, continuing education and open positions.

TRADESHOWS

8261 ■ American Association of Medical Assistants National Convention

American Association of Medical Assistants
20 N. Wacker Dr., Ste. 1575
Chicago, IL 60606
Ph: (312)899-1500
Fax: (312)899-1259
Fr: 800-228-2262
URL: http://www.aama-ntl.org

Annual. Primary Exhibits: Data processing equipment, pharmaceuticals, publications, insurance services, text books, coding system reference guides, health care services, filing and accounting systems, and computer hardware and software.

OTHER SOURCES

8262 ■ American Association of Medical Assistants (AAMA)

20 N Wacker Dr., Ste. 1575
Chicago, IL 60606
Ph: (312)899-1500
Fax: (312)899-1259
Fr: 800-228-2262
E-mail: info@aama-ntl.org
URL: http://www.aama-ntl.org

Description: Medical assistants are allied health professionals who work primarily in ambulatory (outpatient) settings and perform clinical and administrative procedures. Activities include a certification program consisting of study and an examination, passage of which entitles the individual to become credentialed as a Certified Medical Assistant. Conducts accreditation of one and two-year programs in medical assisting in conjunction with the commission on Accreditation of Allied Health Education Programs. Provides assistance and information to institutions of higher learning desirous of initiating courses for medical assistants. Awards continuing education units for selected educational programs.

8263 ■ American Medical Technologists (AMT)

10700 W Higgins Rd., Ste. 150
Rosemont, IL 60018
Ph: (847)823-5169
Fax: (847)823-0458
Fr: 800-275-1268
E-mail: membership@amt1.com
URL: http://www.amt1.com

Description: Represents medical technologists, medical laboratory technicians, medical assistants, medical administrative specialists, dental assistants, office laboratory technicians, phlebotomy technicians, laboratory consultants, and allied health technicians. Provides allied health professionals with professional certification services and membership programs to enhance their professional and personal growth. Aims to issue certification credentials to medical and dental assistants, clinical laboratory personnel, laboratory consultants, and allied health instructors.

8264 ■ American Society of Podiatric Medical Assistants (ASPMA)

1616 N 78th Ct.
Elmwood Park, IL 60707
Fr: 888-882-7762
E-mail: aspmaex@aol.com
URL: http://www.aspma.org

Description: Represents podiatric assistants. Holds educational seminars and administers certification examinations.

8265 ■ Health Professions Network (HPN)

PO Box 112
Shillington, PA 19607-0112
Ph: (678)200-2619
Fax: (206)426-6469
E-mail: info@healthpronet.org
URL: http://www.healthpronet.org

Description: Represents health care professionals who specialize in various allied health professions, including provider organizations, educators, accreditors, credentialing agencies, and administrators. Seeks to address issues relevant to workforce development and delivery of quality health care in the United States. Facilitates interdisciplinary communication, discussion, and collaboration among its members.

8266 ■ National Association of Certified Professional Midwives (NACPM)

243 Banning Rd.
Putney, VT 05346
E-mail: president@nacpm.org
URL: http://www.nacpm.org

Description: Strives to ensure that Certified Professional Midwives (CPMs) will achieve their appropriate place in the delivery of maternity care in the United States. Increases women's access to midwives by supporting the work and practice of CPMs. Educates legislators and policy makers about the practice of Certified Professional Midwifery. Works to increase reimbursement for the services of CPMs.

8267 ■ Careers in Focus—Medical Technicians and Technologists
Facts On File Inc.
132 W 31st St., 17th Fl.
New York, NY 10001
Ph: (212)967-8800
Fax: 800-678-3633
Fr: 800-322-8755
URL: http://www.infobasepublishing.com

Latest edition 5th; Published July, 2009. $32.95 for individuals. Covers: An overview of medical technicians, followed by a selection of jobs profiled in detail, including the nature of the job, earnings, prospects for employment, what kind of training and skills it requires, and sources for further information.

8268 ■ Crain's List—Chicago's Largest Hospitals
Crain Communications Inc.
360 N Michigan Ave.
Chicago, IL 60601
Ph: (312)649-5200
URL: http://www.chicagobusiness.com/section/lists

Published November, 2010. $25.00 for individuals; $45.00 for individuals. Covers: 25 hospitals in Chicago area ranked by net patient revenues. Entries include: Name, address, phone number, fax, web address, corporate e-mail, hospital administrator, network affiliation, 2009 net patient revenue, percentage change from 2008, 2009 net profits, percentage change from 2008, inpatient days, available beds, daily occupancy rate, number of hospital employees as of December 31, 2009, fiscal year end, Chairman, President, CEO, Chief Financial Officer, Human Resources Manager, Media Relations/Public Relations Director, and Hospital Administrator.

8269 ■ Directory of Hospital Personnel
Grey House Publishing
4919 Rte. 22
PO Box 56
Amenia, NY 12501
Ph: (518)789-8700
Fax: (518)789-0556
Fr: 800-562-2139
URL: http://www.greyhouse.com/hospital_personnel.htm

Annual, Latest edition 2011. $325.00 for individuals. Covers: 200,000 executives at 6,000 U.S. Hospitals. Entries include: Name of hospital, address, phone, number of beds, type and JCAHO status of hospital, names and titles of key department heads and staff, medical and nursing school affiliations; number of residents, interns, and nursing students. Arrangement: Geographical. Indexes: Hospital name, personnel, hospital size.

8270 ■ Hospital Blue Book
Billian Publishing Inc. and Trans World Publishing Inc.
2100 River Edge Pky.
Atlanta, GA 30328
Ph: (770)955-5656
Fax: (770)952-0669
Fr: 800-800-5668
E-mail: blu-book@billian.com
URL: http://www.billianshealthdata.com/Products/bluebook.html

Annual, Latest edition 2010. $575.00 for individuals; $575.00 for individuals. Covers: More than 6,500 hospitals; some listings also appear in a separate southern edition of this publication. Entries include: Name of hospital, accreditation, mailing address, phone, fax, number of beds, type of facility (nonprofit, general, state, etc.); list of administrative personnel and chiefs of medical services, with specific titles. Arrangement: Geographical.

8271 ■ Medical and Health Information Directory
Gale
PO Box 6904
Florence, KY 41022-6904
Fr: 800-354-9706
URL: http://www.gale.cengage.com

Annual, Latest edition April 2011. $1190.00 for individuals; $501.00 for individuals. Covers: In volume 1, more than 33,000 medical and health oriented associations, organizations, institutions, and government agencies, including health maintenance organizations (HMOs), preferred provider organizations (PPOs), insurance companies, pharmaceutical companies, research centers, and medical and allied health schools. In Volume 2, over 20,000 medical book publishers; medical periodicals, directories, audiovisual producers and services, medical libraries and information centers, electronic resources, and health-related internet search engines. In Volume 3, more than 40,500 clinics, treatment centers, care programs, and counseling/diagnostic services for 34 subject areas. Entries include: Institution, service, or firm name, address, phone, fax, email and URL; many include names of key personnel and, when pertinent, descriptive annotation. Volume 3 was formerly listed separately as Health Services Directory. Arrangement: Classified by organization activity, service, etc. Indexes: Each volume has a complete alphabetical name and keyword index.

HANDBOOKS AND MANUALS

8272 ■ Careers in Health Care
The McGraw-Hill Companies
PO Box 182604
Columbus, OH 43272
Fax: (614)759-3749
Fr: 877-883-5524
E-mail: customer.service@mcgraw-hill.com
URL: http://www.mhprofessional.com/product.php?isbn=0071466533

Barbara M. Swanson. Fifth edition, 2005. $19.95 (paper). 192 pages. Describes job duties, work settings, salaries, licensing and certification requirements, educational preparation, and future outlook. Gives ideas on how to secure a job.

8273 ■ Expert Resumes for Health Care Careers
Jist Works
875 Montreal Way
St. Paul, MN 55102
Fr: 800-648-5478
E-mail: educate@emcp.com
URL: http://www.jist.com

Wendy S. Enelow and Louise M. Kursmark. 2010. $16.95. 288 pages.

8274 ■ Exploring Health Care Careers, Second Edition
JIST Publishing
875 Montreal Way
St. Paul, MN 55102
Fax: 800-547-8329
Fr: 800-648-5478
E-mail: info@jist.com
URL: http://www.jist.com

2006. $125.00. 992 pages. Information about careers in the health industry, including education and certification requirements, earnings, and job outlook.

8275 ■ Health Careers Today
Elsevier
11830 Westline Industrial Dr.
St. Louis, MO 63146
Ph: (314)453-7010
Fax: (314)453-7095
Fr: 800-545-2522
E-mail: usbkinfo@elsevier.com
URL: http://www.elsevier.com

Gerdin, Judith. Fourth edition. 2007. $74.95. 496 pages. Covers more than 45 health careers. Discusses the roles and responsibilities of various occupations and provides a solid foundation in the skills needed for all health careers.

8276 ■ Introduction to the Health Professions
Jones & Bartlett Learning, LLC
PO Box 417289
Boston, MA 02241-7289
Ph: (978)443-5000
Fax: (978)443-8000
Fr: 800-832-0034
E-mail: info@jblearning.com
URL: http://www.jblearning.com

Peggy S. Stanfield, Y. H. Hui and Nanna Cross. 2012. $93.95. 502 pages. Sixth edition. Provides current coverage of all major health professions. Outlines health-related careers, a review of the U.S. healthcare delivery system, managed care, and impact of new technology on healthcare services.

8277 ■ Opportunities in Health and Medical Careers

The McGraw-Hill Companies
PO Box 182604
Columbus, OH 43272
Fax: (614)759-3749
Fr: 877-883-5524
E-mail: customer.service@mcgraw-hill.com
URL: http://www.mhprofessional.com/
product.php?isbn=0071437274

I. Donald Snook, Jr. and Leo D'Orazio. 2004. $14.95 (paper). 157 pages. Covers the full range of medical and health occupations. Illustrated.

8278 ■ Plunkett's Health Care Industry Almanac 2012

Plunkett Research, Ltd.
PO Drawer 541737
Houston, TX 77254-1737
Ph: (713)932-0000
Fax: (713)932-7080
E-mail: customersupport@plunkettresearch.com
URL: http://www.plunkettresearch.com

Jack W. Plunkett. 2011. $299.99. 717 pages. Features in-depth profiles of leading companies, associations and professional societies in the healthcare field. Covers major issues and trends, market forecasts and industry statistics.

8279 ■ Resumes for Health and Medical Careers

The McGraw-Hill Companies
PO Box 182604
Columbus, OH 43272
Fax: (614)759-3749
Fr: 877-883-5524
E-mail: customer.service@mcgraw-hill.com
URL: http://www.mhprofessional.com/
product.php?isbn=0071545352

Third edition, 2008. $12.95 (paper). 144 pages.

EMPLOYMENT AGENCIES AND SEARCH FIRMS

8280 ■ Davis-Smith, Inc.

27656 Franklin Rd.
Southfield, MI 48034
Ph: (248)354-4100
Fax: (248)354-6702
E-mail: info@davissmith.com
URL: http://www.davissmith.com

Healthcare staffing agency. Executive search firm.

8281 ■ Harper Associates

31000 NW Hwy., Ste. 240
Farmington Hills, MI 48334
Ph: (248)932-1170
Fax: (248)932-1214
E-mail: info@harperjobs.com
URL: http://www.harperjobs.com

Executive search firm and employment agency.

8282 ■ JPM International

26034 Acero
Mission Viejo, CA 92691
Ph: (949)699-4300
Fax: (949)699-4333

Fr: 800-685-7856
E-mail: qtek37@yahoo.com
URL: http://www.jpmintl.com/pages/qss.html

Executive search firm and employment agency.

8283 ■ Professional Placement Associates, Inc.

287 Bowman Ave.
Purchase, NY 10577-2517
Ph: (914)251-1000
Fax: (914)251-1055
E-mail: careers@ppasearch.com
URL: http://www.ppasearch.com

Executive search firm specializing in the health and medical field.

8284 ■ SHS Careers Front Page

711 DeLasalle Ct.
Naperville, IL 60565
Ph: (630)718-1704
Fax: (630)718-1709
URL: http://www.shsinc.com

Executive search firm for pharmaceutical advertising, medical communications and education, healthcare public relations, and biotechnology industries.

ONLINE JOB SOURCES AND SERVICES

8285 ■ HEALTHeCAREERS Network

Fr: 888-884-8242
E-mail: info@healthecareers.com
URL: http://www.healthecareers.com

Description: Career search site for jobs in all health care specialties; educational resources; visa and licensing information for relocation; interesting articles; relocation tools; links to professional organizations and general resources.

8286 ■ Hospital Jobs OnLine

E-mail: support@hospitaljobsonline.com
URL: http://www.hospitaljobsonline.com

Description: Serves as a niche healthcare job board designed exclusively for hospitals, healthcare companies, and healthcare job seekers.

8287 ■ ProHealthJobs.com

Ph: (484)443-8545
Fax: (484)443-8549
E-mail: info@prohealthjobs.com
URL: http://prohealthjobs.com/jobboard

Description: Career resources site for the medical and health care field. Lists professional opportunities, product information, continuing education and open positions.

OTHER SOURCES

8288 ■ American Association of Clinical Coders and Auditors (AACCA)

1142 S Diamond Bar Blvd., No. 796
Diamond Bar, CA 91765
Ph: (909)579-0507
Fax: (909)680-3157
URL: http://www.aacca.net

Description: Fosters the advancement of the clinical coding and auditing profession. Promotes correct documentation and coding of all medical and surgical services, and the professional and technical components of these services.

8289 ■ American Health Information Management Association (AHIMA)

233 N Michigan Ave., 21st Fl.
Chicago, IL 60601
Ph: (312)233-1100
Fax: (312)233-1090
Fr: 800-335-5535
E-mail: info@ahima.org
URL: http://www.ahima.org

Description: Registered record administrators; accredited record technicians with expertise in health information management, biostatistics, classification systems, and systems analysis. Sponsors Independent Study Programs in Medical Record Technology and coding. Conducts annual qualification examinations to credential medical record personnel as Registered Record Administrators (RRA), Accredited Record Technicians (ART) and Certified Coding Specialists (CCS). Maintains Foundation of Research and Education Library, Scholarships and loans.

8290 ■ American Medical Informatics Association

4720 Montgomery Ln., Ste. 500
Bethesda, MD 20814
Ph: (301)657-1291
Fax: (301)657-1296
E-mail: mail@amia.org
URL: http://www.amia.org

Description: Medical personnel, physicians, physical scientists, engineers, data processors, researchers, educators, hospital administrators, nurses, medical record administrators, and computer professionals. Supports the use of health information and communications technology in clinical care and clinical research, personal health management, public health/population, and translational science.

8291 ■ ARMA International - The Association of Information Management Professionals

11880 College Blvd., Ste. 450
Overland Park, KS 66210
Ph: (913)341-3808
Fax: (913)341-3742
Fr: 800-422-2762
URL: http://www.arma.org

Description: Provides education, research, and networking opportunities to information professionals to enable them to use their skills and experience to leverage the value of records, information and knowledge as corporate assets and as contributors to organizational success.

8292 ■ National Association for Healthcare Quality (NAHQ)

4700 W Lake Ave.
Glenview, IL 60025
Ph: (847)375-4720
Fax: (847)375-6320
Fr: 800-966-9392
E-mail: info@nahq.org
URL: http://www.nahq.org

Description: Healthcare professionals in quality assessment and improvement, utilization and risk management, case management, infection control, managed care, nursing, and medical records. Objectives are: to encourage, develop, and provide continuing education for all persons involved in health care quality; to give the patient primary consideration in all actions affecting his or her health and welfare; to promote the sharing of knowledge and encourage a high degree of professional ethics in health care quality. Offers accredited certification in the field of healthcare quality, utilization, and risk management. Facilitates communication and cooperation among members, medical staff, and health care government agencies. Conducts educational seminars and conferences.

SOURCES OF HELP-WANTED ADS

8293 ■ Advanced Materials & Processes
ASM International
9639 Kinsman Rd.
Novelty, OH 44073-0001
Ph: (440)338-5151
Fax: (440)338-4634
Fr: 800-336-5152
URL: http://www.asminternational.org/portal/site/
www/membership/b

Monthly. Magazine covering advances in metal, materials, testing technology and more.

8294 ■ AIE Perspectives Newsmagazine
American Institute of Engineers
4630 Appian Way, Ste. 206
El Sobrante, CA 94803-1875
Ph: (510)758-6240
Fax: (510)758-6240
URL: http://www.members-aie.org

Monthly. Professional magazine covering engineering.

8295 ■ American Machinist
Penton Media Inc.
249 W 17th St.
New York, NY 10011
Ph: (212)204-4200
URL: http://www.americanmachinist.com/

Monthly. Magazine serving the metalworking marketplace, consisting of plants in industries primarily engaged in manufacturing durable goods and other metal products.

8296 ■ Composites
Begell House Inc.
50 Cross Hwy.
Redding, CT 06896
Ph: (203)938-1300
Fax: (203)938-1304
URL: http://www.begellhouse.com/journals/
36ff4a142dec9609

$708.00/year for institutions. Journal featuring basic ideas in the mechanics of composite materials and structures between research workers and engineers.

8297 ■ The Electrochemical Society Interface
Electrochemical Society Inc.
65 S Main St., Bldg. D
Pennington, NJ 08534-2839
Ph: (609)737-1902
Fax: (609)737-2743
E-mail: interface@electrochem.org
URL: http://www.electrochem.org/dl/interface/

Quarterly. $64.00/year for individuals, print & online; $82.00/year for other countries, tier 1, print & online. Publication featuring news and articles of interest to members of the Electrochemical Society.

8298 ■ Engineering
Scientific Research Publishing
PO Box 54821
Irvine, CA 92619-4821
E-mail: eng@scirp.org
URL: http://www.scirp.org/journal/eng/

Monthly. $708.00/year for individuals. Peer-reviewed journal publishing articles on the latest advancements in engineering.

8299 ■ Engineering Conferences International Symposium Series
Berkeley Electronic Press
2809 Telegraph Ave., Ste. 202
Berkeley, CA 94705-1167
Ph: (510)665-1200
Fax: (510)665-1201
URL: http://services.bepress.com/eci/

Journal focusing on advance engineering science.

8300 ■ ENR: Engineering News-Record
McGraw-Hill Inc.
PO Box 182604
Columbus, OH 43218
Ph: (614)430-4000
Fax: (614)759-3749
Fr: 877-833-5524
URL: http://enr.construction.com/Default.asp

Weekly. $49.00/year for individuals, print; $89.00/year for Canada, print; $125.00/year for other countries, print. Magazine focusing on engineering and construction.

8301 ■ Graduating Engineer & Computer Careers
Career Recruitment Media
2 LAN Dr., Ste. 100
Westford, MA 01886
Ph: (978)692-5092
Fax: (978)692-4174
URL: http://www.graduatingengineer.com

Quarterly. $16.95/year for individuals. Magazine focusing on employment, education, and career development for entry-level engineers and computer scientists.

8302 ■ High Technology Careers Magazine
HTC
4701 Patrick Henry Dr., No. 1901
Santa Clara, CA 95054
Fax: (408)567-0242
URL: http://www.hightechcareers.com

Bimonthly. $29.00/year; $35.00/year for Canada; $85.00/year for out of country. Magazine (tabloid) containing employment opportunity information for the engineering and technical community.

8303 ■ InterJournal
New England Complex Systems Institute
283 Main St., Ste. 319
Cambridge, MA 02142
Ph: (617)547-4100

Fax: (617)661-7711
URL: http://www.interjournal.org/

Journal covering the fields of science and engineering.

8304 ■ International Journal of Powder Metallurgy
APMI International
105 College Rd. E
Princeton, NJ 08540-6992
Ph: (609)452-7700
Fax: (609)987-8523
URL: http://www.mpif.org/apmi/intljournal.html

Bimonthly. Powder metallurgy journal.

8305 ■ Iron & Steel Technology
Association for Iron & Steel Technology
186 Thorn Hill Rd.
Warrendale, PA 15086
Ph: (724)814-3000
Fax: (724)814-3001
URL: http://www.aist.org/magazine/preview.htm

Monthly. $155.00/year for U.S., Canada, and Mexico; $195.00/year for other countries; $20.00/year for U.S., Canada, and Mexico, single copy; $25.00/year for other countries, single copy; free to members only. Journal offers information on metallurgical, engineering, operating and maintenance of the iron and steel industries.

8306 ■ JOM
The Minerals, Metals & Materials Society
184 Thorn Hill Rd.
Warrendale, PA 15086-7514
Ph: (724)776-9000
Fax: (724)776-3770
Fr: 800-759-4867
URL: http://www.tms.org

Monthly. Covers an array of materials-related subjects from minerals characterization and developments in extraction to the production of advanced electronic materials and the performance of tomorrow's aerospace structural components.

8307 ■ Journal of Engineering Education
American Society for Engineering Education
1818 N St. NW, Ste. 600
Washington, DC 20036-2479
Ph: (202)331-3500
Fax: (202)265-8504
URL: http://www.jee.org

Quarterly. $100.00/year for libraries, online; $160.00/year for other countries, library; $150.00/year for U.S., Canada, and Mexico, library; $160.00/year for other countries, library. Peer-reviewed journal covering scholarly research in engineering education.

8308 ■ Journal of Surface Engineered Materials and Advanced Technology
Scientific Research Publishing
PO Box 54821
Irvine, CA 92619-4821
E-mail: jsemat@scirp.org
URL: http://www.scirp.org/journal/jsemat/

Quarterly. $117.00/year for individuals. Peer-reviewed journal publishing articles on surface sciences, surface properties, techniques of characterization and generated applications.

8309 ■ *Journal of Women and Minorities in Science and Engineering*
Begell House Inc.
50 Cross Hwy.
Redding, CT 06896
Ph: (203)938-1300
Fax: (203)938-1304
URL: http://www.begellhouse.com/journals/00551c876cc2f027

$248.00/year for institutions. Peer-reviewed journal featuring innovative ideas and programs for classroom teachers, scientific studies, and formulation of concepts related to the education, recruitment, and retention of under-represented groups in science and engineering.

8310 ■ *Light Metal Age*
Fellom Publishing Co.
170 S Spruce Ave., Ste. 120
South San Francisco, CA 94080
Ph: (650)588-8832
Fax: (650)588-0901
URL: http://www.lightmetalage.com/

Bimonthly. $49.00/year for individuals; $64.00/year for two years; $79.00/year for individuals, three years; $84.00/year for out of country, seamail; $129.00/year for two years, seamail; $174.00/year for out of country, three years, seamail; $119.00/year for out of country, airmail; $204.00/year for two years, airmail; $289.00/year for out of country, three years, airmail. Magazine serving primary and semi-fabrication metal plants that produce, semi-fabricate, process or manufacture the light metals: aluminum, magnesium, titanium, beryllium and their alloys, and/or the nonferrous metals copper and zinc.

8311 ■ *Materials Performance*
NACE International
1440 S Creek Dr.
Houston, TX 77084-4906
Ph: (281)228-6200
Fax: (281)228-6300
Fr: 800-797-6223
URL: http://www.nace.org/content.cfm?parentid=1012&currentID=1391

Monthly. $115.00/year for nonmembers, USA; $205.00/year for libraries; $130.00/year for nonmembers, foreign; $220.00/year for libraries, foreign; free to members. Magazine on performance and protection of materials in a corrosive environment.

8312 ■ *Metalforming*
Precision Metalforming Association
6363 Oak Tree Blvd.
Independence, OH 44131-2500
Ph: (216)901-8800
Fax: (216)901-9190
E-mail: metalforming@pma.org
URL: http://www.metalformingmagazine.com

Monthly. $40.00/year for individuals, North America; $225.00/year for other countries; free to qualified subscribers, Canada, Mexico, USA. Serving those who add value to sheetmetal.

8313 ■ *MetalMag*
Hanley Wood L.L.C.
1 Thomas Cir. NW, Ste. 600
Washington, DC 20005-5803
Ph: (202)452-0800
Fax: (202)785-1974
Fr: 877-275-8647
E-mail: mtm@omeda.com
URL: http://www.metalmag.com/

Bimonthly. Free to qualified subscribers. Magazine for industrial construction professionals.

8314 ■ *Modern Casting Magazine*
American Foundry Society
1695 N Penny Ln.
Schaumburg, IL 60173-4555
Ph: (847)824-0181
Fax: (847)824-7848
Fr: 800-537-4237
URL: http://www.moderncasting.com/

Monthly. $40.00/year for individuals; $5.00/year for single issue; $50.00/year for individuals; $75.00/year for by mail. Magazine on metal casting plants and pattern shops.

8315 ■ *Modern Metals*
Trend Publishing
625 N Michigan Ave., Ste. 1100
Chicago, IL 60611-3118
Ph: (312)654-2300
Fax: (312)654-2323
Fr: 800-278-7363
URL: http://www.modernmetals.com

Monthly. $180.00/year for individuals; $270.00/year for two years; $260.00/year for individuals, airmail; $430.00/year for two years, airmail. Metals fabrication magazine.

8316 ■ *MRS Bulletin*
Materials Research Society
506 Keystone Dr.
Warrendale, PA 15086
Ph: (724)779-3003
Fax: (724)779-8313
E-mail: info@mrs.org
URL: http://www.mrs.org

Monthly. $363.00/year. Features news, trends, and event listing that keep the materials community apprised of information important to their research and their profession. Includes classified listings.

8317 ■ *New Journal of Glass and Ceramics*
Scientific Research Publishing
PO Box 54821
Irvine, CA 92619-4821
E-mail: njgc@scirp.org
URL: http://www.scirp.org/journal/njgc/

Quarterly. $117.00/year for individuals. Peer-reviewed journal publishing articles on all branches of glass and ceramics.

8318 ■ *NSBE Magazine*
NSBE Publications
205 Daingerfield Rd.
Alexandria, VA 22314
Ph: (703)549-2207
Fax: (703)683-5312
URL: http://www.nsbe.org/News-Media/Magazines/About-NSBE-Magazine

$20.00/year for individuals; $35.00/year for other countries; $15.00/year for students. Journal providing information on engineering careers, self-development, and cultural issues for recent graduates with technical majors.

8319 ■ *PE*
National Society of Professional Engineers
1420 King St.
Alexandria, VA 22314
Ph: (703)684-2800
Fax: (703)684-4875
URL: http://www.nspe.org/PEmagazine/index.html

Monthly. Magazine (tabloid) covering professional, legislative, and techology issues for an engineering audience.

8320 ■ *Snips Magazine*
Snips Magazine
2401 W Big Beaver Rd., Ste. 700
Troy, MI 48084-3333
Ph: (248)362-3700
Fax: (248)362-0317
URL: http://www.snipsmag.com/

Monthly. Free. Magazine for the sheet metal, warm-air heating, ventilating and air conditioning industry. Provides helpful hints for contractors.

8321 ■ *SWE, Magazine of the Society of Women Engineers*
Society of Women Engineers
120 S La Salle St., Ste. 1515
Chicago, IL 60603
Ph: (312)596-5223
Fr: 877-793-4636
URL: http://societyofwomenengineers.swe.org/index.php

Quarterly. $30.00/year for nonmembers. Magazine for engineering students and for women and men working in the engineering and technology fields. Covers career guidance, continuing development and topical issues.

8322 ■ *Tooling & Production*
Nelson Publishing Inc.
2500 Tamiami Trl. N
Nokomis, FL 34275
Ph: (941)966-9521
Fax: (941)966-2590
URL: http://www.manufacturingcenter.com

Monthly. Free. Magazine concerning metalworking.

8323 ■ *WEPANEWS*
Women in Engineering Programs & Advocates Network
1901 E Asbury Ave., Ste. 220
Denver, CO 80208
Ph: (303)871-4643
Fax: (303)871-4628
E-mail: dmatt@wepan.org
URL: http://www.wepan.org

Description: 2/year. Seeks to provide greater access for women to careers in engineering. Includes news of graduate, undergraduate, freshmen, precollege, and re-entry engineering programs for women. Recurring features include job listings, faculty, grant, and conference news, international engineering program news, action group news, notices of publications available, and a column titled Kudos.

8324 ■ *Woman Engineer*
Equal Opportunity Publications, Inc.
445 Broadhollow Rd., Ste. 425
Melville, NY 11747
Ph: (631)421-9421
Fax: (631)421-1352
E-mail: info@eop.com
URL: http://www.eop.com

Annual. Magazine that is offered at no charge to qualified female engineering, computer-science, and information-technology students and professionals seeking to find employment and advancement in their careers.

EMPLOYER DIRECTORIES AND NETWORKING LISTS

8325 ■ *American Men and Women of Science*
Gale
PO Box 6904
Florence, KY 41022-6904
Fr: 800-354-9706
URL: http://www.gale.cengage.com

Biennial, even years; New edition expected 29th, June 2011. $1,368.00 for individuals. Covers: Over 135,000 U.S. and Canadian scientists active in the physical, biological, mathematical, computer science, and engineering fields; includes references to previous edition for deceased scientists and nonrespondents. Entries include: Name, address, education, personal and career data, memberships, honors and awards, research interest. Arrangement: Alphabetical. Indexes: Discipline (in separate volume).

8326 ■ *Careers in Focus—Engineering*
Facts On File Inc.
132 W 31st St., 17th Fl.
New York, NY 10001
Ph: (212)967-8800
Fax: 800-678-3633
Fr: 800-322-8755
URL: http://www.infobasepublishing.com
Latest edition 3rd; Published July, 2007. $32.95 for individuals. Covers: An overview of engineering, followed by a selection of jobs profiled in detail, including the nature of the job, earnings, prospects for employment, what kind of training and skills it requires, and sources for further information.

8327 ■ *Directory of Contract Staffing Firms*
C.E. Publications Inc.
PO Box 3006
Bothell, WA 98041-3006
Ph: (425)806-5200
Fax: (425)806-5585
URL: http://www.cjhunter.com/dcsf/overview.html
Annual. Covers: Nearly 1,300 contract firms actively engaged in the employment of engineering, IT/IS, and technical personnel for 'temporary' contract assignments throughout the world. Entries include: Company name, address, phone, name of contact, email, web address. Arrangement: Alphabetical. Indexes: Geographical.

8328 ■ *The Minerals, Metals & Materials Society Membership Directory*
American Institute of Mining, Metallurgical and Petroleum Engineers
12999 E Adam Aircraft Cir.
Englewood, CO 80112
Ph: (303)325-5185
Fax: 888-702-0049
E-mail: tmsorg@multiview.com
URL: http://tmsmarketplace.com
Annual, July. Covers: 8,300 metallurgists, metallurgical engineers, and materials scientists, worldwide. Entries include: Name, office address, career data, telephone number. Arrangement: Alphabetical; geographical. Indexes: Geographical.

HANDBOOKS AND MANUALS

8329 ■ *Great Jobs for Engineering Majors*
The McGraw-Hill Companies
PO Box 182604
Columbus, OH 43272
Fax: (614)759-3749
Fr: 877-883-5524
E-mail: customer.service@mcgraw-hill.com
URL: http://www.mhprofessional.com/
   product.php?isbn=0071641963
Geraldine O. Garner. Second edition, 2008. $16.95. 192 pages. Covers all the career options open to students majoring in engineering.

8330 ■ *Resumes for Scientific and Technical Careers*
The McGraw-Hill Companies
PO Box 182604
Columbus, OH 43272
Fax: (614)759-3749
Fr: 877-883-5524
E-mail: customer.service@mcgraw-hill.com
URL: http://www.mhprofessional.com/
   product.php?isbn=0071482199
Third edition, 2007. $12.95 (paper). 144 pages. Provides resume advice for individuals interested in working in scientific and technical careers. Includes sample resumes and cover letters.

EMPLOYMENT AGENCIES AND SEARCH FIRMS

8331 ■ Elite Resources Group
1239 Stetson Ln.
Sevierville, TN 37876

Ph: (865)774-8228
Fax: (865)774-8229
URL: http://www.elite-rg.com
Executive search firm.

8332 ■ Empire International
1147 Lancaster Ave.
Berwyn, PA 19312
Ph: (610)647-7976
Fax: (610)647-8488
Fr: 800-539-0231
E-mail: info@empire-internl.com
URL: http://www.empire-internl.com
Executive search firm.

8333 ■ Engineer One, Inc.
PO Box 23037
Knoxville, TN 37933
Fax: (865)691-0110
E-mail: engineerone@engineerone.com
URL: http://www.engineerone.com
Engineering employment service specializing in engineering and management in the chemical process, power utilities, manufacturing, mechanical, electrical, and electronic industries. Maintains an Information Technology Division that works nationwide across all industries. Also provides systems analysis consulting services specializing in VAX based systems.

8334 ■ Executive Directions
PO Box 5742
Sarasota, FL 34277
Ph: (941)922-9180
E-mail: info@execdir.com
URL: http://www.executivedirections.com
Executive search firm.

8335 ■ Executive Resource Group Inc.
1330 Cedar Point, No. 201
Amelia, OH 45102
Ph: (513)947-1447
Fax: (513)752-3026
URL: http://www.executiveresource.net
Executive search firm.

8336 ■ Executives Unlimited Inc.
5000 E Spring St., Ste. 395
Long Beach, CA 90815
Ph: (562)627-3800
Fax: (562)627-1092
Fr: (866)957-4466
URL: http://www.executivesunlimited.com
Executive search firm. Branches in Western Springs, IL; Scotch Plains, NJ; Long Beach, CA.

8337 ■ First Choice Search
PO Box 946
Danville, WA 94526
Ph: (925)552-9985
E-mail: info@firstchoicesearch.com
URL: http://www.firstchoicesearch.com
Executive search firm.

8338 ■ Global Employment Solutions
10375 Park Meadows Dr., Ste. 375
Littleton, CO 80124
Ph: (303)216-9500
Fax: (303)216-9533
URL: http://www.gesnetwork.com
Employment agency.

8339 ■ International Staffing Consultants
31655 2nd Ave.
Laguna Beach, CA 92651
Ph: (949)255-5857
Fax: (949)767-5959
E-mail: iscinc@iscworld.com
URL: http://www.iscworld.com
Employment agency. Provides placement on regular or temporary basis. Affiliate office in London.

8340 ■ National Recruiting Service
1832 Hart St.
PO Box 218
Dyer, IN 46311-1564
Ph: (219)865-2373
Fax: (219)865-2375
E-mail: stan.hendricks@
   nationalrecruitingservice.com
URL: http://www.nationalrecruitingservice.com
A privately held Midwestern human resource firm, which specializes in the identification and screening of personnel exclusively to the pipe and tubing industry. In addition to the recruiting function the firm also offers a comprehensive outplacement and employee termination service, which can be used for all levels of management. Through executive search, psychological evaluations, contingency methods, consulting and outplacement services, firm helps organizations to fully utilize client personnel as a cost effective asset. Industries served: metals.

ONLINE JOB SOURCES AND SERVICES

8341 ■ Builder Jobs
URL: http://www.builderjobs.com
Description: Serves as an online career resource for home building professionals. Features career development articles, salary tools, home building and construction job listings, resume postings, and job alerts.

8342 ■ EngineerJobs.com
URL: http://www.engineerjobs.com
Description: Provides job opportunities for engineering professionals in the following disciplines: aerospace, agricultural, biomedical, chemical, civil, electrical, environmental, industrial, manufacturing, marine, materials, mechanical, mining, nuclear, petroleum, process, project, quality, sales, software, solar, systems, and structural.

8343 ■ MaterialsEngineerJob.com
URL: http://www.materialsengineerjobs.com
Description: Offers career opportunities to materials engineering professionals. Features networking and job opportunities throughout the country.

8344 ■ Spherion
2050 Spectrum Blvd.
Fort Lauderdale, FL 33309
Ph: (954)308-7600
Fr: 800-774-3746
E-mail: help@spherion.com
URL: http://www.spherion.com
Description: Recruitment firm specializing in accounting and finance, sales and marketing, interim executives, technology, engineering, retail and human resources.

8345 ■ ThinkEnergyGroup.com
E-mail: resumes@thinkjobs.com
URL: http://www.thinkenergygroup.com
Description: Serves as a job board for professionals looking for positions in engineering, power plant, energy, and technical fields. Contains advice and tips on interviews, job searching, resume writing, hiring, and management. Provides choices of work location, pay rates in the field of expertise and contract, temp-to-hire, and direct hiring options.

TRADESHOWS

8346 ■ METALFORM Mexico
Precision Metalforming Association
6363 Oak Tree Blvd.
Independence, OH 44131-2500
Ph: (216)901-8800
Fax: (216)901-9190
E-mail: pma@pma.org
URL: http://www.metalforming.com

Annual. Primary Exhibits: Presses and stamping equipment, tooling and fabricating machines, management aids, and related materials. Dates and Locations: 2012 May 02-04; Monterrey, NL, Mexico; Cintermex.

8347 ■ TMS Annual Meeting and Exhibition

Minerals, Metals and Materials Society TMS
184 Thorn Hill Rd.
Warrendale, PA 15086-7514
Ph: (724)776-9000
Fax: (724)776-3770
Fr: 800-759-4867
URL: http://www.tms.org

Annual. Primary Exhibits: Equipment, supplies, and services for those involved in the scientific and technological aspects of the minerals, metals, and materials industries. Dates and Locations: 2012 Mar 11-15; Orlando, FL; Walt Disney World Swan & Dolphin Resort.

8348 ■ WELDEX - International Exhibition for Welding Materials, Equipment and Technologies

Reed Exhibitions North American Headquarters
383 Main Ave.
Norwalk, CT 06851
Ph: (203)840-4800
Fax: (203)840-5805
E-mail: inquiry@reedexpo.com
URL: http://www.reedexpo.com

Quadrennial. Primary Exhibits: Plant, equipment, and consumables for welding, brazing, soldering, and surfacing; equipment for safety and fume extraction, gases and gas, industrial robots and automated welding, metal working and machinery, and inspection; fasteners, and hand and power tools. Dates and Locations: 2012 Oct 23-26; Moscow, Russia; Eco-Centre Sokolniki.

OTHER SOURCES

8349 ■ American Association of Engineering Societies (AAES)

1801 Alexander Bell Dr.
Reston, VA 20191
Ph: (202)296-2237
Fax: (202)296-1151
Fr: 888-400-2237
E-mail: dbateson@aaes.org
URL: http://www.aaes.org

Description: Coordinates the efforts of the member societies in the provision of reliable and objective information to the general public concerning issues which affect the engineering profession and the field of engineering as a whole; collects, analyzes, documents, and disseminates data which will inform the general public of the relationship between engineering and the national welfare; provides a forum for the engineering societies to exchange and discuss their views on matters of common interest; and represents the U.S. engineering community abroad through representation in WFEO and UPADI.

8350 ■ American Ceramic Society (ACerS)

600 N Cleveland Ave., Ste. 210
Westerville, OH 43082
Ph: (614)794-5855
Fax: (301)206-9789
Fr: (866)721-3322
E-mail: customerservice@ceramics.org
URL: http://ceramics.org

Description: Professional society of scientists, engineers, educators, plant operators, and others interested in the glass, cements, refractories, nuclear ceramics, whitewares, electronics, engineering, and structural clay products industries. Disseminates scientific and technical information through its publications and technical meetings. Conducts continuing education courses and training such as the Precollege Education Program. Sponsors over 10 meetings yearly; encourages high school and college

students' interest in ceramics. Maintains Ross C. Purdy Museum of Ceramics; offers placement service and speakers' bureau.

8351 ■ American Indian Science and Engineering Society (AISES)

PO Box 9828
Albuquerque, NM 87119-9828
Ph: (505)765-1052
Fax: (505)765-5608
E-mail: info@aises.org
URL: http://www.aises.org

Description: Represents American Indian and non-Indian students and professionals in science, technology, and engineering fields; corporations representing energy, mining, aerospace, electronic, and computer fields. Seeks to motivate and encourage students to pursue undergraduate and graduate studies in science, engineering, and technology. Sponsors science fairs in grade schools, teacher training workshops, summer math/science sessions for 8th-12th graders, professional chapters, and student chapters in colleges. Offers scholarships. Adult members serve as role models, advisers, and mentors for students. Operates placement service.

8352 ■ APMI International

105 College Rd. E
Princeton, NJ 08540-6692
Ph: (609)452-7700
Fax: (609)987-8523
E-mail: apmi@mpif.org
URL: http://www.mpif.org/apmi/index_frame.html

Description: Technical society for powder metallurgists and others interested in powder metallurgy and particulate materials, and their applications. Maintains speakers' bureau and placement service.

8353 ■ ASM International (ASM)

9639 Kinsman Rd.
Novelty, OH 44072
Ph: (440)338-5151
Fax: (440)338-4634
Fr: 800-336-5152
E-mail: customerservice@asminternational.org
URL: http://www.asminternational.org/portal/site/www

Description: Metallurgists, materials engineers, executives in materials producing and consuming industries; teachers and students. Disseminates technical information about the manufacture, use, and treatment of engineered materials. Offers in-plant, home study, and intensive courses through Materials Engineering Institute. Conducts career development program. Established ASM Foundation for Education and Research.

8354 ■ Association for International Practical Training (AIPT)

10400 Little Patuxent Pkwy., Ste. 250
Columbia, MD 21044-3519
Ph: (410)997-2200
Fax: (410)992-3924
E-mail: aipt@aipt.org
URL: http://www.aipt.org

Description: Provides worldwide of on-the-job training programs for students and professionals seeking international career development and life-changing experiences. Arranges workplace exchanges in hundreds of professional fields, bringing employers and trainees together from around the world. Client list ranges from small farming communities to Fortune 500 companies.

8355 ■ Engineering Society of Detroit (ESD)

20700 Civic Center Dr., Ste. 450
Southfield, MI 48076
Ph: (248)353-0735
Fax: (248)353-0736
E-mail: esd@esd.org
URL: http://ww2.esd.org/home.htm

Description: Engineers from all disciplines; scientists and technologists. Conducts technical programs and engineering refresher courses; sponsors conferences and expositions. Maintains speakers' bureau; offers

placement services; although based in Detroit, MI, society membership is international.

8356 ■ Global Semiconductor Alliance

Churchill Tower
12400 Coit Rd., Ste. 650
Dallas, TX 75251
Ph: (972)866-7579
Fax: (972)239-2292
E-mail: jshelton@gsaglobal.org
URL: http://www.gsaglobal.org

Description: Represents semiconductor companies including fabless, fab-lite, and integrated device manufacturers. Aims to accelerate the growth and increase of return on invested capital in the global semiconductor industry by fostering a more effective fabless ecosystem through collaboration, integration, and innovation.

8357 ■ International Society of Automation (ISA)

67 Alexander Dr.
PO Box 12277
Research Triangle Park, NC 27709
Ph: (919)549-8411
Fax: (919)549-8288
E-mail: info@isa.org
URL: http://www.isa.org

Description: Sets the standard for automation by helping over 30,000 worldwide members and other professionals solve difficult technical problems, while enhancing their leadership and personal career capabilities. Develops standards; certifies industry professionals; provides education and training; publishes books and technical articles; and hosts the largest conference and exhibition for automation professionals in the Western Hemisphere. Is the founding sponsor of The Automation Federation.

8358 ■ Korean-American Scientists and Engineers Association (KSEA)

1952 Gallows Rd., Ste. 300
Vienna, VA 22182
Ph: (703)748-1221
Fax: (703)748-1331
E-mail: sejong@ksea.org
URL: http://www.ksea.org

Description: Represents scientists and engineers holding single or advanced degrees. Promotes friendship and mutuality among Korean and American scientists and engineers; contributes to Korea's scientific, technological, industrial, and economic developments; strengthens the scientific, technological, and cultural bonds between Korea and the U.S. Sponsors symposium. Maintains speakers' bureau, placement service, and biographical archives. Compiles statistics.

8359 ■ Materials Research Society

506 Keystone Dr.
Warrendale, PA 15086
Ph: (724)779-3003
Fax: (724)779-8313
E-mail: info@mrs.org
URL: http://www.mrs.org

Description: Represents the interests of materials researchers from academia, industry, and government. Promotes advancement of interdisciplinary materials research to improve the quality of life. Encourages interaction among materials professionals.

8360 ■ Metal Powder Industries Federation (MPIF)

105 College Rd. E
Princeton, NJ 08540-6692
Ph: (609)452-7700
Fax: (609)987-8523
E-mail: info@mpif.org
URL: http://www.mpif.org

Description: Manufacturers of metal powders, powder metallurgy processing equipment and tools, powder metallurgy products, and refractory and reactive metals. Member associations are: Metal Injection

Molding Association; Metal Powder Producers Association; Advanced Particulate Materials Association; Powder Metallurgy Equipment Association; Powder Metallurgy Parts Association; Refractory Metals Association. Promotes the science and industry of powder metallurgy and metal powder application through: sponsorship of technical meetings, seminars, and exhibits; establishment of standards; compilation of statistics; public relations; publications. Maintains speakers' bureau and placement service; conducts research.

8361 ■ National Action Council for Minorities in Engineering (NACME)
440 Hamilton Ave., Ste. 302
White Plains, NY 10601-1813
Ph: (914)539-4010
Fax: (914)539-4032
E-mail: info@nacme.org
URL: http://www.nacme.org
Description: Leads the national effort to increase access to careers in engineering and other science-based disciplines. Conducts research and public policy analysis, develops and operates national demonstration programs at precollege and university levels, and disseminates information through publications, conferences and electronic media. Serves as a privately funded source of scholarships for minority students in engineering.

8362 ■ National Institute of Ceramic Engineers (NICE)
2840 Windrush Ln.
Roswell, GA 30076
Ph: (770)891-2212
E-mail: eajudson@comcast.net
URL: http://ceramics.org/classes/national-institute-of-ceramic-engineers
Description: Promotes the profession of ceramic engineering, accreditation of educational programs in ceramic and glass engineering and science, and in materials science and engineering and high ethical engineering standards and practices. Sponsors continuing education courses. Offers employment service and promotes professional engineer registration. Responsible for Professional Engineering exams in Ceramic Engineering.

8363 ■ National Society of Professional Engineers (NSPE)
1420 King St.
Alexandria, VA 22314-2794
Ph: (703)684-2800

Fax: (703)836-4875
Fr: 888-285-6773
E-mail: memserv@nspe.org
URL: http://www.nspe.org
Description: Represents professional engineers and engineers-in-training in all fields registered in accordance with the laws of states or territories of the U.S. or provinces of Canada; qualified graduate engineers, student members, and registered land surveyors. Is concerned with social, professional, ethical, and economic considerations of engineering as a profession; encompasses programs in public relations, employment practices, ethical considerations, education, and career guidance. Monitors legislative and regulatory actions of interest to the engineering profession.

8364 ■ North American Die Casting Association
241 Holbrook Dr.
Wheeling, IL 60090
Ph: (847)279-0001
Fax: (847)279-0002
E-mail: nadca@diecasting.org
URL: http://www.diecasting.org

Description: Promotes industry awareness, domestic growth in the global marketplace and member exposure. Provides educational and employment opportunities for members.

8365 ■ Society for the Advancement of Material and Process Engineering (SAMPE)
1161 Park View Dr., Ste. 200
Covina, CA 91724-3751
Ph: (626)331-0616
Fax: (626)332-8929
Fr: 800-562-7360
E-mail: sampeibo@sampe.org
URL: http://www.sampe.org

Description: Material and process engineers, scientists, and other professionals engaged in development of advanced materials and processing technology in airframe, missile, aerospace, propulsion, electronics, life sciences, management, and related industries. International and local chapters sponsor scholarships for science students seeking financial

assistance. Provides placement service for members.

8366 ■ Society of Hispanic Professional Engineers (SHPE)
13181 Crossroads Pkwy. N, Ste. 450
City of Industry, CA 91746-3496
Ph: (323)725-3970
Fax: (323)725-0316
E-mail: shpenational@shpe.org
URL: http://oneshpe.shpe.org/wps/portal/national
Description: Represents engineers, student engineers, and scientists. Aims to increase the number of Hispanic engineers by providing motivation and support to students. Sponsors competitions and educational programs. Maintains placement service and speakers' bureau; compiles statistics.

8367 ■ Society for Mining, Metallurgy, and Exploration (SME)
12999 E Adam Aircraft Cir.
Englewood, CO 80112
Ph: (303)948-4200
Fax: (303)973-3845
Fr: 800-763-3132
E-mail: cs@smenet.org
URL: http://www.smenet.org
Description: A member society of the American Institute of Mining, Metallurgical and Petroleum Engineers. Persons engaged in the finding, exploitation, treatment, and marketing of all classes of minerals (metal ores, industrial minerals, and solid fuels) except petroleum. Promotes the arts and sciences connected with the production of useful minerals and metals. Offers specialized education programs; compiles enrollment and graduation statistics from schools offering engineering degrees in mining, mineral, mineral processing/metallurgical, geological, geophysical, and mining technology. Provides placement service and sponsors charitable programs.

8368 ■ Society of Women Engineers (SWE)
203 N La Salle St., Ste. 1675
Chicago, IL 60601
Ph: (312)596-5223
Fax: (312)596-5252
Fr: 877-SWE-INFO
E-mail: hq@swe.org
URL: http://societyofwomenengineers.swe.org
Description: Educational and service organization representing both students and professional women in engineering and technical fields.

8369 ■ Climate Alert
The Climate Institute
900 17th St. NW, Ste. 700
Washington, DC 20006
Ph: (202)552-4723
Fax: (202)737-6410
E-mail: info@climate.org
URL: http://www.climate.org/publications/climate-alert.html

Description: Quarterly. Addresses global climate issues in terms of science and policy.

8370 ■ Nature International Weekly Journal of Science
Nature Publishing Group
75 Varick St., 9th Fl.
New York, NY 10013-1917
Ph: (212)726-9200
Fax: (212)696-9006
Fr: 888-331-6288
E-mail: nature@natureny.com
URL: http://www.nature.com/nature/index.html

Weekly. $199.00/year for individuals, print and online; $338.00/year for two years, print and online. Magazine covering science and technology, including the fields of biology, biochemistry, genetics, medicine, earth sciences, physics, pharmacology, and behavioral sciences.

8371 ■ PALAIOS
SEPM Publications
4111 S Darlington, Ste. 100
Tulsa, OK 74135-6373
Ph: (918)610-3361
Fax: (918)621-1685
Fr: 800-865-9765
E-mail: palois@ku.edu
URL: http://palaios.ku.edu/

Monthly. $315.00/year for individuals, for U.S.; online version with CD-ROM; $415.00/year for individuals, for U.S.; print and online version with CD-ROM; $315.00/year for other countries, online version with CD-ROM; $425.00/year for other countries, print and online version with CD-ROM. Journal providing information on the impact of life on Earth history as recorded in the paleontological and sedimentological records. Covers areas such as biogeochemistry, ichnology, sedimentology, stratigraphy, paleoecology, paleoclimatology, and paleoceanography.

8372 ■ PE & RS Photogrammetric Engineering & Remote Sensing
The Imaging and Geospatial Information Society
5410 Grosvenor Ln., Ste. 210
Bethesda, MD 20814-2160
Ph: (301)493-0290
Fax: (301)493-0208
URL: http://www.asprs.org/PE-RS-Journal/

Monthly. $410.00/year for individuals, first class

mail; $426.00/year for Canada, airmail; $420.00/year for other countries, air standard. Peer-reviewed journal covering photogrammetry, remote sensing, geographic information systems, cartography, and surveying, global positioning systems, digital photogrammetry.

8373 ■ The Scientist
The Scientist Inc.
121 W 27th St., Ste. 604
New York, NY 10001
Ph: (212)461-4470
Fax: (347)626-2385
URL: http://www.the-scientist.com

Monthly. $39.95/year for individuals, print only; $49.95/year for individuals, print & online; $64.95/year for other countries, print only; $74.95/year for other countries, print & online. News journal (tabloid) for life scientists featuring news, opinions, research, and professional section.

8374 ■ Weatherwise
Routledge
711 3 Ave., 8 Fl.
New York, NY 10016
Ph: (212)216-7800
Fax: (212)563-2269
Fr: 800-634-7064
URL: http://www.weatherwise.org/

Bimonthly. $48.00/year for individuals, print and online; $162.00/year for institutions, print and online; $162.00/year for institutions, print only. Popular weather magazine for students, teachers, and professionals.

EMPLOYER DIRECTORIES AND NETWORKING LISTS

8375 ■ American Men and Women of Science
Gale
PO Box 6904
Florence, KY 41022-6904
Fr: 800-354-9706
URL: http://www.gale.cengage.com

Biennial, even years; New edition expected 29th, June 2011. $1,368.00 for individuals. Covers: Over 135,000 U.S. and Canadian scientists active in the physical, biological, mathematical, computer science, and engineering fields; includes references to previous edition for deceased scientists and nonrespondents. Entries include: Name, address, education, personal and career data, memberships, honors and awards, research interest. Arrangement: Alphabetical. Indexes: Discipline (in separate volume).

8376 ■ National Weather Service Offices and Stations
U.S. National Weather Service
1325 East-West Hwy.
Silver Spring, MD 20910

Ph: (301)713-1698
URL: http://www.nws.noaa.gov
Annual, September. Covers: Offices and stations operated by or under the supervision of the National Weather Service in the United States, Mexico, the Caribbean, Central and South America, and Oceania. Entries include: Station and airport name, type of station, call letters, International Index Number, latitude, longitude, elevation; and number, type, and frequency of weather observations. Arrangement: Geographical.

ONLINE JOB SOURCES AND SERVICES

8377 ■ meteorologistjobs.net
URL: http://meteorologistjobs.net
Description: Focuses on meteorologist employment opportunities and candidate recruiting. Helps job seekers find meteorologist career opportunities with the best companies.

8378 ■ MeteorologyCareers.com
URL: http://www.meteorologycareers.com
Description: Provides information and resources for job seekers searching for meteorology job openings. Includes job title, company, location, job type, salaries, employers, and recruiters.

8379 ■ MeteorologyJobs.com
URL: http://www.meteorologyjobs.com
Description: Allows registered users to post and distribute resumes, as well as search job postings.

8380 ■ TheWeatherPrediction.com
URL: http://www.theweatherprediction.com
Description: Compares and contrasts jobs with different meteorological agencies. Provides links to jobs sites and postings.

TRADESHOWS

8381 ■ AMS Annual Meeting
American Meteorological Society
45 Beacon St.
Boston, MA 02108-3693
Ph: (617)227-2425
Fax: (617)742-8718
E-mail: amsmtgs@ametsoc.org
URL: http://www.ametsoc.org

Annual. Primary Exhibits: Satellite weather data systems, meteorological data integration systems, hydro-meteorological instruments, and aerostatic vehicles. Dates and Locations: 2013 Jan 06-10; Austin, TX; 2014 Feb 02-06; Atlanta, GA; 2015 Jan 04-08; Phoenix, AZ.

OTHER SOURCES

8382 ■ American Meteorological Society (AMS)
45 Beacon St.
Boston, MA 02108-3693
Ph: (617)227-2425

Fax: (617)742-8718
E-mail: amsinfo@ametsoc.org
URL: http://www.ametsoc.org
Description: Professional meteorologists, oceanographers, and hydrologists; interested students and nonprofessionals. Develops and disseminates information on the atmospheric and related oceanic and hydrospheric sciences; seeks to advance professional applications. Activities include guidance service, scholarship programs, career information, certification of consulting meteorologists, and a seal of approval program to recognize competence in radio and television weathercasting. Issues statements of policy to assist public understanding on subjects such as weather modification, forecasting, tornadoes, hurricanes, flash floods, and meteorological satellites. Provides abstracting services. Prepares educational films, filmstrips, and slides for a new curriculum in meteorology at the ninth grade level. Issues monthly announcements of job openings for meteorologists.

8383 ■ ASPRS - The Imaging and Geospatial Information Society
5410 Grosvenor Ln., Ste. 210
Bethesda, MD 20814-2160
Ph: (301)493-0290
Fax: (301)493-0208
E-mail: asprs@asprs.org
URL: http://www.asprs.org

Description: Firms, individuals, government employees and academicians engaged in photogrammetry, photointerpretation, remote sensing, and geographic information systems and their application to such fields as archaeology, geographic information systems, military reconnaissance, urban planning, engineering, traffic surveys, meteorological observations, medicine, geology, forestry, agriculture, construction and topographic mapping. Seeks to advance knowledge and improve understanding of these sciences and promote responsible applications. Offers voluntary certification program open to persons associated with one or more functional area of photogrammetry, remote sensing and GIS. Surveys the profession of private firms in photogrammetry and remote sensing in the areas of products and services.

8384 ■ Association for International Practical Training (AIPT)
10400 Little Patuxent Pkwy., Ste. 250
Columbia, MD 21044-3519
Ph: (410)997-2200
Fax: (410)992-3924
E-mail: aipt@aipt.org
URL: http://www.aipt.org

Description: Providers worldwide of on-the-job training programs for students and professionals seeking international career development and life-changing experiences. Arranges workplace exchanges in hundreds of professional fields, bringing employers and trainees together from around the world. Client list ranges from small farming communities to Fortune 500 companies.

8385 ■ National Severe Storms Laboratory
120 David L Boren Blvd.
Norman, OK 73072
Ph: (405)325-3620
URL: http://www.nssl.noaa.gov

Description: Offers training materials and information on college programs for meteorology, along with a career guide. Internships are available, and links to job postings are posted in the FAQ section of the Web site.

8386 ■ National Weather Association
228 W Millbrook Rd.
Raleigh, NC 27609
Ph: (919)845-1546
Fax: (919)845-2956
URL: http://www.nwas.org/jobs.php

Description: Provides members with the opportunity to network and to participate in activities related to meteorology.

ONLINE JOB SOURCES AND SERVICES

8387 ■ **Millwright Jobs**
URL: http://millwrightjobs.net
Description: Features job listings for millwrights.

SOURCES OF HELP-WANTED ADS

8388 ■ AEG News
Association of Environmental & Engineering Geologists
PO Box 460518
Denver, CO 80246
Ph: (303)757-2926
E-mail: aeg@aegweb.org
URL: http://www.aegweb.org
Description: Bimonthly. $40 per year for nonmember. Covers news of the engineering geology profession and the Association, whose members are engineering geologists and geological engineers worldwide. Recurring features include letters to the editor, a calendar of events, news of research, and short articles of technical interest.

8389 ■ Coal Age
Mining Media Inc.
8751 E Hampden Ave., Ste. B-1
Denver, CO 80231
Ph: (303)283-0640
Fax: (303)283-0641
URL: http://www.mining-media.com/publications/coal_age/index.php#
Monthly. Free. Coal production magazine.

8390 ■ Engineering
Scientific Research Publishing
PO Box 54821
Irvine, CA 92619-4821
E-mail: eng@scirp.org
URL: http://www.scirp.org/journal/eng/
Monthly. $708.00/year for individuals. Peer-reviewed journal publishing articles on the latest advancements in engineering.

8391 ■ Engineering Economist
Taylor & Francis Group
270 Madison Ave.
New York, NY 10016
Fax: (212)244-4561
URL: http://www.tandf.co.uk/journals/titles/0013791x.asp
Quarterly. $89.00/year for individuals, print; $153.00/year for institutions, online only; $170.00/year for institutions, print & online. Publication covering business issues in the energy, petroleum and mining industries.

8392 ■ Engineering and Mining Journal
Mining Media Inc.
8751 E Hampden Ave., Ste. B-1
Denver, CO 80231
Ph: (303)283-0640
Fax: (303)283-0641
URL: http://www.mining-media.com/publications/emj/
Monthly. Provides professionals in metallic and nonmetallic ores and minerals industries with news and technical economic information.

8393 ■ ENR: Engineering News-Record
McGraw-Hill Inc.
PO Box 182604
Columbus, OH 43218
Ph: (614)430-4000
Fax: (614)759-3749
Fr: 877-833-5524
URL: http://enr.construction.com/Default.asp
Weekly. $49.00/year for individuals, print; $89.00/year for Canada, print; $125.00/year for other countries, print. Magazine focusing on engineering and construction.

8394 ■ Graduating Engineer & Computer Careers
Career Recruitment Media
2 LAN Dr., Ste. 100
Westford, MA 01886
Ph: (978)692-5092
Fax: (978)692-4174
URL: http://www.graduatingengineer.com
Quarterly. $16.95/year for individuals. Magazine focusing on employment, education, and career development for entry-level engineers and computer scientists.

8395 ■ High Technology Careers Magazine
HTC
4701 Patrick Henry Dr., No. 1901
Santa Clara, CA 95054
Fax: (408)567-0242
URL: http://www.hightechcareers.com
Bimonthly. $29.00/year; $35.00/year for Canada; $85.00/year for out of country. Magazine (tabloid) containing employment opportunity information for the engineering and technical community.

8396 ■ International California Mining Journal
International California Mining Journal
PO Box 2260
Aptos, CA 95001-2260
Ph: (831)479-1500
Fax: (831)479-4385
URL: http://www.icmj.com
Monthly. $27.95/year for individuals; $49.90/year for two years; $72.85/year for U.S., three years; $41.95/year for Canada; $77.90/year for Canada, two years; $114.85/year for Canada, three years; $44.95/year for other countries; $83.90/year for other countries, two years; $123.85/year for out of country, three years. Mining trade magazine covering prospecting and mining throughout the world.

8397 ■ Journal of Women and Minorities in Science and Engineering
Begell House Inc.
50 Cross Hwy.
Redding, CT 06896
Ph: (203)938-1300
Fax: (203)938-1304
URL: http://www.begellhouse.com/journals/00551c876cc2f027
$248.00/year for institutions. Peer-reviewed journal featuring innovative ideas and programs for classroom teachers, scientific studies, and formulation of concepts related to the education, recruitment, and retention of under-represented groups in science and engineering.

8398 ■ The Mining Record
Howell International Enterprises
PO Box 1630
Castle Rock, CO 80104-6130
Ph: (303)663-7820
Fax: (303)663-7823
Fr: 800-441-4748
URL: http://www.miningrecord.com/
Monthly. $55.00/year for individuals; $85.00/year for two years; $120.00/year for individuals, 3 years; $85.00/year for Canada and Mexico; $85.00/year for by mail; $99.00/year for other countries. International mining industry newspaper. Features reporting on exploration, discovery, development, production, joint ventures, operating results, legislation, government reports, and metals prices.

8399 ■ Monthly Energy Review
U.S. Government Printing Office and Superintendent of Documents
Mail Stop: IDCC
732 N Capitol St. NW
Washington, DC 20401
Ph: (202)512-1800
Fax: (202)512-2104
Fr: (866)512-1800
URL: http://www.eia.doe.gov/emeu/mer/contents.html
Monthly. $147.00/year for individuals; $205.80/year for other countries; $27.00/year for single issue; $37.80/year for other countries, single copy. Publication covering the petroleum, energy and mining industries.

8400 ■ NSBE Magazine
NSBE Publications
205 Daingerfield Rd.
Alexandria, VA 22314
Ph: (703)549-2207
Fax: (703)683-5312
URL: http://www.nsbe.org/News-Media/Magazines/About-NSBE-Magazine
$20.00/year for individuals; $35.00/year for other countries; $15.00/year for students. Journal providing information on engineering careers, self-development, and cultural issues for recent graduates with technical majors.

8401 ■ Pay Dirt Magazine
Copper Queen Publishing Company Inc.
PO Box 48
Bisbee, AZ 85603

Ph: (520)432-2244
Fax: (520)432-2247
E-mail: paydirt@theriver.com
URL: http://paydirtmagazine.com/

Monthly. $30.00/year for individuals; $3.00/year for single issue. Magazine bringing mining developments, government mining policies, environmental issues, and mining heritage to the U.S. and around the world.

8402 ■ PE
National Society of Professional Engineers
1420 King St.
Alexandria, VA 22314
Ph: (703)684-2800
Fax: (703)684-4875
URL: http://www.nspe.org/PEmagazine/index.html

Monthly. Magazine (tabloid) covering professional, legislative, and techology issues for an engineering audience.

8403 ■ Sustainable Facility
BNP Media
2401 W Big Beaver Rd., Ste. 700
Troy, MI 48084-3333
Ph: (847)763-9534
Fax: (847)763-9538
URL: http://www.sustainablefacility.com/

Monthly. Magazine reporting on the energy management market as it relates to commercial, industrial, and institutional facilities.

8404 ■ SWE, Magazine of the Society of Women Engineers
Society of Women Engineers
120 S La Salle St., Ste. 1515
Chicago, IL 60603
Ph: (312)596-5223
Fr: 877-793-4636
URL: http://societyofwomenengineers.swe.org/index.php

Quarterly. $30.00/year for nonmembers. Magazine for engineering students and for women and men working in the engineering and technology fields. Covers career guidance, continuing development and topical issues.

8405 ■ WEPANEWS
Women in Engineering Programs & Advocates Network
1901 E Asbury Ave., Ste. 220
Denver, CO 80208
Ph: (303)871-4643
Fax: (303)871-4628
E-mail: dmatt@wepan.org
URL: http://www.wepan.org

Description: 2/year. Seeks to provide greater access for women to careers in engineering. Includes news of graduate, undergraduate, freshmen, precollege, and re-entry engineering programs for women. Recurring features include job listings, faculty, grant, and conference news, international engineering program news, action group news, notices of publications available, and a column titled Kudos.

8406 ■ Woman Engineer
Equal Opportunity Publications, Inc.
445 Broadhollow Rd., Ste. 425
Melville, NY 11747
Ph: (631)421-9421
Fax: (631)421-1352
E-mail: info@eop.com
URL: http://www.eop.com

Annual. Magazine that is offered at no charge to qualified female engineering, computer-science, and information-technology students and professionals seeking to find employment and advancement in their careers.

EMPLOYER DIRECTORIES AND NETWORKING LISTS

8407 ■ American Men and Women of Science
Gale
PO Box 6904
Florence, KY 41022-6904
Fr: 800-354-9706
URL: http://www.gale.cengage.com

Biennial, even years; New edition expected 29th, June 2011. $1,368.00 for individuals. Covers: Over 135,000 U.S. and Canadian scientists active in the physical, biological, mathematical, computer science, and engineering fields; includes references to previous edition for deceased scientists and nonrespondents. Entries include: Name, address, education, personal and career data, memberships, honors and awards, research interest. Arrangement: Alphabetical. Indexes: Discipline (in separate volume).

8408 ■ Careers in Focus—Engineering
Facts On File Inc.
132 W 31st St., 17th Fl.
New York, NY 10001
Ph: (212)967-8800
Fax: 800-678-3633
Fr: 800-322-8755
URL: http://www.infobasepublishing.com

Latest edition 3rd; Published July, 2007. $32.95 for individuals. Covers: An overview of engineering, followed by a selection of jobs profiled in detail, including the nature of the job, earnings, prospects for employment, what kind of training and skills it requires, and sources for further information.

8409 ■ Directory of Contract Staffing Firms
C.E. Publications Inc.
PO Box 3006
Bothell, WA 98041-3006
Ph: (425)806-5200
Fax: (425)806-5585
URL: http://www.cjhunter.com/dcsf/overview.html

Annual. Covers: Nearly 1,300 contract firms actively engaged in the employment of engineering, IT/IS, and technical personnel for 'temporary' contract assignments throughout the world. Entries include: Company name, address, phone, name of contact, email, web address. Arrangement: Alphabetical. Indexes: Geographical.

8410 ■ The Geophysical Directory
Geophysical Directory Inc.
PO Box 130508
Houston, TX 77219
Ph: (713)529-8789
Fax: (713)529-3646
Fr: 800-929-2462
E-mail: info@geophysicaldirectory.com
URL: http://www.geophysicaldirectory.com

Annual, Latest edition 66th; 2011. $150.00 for individuals; $165.00 for individuals. Covers: About 4,581 companies that provide geophysical equipment, supplies, or services, and mining and petroleum companies that use geophysical techniques; international coverage. Entries include: Company name, address, phone, fax, names of principal executives, operations, and 9,719 key personnel; similar information for branch locations. Arrangement: Classified by product or service. Indexes: Company name, personal name.

8411 ■ Indiana Society of Professional Engineers—Directory
Indiana Society of Professional Engineers
PO Box 20806
Indianapolis, IN 46220
Ph: (317)255-2267
Fax: (317)255-2530
URL: http://www.indspe.org

Annual, fall. Covers: Member registered engineers, land surveyors, engineering students, and engineers in training. Entries include: Member name, address, phone, type of membership, business information, specialty. Arrangement: Alpha by chapter area.

8412 ■ Western Mining Directory
Howell International Enterprises
PO Box 1630
Castle Rock, CO 80104-6130
Ph: (303)663-7820
Fax: (303)663-7823
Fr: 800-441-4748
URL: http://www.miningrecord.com

Annual, Latest edition 2010-2011. $49.00 for U.S. and Canada; $55.00 for other countries; $85.00 for U.S. and Canada; $95.00 for other countries. Covers: About 230 mining firms and organizations in the mining industry of the western United States, including active hardrock and coal mines, uranium and vanadium mines; mining firms, consultants, contractors-developers, suppliers of equipment and services, exploration and drilling companies; educational institutions; mining associations; related government agencies; mining exhibitions and conferences. Entries include: For mining companies—Name, corporate, regional, and exploration office addresses; information regarding companies that are privately or publicly held; stock exchange information; trading symbol. For mines—Names of managers, location, open pit, underground, type of recovery, product, operator, reserves, grade, mining rates, number of employees. Arrangement: Alphabetical and geographical. Indexes: Mining location.

HANDBOOKS AND MANUALS

8413 ■ Resumes for Scientific and Technical Careers
The McGraw-Hill Companies
PO Box 182604
Columbus, OH 43272
Fax: (614)759-3749
Fr: 877-883-5524
E-mail: customer.service@mcgraw-hill.com
URL: http://www.mhprofessional.com/product.php?isbn=0071482199

Third edition, 2007. $12.95 (paper). 144 pages. Provides resume advice for individuals interested in working in scientific and technical careers. Includes sample resumes and cover letters.

8414 ■ Sustainable Development in Practice: Case Studies for Engineers and Scientists
John Wiley & Sons, Inc.
111 River St.
Hoboken, NJ 07030-5774
Ph: (201)748-6000
Fax: (201)748-6088
E-mail: info@wiley.com
URL: http://www.wiley.com

Adisa Azapagic and Slobodan Perdan. 2011. $139.95 (hardcover). 536 pages. 2nd edition. Covers a wide range of sustainability issues in both developed and developing countries. Includes case studies. Serves as reading guide for engineers and scientists concerned with sustainable development.

EMPLOYMENT AGENCIES AND SEARCH FIRMS

8415 ■ Engineer One, Inc.
PO Box 23037
Knoxville, TN 37933
Fax: (865)691-0110
E-mail: engineerone@engineerone.com
URL: http://www.engineerone.com

Engineering employment service specializing in engineering and management in the chemical process, power utilities, manufacturing, mechanical, electrical, and electronic industries. Maintains an Information Technology Division that works nationwide across all industries. Also provides systems analysis consulting services specializing in VAX based systems.

8416 ■ Global Employment Solutions
10375 Park Meadows Dr., Ste. 375
Littleton, CO 80124
Ph: (303)216-9500
Fax: (303)216-9533
URL: http://www.gesnetwork.com
Employment agency.

8417 ■ Power Source Systems
515 E Carefree Hwy.
PMB 470
Phoenix, AZ 85085
Ph: (623)465-5855
Fax: (623)465-0979
E-mail: powersource@powersourceglobal.com
URL: http://www.powersourceglobal.com

Serves as a search firm for the mining, mineral processing, paper, and other heavy industries. Provides hiring authorities with candidates who meet the specified requirements and assists both parties throughout the entire interview and placement process.

8418 ■ SPECTRA Associates
PO Box 688
Stevensville, MT 59870
Ph: (406)369-1188
E-mail: engineering@spectra-assoc.com
URL: http://www.spectra-assoc.com

Description: Serves as an executive search firm specializing in recruitment for engineering markets including companies involved with manufacturing, production and engineering.

ONLINE JOB SOURCES AND SERVICES

8419 ■ EngineerJobs.com
URL: http://www.engineerjobs.com

Description: Provides job opportunities for engineering professionals in the following disciplines: aerospace, agricultural, biomedical, chemical, civil, electrical, environmental, industrial, manufacturing, marine, materials, mechanical, mining, nuclear, petroleum, process, project, quality, sales, software, solar, systems, and structural.

8420 ■ Jobs4Mining
URL: http://www.jobs4mining.com

Description: Serves as a job board dedicated to the mineral mining and quarrying industries worldwide. Features job listings from mining companies and recruitment agencies.

8421 ■ Mining Engineering Jobs
URL: http://www.miningengineeringjobs.org

Description: Serves as a job board for mining engineers. Offers updated job listings for candidates and job posting for employers.

8422 ■ Misco Jobs
E-mail: support@miscojobs.com
URL: http://www.miscojobs.com

Description: Provides international mining, petroleum, oil, gas, construction, and environmental job opportunities. Includes industry portal web sites, newspapers, magazines, corporate web sites, direct postings from both employers and candidates and more.

8423 ■ Spherion
2050 Spectrum Blvd.
Fort Lauderdale, FL 33309
Ph: (954)308-7600

Fr: 800-774-3746
E-mail: help@spherion.com
URL: http://www.spherion.com

Description: Recruitment firm specializing in accounting and finance, sales and marketing, interim executives, technology, engineering, retail and human resources.

8424 ■ ThinkEnergyGroup.com
E-mail: resumes@thinkjobs.com
URL: http://www.thinkenergygroup.com

Description: Serves as a job board for professionals looking for positions in engineering, power plant, energy, and technical fields. Contains advice and tips on interviews, job searching, resume writing, hiring, and management. Provides choices of work location, pay rates in the field of expertise and contract, temp-to-hire, and direct hiring options.

TRADESHOWS

8425 ■ American Society of Mining and Reclamation
American Society of Mining and Reclamation
3134 Montevesta Rd.
Lexington, KY 40502
Ph: (859)335-6529
Fax: (859)335-6529
E-mail: asmr@insightbb.com
URL: http://www.asmr.us

Annual. Primary Exhibits: Exhibits relating to the protection and enhancement of land disturbed by mining. Dates and Locations: 2012 Jun 08-15; Tupelo, MS.

8426 ■ Rapid Excavation & Tunneling Conference & Exhibit
Society for Mining, Metallurgy, and Exploration, Inc.
12999 E. Adam Aircraft Cir.
Englewood, CO 80112
Ph: (303)948-4200
Fax: (303)973-3845
Fr: 800-763-3132
E-mail: cs@smenet.org
URL: http://www.smenet.org

Biennial. Primary Exhibits: Excavation equipment. Dates and Locations: 2013 Jun 23-26; Washington, DC.

OTHER SOURCES

8427 ■ American Association of Blacks in Energy (AABE)
1625 K St. NW, Ste. 405
Washington, DC 20006
Ph: (202)371-9530
Fax: (202)371-9218
Fr: 800-466-0204
E-mail: info@aabe.org
URL: http://www.aabe.org

Description: Seeks to increase the knowledge, understanding, and awareness of the minority community in energy issues by serving as an energy information source for policymakers, recommending blacks and other minorities to appropriate energy officials and executives, encouraging students to pursue professional careers in the energy industry, and advocating the participation of blacks and other minorities in energy programs and policymaking activities. Updates members on key legislation and regulations being developed by the Department of Energy, the Department of Interior, the Department of Commerce, the Small Business Administration, and other federal and state agencies.

8428 ■ American Association of Engineering Societies (AAES)
1801 Alexander Bell Dr.
Reston, VA 20191
Ph: (202)296-2237

Fax: (202)296-1151
Fr: 888-400-2237
E-mail: dbateson@aaes.org
URL: http://www.aaes.org

Description: Coordinates the efforts of the member societies in the provision of reliable and objective information to the general public concerning issues which affect the engineering profession and the field of engineering as a whole; collects, analyzes, documents, and disseminates data which will inform the general public of the relationship between engineering and the national welfare; provides a forum for the engineering societies to exchange and discuss their views on matters of common interest; and represents the U.S. engineering community abroad through representation in WFEO and UPADI.

8429 ■ American Indian Science and Engineering Society (AISES)
PO Box 9828
Albuquerque, NM 87119-9828
Ph: (505)765-1052
Fax: (505)765-5608
E-mail: info@aises.org
URL: http://www.aises.org

Description: Represents American Indian and non-Indian students and professionals in science, technology, and engineering fields; corporations representing energy, mining, aerospace, electronic, and computer fields. Seeks to motivate and encourage students to pursue undergraduate and graduate studies in science, engineering, and technology. Sponsors science fairs in grade schools, teacher training workshops, summer math/science sessions for 8th-12th graders, professional chapters, and student chapters in colleges. Offers scholarships. Adult members serve as role models, advisers, and mentors for students. Operates placement service.

8430 ■ Association for International Practical Training (AIPT)
10400 Little Patuxent Pkwy., Ste. 250
Columbia, MD 21044-3519
Ph: (410)997-2200
Fax: (410)992-3924
E-mail: aipt@aipt.org
URL: http://www.aipt.org

Description: Providers worldwide of on-the-job training programs for students and professionals seeking international career development and life-changing experiences. Arranges workplace exchanges in hundreds of professional fields, bringing employers and trainees together from around the world. Client list ranges from small farming communities to Fortune 500 companies.

8431 ■ Engineering Society of Detroit (ESD)
20700 Civic Center Dr., Ste. 450
Southfield, MI 48076
Ph: (248)353-0735
Fax: (248)353-0736
E-mail: esd@esd.org
URL: http://ww2.esd.org/home.htm

Description: Engineers from all disciplines; scientists and technologists. Conducts technical programs and engineering refresher courses; sponsors conferences and expositions. Maintains speakers' bureau; offers placement services; although based in Detroit, MI, society membership is international.

8432 ■ Korean-American Scientists and Engineers Association (KSEA)
1952 Gallows Rd., Ste. 300
Vienna, VA 22182
Ph: (703)748-1221
Fax: (703)748-1331
E-mail: sejong@ksea.org
URL: http://www.ksea.org

Description: Represents scientists and engineers holding single or advanced degrees. Promotes friendship and mutuality among Korean and American scientists and engineers; contributes to Korea's scientific, technological, industrial, and economic developments; strengthens the scientific, technological, and cultural bonds between Korea and the U.S. Sponsors symposium. Maintains speakers' bureau, placement service, and biographical archives. Compiles statistics.

8433 ■ National Action Council for Minorities in Engineering (NACME)

440 Hamilton Ave., Ste. 302
White Plains, NY 10601-1813
Ph: (914)539-4010
Fax: (914)539-4032
E-mail: info@nacme.org
URL: http://www.nacme.org

Description: Leads the national effort to increase access to careers in engineering and other science-based disciplines. Conducts research and public policy analysis, develops and operates national demonstration programs at precollege and university levels, and disseminates information through publications, conferences and electronic media. Serves as a privately funded source of scholarships for minority students in engineering.

8434 ■ National Society of Professional Engineers (NSPE)

1420 King St.
Alexandria, VA 22314-2794
Ph: (703)684-2800
Fax: (703)836-4875
Fr: 888-285-6773
E-mail: memserv@nspe.org
URL: http://www.nspe.org

Description: Represents professional engineers and engineers-in-training in all fields registered in accordance with the laws of states or territories of the U.S. or provinces of Canada; qualified graduate engineers, student members, and registered land surveyors. Is concerned with social, professional, ethical, and economic considerations of engineering as a profession; encompasses programs in public relations, employment practices, ethical considerations, education, and career guidance. Monitors legislative and regulatory actions of interest to the engineering profession.

8435 ■ Society of Hispanic Professional Engineers (SHPE)

13181 Crossroads Pkwy. N, Ste. 450
City of Industry, CA 91746-3496
Ph: (323)725-3970
Fax: (323)725-0316
E-mail: shpenational@shpe.org
URL: http://oneshpe.shpe.org/wps/portal/national

Description: Represents engineers, student engineers, and scientists. Aims to increase the number of Hispanic engineers by providing motivation and support to students. Sponsors competitions and educational programs. Maintains placement service and speakers' bureau; compiles statistics.

8436 ■ Society for Mining, Metallurgy, and Exploration (SME)

12999 E Adam Aircraft Cir.
Englewood, CO 80112

Ph: (303)948-4200
Fax: (303)973-3845
Fr: 800-763-3132
E-mail: cs@smenet.org
URL: http://www.smenet.org

Description: A member society of the American Institute of Mining, Metallurgical and Petroleum Engineers. Persons engaged in the finding, exploitation, treatment, and marketing of all classes of minerals (metal ores, industrial minerals, and solid fuels) except petroleum. Promotes the arts and sciences connected with the production of useful minerals and metals. Offers specialized education programs; compiles enrollment and graduation statistics from schools offering engineering degrees in mining, mineral, mineral processing/metallurgical, geological, geophysical, and mining technology. Provides placement service and sponsors charitable programs.

8437 ■ Society of Women Engineers (SWE)

203 N La Salle St., Ste. 1675
Chicago, IL 60601
Ph: (312)596-5223
Fax: (312)596-5252
Fr: 877-SWE-INFO
E-mail: hq@swe.org
URL: http://societyofwomenengineers.swe.org

Description: Educational and service organization representing both students and professional women in engineering and technical fields.

SOURCES OF HELP-WANTED ADS

8438 ■ The Christian Century
Christian Century Foundation
104 S Michigan Ave., Ste. 700
Chicago, IL 60603
Ph: (312)263-7510
Fax: (312)263-7540
Fr: 800-208-4097
E-mail: main@christiancentury.org
URL: http://www.christiancentury.org

Biweekly. $59/year (print and online); $39/year (online only). Contains religious news; commentary on theological, moral and cultural issues; and reviews of the latest books and movies. Maintains a group blog and hosts a network of outside bloggers.

8439 ■ The Lutheran
Augsburg Fortress, Publishers
PO Box 1209
Minneapolis, MN 55440
Ph: (612)330-3300
Fax: (612)330-3455
E-mail: lutheran@thelutheran.org
URL: http://www.thelutheran.org

Monthly. $17.95/year for individuals; $30.95/year for two years; $40.95/year for individuals, three years. Magazine of the Evangelical Lutheran Church in America.

8440 ■ Panorama
Pittsburgh Theological Seminary
616 N Highland Ave.
Pittsburgh, PA 15206-2596
Ph: (412)362-5610
Fax: (412)363-3260
URL: http://www.pts.edu/Publications

Description: Two issues/year. Provides news for seminary faculty and staff. Recurring features include interviews, news of research, calendar of events, news of educational opportunities, job listings, book reviews, notices of publications available.

8441 ■ Sojourners
Sojourners
3333 14th St., NW Ste. 200
Washington, DC 20010
Ph: (202)328-8842
Fax: (202)328-8757
Fr: 800-714-7474
URL: http://www.sojo.net/

Monthly. $39.95/year for individuals; $49.95/year for Canada; $59.95/year for other countries. Independent, ecumenical Christian magazine which analyzes faith, politics, and culture from a progressive, justice-oriented perspective.

8442 ■ United Church News
United Church of Christ
700 Prospect Ave.
Cleveland, OH 44115
Ph: (216)736-2100
Fr: 888-822-3863
E-mail: newsroom@ucc.org
URL: http://www.ucc.org/ucnews

Description: Bimonthly. Concerned with the programs and activities of the United Church of Christ. Reports news of the UCC's 39 regional groupings and carries notices of pastoral changes within the UCC. Recurring features include letters to the editor, interviews, reports of meetings, news of resources and educational opportunities, and job listings. Also includes columns titled Focus on Faith, Heart Warmers, As I See It, and Current Comment.

8443 ■ Vision
National Association of Catholic Chaplains
4915 S Howell Ave., Ste. 501
Milwaukee, WI 53207-5939
Ph: (414)483-4898
Fax: (414)483-6712
E-mail: info@nacc.org
URL: http://www.nacc.org/vision/

Description: Six issues/year. Serves Catholic lay persons, priests, and religious personnel in professional health care, related institutional ministries and parishes. Recurring features include book reviews of publications on pastoral care, employment opportunities, and notices of conferences and meetings.

EMPLOYER DIRECTORIES AND NETWORKING LISTS

8444 ■ Christian Schools International—Directory
Christian Schools International
3350 E Paris Ave. SE
Grand Rapids, MI 49512-2907
Ph: (616)957-1070
Fax: (616)957-5022
Fr: 800-635-8288
URL: http://www.store.csionline.org/index.php?main_page=index&cPath=

Annual, Latest edition 2007-2008. $15.00 for members. Covers: Nearly 450 Reformed Christian elementary and secondary schools; related associations; societies without schools. Entries include: For schools—School name, address, phone; name, title, and address of officers; names of faculty members. Arrangement: Geographical.

8445 ■ Directory of Catholic Charities USA Directories
Catholic Charities USA
66 Canal Center Pl., Ste. 600
Alexandria, VA 22314-1583
Ph: (703)549-1390
Fax: (703)549-1656
URL: http://www.catholiccharitiesusa.org

Annual. $25.00 for individuals. Covers: Nearly 1,200 Catholic community and social service agencies. List-ings include diocesan agencies, state Catholic conferences. Entries include: Organization name, address, name and title of director, phone, fax. Arrangement: Geographical by state, then classified by diocese.

8446 ■ Ganley's Catholic Schools in America—Elementary/Secondary/College & University
Fisher Publishing Co.
PO Box 5729
Sun City West, AZ 85376
Ph: (623)328-8326
URL: http://www.ganleyscatholicschools.com

Annual, summer; Latest edition 38th, 2010. $67.00 for individuals. Covers: over 8,400 Catholic K-12 Schools. Arrangement: Geographical by state, then alphabetical by Diocese name.

8447 ■ Official Traditional Catholic Directory
iUniverse Inc.
1663 Liberty Dr.
Bloomington, IN 47403
Ph: (402)323-7800
Fax: (812)355-4085
Fr: 800-288-4677
URL: http://www.iuniverse.com/Bookstore/BookstoreHome.aspx

$15.95 for individuals. Publication includes: Listing of over 600 traditional Latin masses regularly and publicly celebrated in the United States and Canada. Also provides extensive lists of traditional resources, including traditional Catholic organizations, seminaries, religious orders, lay societies, periodicals, suppliers, retreats, and schooling, as well as contacts for traditional Latin masses outside the United States and Canada. Indexes: Alphabetical.

HANDBOOKS AND MANUALS

8448 ■ Careers in Social and Rehabilitation Services
The McGraw-Hill Companies
PO Box 182604
Columbus, OH 43272
Fax: (614)759-3749
Fr: 877-883-5524
E-mail: customer.service@mcgraw-hill.com
URL: http://www.mhprofessional.com/product.php?isbn=0071641955

Geraldine O. Garner. 2008. $16.95. 192 pages.

ONLINE JOB SOURCES AND SERVICES

8449 ■ ChristianCareerCenter.com
URL: http://www.christiancareercenter.com

Description: Provides career resources for Christian men and women. Lists Christian jobs and ministries and maintains an employment center.

8450 ■ ChristianJobs1.net
URL: http://www.christianjobs1.net
Description: Provides job openings and ministry positions for Christian schools, ministries, and other businesses that have Christian owners.

8451 ■ ChurchEmployment.com
URL: http://www.churchemployment.com
Description: Provides job search and recruitment services for Christian businesses, ministries, educational institutions, mission agencies, and churches.

8452 ■ ChurchJobs.net
URL: http://www.churchjobs.net
Description: Allows job seekers to search national church jobs, Christian jobs, other ministry jobs and pastor jobs and positions. Offers users the ability to create custom job and resume listings.

8453 ■ ChurchStaffing.com
URL: http://www.churchstaffing.com
Description: Provides information for churches and church staff members in the area of personnel and staff relations.

8454 ■ Kingdom Careers
URL: http://www.kingdomcareers.com
Description: Serves the evangelical church community. Offers resume postings and job search services to assist evangelical churches and ministries in finding qualified job candidates.

8455 ■ MinistryJobs.com
URL: http://www.ministryjobs.com
Description: Provides listing of job openings for ministers.

8456 ■ MinistrySearch.com
URL: http://www.ministrysearch.com
Description: Provides listings of available Christian ministry jobs. Includes senior pastors, worship leaders, youth pastors, and other church leadership positions.

8457 ■ PastorFinder.com
URL: http://www.pastorfinder.com
Description: Serves as a job site where churches leaders come to find or fill a job.

8458 ■ YouthPastor.Com
URL: http://www.youthpastor.com
Description: Provides youth ministry resources for youth pastors, ministers, workers, and volunteers. Features a job center and a searchable directory of ministries.

TRADESHOWS

8459 ■ Association of Professional Chaplains Annual Conference
Association of Professional Chaplains
1701 E Woodfield Rd., Ste. 400
Schaumburg, IL 60173
Ph: (847)240-1014
Fax: (847)240-1015
E-mail: info@professionalchaplains.org
URL: http://www.professionalchaplains.org
Annual. Features latest trends in chaplaincy and develops and nurtures relationships with other chaplaincy professionals.

8460 ■ Society for the Scientific Study of Religion Annual Meeting
Exhibit Promotions Plus, Inc.
11620 Vixens Path
Ellicott City, MD 21042-1539
Ph: (410)997-0763
Fax: (410)997-0764
E-mail: exhibit@epponline.com
URL: http://www.epponline.com

Annual. Primary Exhibits: Publications and films and other resources in the fields of religion, philosophy, sociology, psychology and anthropology. Dates and Locations: 2012 Nov 09-11; Phoenix, AZ; Hyatt Regency Phoenix; 2013 Nov 08-10; Boston, MA; Boston Westin Waterfront; 2014 Oct 31 - Nov 02; Indianapolis, IN; JW Marriott Indianapolis.

OTHER SOURCES

8461 ■ Administrative Personnel Association of the Presbyterian Church (APA)
1201 W Wall
Midland, TX 79701-6619
Ph: (432)682-5297
Fax: (432)687-6120
E-mail: apa-office@tresrios.org
URL: http://www.pcusa-apa.org
Description: Works to govern bodies, agencies and institutions of the Presbyterian Church. Offers opportunities for professional and personal development to the support staff of the Presbyterian Church. Provides opportunities for continuing education.

8462 ■ American Association of Christian Schools (AACS)
602 Belvoir Ave.
East Ridge, TN 37412
Ph: (423)629-4280
Fax: (423)622-7461
E-mail: info@aacs.org
URL: http://www.aacs.org
Description: Maintains teacher/administrator certification program and placement service. Participates in school accreditation program. Sponsors National Academic Tournament. Maintains American Christian Honor Society. Compiles statistics; maintains speakers' bureau and placement service.

8463 ■ American Association of Pastoral Counselors (AAPC)
9504A Lee Hwy.
Fairfax, VA 22031-2303
Ph: (703)385-6967
Fax: (703)352-7725
E-mail: info@aapc.org
URL: http://aapc.org
Description: Employs counselors who are certified mental health professionals and have had in-depth religious and/or theological training. Represents and sets standards for the profession around the world. Certifies counselors, accredits pastoral counseling centers and approves training programs. Encourages all counselors to respect the spiritual commitments and religious traditions of those who need assistance by not imposing counselor beliefs onto the client. Facilitates growth and innovation in the ministry of pastoral counseling and provides both specialized in-service training and supervision in pastoral counseling.

8464 ■ American Orff-Schulwerk Association (AOSA)
PO Box 391089
Cleveland, OH 44139-8089
Ph: (440)543-5366
Fax: (440)543-2687
E-mail: info@aosa.org
URL: http://www.aosa.org
Description: Music and movement educators, music therapists, and church choir directors united to promote and encourage the philosophy of Carl Orff's (1895-1982, German composer) Schulwerk (Music for Children) in America. Distributes information on the activities and growth of Orff Schulwerk in America. Conducts research; offers information on teacher training. Operates clearinghouse.

8465 ■ Association of Christian Schools International (ACSI)
PO Box 65130
Colorado Springs, CO 80962-5130

Fax: (719)531-0631
Fr: 800-367-0798
E-mail: acsi_email@acsi.org
URL: http://www.acsi.org
Description: Seeks to enable Christian educators and schools worldwide to effectively prepare students for life.

8466 ■ Association of North American Missions (ANAM)
PO Box 610
Salem, MO 65560
Ph: (573)261-0057
E-mail: director@anamissions.org
URL: http://www.anamissions.org
Description: Missions of more than five missionaries operating in North America. Aims to make missions more credible and visible; to promote unity and cooperation among members; to collect, organize, and disseminate information relating to missionary work to the public and to act as clearinghouse for members. Offers referral and placement service to qualified missionaries not serving with member missions. Provides information about missions to pastors and schools. Offers workshops and in-depth seminars for mission leaders and missionaries.

8467 ■ Association of Professional Chaplains
1701 E Woodfield Rd., Ste. 400
Schaumburg, IL 60173
Ph: (847)240-1014
Fax: (847)240-1015
E-mail: info@professionalchaplains.org
URL: http://www.professionalchaplains.org
Description: Advocates for quality spiritual care of all persons in healthcare facilities, correctional institutions, long term care units, rehabilitation centers, hospice, the military and other specialized settings. Provides pastoral care and counseling through the association's various programs and activities. Certifies and serves membership to promote professional chaplaincy.

8468 ■ Association of Unity Churches International
PO Box 610
Lee's Summit, MO 64063
Ph: (816)524-7414
Fax: (816)525-4020
E-mail: info@unity.org
URL: http://www.unity.org
Description: Ministers licensed Unity teachers, and interested members of Unity Churches and study groups. Serves and supports member ministries by providing human resources, administrative and educational programs, and consultation in accordance with the teachings of the Unity School of Christianity founded by Charles and Myrtle Fillmore. Trains and licenses teachers, ministers, and youth advisors; offers continuing education programs and minister employment service. Holds skills development seminars and workshops. Offers media service consultation. Assists with the development of local groups.

8469 ■ Baptist Women in Ministry/Folio (BWIM/FOLIO)
PO Box 941294
Atlanta, GA 31141-1294
Ph: (678)547-6475
E-mail: pamdurso@bwim.info
URL: http://www.bwim.info
Description: Ordained and unordained female Baptist ministers; students of the Baptist ministry; interested individuals. Promotes the image of women as ministers. Fosters support and communication among members. Conducts educational and research programs.

8470 ■ Catholic Campus Ministry Association (CCMA)
1118 Pendleton St., Ste. 300
Cincinnati, OH 45202-8805

Ph: (513)842-0167
Fax: (513)842-0171
Fr: 888-714-6631
E-mail: info@ccmanet.org
URL: http://www.ccmanet.org

Description: Aims to: form a strong and coordinated voice for the Church's ministry in higher education; provide continuing education programs for members; provide liaison with other individuals and agencies of the church interested in campus ministry and the role of the Church in higher education; advance ecumenical and interfaith understanding and cooperation; provide guidelines for, and assistance in, developing effective campus ministries. Maintains placement service; offers colleague consultation service.

8471 ■ Catholic Press Association (CPA)
205 W Monroe St., Ste. 470
Chicago, IL 60606
Ph: (312)380-6789
Fax: (312)361-0256
E-mail: cathjourn@catholicpress.org
URL: http://www.catholicpress.org

Description: Consists of Catholic writers and publishers of Catholic newspapers, magazines, newsletters and books. Maintains 25 committees, including Freedom of Information, Fair Publishing Practices Code, Catholic News Service Liaison.

8472 ■ Chinese Christian Mission (CCM)
PO Box 750759
Petaluma, CA 94975-0759
Ph: (707)762-1314
Fax: (707)762-1713
E-mail: ccm@ccmusa.org
URL: http://www.ccmusa.org

Description: Serves as an evangelical faith mission dedicated to reaching Chinese people around the world with the gospel of Jesus Christ. Broadcasts radio programs to foster Christianity in China. Operates placement service providing ministers with churches. Sponsors short-term mission trips to Latin America and East Asia.

8473 ■ Christian Chiropractors Association (CCA)
2550 Stover St., No. B-102
Fort Collins, CO 80525
Ph: (970)482-1404
Fax: (970)482-1538
Fr: 800-999-1970
URL: http://www.christianchiropractors.org

Description: Works to spread the Gospel of Christ throughout the U.S. and abroad. Offers Christian fellowship and works to unify Christian chiropractors around the essentials of the faith, "leaving minor points of doctrine to the conscience of the individual believer." Focuses on world missions; organizing short-term trips and aiding in the placement of Christian chiropractors as missionaries.

8474 ■ A Christian Ministry in the National Parks (ACMNP)
9185 E Kenyon Ave., Ste. 230
Denver, CO 80237
Ph: (303)220-2808
Fax: (303)220-0128
Fr: 800-786-3450
E-mail: info@acmnp.com
URL: http://www.acmnp.com

Description: Recommends employment for seminary and college students with private concessionaires operating lodges, inns, restaurants, and stores within national parks; aims to offer students the opportunity to conduct interdenominational worship services and Bible studies for park employees and visitors.

8475 ■ Conservative Baptist Association of America
3686 Stagecoach Rd., Ste. F
Longmont, CO 80504-5660
Ph: (303)772-1205
Fax: (303)772-5690

Fr: 888-366-3010
E-mail: info@cbamerica.org
URL: http://www.cbamerica.org

Description: Provides leadership, fellowship, counseling services, and specialized support ministries to 1,200 member churches in an effort "to advance the cause of Christ through worship, evangelism, instruction, and service throughout the world". Conducts charitable program; offers placement service, chaplaincy endorsement.

8476 ■ Council for Health and Human Service Ministries of the United Church of Christ (CHHSM)
700 Prospect Ave.
Cleveland, OH 44115
Ph: (216)736-2260
Fax: (216)736-2251
Fr: (866)822-8224
E-mail: sickberb@chhsm.org
URL: http://www.chhsm.org

Description: Health and human service institutions related to the United Church of Christ. Seeks to study, plan, and implement a program in health and human services; assist members in developing and providing quality services and in financing institutional and non-institutional health and human service ministries; stimulate awareness of and support for these programs; inform the UCC of policies that affect the needs, problems, and conditions of patients; cooperate with interdenominational agencies and others in the field. Maintains placement service and hall of fame. Compiles statistics; provides specialized education programs.

8477 ■ Evangelical Press Association (EPA)
PO Box 28129
Crystal, MN 55428
Ph: (763)535-4793
Fax: (763)535-4794
E-mail: director@epassoc.org
URL: http://www.epassoc.org

Description: Editors and publishers of Christian periodicals. Maintains placement service.

8478 ■ Forward in Faith North America (FiF)
PO Box 210248
Bedford, TX 76095-7248
Fr: 800-225-3661
E-mail: michael.howell@fifna.org
URL: http://www.forwardinfaith.com

Description: Dioceses, parishes, institutions, and societies of Anglican laity and clergy in North America, Central America, South America and the Caribbean who "embrace the Gospel of Jesus Christ and uphold evangelical faith and order, laboring with zeal for the reform and renewal of the church." Promotes the establishment and implementation of cooperative programs.

8479 ■ IFCA International
PO Box 810
Grandville, MI 49468-0810
Ph: (616)531-1840
Fax: (616)531-1814
Fr: 800-347-1840
E-mail: office@ifca.org
URL: http://www.ifca.org

Description: Ministers, missionaries, youth leaders, musicians, and ministerial students; churches and organizations. Seeks to offer independent churches the benefits of unity, while allowing them to keep their autonomy. Supports active evangelism; encourages churches to extend their ministry into neighboring communities, the military, and other Christian churches, which the group believes are in harmony with the Word of God. Serves to reinforce members' doctrinal beliefs; provides interchurch fellowship and the sharing of ministers; trains pastors and lay workers.

8480 ■ International Association of Christian Chaplains (IACC)
5804 Babcock Rd.
PMB 189
San Antonio, TX 78240-2134
Ph: (210)696-7313
Fax: (210)558-0701
E-mail: iacc@christianchaplains.com
URL: http://www.christianchaplains.com

Description: Provides pastoral fellowship, professional certification and continuing educational opportunities, enabling the chaplain to provide the best spiritual care possible. Assists members with professional and pastoral support. Promotes a participative, creative and horizontal type of democracy and government.

8481 ■ International Catholic Stewardship Council (ICSC)
1275 K St. NW, Ste. 880
Washington, DC 20005-4077
Ph: (202)289-1093
Fax: (202)682-9018
Fr: 800-352-3452
E-mail: info@catholicstewardship.org
URL: http://catholicstewardship.org

Description: Commits to promote the right use of God's gifts of time, talent, and treasure through diocesan and parish leadership. Encourages the adoption of the holistic stewardship concept which stresses that everything is a gift from God, and that gratitude for gifts received is best expressed in right management and ministry to others. Fosters the exchange of ideas and materials among dioceses, parishes, and other church organizations. Maintains speakers' bureau and placement service. Compiles statistics.

8482 ■ International Council of Community Churches (ICCC)
21116 Washington Pkwy.
Frankfort, IL 60423
Ph: (815)464-5690
Fax: (815)464-5692
E-mail: iccc60423@sbcglobal.net
URL: http://www.icccusa.com

Description: Promotes the fellowship of community churches, provides an annual meeting for worship, study, fellowship; relates to the larger church through membership in the NCCCUSA and the WCC. Assists congregations in pastoral search process. Provides pension plan and health benefits for members.

8483 ■ Jesuit Association of Student Personnel Administrators (JASPA)
2500 California Plz.
Omaha, NE 68178
Ph: (402)280-2717
Fax: (402)280-1275
E-mail: waynejr@creighton.edu
URL: http://jaspa.creighton.edu

Description: Represents administrators of student personnel programs in 28 Jesuit colleges and universities in the United States. Sponsors institutes and seminars for personnel in Jesuit colleges. Cooperates with Catholic and non-Catholic educational associations in various projects. Maintains placement service and conducts workshops. Operates organizational archives and compiles statistics.

8484 ■ Lutheran Deaconess Conference (LDC)
1304 LaPorte Ave.
Valparaiso, IN 46383
Ph: (219)464-6925
Fax: (219)464-6928
E-mail: deacserv@valpo.edu
URL: http://www.thelda.org/about/ldc.php

Description: Consecrated deaconesses having completed the educational requirements of the Lutheran Deaconess Association; students in training. Seeks to: develop sisterhood and community among deaconesses; present an opportunity for renewed inspiration and personal and professional growth;

encourage women in the church to use their full potential and to shape, promote, and support the total deaconess program.

8485 ■ National Association of Church Business Administration (NACBA)

100 N Central Expy., Ste. 914
Richardson, TX 75080-5326
Ph: (972)699-7555
Fax: (972)699-7617
Fr: 800-898-8085
E-mail: info@nacba.net
URL: http://www.nacba.net

Description: Represents business administrators and managers employed by local churches or institutions of the Christian church. Aims to train, certify and provide resources for those serving in the field of church administration. Offers placement service; conducts research programs; and compiles statistics. Maintains hall of fame.

8486 ■ National Association of Congregational Christian Churches (NACCC)

PO Box 288
Oak Creek, WI 53154-0288
Ph: (414)764-1620
Fax: (414)764-0319
Fr: 800-262-1620
E-mail: naccc@naccc.org
URL: http://www.naccc.org

Description: Aims to provide a means whereby Congregational Christian churches may consult and exchange advise on spiritual and temporal matters of common concern; and to encourage the continuance of Christian purposes and practices that have been the historic and accepted characteristics of Congregational Christian churches. Supports the education of ministers through its Congregational Foundation for Theological Studies. Compiles statistics. Operates placement service and mission program. Provides a variety of financial services. Supports youth programming from coast to coast and hosts annual meeting.

8487 ■ National Association of Episcopal Schools (NAES)

815 2nd Ave., Ste. 819
New York, NY 10017-4594
Ph: (212)716-6134
Fax: (212)286-9366
Fr: 800-334-7626
E-mail: info@episcopalschools.org
URL: http://www.episcopalschools.org

Description: Represents Episcopal day and boarding schools and preschools. Promotes the educational ministry of the Episcopal Church. Provides publications, consultation services and conference focusing on Episcopal identity of schools, worship, religious education, spirituality, leadership development and governance for heads/directors, administrators, chaplains and teachers of religion, trustees, rectors and other church and school leaders.

8488 ■ National Association of Parish Catechetical Directors (NPCD)

1005 N Glebe Rd., Ste. 525
Arlington, VA 22201
Ph: (202)337-6232
Fax: (202)333-6706
Fr: 800-711-6232
E-mail: npcd@ncea.org
URL: http://www.ncea.org/departments/npcd

Description: A subdivision of the National Catholic Educational Association. Directors, coordinators and administrators of religious education/catechesis in Roman Catholic parishes; students considering careers as catechetical leaders; clergy, laity, and others involved in the religious community. Works to act as a representative and advocate for professionals who administer parish catechetical programs; foster cooperation and communication among organizations serving parish catechesis including other NCEA groups and independent associations; promote the spiritual, personal, and professional growth of parish

DREs and encourage careers in catechetical ministry. Supports and develops the practice of family catechesis and encourages efforts in adult religious education; urges cooperation among parishleadership, especially parish staff members; promotes competency standards. Provides guidelines for members' contracts, salaries, benefits, and job descriptions. Disseminates information on members' jobs, educational background, salaries, and benefits; reports on parish program activities and surveys. Conducts research

8489 ■ National Association of Pastoral Musicians (NPM)

962 Wayne Ave., Ste. 210
Silver Spring, MD 20910-4461
Ph: (240)247-3000
Fax: (240)247-3001
E-mail: npmsing@npm.org
URL: http://www.npm.org

Description: Fosters the art of musical liturgy. Members serve the Catholic Church in the United States as musicians, clergy, liturgists, and other leaders of prayer. Provides ongoing formation for musicians and clergy through annual conventions, educational institutes, and events in more than 70 diocesan chapters. Also provides certification programs for cantors, organists, and directors of music ministries.

8490 ■ National Association of Veterans Affairs Chaplains (NAVAC)

PO Box 69004
Alexandria, LA 71306
Ph: (318)473-0010
E-mail: stephen.brandow@va.gov
URL: http://www.navac.net

Description: Promotes professional collegiality, personal growth, and professional development of Veterans Affairs (VA) chaplains. Fosters enhanced pastoral care for veteran patients and their families. Serves as a certifying body for clinical and board chaplaincy.

8491 ■ National Conference for Catechetical Leadership (NCCL)

125 Michigan Ave. NE
Washington, DC 20017
Ph: (202)884-9753
Fax: (202)884-9756
E-mail: nccl@nccl.org
URL: http://www.nccl.org

Description: Diocesan directors of religious education and their staff; publishers, academics, Diocesan religious education, Associations, and individuals interested in religious education. Fosters communication and unity among members. Addresses the special responsibility to provide lifelong religious education within the Catholic Church; assists members with increasing religious education needs; coordinates religious education and helps to supply needed materials. Aids in formal religious education for children, adults, and handicapped persons. Compiles statistics; provides placement service; operates research programs; conducts charitable program; maintains speakers' bureau.

8492 ■ National Lutheran Outdoors Ministry Association (NLOMA)

PO Box 1672
Tahlequah, OK 74465
Ph: (918)458-0704
Fax: (918)456-2919
E-mail: nloma@nloma.org
URL: http://www.nloma.net

Description: Individuals and camps joined to aid in the mission of the Lutheran church and to promote Christian camping and related experience. Provides support for all areas of outdoor ministry. Serves as resource base for camps in the areas of personnel development, site evaluation, program development, and staff recruitment. Conducts seminars and training sessions. Maintains placement service for individuals seeking employment at a member camp.

8493 ■ North American Association of Christians in Social Work (NACSW)

PO Box 121
Botsford, CT 06404-0121
Fr: 888-426-4712
E-mail: info@nacsw.org
URL: http://www.nacsw.org

Description: Professional social workers and related professionals, students, interested individuals. Supports the integration of Christian faith and professional social work practice in the lives of its members, the profession and the church, promoting love and justice in social service and social reform. Provides opportunities for Christian fellowship, education and service opportunities; articulates informed Christian voice on social welfare practice and policy to the social work profession; provides professional understanding and help for the social ministry of the church; and promotes social welfare services and policies in society that bring about greater justice and meet basic human needs.

8494 ■ North American Maritime Ministry Association (NAMMA)

PO Box 2434
Niagara Falls, NY 14302
Ph: (905)892-7525
E-mail: namma@cogeco.ca
URL: http://www.namma.org

Description: Spiritual and social welfare agencies from the U.S., Canada, and the Caribbean providing facilities and services for merchant seafarers. Sponsors Chaplain Training School; operates placement service. Maintains archives; conducts research programs.

8495 ■ OMF International U.S.A.

10 W Dry Creek Cir.
Littleton, CO 80120-4413
Ph: (303)730-4160
Fax: (303)730-4165
Fr: 800-422-5330
E-mail: info@omf.org
URL: http://www.omf.org/us

Description: Protestant missionaries. American office of international missionary society, which originated in England in 1865 for work in inland China. Church planting, evangelism, training and development work now carried out in most countries of East Asia. Through its publications, the group seeks to mobilize new missionaries and supporters, and educate the public.

8496 ■ Presbyterian Association of Musicians (PAM)

100 Witherspoon St.
Louisville, KY 40202-1396
Ph: (502)569-5288
Fax: (502)569-8465
Fr: 888-728-7228
E-mail: alan.barthel@pcusa.org
URL: http://www.presbymusic.org

Description: Represents organists, choir directors, singers, churches, clergy, directors of Christian education, and interested persons of all denominations. Aims to develop the use of music and the arts in the life and worship of individual congregations. Offers assistance in the areas of worship, music, and the arts. Conducts continuing education. Acts as a clearinghouse for job referrals; promotes the professional status of church musicians and recommends salaries and benefits to churches; certifies church musicians.

8497 ■ Presbyterian-Reformed Ministries International (PRMI)

PO Box 429
Black Mountain, NC 28711-0429
Ph: (828)669-7373
Fax: (828)669-4880
E-mail: prmi@prmi.org
URL: http://www.prmi.org

Description: Aims to ignite the Church in the power of the Holy Spirit through prayer, leadership development, congregational renewal, and mission outreach. Seeks to call the church to prayer and teach the work of prayer, equip clergy and laity for Holy Spirit-empowered ministry, assist congregations in their renewal process and promote the Holy Spirit for the advancement of the Kingdom of God.

8498 ■ Presbyterians for Renewal (PFR)
8134 New LaGrange Rd.
Louisville, KY 40222-4673
Ph: (502)425-4630
Fax: (502)423-8329
E-mail: pfroffice@pfrenewal.org
URL: http://www.pfrenewal.org

Description: Supporters are individuals, congregations, and foundations. Trains church officers. Conducts renewal weekends, officer retreats, and marriage enrichment programs. Provides placement service; bestows awards; compiles statistics. Operates charitable program and speakers' bureau.

8499 ■ Society of Biblical Literature (SBL)
Luce Center
825 Houston Mill Rd.
Atlanta, GA 30329
Ph: (404)727-3100
Fax: (404)727-3101
Fr: (866)727-9955
E-mail: sblexec@sbl-site.org
URL: http://www.sbl-site.org

Description: Professors and persons interested in biblical studies, ancient world and religious studies. Seeks to "stimulate the critical investigation of classical biblical literature, together with other related literature, by the exchange of scholarly research both in published form and in public forum". Endeavors to support those disciplines and sub disciplines pertinent to the illumination of the literatures and religions of the ancient Near Eastern and Mediterranean regions, including the study of ancient languages, textual criticism, history, and archaeology. Supports and cooperates with several national and international groups. Conducts research programs; offers placement services.

8500 ■ Teen Missions International (TMI)
885 E Hall Rd.
Merritt Island, FL 32953
Ph: (321)453-0350
Fax: (321)452-7988
E-mail: info@teenmissions.org
URL: http://www.teenmissions.org

Description: Organizes interdenominational evangelical missionary work projects in areas such as agriculture and community development; programs have operated in 60 countries, including Australia, Brazil, Mongolia, India, Indonesia, Mexico, South Africa, and Zimbabwe. Trains teen and adult missionaries through camps and conferences; operates placement service. Promotes the Christian gospel through the production of films, videos, printed materials, and media presentations. Assists in establishing local teen mission clubs in an effort to encourage evangelical outreach.

8501 ■ United Church of Christ Justice and Witness Ministries
700 Prospect Ave.
Cleveland, OH 44115-1110
Ph: (216)736-2100
E-mail: ogm@ucc.org
URL: http://www.ucc.org/justice/index.html

Description: Represents ministers of United Church of Christ who work to maximize the impact of African American and other people of color constituencies within the UCC.

8502 ■ Youth for Christ/U.S.A. (YFC/USA)
PO Box 4478
Englewood, CO 80155
Ph: (303)843-9000
Fax: (303)843-9002
E-mail: info@yfc.net
URL: http://www.yfc.net

Description: Fights juvenile delinquency through counseling and Youth Guidance programs for youth penal institutions. Carries on projects in various countries through Youth for Christ International. Maintains placement service. Programs for staffs are: area refreshers; college training; intern training; and summer training. Programs for youth are: camps; Campus Life Clubs; counseling; short-term missions and work projects overseas; and Youth Guidance work with troubled teenagers. Sponsors "Lighten Up!" radio.

Musicians

SOURCES OF HELP-WANTED ADS

8503 ■ The American Organist Magazine
American Guild of Organists
475 Riverside Dr., Ste. 1260
New York, NY 10115
Ph: (212)870-2310
Fax: (212)870-2163
E-mail: info@agohq.org
URL: http://www.agohq.org

Monthly. Devoted to organ and choral music across the globe. Facilitates personal contact with colleagues locally and nationally. Keeps members up to date with the profession by providing them with both scholarly and practical features as well as timely news of the Guild and its members. Contains listings of positions available to keep members aware of employment opportunities nationwide.

8504 ■ ArtSEARCH
Theatre Communications Group
520 8th Ave., 24th Fl.
New York, NY 10018-4156
Ph: (212)609-5900
Fax: (212)609-5901
E-mail: tcg@tcg.org
URL: http://www.tcg.org

Description: Biweekly. Publishes classified listings for job opportunities in the arts, especially theatre, dance, music, and educational institutions. Listings include opportunities in administration, artistic, education, production, and career development.

8505 ■ Daily Variety
Reed Business Information
360 Park Ave. S
New York, NY 10010-1710
Ph: (646)746-7764
Fax: (646)746-7583
URL: http://www.reedbusiness.com/
index.asp?layout=theListProfile&

Daily. $329.99/year for individuals. Global entertainment newspaper (tabloid).

8506 ■ The Diapason
Scranton Gillette Communications Inc.
3030 W Salt Creek Ln., Ste. 201
Arlington Heights, IL 60005-5025
Ph: (847)391-1000
Fax: (847)390-0408
URL: http://www.thediapason.com

Monthly. $70.00/year for individuals, 3 years; $55.00/year for two years; $35.00/year for individuals; $85.00/year for other countries, 3 years; $65.00/year for other countries, 2 years; $45.00/year for other countries. Magazine devoted to pipe organ building, organ and church music performance, and repertoire.

8507 ■ Down Beat
Maher Publications Inc.
102 N Haven Rd.
Elmhurst, IL 60126

Ph: (630)941-2030
Fr: 800-554-7470
URL: http://www.downbeat.com

Monthly. $48.99/year for two years; $26.99/year for individuals; $48.99/year for other countries; $92.99/year for other countries, two years; $37.99/year for Canada; $70.99/year for Canada, two years. Magazine edited for the learning musician.

8508 ■ Electronic Musician
Penton Media
249 W 17th St.
New York, NY 10011-5390
Ph: (212)204-4200
E-mail: emeditorial@prismb2b.com
URL: http://emusician.com/

Monthly. $23.97/year for individuals, digital; $29.97/year for individuals, print and digital; $23.97/year for individuals, print. Magazine on music and home or personal recording industry technology.

8509 ■ Jelly
Peppercorn Press
68158 Red Arrow Hwy.
Hartford, MI 49057
Ph: (269)621-2733
Fax: (269)621-2709
E-mail: inbox@jellyroll.com
URL: http://www.jellyroll.com/

Magazine covering blues, jazz, country, soul and rock'n'roll music.

8510 ■ Journal of the AMIS
American Musical Instrument Society
The Guild Associates, Inc.
389 Main St., Ste. 202
Malden, MA 02148
Ph: (781)397-8870
Fax: (781)397-8887
URL: http://www.amis.org/publications/journal

Annual. Journal covering all aspects of musical instruments.

8511 ■ Music Educators Journal
MENC: The National Association for Music Education
1806 Robert Fulton Dr.
Reston, VA 20191
Ph: (703)860-4000
Fax: (703)860-1531
Fr: 800-336-3768
URL: http://www.menc.org/resources/view/menc-journals

$165.00/year for institutions, print & E-access; $149.00/year for institutions, E-access; $162.00/year for institutions, print only. Journal covering all levels of music education. Published on alternate months with Teaching Music.

8512 ■ Music and Media
Nielsen Business Media
770 Broadway
New York, NY 10003-9595
URL: http://www.vnubusinessmedia.com

Weekly. Publication covering the music and entertainment industries.

8513 ■ Music Trades
Music Trades Corp.
80 West St.
Englewood, NJ 07631
Ph: (201)871-1965
Fax: (201)871-0455
Fr: 800-423-6530
URL: http://www.musictrades.com/

Monthly. $45.00/year for individuals, foreign; $23.00/year for two years, domestic; $16.00/year for individuals, domestic. Music trade magazine.

8514 ■ Music Vacancy List
College Music Society
312 E Pine St.
Missoula, MT 59802
Ph: (406)721-9616
Fax: (406)721-9419
E-mail: cms@music.org
URL: http://www.music.org/cgi-bin/showpage.pl

Weekly. Features employment opportunities in the field of music and higher education and career opportunities in allied professions.

8515 ■ Musical News
Musicians Union Local 6
116 Ninth St.
San Francisco, CA 94103
Ph: (415)575-0777
URL: http://www.afm6.org/MusicalNews.htm

Description: Bimonthly. Contains union news and information of importance to members of the American Federation of Musicians.

8516 ■ Paste
Paste Media Group L.L.C.
PO Box 1606
Decatur, GA 30031
Ph: (404)664-4320
Fax: (404)377-4508
Fr: (866)370-9067
URL: http://www.pastemagazine.com

$19.95/year for individuals; $39.90/year for two years; $50.00/year for other countries; $25.00/year for Canada and Mexico. Music magazine.

8517 ■ The Sinfonian
Phi Mu Alpha - Sinfonia
National Headquarters
10600 Old State Rd.
Evansville, IN 47711
Ph: (812)867-2433
Fax: (812)867-0633

Fr: 800-473-2649
E-mail: lyrecrest@sinfonia.org
URL: http://www.sinfonia.org

Description: 2/year. Announces and reviews activities and programs of the fraternity. Profiles members and their careers. Discusses major developments in the music industry and education.

8518 ■ Sounding Board
American Composers Forum
332 Minnesota St., Ste. E 145
St. Paul, MN 55101
Ph: (651)228-1407
Fax: (651)291-7978
URL: http://www.composersforum.org

Description: Bimonthly. Features news and updates on Forum programming, articles of interest to composers, musicians, and others in the new music community. Provides a listing of opportunities including grants, fellowships, and calls for scores.

8519 ■ SYMPHONY
American Symphony Orchestra League
33 W 60th St., 5th Fl.
New York, NY 10023-7905
Ph: (212)262-5161
Fax: (212)262-5198
E-mail: league@symphony.org
URL: http://www.americanorchestras.org/symphony_magazine/symphony

Bimonthly. $25.00/year for individuals. Magazine with news and articles for symphony orchestra managers, trustees, conductors, volunteers, and musicians.

8520 ■ UMS E-News
University Musical Society (UMS)
Burton Memorial Tower
881 N University Ave.
Ann Arbor, MI 48109-1011
Ph: (734)764-2538
Fax: (734)647-1171
URL: http://www.ums.org

Features articles and news of events involving classical music and musicians. Covers festivals, concerts, and other programs. Includes a calendar of events, a column titled Remembrances, and news of Society activities.

8521 ■ Variety
Reed Business Information
360 Park Ave. S
New York, NY 10010-1710
Ph: (646)746-7764
Fax: (646)746-7583
URL: http://www.reedbusiness.com/us.html

Weekly. $259.00/year for individuals; $25.00/year for individuals, monthly. Newspaper (tabloid) reporting on theatre, television, radio, music, records, and movies.

PLACEMENT AND JOB REFERRAL SERVICES

8522 ■ Musicians Contact
PO Box 788
Woodland Hills, CA 91365
Ph: (818)888-7879
E-mail: information@musicianscontact.com
URL: http://www.musicianscontact.com

Description: Job source for musicians, singers, bands, managers, employers and agents. Connects musicians and singers to paying jobs. Caters to both employers in need of musicians and musicians in need of placement.

EMPLOYER DIRECTORIES AND NETWORKING LISTS

8523 ■ Careers in Focus—Music
Facts On File Inc.
132 W 31st St., 17th Fl.
New York, NY 10001

Ph: (212)967-8800
Fax: 800-678-3633
Fr: 800-322-8755
URL: http://www.infobasepublishing.com

Latest edition 2nd; Published July, 2009. $32.95 for individuals. Covers: An overview of music, followed by a selection of jobs profiled in detail, including the nature of the job, earnings, prospects for employment, what kind of training and skills it requires, and sources for further information.

8524 ■ Chamber Music America—Membership Directory
Chamber Music America
305 7th Ave.
New York, NY 10001
Ph: (212)242-2022
Fax: (212)242-7955
URL: http://www.chamber-music.org

Annual, in the September issue of Chamber Music Magazine. $85.00 for individuals; $60.00 for individuals; $35.00 for individuals. Covers: Over 800 member ensembles, presenters, festivals, and training programs; over 4,000 associate members, including managers, publishers, arts organizations, instrument manufacturers, libraries and individuals. Entries include: For members—Name, address, phone, name of contact, activities, awards, year established. For associates—Name, address, phone. Arrangement: Separate geographical sections for ensembles, presenters, festivals and training programs; associate members are classified by type of organization, then alphabetical. Indexes: General, subject.

8525 ■ Chicago Creative Directory
Chicago Creative Directory
4149 N Leamington Ave.
Chicago, IL 60601
Ph: (773)427-7777
Fax: (773)427-7771
URL: http://creativedir.com

Annual, March. Covers: Over 6,000 advertising agencies, photographers, sound studios, talent agencies, audiovisual services, and others offering creative and production services. Entries include: For most listings—Company name, address, phone, list of officers, description of services. For freelance listings—Name, talent, address, phone. Arrangement: Classified by specialty.

8526 ■ Instrumentalist—Directory of Summer Music Camps, Clinics, and Workshops Issue
Instrumentalist Co.
200 Northfield Rd.
Northfield, IL 60093
Ph: (847)446-5000
Fax: (847)446-6263
Fr: 888-446-6888
E-mail: editor@theinstrumentalist.com
URL: http://www.theinstrumentalist.com

Annual, Latest edition 2009. $2.50. Publication includes: List of nearly 250 summer music camps, clinics, and workshops in the United States; limited Canadian and foreign coverage. Entries include: Camp name, location, name of director, opening and closing dates, tuition fees, courses offered. Arrangement: Geographical.

8527 ■ Music Publisher Registry
The Music Business Registry Inc.
7510 Sunset Blvd., No. 1041
Los Angeles, CA 90046-3400
Ph: (818)781-1974
Fax: (740)587-3916
Fr: 800-377-7411
URL: http://musicregistry.com/frame.html

$75.00 for single issue. Covers: Lists of all major publishers and significant independents in LA, NY, Nashville, London and Toronto. Entries include: Creative staff, direct dial numbers, assistant's names and e-mail addresses.

8528 ■ National Directory of Arts Internships
National Network for Artist Placement
935 West Ave. 37
Los Angeles, CA 90065
Ph: (323)222-4035
E-mail: info@artistplacement.com
URL: http://www.artistplacement.com

Biennial, odd years; latest edition 11th. $95.00 for individuals. Covers: Over 5,000 internship opportunities in dance, music, theater, art, design, film, and video & over 1,250 host organizations Entries include: Name of sponsoring organization, address, name of contact; description of positions available, eligibility requirements, stipend or salary (if any), application procedures. Arrangement: Classified by discipline, then geographical.

8529 ■ The R & R Directory
Billboard.biz
PO Box 3595
Northbrook, IL 60065-3595
Ph: (847)559-7531
Fr: 800-658-8372
E-mail: moreinfo@rronline.com
URL: http://www.radioandrecords.com/RRDirectory/Directory_Main.as

Semiannual, Spring and Fall. $75.00. Covers: More than 3,000 radio group owners, equipment manufacturers, jingle producers, TV production houses and spot producers, record companies, representative firms, research companies, consulting firms, media brokers, networks, program suppliers, trade associations, and other organizations involved in the radio and record industry. Entries include: Organization name, address, phone, fax, E-mail, name and title of contacts, branch offices or subsidiary names and locations. Arrangement: Alphabetical; classified by subject. Indexes: Company.

8530 ■ Regional Theater Directory
American Theatre Works Inc.
2349 West Rd.
PO Box 159
Dorset, VT 05251
Ph: (802)867-9333
Fax: (802)867-2297
URL: http://www.theatredirectories.com

Annual, May. $38.50 for individuals. Covers: Regional theater companies and dinner theatres with employment opportunities in acting, design, production, and management. Entries include: Company name, address, phone, name and title of contact; type of company, activities, and size of house; whether union affiliated, whether nonprofit or commercial; year established; hiring procedure and number of positions hired annually, season; description of stage; internships, description of artistic policy and audience. Arrangement: Geographical. Indexes: Company name, type of plays produced.

8531 ■ Songwriter's Market
Writer's Digest Books
4700 E Galbraith Rd.
Cincinnati, OH 45236
Ph: (715)445-4612
Fr: 800-258-0929
E-mail: songmarket@fwpubs.com
URL: http://www.writersdigest.com

Annual, Latest edition 2010. $19.79 for individuals. Covers: 2,000 music publishers, jingle writers, advertising agencies, audiovisual firms, radio and television stations, booking agents, and other buyers of musical compositions and lyrics; also lists contests, competitions, and workshops. Entries include: Buyer's name and address, phone, payment rates, submission requirements, etc. Arrangement: Classified by type of market. Indexes: Geographical.

8532 ■ Summer Theater Directory
American Theatre Works Inc.
2349 West Rd.
PO Box 159
Dorset, VT 05251
Ph: (802)867-9333

Fax: (802)867-2297
URL: http://www.theatredirectories.com
Annual, Latest edition 2009. $38.50 for individuals.
Covers: Summer theater companies, theme parks
and cruise lines that offer employment opportunities
in acting, design, production, and management; summer theater training programs. Entries include:
Company name, address, phone, name and title of
contact; type of company, activities and size of house;
whether union affiliated, whether nonprofit or commercial; year established; hiring procedure and
number of positions hired annually, season; description of stage; internships; description of company's
artistic goals and audience. Arrangement:
Geographical. Indexes: Company name.

HANDBOOKS AND MANUALS

8533 ■ 100 Careers in the Music Business
Barron's Educational Series, Inc.
250 Wireless Blvd.
Hauppauge, NY 11788
Fax: (631)434-3723
Fr: 800-645-3476
E-mail: fbrown@barronseduc.com
URL: http://barronseduc.com

Tanja L. Crouch. 2008. $15.29 (paper). 320 pages.
Includes descriptions of job opportunities in the music
industry. Provides information on how and where to
find employment opportunities. Informs beginners on
how to match their own qualifications with potential
job openings, seek and find job interviews, and get
into the music business. Contains lists of skills
needed in each job designation, describes a typical
workday, and presents actual case studies of men
and women who have found music career openings.
Includes lists of names, addresses, and websites of
music unions, organizations, directories, magazines,
and schools offering degrees in music business
management. Contains career tips and a glossary of
music business and technical terms.

**8534 ■ Beyond Talent: Creating a Successful
Career in Music**
Oxford University Press
198 Madison Ave.
New York, NY 10016
Ph: (212)726-6000
Fax: (919)677-1303
Fr: 800-445-9714
E-mail: custserv.us@oup.com
URL: http://www.oup.com

Angela Myles Beeching. 2010. $21.95 (paper). 400
pages. Provides updated user-friendly advice, inspiring examples, and practical tools to advance a career
in music. Covers topics on social networking tools;
commissioning; branding; online fundraising; tips on
staying motivated; assessing one's strengths and
weaknesses; and managing time, money, and stress.

**8535 ■ Career Opportunities in the Music
Industry**
Facts On File Inc.
132 W 31st St., 17th Fl.
New York, NY 10001-2006
Ph: (212)967-8800
Fax: 800-678-3633
Fr: 800-322-8755
E-mail: custserv@factsonfile.com
URL: http://factsonfile.infobasepublishing.com

Shelly Field. Sixth edition, 2009. $49.50.

**8536 ■ Creative Careers: Paths for Aspiring
Actors, Artists, Dancers, Musicians and
Writers**
SuperCollege, LLC
3286 Oak Ct.
Belmont, CA 94002
Ph: (650)618-2221
URL: http://www.supercollege.com

Elaina Loveland. 2009. $17.95. 352 pages. Provides
tips and advice for job seekers aiming for a career in

the field of arts. Includes details on salaries, job
descriptions, job outlook, training and education
requirements for each artistic career.

8537 ■ Great Jobs for Music Majors
The McGraw-Hill Companies
PO Box 182604
Columbus, OH 43272
Fax: (614)759-3749
Fr: 877-883-5524
E-mail: customer.service@mcgraw-hill.com
URL: http://www.mhprofessional.com/
    product.php?isbn=0071454616

Jan Goldberg. Second edition, 2004. $15.95 (paper).
180 pages.

**8538 ■ How to Get a Job in the Music
Industry**
Berklee College of Music
1140 Boylston St.
Boston, MA 02215
Ph: (617)266-1400
Fax: (617)747-2047
Fr: 800-237-5533
URL: http://berkleepress.com

Keith Hatschek. 2007. $27.95 (paper). 272 pages.
Contains details on booming job prospects in new
media, including gaming and the internet and strategies for networking. Serves as a resource directory
of key publications, websites, and trade organizations.
Contains workshops to assess and develop a person-
alized career path. Includes interviews with pros who
discuss how they got their starts plus a step-by-step
guidance for developing a resume and acing
interviews.

**8539 ■ How to Make It in the New Music
Business: Lessons, Tips and Inspiration
from Music's Biggest and Best**
Watson-Guptill Publications
1745 Broadway
New York, NY 10003
Ph: (212)782-9000
Fax: (212)940-7381
Fr: 800-733-3000
E-mail: info@watsonguptill.com
URL: http://www.randomhouse.com/crown/
    watsonguptill

Robert Wolff. April 2004. $19.95 (paper). Illustrated.
288 pages.

8540 ■ Jumpstart Your Music Career
Course Technology PTR
20 Channel Center St.
Boston, MA 02210
Fr: 800-354-9706
URL: http://www.courseptr.com

Simon Cann. 2011. $29.99. 304 pages. Offers
information and strategies needed to build a career
in music. Contains updates on recent changes in the
music industry.

**8541 ■ Making Music Your Business: A
Guide for Young Musicians**
Sphinx Publishing
1935 Brookdale Rd., Ste. 139
Naperville, IL 60563
Ph: (630)961-3900
Fax: (630)961-2168
Fr: 800-432-7444
URL: http://www.sphinxlegal.com

Traci Truly. 2005. $19.95. 142 pages. Covers many
aspects of the music business.

**8542 ■ Making Your Living As a String
Player: Career Guidance from the Experts
at Strings Magazine**
String Letter Publishing
255 W End Ave.
San Rafael, CA 94901
Ph: (415)485-6946

Fax: (415)485-0831
URL: http://www.stringletter.com
Greg Cahill. January 2004. $12.95. 96 pages.

**8543 ■ Monsters and Angels: Surviving a
Career in Music**
Manduca Music
861 Washington Ave.
Portland, ME 04103
Ph: (207)773-7012
URL: http://www.manducamusic.com/
    BernsteinTextbooks1.htm
Seymour Bernstein. March 2004. $30.00. 507 pages.

**8544 ■ Music Business Handbook and
Career Guide**
SAGE Publications
2455 Teller Rd.
Thousand Oaks, CA 91320
Ph: (805)499-0721
Fax: 800-583-2665
Fr: 800-818-7243
E-mail: info@sagepub.com
URL: http://www.sagepub.com

David Baskerville and Tim Baskerville. 2010. $83.00
(hardcover) 600 pages. Serves as a guide to the
music industry. Discusses digital technology and its
implications for the music industry.

**8545 ■ Music Business Made Simple: A
Guide to Becoming a Recording Artist**
Music Sales Corporation
257 Park Ave., S., 20th Fl.
New York, NY 10010
Ph: (212)254-2100
Fax: (212)254-2103
URL: http://www.musicsales.com

J. Scott Rudsenke and James P. Denk. April 2004.
$9.95. Illustrated. 144 pages. Music Business Made
Simpler Series.

8546 ■ Resumes for Performing Arts Careers
The McGraw-Hill Companies
PO Box 182604
Columbus, OH 43272
Fax: (614)759-3749
Fr: 877-883-5524
E-mail: customer.service@mcgraw-hill.com
URL: http://www.mhprofessional.com/
    product.php?isbn=0071442464

2004. $10.95 (paper). 160 pages.

**8547 ■ Songwriting Success: How to Write
Songs for Fun and (Maybe) Profit**
Routledge
711 3rd Ave., 8th Fl.
New York, NY 10017
Ph: (212)216-7800
Fax: (212)563-2269
URL: http://www.routledge.com

Michael Lydon. Book & CD edition. May 2004. $19.99
(paper). Illustrated. 208 pages.

**8548 ■ What's Up Dawg: How to Become a
Superstar in the Music Business**
Hyperion Books
114 Fifth Ave.
New York, NY 10011
Ph: (917)661-2072
Fax: (917)661-6411
Fr: 800-242-7737
URL: http://www.hyperionbooks.com

Randy Jackson and K.C. Baker. 2004. $19.95
(paper). 208 pages.

EMPLOYMENT AGENCIES AND SEARCH FIRMS

8549 ■ Filcro Media Staffing
521 5th Ave., Fl. 18
New York, NY 10175

Ph: (212)599-0909
Fax: (212)599-1023
E-mail: mail@executivesearch.tv
URL: http://www.executivesearch.tv

Executive search firm for the entertainment industry.

8550 ■ NMC Inc.
24 Music Sq. W
Nashville, TN 37203
Ph: (615)345-4976

Consults aspiring country music singers and song-writers by listening to their works prior to submission to record labels and publishing companies. Singers and songwriters who the firm feels are not ready will be given the opportunity to resubmit material after six months at no additional charge.

ONLINE JOB SOURCES AND SERVICES

8551 ■ GetGigs.com
URL: http://www.getgigs.com

Description: Seeks to provide an on-line experience for creative types, performing artists, and musicians around the world by integrating internet technologies into a one-stop information resource. Also functions as a creative directory and talent network.

8552 ■ Music Jobs USA
URL: http://us.music-jobs.com

Description: Serves as an online database of U.S. music professionals' resumes. Features forums, media center, testimonials, company directory, freelancer profiles, employment opportunities, and descriptions of various jobs in the music industry.

8553 ■ MyMusicJob.com
URL: http://www.mymusicjob.com

Description: Provides international music industry jobs, employment, and internships.

TRADESHOWS

8554 ■ American Harp Society National Conference
American Harp Society
c/o Ashanti Pretlow
3416 Primm Ln.
Birmingham, AL 35216
Ph: (205)795-7130
Fax: (205)823-2760
E-mail: execsecretary@harpsociety.org
URL: http://www.harpsociety.org

Annual. Primary Exhibits: Harps and related materials. Dates and Locations: 2012 Jun 30 - Jul 03; New York, NY; Marriott Marquis.

8555 ■ American Orff-Schulwerk Association National Conference
American Orff-Schulwerk Association Inc.
PO Box 391089
Cleveland, OH 44139-8089
Ph: (440)543-5366
Fax: (440)543-2687
E-mail: info@aosa.org
URL: http://www.aosa.org

Annual. Primary Exhibits: Music, music books, instruments, pitched and unpitched percussion, early music instruments, records and music gifts, computer music software.

8556 ■ ASTA National Conference
American String Teachers Association
4155 Chain Bridge Rd.
Fairfax, VA 22030
Ph: (703)279-2113
Fax: (703)279-2114
E-mail: asta@astaweb.com
URL: http://www.astaweb.com

Annual. Includes exhibits of instruments and bows.

8557 ■ Chamber Music America National Conference
Chamber Music America
305 7th Ave., 5th Fl.
New York, NY 10001-6008
Ph: (212)242-2022
Fax: (212)242-7955
URL: http://www.chamber-music.org

Annual. Primary Exhibits: Professional chamber music ensembles and presenters; organizations, foundations, and individuals actively supporting chamber music performances. Dates and Locations: 2013 Jan 17-20; New York, NY; The Westin Hotel.

8558 ■ College Music Society National Conference
The College Music Society
312 E. Pine St.
Missoula, MT 59802
Ph: (406)721-9616
Fax: (406)721-9419
Fr: 800-729-0235
E-mail: cms@music.org
URL: http://www.music.org

Annual. Primary Exhibits: Music publishers, instrument manufacturers, music retailers, non-profit associations, music hardware and software manufacturers. Dates and Locations: 2012 Nov 15-18; San Diego, CA; Manschester Grand Hyatt.

8559 ■ The Midwest Clinic An International Band and Orchestra Conference
The Midwest Clinic
1111 E. Touhy, Ste. 250
Des Plaines, IL 60018
Ph: (847)424-4163
Fax: (773)321-1509
E-mail: info@midwestclinic.org
URL: http://www.midwestclinic.org

Annual. Primary Exhibits: Music instruments and publications, supplies, and services, universities, military organizations, fund raisers, music publishers. Dates and Locations: 2012 Dec 19-22.

8560 ■ MTNA National Conference
Music Teachers National Association
441 Vine St., Ste. 3100
Cincinnati, OH 45202-3004
Ph: (513)421-1420
Fax: (513)421-2503
Fr: 888-512-5278
E-mail: mtnanet@mtna.org
URL: http://www.mtna.org

Annual. Primary Exhibits: Musical equipment, supplies, and services.

8561 ■ MUSICORA - Classical and Jazz Music Show
Secession
E-mail: secession@secession.fr
URL: http://www.secession.at

Annual. Primary Exhibits: Instruments, records, scores, books, and antiques related to classical music.

8562 ■ NAMM - Summer Session
NAMM - International Music Products Association
5790 Armada Dr.
Carlsbad, CA 92008
Ph: (760)438-8001
Fax: (760)438-7327
Fr: 800-767-6266
URL: http://www.namm.org

Annual. Primary Exhibits: Musical instruments and accessories, acoustical equipment, and sheet music publications. Dates and Locations: 2012 Jul 12-14; Nashville, TN; Nashville Convention Center; 2013 Jul 11-13; Nashville, TN; Nashville Convention Center.

8563 ■ National Association of Pastoral Musicians National Convention
National Association of Pastoral Musicians
962 Wayne Ave., Ste. 210
Silver Spring, MD 20910-4461
Ph: (240)247-3000
Fax: (240)247-3001
E-mail: npmsing@npm.org
URL: http://npm.org

Annual. Primary Exhibits: Music, musical instruments, books, church furnishings and art. Dates and Locations: 2012 Jul 23-27; Pittsburgh, PA; David L. Lawrence Convention Center.

8564 ■ National Flute Association Convention
National Flute Association
26951 Ruether Ave., Ste. H
Santa Clarita, CA 91351
Ph: (661)713-6013
Fax: (661)299-6681
E-mail: conventionservices@nfaonline.org
URL: http://www.nfaonline.org

Annual. Features competitions, flute choirs, performance health workshops, and concerts and recitals galore for professionals, teachers, students, amateurs, flute enthusiasts and their families. 2012 August 9-12; Las Vegas, NV; Caesars Place.

8565 ■ Violin Society of America Convention
Violin Society of America
341 N. Maitland Ave., Ste. 130
Maitland, FL 32751
Ph: (407)647-8839
Fr: (407)629-2502
E-mail: info@vsaweb.org
URL: http://www.vsa.to

Annual. Primary Exhibits: Violins, violas, cellos, and their bows, strings, and other accessories; books; tone and bow woods.

8566 ■ Western Division Choral Directors Association Conference
American Choral Directors Association
545 Couch Dr.
PO Box 2720
Oklahoma City, OK 73102-2207
Ph: (405)232-8161
Fax: (405)232-8162
E-mail: acda@acdaonline.org
URL: http://www.acdaonline.org

Biennial. Primary Exhibits: Exhibits of interest to choral directors. Dates and Locations: 2012 Feb 29 - Mar 03; Reno, NV.

OTHER SOURCES

8567 ■ Acoustical Society of America
2 Huntington Quadrangle, Ste. 1NO1
Melville, NY 11747-4502
Ph: (516)576-2360
Fax: (516)576-2377
E-mail: asa@aip.org
URL: http://acousticalsociety.org

Description: Represents members from various fields related to sound including physics, electrical, mechanical and aeronautical engineering, oceanography, biology, physiology, psychology, architecture, speech, noise and noise control, and music. Aims to increase and diffuse the knowledge of acoustics and its practical applications. Organizes meetings, provides reprints of out-of-print classic texts in acoustics, and translation books.

8568 ■ American Federation of Musicians of the United States and Canada (AFM)
1501 Broadway, Ste. 600
New York, NY 10036
Ph: (212)869-1330
Fax: (212)764-6134
E-mail: presoffice@afm.org
URL: http://www.afm.org

Description: Union representing the interests of professional musicians through collective bargaining, benefits, and services.

8569 ■ American Guild of Musical Artists (AGMA)
1430 Broadway, 14th Fl.
New York, NY 10018
Ph: (212)265-3687
Fax: (212)262-9088
Fr: 800-543-2462
E-mail: agma@musicalartists.org
URL: http://www.musicalartists.org

Description: AFL-CIO. Represents opera and classical concert singers, classical ballet and modern dance performers, and affiliated stage directors, stage managers and choreographers.

8570 ■ American Guild of Organists (AGO)
475 Riverside Dr., Ste. 1260
New York, NY 10115
Ph: (212)870-2310
Fax: (212)870-2163
Fr: 800-AGO-5115
E-mail: info@agohq.org
URL: http://www.agohq.org

Description: Educational and service organization organized to advance the cause of organ and choral music and to maintain standards of artistic excellence of organists and choral conductors. Offers professional certification in organ playing, choral and instrumental training, and theory and general knowledge of music.

8571 ■ American Society Of Composers, Authors, And Publishers
One Lincoln Plz.
New York, NY 10023
Ph: (212)621-6000
Fax: (212)621-8453
E-mail: info@ascap.com
URL: http://www.ascap.com

Description: Represents composers, songwriters, lyricists, and music publishers of every kind of music. Aims to ensure that music creators are fairly compensated for the public performance of their works and that their rights are properly protected. Organizes workshops and showcases. Provides publications and benefits packages that include health and instrument insurance, a credit union, discounts on musical accessories, travel, and more.

8572 ■ American String Teachers Association
4155 Chain Bridge Rd.
Fairfax, VA 22030
Ph: (703)279-2113
Fax: (703)279-2114
E-mail: asta@astaweb.com
URL: http://www.astaweb.com

Description: Represents string and orchestra teachers and players. Promotes excellence in string and orchestra teaching and playing. Provides services including instrument insurance, publications and resources, annual professional development opportunities, and access to a collegial network of colleagues throughout the string profession.

8573 ■ American Viola Society
14070 Proton Rd., Ste. 100, LB 9
Dallas, TX 75244
Ph: (972)233-9107
E-mail: info@avsnationaloffice.org
URL: http://americanviolasociety.org

Description: Promotes interest in the viola by encouraging performance and recording at the highest artistic level, by the continued study and research of the instrument and its repertoire, and by providing a vehicle for the ongoing development of the fraternal bond among violists.

8574 ■ Association of Anglican Musicians (AAM)
PO Box 7530
Little Rock, AR 72217
Ph: (501)661-9925
Fax: (501)661-9925
E-mail: anglicanm@aol.com
URL: http://anglicanmusicians.org

Description: Represents church musicians (laypersons or clergy) serving Episcopal and Anglican churches. Seeks to promote excellence in church music. Fosters a relationship of mutual respect and trust between clergy and musicians actively encouraging and supporting composers and other artists to create works for the church. Maintains communication with and supporting the work of the Standing Commission on Liturgy and Church. Encourages equitable compensation and benefits for professional church musicians. Works closely with seminaries toward the establishment and continuation of courses in music and the allied arts as they relate to worship and theology. Maintains placement service.

8575 ■ Association of Lutheran Church Musicians
Valparaiso University
810 Freeman St.
Valparaiso, IN 46383
Ph: (219)548-2526
Fr: 800-624-2526
E-mail: alcm.ofc@comcast.net
URL: http://www.alcm.org

Description: Promotes and preserves Lutheran liturgical heritage. Provides opportunities for educational, spiritual, and theological growth for Lutheran musicians and clergy. Fosters professional exchange and fellowship within the Lutheran musical community.

8576 ■ Church Music Association of America
12421 New Point Dr.
Richmond, VA 23233
Ph: (334)703-0884
Fax: (334)460-9924
E-mail: contact@musicasacra.com
URL: http://musicasacra.com

Description: Represents Catholic musicians and others interested in Roman Catholic liturgical music. Promotes the advancement of sacred music in Catholic liturgy through workshops and publications.

8577 ■ Country Music Showcase International (CMSI)
PO Box 368
Carlisle, IA 50047-0368
Ph: (515)989-3748
E-mail: haroldl@cmshowcase.org
URL: http://www.cmshowcase.org

Description: Helps songwriters and entertainers learn more about songwriting and the general music industry. Sponsors Song Evaluation and Critiques Service, songwriting seminars and workshops and songwriter showcases. Operates a BMI Music Publishing Company for the benefit of members whose songs qualify for publishing. Configures specially made computers for songwriters, musicians, and entertainers to use. Owns and operates: Country Music Showcase International, Inc.; Attraction Booking Agency, which serves fairs, festivals and corporate fund raising events providing them access to all 14 Art Forms of Country Music Entertainers and Stage Shows. Serves as the trustee for the Iowa/Midwest Country Music Heritage "Virtual" Museum, Library and Hall Of Fame.

8578 ■ Early Music America
2366 Eastlake Ave. E, Ste. 429
Seattle, WA 98102
Ph: (206)720-6270
Fax: (206)720-6290
Fr: 888-722-5288
E-mail: info@earlymusic.org
URL: http://earlymusic.org

Description: Represents professional performers, ensembles, presenters, instrument makers, amateur musicians, and audience members. Serves and strengthens the early music community in North America and raises public awareness of early music. Aims to expand awareness of, and interest in, the music of the Medieval, Renaissance, Baroque, and Classical periods performed on period instruments using historical performance practices.

8579 ■ High School Band Directors National Association (HSBDNA)
PO Box 886
Fortson, GA 31808
Ph: (706)568-0760
E-mail: oboone9007@bellsouth.net
URL: http://www.hsbdna.com

Description: Promotes the excellence of high school band performance throughout the United States. Advocates for the promotion of bands in the educational curriculum. Fosters pride and continued enthusiasm among high school band directors.

8580 ■ League of American Orchestras
33 W 60th St., 5th Fl.
New York, NY 10023
Ph: (212)262-5161
Fax: (212)262-5198
E-mail: member@americanorchestras.org
URL: http://www.americanorchestras.org

Description: Symphony orchestras; associate members include educational institutions, arts councils, public libraries, business firms, orchestra professionals, and individuals interested in symphony orchestras. Engages in extensive research on diverse facets of symphony orchestra operations and development. Provides consulting services for orchestras, their boards, and volunteer organizations. Sponsors management seminars and workshops for professional symphony orchestra administrative and artistic staff, volunteers, and prospective management personnel. Maintains employment services; collects and distributes resource materials, financial data, and statistical reports on many aspects of orchestra operations. Compiles statistics; sponsors educational programs; maintains resource center.

8581 ■ MENC: The National Association for Music Education (MENC)
1806 Robert Fulton Dr.
Reston, VA 20191
Ph: (703)860-4000
Fax: (703)860-1531
Fr: 800-336-3768
E-mail: mbrserv@menc2.org
URL: http://www.menc.org

Description: Comprised of music educators, administrators, supervisors, consultants, and music education majors in colleges. Publishes materials for music educators, presents conferences, compiles statistics.

8582 ■ Music Teachers National Association (MTNA)
441 Vine St., Ste. 3100
Cincinnati, OH 45202-3004
Ph: (513)421-1420
Fax: (513)421-2503
Fr: 888-512-5278
E-mail: mtnanet@mtna.org
URL: http://www.mtna.org

Description: Professional society of independent and collegiate music teachers committed to furthering the art of music through programs that encourage and support teaching, performance, composition, and scholarly research.

8583 ■ National Association of Pastoral Musicians (NPM)
962 Wayne Ave., Ste. 210
Silver Spring, MD 20910-4461
Ph: (240)247-3000
Fax: (240)247-3001
E-mail: npmsing@npm.org
URL: http://www.npm.org

Description: Fosters the art of musical liturgy.

Members serve the Catholic Church in the United States as musicians, clergy, liturgists, and other leaders of prayer. Provides ongoing formation for musicians and clergy through annual conventions, educational institutes, and events in more than 70 diocesan chapters. Also provides certification programs for cantors, organists, and directors of music ministries.

8584 ■ National Association of Teachers of Singing (NATS)

9957 Moorings Dr., Ste. 401
Jacksonville, FL 32257
Ph: (904)992-9101
Fax: (904)262-2587
E-mail: info@nats.org
URL: http://www.nats.org

Description: Serves as a professional society of teachers of singing. Encourages the highest standards of the vocal art and of ethical principles in the teaching of singing. Promotes vocal education and research at all levels, both for the enrichment of the general public and for the professional advancement of the talented.

8585 ■ National Flute Association

26951 Ruether Ave., Ste. H
Santa Clarita, CA 91351
Ph: (661)299-6680
Fax: (661)299-6681
E-mail: conventionservices@nfaonline.org
URL: http://www.nfaonline.org

Description: Promotes flute performance, pedagogy, and development by providing a forum for the exchange of ideas. Enriches the repertoire for the flute through commissioning, special publications, and related activities. Inspires and cultivates personal, professional, and artistic excellence among its members.

8586 ■ National Traditional Country Music Association (NTCMA)

PO Box 492
Anita, IA 50020
Ph: (712)762-4363
E-mail: bobeverhart@yahoo.com
URL: http://www.orgsites.com/ia/oldtimemusic

Description: Individuals interested in the preservation, presentation, and perpetuation of traditional acoustic country, folk, honky-tonk, ragtime, mountain, and bluegrass music celebrating contributions of U.S. settlers and pioneers; country music associations. Supports what the association views as related, traditional values. Holds jam sessions; sponsors booths and offers hands-on music and craft experiences; operates charitable program; offers children's services; maintains placement service. Sponsors championship contests in numerous categories, including: Great Plains Story Telling; Hank Williams Songwriting; International Country Singer; Jimmie Rodgers Yodeling; National Bluegrass Band; National Harmonica Playing. Programs are taped and televised by various local, national, and international stations. Established the "Old-Time Music Hour" radio program at the Walnut Country Opera House, Pioneer Music Museum, America Old-Time Fiddlers Hall of Fame, and America Country Music Hall of Fame.

8587 ■ Organization of American Kodaly Educators (OAKE)

1612 29th Ave. S
Moorhead, MN 56560
Ph: (218)227-6253
Fax: (218)277-6254
E-mail: oakeoffice@oake.org
URL: http://www.oake.org

Description: Represents music educators, students, organizations, schools, and libraries interested in the Kodaly concept of music education. Zoltan Kodaly (1882-1967), Hungarian composer and educator, originated a concept of music education that seeks to develop the sensibilities, intellectual facilities, and skills of children, with the intention of creating a musically educated public. Objectives are: to encourage communication and cooperation among Kodaly educators; to encourage musical and human growth; to provide a forum for comment on the impact of the Kodaly concept; to recognize, identify, and convey the multicultural musical heritage of American society; to contribute to and encourage the aesthetic education of the child. Conducts clinics and other small unit activities.

8588 ■ Presbyterian Association of Musicians (PAM)

100 Witherspoon St.
Louisville, KY 40202-1396
Ph: (502)569-5288
Fax: (502)569-8465
Fr: 888-728-7228
E-mail: alan.barthel@pcusa.org
URL: http://www.presbymusic.org

Description: Represents organists, choir directors, singers, churches, clergy, directors of Christian education, and interested persons of all denominations. Aims to develop the use of music and the arts in the life and worship of individual congregations. Offers assistance in the areas of worship, music, and the arts. Conducts continuing education. Acts as a clearinghouse for job referrals; promotes the professional status of church musicians and recommends salaries and benefits to churches; certifies church musicians.

8589 ■ Professional Women Singers Association (PWSA)

PO Box 884
New York, NY 10159
E-mail: info@womensingers.org
URL: http://www.womensingers.org

Description: Professional women singers. Promotes career advancement of women singers. Serves as a network for singers looking for career support.

8590 ■ Reverb

386 Fore St., No. 202
Portland, ME 04101
Ph: (207)221-6553
E-mail: info@reverb.org
URL: http://www.reverb.org

Description: Seeks to educate and engage musicians and their fans to participate in protecting the environment. Conducts outreach programs and engages music fans online and in concerts while greening musicians' tours. Conducts presentations at music shows to promote carbon offset programs and to encourage fans to participate in eco-village activities.

8591 ■ Texas International Theatrical Arts Society (TITAS)

3625 N Hall St., Ste. 740
Dallas, TX 75219
Ph: (214)528-6112
Fax: (214)528-2617
E-mail: csantos@titas.org
URL: http://www.titas.org

Description: Theatrical agencies working to book entertainers and international acts into all live music venues. Provides placement service; conducts educational seminars.

Sources of Help-Wanted Ads

8592 ■ *Engineering*
Scientific Research Publishing
PO Box 54821
Irvine, CA 92619-4821
E-mail: eng@scirp.org
URL: http://www.scirp.org/journal/eng/

Monthly. $708.00/year for individuals. Peer-reviewed journal publishing articles on the latest advancements in engineering.

8593 ■ *Engineering Economist*
Taylor & Francis Group
270 Madison Ave.
New York, NY 10016
Fax: (212)244-4561
URL: http://www.tandf.co.uk/journals/titles/ 0013791x.asp

Quarterly. $89.00/year for individuals, print; $153.00/ year for institutions, online only; $170.00/year for institutions, print & online. Publication covering business issues in the energy, petroleum and mining industries.

8594 ■ *ENR: Engineering News-Record*
McGraw-Hill Inc.
PO Box 182604
Columbus, OH 43218
Ph: (614)430-4000
Fax: (614)759-3749
Fr: 877-833-5524
URL: http://enr.construction.com/Default.asp

Weekly. $49.00/year for individuals, print; $89.00/ year for Canada, print; $125.00/year for other countries, print. Magazine focusing on engineering and construction.

8595 ■ *Graduating Engineer & Computer Careers*
Career Recruitment Media
2 LAN Dr., Ste. 100
Westford, MA 01886
Ph: (978)692-5092
Fax: (978)692-4174
URL: http://www.graduatingengineer.com

Quarterly. $16.95/year for individuals. Magazine focusing on employment, education, and career development for entry-level engineers and computer scientists.

8596 ■ *High Technology Careers Magazine*
HTC
4701 Patrick Henry Dr., No. 1901
Santa Clara, CA 95054
Fax: (408)567-0242
URL: http://www.hightechcareers.com

Bimonthly. $29.00/year; $35.00/year for Canada; $85.00/year for out of country. Magazine (tabloid)

containing employment opportunity information for the engineering and technical community.

8597 ■ *IEEE Spectrum*
Institute of Electrical and Electronics Engineers Inc.
3 Park Ave., 17th Fl.
New York, NY 10016-5997
Ph: (212)419-7900
Fax: (212)705-8999
URL: http://www.spectrum.ieee.org/mc_online

Monthly. $29.95/year for U.S. and Canada; $99.95/ year for other countries. Magazine for the scientific and engineering professional. Provides information on developments and trends in engineering, physics, mathematics, chemistry, medicine/biology, and the nuclear sciences.

8598 ■ *International Journal of Energetic Materials and Chemical Propulsion*
Begell House Inc.
50 Cross Hwy.
Redding, CT 06896
Ph: (203)938-1300
Fax: (203)938-1304
URL: http://www.begellhouse.com/journals/ 17bbb47e377ce023

$1,240.00/year for institutions. Journal promoting scientific investigation, technical advancements and information exchange on energetic materials and chemical propulsion.

8599 ■ *Journal of Women and Minorities in Science and Engineering*
Begell House Inc.
50 Cross Hwy.
Redding, CT 06896
Ph: (203)938-1300
Fax: (203)938-1304
URL: http://www.begellhouse.com/journals/ 00551c876cc2f027

$248.00/year for institutions. Peer-reviewed journal featuring innovative ideas and programs for classroom teachers, scientific studies, and formulation of concepts related to the education, recruitment, and retention of under-represented groups in science and engineering.

8600 ■ *NSBE Magazine*
NSBE Publications
205 Daingerfield Rd.
Alexandria, VA 22314
Ph: (703)549-2207
Fax: (703)683-5312
URL: http://www.nsbe.org/News-Media/Magazines/ About-NSBE-Magazine

$20.00/year for individuals; $35.00/year for other countries; $15.00/year for students. Journal providing information on engineering careers, self-development, and cultural issues for recent graduates with technical majors.

8601 ■ *Nuclear Plant Journal*
Nuclear Plant Journal
1400 Opus Pl., Ste. 904
Downers Grove, IL 60515
Ph: (630)858-6161
Fax: (630)858-8787
E-mail: npj@goinfo.com
URL: http://www.nuclearplantjournal.com

Bimonthly. Free, to industry professionals. Magazine focusing on nuclear power plants.

8602 ■ *PE*
National Society of Professional Engineers
1420 King St.
Alexandria, VA 22314
Ph: (703)684-2800
Fax: (703)684-4875
URL: http://www.nspe.org/PEmagazine/index.html

Monthly. Magazine (tabloid) covering professional, legislative, and techology issues for an engineering audience.

8603 ■ *Power Engineering*
PennWell Corp.
1421 S Sheridan Rd.
Tulsa, OK 74112
Ph: (918)835-3161
Fax: (918)831-9497
Fr: 800-331-4463
E-mail: pe@pennwell.com
URL: http://www.powergenworldwide.com/index.html

Monthly. $88.00/year for U.S.; $98.00/year for Canada and Mexico; $242.00/year for other countries. Magazine focusing on power generation.

8604 ■ *Radwaste Solutions*
American Nuclear Society
555 N Kensington Ave.
La Grange Park, IL 60526-5535
Ph: (708)352-6611
Fax: (708)352-0499
Fr: 800-323-3044
URL: http://www.new.ans.org/pubs/magazines/rs/

$460.00/year for individuals, print. Magazine promoting awareness and understanding of the application of nuclear science and technology.

8605 ■ *Sustainable Facility*
BNP Media
2401 W Big Beaver Rd., Ste. 700
Troy, MI 48084-3333
Ph: (847)763-9534
Fax: (847)763-9538
URL: http://www.sustainablefacility.com/

Monthly. Magazine reporting on the energy management market as it relates to commercial, industrial, and institutional facilities.

8606 ■ *SWE, Magazine of the Society of Women Engineers*
Society of Women Engineers
120 S La Salle St., Ste. 1515
Chicago, IL 60603
Ph: (312)596-5223
Fr: 877-793-4636
URL: http://societyofwomenengineers.swe.org/index.php

Quarterly. $30.00/year for nonmembers. Magazine for engineering students and for women and men working in the engineering and technology fields. Covers career guidance, continuing development and topical issues.

8607 ■ *WEPANEWS*
Women in Engineering Programs & Advocates Network
1901 E Asbury Ave., Ste. 220
Denver, CO 80208
Ph: (303)871-4643
Fax: (303)871-4628
E-mail: dmatt@wepan.org
URL: http://www.wepan.org

Description: 2/year. Seeks to provide greater access for women to careers in engineering. Includes news of graduate, undergraduate, freshmen, pre-college, and re-entry engineering programs for women. Recurring features include job listings, faculty, grant, and conference news, international engineering program news, action group news, notices of publications available, and a column titled Kudos.

8608 ■ *Woman Engineer*
Equal Opportunity Publications, Inc.
445 Broadhollow Rd., Ste. 425
Melville, NY 11747
Ph: (631)421-9421
Fax: (631)421-1352
E-mail: info@eop.com
URL: http://www.eop.com

Annual. Magazine that is offered at no charge to qualified female engineering, computer-science, and information-technology students and professionals seeking to find employment and advancement in their careers.

EMPLOYER DIRECTORIES AND NETWORKING LISTS

8609 ■ *American Men and Women of Science*
Gale
PO Box 6904
Florence, KY 41022-6904
Fr: 800-354-9706
URL: http://www.gale.cengage.com

Biennial, even years; New edition expected 29th, June 2011. $1,368.00 for individuals. Covers: Over 135,000 U.S. and Canadian scientists active in the physical, biological, mathematical, computer science, and engineering fields; includes references to previous edition for deceased scientists and nonrespondents. Entries include: Name, address, education, personal and career data, memberships, honors and awards, research interest. Arrangement: Alphabetical. Indexes: Discipline (in separate volume).

8610 ■ *Careers in Focus—Engineering*
Facts On File Inc.
132 W 31st St., 17th Fl.
New York, NY 10001
Ph: (212)967-8800
Fax: 800-678-3633
Fr: 800-322-8755
URL: http://www.infobasepublishing.com

Latest edition 3rd; Published July, 2007. $32.95 for individuals. Covers: An overview of engineering, followed by a selection of jobs profiled in detail, includ-

ing the nature of the job, earnings, prospects for employment, what kind of training and skills it requires, and sources for further information.

8611 ■ *Directory of Contract Staffing Firms*
C.E. Publications Inc.
PO Box 3006
Bothell, WA 98041-3006
Ph: (425)806-5200
Fax: (425)806-5585
URL: http://www.cjhunter.com/dcsf/overview.html

Annual. Covers: Nearly 1,300 contract firms actively engaged in the employment of engineering, IT/IS, and technical personnel for 'temporary' contract assignments throughout the world. Entries include: Company name, address, phone, name of contact, email, web address. Arrangement: Alphabetical. Indexes: Geographical.

8612 ■ *Indiana Society of Professional Engineers—Directory*
Indiana Society of Professional Engineers
PO Box 20806
Indianapolis, IN 46220
Ph: (317)255-2267
Fax: (317)255-2530
URL: http://www.indspe.org

Annual, fall. Covers: Member registered engineers, land surveyors, engineering students, and engineers in training. Entries include: Member name, address, phone, type of membership, business information, specialty. Arrangement: Alpha by chapter area.

HANDBOOKS AND MANUALS

8613 ■ *Great Jobs for Engineering Majors*
The McGraw-Hill Companies
PO Box 182604
Columbus, OH 43272
Fax: (614)759-3749
Fr: 877-883-5524
E-mail: customer.service@mcgraw-hill.com
URL: http://www.mhprofessional.com/product.php?isbn=0071641963

Geraldine O. Garner. Second edition, 2008. $16.95. 192 pages. Covers all the career options open to students majoring in engineering.

8614 ■ *Resumes for Scientific and Technical Careers*
The McGraw-Hill Companies
PO Box 182604
Columbus, OH 43272
Fax: (614)759-3749
Fr: 877-883-5524
E-mail: customer.service@mcgraw-hill.com
URL: http://www.mhprofessional.com/product.php?isbn=0071482199

Third edition, 2007. $12.95 (paper). 144 pages. Provides resume advice for individuals interested in working in scientific and technical careers. Includes sample resumes and cover letters.

EMPLOYMENT AGENCIES AND SEARCH FIRMS

8615 ■ *Engineer One, Inc.*
PO Box 23037
Knoxville, TN 37933
Fax: (865)691-0110
E-mail: engineerone@engineerone.com
URL: http://www.engineerone.com

Engineering employment service specializing in engineering and management in the chemical process, power utilities, manufacturing, mechanical, electrical, and electronic industries. Maintains an Information Technology Division that works nationwide across all industries. Also provides systems

analysis consulting services specializing in VAX based systems.

8616 ■ *Global Employment Solutions*
10375 Park Meadows Dr., Ste. 375
Littleton, CO 80124
Ph: (303)216-9500
Fax: (303)216-9533
URL: http://www.gesnetwork.com

Employment agency.

8617 ■ *International Staffing Consultants*
31655 2nd Ave.
Laguna Beach, CA 92651
Ph: (949)255-5857
Fax: (949)767-5959
E-mail: iscinc@iscworld.com
URL: http://www.iscworld.com

Employment agency. Provides placement on regular or temporary basis. Affiliate office in London.

ONLINE JOB SOURCES AND SERVICES

8618 ■ *AlternativeEnergyJobStore.com*
URL: http://www.alternativeenergyjobstore.com

Description: Provides alternative energy jobs including solar, wind, biomass, hydropower, geothermal, and renewable energy nationwide. Features job videos, search agents, salary information, salary surveys, resume tips, news, educational programs, and other career resources.

8619 ■ *EnergyCentralJobs.com*
E-mail: service@energycentral.com
URL: http://www.energycentraljobs.com

Description: Serves as an on-line job resource for candidates and power companies worldwide. Maintains a job search database dedicated to the power, nuclear, oil and gas career fields.

8620 ■ *EngineerJobs.com*
URL: http://www.engineerjobs.com

Description: Provides job opportunities for engineering professionals in the following disciplines: aerospace, agricultural, biomedical, chemical, civil, electrical, environmental, industrial, manufacturing, marine, materials, mechanical, mining, nuclear, petroleum, process, project, quality, sales, software, solar, systems, and structural.

8621 ■ *Nuclear Engineering Jobs*
URL: http://www.nuclearengineeringjobs.org

Description: Provides career opportunities for nuclear engineering professionals. Features updated job listings for candidates and job posting for employers.

8622 ■ *Nuclear Jobs*
URL: http://www.nukejob.net

Description: Serves as an online tool that helps job seekers find information and postings related to nuclear career opportunities.

8623 ■ *Nuclear Street*
URL: http://nuclearstreet.com

Description: Features news, jobs, careers, and companies in the nuclear power industry. Maintains an online forum and provides job hunting tools for industry professionals.

8624 ■ *NuclearEngineerJobs.com*
URL: http://www.nuclearengineerjobs.com

Description: Lists job openings and employment opportunities for nuclear engineers.

8625 ■ *NuclearMarket.com*
E-mail: info@nuclearmarket.com
URL: http://www.nuclearmarket.com

Description: Nuclear Market's Career Center allows seekers to search a database of nuclear jobs in the

United States, Europe and beyond. Candidates also have the option of registering their profile in database in order to receive email notification of any relevant vacancies.

8626 ■ NukeWorker.com
URL: http://www.nukeworker.com

Description: Serves as a job site for nuclear power workers. Features job listings and resume posting.

8627 ■ PowerPlantPro.com
E-mail: support@powerplantpro.com
URL: http://www.powerplantpro.com/main/sendform/4/18/3472

Description: Dedicated to professionals in the power and energy industry. Features career advice and employer listings.

8628 ■ Spherion
2050 Spectrum Blvd.
Fort Lauderdale, FL 33309
Ph: (954)308-7600
Fr: 800-774-3746
E-mail: help@spherion.com
URL: http://www.spherion.com

Description: Recruitment firm specializing in accounting and finance, sales and marketing, interim executives, technology, engineering, retail and human resources.

8629 ■ ThinkEnergyGroup.com
E-mail: resumes@thinkjobs.com
URL: http://www.thinkenergygroup.com

Description: Serves as a job board for professionals looking for positions in engineering, power plant, energy, and technical fields. Contains advice and tips on interviews, job searching, resume writing, hiring, and management. Provides choices of work location, pay rates in the field of expertise and contract, temp-to-hire, and direct hiring options.

OTHER SOURCES

8630 ■ American Association of Blacks in Energy (AABE)
1625 K St. NW, Ste. 405
Washington, DC 20006
Ph: (202)371-9530
Fax: (202)371-9218
Fr: 800-466-0204
E-mail: info@aabe.org
URL: http://www.aabe.org

Description: Seeks to increase the knowledge, understanding, and awareness of the minority community in energy issues by serving as an energy information source for policymakers, recommending blacks and other minorities to appropriate energy officials and executives, encouraging students to pursue professional careers in the energy industry, and advocating the participation of blacks and other minorities in energy programs and policymaking activities. Updates members on key legislation and regulations being developed by the Department of Energy, the Department of Interior, the Department of Commerce, the Small Business Administration, and other federal and state agencies.

8631 ■ American Association of Engineering Societies (AAES)
1801 Alexander Bell Dr.
Reston, VA 20191
Ph: (202)296-2237
Fax: (202)296-1151
Fr: 888-400-2237
E-mail: dbateson@aaes.org
URL: http://www.aaes.org

Description: Coordinates the efforts of the member societies in the provision of reliable and objective information to the general public concerning issues which affect the engineering profession and the field of engineering as a whole; collects, analyzes, documents, and disseminates data which will inform the general public of the relationship between engineering and the national welfare; provides a forum for the engineering societies to exchange and discuss their views on matters of common interest; and represents the U.S. engineering community abroad through representation in WFEO and UPADI.

8632 ■ American Engineering Association (AEA)
533 Waterside Blvd.
Monroe Township, NJ 08831
Ph: (201)664-6954
E-mail: aea@aea.org
URL: http://www.aea.org

Description: Members consist of Engineers and engineering professionals. Purpose to advance the engineering profession and U.S. engineering capabilities. Issues of concern include age discrimination, immigration laws, displacement of U.S. Engineers by foreign workers, trade agreements, off shoring of U.S. Engineering and manufacturing jobs, loss of U.S. manufacturing and engineering capability, and recruitment of foreign students. Testifies before Congress. Holds local Chapter meetings.

8633 ■ American Indian Science and Engineering Society (AISES)
PO Box 9828
Albuquerque, NM 87119-9828
Ph: (505)765-1052
Fax: (505)765-5608
E-mail: info@aises.org
URL: http://www.aises.org

Description: Represents American Indian and non-Indian students and professionals in science, technology, and engineering fields; corporations representing energy, mining, aerospace, electronic, and computer fields. Seeks to motivate and encourage students to pursue undergraduate and graduate studies in science, engineering, and technology. Sponsors science fairs in grade schools, teacher training workshops, summer math/science sessions for 8th-12th graders, professional chapters, and student chapters in colleges. Offers scholarships. Adult members serve as role models, advisers, and mentors for students. Operates placement service.

8634 ■ American Nuclear Society (ANS)
555 N Kensington Ave.
La Grange Park, IL 60526
Ph: (708)352-6611
Fax: (708)352-0499
Fr: 800-323-3044
E-mail: members@ans.org
URL: http://www.new.ans.org

Description: Physicists, chemists, educators, mathematicians, life scientists, engineers, metallurgists, managers, and administrators with professional experience in nuclear science or nuclear engineering. Works to advance science and engineering in the nuclear industry. Disseminates information; promotes research; conducts meetings devoted to scientific and technical papers; works with government agencies, educational institutions, and other organizations dealing with nuclear issues.

8635 ■ Association for International Practical Training (AIPT)
10400 Little Patuxent Pkwy., Ste. 250
Columbia, MD 21044-3519
Ph: (410)997-2200
Fax: (410)992-3924
E-mail: aipt@aipt.org
URL: http://www.aipt.org

Description: Providers worldwide of on-the-job training programs for students and professionals seeking international career development and life-changing experiences. Arranges workplace exchanges in hundreds of professional fields, bringing employers and trainees together from around the world. Client list ranges from small farming communities to Fortune 500 companies.

8636 ■ Engineering Society of Detroit (ESD)
20700 Civic Center Dr., Ste. 450
Southfield, MI 48076
Ph: (248)353-0735
Fax: (248)353-0736
E-mail: esd@esd.org
URL: http://ww2.esd.org/home.htm

Description: Engineers from all disciplines; scientists and technologists. Conducts technical programs and engineering refresher courses; sponsors conferences and expositions. Maintains speakers' bureau; offers placement services; although based in Detroit, MI, society membership is international.

8637 ■ Korean-American Scientists and Engineers Association (KSEA)
1952 Gallows Rd., Ste. 300
Vienna, VA 22182
Ph: (703)748-1221
Fax: (703)748-1331
E-mail: sejong@ksea.org
URL: http://www.ksea.org

Description: Represents scientists and engineers holding single or advanced degrees. Promotes friendship and mutuality among Korean and American scientists and engineers; contributes to Korea's scientific, technological, industrial, and economic developments; strengthens the scientific, technological, and cultural bonds between Korea and the U.S. Sponsors symposium. Maintains speakers' bureau, placement service, and biographical archives. Compiles statistics.

8638 ■ National Action Council for Minorities in Engineering (NACME)
440 Hamilton Ave., Ste. 302
White Plains, NY 10601-1813
Ph: (914)539-4010
Fax: (914)539-4032
E-mail: info@nacme.org
URL: http://www.nacme.org

Description: Leads the national effort to increase access to careers in engineering and other science-based disciplines. Conducts research and public policy analysis, develops and operates national demonstration programs at precollege and university levels, and disseminates information through publications, conferences and electronic media. Serves as a privately funded source of scholarships for minority students in engineering.

8639 ■ National Society of Professional Engineers (NSPE)
1420 King St.
Alexandria, VA 22314-2794
Ph: (703)684-2800
Fax: (703)836-4875
Fr: 888-285-6773
E-mail: memserv@nspe.org
URL: http://www.nspe.org

Description: Represents professional engineers and engineers-in-training in all fields registered in accordance with the laws of states or territories of the U.S. or provinces of Canada; qualified graduate engineers, student members, and registered land surveyors. Is concerned with social, professional, ethical, and economic considerations of engineering as a profession; encompasses programs in public relations, employment practices, ethical considerations, education, and career guidance. Monitors legislative and regulatory actions of interest to the engineering profession.

8640 ■ Nuclear Energy Institute
1776 I St. NW, Ste. 400
Washington, DC 20006
Ph: (202)739-8000
Fax: (202)785-4019
URL: http://www.nei.org

Description: Serves as the policy organization for the nuclear energy and technologies industry. Promotes the beneficial uses of nuclear energy and technologies in the United States and around the world. Develops policies on key legislative and regulatory issues affecting the industry.

8641 ■ Radiochemistry Society
PO Box 3091
Richland, WA 99354
Fr: 800-371-0542
E-mail: rad-info@radiochemistry.org
URL: http://www.radiochemistry.org

Description: Aims to promote education and public outreach for the safe use, handling and benefits of radioisotopes in security, energy, agriculture, environment, food safety and medicine. Conducts seminars, trainings, scholarships, meetings and exchange of scientific information.

8642 ■ Society of Hispanic Professional Engineers (SHPE)
13181 Crossroads Pkwy. N, Ste. 450
City of Industry, CA 91746-3496
Ph: (323)725-3970
Fax: (323)725-0316
E-mail: shpenational@shpe.org
URL: http://oneshpe.shpe.org/wps/portal/national

Description: Represents engineers, student engineers, and scientists. Aims to increase the number of Hispanic engineers by providing motivation and support to students. Sponsors competitions and educational programs. Maintains placement service and speakers' bureau; compiles statistics.

8643 ■ Society of Women Engineers (SWE)
203 N La Salle St., Ste. 1675
Chicago, IL 60601
Ph: (312)596-5223
Fax: (312)596-5252
Fr: 877-SWE-INFO
E-mail: hq@swe.org
URL: http://societyofwomenengineers.swe.org

Description: Educational and service organization representing both students and professional women in engineering and technical fields.

8644 ■ Young Professionals in Energy (YPE)
600 Travis St., Ste. 2310
Houston, TX 77002
Ph: (832)429-6344
E-mail: contact@ypenergy.org
URL: http://www.ypenergy.org

Description: Facilitates the advancement of young professionals in the energy industry around the world. Provides a forum for networking and career development for professionals in the energy industry.

SOURCES OF HELP-WANTED ADS

8645 ■ Applied Radiation and Isotopes
Mosby Inc.
11830 Westline Industrial Dr.
St. Louis, MO 63146-3326
Ph: (314)872-8370
Fax: (314)432-1380
Fr: 800-325-4177
URL: http://www.elsevier.com/wps/find/
journaldescription.cws_home

Monthly. $3,616.00/year for institutions, for all countries except Europe, Japan and Iran; $3,230.00/year for institutions, for European countries and Iran; $429,300.00/year for institutions. Journal for radiologists.

8646 ■ ASTRO News
American Society for Therapeutic Radiology and Oncology
8280 Willow Oaks Corporate Dr., Ste. 500
Fairfax, VA 22031
Ph: (703)502-1550
Fax: (703)502-7852
Fr: 800-962-7876
URL: http://www.astro.org/publications/astronews/

Quarterly. Included in membership. Professional magazine covering radiology.

8647 ■ Clinical Nuclear Medicine
Lippincott Williams & Wilkins
530 Walnut St.
Philadelphia, PA 19106-3619
Ph: (215)521-8300
Fax: (215)521-8902
Fr: 800-638-3030
E-mail: cnm.mlk@verizon.net
URL: http://journals.lww.com/nuclearmed/pages/
default.aspx

Monthly. $410.00/year for individuals; $844.00/year for institutions; $576.00/year for other countries; $1,051.00/year for institutions, other countries; $234.10/year for other countries, in-training; $211.00/year for individuals, in-training. Journal publishing original manuscripts about scanning, imaging, and related subjects.

8648 ■ CME Supplement to Radiologic Clinics of North America
Elsevier Science Inc.
360 Park Ave. S
New York, NY 10010-1710
Ph: (212)989-5800
Fax: (212)633-3990
Fr: 888-437-4636
URL: http://www.elsevier.com/wps/find/
journaldescription.cws_home

$283.00/year for individuals; $283.00/year for other countries. Journal covering radiology, nuclear medicine and medical imaging.

8649 ■ Diagnostic Imaging
United business Media L.L.C
240 W 35th St.
New York, NY 10001
Ph: (516)562-5000
URL: http://www.diagnosticimaging.com/

Monthly. News and analysis on clinical and economic developments in medical imaging.

8650 ■ Journal of Nuclear Medicine Technology
Society of Nuclear Medicine Inc.
1850 Samuel Morse Dr.
Reston, VA 20190
Ph: (703)708-9000
Fax: (703)708-9015
Fr: 800-487-5620
URL: http://tech.snmjournals.org

Quarterly. $117.00/year for individuals, print & online; $126.00/year for by mail, overseas; $198.00/year for institutions. Peer-reviewed scientific journal for technologists presenting original research, clinical reports, continuing education articles, and commentary on scientific trends and discoveries in nuclear medicine.

8651 ■ Magnetic Resonance Imaging Clinics
Mosby Inc.
11830 Westline Industrial Dr.
St. Louis, MO 63146-3326
Ph: (314)872-8370
Fax: (314)432-1380
Fr: 800-325-4177
URL: http://www.mri.theclinics.com

Quarterly. $448.00/year for other countries; $628.00/year for institutions, other countries; $228.00/year for students, other countries; $309.00/year for individuals; $501.00/year for institutions; $158.00/year for students; $628.00/year for institutions, Canada; $228.00/year for students, Canada; $345.00/year for Canada. Journal publishing articles and research on the latest trends in magnetic resonance imagining clinics and patient management.

8652 ■ Magnetic Resonance in Medicine
International Society for Magnetic Resonance in Medicine
2030 Addison St., 7th Fl.
Berkeley, CA 94704
Ph: (510)841-1899
Fax: (510)841-2340
URL: http://www.ismrm.org/journals.htm

Monthly. $903.00/year for individuals, online; $903.00/year for Canada and Mexico, online; $903.00/year for other countries, online; $2,714.00/year for institutions, print or online; $3,121.00/year for institutions, Canada and Mexico; $3,373.00/year for institutions, other countries, print & online. Journal covering radiology worldwide.

8653 ■ Neuroimaging Clinics of North America
Mosby Inc.
11830 Westline Industrial Dr.
St. Louis, MO 63146-3326
Ph: (314)872-8370
Fax: (314)432-1380
Fr: 800-325-4177
URL: http://www.neuroimaging.theclinics.com

Quarterly. $546.00/year for institutions, international; $461.00/year for individuals, international; $226.00/year for students, international; $436.00/year for institutions, U.S.; $158.00/year for students, U.S.; $363.00/year for individuals, Canada; $226.00/year for students, Canada; $546.00/year for institutions, Canada. Journal publishing articles on newest advances in neuroimaging and patient treatment options.

8654 ■ Practical Radiation Oncology
Elsevier
1600 John F. Kennedy Blvd., Ste. 1800
Philadelphia, PA 19103-2822
Ph: (215)239-3900
Fax: (215)238-7883
E-mail: pro@astro.org
URL: http://www.practicalradonc.org/

Peer-reviewed journal featuring information about radiation oncology practice.

8655 ■ Radiologic Clinics of North America
Mountain Association for Community Economic Development
433 Chestnut St.
Berea, KY 40403-1510
Ph: (859)986-2373
Fax: (859)986-1299
URL: http://www.radiologic.theclinics.com

$386.00/year for individuals; $185.00/year for students; $450.00/year for Canada; $266.00/year for students, Canada; $556.00/year for other countries; $266.00/year for students, other countries. Journal publishing articles written by leading experts, along with high-quality reproductions of radiographs, MR images, CT scans and sonograms.

8656 ■ Radiologic Technology
American Society of Radiologic Technologists
15000 Central Ave. SE
Albuquerque, NM 87123-3909
Ph: (505)298-4500
Fax: (505)298-5063
Fr: 800-444-2778
E-mail: communications@asrt.org
URL: http://www.asrt.org/content/Publications/
radiologictechnolo

Bimonthly. $60.00/year for individuals; $90.00/year for other countries; $108.00/year for two years; $162.00/year for two years, other countries; $108.00/year for institutions, 2 years. Medical imaging technology. Includes annual index.

8657 ■ Seminars in Roentgenology

Mosby Inc.
11830 Westline Industrial Dr.
St. Louis, MO 63146-3326
Ph: (314)872-8370
Fax: (314)432-1380
Fr: 800-325-4177
URL: http://www.seminarsinroentgenology.com/

Quarterly. $286.00/year for individuals, U.S.; $144.00/year for students, U.S.; $440.00/year for other countries; $220.00/year for students, other countries; $500.00/year for institutions; $633.00/year for institutions, other countries. Journal covering for the practicing radiologist and for the resident.

EMPLOYER DIRECTORIES AND NETWORKING LISTS

8658 ■ Crain's List—Chicago's Largest Hospitals

Crain Communications Inc.
360 N Michigan Ave.
Chicago, IL 60601
Ph: (312)649-5200
URL: http://www.chicagobusiness.com/section/lists

Published November, 2010. $25.00 for individuals; $45.00 for individuals. Covers: 25 hospitals in Chicago area ranked by net patient revenues. Entries include: Name, address, phone number, fax, web address, corporate e-mail, hospital administrator, network affiliation, 2009 net patient revenue, percentage change from 2008, 2009 net profits, percentage change from 2008, inpatient days, available beds, daily occupancy rate, number of hospital employees as of December 31, 2009, fiscal year end, Chairman, President, CEO, Chief Financial Officer, Human Resources Manager, Media Relations/Public Relations Director, and Hospital Administrator.

8659 ■ Directory of Hospital Personnel

Grey House Publishing
4919 Rte. 22
PO Box 56
Amenia, NY 12501
Ph: (518)789-8700
Fax: (518)789-0556
Fr: 800-562-2139
URL: http://www.greyhouse.com/hospital_
personnel.htm

Annual, Latest edition 2011. $325.00 for individuals. Covers: 200,000 executives at 6,000 U.S. Hospitals. Entries include: Name of hospital, address, phone, number of beds, type and JCAHO status of hospital, names and titles of key department heads and staff, medical and nursing school affiliations; number of residents, interns, and nursing students. Arrangement: Geographical. Indexes: Hospital name, personnel, hospital size.

8660 ■ Hospital Blue Book

Billian Publishing Inc. and Trans World Publishing Inc.
2100 River Edge Pky.
Atlanta, GA 30328
Ph: (770)955-5656
Fax: (770)952-0669
Fr: 800-800-5668
E-mail: blu-book@billian.com
URL: http://www.billianshealthdata.com/Products/
bluebook.html

Annual, Latest edition 2010. $575.00 for individuals; $575.00 for individuals. Covers: More than 6,500 hospitals; some listings also appear in a separate southern edition of this publication. Entries include: Name of hospital, accreditation, mailing address, phone, fax, number of beds, type of facility (nonprofit, general, state, etc.); list of administrative personnel and chiefs of medical services, with specific titles. Arrangement: Geographical.

8661 ■ Medical and Health Information Directory

Gale
PO Box 6904
Florence, KY 41022-6904
Fr: 800-354-9706
URL: http://www.gale.cengage.com

Annual, Latest edition April 2011. $1190.00 for individuals; $501.00 for individuals. Covers: In volume 1, more than 33,000 medical and health oriented associations, organizations, institutions, and government agencies, including health maintenance organizations (HMOs), preferred provider organizations (PPOs), insurance companies, pharmaceutical companies, research centers, and medical and allied health schools. In Volume 2, over 20,000 medical book publishers; medical periodicals, directories, audiovisual producers and services, medical libraries and information centers, electronic resources, and health-related internet search engines. In Volume 3, more than 40,500 clinics, treatment centers, care programs, and counseling/diagnostic services for 34 subject areas. Entries include: Institution, service, or firm name, address, phone, fax, email and URL; many include names of key personnel and, when pertinent, descriptive annotation. Volume 3 was formerly listed separately as Health Services Directory. Arrangement: Classified by organization activity, service, etc. Indexes: Each volume has a complete alphabetical name and keyword index.

HANDBOOKS AND MANUALS

8662 ■ Careers in Health Care

The McGraw-Hill Companies
PO Box 182604
Columbus, OH 43272
Fax: (614)759-3749
Fr: 877-883-5524
E-mail: customer.service@mcgraw-hill.com
URL: http://www.mhprofessional.com/
product.php?isbn=0071466533

Barbara M. Swanson. Fifth edition, 2005. $19.95 (paper). 192 pages. Describes job duties, work settings, salaries, licensing and certification requirements, educational preparation, and future outlook. Gives ideas on how to secure a job.

8663 ■ Expert Resumes for Health Care Careers

Jist Works
875 Montreal Way
St. Paul, MN 55102
Fr: 800-648-5478
E-mail: educate@emcp.com
URL: http://www.jist.com

Wendy S. Enelow and Louise M. Kursmark. 2010. $16.95. 288 pages.

8664 ■ Health Careers Today

Elsevier
11830 Westline Industrial Dr.
St. Louis, MO 63146
Ph: (314)453-7010
Fax: (314)453-7095
Fr: 800-545-2522
E-mail: usbkinfo@elsevier.com
URL: http://www.elsevier.com

Gerdin, Judith. Fourth edition. 2007. $74.95. 496 pages. Covers more than 45 health careers. Discusses the roles and responsibilities of various occupations and provides a solid foundation in the skills needed for all health careers.

8665 ■ Opportunities in Health and Medical Careers

The McGraw-Hill Companies
PO Box 182604
Columbus, OH 43272
Fax: (614)759-3749

Fr: 877-883-5524
E-mail: customer.service@mcgraw-hill.com
URL: http://www.mcgraw-hill.com/
product.php?isbn=0071437274

I. Donald Snook, Jr. and Leo D'Orazio. 2004. $14.95 (paper). 157 pages. Covers the full range of medical and health occupations. Illustrated.

8666 ■ Resumes for Health and Medical Careers

The McGraw-Hill Companies
PO Box 182604
Columbus, OH 43272
Fax: (614)759-3749
Fr: 877-883-5524
E-mail: customer.service@mcgraw-hill.com
URL: http://www.mhprofessional.com/
product.php?isbn=0071545352

Third edition, 2008. $12.95 (paper). 144 pages.

EMPLOYMENT AGENCIES AND SEARCH FIRMS

8667 ■ JPM International

26034 Acero
Mission Viejo, CA 92691
Ph: (949)699-4300
Fax: (949)699-4333
Fr: 800-685-7856
E-mail: qtek37@yahoo.com
URL: http://www.jpmintl.com/pages/qss.html

Executive search firm and employment agency.

8668 ■ MedTeam Staffing

160 International Pkwy., Ste. 110
Heathrow, FL 32746
Ph: (407)936-0411
Fax: (407)936-0417
Fr: 888-864-3030
E-mail: info@medteamstaffing.com
URL: http://www.medteamstaffing.com

Description: Specializes in the nationwide recruitment of healthcare professionals. Offers employment opportunities for radiology, ultrasound, nuclear medicine and related allied health careers.

ONLINE JOB SOURCES AND SERVICES

8669 ■ HEALTHeCAREERS Network

Fr: 888-884-8242
E-mail: info@healthecareers.com
URL: http://www.healthecareers.com

Description: Career search site for jobs in all health care specialties; educational resources; visa and licensing information for relocation; interesting articles; relocation tools; links to professional organizations and general resources.

8670 ■ Hot Radiology Jobs

E-mail: info@hotradiologyjobs.com
URL: http://www.hotradiologyjobs.com

Description: Provides a database of job listings in the field of radiology. Features a resume database for its users.

8671 ■ Nuclear Jobs

URL: http://www.nukejob.net

Description: Serves as an online tool that helps job seekers find information and postings related to nuclear career opportunities.

8672 ■ Nuclear Medicine Tech Jobs

URL: http://www.nuclearmedicinetechjobs.com

Description: Serves as a niche job board for nuclear medicine technologists. Offers employment opportunities and candidate recruiting.

8673 ■ ProHealthJobs.com
Ph: (484)443-8545
Fax: (484)443-8549
E-mail: info@prohealthjobs.com
URL: http://prohealthjobs.com/jobboard

Description: Career resources site for the medical and health care field. Lists professional opportunities, product information, continuing education and open positions.

TRADESHOWS

8674 ■ American Association of Physicists in Medicine Annual Meeting
American Association of Physicists in Medicine
1 Physics Ellipse
College Park, MD 20740-3846
Ph: (301)209-3350
Fax: (301)209-0862
E-mail: 2011.aapm@aapm.org
URL: http://www.aapm.org

Annual. Primary Exhibits: Radiation therapy, diagnostic radiology, radiation protection, hyperthermia, nuclear medicine, and magnetic resonance imaging. Dates and Locations: 2012 Jul 29 - Aug 02; Charlotte, NC; 2013 Aug 04-08; Indianapolis, IN; 2014 Jul 20-24; Austin, TX; 2015 Jul 12-16; Anaheim, CA.

8675 ■ Society of Nuclear Medicine Annual Meeting
Society of Nuclear Medicine
1850 Samuel Morse Dr.
Reston, VA 20190-5316
Ph: (703)708-9000
Fax: (703)708-9015
URL: http://interactive.snm.org

Annual. Primary Exhibits: Nuclear medicine equipment, supplies, and services and radiopharmaceuticals.

OTHER SOURCES

8676 ■ American Association for Women Radiologists
4550 Post Oak Pl., Ste. 342
Houston, TX 77027

Ph: (713)965-0566
Fax: (713)960-0488
E-mail: admin@aawr.org
URL: http://www.aawr.org

Description: Physicians involved in diagnostic or therapeutic radiology, nuclear medicine, or radiologic physics. Serves as resource organization for women in the practice of radiology and medicine and as a support for women training in radiology. Provides a forum wherein radiologists can consider, discuss, develop and disseminate knowledge and information concerning the fields of radiology and medicine. Sponsors meetings, forums, seminars and educational institutes dealing with the subject of radiology and related topics.

8677 ■ American Registry of Radiologic Technologists (ARRT)
1255 Northland Dr.
St. Paul, MN 55120-1155
Ph: (651)687-0048
URL: http://www.arrt.org

Description: Radiologic technologist certification board that administers examinations, issues certificates of registration to radiographers, nuclear medicine technologists, and radiation therapists, and investigates the qualifications of practicing radiologic technologists. Governed by trustees appointed from American College of Radiology and American Society of Radiologic Technologists.

8678 ■ American Society of Radiologic Technologists (ASRT)
15000 Central Ave. SE
Albuquerque, NM 87123-3909
Ph: (505)298-4500
Fax: (505)298-5063
Fr: 800-444-2778
E-mail: memberservices@asrt.org
URL: http://www.asrt.org

Description: Serves as professional society of diagnostic radiography, radiation therapy, ultrasound, and nuclear medicine technologists. Advances the science of radiologic technology; establishes and maintains high standards of education; evaluates the quality of patient care; improves the welfare and socioeconomics of radiologic technologists. Operates ASRT Education and Research Foundation, which

provides educational materials to radiologic technologists.

8679 ■ Nuclear Medicine Technology Certification Board (NMTCB)
3558 Habersham at Northlake, Bldg. I
Tucker, GA 30084
Ph: (404)315-1739
Fax: (404)315-6502
Fr: 800-659-3953
E-mail: board@nmtcb.org
URL: http://www.nmtcb.org

Description: Aims to provide for the certification of nuclear medical technologists and to develop, assess, and administer basic and specialty examinations relevant to nuclear medicine technology.

8680 ■ Radiochemistry Society
PO Box 3091
Richland, WA 99354
Fr: 800-371-0542
E-mail: rad-info@radiochemistry.org
URL: http://www.radiochemistry.org

Description: Aims to promote education and public outreach for the safe use, handling and benefits of radioisotopes in security, energy, agriculture, environment, food safety and medicine. Conducts seminars, trainings, scholarships, meetings and exchange of scientific information.

8681 ■ Society of Nuclear Medicine (SNM)
1850 Samuel Morse Dr.
Reston, VA 20190-5316
Ph: (703)708-9000
Fax: (703)708-9015
E-mail: feedback@snm.org
URL: http://www.snm.org

Description: Serves as professional society of physicians, physicists, chemists, radiopharmacists, nuclear medicine technologists, and others interested in nuclear medicine, nuclear magnetic resonance, and the use of radioactive isotopes in clinical practice, research, and teaching. Disseminates information concerning the utilization of nuclear phenomena in the diagnosis and treatment of disease. Oversees the Technologist Section of the Society of Nuclear Medicine.

SOURCES OF HELP-WANTED ADS

8682 ■ AAAP News
American Academy of Addiction Psychiatry
400 Massasoit Ave., Ste. 307, 2nd Fl.
East Providence, RI 02914
Ph: (401)524-3076
Fax: (401)272-0922
URL: http://www2.aaap.org/advertising/newsletter-
   advertising

$45.00/year for individuals, per year; $15.00/year for individuals, per issue; $50.00/year for individuals, international; $20.00/year for individuals, per issue. Professional journal covering addiction psychiatry.

8683 ■ AANA Journal
AANA Publishing Inc.
222 S Prospect Ave.
Park Ridge, IL 60068-4001
Ph: (847)692-7050
Fax: (847)692-6968
URL: http://www.aana.com/
   Resources.aspx?id=5324&linkidentifier=id

Bimonthly. Nursing and anesthesia journal.

8684 ■ AAOHN Journal
SLACK Incorporated
6900 Grove Rd.
Thorofare, NJ 08086-9447
Ph: (856)848-1000
Fax: (856)848-6091
E-mail: aaohn@slackinc.com
URL: http://www.slackjournals.com/aaohn

Monthly. $115.00/year for individuals; $230.00/year for individuals, two years; $345.00/year for individuals, three years; $259.00/year for institutions; $518.00/year for institutions, two years; $777.00/year for institutions, three years; $29.00/year for single issue. Official journal of the American Association of Occupational Health Nurses.

8685 ■ Academic Psychiatry
American Psychiatric Publishing Inc.
1000 Wilson Blvd., Ste. 1825
Arlington, VA 22209-3924
Ph: (703)907-7322
Fax: (703)907-1091
Fr: 800-368-5777
URL: http://ap.psychiatryonline.org/

$42.00/year for members, in-training; online only; $178.00/year for members, print + online; $223.00/year for nonmembers, print + online; $268.00/year for members, international: print + online; $335.00/year for nonmembers, international, print + online. Journal contributing to the efforts in furthering psychiatry as a profession and to knowledge pool of medicine.

8686 ■ ADVANCE for Nurse Practitioners
Merion Publications Inc.
2900 Horizon Dr.
PO Box 61556
King of Prussia, PA 19406-0956
Ph: (610)278-1400
Fr: 800-355-5627
URL: http://nurse-practitioners-and-physician-
   assistants.advancew

Monthly. Free to qualified subscribers. For practicing nurse practitioner students with senior status.

8687 ■ Advances in Nursing Science (ANS)
Lippincott Williams & Wilkins
530 Walnut St.
Philadelphia, PA 19106-3619
Ph: (215)521-8300
Fax: (215)521-8902
Fr: 800-638-3030
URL: http://www.lww.com/product/?0161-9268

Quarterly. $114.99/year for individuals; $432.00/year for institutions; $68.49/year for individuals, in-training; $219.73/year for other countries; $561.73/year for institutions, other countries. Academic medical journal focusing on nursing research and education.

8688 ■ American Journal of Geriatric Psychiatry
American Association for Geriatric Psychiatry
7910 Woodmont Ave., Ste. 1050
Bethesda, MD 20814-3004
Ph: (301)654-7850
Fax: (301)654-4137
URL: http://journals.lww.com/ajgponline/pages/
   default.aspx

Monthly. $396.74/year for individuals; $1,157.40/year for institutions; $554.06/year for other countries; $1,457.12/year for institutions, other countries; $214.00/year for individuals, in-training; $238.00/year for other countries, in-training. Peer-reviewed professional journal covering geriatric psychiatry.

8689 ■ American Journal of Nursing
American Journal of Nursing
c/o Lippincott, Williams & Wilkins
2 Commerce Sq., 2001 Market St.
Philadelphia, PA 19103
Ph: (215)521-8300
Fax: (215)521-8902
URL: http://www.nursingcenter.com

Monthly. $51.00/year for individuals; $425.00/year for institutions; $129.00/year for other countries; $465.00/year for institutions, other countries. Peer-reviewed journal promoting excellence in nursing and health care.

8690 ■ American Journal of Psychology
University of Illinois Press
1325 S Oak St.
Champaign, IL 61820-6903
Ph: (217)333-0950

Fax: (217)244-8082
E-mail: ajp@psych.purdue.edu
URL: http://www.press.uillinois.edu/journals/ajp.html

Quarterly. $74.00/year for individuals, print or online; $81.00/year for individuals, print + online; $236.00/year for institutions, print or online; $260.00/year for institutions, print + online; $30.00/year for students, online only; $60.00/year for single issue. Journal dealing with experimental psychology and basic principles of psychology.

8691 ■ The American Nurse
American Nurses Association
8515 Georgia Ave., Ste. 400
Silver Spring, MD 20910
Ph: (301)628-5000
Fax: (301)628-5001
Fr: 800-274-4262
E-mail: adsales@ana.org
URL: http://nursingworld.org/tan/

Monthly. $20.00/year for individuals, practicing nurses; $10.00/year for students. Newspaper (tabloid) for the nursing profession.

8692 ■ Annual Review of Psychology
Annual Reviews Inc.
4139 El Camino Way
Palo Alto, CA 94306
Ph: (650)493-4400
Fax: (650)424-0910
Fr: 800-523-8635
URL: http://www.annualreviews.org/journal/psych

Annual. $80.00/year for individuals, print and online; $202.00/year for institutions, print only; $202.00/year for institutions, online only; $242.00/year for institutions, print and online. Publication covering psychology and mental health issues.

8693 ■ Cancer Nursing
Lippincott Williams & Wilkins
530 Walnut St.
Philadelphia, PA 19106-3619
Ph: (215)521-8300
Fax: (215)521-8902
Fr: 800-638-3030
E-mail: editor@gator.net
URL: http://journals.lww.com/cancernursingonline/
   pages/default.as

Bimonthly. $109.99/year for individuals; $378.00/year for institutions; $63.99/year for individuals, in-training; $203.22/year for other countries; $518.22/year for institutions, other countries. Medical journal covering problems arising in the care and support of cancer patients.

8694 ■ Children & Society
John Wiley & Sons Inc.
111 River St.
Hoboken, NJ 07030-5773
Ph: (201)748-6000
Fax: (201)748-6088

Fr: 800-825-7550
URL: http://onlinelibrary.wiley.com/journal/10.1111/
(ISSN)1099-08

Bimonthly. $211.00/year for individuals, print & on-
line; $171.00/year for individuals, print & online;
$114.00/year for individuals, print & online; $126.00/
year for other countries, print & online, rest of World;
$756.00/year for institutions, print & online; $374.00/
year for individuals, print & online; $475.00/year for
institutions, print & online; $807.00/year for institu-
tions, other countries, print & online. Journal focusing
on children and services for children.

8695 ■ Clinical Nurse Specialist

Lippincott Williams & Wilkins
530 Walnut St.
Philadelphia, PA 19106-3619
Ph: (215)521-8300
Fax: (215)521-8902
Fr: 800-638-3030
E-mail: jasfulto@iupui.edu
URL: http://journals.lww.com/cns-journal/pages/
default.aspx

Bimonthly. $104.99/year for individuals; $356.00/year
for institutions; $63.99/year for individuals, in-training;
$218.22/year for other countries; $535.22/year for
institutions, other countries. Nursing journal.

8696 ■ Clinical Psychiatry News

International Medical News Group
60 Columbia Rd., Bldg. B
Morristown, NJ 07960
Ph: (973)290-8200
Fax: (973)290-8250
E-mail: cpnews@elsevier.com
URL: http://journals.elsevierhealth.com/periodicals/
cpnews

Monthly. $109.00/year for individuals; $173.00/year
for other countries. Medical and psychiatry tabloid.

8697 ■ CNS Senior Care

The McMahon Publishing Group
545 W 45th St.
New York, NY 10036
Ph: (212)957-5300
Fax: (212)957-7230
URL: http://www.cnsseniorcare.com/index.asp

Medical newspaper providing current, practical
information, and education for healthcare professionals managing geriatric patients with neurologic and
psychiatric disorders in long-term care and other
treatment settings.

8698 ■ Counselling Psychology Quarterly

Routledge Journals
270 Madison Ave.
New York, NY 10016-0601
Ph: (212)216-7800
Fax: (212)563-2269
URL: http://www.tandf.co.uk/journals/titles/
09515070.asp

Quarterly. $754.00/year for institutions, print + on-
line; $1,266.00/year for institutions, print + online;
$679.00/year for institutions, online only; $1,139.00/
year for institutions, online only; $206.00/year for
individuals, print only; $347.00/year for individuals,
print only; $40.00/year for institutions, society;
$66.00/year for institutions, society. Journal covering
practical counseling, clinical, occupational and medical psychology.

8699 ■ Ethical Human Psychology and Psychiatry

Springer Publishing Co.
11 W 42nd St., 15th Fl.
New York, NY 10036
Ph: (212)431-4370
Fax: (212)941-7842
Fr: 877-687-7476
URL: http://www.springerpub.com/
journal.aspx?jid=1559-4343

$90.00/year for individuals, print; $125.00/year for
individuals, print and online; $230.00/year for institu-

tions, print; $275.00/year for institutions, print and
online. Books on nursing, psychology, gerontology,
geriatrics, social work, counseling, public health,
rehabilitation and medical education.

8700 ■ GradPsych

American Psychoanalytic Association
309 E 49th St.
New York, NY 10017-1601
Ph: (212)752-0450
Fax: (212)593-0571
E-mail: gradpsych@apa.org
URL: http://www.apa.org/gradpsych

Quarterly. $17.50/year for members, domestic;
$35.00/year for individuals, non-members; $70.00/
year for institutions; $17.50/year for other countries,
international affiliates; $17.50/year for individuals,
high school teacher affiliates; $27.50/year for mem-
bers, international surface; $50.00/year for individu-
als, international surface; $39.50/year for members,
international air mail; $60.00/year for individuals,
international air mail; $115.00/year for institutions,
international air mail. Magazine that offers information about psychology careers, finance, and emerging trends in psychology practice, research, and
education.

8701 ■ Home Healthcare Nurse

Lippincott Williams & Wilkins
530 Walnut St.
Philadelphia, PA 19106-3619
Ph: (215)521-8300
Fax: (215)521-8902
Fr: 800-638-3030
URL: http://journals.lww.com/
homehealthcarenurseonline/pages/defa

$62.14/year for individuals; $324.00/year for institutions; $156.11/year for other countries; $481.11/year
for institutions, other countries; $40.99/year for
individuals, in-training. Magazine for the practicing
professional nurse working in the home health, community health, and public health areas.

8702 ■ HomeCare Magazine

Penton Media
249 W 17th St.
New York, NY 10011-5390
Ph: (212)204-4200
URL: http://homecaremag.com/

Monthly. Free, in US; $135.00/year for Canada;
$150.00/year for two years, Canada; $250.00/year
for other countries; $250.00/year for two years, other
countries. Magazine serving home medical equipment suppliers, including independent and chain
centers specializing in home care, pharmacies or
chain drug stores with home care products, and joint-
ventured hospital home health care businesses.
Contains industry news and new product launches
and marketing strategies.

8703 ■ Hospitals & Health Networks

Health Forum L.L.C.
155 N Wacker Dr., Ste. 400
Chicago, IL 60606
Ph: (312)893-6800
Fax: (312)422-4500
Fr: 800-821-2039
URL: http://www.hhnmag.com

Weekly. Free. Publication covering the health care
industry.

8704 ■ The IHS Primary Care Provider

Indian Health Service
The Reyes Bldg.
801 Thompson Ave., Ste. 400
Rockville, MD 20852-1627
Ph: (301)443-1011
URL: http://www.ihs.gov/provider

Monthly. Journal for health care professionals, physicians, nurses, pharmacists, dentists, and dietitians.

8705 ■ Intensive and Critical Care Nursing

Mosby Inc.
11830 Westline Industrial Dr.
St. Louis, MO 63146-3326
Ph: (314)872-8370
Fax: (314)432-1380
Fr: 800-325-4177
URL: http://www.elsevier.com/wps/find/
journaldescription.cws_home

Bimonthly. $114.00/year for individuals, for all
countries except Europe, Japan & Iran; $501.00/year
for institutions, for all countries except Europe, Japan
& Iran; $124.00/year for individuals, for European
countries and Iran; $565.00/year for institutions, for
European countries and Iran. Journal for nurses in
intensive and critical care nursing.

8706 ■ International Journal of Nursing Education Scholarship

Berkeley Electronic Press
2809 Telegraph Ave., Ste. 202
Berkeley, CA 94705-1167
Ph: (510)665-1200
Fax: (510)665-1201
URL: http://www.bepress.com/ijnes

Annual. $525.00/year corporate; $175.00/year
academic. Journal that publishes original papers on
nursing education issues and research.

8707 ■ International Journal of Nursing Practice

John Wiley & Sons Inc.
350 Main St., Commerce Pl.
Malden, MA 02148-5089
Ph: (781)388-8200
Fax: (781)388-8210
URL: http://www.wiley.com/bw/journal.asp?ref=1322-
7114

Bimonthly. $146.00/year for individuals, print and on-
line; $1,053.00/year for institutions, print and online;
$916.00/year for institutions, print or online; $651.00/
year for institutions, other countries, print and online;
$566.00/year for institutions, other countries, print or
online; $850.00/year for institutions, print and pre-
mium online, Australia/New Zealand; $739.00/year
for institutions, print or online, Australia/New Zealand.
Journal publishing articles about advances the
international understanding and development of nursing, both as a profession and as an academic
discipline.

8708 ■ International Journal of Orthopaedic and Trauma Nursing

Mosby Inc.
11830 Westline Industrial Dr.
St. Louis, MO 63146-3326
Ph: (314)872-8370
Fax: (314)432-1380
Fr: 800-325-4177
URL: http://www.elsevier.com/wps/find/
journaldescription.cws_home

Quarterly. $106.00/year for individuals, for all coun-
tries except Europe, Japan and Iran; $409.00/year
for institutions, for all countries except Europe, Japan
and Iran. Journal for orthopaedic nurses.

8709 ■ International Journal of Psychiatry in Clinical Practice

Informa Healthcare
52 Vanderbilt Ave., 7th Fl.
New York, NY 10017-3846
Ph: (212)520-2777
URL: http://informahealthcare.com/journal/jpc

Quarterly. $460.00/year for institutions; $765.00/year
for institutions; $610.00/year for institutions. Journal
for health professionals with clinical, academic, and
research interests in psychiatry.

8710 ■ International Journal of Psychology

Psychology Press
270 Madison Ave.
New York, NY 10016-0601
Fax: 800-248-4724

Fr: 800-634-7064
URL: http://www.tandf.co.uk/journals/titles/
00207594.asp

$567.00/year for institutions, print + online; $510.00/
year for institutions, online; $125.00/year for individu-
als, print; $938.00/year for institutions, print + online;
$844.00/year for institutions, online; $210.00/year for
individuals, print; $747.00/year for institutions, print +
online; $672.00/year for institutions, online; $166.00/
year for individuals, print. Journal dealing with all
aspects of development of international psychological
science.

8711 ■ International Nursing Review
John Wiley & Sons Inc.
350 Main St., Commerce Pl.
Malden, MA 02148-5089
Ph: (781)388-8200
Fax: (781)388-8210
URL: http://www.wiley.com/bw/journal.asp?ref=0020-
8132

Quarterly. $63.00/year for individuals, UK & non Euro
zone; print + online; $71.00/year for U.S. and other
countries, members; $223.00/year for institutions,
print + online; $202.00/year for institutions, print or
online; $118.00/year for individuals, print + online;
$431.00/year for institutions, print + online; $374.00/
year for institutions, print or online; $95.00/year for
individuals, print + online; $295.00/year for institu-
tions, print + online; $256.00/year for institutions,
print or online. Journal focusing on current concerns
and issues of modern day nursing and health care
from an international perspective.

8712 ■ Journal of Addictions Nursing
Informa Healthcare
52 Vanderbilt Ave., 7th Fl.
New York, NY 10017-3846
Ph: (212)520-2777
URL: http://informahealthcare.com/journal/jan

$342.00/year for institutions; $556.00/year for institutions; $444.00/year for institutions. Journal for nurs-
ing addiction professionals.

8713 ■ Journal of Business and Psychology
Springer-Verlag New York Inc.
233 Spring St.
New York, NY 10013-1578
Ph: (212)460-1500
Fax: (212)460-1575
Fr: 800-777-4643
URL: http://www.springer.com/psychology/
community+%26+environment

$904.00/year for institutions, print or online;
$1,085.00/year for institutions, print & enchanced
access. Journal covering all aspects of psychology
that apply to the business segment. Includes topics
such as personnel selection and training, organizational assessment and development, risk management and loss control, marketing and consumer
behavior research.

8714 ■ Journal of Clinical Nursing
John Wiley & Sons Inc.
350 Main St., Commerce Pl.
Malden, MA 02148-5089
Ph: (781)388-8200
Fax: (781)388-8210
E-mail: jcn@oxon.blackwellpublishing.com
URL: http://www.wiley.com/bw/journal.asp?ref=0962-
1067

Monthly. $381.00/year for individuals, print and on-
line; $208.00/year for students, print and online;
$2,428.00/year for institutions, print and online;
$2,111.00/year for institutions, print or online;
$312.00/year for individuals, print and online;
$167.00/year for students, print and online;
$1,315.00/year for institutions, other countries, print
and online; $1,143.00/year for institutions, other
countries, print or online. Peer-reviewed scientific
journal that seeks to promote the development and
exchange of knowledge that is directly relevant to
spheres of nursing and midwifery practice.

8715 ■ Journal of Clinical Psychology
John Wiley & Sons Inc.
111 River St.
Hoboken, NJ 07030-5773
Ph: (201)748-6000
Fax: (201)748-6088
Fr: 800-825-7550
URL: http://onlinelibrary.wiley.com/journal/10.1002/
(ISSN)1097-46

Monthly. $129.00/year for U.S., Canada, and Mexico,
print only; $973.00/year for institutions, print only;
$1,057.00/year for institutions, other countries, print
only; $1,119.00/year for institutions, print with online;
$1,203.00/year for institutions, other countries, print
with online. Peer-reviewed journal for professionals
in the field of psychology.

**8716 ■ The Journal of Continuing Education
in Nursing**
SLACK Incorporated
6900 Grove Rd.
Thorofare, NJ 08086-9447
Ph: (856)848-1000
Fax: (856)848-6091
E-mail: jcen@slackinc.com
URL: http://www.slackjournals.com/jcen

Monthly. $124.00/year for individuals; $248.00/year
for two years; $29.00/year for single issue; $355.00/
year for institutions. Peer-reviewed journal for nurses
involved in planning and implementing educational
programs for the practitioner and others in patient
care.

8717 ■ Journal of Gerontological Nursing
SLACK Incorporated
6900 Grove Rd.
Thorofare, NJ 08086-9447
Ph: (856)848-1000
Fax: (856)848-6091
E-mail: jgn@slackinc.com
URL: http://www.slackjournals.com/jgn

Monthly. $95.00/year for individuals; $190.00/year for
two years; $315.00/year for institutions; $630.00/year
for institutions, two years; $29.00/year for single
issue. Gerontological nursing journal.

**8718 ■ Journal of Nursing Administration
(JONA)**
Lippincott Williams & Wilkins
530 Walnut St.
Philadelphia, PA 19106-3619
Ph: (215)521-8300
Fax: (215)521-8902
Fr: 800-638-3030
E-mail: jonaeditor@aol.com
URL: http://journals.lww.com/jonajournal/pages/
default.aspx

$126.99/year for individuals; $69.99/year for individuals, in-training; $261.10/year for other countries;
$544.00/year for institutions; $74.63/year for individuals, in-training; $690.70/year for institutions, other
countries. Journal covering developments and
advances in nursing administration and management.

8719 ■ Journal of Nursing Scholarship
John Wiley & Sons Inc.
350 Main St., Commerce Pl.
Malden, MA 02148-5089
Ph: (781)388-8200
Fax: (781)388-8210
URL: http://www.wiley.com/bw/journal.asp?ref=1527-
6546&site=1

Quarterly. $63.00/year for individuals, print & online;
$263.00/year for institutions, print & online; $228.00/
year for institutions, print, online; $73.00/year for
individuals, print & online; $191.00/year for institu-
tions, other countries, print & online; $243.00/year for
institutions, print & online; $49.00/year for individuals,
print & online. Peer-reviewed journal covering
nursing.

**8720 ■ Journal of Obstetric, Gynecologic
and Neonatal Nursing (JOGNN)**
John Wiley & Sons Inc.
350 Main St., Commerce Pl.
Malden, MA 02148-5089
Ph: (781)388-8200
Fax: (781)388-8210
URL: http://www.wiley.com/bw/journal.asp?ref=0884-
2175&site=1

Bimonthly. $121.00/year for individuals, print & on-
line; $1,117.00/year for institutions, print & online;
$971.00/year for institutions, online only; $102.00/
year for individuals, print & online; $788.00/year for
institutions, print & online; $685.00/year for institu-
tions, online only; $68.00/year for individuals, print &
online; $621.00/year for institutions, print & online;
$540.00/year for institutions, online only. Journal
covering trends, policies, and research. Official
publication of the Association of Women's Health,
Obstetric, and Neonatal Nurses (AWHONN).

**8721 ■ Journal of Positive Behavior
Interventions**
PRO-ED Inc.
8700 Shoal Creek Blvd.
Austin, TX 78757-6897
Ph: (512)451-3246
Fax: (512)451-8542
Fr: 800-897-3202
URL: http://www.proedinc.com/customer/
content.aspx?redid=24

Quarterly. $164.00/year for institutions, print &
e-access; $148.00/year for institutions, e-access;
$161.00/year for institutions, print; $61.00/year for
individuals, print & e-access; $44.00/year for institu-
tions, single print; $20.00/year for single issue, print.
Journal covering issues in mental health and
psychology.

**8722 ■ Journal of Psychosocial Nursing and
Mental Health Services**
SLACK Incorporated
6900 Grove Rd.
Thorofare, NJ 08086-9447
Ph: (856)848-1000
Fax: (856)848-6091
E-mail: jpn@slackinc.com
URL: http://www.slackjournals.com/jpn

Monthly. $95.00/year for individuals; $190.00/year for
individuals, two years; $315.00/year for institutions;
$630.00/year for institutions, two years; $29.00/year
for single issue. Peer-reviewed journal presenting
original, peer-reviewed articles on psychiatric/mental
health nursing.

8723 ■ Journal of Radiology Nursing
Mosby Inc.
11830 Westline Industrial Dr.
St. Louis, MO 63146-3326
Ph: (314)872-8370
Fax: (314)432-1380
Fr: 800-325-4177
URL: http://www.radiologynursing.org

Quarterly. $80.00/year for individuals, U.S.; $152.00/
year for institutions, U.S.; $121.00/year for individu-
als, International; $202.00/year for institutions,
International. Journal publishing articles about patient
care in the diagnostic and therapeutic imaging
environments.

8724 ■ LPN2009
Lippincott Williams & Wilkins
530 Walnut St.
Philadelphia, PA 19106-3619
Ph: (215)521-8300
Fax: (215)521-8902
Fr: 800-638-3030
URL: http://www.lww.com/product/?1553-0582

Bimonthly. $149.96/year for institutions; $29.96/year
for individuals; $22.75/year for individuals, in-training;
$75.96/year for other countries; $214.96/year for
institutions, other countries. Peer-reviewed journal
that focuses on bedside care skills for practical
nurses.

8725 ■ McKnight's Long-Term Care News
McKnight's Long-Term Care News
1 Northfield Plz., Ste. 521
Northfield, IL 60093-1216
Ph: (847)784-8706
Fax: (847)784-9346
Fr: 800-558-1703
URL: http://www.mcknightsonline.com/home

$60.00/year for individuals; $108.00/year for two years; $75.00/year for Canada; $135.00/year for Canada, two years; $75.00/year for other countries; $135.00/year for other countries, two years. Professional magazine.

8726 ■ MCN, The American Journal of Maternal/Child Nursing
Lippincott Williams & Wilkins
530 Walnut St.
Philadelphia, PA 19106-3619
Ph: (215)521-8300
Fax: (215)521-8902
Fr: 800-638-3030
URL: http://journals.lww.com/mcnjournal/pages/default.aspx

Bimonthly. $63.99/year for individuals; $300.00/year for institutions; $149.22/year for other countries; $421.22/year for institutions, other countries; $42.43/year for individuals, in-training. Peer-reviewed journal focusing on maternal/child nursing and health.

8727 ■ Modern Healthcare
Crain Communications Inc.
360 N Michigan Ave.
Chicago, IL 60601
Ph: (312)649-5200
E-mail: subs@crain.com
URL: http://www.modernhealthcare.com

Weekly. $164.00/year for individuals; $255.00/year for Canada; $218.00/year for other countries. Weekly business news magazine for healthcare management.

8728 ■ Monitor on Psychology
American Psychological Association
750 1st St. NE
Washington, DC 20002-4242
Ph: (202)336-5500
Fax: (202)336-5549
Fr: 800-374-2721
E-mail: journals@apa.org
URL: http://www.apa.org/monitor/

$50.00/year for nonmembers; $99.00/year for individuals, foreign, surface freight; $126.00/year for individuals, foreign, air mail; $93.00/year for institutions; $190.00/year for institutions, surface freight; $217.00/year for institutions, air freight; $20.00/year for single issue. Magazine of the APA. Reports on the science, profession, and social responsibility of psychology, including latest legislative developments affecting mental health, education, and research support.

8729 ■ Nurse Education in Practice
Mosby Inc.
11830 Westline Industrial Dr.
St. Louis, MO 63146-3326
Ph: (314)872-8370
Fax: (314)432-1380
Fr: 800-325-4177
URL: http://www.elsevier.com/wps/find/journaldescription.cws_home

Bimonthly. $105.00/year for individuals, for all countries except Europe, Japan & Iran; $399.00/year for institutions, for all countries except Europe, Japan & Iran. Journal enabling lecturers and practitioners to both share and disseminate evidence that demonstrates the actual practice of education as it is experienced in the realities of their respective work environments.

8730 ■ Nursing Clinics of North America
Mosby Inc.
11830 Westline Industrial Dr.
St. Louis, MO 63146-3326

Ph: (314)872-8370
Fax: (314)432-1380
Fr: 800-325-4177
URL: http://www.elsevier.com/wps/find/journaldescription.cws_home

Quarterly. $135.00/year for individuals; $343.00/year for institutions; $74.00/year for students; $197.00/year for Canada; $419.00/year for institutions, Canada; $121.00/year for students, Canada. Journal publishing articles by experts in the field provide current, practical information geared to the active nurse.

8731 ■ Nursing Education Perspectives
National League for Nursing
61 Broadway, 33rd Fl.
New York, NY 10006-2701
Ph: (212)363-5555
Fax: (212)812-0393
Fr: 800-669-1656
URL: http://www.nln.org/nlnjournal/index.htm

Bimonthly. $40.00/year for individuals; $90.00/year for nonmembers; $110.00/year for Canada, nonmembers; $120.00/year for other countries, nonmember; $152.00/year for institutions; $172.00/year for libraries; $182.00/year for other countries, libraries. Professional journal for nurses. Includes articles on health policy, social and economic issues affecting health care, and nursing education and practice.

8732 ■ Nursing Management
Lippincott Williams & Wilkins
530 Walnut St.
Philadelphia, PA 19106-3621
Ph: (215)521-8300
Fax: (215)521-8902
URL: http://journals.lww.com/nursingmanagement/pages/default.aspx

Monthly. $76.76/year for individuals; $371.76/year for institutions; $168.49/year for other countries; $518.49/year for institutions, other countries. Magazine focusing on nursing management.

8733 ■ Nursing Outlook
Mosby Inc.
10801 Executive Center Dr., Ste. 509
Little Rock, AR 72211
Ph: (501)223-5165
Fax: (501)223-0519
URL: http://journals.elsevierhealth.com/periodicals/ymno

Bimonthly. $133.00/year for Canada; $84.00/year for individuals; $133.00/year for individuals, Mexico; $133.00/year for other countries. Official journal of the American Academy of Nursing, reporting on trends and issues in nursing.

8734 ■ Patient Education and Counseling
Mosby Inc.
11830 Westline Industrial Dr.
St. Louis, MO 63146-3326
Ph: (314)872-8370
Fax: (314)432-1380
Fr: 800-325-4177
URL: http://www.elsevier.com/wps/find/journaldescription.cws_home

Monthly. $284.00/year for individuals, all countries except Europe, Japan and Iran; $2,648.00/year for institutions, all countries except Europe, Japan and Iran; $314,200.00/year for institutions; $33,700.00/year for individuals. Journal publishing articles on patient education and health promotion researchers, managers, physicians, nurses and other health care provider.

8735 ■ Provider
American Health Care Association
1201 L St. NW
Washington, DC 20005
Ph: (202)842-4444
Fax: (202)842-3860
E-mail: sales@ahca.org
URL: http://www.providermagazine.com

Monthly. $48.00/year for U.S.; $61.00/year for Canada and Mexico; $85.00/year for other countries; free to qualified subscribers. Provider Magazine.

8736 ■ Psychiatric Annals
SLACK Incorporated
6900 Grove Rd.
Thorofare, NJ 08086-9447
Ph: (856)848-1000
Fax: (856)848-6091
E-mail: psyann@slackinc.com
URL: http://www.psychiatricannalsonline.com/

Monthly. $229.00/year for individuals; $458.00/year for two years; $687.00/year for individuals, three years; $379.00/year for institutions; $758.00/year for institutions, two years; $1,137.00/year for institutions, three years; $114.00/year for individuals, resident; $53.00/year for individuals, outside the U.S.; $39.00/year for single issue. Peer-reviewed journal analyzing concepts and practices in every area of psychiatry.

8737 ■ Psychiatric News
American Psychiatric Publishing Inc.
1000 Wilson Blvd., Ste. 1825
Arlington, VA 22209-3924
Ph: (703)907-7322
Fax: (703)907-1091
Fr: 800-368-5777
URL: http://pn.psychiatryonline.org/

Semimonthly. $111.00/year for nonmembers, print and online; $151.00/year for members, international, print & online; $167.00/year for nonmembers, international, print & online; $22.00/year for single issue, United States; $37.00/year for single issue, international. Professional magazine of the American Psychiatric Assn.

8738 ■ Psychological Bulletin
American Psychological Association
750 1st St. NE
Washington, DC 20002-4242
Ph: (202)336-5500
Fax: (202)336-5549
Fr: 800-374-2721
E-mail: journals@apa.org
URL: http://www.apa.org/pubs/journals/bul/index.aspx

Bimonthly. $106.00/year for members, domestic; $130.00/year for members, foreign, surface; $149.00/year for members, foreign, air mail; $84.00/year for students, domestic; $108.00/year for students, foreign, surface; $127.00/year for students, foreign, air mail; $280.00/year for nonmembers, domestic; $312.00/year for nonmembers, foreign, surface; $327.00/year for nonmembers, foreign, air mail; $765.00/year for institutions, domestic. Journal presenting comprehensive and integrative reviews and interpretations of critical substantive and methodological issues and practical problems from all the diverse areas of psychology.

8739 ■ Psychological Services
American Psychological Association
750 1st St. NE
Washington, DC 20002-4242
Ph: (202)336-5500
Fax: (202)336-5549
Fr: 800-374-2721
URL: http://www.apa.org/pubs/journals/ser/index.aspx

Quarterly. $63.00/year for members; $85.00/year for members, international surface; $97.00/year for members, international airmail; $63.00/year for students; $85.00/year for students, other countries, surface; $97.00/year for students, other countries, airmail; $98.00/year for nonmembers; $125.00/year for nonmembers, international surface; $136.00/year for nonmembers, international airmail; $403.00/year for institutions. Journal of the Division of Psychologists in Public Service, publishing data-based articles on the broad range of psychological services.

8740 ■ *Psychology Journal*
Psychological Publishing
PO Box 176
Natchitoches, LA 71458
E-mail: psychjournal@aol.com
URL: http://www.psychologicalpublishing.com/

Quarterly. $90.00/year for individuals; $175.00/year for institutions. Journal dedicated to all areas of the science and practice of counseling and clinical psychology.

8741 ■ *Rehabilitation Nursing*
Rehabilitation Nursing
4700 W Lake Ave.
Glenview, IL 60025
Ph: (847)375-4710
Fax: (847)375-6481
Fr: 800-229-7530
E-mail: info@rehabnurse.org
URL: http://awebsource.com/clients/arn/ws_resource/public_index.p

Bimonthly. $120.00/year for individuals, regular; $150.00/year for individuals, premium; $195.00/year for other countries, regular; $240.00/year for other countries, premium; $175.00/year for institutions, regular (USA); $220.00/year for institutions, premium (USA); $195.00/year for institutions, regular (international); $240.00/year for institutions, premium (international). Magazine focusing on rehabilitation nursing involving clinical practice, research, education, and administration.

8742 ■ *Research in Nursing & Health*
John Wiley & Sons Inc.
111 River St.
Hoboken, NJ 07030-5773
Ph: (201)748-6000
Fax: (201)748-6088
Fr: 800-825-7550
URL: http://onlinelibrary.wiley.com/journal/10.1002/(ISSN)1098-24

Bimonthly. $164.00/year for U.S., Canada, and Mexico, print only; $206.00/year for other countries, print only; $1,483.00/year for institutions, print only; $1,567.00/year for institutions, Canada and Mexico, print only; $1,609.00/year for institutions, other countries, print only. Peer-reviewed journal publishing wide range of research and theory that will inform the practice of nursing and other health disciplines.

8743 ■ *Review of General Psychology*
American Psychological Association
750 1st St. NE
Washington, DC 20002-4242
Ph: (202)336-5500
Fax: (202)336-5549
Fr: 800-374-2721
URL: http://www.apa.org/pubs/journals/gpr/index.aspx

Quarterly. $63.00/year for members; $63.00/year for students; $110.00/year for nonmembers; $415.00/year for institutions; $85.00/year for members, international, surface; $85.00/year for students, other countries, surface; $137.00/year for nonmembers, international, surface; $460.00/year for institutions, other countries, surface; $97.00/year for members, international, airmail; $97.00/year for students, other countries, airmail. Journal including a wide variety of psychological research-related articles.

8744 ■ *Seminars in Oncology Nursing*
Mosby Inc.
11830 Westline Industrial Dr.
St. Louis, MO 63146-3326
Ph: (314)872-8370
Fax: (314)432-1380
Fr: 800-325-4177
URL: http://www.nursingoncology.com

Quarterly. $105.00/year for individuals; $298.00/year for institutions; $212.00/year for individuals, International; $402.00/year for institutions, other countries. Journal publishing material to disseminate knowledge in the complex field of cancer nursing.

8745 ■ *Supporting Innovations in Gerontological Nursing*
National Gerontological Nursing Association
3493 Lansdowne Dr., Ste. 2
Lexington, KY 40517
Ph: (859)977-7453
Fax: (859)271-0607
Fr: 800-723-0560
E-mail: info@ngna.org
URL: http://www.ngna.org

Bimonthly. Provides updates on NGNA's activities as well as other information of interest to gerontological nurses. Features job opportunities in the field.

8746 ■ *Teaching and Learning in Nursing*
Elsevier Science Inc.
360 Park Ave. S
New York, NY 10010-1710
Ph: (212)989-5800
Fax: (212)633-3990
Fr: 888-437-4636
URL: http://www.elsevier.com/wps/find/journaldescription.cws_home

Quarterly. $232.00/year for institutions, other countries; $134.00/year for other countries; $160.00/year for institutions; $91.00/year for individuals. Journal devoted to associate degree nursing education and practice.

8747 ■ *USA Body Psychotherapy Journal*
United States Association for Body Psychotherapy
8639 B 16th St., Ste. 119
Silver Spring, MD 20910
Ph: (202)466-1619
E-mail: admin@usabp.org
URL: http://www.usabp.org/displaycommon.cfm?an=4

Semiannual. Academic journal that seeks to support, promote and stimulate the exchange of ideas, scholarship and research within the field of body psychotherapy as well as an interdisciplinary exchange with related fields of clinical practice and inquiry.

8748 ■ *Worldviews on Evidence-Based Nursing*
John Wiley & Sons Inc.
350 Main St., Commerce Pl.
Malden, MA 02148-5089
Ph: (781)388-8200
Fax: (781)388-8210
URL: http://www.wiley.com/bw/journal.asp?ref=1545-102X

Quarterly. $149.00/year for individuals, print and online; $142.00/year for individuals, online only; $450.00/year for institutions, print and online; $391.00/year for institutions, print or online; $161.00/year for individuals, print and online; $154.00/year for individuals, online only. Peer-reviewed journal that offers research, policy and practice, education and management for nursing.

Employer Directories and Networking Lists

8749 ■ *Crain's List—Chicago's Largest Hospitals*
Crain Communications Inc.
360 N Michigan Ave.
Chicago, IL 60601
Ph: (312)649-5200
URL: http://www.chicagobusiness.com/section/lists

Published November, 2010. $25.00 for individuals; $45.00 for individuals. Covers: 25 hospitals in Chicago area ranked by net patient revenues. Entries include: Name, address, phone number, fax, web address, corporate e-mail, hospital administrator, network affiliation, 2009 net patient revenue, percentage change from 2008, 2009 net profits, percentage change from 2008, inpatient days, available beds, daily occupancy rate, number of hospital employees

as of December 31, 2009, fiscal year end, Chairman, President, CEO, Chief Financial Officer, Human Resources Manager, Media Relations/Public Relations Director, and Hospital Administrator.

8750 ■ *Directory of Hospital Personnel*
Grey House Publishing
4919 Rte. 22
PO Box 56
Amenia, NY 12501
Ph: (518)789-8700
Fax: (518)789-0556
Fr: 800-562-2139
URL: http://www.greyhouse.com/hospital_personnel.htm

Annual, Latest edition 2011. $325.00 for individuals. Covers: 200,000 executives at 6,000 U.S. Hospitals. Entries include: Name of hospital, address, phone, number of beds, type and JCAHO status of hospital, names and titles of key department heads and staff, medical and nursing school affiliations; number of residents, interns, and nursing students. Arrangement: Geographical. Indexes: Hospital name, personnel, hospital size.

8751 ■ *Hospital Blue Book*
Billian Publishing Inc. and Trans World Publishing Inc.
2100 River Edge Pky.
Atlanta, GA 30328
Ph: (770)955-5656
Fax: (770)952-0669
Fr: 800-800-5668
E-mail: blu-book@billian.com
URL: http://www.billianshealthdata.com/Products/bluebook.html

Annual, Latest edition 2010. $575.00 for individuals; $575.00 for individuals. Covers: More than 6,500 hospitals; some listings also appear in a separate southern edition of this publication. Entries include: Name of hospital, accreditation, mailing address, phone, fax, number of beds, type of facility (nonprofit, general, state, etc.); list of administrative personnel and chiefs of medical services, with specific titles. Arrangement: Geographical.

8752 ■ *How to Survive and Maybe Even Love Nursing School!*
F.A. Davis Co.
1915 Arch St.
Philadelphia, PA 19103
Ph: (215)568-2270
Fax: (215)568-5065
Fr: 800-523-4049
URL: http://www.fadavis.com

Latest edition 3rd. $28.95 for individuals. Publication includes: List of resources for nursing students such as Web sites and organizations. Principal content of publication is information about succeeding in nursing school.

8753 ■ *Legal and Ethical Dictionary for Mental Health Professionals*
University Press of America Inc.
4501 Forbes Blvd., Ste. 200
Lanham, MD 20706
Ph: (301)459-3366
Fax: (301)429-5748
Fr: 800-462-6420
URL: http://www.univpress.com

Latest edition 2009. $61.99 for individuals; $29.99 for individuals. Publication includes: Lists of state licensure boards and Web sites for mental health organizations. Principal content of publication is a dictionary of legal and ethical responsibilities for mental health professionals.

8754 ■ *Medical and Health Information Directory*
Gale
PO Box 6904
Florence, KY 41022-6904
Fr: 800-354-9706
URL: http://www.gale.cengage.com

Annual, Latest edition April 2011. $1190.00 for individuals; $501.00 for individuals. Covers: In volume 1, more than 33,000 medical and health oriented associations, organizations, institutions, and government agencies, including health maintenance organizations (HMOs), preferred provider organizations (PPOs), insurance companies, pharmaceutical companies, research centers, and medical and allied health schools. In Volume 2, over 20,000 medical book publishers; medical periodicals, directories, audiovisual producers and services, medical libraries and information centers, electronic resources, and health-related internet search engines. In Volume 3, more than 40,500 clinics, treatment centers, care programs, and counseling/diagnostic services for 34 subject areas. Entries include: Institution, service, or firm name, address, phone, fax, email and URL; many include names of key personnel and, when pertinent, descriptive annotation. Volume 3 was formerly listed separately as Health Services Directory. Arrangement: Classified by organization activity, service, etc. Indexes: Each volume has a complete alphabetical name and keyword index.

8755 ■ Online Resources for Senior Citizens
McFarland & Company Inc., Publishers
960 NC Hwy. 88 W
PO Box 611
Jefferson, NC 28640
Ph: (336)246-4460
Fax: (336)246-5018
Fr: 800-253-2187
URL: http://www.mcfarlandpub.com/book-
    2.php?id=978-0-7864-2803-8

latest edition 2nd; Published 2006. $39.95 for individuals. Covers: Federal government resources, general resources, and resources listed by topic such as caregivers, death and dying, volunteering, employment, grandparenting, health care, and travel.

HANDBOOKS AND MANUALS

8756 ■ Being a Nursing Assistant
Prentice Hall PTR
1 Lake St.
Upper Saddle River, NJ 07458
Ph: (201)236-7000
Fax: (317)428-3343
Fr: 800-922-0579
URL: http://www.pearsonhighered.com

Francie Wolgin. Ninth edition, 2005. $76.13 (paper). 800 pages.

8757 ■ Careers in Health Care
The McGraw-Hill Companies
PO Box 182604
Columbus, OH 43272
Fax: (614)759-3749
Fr: 877-883-5524
E-mail: customer.service@mcgraw-hill.com
URL: http://www.mhprofessional.com/
    product.php?isbn=0071466533

Barbara M. Swanson. Fifth edition, 2005. $19.95 (paper). 192 pages. Describes job duties, work settings, salaries, licensing and certification requirements, educational preparation, and future outlook. Gives ideas on how to secure a job.

8758 ■ Developing Your Career in Nursing
Sage Publications, Inc.
2455 Teller Rd.
Thousand Oaks, CA 91320-2218
Fax: 800-583-2665
Fr: 800-818-7243
E-mail: info@sagepub.com
URL: http://www.sagepub.com/books/Book226518

Robert Newell, editor. $37.95. 184 pages.

8759 ■ Expert Resumes for Health Care Careers
Jist Works
875 Montreal Way
St. Paul, MN 55102

Fr: 800-648-5478
E-mail: educate@emcp.com
URL: http://www.jist.com

Wendy S. Enelow and Louise M. Kursmark. 2010. $16.95. 288 pages.

8760 ■ Health Careers Today
Elsevier
11830 Westline Industrial Dr.
St. Louis, MO 63146
Ph: (314)453-7010
Fax: (314)453-7095
Fr: 800-545-2522
E-mail: usbkinfo@elsevier.com
URL: http://www.elsevier.com

Gerdin, Judith. Fourth edition. 2007. $74.95. 496 pages. Covers more than 45 health careers. Discusses the roles and responsibilities of various occupations and provides a solid foundation in the skills needed for all health careers.

8761 ■ Introduction to the Health Professions
Jones & Bartlett Learning, LLC
PO Box 417289
Boston, MA 02241-7289
Ph: (978)443-5000
Fax: (978)443-8000
Fr: 800-832-0034
E-mail: info@jblearning.com
URL: http://www.jblearning.com

Peggy S. Stanfield, Y. H. Hui and Nanna Cross. 2012. $93.95. 502 pages. Sixth edition. Provides current coverage of all major health professions. Outlines health-related careers, a review of the U.S. healthcare delivery system, managed care, and impact of new technology on healthcare services.

8762 ■ Nursing Assistant: A Nursing Process Approach
Cengage Learning
PO Box 6904
Florence, KY 41022
Fax: 800-487-8488
Fr: 800-354-9706
E-mail: esales@cengage.com
URL: http://www.cengage.com

Barbara Hegner, Barbara Acello and Esther Caldwell. 2010. $72.95 (paper).

8763 ■ Nursing Assistants: A Basic Study Guide
First Class Books, Inc.
PO Box 28493
Spokane, WA 99228
Ph: (509)276-8000
Fax: (509)276-8008
Fr: 800-524-6911
E-mail: fcb@hughes.net
URL: http://firstclassbooks.net/basicGuide.htm

Beverly Robertson. Seventh edition. $18.00 (paper).

8764 ■ The Nursing Experience: Trends, Challenges & Transitions
The McGraw-Hill Companies
PO Box 182604
Columbus, OH 43272
Fax: (614)759-3749
Fr: 877-883-5524
E-mail: customer.service@mcgraw-hill.com
URL: http://www.mhprofessional.com

Lucille A. Joel and L.Y. Kelly. Fifth edition, 2006. $44.95 (paper). 792 pages.

8765 ■ Nursing Today: Transition and Trends
W. B. Saunders Co.
6277 Sea Harbor Dr.
Orlando, FL 32887
Ph: (407)345-2000
Fr: 800-545-2522
URL: http://www.elsevier.com

JoAnn Zerwekh and Jo C. Claborn, editors. Sixth edition, 2009. $52.95 (paper). 640 pages.

8766 ■ Opportunities in Health and Medical Careers
The McGraw-Hill Companies
PO Box 182604
Columbus, OH 43272
Fax: (614)759-3749
Fr: 877-883-5524
E-mail: customer.service@mcgraw-hill.com
URL: http://www.mhprofessional.com/
    product.php?isbn=0071437274

I. Donald Snook, Jr. and Leo D'Orazio. 2004. $14.95 (paper). 157 pages. Covers the full range of medical and health occupations. Illustrated.

8767 ■ Plunkett's Health Care Industry Almanac 2012
Plunkett Research, Ltd.
PO Drawer 541737
Houston, TX 77254-1737
Ph: (713)932-0000
Fax: (713)932-7080
E-mail: customersupport@plunkettresearch.com
URL: http://www.plunkettresearch.com

Jack W. Plunkett. 2011. $299.99. 717 pages. Features in-depth profiles of leading companies, associations and professional societies in the healthcare field. Covers major issues and trends, market forecasts and industry statistics.

8768 ■ Resumes for Health and Medical Careers
The McGraw-Hill Companies
PO Box 182604
Columbus, OH 43272
Fax: (614)759-3749
Fr: 877-883-5524
E-mail: customer.service@mcgraw-hill.com
URL: http://www.mhprofessional.com/
    product.php?isbn=0071545352

Third edition, 2008. $12.95 (paper). 144 pages.

EMPLOYMENT AGENCIES AND SEARCH FIRMS

8769 ■ Axis Medical Staffing
100 W Harrison St., Ste. 550
Seattle, WA 98119
Ph: (206)285-6300
Fax: (206)285-6302
Fr: 888-299-AXIS
E-mail: hr@axismedicalstaffing.com
URL: http://www.axismedicalstaffing.com

Description: Focuses on recruiting medical professionals and matching their requirements to the needs of facilities. Provides quality medical staffing for facilities nationwide. Specializes in per diem staffing, local/national travel assignments and direct hire full-time placements for nursing/nursing aides, radiological technologists and business services.

8770 ■ CompHealth
PO Box 713100
Salt Lake City, UT 84171-3100
Ph: (801)930-3000
Fax: (801)930-4517
Fr: 800-453-3030
E-mail: info@comphealth.com
URL: http://www.comphealth.com

Provides healthcare staffing and recruiting services covering certified registered nurse anesthetist, dosimetrist, imaging and radiation therapy, laboratory technology, medical physicist, nurse practitioner, nursing, pharmacy, physician, physician assistant, rehab therapy and respiratory therapy.

8771 ■ Cross Country TravCorps
6551 Park of Commerce Blvd.
Boca Raton, FL 33487-8247

Fax: (561)998-8533
Fr: 800-530-6125
E-mail: sms@cctc.com
URL: http://www.crosscountrytravcorps.com/cctc/

Places traveling nurses in assignments nationwide.

8772 ■ Daudlin, De Beaupre & Company Inc.
18530 Mack Ave., No. 315
Grosse Pointe Farms, MI 48236
Ph: (313)885-1235
E-mail: ptd@daudlindebeaupre.com
URL: http://www.daudlindebeaupre.com

Executive search firm focused on the healthcare industry.

8773 ■ Davis-Smith, Inc.
27656 Franklin Rd.
Southfield, MI 48034
Ph: (248)354-4100
Fax: (248)354-6702
E-mail: info@davissmith.com
URL: http://www.davissmith.com

Healthcare staffing agency. Executive search firm.

8774 ■ Diversified Staffing Group, Inc.
85 Newbury St.
Boston, MA 02116
Ph: (617)259-1001
Fax: (617)259-1009
Fr: 877-229-1118
E-mail: info@dsgworld.com
URL: http://www.dsgworld.com/main.htm

Description: Serves as an executive search firm for nursing professionals.

8775 ■ Harper Associates
31000 NW Hwy., Ste. 240
Farmington Hills, MI 48334
Ph: (248)932-1170
Fax: (248)932-1214
E-mail: info@harperjobs.com
URL: http://www.harperjobs.com

Executive search firm and employment agency.

8776 ■ MEDCareerNET
23072 Lake Center Dr., Ste. 210
Lake Forest, CA 92630
Ph: (949)380-4800
Fax: (949)380-7477
E-mail: vic@medcareernet.com
URL: http://www.medcareernet.com

Firm provides medical career professionals with a choice of career alternatives that extend their reach within their respective disciplines.

8777 ■ Nursefinders
524 E Lamar Blvd., Ste. 300
Arlington, TX 76011
Ph: (817)460-1181
Fax: (817)462-9146
Fr: 800-445-0459
E-mail: info@nursefinders.com
URL: http://www.nursefinders.com

Description: Serves as a health care staffing company for nursing jobs, travel nursing jobs, home health care positions, therapy, technicians, physicians, allied health and more.

8778 ■ Professional Placement Associates, Inc.
287 Bowman Ave.
Purchase, NY 10577-2517
Ph: (914)251-1000
Fax: (914)251-1055
E-mail: careers@ppasearch.com
URL: http://www.ppasearch.com

Executive search firm specializing in the health and medical field.

ONLINE JOB SOURCES AND SERVICES

8779 ■ Delta T Group
E-mail: cfassl@deltatg.com
URL: http://www.delta-tgroup.com

Description: Specialized contract temporary staffing source for healthcare professionals in the fields of social service, psychiatry, mental health, and substance abuse. Organizations may request services and staffing; job seekers may view services provided, submit a resume, or peruse jobs available.

8780 ■ EmployMED: Healthcare Job Listings
E-mail: customerservice@evalumed.com
URL: http://www.evalumed.com/EmployMed.aspx

Description: Lists practice opportunities throughout North America for all medical specialties. Contains job listings directory. Posting option is available for those who wish to advertise jobs. Fee: $25 per month per posting for minimum of two months.

8781 ■ FCS - The 1st Choice in Psychiatric Recruitment
1711 Ashley Cir., Ste. 6
Bowling Green, KY 42104-5801
Fax: (270)782-1055
Fr: 800-783-9152
E-mail: admin@fcspsy.com
URL: http://www.fcspsy.com

Description: Physician search firm specializing in the recruitment of psychiatrists. After the applicant fills out an interest survey, a tailored search is run on the jobs database. Confidential and free.

8782 ■ Health Care Recruitment Online
E-mail: info@healthcarerecruitment.com
URL: http://healthcarerecruitment.com

Description: Helps seekers find healthcare positions through on-line postings with national staffing companies and hospital partners. Main files include: Featured Employers, Job Search, Immediate Openings, Relocating, Career Management, State boards, and more.

8783 ■ HEALTHeCAREERS Network
Fr: 888-884-8242
E-mail: info@healthecareers.com
URL: http://www.healthecareers.com

Description: Career search site for jobs in all health care specialties; educational resources; visa and licensing information for relocation; interesting articles; relocation tools; links to professional organizations and general resources.

8784 ■ HireNursing.com
URL: http://www.hirenursing.com

Description: Provides job opportunities for professional nurses. Features career tools, educational resources, networking, and industry news.

8785 ■ Hospital Jobs OnLine
E-mail: support@hospitaljobsonline.com
URL: http://www.hospitaljobsonline.com

Description: Serves as a niche healthcare job board designed exclusively for hospitals, healthcare companies, and healthcare job seekers.

8786 ■ Locate Nurse Jobs
URL: http://www.locatenursejobs.com

Description: Serves as an online job search and employee recruiting resource. Provides opportunities for nurses in a wide range of health care settings from hospitals to home health care.

8787 ■ Medzilla.com
URL: http://www.medzilla.com

Description: General medical website which matches employers and job hunters to their ideal employees and jobs through search capabilities. Main files include: Post Jobs, Search Resumes, Post Resumes, Search Jobs, Head Hunters, Articles, Salary Survey.

8788 ■ Nurse Aide Jobs
URL: http://www.nurseaidejobs.net

Description: Features a searchable database of employment opportunities for nurse aides.

8789 ■ NursePath.com
URL: http://www.nursepath.com

Description: Serves as a clearinghouse for those seeking nursing positions. Contains job postings by specialty in critical care, education, emergency, gerontology, and psychiatry.

8790 ■ NursesRX.com
12400 High Bluff Dr.
Huntersville, NC 28078
Fax: 877-744-9052
Fr: 800-733-9354
E-mail: info@nursesrx.com
URL: http://www.nursesrx.com

Description: Job board site for travel nursing. In addition to traditional travel nursing, Nurses RX provides staffing possibilities from temporary-to-permanent, traditional permanent placement, staffing/recruitment outsourcing, new graduate internship programs, and a full Canadian Placement Division.

8791 ■ NursingCrossing.com
URL: http://www.nursingcrossing.com

Description: Provides job listings and other resources related to nursing employment opportunities.

8792 ■ ProHealthJobs.com
Ph: (484)443-8545
Fax: (484)443-8549
E-mail: info@prohealthjobs.com
URL: http://prohealthjobs.com/jobboard

Description: Career resources site for the medical and health care field. Lists professional opportunities, product information, continuing education and open positions.

8793 ■ United Search Associates: Health Network USA
PO Box 342
Vinita, OK 74301
Ph: (918)323-4165
E-mail: jobs@hnusa.com
URL: http://homepage.mac.com/hnusa

Description: Visitors may explore healthcare positions, submit an electronic resume, or advertise with the site.

TRADESHOWS

8794 ■ American Psychiatric Association Annual Meeting
American Psychiatric Association
1000 Wilson Blvd., Ste. 1825
Arlington, VA 22209-3901
Ph: (703)907-7300
Fax: (703)907-1097
Fr: 888-357-7924
E-mail: apa@psych.org
URL: http://www.psych.org

Annual. Primary Exhibits: Computer software online service, media product, criminal justice, diagnostic tool, ECT educational, insurance, market research, professional/support organizations, publishers, recruitment, store/federal and pharmaceuticals. Dates and Locations: 2012 May 05-09; Philadelphia, PA; 2013 May 18-22; San Francisco, CA; 2014 May 03-07; New York, NY; 2015 May 16-20; Toronto, ON, Canada.

8795 ■ International Society of Psychiatric-Mental Health Nurses Annual Conference
International Society of Psychiatric - Mental Health Nurses
2424 American Ln.
Madison, WI 53704-3102
Ph: (608)443-2463
Fax: (608)443-2474
Fr: (866)330-7227
E-mail: info@ispn-psych.org
URL: http://www.ispn-psych.org

Annual. Primary Exhibits: Psychiatric nursing equipment, supplies, and services.

OTHER SOURCES

8796 ■ Academy of Medical-Surgical Nurses
East Holly Ave.
Box 56
Pitman, NJ 08071
Ph: (856)256-2422
Fax: (856)589-7463
Fr: (866)877-2676
E-mail: amsn@ajj.com
URL: http://www.amsn.org

Description: Represents registered, licensed practical, licensed vocational nurses, clinical nurse specialists, nurse practitioners, educators, researchers, administrators, and students. Promotes standards of nursing practice and facilitates the implementation of practice guidelines. Provides education programs for members, fosters scholarly activities and disseminates new ideas for all areas of adult health/medical-surgical nursing.

8797 ■ Academy of Medical-Surgical Nurses Annual Convention
Academy of Medical-Surgical Nurses
East Holly Ave.
Box 56
Pitman, NJ 08071
Fr: (866)877-2676
E-mail: amsn@ajj.com
URL: http://www.amsn.org

Annual. Includes exhibits of various products, technologies, and publications specific to medical-surgical nursing care and services. 2012 October 4-7; Salt Lake City, UT; Salt Palace Convention Center.

8798 ■ American Academy of Addiction Psychiatry (AAAP)
400 Massasoit Ave., Ste. 307
East Providence, RI 02914
Ph: (401)524-3076
Fax: (401)272-0922
E-mail: information@aaap.org
URL: http://www.aaap.org

Description: Psychiatrists and other health care and mental health professionals treating people with addictive behaviors. Promotes accessibility to highest quality treatment for all who need it; promotes excellence in clinical practice in addiction psychiatry; educates the public to influence public policy regarding addictive illness; provides continuing education for addiction professionals; disseminates new information in the field of addiction psychiatry; and encourages research on the etiology, prevention, identification, and treatment of the addictions.

8799 ■ American Assisted Living Nurses Association (AALNA)
PO Box 10469
Napa, CA 94581
Ph: (707)253-7299
Fax: (707)253-8228
URL: http://www.alnursing.org

Description: Promotes the interests of nurses working in assisted living. Works to enhance the quality of life for the population it serves. Fosters better nursing practice in assisted living programs. Advocates for long-term care and assisted living issues.

8800 ■ American Association for Geriatric Psychiatry (AAGP)
7910 Woodmont Ave., Ste. 1050
Bethesda, MD 20814-3004
Ph: (301)654-7850
Fax: (301)654-4137
E-mail: main@aagponline.org
URL: http://www.aagponline.org

Description: Psychiatrists interested in promoting better mental health care for the elderly. Maintains placement service and speakers' bureau.

8801 ■ American Association for Long Term Care Nursing
PO Box 62956
Cincinnati, OH 45262-0956
Fax: (513)791-1477
Fr: 888-458-2687
E-mail: charlotte@ltcnursing.org
URL: http://ltcnursing.org

Description: Represents the interests of long-term care nurses and other professionals who wish to achieve excellence in the specialty of long-tem care nursing. Provides educational resources that bridge current practices with managerial and clinical activities.

8802 ■ American Association of Psychiatric Technicians (AAPT)
1220 S St., Ste. 100
Sacramento, CA 95811-7138
Fax: (916)329-9145
Fr: 800-391-7589
E-mail: aapt@psychtechs.net
URL: http://www.psychtechs.org

Description: Administers the Nationally Certified Psychiatric Technician examination to non-licensed direct-care workers in the fields of mental illness, developmental disabilities and substance abuse.

8803 ■ American Health Care Association (AHCA)
1201 L St. NW
Washington, DC 20005
Ph: (202)842-4444
Fax: (202)842-3860
E-mail: hr@ahca.org
URL: http://www.ahcancal.org/Pages/Default.aspx

Description: Federation of state associations of long-term health care facilities. Promotes standards for professionals in long-term health care delivery and quality care for patients and residents in a safe environment. Focuses on issues of availability, quality, affordability, and fair payment. Operates as liaison with governmental agencies, Congress, and professional associations. Compiles statistics.

8804 ■ American Hospital Association (AHA)
155 N Wacker Dr.
Chicago, IL 60606
Ph: (312)422-3000
Fax: (312)422-4796
E-mail: rich@aha.org
URL: http://www.aha.org

Description: Represents health care provider organizations. Seeks to advance the health of individuals and communities. Leads, represents, and serves health care provider organizations that are accountable to the community and committed to health improvement.

8805 ■ American Mental Health Alliance (AMHA)
PO Box 4075
Portland, OR 97208-4075
Ph: (503)227-2027
Fr: 888-826-3682
E-mail: memberinfo@americanmentalhealth.com
URL: http://www.americanmentalhealth.com

Description: Represents mental health professionals licensed or certified for independent practice. Creates a professional community that provides therapy of the highest quality and ethical standards. Supports

and markets competent, ethical mental health services that preserve privacy and confidentiality. Supports education, supervision, and research opportunities for members. Opposes legislation and regulations that invade patent privacy and confidentiality.

8806 ■ American Psychiatric Nurses Association
1555 Wilson Blvd., Ste. 530
Arlington, VA 22209
Ph: (703)243-2443
Fax: (703)243-3390
Fr: (866)243-2443
E-mail: ncroce@apna.org
URL: http://www.apna.org

Description: Represents psychiatric nurses who are at all levels of education from basic to doctoral and work in a variety of settings including inpatient, outpatient, research, education, administration, clinical, private practice, military, and forensic.

8807 ■ American Public Health Association (APHA)
800 I St. NW
Washington, DC 20001
Ph: (202)777-2742
Fax: (202)777-2534
E-mail: comments@apha.org
URL: http://www.apha.org

Description: Professional organization of physicians, nurses, educators, academicians, environmentalists, epidemiologists, new professionals, social workers, health administrators, optometrists, podiatrists, pharmacists, dentists, nutritionists, health planners, other community and mental health specialists, and interested consumers. Seeks to protect and promote personal, mental, and environmental health. Services include: promulgation of standards; establishment of uniform practices and procedures; development of the etiology of communicable diseases; research in public health; exploration of medical care programs and their relationships to public health. Sponsors job placement service.

8808 ■ American School Health Association (ASHA)
4340 East West Hwy., Ste. 403
Bethesda, MD 20814
Ph: (301)652-8072
Fax: (301)652-8077
Fr: 800-445-2742
E-mail: info@ashaweb.org
URL: http://www.ashaweb.org

Description: School physicians, school nurses, counselors, nutritionists, psychologists, social workers, administrators, school health coordinators, health educators, and physical educators working in schools, professional preparation programs, public health, and community-based organizations. Promotes coordinated school health programs that include health education, health services, a healthful school environment, physical education, nutrition services, and psycho-social health services offered in schools collaboratively with families and other members of the community. Offers professional reference materials and professional development opportunities. Conducts pilot programs that inform materials development, provides technical assistance to school professionals, advocates for school health.

8809 ■ Association of Black Nursing Faculty (ABNF)
PO Box 580
Lisle, IL 60532
Ph: (630)969-0221
Fax: (630)969-3895
E-mail: drsallie@gmail.com
URL: http://www.abnf.net

Description: Black nursing faculty teaching in nursing programs accredited by the National League for Nursing. Works to promote health-related issues and educational concerns of interest to the black community and ABNF. Serves as a forum for communication and the exchange of information among members; develops strategies for expressing concerns to other individuals, institutions, and communities. Assists members in professional development; develops and sponsors continuing education activities; fosters networking and guidance in employment and recruitment activities. Promotes health-related issues of legislation, government programs, and community activities. Supports black consumer advocacy issues. Encourages research. Maintains speakers' bureau and hall of fame.

8810 ■ Institute on Psychiatric Services
American Psychiatric Association
1000 Wilson Blvd., Ste. 1825
Arlington, VA 22209-3901
Ph: (703)907-7300
Fax: (703)907-1085
Fr: 888-357-7924
E-mail: apa@psych.org
URL: http://www.psych.org

Description: Annual meeting sponsored by the American Psychiatric Association. Open to Physicians and all mental health professionals of all psychiatric and related health and educational facilities. Includes lectures by experts in the field and workshops and accredited courses on problems, programs, and trends. Offers on-site Job Bank, which lists opportunities for mental health professionals. Organized scientific exhibits.

8811 ■ National Gerontological Nursing Association
3493 Landowne Dr., Ste. 2
Lexington, KY 40517
Ph: (859)977-7453

Fax: (859)271--060
Fr: 800-723-0560
E-mail: info@ngna.org
URL: http://www.ngna.org

Description: Dedicated to the clinical care of older adults across diverse care settings. Represents the interests of clinicians, educators, and researchers with vastly different educational preparation, clinical roles, and interests in practice issues.

8812 ■ National League for Nursing (NLN)
61 Broadway, 33rd Fl.
New York, NY 10006
Ph: (212)363-5555
Fax: (212)812-0391
Fr: 800-669-1656
E-mail: generalinfo@nln.org
URL: http://www.nln.org

Description: Champions the pursuit of quality nursing education. A professional association of nursing faculty, education agencies, health care agencies, allied/public agencies, and public members whose mission is to advance quality nursing education that prepares the nursing workforce to meet the needs of diverse populations in an ever-changing health care environment. Serves as the primary source of information about every type of nursing education program, from the LVN and LPN to the EdD and PhD. There are 20 affiliated constituent leagues that provide a local forum for members. The National League for Nursing Accrediting Commission is an independent corporate affiliate of the NLN, responsible for providing accreditation services to all levels of nursing education.

8813 ■ National Rural Health Association (NRHA)
Administrative Office
521 E 63rd St.
Kansas City, MO 64110-3329
Ph: (816)756-3140
Fax: (816)756-3144
E-mail: mail@nrharural.org
URL: http://www.ruralhealthweb.org

Description: Administrators, physicians, nurses, physician assistants, health planners, academicians, and others interested or involved in rural health care. Creates a better understanding of health care problems unique to rural areas; utilizes a collective approach in finding positive solutions; articulates and represents the health care needs of rural America; supplies current information to rural health care providers; serves as a liaison between rural health care programs throughout the country. Offers continuing education credits for medical, dental, nursing, and management courses.

8814 ■ Visiting Nurse Associations of America (VNAA)
900 19th St. NW, Ste. 200
Washington, DC 20006
Ph: (202)384-1420
Fax: (202)384-1444
Fr: 888-866-8773
E-mail: vnaa@vnaa.org
URL: http://www.vnaa.org

Description: Home health care agencies. Develops competitive strength among community-based non-profit visiting nurse organizations; works to strengthen business resources and economic programs through contracting, marketing, governmental affairs and publications.

Occupational Health and Safety Specialists and Technicians

SOURCES OF HELP-WANTED ADS

8815 ■ *BNA's SafetyNet*
Bureau of National Affairs Inc.
1801 S Bell St.
Arlington, VA 22202
Fax: 800-253-0332
Fr: 800-372-1033
URL: http://www.bna.com/safetynet-p6625

Description: Biweekly. Designed to help employers deal with occupational safety and health regulations, policies, standards, and practices, and to understand the effects of compliance on employee relations. Covers the establishment, management, evaluation, maintenance, and administration of health and safety programs. Carries information on recordkeeping, inspections, enforcement, employer defenses, and training.

8816 ■ *Conflict, Security and Development*
Routledge Journals
270 Madison Ave.
New York, NY 10016-0601
Ph: (212)216-7800
Fax: (212)563-2269
URL: http://www.tandf.co.uk/journals/titles/
    14678802.asp

Quarterly. $400.00/year for institutions, print + online; $360.00/year for institutions, online only; $109.00/year for individuals, print only; $668.00/year for institutions, print + online; $601.00/year for institutions, online only; $187.00/year for individuals, print only. Journal focusing on traditional development and security studies.

8817 ■ *ISHN*
BNP Media
2401 W Big Beaver Rd., Ste. 700
Troy, MI 48084-3333

Ph: (847)763-9534
Fax: (847)763-9538
URL: http://www.ishn.com/

Monthly. Free. Business-to-business magazine for safety and health managers at high-hazard worksites in manufacturing, construction, health facilities, and service industries. Content covering OSHA and EPA regulations, howto features, safety and health management topics, and the latest product news.

8818 ■ *Job Safety and Health Quarterly*
Occupational Safety and Health Administration
200 Constitution Ave., NW
Washington, DC 20210
Ph: (202)693-1999
Fax: (202)693-2498
Fr: 800-321-OSHA
URL: http://www.osha.gov/html/jshq-index.html

Description: Quarterly. Informs readers of changes, developments, and new rulings made by the Occupational Safety and Health Administration (OSHA).

8819 ■ *Journal of Safety Management*
National Safety Management Society
PO Box 4460
Walnut Creek, CA 94596-0460
Fr: 800-321-2910
URL: http://www.nsms.us/pages/c12991.htm

Quarterly. Journal covering issues in the field of safety.

8820 ■ *Occupational Safety & Health
    Reporter*
Bureau of National Affairs Inc.
1801 S Bell St.
Arlington, VA 22202
Fax: 800-253-0332

Fr: 800-372-1033
URL: http://www.bna.com/occupational-safety--p4900

Description: Weekly, except week preceding Labor Day and last week of year. Provides a notification and reference service covering federal and state regulation of occupational safety and health, standards, legislation, enforcement activities, research, and legal decisions. Recurring features include a calendar of meetings and seminars and the full text of selected administrative rulings, proposed standards, criteria documents, variance notices, and compliance manuals.

HANDBOOKS AND MANUALS

8821 ■ *Safety Consultant*
National Learning Corporation
212 Michael Dr.
Syosset, NY 11791
Ph: (516)921-8888
Fax: (516)921-8743
Fr: 800-632-8888
URL: http://www.passbooks.com

National Learning Corporation (editor). 2005. $34.95 (Trade paper).

ONLINE JOB SOURCES AND SERVICES

8822 ■ *OccupationalHealthSafetyTechnician.com*
URL: http://
    www.occupationalhealthsafetytechnician.com

Description: Provides job and career opportunities for aspiring occupational health safety technicians. Offers links, job listings, sample resumes and more.

SOURCES OF HELP-WANTED ADS

8823 ■ *ADVANCE for Occupational Therapy Practitioners*
Merion Publications Inc.
2900 Horizon Dr.
PO Box 61556
King of Prussia, PA 19406-0956
Ph: (610)278-1400
Fr: 800-355-5627
E-mail: advance@merion.com
URL: http://occupational-therapy.advanceweb.com/Default.aspx

Biweekly. Serves licensed and registered occupational therapists, certified occupational therapy assistants, and senior OT students nationwide.

8824 ■ *The American Journal of Occupational Therapy*
American Occupational Therapy Association Inc.
4720 Montgomery Ln.
PO Box 31220
Bethesda, MD 20824-1220
Ph: (301)652-2682
Fax: (301)652-7711
Fr: 800-377-8555
E-mail: cdavis@aota.org
URL: http://www.aota.org

$114.00/year for individuals, U.S.; $182.50/year for institutions, U.S.; $159.75/year for individuals, Canada; $214.00/year for institutions, Canada; $285.00/year for individuals, foreign (via airmail); $310.00/year for institutions, foreign (via airmail). Peer-reviewed journal focuses on research, practice and health care issues in the field of occupational therapy.

8825 ■ *American Journal of Physical Medicine and Rehabilitation*
Lippincott Williams & Wilkins
530 Walnut St.
Philadelphia, PA 19106-3619
Ph: (215)521-8300
Fax: (215)521-8902
Fr: 800-638-3030
URL: http://journals.lww.com/ajpmr/pages/default.aspx

Monthly. $343.00/year for individuals; $579.00/year for institutions; $210.00/year for individuals, in-training; $498.00/year for other countries; $768.00/year for institutions, other countries; $358.00/year for other countries, in-training. Medical journal.

8826 ■ *Journal of Learning Disabilities*
Sage Publications Inc.
2455 Teller Rd.
Thousand Oaks, CA 91320-2218
Ph: (805)499-9774
Fax: (805)583-2665

Fr: 800-818-7243
URL: http://www.sagepub.com/journalsProdDesc.nav?ct_p=boardsII

Bimonthly. $77.00/year for individuals, print & e-access; $260.00/year for institutions, print & e-access; $255.00/year for institutions, print only; $234.00/year for institutions, e-access. Special education journal.

8827 ■ *Occupational Therapy in Health Care*
Informa Healthcare
52 Vanderbilt Ave., 7th Fl.
New York, NY 10017-3846
Ph: (212)520-2777
URL: http://informahealthcare.com/loi/ohc

Quarterly. $585.00/year for institutions; $435.00/year for institutions. Journal for occupational therapists.

8828 ■ *Occupational Therapy in Mental Health*
Routledge Journals
270 Madison Ave.
New York, NY 10016-0601
Ph: (212)216-7800
Fax: (212)563-2269
URL: http://www.tandf.co.uk/journals/WOMH

Quarterly. $110.00/year for individuals, online only; $118.00/year for individuals, print + online; $584.00/year for institutions, online only; $649.00/year for institutions, print + online. Journal for occupational therapists working in the mental health field.

8829 ■ *OT Practice*
American Occupational Therapy Association Inc.
4720 Montgomery Ln.
PO Box 31220
Bethesda, MD 20824-1220
Ph: (301)652-2682
Fax: (301)652-7711
Fr: 800-377-8555
E-mail: otpractice@aota.org
URL: http://www.aota.org/Pubs/OTP.aspx

$142.50/year for nonmembers; $216.50/year for institutions; $205.25/year for Canada, non member; $262.50/year for institutions, Canada; $310.00/year for other countries, airmail; $365.00/year for institutions, other countries, airmail. Professional magazine for occupational therapy practitioners.

8830 ■ *Physical and Occupational Therapy in Pediatrics*
Informa Healthcare
52 Vanderbilt Ave., 7th Fl.
New York, NY 10017-3846
Ph: (212)520-2777
URL: http://informahealthcare.com/loi/pop

Quarterly. $945.00/year for institutions; $1,900.00/year for institutions, corporate; $700.00/year for institutions; $530.00/year for institutions; $1,065.00/year corporate; $1,410.00/year corporate. Journal for therapists involved in developmental and physical rehabilitation of infants and children.

8831 ■ *Teaching Exceptional Children*
Council for Exceptional Children
2900 Crystal Dr., Ste. 1000
Arlington, VA 22202
Ph: (703)620-3660
Fax: (703)264-9494
Fr: 888-232-7733
URL: http://www.cec.sped.org/Content/NavigationMenu/Publications2

$90.00/year for individuals, print; $152.00/year for two years, print; $101.00/year for Canada, print; $169.00/year for two years, Canada; $197.00/year for institutions, print; $332.00/year for two years, print; $208.00/year for institutions, Canada, print; $236.00/year for institutions, other countries, print; $399.00/year for two years, institutional (print); $225.00/year for institutions, Canada, print and online. Peer-reviewed journal exploring practical methods for teaching students who have exceptionalities and those who are gifted and talented.

EMPLOYER DIRECTORIES AND NETWORKING LISTS

8832 ■ *Careers in Focus—Therapists*
Facts On File Inc.
132 W 31st St., 17th Fl.
New York, NY 10001
Ph: (212)967-8800
Fax: 800-678-3633
Fr: 800-322-8755
URL: http://www.infobasepublishing.com

Latest edition 2nd; Published August, 2008. $32.95 for individuals. Covers: An overview of therapists, followed by a selection of jobs profiled in detail, including the nature of the job, earnings, prospects for employment, what kind of training and skills it requires, and sources for further information.

8833 ■ *Crain's List—Chicago's Largest Hospitals*
Crain Communications Inc.
360 N Michigan Ave.
Chicago, IL 60601
Ph: (312)649-5200
URL: http://www.chicagobusiness.com/section/lists

Published November, 2010. $25.00 for individuals; $45.00 for individuals. Covers: 25 hospitals in Chicago area ranked by net patient revenues. Entries include: Name, address, phone number, fax, web address, corporate e-mail, hospital administrator, network affiliation, 2009 net patient revenue, percentage change from 2008, 2009 net profits, percentage change from 2008, inpatient days, available beds, daily occupancy rate, number of hospital employees as of December 31, 2009, fiscal year end, Chairman, President, CEO, Chief Financial Officer, Human Resources Manager, Media Relations/Public Relations Director, and Hospital Administrator.

8834 ■ Directory of Hospital Personnel
Grey House Publishing
4919 Rte. 22
PO Box 56
Amenia, NY 12501
Ph: (518)789-8700
Fax: (518)789-0556
Fr: 800-562-2139
URL: http://www.greyhouse.com/hospital_
   personnel.htm

Annual, Latest edition 2011. $325.00 for individuals. Covers: 200,000 executives at 6,000 U.S. Hospitals. Entries include: Name of hospital, address, phone, number of beds, type and JCAHO status of hospital, names and titles of key department heads and staff, medical and nursing school affiliations; number of residents, interns, and nursing students. Arrangement: Geographical. Indexes: Hospital name, personnel, hospital size.

8835 ■ Hospital Blue Book
Billian Publishing Inc. and Trans World Publishing Inc.
2100 River Edge Pky.
Atlanta, GA 30328
Ph: (770)955-5656
Fax: (770)952-0669
Fr: 800-800-5668
E-mail: blu-book@billian.com
URL: http://www.billianshealthdata.com/Products/
   bluebook.html

Annual, Latest edition 2010. $575.00 for individuals; $575.00 for individuals. Covers: More than 6,500 hospitals; some listings also appear in a separate southern edition of this publication. Entries include: Name of hospital, accreditation, mailing address, phone, fax, number of beds, type of facility (nonprofit, general, state, etc.); list of administrative personnel and chiefs of medical services, with specific titles. Arrangement: Geographical.

8836 ■ Medical and Health Information Directory
Gale
PO Box 6904
Florence, KY 41022-6904
Fr: 800-354-9706
URL: http://www.gale.cengage.com

Annual, Latest edition April 2011. $1190.00 for individuals; $501.00 for individuals. Covers: In volume 1, more than 33,000 medical and health oriented associations, organizations, institutions, and government agencies, including health maintenance organizations (HMOs), preferred provider organizations (PPOs), insurance companies, pharmaceutical companies, research centers, and medical and allied health schools. In Volume 2, over 20,000 medical book publishers; medical periodicals, directories, audiovisual producers and services, medical libraries and information centers, electronic resources, and health-related internet search engines. In Volume 3, more than 40,500 clinics, treatment centers, care programs, and counseling/diagnostic services for 34 subject areas. Entries include: Institution, service, or firm name, address, phone, fax, email and URL; many include names of key personnel and, when pertinent, descriptive annotation. Volume 3 was formerly listed separately as Health Services Directory. Arrangement: Classified by organization activity, service, etc. Indexes: Each volume has a complete alphabetical name and keyword index.

HANDBOOKS AND MANUALS

8837 ■ Careers in Health Care
The McGraw-Hill Companies
PO Box 182604
Columbus, OH 43272
Fax: (614)759-3749
Fr: 877-883-5524
E-mail: customer.service@mcgraw-hill.com
URL: http://www.mhprofessional.com/
   product.php?isbn=0071466533

Barbara M. Swanson. Fifth edition, 2005. $19.95 (paper). 192 pages. Describes job duties, work settings, salaries, licensing and certification requirements, educational preparation, and future outlook. Gives ideas on how to secure a job.

8838 ■ Careers for Health Nuts and Others Who Like to Stay Fit
The McGraw-Hill Companies
PO Box 182604
Columbus, OH 43272
Fax: (614)759-3749
Fr: 877-883-5524
E-mail: customer.service@mcgraw-hill.com
URL: http://www.mhprofessional.com

Blythe Camenson. Second edition. $13.95 (paper). 208 pages.

8839 ■ Careers in Social and Rehabilitation Services
The McGraw-Hill Companies
PO Box 182604
Columbus, OH 43272
Fax: (614)759-3749
Fr: 877-883-5524
E-mail: customer.service@mcgraw-hill.com
URL: http://www.mhprofessional.com/
   product.php?isbn=0071641955

Geraldine O. Garner. 2008. $16.95. 192 pages.

8840 ■ Chief Occupational Therapist
National Learning Corporation
212 Michael Dr.
Syosset, NY 11791
Fr: 800-632-8888
URL: http://www.passbooks.com

2009. $39.95 (paper). Serves as an exam preparation guide for chief occupational therapists.

8841 ■ Opportunities in Health and Medical Careers
The McGraw-Hill Companies
PO Box 182604
Columbus, OH 43272
Fax: (614)759-3749
Fr: 877-883-5524
E-mail: customer.service@mcgraw-hill.com
URL: http://www.mhprofessional.com/
   product.php?isbn=0071437274

I. Donald Snook, Jr. and Leo D'Orazio. 2004. $14.95 (paper). 157 pages. Covers the full range of medical and health occupations. Illustrated.

8842 ■ Opportunities in Occupational Therapy Careers
The McGraw-Hill Companies
PO Box 182604
Columbus, OH 43272
Fax: (614)759-3749
Fr: 877-883-5524
E-mail: customer.service@mcgraw-hill.com
URL: http://www.mhprofessional.com/
   product.php?isbn=007146770X

Zona R. Weeks. 2006. $14.95. 160 pages. Provides an overview of opportunities in clinical positions, government and nonprofit agencies, rehabilitation centers, hospices, and other areas, and provides job-hunting guidance. Illustrated.

8843 ■ Pocket Orthopaedics: Evidence-Based Survival Guide
Jones & Bartlett Learning
5 Wall St.
Burlington, MA 01803
Fax: (978)443-8000
Fr: 800-832-0034
E-mail: info@jblearning.com
URL: http://www.jblearning.com

Michael S. Wong. 2011. $41.95 (spiral/paperback). 412 pages. Serves as learning aide in evidence-based practice for both students and clinicians.

EMPLOYMENT AGENCIES AND SEARCH FIRMS

8844 ■ Access Staffing
360 Lexington Ave., 8th Fl.
New York, NY 10017
Ph: (212)687-5440
Fax: (212)557-2544
URL: http://www.accessstaffingco.com

Serves as a staffing firm covering accounting/financial, advertising, bilingual Japanese, creative, event planning, fashion/retail, healthcare/ human services, human resources, information technology, insurance, legal, light industrial and office support.

8845 ■ Advanced Medical Personnel Services
5535 S Williamson Blvd., Ste. 774
Port Orange, FL 32128
Ph: (386)756-4395
Fr: 800-330-7711
URL: http://www.advanced-medical.net

Specializes in the placement of physical therapists, physical therapy assistants, occupational therapists, certified occupational therapy assistants and speech-language pathologists in assignments across the United States.

8846 ■ Cobb Pediatric Therapy Services
3104 Creekside Village Dr., Ste. 404
Kennesaw, GA 30144
Ph: (770)218-6274
Fax: (770)218-8568
Fr: 888-288-1048
E-mail: info@cobbpediatric.com
URL: http://www.cobbpediatric.com

Description: Staffing company that works primarily with school systems to match them with qualified speech language pathologists, occupational therapists, and physical therapists.

8847 ■ CompHealth
PO Box 713100
Salt Lake City, UT 84171-3100
Ph: (801)930-3000
Fax: (801)930-4517
Fr: 800-453-3030
E-mail: info@comphealth.com
URL: http://www.comphealth.com

Provides healthcare staffing and recruiting services covering certified registered nurse anesthetist, dosimetrist, imaging and radiation therapy, laboratory technology, medical physicist, nurse practitioner, nursing, pharmacy, physician, physician assistant, rehab therapy and respiratory therapy.

8848 ■ Cross Country TravCorps
6551 Park of Commerce Blvd.
Boca Raton, FL 33487-8247
Fax: (561)998-8533
Fr: 800-530-6125
E-mail: sms@cctc.com
URL: http://www.crosscountrytravcorps.com/cctc/

Places traveling nurses in assignments nationwide.

8849 ■ Foundation Rehab Staffing
416 W 15th St., Bldg. 600
Edmond, OK 73013
Fax: 800-774-9252
Fr: (866)337-6113
URL: http://www.foundationrehabstaffing.com

Provides staffing services; specializes in rehabilitation therapy.

8850 ■ Harper Associates
31000 NW Hwy., Ste. 240
Farmington Hills, MI 48334
Ph: (248)932-1170

Fax: (248)932-1214
E-mail: info@harperjobs.com
URL: http://www.harperjobs.com
Executive search firm and employment agency.

8851 ■ Jackson Therapy Partners
11315 Corporate Blvd., Ste. 100
Orlando, FL 32817
Fr: 800-774-7785
URL: http://www.jacksontherapy.com

Serves as a therapy recruiting firm. Features therapy jobs available across the United States including permanent and travel opportunities.

8852 ■ JPM International
26034 Acero
Mission Viejo, CA 92691
Ph: (949)699-4300
Fax: (949)699-4333
Fr: 800-685-7856
E-mail: qtek37@yahoo.com
URL: http://www.jpmintl.com/pages/qss.html

Executive search firm and employment agency.

8853 ■ MedPro Healthcare Staffing
1580 Sawgrass Corporate Pkwy., Ste. 100
Sunrise, FL 33323
Ph: (954)739-4247
Fax: 800-370-0755
Fr: 800-886-8108
E-mail: medprogeneralinquiries@medprostaffing.com
URL: http://www.medprostaffing.com

Provides temporary and contract staffing services to healthcare facilities.

8854 ■ Professional Placement Associates, Inc.
287 Bowman Ave.
Purchase, NY 10577-2517
Ph: (914)251-1000
Fax: (914)251-1055
E-mail: careers@ppasearch.com
URL: http://www.ppasearch.com

Executive search firm specializing in the health and medical field.

8855 ■ TheraKare
8596 E 101st St., Ste. H
Tulsa, OK 74146
Ph: (918)251-5982
Fax: (918)251-6047
Fr: 800-258-1036
E-mail: info@therakare.com
URL: http://www.therakare.com

Description: Specializes in providing temporary and permanent placement options for rehabilitation therapy professionals, including physical therapists, occupational therapists and speech language pathologists.

ONLINE JOB SOURCES AND SERVICES

8856 ■ CareerVitals.com
URL: http://www.careervitals.com

Description: Serves as a job board for healthcare professionals in different specializations.

8857 ■ HEALTHeCAREERS Network
Fr: 888-884-8242
E-mail: info@healthecareers.com
URL: http://www.healthecareers.com

Description: Career search site for jobs in all health care specialties; educational resources; visa and licensing information for relocation; interesting articles; relocation tools; links to professional organizations and general resources.

8858 ■ Hospital Jobs OnLine
E-mail: support@hospitaljobsonline.com
URL: http://www.hospitaljobsonline.com

Description: Serves as a niche healthcare job board designed exclusively for hospitals, healthcare companies, and healthcare job seekers.

8859 ■ JobsInLTC.com
URL: http://www.jobsinltc.com

Description: Serves as a job board for long-term care jobs for nursing home administrators, assisted living staff, directors of nursing, MDS coordinators, and other related fields.

8860 ■ JobsOT.com
URL: http://www.jobsot.com

Description: Provides solutions for finding job opportunities and job candidates dedicated specifically to the occupational therapy profession.

8861 ■ Medzilla.com
URL: http://www.medzilla.com

Description: General medical website which matches employers and job hunters to their ideal employees and jobs through search capabilities. Main files include: Post Jobs, Search Resumes, Post Resumes, Search Jobs, Head Hunters, Articles, Salary Survey.

8862 ■ nurse-recruiter.com
URL: http://www.nurse-recruiter.com

Description: Serves as a resource of jobs for the nursing and allied health fields.

8863 ■ OccupationalTherapistJobs.com
E-mail: jobs@healthcarejobstore.com
URL: http://www.occupationaltherapistjobs.com

Description: Includes occupational therapy job listings from all over the United States.

8864 ■ OccupationalTherapyCrossing.com
URL: http://www.occupationaltherapycrossing.com

Description: Provides instant access to job listings based on a job hunter's area of focus. Lists occupational therapy jobs from all Fortune 500 and Fortune 1,000 companies.

8865 ■ OTJobs.com
URL: http://www.otjobs.com

Description: Serves as an occupational therapy resource featuring a job board built specifically for occupational therapists and certified occupational therapy assistants. Provides job search tools, occupational therapy licensure information, career resources, resume posting, career development resources and a salary wizard.

8866 ■ ProHealthJobs.com
Ph: (484)443-8545
Fax: (484)443-8549
E-mail: info@prohealthjobs.com
URL: http://prohealthjobs.com/jobboard

Description: Career resources site for the medical and health care field. Lists professional opportunities, product information, continuing education and open positions.

8867 ■ RehabCareer.com
URL: http://www.rehabcareer.com

Description: Serves as a job site for physical, occupational and speech therapy.

8868 ■ RehabJobs Online
E-mail: support@atsrehabjobs.com
URL: http://www.rehabjobsonline.com

Description: Resource center for the professional therapist. Main files include: Therapists Only, Therapy Forums, Nationwide Job Search (database), Therapy Job Outlook, Therapy Job Search Utilities, Therapy Links, Information for Employers and Recruiters.

8869 ■ RehabWorld.com
URL: http://www.rehabworld.com

Description: Site for rehabilitation professionals to learn about the profession and locate jobs. Includes user groups, salary surveys, and chat capabilities. Main files include: Physical Therapy, Occupational Therapy, Speech Therapy, Mental Health, Employer World, Student World, International World, Forum.

8870 ■ TherapistsCentral.com
URL: http://www.therapistscentral.com

Description: Provides lists of job and career opportunities to physical therapists, speech therapists and occupational therapists.

8871 ■ TherapyJobBoard.com
URL: http://www.therapyjobboard.com

Description: Serves as an employment resource for job seekers and employers in the physical therapy, occupational therapy, speech therapy and respiratory therapy professions.

8872 ■ TherapyJobs.com
URL: http://www.therapyjobs.com

Description: Serves as an online career center bringing therapy employers and candidates together.

TRADESHOWS

8873 ■ American Occupational Health Conference & Exhibits
Slack, Inc.
6900 Grove Rd.
Thorofare, NJ 08086-9447
Ph: (856)848-1000
Fax: (856)853-5991
URL: http://www.slackinc.com

Annual. Primary Exhibits: Pharmaceuticals, medical equipment, computer software packages for medical offices, lab services, diagnostic testing, EAPs, ergonomics, environmental products and services. Dates and Locations: 2012 Apr 29 - May 02; Los Angeles, CA; Hyatt Regency Century Plaza.

8874 ■ American Society of Hand Therapists Annual Meeting
Smith, Bucklin and Associates, Inc. (Chicago, Illinois)
401 N Michigan Ave.
Chicago, IL 60611-4267
Ph: (312)321-6610
Fax: (312)673-6670
Fr: 800-289-NAON
E-mail: info@smithbucklin.com
URL: http://www.smithbucklin.com

Annual. Primary Exhibits: Hand therapy equipment and products. Dates and Locations: 2012 Sep 18-21; San Diego, CA; Sheraton San Diego Hotel & Marina.

8875 ■ AOTA Conference & Expo
American Occupational Therapy Association
PO Box 31220
Bethesda, MD 20824-1220
Ph: (301)652-2682
Fax: (301)652-7711
Fr: 800-377-8555
URL: http://www.aota.org/ConfandEvents/2012Conference.aspx

Annual. Provides news, information, and discussion about the serious challenges OT faces and offers guidance on navigating through these challenges.

8876 ■ Occupational Therapy Association of California Conference
Occupational Therapy Association of California
PO Box 276567
Sacramento, CA 95827
Ph: (916)567-7000
Fax: (916)567-7001
Fr: 888-686-3225
E-mail: info@otaconline.org
URL: http://www.otaconline.org

Annual. Primary Exhibits: Occupational therapy equipment, supplies, and services.

OTHER SOURCES

8877 ■ American Health Care Association (AHCA)
1201 L St. NW
Washington, DC 20005
Ph: (202)842-4444
Fax: (202)842-3860
E-mail: hr@ahca.org
URL: http://www.ahcancal.org/Pages/Default.aspx

Description: Federation of state associations of long-term health care facilities. Promotes standards for professionals in long-term health care delivery and quality care for patients and residents in a safe environment. Focuses on issues of availability, quality, affordability, and fair payment. Operates as liaison with governmental agencies, Congress, and professional associations. Compiles statistics.

8878 ■ American Kinesiotherapy Association (AKTA)
118 College Dr., No. 5142
Hattiesburg, MS 39406
Fr: 800-296-2582
E-mail: info@akta.org
URL: http://www.akta.org

Description: Professional society of kinesiotherapists, associate and student members with interest in therapeutic exercise and education. Kinesiotherapy is the application of scientifically-based exercise principles adapted to enhance the strength, endurance and mobility of individuals with functional limitations of those requiring extended physical reconditioning. Seeks to serve the interest of members and represent the profession to the public through the promotion of continuing competency and continuing educational opportunities.

8879 ■ American Occupational Therapy Association (AOTA)
4720 Montgomery Ln.
PO Box 31220
Bethesda, MD 20824-1220
Ph: (301)652-2682
Fax: (301)652-7711
Fr: 800-377-8555
E-mail: members@aota.org
URL: http://www.aota.org

Description: Occupational therapists and occupational therapy assistants. Provides services to people whose lives have been disrupted by physical injury or illness, developmental problems, the aging process, or social or psychological difficulties. Occupational therapy focuses on the active involvement of the patient in specially designed therapeutic tasks and activities to improve function, performance capacity, and the ability to cope with demands of daily living.

8880 ■ American Public Health Association (APHA)
800 I St. NW
Washington, DC 20001
Ph: (202)777-2742
Fax: (202)777-2534
E-mail: comments@apha.org
URL: http://www.apha.org

Description: Professional organization of physicians, nurses, educators, academicians, environmentalists, epidemiologists, new professionals, social workers, health administrators, optometrists, podiatrists, pharmacists, dentists, nutritionists, health planners, other community and mental health specialists, and interested consumers. Seeks to protect and promote personal, mental, and environmental health. Services include: promulgation of standards; establishment of uniform practices and procedures; development of the etiology of communicable diseases; research in public health; exploration of medical care programs and their relationships to public health. Sponsors job placement service.

8881 ■ American Society of Hand Therapists (ASHT)
15000 Commerce Pkwy., Ste. C
Mount Laurel, NJ 08054
Ph: (856)380-6856
Fax: (856)439-0525
E-mail: asht@asht.org
URL: http://www.asht.org

Description: Registered and licensed occupational and physical therapists specializing in hand therapy and committed to excellence and professionalism in hand rehabilitation. Works to promote research, publish information, improve treatment techniques, and standardize hand evaluation and care. Fosters education and communication between therapists in the U.S. and abroad. Compiles statistics; conducts research and education programs and continuing education seminars.

8882 ■ Association on Higher Education and Disability (AHEAD)
107 Commerce Center Dr., Ste. 204
Huntersville, NC 28078
Ph: (704)947-7779
Fax: (704)948-7779
E-mail: ahead@ahead.org
URL: http://www.ahead.org

Description: Individuals interested in promoting the equal rights and opportunities of disabled postsecondary students, staff, faculty, and graduates. Provides an exchange of communication for those professionally involved with disabled students; collects, evaluates, and disseminates information; encourages and supports legislation for the benefit of disabled students. Conducts surveys on issues pertinent to college students with disabilities; offers resource referral system and employment exchange for positions in disability student services. Conducts research programs; compiles statistics.

8883 ■ National Board for Certification in Occupational Therapy (NBCOT)
12 S Summit Ave., Ste. 100
Gaithersburg, MD 20877-4150
Ph: (301)990-7979
Fax: (301)869-8492
E-mail: info@nbcot.org
URL: http://www.nbcot.org

Description: Participants are occupational therapists and occupational therapy assistants. Administers certification program and maintains certification records of certificants; operates disciplinary mechanisms.

8884 ■ National Rehabilitation Association (NRA)
633 S Washington St.
Alexandria, VA 22314
Ph: (703)836-0850
Fax: (703)836-0848
E-mail: info@nationalrehab.org
URL: http://www.nationalrehab.org

Description: Provides opportunities through knowledge and diversity for professionals in the fields of rehabilitation of people with disabilities.

8885 ■ Neuro-Developmental Treatment Association (NDTA)
1540 S Coast Hwy., Ste. 203
Laguna Beach, CA 92651
Fax: (949)376-3456
Fr: 800-869-9295
E-mail: info@ndta.org
URL: http://www.ndta.org

Description: Physical and occupational therapists, speech pathologists, special educators, physicians, parents, and others interested in neurodevelopmental treatment. (NDT is a form of therapy for individuals who suffer from central nervous system disorders resulting in abnormal movement. Treatment attempts to initiate or refine normal stages and processes in the development of movement.) Informs members of new developments in the field and with ideas that will eventually improve fundamental independence. Locates articles related to NDT.

SOURCES OF HELP-WANTED ADS

8886 ■ ADVANCE for Occupational Therapy Practitioners
Merion Publications Inc.
2900 Horizon Dr.
PO Box 61556
King of Prussia, PA 19406-0956
Ph: (610)278-1400
Fr: 800-355-5627
E-mail: advance@merion.com
URL: http://occupational-therapy.advanceweb.com/Default.aspx

Biweekly. Serves licensed and registered occupational therapists, certified occupational therapy assistants, and senior OT students nationwide.

8887 ■ The American Journal of Occupational Therapy
American Occupational Therapy Association Inc.
4720 Montgomery Ln.
PO Box 31220
Bethesda, MD 20824-1220
Ph: (301)652-2682
Fax: (301)652-7711
Fr: 800-377-8555
E-mail: cdavis@aota.org
URL: http://www.aota.org

$114.00/year for individuals, U.S.; $182.50/year for institutions, U.S.; $159.75/year for individuals, Canada; $214.00/year for institutions, Canada; $285.00/year for individuals, foreign (via airmail); $310.00/year for institutions, foreign (via airmail). Peer-reviewed journal focuses on research, practice and health care issues in the field of occupational therapy.

8888 ■ American Journal of Physical Medicine and Rehabilitation
Lippincott Williams & Wilkins
530 Walnut St.
Philadelphia, PA 19106-3619
Ph: (215)521-8300
Fax: (215)521-8902
Fr: 800-638-3030
URL: http://journals.lww.com/ajpmr/pages/default.aspx

Monthly. $343.00/year for individuals; $579.00/year for institutions; $210.00/year for individuals, in-training; $498.00/year for other countries; $768.00/year for institutions, other countries; $358.00/year for other countries, in-training. Medical journal.

8889 ■ Occupational Therapy in Health Care
Informa Healthcare
52 Vanderbilt Ave., 7th Fl.
New York, NY 10017-3846
Ph: (212)520-2777
URL: http://informahealthcare.com/loi/ohc

Quarterly. $585.00/year for institutions; $435.00/year for institutions. Journal for occupational therapists.

8890 ■ Occupational Therapy in Mental Health
Routledge Journals
270 Madison Ave.
New York, NY 10016-0601
Ph: (212)216-7800
Fax: (212)563-2269
URL: http://www.tandf.co.uk/journals/WOMH

Quarterly. $110.00/year for individuals, online only; $118.00/year for individuals, print + online; $584.00/year for institutions, online only; $649.00/year for institutions, print + online. Journal for occupational therapists working in the mental health field.

8891 ■ OT Practice
American Occupational Therapy Association Inc.
4720 Montgomery Ln.
PO Box 31220
Bethesda, MD 20824-1220
Ph: (301)652-2682
Fax: (301)652-7711
Fr: 800-377-8555
E-mail: otpractice@aota.org
URL: http://www.aota.org/Pubs/OTP.aspx

$142.50/year for nonmembers; $216.50/year for institutions; $205.25/year for Canada, non member; $262.50/year for institutions, Canada; $310.00/year for other countries, airmail; $365.00/year for institutions, other countries, airmail. Professional magazine for occupational therapy practitioners.

8892 ■ Physical & Occupational Therapy in Geriatrics
Informa Healthcare
52 Vanderbilt Ave., 7th Fl.
New York, NY 10017-3846
Ph: (212)520-2777
URL: http://informahealthcare.com/pog

Quarterly. $520.00/year for institutions; $920.00/year for institutions; $685.00/year for institutions. Journal for allied health professionals focusing on current practice and emerging issues in the health care of and rehabilitation of the older client.

8893 ■ Physical and Occupational Therapy in Pediatrics
Informa Healthcare
52 Vanderbilt Ave., 7th Fl.
New York, NY 10017-3846
Ph: (212)520-2777
URL: http://informahealthcare.com/loi/pop

Quarterly. $945.00/year for institutions; $1,900.00/year for institutions, corporate; $700.00/year for institutions; $530.00/year for institutions; $1,065.00/year corporate; $1,410.00/year corporate. Journal for therapists involved in developmental and physical rehabilitation of infants and children.

EMPLOYER DIRECTORIES AND NETWORKING LISTS

8894 ■ Careers in Focus—Therapists
Facts On File Inc.
132 W 31st St., 17th Fl.
New York, NY 10001

Ph: (212)967-8800
Fax: 800-678-3633
Fr: 800-322-8755
URL: http://www.infobasepublishing.com

Latest edition 2nd; Published August, 2008. $32.95 for individuals. Covers: An overview of therapists, followed by a selection of jobs profiled in detail, including the nature of the job, earnings, prospects for employment, what kind of training and skills it requires, and sources for further information.

8895 ■ Crain's List—Chicago's Largest Hospitals
Crain Communications Inc.
360 N Michigan Ave.
Chicago, IL 60601
Ph: (312)649-5200
URL: http://www.chicagobusiness.com/section/lists

Published November, 2010. $25.00 for individuals; $45.00 for individuals. Covers: 25 hospitals in Chicago area ranked by net patient revenues. Entries include: Name, address, phone number, fax, web address, corporate e-mail, hospital administrator, network affiliation, 2009 net patient revenue, percentage change from 2008, 2009 net profits, percentage change from 2008, inpatient days, available beds, daily occupancy rate, number of hospital employees as of December 31, 2009, fiscal year end, Chairman, President, CEO, Chief Financial Officer, Human Resources Manager, Media Relations/Public Relations Director, and Hospital Administrator.

8896 ■ Health Care Careers Directory
American Medical Association
515 N State St.
Chicago, IL 60654
Fr: 800-621-8335
E-mail: dorothy-grant@ama-assn.org
URL: http://www.ama-assn.org

Annual, Latest edition 2010-2011. $30.00 for individuals. Covers: More than 8,600 health career educational programs in over 82 health occupations at 2,700 sponsoring institutions. Entries include: Occupational descriptions, employment characteristics, and information on education programs, such as length, curriculum, and prerequisites. Arrangement: Classified by occupation, then geographical. Indexes: Institution name, program name.

8897 ■ Occupational Therapy Educational Programs List
American Occupational Therapy Association Inc.
4720 Montgomery Ln.
PO Box 31220
Bethesda, MD 20824-1220
Ph: (301)652-2682
Fax: (301)652-7711
Fr: 800-377-8555
E-mail: accred@aota.org
URL: http://www.aota.org

Database covers: Approximately 150 accredited, developing, and applicant programs in occupational therapy and 149 accredited, developing, and applicant occupational therapy assistant programs. Database includes: Institution name, address, phone, URL, level of program. Telecommunications Device for the Deaf, 800-377-8555. Arrangement: Geographical, then classified by educational institution. Separate listings for accredited, developing, and applicant OT and OTA programs.

Handbooks and Manuals

8898 ■ *Careers for Health Nuts and Others Who Like to Stay Fit*
The McGraw-Hill Companies
PO Box 182604
Columbus, OH 43272
Fax: (614)759-3749
Fr: 877-883-5524
E-mail: customer.service@mcgraw-hill.com
URL: http://www.mhprofessional.com

Blythe Camenson. Second edition. $13.95 (paper). 208 pages.

8899 ■ *Careers in Social and Rehabilitation Services*
The McGraw-Hill Companies
PO Box 182604
Columbus, OH 43277
Fax: (614)759-3749
Fr: 877-883-5524
E-mail: customer.service@mcgraw-hill.com
URL: http://www.mhprofessional.com/ product.php?isbn=0071641955

Geraldine O. Garner. 2008. $16.95. 192 pages.

8900 ■ *Opportunities in Health and Medical Careers*
The McGraw-Hill Companies
PO Box 182604
Columbus, OH 43272
Fax: (614)759-3749
Fr: 877-883-5524
E-mail: customer.service@mcgraw-hill.com
URL: http://www.mhprofessional.com/ product.php?isbn=0071437274

I. Donald Snook, Jr. and Leo D'Orazio. 2004. $14.95 (paper). 157 pages. Covers the full range of medical and health occupations. Illustrated.

8901 ■ *Opportunities in Occupational Therapy Careers*
The McGraw-Hill Companies
PO Box 182604
Columbus, OH 43272
Fax: (614)759-3749
Fr: 877-883-5524
E-mail: customer.service@mcgraw-hill.com
URL: http://www.mhprofessional.com/ product.php?isbn=007146770X

Zona R. Weeks. 2006. $14.95. 160 pages. Provides an overview of opportunities in clinical positions, government and nonprofit agencies, rehabilitation centers, hospices, and other areas, and provides job-hunting guidance. Illustrated.

8902 ■ *Pocket Orthopaedics: Evidence-Based Survival Guide*
Jones & Bartlett Learning
5 Wall St.
Burlington, MA 01803
Fax: (978)443-8000
Fr: 800-832-0034
E-mail: info@jblearning.com
URL: http://www.jblearning.com

Michael S. Wong. 2011. $41.95 (spiral/paperback). 412 pages. Serves as learning aide in evidence-based practice for both students and clinicians.

Employment Agencies and Search Firms

8903 ■ Advanced Medical Personnel Services
5535 S Williamson Blvd., Ste. 774
Port Orange, FL 32128
Ph: (386)756-4395
Fr: 800-330-7711
URL: http://www.advanced-medical.net

Specializes in the placement of physical therapists, physical therapy assistants, occupational therapists, certified occupational therapy assistants and speech-language pathologists in assignments across the United States.

8904 ■ Cross Country TravCorps
6551 Park of Commerce Blvd.
Boca Raton, FL 33487-8247
Fax: (561)998-8533
Fr: 800-530-6125
E-mail: sms@cctc.com
URL: http://www.crosscountrytravcorps.com/cctc/

Places traveling nurses in assignments nationwide.

8905 ■ Jackson Therapy Partners
11315 Corporate Blvd., Ste. 100
Orlando, FL 32817
Fr: 800-774-7785
URL: http://www.jacksontherapy.com

Serves as a therapy recruiting firm. Features therapy jobs available across the United States including permanent and travel opportunities.

8906 ■ MedPro Healthcare Staffing
1580 Sawgrass Corporate Pkwy., Ste. 100
Sunrise, FL 33323
Ph: (954)739-4247
Fax: 800-370-0755
Fr: 800-886-8108
E-mail: medprogeneralinquiries@medprostaffing.com
URL: http://www.medprostaffing.com

Provides temporary and contract staffing services to healthcare facilities.

8907 ■ Team Placement Service, Inc.
1414 Prince St., Ste. 202
Alexandria, VA 22314
Ph: (703)820-8618
Fax: (703)820-3368
Fr: 800-495-6767
E-mail: 4jobs@teamplace.com
URL: http://www.teamplace.com

Full-service personnel consultants provide placement for healthcare staff, physician and dentist, private practice, and hospitals. Conduct interviews, tests, and reference checks to select the top 20% of applicants. Survey applicants' skill levels, provide backup information on each candidate, select compatible candidates for consideration, and insure the hiring process minimizes potential legal liability. Industries served: healthcare and government agencies providing medical, dental, biotech, laboratory, hospitals, and physician search.

Online Job Sources and Services

8908 ■ OccupationalTherapistAssistant.com
URL: http://www.occupationaltherapistassistant.com

Description: Provides career and employment information for aspiring occupational therapist assistants. Offers links, job listings, sample resumes and more.

8909 ■ OTJobs.com
URL: http://www.otjobs.com

Description: Serves as an occupational therapy resource featuring a job board built specifically for occupational therapists and certified occupational

therapy assistants. Provides job search tools, occupational therapy licensure information, career resources, resume posting, career development resources and a salary wizard.

8910 ■ RehabJobs Online
E-mail: support@atsrehabjobs.com
URL: http://www.rehabjobsonline.com

Description: Resource center for the professional therapist. Main files include: Therapists Only, Therapy Forums, Nationwide Job Search (database), Therapy Job Outlook, Therapy Job Search Utilities, Therapy Links, Information for Employers and Recruiters.

8911 ■ RehabWorld.com
URL: http://www.rehabworld.com

Description: Site for rehabilitation professionals to learn about the profession and locate jobs. Includes user groups, salary surveys, and chat capabilities. Main files include: Physical Therapy, Occupational Therapy, Speech Therapy, Mental Health, Employer World, Student World, International World, Forum.

8912 ■ TherapyJobBoard.com
URL: http://www.therapyjobboard.com

Description: Serves as an employment resource for job seekers and employers in the physical therapy, occupational therapy, speech therapy and respiratory therapy professions.

Other Sources

8913 ■ American Occupational Therapy Association (AOTA)
4720 Montgomery Ln.
PO Box 31220
Bethesda, MD 20824-1220
Ph: (301)652-2682
Fax: (301)652-7711
Fr: 800-377-8555
E-mail: members@aota.org
URL: http://www.aota.org

Description: Occupational therapists and occupational therapy assistants. Provides services to people whose lives have been disrupted by physical injury or illness, developmental problems, the aging process, or social or psychological difficulties. Occupational therapy focuses on the active involvement of the patient in specially designed therapeutic tasks and activities to improve function, performance capacity, and the ability to cope with demands of daily living.

8914 ■ National Board for Certification in Occupational Therapy (NBCOT)
12 S Summit Ave., Ste. 100
Gaithersburg, MD 20877-4150
Ph: (301)990-7979
Fax: (301)869-8492
E-mail: info@nbcot.org
URL: http://www.nbcot.org

Description: Participants are occupational therapists and occupational therapy assistants. Administers certification program and maintains certification records of certificants; operates disciplinary mechanisms.

8915 ■ Neuro-Developmental Treatment Association (NDTA)
1540 S Coast Hwy., Ste. 203
Laguna Beach, CA 92651
Fax: (949)376-3456
Fr: 800-869-9295
E-mail: info@ndta.org
URL: http://www.ndta.org

Description: Physical and occupational therapists, speech pathologists, special educators, physicians, parents, and others interested in neurodevelopmental treatment. (NDT is a form of therapy for individuals who suffer from central nervous system disorders resulting in abnormal movement. Treatment attempts to initiate or refine normal stages and processes in the development of movement.) Informs members of new developments in the field and with ideas that will

eventually improve fundamental independence.

Locates articles related to NDT.

SOURCES OF HELP-WANTED ADS

8916 ■ *Academy of Management Journal*
Academy of Management
235 Elm Rd.
PO Box 3020
Briarcliff Manor, NY 10510-8020
Ph: (914)923-2607
Fax: (914)923-2615
URL: http://journals.aomonline.org/amj/
Bimonthly. Professional journal covering management.

8917 ■ *Academy of Management Learning & Education*
Academy of Management
235 Elm Rd.
PO Box 3020
Briarcliff Manor, NY 10510-8020
Ph: (914)923-2607
Fax: (914)923-2615
URL: http://journals.aomonline.org/amle
Quarterly. $85.00/year for individuals, print; $130.00/year for individuals, print & online; $125.00/year for libraries, print; $170.00/year for libraries, print and online; $105.00/year for other countries, print; $150.00/year for other countries, print & online; $195.00/year for other countries, print, corporate library; $235.00/year for other countries, print & online, corporate library. Journal covering management issues for professionals.

8918 ■ *Business Performance Management*
Penton Media Inc.
249 W 17th St.
New York, NY 10011
Ph: (212)204-4200
URL: http://www.bpmmag.net/
Free to qualified subscribers. Magazine for business managers. Covers organizing, automating, and analyzing of business methodologies and processes.

8919 ■ *CXO*
IDG Communications Inc.
3 Speen St.
Framingham, MA 01701
Ph: (508)875-5000
URL: http://www.idg.com/www/IDGProducts.nsf/0/022796185EED5984852
Monthly. Magazine providing technology information for chief officers and managers.

8920 ■ *D & O Advisor*
American Lawyer Media L.P.
120 Broadway, 5th Fl.
New York, NY 10271
Ph: (212)457-9400
Fax: (646)417-7705
Fr: 800-603-6571
URL: http://www.alm.com
Quarterly. Magazine that offers advice and perspective on corporate oversight responsibilities for directors and officers.

8921 ■ *E Journal of Organizational Learning and Leadership*
WeLEAD Inc.
PO Box 202
Litchfield, OH 44253
Fr: 877-778-5494
URL: http://www.leadingtoday.org/weleadinlearning/
Semiannual. Free. Online academic journal about organizational leadership.

8922 ■ *Event Management*
Cognizant Communications Corp.
3 Hartsdale Rd.
Elmsford, NY 10523-3701
Ph: (914)592-7720
Fax: (914)592-8981
URL: http://www.cognizantcommunication.com/journal-titles/event-
Quarterly. $445.00/year for institutions, online only; $525.00/year for institutions, online & hard copy; $52.00/year for individuals, professional; $50.00/year for members, online & hard copy; $65.00/year for single issue. Peer-reviewed journal covering research and analytic needs of a rapidly growing profession focused on events.

8923 ■ *Executive Legal Adviser*
Incisive Media
120 Broadway, 5th Fl.
New York, NY 10271
Ph: (212)457-9400
Fax: (646)417-7705
URL: http://www.executivelegaladviser.com
Bimonthly. Free to qualified subscribers. Magazine that offers legal advice for corporate executives.

8924 ■ *Fleet Maintenance*
Cygnus Business Media Inc.
3 Huntington Quadrangle, Ste. 301 N
Melville, NY 11747
Ph: (631)845-2700
Fax: (631)845-7109
Fr: 800-308-6397
URL: http://www.fleetmag.com
Business tabloid magazine offering a chapterized curriculum of technical, regulatory and managerial information designed to help maintenance managers, directors and supervisors better perform their jobs and reduce their overall cost-per-mile.

8925 ■ *Forrester*
Forrester Research Inc.
400 Technology Sq.
Cambridge, MA 02139
Ph: (617)613-5730
Fr: (866)367-7378
URL: http://www.forrester.com/mag
Free. Journal that aims to provide ideas and advice that is relevant to today's CEOs.

8926 ■ *International Journal of Business Research*
International Academy of Business and Economics
PO Box 2536
Ceres, CA 95307
Ph: (702)560-0653
Fax: (702)508-9166
URL: http://www.iabe.eu/domains/iabeX/journal.aspx?journalid=12
Peer-reviewed journal publishing theoretical, conceptual, and applied research on topics related to research, practice and teaching in all areas of business, management, and marketing.

8927 ■ *Journal of Academic Leadership*
Academic Leadership
600 Park St.
Rarick Hall 219
Hays, KS 67601-4099
Ph: (785)628-4547
URL: http://www.academicleadership.org/
Journal focusing on the leadership issues in the academic world.

8928 ■ *Journal of Business and Psychology*
Springer-Verlag New York Inc.
233 Spring St.
New York, NY 10013-1578
Ph: (212)460-1500
Fax: (212)460-1575
Fr: 800-777-4643
URL: http://www.springer.com/psychology/community+%26+environment
$904.00/year for institutions, print or online; $1,085.00/year for institutions, print & enchanced access. Journal covering all aspects of psychology that apply to the business segment. Includes topics such as personnel selection and training, organizational assessment and development, risk management and loss control, marketing and consumer behavior research.

8929 ■ *Journal of International Business Strategy*
International Academy of Business and Economics
PO Box 2536
Ceres, CA 95307
Ph: (702)560-0653
Fax: (702)508-9166
URL: http://www.iabe.eu/domains/iabeX/journal.aspx?journalid=7
Peer-reviewed journal publishing theoretical, conceptual, and applied research on topics related to strategy in international business.

8930 ■ Management Research
M.E. Sharpe Inc.
80 Business Pk. Dr.
Armonk, NY 10504
Ph: (914)273-1800
Fax: (914)273-2106
Fr: 800-541-6563
URL: http://www.mesharpe.com/mall/
results1.asp?ACR=JMR

$75.00/year for individuals; $399.00/year for institutions; $87.00/year for other countries; $441.00/year for institutions, other countries. International journal dedicated to advancing the understanding of management in private and public sector organizations through empirical investigation and theoretical analysis. Attempts to promote an international dialogue between researchers, improve the understanding of the nature of management in different settings, and achieve a reasonable transfer of research results to management practice in several contexts. Receptive to research across a broad range of management topics such as human resource management, organizational behavior, organizational theory, and strategic management. While not regional in nature, articles dealing with Iberoamerican issues are particularly welcomed.

8931 ■ OfficePRO
Stratton Publishing and Marketing Inc.
5285 Shawnee Rd., Ste. 510
Alexandria, VA 22312-2334
Ph: (703)914-9200
Fax: (703)914-6777
URL: http://www.iaap-hq.org/publications/officepro

$25.00/year for individuals; $40.00/year for individuals, two years; $57.00/year for individuals, three years; $59.00/year for individuals, international; $109.00/year for individuals, international, two years. Magazine for administrative assistants, office managers, and secretaries featuring information on trends in business, technology, career development, and management.

8932 ■ Organization Management Journal
Eastern Academy of Management
c/o Vicki Fairbanks Taylor, VP
John I. Grove College of Business
45 Keefer Way
Mechanicsburg, PA 17011
Ph: (518)762-4651
Fax: (518)736-1716
E-mail: omj@palgrave.com
URL: http://www1.wnec.edu/omj

Free to qualified subscribers. Refereed, online journal focusing on organization management issues.

8933 ■ Public Performance and Management Review
M.E. Sharpe Inc.
80 Business Pk. Dr.
Armonk, NY 10504
Ph: (914)273-1800
Fax: (914)273-2106
Fr: 800-541-6563
URL: http://www.mesharpe.com/mall/
results1.asp?ACR=pmr

Quarterly. $95.00/year for individuals; $528.00/year for institutions; $111.00/year for other countries; $560.00/year for institutions, other countries. Journal addressing a broad range of factors influencing the performance of public and nonprofit organizations and agencies. Aims to facilitate the development of innovative techniques and encourage a wider application of those already established; stimulate research and critical thinking about the relationship between public and private management theories; present integrated analyses of theories, concepts, strategies and techniques dealing with productivity, measurement and related questions of performance improvement; and provide a forum for practitioner-academic exchange. Continuing themes include managing for productivity, measuring and evaluating performance, improving budget strategies, managing

human resources, building partnerships, and applying new technologies.

8934 ■ Supply Chain Management Review
Reed Business Information
360 Park Ave. S
New York, NY 10010-1710
Ph: (646)746-6400
URL: http://www.scmr.com

$199.00/year for individuals; $199.00/year for Canada; $337.00/year for other countries. Publication covering business and management.

HANDBOOKS AND MANUALS

8935 ■ Administrative Manager
National Learning Corporation
212 Michael Dr.
Syosset, NY 11791
Ph: (516)921-8888
Fax: (516)921-8743
Fr: 800-632-8888
URL: http://www.passbooks.com

Rudman, Jack. 2005. $34.95 (Trade paper).

8936 ■ Real-Resumes for Administrative Support, Office and Secretarial Jobs
PREP Publishing
1110 1/2 Hay St., PMB 66
Fayetteville, NC 28305
Ph: (910)483-6611
Fax: (910)483-2439
URL: http://www.prep-pub.com/Bookstore/
administrative.htm

Anne McKinney (Editor). March 2004. $16.95. Illustrated. 192 pages. Part of the Real-Resumes Series.

EMPLOYMENT AGENCIES AND SEARCH FIRMS

8937 ■ Ambassador Personnel Services Inc.
1541 Fording Island Rd., Ste. 4
Hilton Head Island, SC 29926
Ph: (843)837-9066
Fax: (843)837-6477
E-mail: blufton@teamambassador.com
URL: http://www.teamambassador.com

Full service employment agency that includes local temporary and permanent placements, medical home health provider and regional and national hospitality placement. Industries served: locally: administrative and clerical, home health; regionally: food and beverage and hospitality.

8938 ■ ARI Admin
4902 Tollview Dr.
Rolling Meadows, IL 60008
Ph: (224)232-5880
E-mail: information@ariadmin.com
URL: http://www.ariadmin.com

Description: Specializes in the placement of administrative professionals for direct hire, contract and temporary services.

8939 ■ ATR Professional
1230 Oakmead Pkwy.
Sunnyvale, CA 94085
Ph: (408)328-8000
Fax: (408)328-8001
Fr: 877-412-1100
E-mail: corporate@atr1.com
URL: http://www.atr-professional.com

Description: Serves as an executive search firm specializing in the placement of administrative, clerical, and customer service, HR, and marketing personnel.

8940 ■ Barrett Business Services Inc.
8100 NE Parkway Dr., Ste. 200
Vancouver, WA 98662
Ph: (360)828-0700
Fax: (360)828-0701
Fr: 800-494-5669
E-mail: bbsicorp@bbsihq.com
URL: http://www.barrettbusiness.com

Offers temporary and long-term staffing services and professional employer services. Services focus primarily on light industrial businesses; clerical and technical staffing account for the rest. Also does business as a professional employment organization, providing outsourced human resource services, such as payroll management, benefits administration, recruiting, and placement.

8941 ■ Brattle Temps
50 Congress St., Ste. 935
Boston, MA 02109-4008
Ph: (617)523-4600
Fax: (617)523-3939
E-mail: temps@brattletemps.com

Personnel consulting firm specializes in providing temporary consultants. Skill areas available include: computer operators, secretaries, editors, librarians, graphic artists, and marketing professionals. Industries served: universities, publishing, engineering, manufacturing, and government agencies.

8942 ■ CyberCoders, Inc.
6591 Irvine Center Dr., Ste. 200
Irvine, CA 92618
Ph: (866)421-0200
Fax: (949)885-5150
E-mail: info@cybercoders.com
URL: http://www.cybercoders.com

Description: Recruitment and job search firm specializing in engineering, executive, financial, accounting and sales.

8943 ■ Golden Gate Staffing
1422 Springs Rd., Ste. B
Vallejo, CA 94591
Ph: (707)552-6767
E-mail: info@goldengatestaffing.com
URL: http://www.goldengatestaffing.com

Provides project based, temporary, full-time and permanent placement staffing services.

8944 ■ Hunt Executive Search, Inc.
100 Park Ave.
New York, NY 10017
Ph: (212)861-2680
Fr: 800-486-8476
E-mail: info@hungroup.com
URL: http://www.huntsearch.com

Provides executive search services to consumer products, life sciences, retail, professional services and diversified industrial markets.

8945 ■ Metropolitan Personnel Inc.
1260 Valley Forge Rd., Ste. 109
PO Box 641
Phoenixville, PA 19460
Ph: (610)933-4000
Fax: (610)933-4670
E-mail: office@metpersnl.com
URL: http://www.metpersnl.com

Offers permanent placement services and specializes in office support, medical and technological staffing. Industries served: multi-industry oriented including government agencies. Firm also provides temporary staffing services and is a PEO.

8946 ■ OfficeTeam.com
2884 Sand Hill Rd.
Menlo Park, CA 94025
Fr: 800-804-8367
URL: http://www.officeteam.com

Serves as a specialized temporary staffing service for administrative professionals including executive assistant, administrative assistant, office manager, project coordinator, receptionist, human resource assistant, marketing assistant, customer service representative, and data entry specialist.

8947 ■ Scion Staffing
576 Sacramento St., 2nd Fl.
San Francisco, CA 94111
Ph: (415)392-7500
E-mail: info@scionstaffing.com
URL: http://scionstaffing.com

Serves as an executive search firm and temporary agency for professional candidates.

8948 ■ The Underwood Group Inc.
1209 A Brooks Ave.
Raleigh, NC 27607
Ph: (919)782-3024
Fax: (919)782-2811
Fr: 800-409-4498
E-mail: shari@underwoodgroup.com
URL: http://www.underwoodgroup.com

Personnel consultants provide data processing placement services, both permanent and temporary. Industries served data processing and engineering. Solutions and project delivery.

ONLINE JOB SOURCES AND SERVICES

8949 ■ AdminCareers.com
URL: http://www.admincareers.com

Description: Serves as a niche job board for administrative related jobs, including administrative assistants, receptionists, secretaries, office managers, executive assistants and all office professionals.

TRADESHOWS

8950 ■ Jobbernaut Career Fairs
Jobbernaut, Inc.
PO Box 2267
Lynnwood, WA 98036
Ph: (425)397-7114
Fax: (425)397-7505
URL: http://jobbernautcareerfairs.com

Brings together over 1500 companies to recruit and hire applicants from the following industries: sales, management, restaurant and retail; technical, engineering, computers; administrative, general office,

and customer service; and banking and financial. 2012 October 3; Seattle, WA.

OTHER SOURCES

8951 ■ International Association of Administrative Professionals (IAAP)
10502 NW Ambassador Dr.
PO Box 20404
Kansas City, MO 64195-0404
Ph: (816)891-6600
Fax: (816)891-9118
E-mail: eallen@iaap-hq.org
URL: http://www.iaap-hq.org

Description: IAAP is the world's largest association of administrative support staff, with over 600 chapters and 28,000 members and affiliates worldwide. Provides up-to-date research on office trends, publications, seminars and conferences, and resources to help administrative professionals enhance their skills and become more effective contributors to their employers.

SOURCES OF HELP-WANTED ADS

8952 ■ ORMS Today
Institute for Operations Research and the Management Sciences
7240 Pkwy. Dr., Ste. 300
Hanover, MD 21076-1310
Ph: (443)757-3500
Fax: (443)757-3515
Fr: 800-446-3676
E-mail: informs@informs.org
URL: http://www.orms-today.org

Bimonthly. Covers topics pertaining to the professional and academic operations research and management services.

HANDBOOKS AND MANUALS

8953 ■ Next Generation Product Development: How to Increase Productivity, Cut Costs, and Reduce Cycle Times
McGraw-Hill Companies
PO Box 182604
Columbus, OH 43272
Ph: 877-833-5524
Fax: (614)759-3749
Fr: 800-262-4729
E-mail: customer.service@mcgraw-hill.com
URL: http://www.mhprofessional.com/
    product.php?isbn=0071435123

Michael E. McGrath. 2004. $39.95. 352 pages. A guide to making the most of today's product development breakthroughs.

EMPLOYMENT AGENCIES AND SEARCH FIRMS

8954 ■ Analytic Recruiting, Inc.
144 E 44th St., 3rd Fl.
New York, NY 10017
Ph: (212)545-8511
E-mail: email@analyticrecruiting.com
URL: http://www.analyticrecruiting.com

Executive search firm.

8955 ■ The Aspire Group
711 Boylston St.
Boston, MA 02116-2616
Fax: (617)500-7284
Fr: 800-487-2967
URL: http://www.bmanet.com/Aspire/index.html

Employment agency.

8956 ■ Mfg/Search, Inc.
205 W Jefferson Blvd., Ste. 601
South Bend, IN 46601
Ph: (574)282-2547
Fax: (574)232-0982
E-mail: hmueller@mfgsearch.com
URL: http://www.mfgsearch.com

Executive search firm. Offices in GA, IL, MI, NY.

8957 ■ Placemart Personnel Service
80 Haines St.
Lanoka Harbor, NJ 08734
Ph: (609)242-4346
Fax: (609)242-4347
Fr: 800-394-7522
E-mail: info@placemart.com
URL: http://www.placemart.com

Executive search firm focusing on the field of clinical research.

ONLINE JOB SOURCES AND SERVICES

8958 ■ ResearchingCrossing.com
URL: http://www.researchingcrossing.com

Description: Offers a collection of top research job openings; includes the lists of employer career pages, job websites, newspaper classifieds and recruitment sites.

TRADESHOWS

8959 ■ INFORMS Meeting
Institute for Operations Research & Management Sciences
7240 Pkwy. Dr., Ste. 300
Hanover, MD 21076-1310
Ph: (443)757-3500
Fr: 800-446-3676
E-mail: informs@informs.org
URL: http://www.informs.org/Attend-a-Conference/
    Annual-Meeting

Annual. Provides a forum to seek and explore opportunities for OR research. 2012 October 4-17; Phoeniz, AZ; Phoenix Convention Center; 2013 October 6-9; Minneapolis, MN; Minneapolis Convention Center; 2014 November 16-19; San Francisco, CA; Parc 55 Wyndham.

OTHER SOURCES

8960 ■ American Supplier Institute (ASI)
30200 Telegraph Rd., Ste. 100
Bingham Farms, MI 48025
Ph: (734)464-1395
Fax: (734)464-1399
Fr: 800-462-4500
E-mail: asi@asiusa.com
URL: http://www.amsup.com

Description: Seeks to encourage change in U.S. industry through development and implementation of advanced manufacturing and engineering technologies such as Taguchi Methods, Quality Function Deployment, Statistical Process Control, and Total Quality Management. Offers educational courses, training seminars, and workshops to improve quality, reduce cost, and enhance competitive position of U.S. products. Maintains international network of affiliates for developing training specialists and technologies curriculum. Provides training services to government supplier companies.

8961 ■ APRA (Association of Professional Researchers for Advancement)
401 N Michigan Ave., Ste. 2200
Chicago, IL 60611
Ph: (312)321-5196
Fax: (312)673-6966
E-mail: info@aprahome.org
URL: http://www.aprahome.org

Description: Consists of development professionals who specialize fundraising research, analytics and relationship management. Provides educational and networking opportunities and advocacy and a representative voice for the profession. Promotes high professional standards and ethical guidelines.

8962 ■ Institute for Operations Research and the Management Sciences
7240 Pkwy. Dr., Ste. 300
Hanover, MD 21076-1310
Ph: (443)757-3500
Fr: 800-446-3676
E-mail: informs@informs.org
URL: http://www.informs.org

Description: Consists of operations research educators, investigators, scientists, students, managers and consultants. Serves as a focal point for operations research professionals to communicate with each other and reach out to other professional societies. Organizes national and international conferences for academics and professionals as well as members of the society's special interest groups.

8963 ■ Military Operations Research Society (MORS)
1703 N Beauregard St., Ste. 450
Alexandria, VA 22311
Ph: (703)933-9070
Fax: (703)933-9066
E-mail: morsoffice@mors.org
URL: http://www.mors.org

Description: Works to improve the quality and effectiveness of military operations research. Sponsors colloquia; facilitates exchange of information and peer criticism among students, theoreticians, practitioners, and users of military operations research. Does not make or advocate official policy nor attempts to influence policy formulation.

Ophthalmic Laboratory Technicians

Sources of Help-Wanted Ads

8964 ■ American Optician
Opticians Association of America
4064 E Fir Hill Dr.
Lakeland, TN 38002
Ph: (901)388-2423
Fax: (901)388-2348
URL: http://www.oaa.org

Quarterly. Included in membership. Professional journal covering optometry.

8965 ■ EyeNet
American Academy of Ophthalmology
PO Box 7424
San Francisco, CA 94120-7424
Ph: (415)561-8500
Fax: (415)561-8533
E-mail: eyenet@aao.org
URL: http://www.eyenetmagazine.org

Monthly. $128.00/year for nonmembers, within U.S.; $180.00/year for nonmembers, outside US; $76.00/year for members, international; $20.00/year for individuals, inactive member. Professional magazine of the American Academy of Ophthalmology covering clinical, socioeconomic and political trends affecting their practice for members.

8966 ■ Investigative Ophthalmology & Visual Science
Association for Research in Vision and Ophthalmology
1801 Rockville Pike, Ste. 400
Rockville, MD 20852-1606
Ph: (240)221-2900
Fax: (240)221-0370
E-mail: iovs@arvo.org
URL: http://www.iovs.org

Monthly. $880.00/year for institutions, online only; $550.00/year for individuals, online only; $400.00/year for students, online only. Peer-reviewed journal dealing with all aspects of vision and ophthalmology.

8967 ■ Journal of Electronic Imaging
SPIE
1000 20th St.
PO Box 10
Bellingham, WA 98227-0010
Ph: (360)676-3290
Fax: (360)647-1445
Fr: 888-504-8171
URL: http://spie.org/x620.xml

Quarterly. $45.00/year for individuals, online; $70.00/year for individuals, print; $510.00/year for institutions, print and online; $550.00/year for institutions, other countries, print & online; $395.00/year for institutions, online. Journal covering issues in optical engineering.

8968 ■ Journal of Optical Communications and Networking
Optical Societyof America
2010 Massachusetts Ave. NW
Washington, DC 20036
Ph: (202)223-8130
Fax: (202)223-1096
E-mail: jocn@osa.org
URL: http://www.osa-jon.org/journal/jon/about.cfm

Monthly. $80.00/year for members, print & online; $56.00/year for members, online only; $180.00/year for other countries, members, print & online; $28.00/year for students, online only. Online journal covering for the optical networking community.

8969 ■ Ophthalmology
Mosby Inc.
11830 Westline Industrial Dr.
St. Louis, MO 63146-3326
Ph: (314)872-8370
Fax: (314)432-1380
Fr: 800-325-4177
URL: http://www.elsevier.com/wps/find/journaldescription.cws_home

Monthly. $385.00/year for individuals; $636.00/year for institutions; $385.00/year for Canada; $636.00/year for institutions, Canada. Journal publishing original, peer-reviewed reports of research in ophthalmology, including basic science investigations and clinical studies.

8970 ■ Optometry
American Optometric Association
243 N Lindbergh Blvd.
St. Louis, MO 63141
Ph: (314)983-4133
Fax: (314)991-4101
Fr: 800-365-2219
URL: http://www.optometryjaoa.com/

Monthly. $193.00/year for individuals; $95.00/year for students; $256.00/year for Canada; $153.00/year for students, other countries; $307.00/year for other countries; $153.00/year for students, other countries. Peer-reviewed clinical journal for members of the American Optometric Association.

8971 ■ Optometry and Vision Science
Lippincott Williams & Wilkins
351 W Camden St.
Baltimore, MD 21201
Ph: (410)528-4000
Fr: 800-638-3030
E-mail: ovs@osu.edu
URL: http://journals.lww.com/optvissci/pages/default.aspx

Monthly. $420.00/year for individuals; $619.00/year for institutions; $567.30/year for other countries; $841.30/year for institutions, other countries. Peer-reviewed journal providing the current developments and research in optometry, physiological optics, and vision science.

8972 ■ Review of Optometry
Jobson Professional Publications Group
11 Campus Blvd., Ste. 100
Newtown Square, PA 19073
Ph: (610)492-1000
Fax: (610)492-1039
URL: http://www.revoptom.com/

Monthly. Journal for the optometric profession and optical industry.

Employer Directories and Networking Lists

8973 ■ Eye Care Sourcebook
Omnigraphics Inc.
PO Box 31-1640
Detroit, MI 48231
Fr: 800-234-1340
URL: http://www.omnigraphics.com

latest edition 3rd, 2008. $85.00 for individuals. Publication includes: List of eye care organizations. Principal content of publication is information on various eye-related problems and solutions. Indexes: Alphabetical.

Handbooks and Manuals

8974 ■ Careers in Health Care
The McGraw-Hill Companies
PO Box 182604
Columbus, OH 43272
Fax: (614)759-3749
Fr: 877-883-5524
E-mail: customer.service@mcgraw-hill.com
URL: http://www.mhprofessional.com/product.php?isbn=0071466533

Barbara M. Swanson. Fifth edition, 2005. $19.95 (paper). 192 pages. Describes job duties, work settings, salaries, licensing and certification requirements, educational preparation, and future outlook. Gives ideas on how to secure a job.

8975 ■ Certified Ophthalmic Technician Exam Review Manual
SLACK, Inc.
6900 Grove Rd.
Thorofare, NJ 08086-9447
Ph: (856)848-1000
Fax: (856)848-6091
Fr: 800-257-8290
URL: http://www.slackinc.com

Janice K. Ledford. Second edition, 2004. $50.95 (paper). 272 pages. Part of the Basic Bookshelf for Eyecare Professionals Series.

8976 ■ Expert Resumes for Health Care Careers
Jist Works
875 Montreal Way
St. Paul, MN 55102

Fr: 800-648-5478
E-mail: educate@emcp.com
URL: http://www.jist.com

Wendy S. Enelow and Louise M. Kursmark. 2010. $16.95. 288 pages.

8977 ■ *Health Careers Today*
Elsevier
11830 Westline Industrial Dr.
St. Louis, MO 63146
Ph: (314)453-7010
Fax: (314)453-7095
Fr: 800-545-2522
E-mail: usbkinfo@elsevier.com
URL: http://www.elsevier.com

Gerdin, Judith. Fourth edition. 2007. $74.95. 496 pages. Covers more than 45 health careers. Discusses the roles and responsibilities of various occupations and provides a solid foundation in the skills needed for all health careers.

8978 ■ *Resumes for Health and Medical Careers*
The McGraw-Hill Companies
PO Box 182604
Columbus, OH 43272
Fax: (614)759-3749
Fr: 877-883-5524
E-mail: customer.service@mcgraw-hill.com
URL: http://www.mhprofessional.com/
   product.php?isbn=0071545352

Third edition, 2008. $12.95 (paper). 144 pages.

EMPLOYMENT AGENCIES AND SEARCH FIRMS

8979 ■ Retail Recruiters
2189 Silas Deane Hwy.
Rocky Hill, CT 06067
Ph: (860)721-9550
Fax: (860)257-8813
E-mail: careers@retailrecruitersusa.com
URL: http://www.retailrecruitersusa.com

Employment agency. Affiliate offices in many locations across the country.

ONLINE JOB SOURCES AND SERVICES

8980 ■ American Academy of Ophthalmology Professional Choices Career Center
American Academy of Ophthalmology
655 Beach St.
PO Box 7424
San Francisco, CA 94120-7424
Ph: (415)561-8500
Fax: (415)561-8533
E-mail: pchoices@aao.org
URL: http://www.aao.org/careers

Description: A site providing regularly updated ophthalmology positions. Applicants for jobs contact the AAO with resume, cover letter, and listing reference number. Job hunters may post resumes for free. Employers may post 90-day job listings at the rate of $335 for members, $535 for nonmembers.

8981 ■ HEALTHeCAREERS Network
Fr: 888-884-8242
E-mail: info@healthecareers.com
URL: http://www.healthecareers.com

Description: Career search site for jobs in all health

care specialties; educational resources; visa and licensing information for relocation; interesting articles; relocation tools; links to professional organizations and general resources.

8982 ■ ProHealthJobs.com
Ph: (484)443-8545
Fax: (484)443-8549
E-mail: info@prohealthjobs.com
URL: http://prohealthjobs.com/jobboard

Description: Career resources site for the medical and health care field. Lists professional opportunities, product information, continuing education and open positions.

TRADESHOWS

8983 ■ Annual Meeting of the American Academy of Ophthalmology
American Academy of Ophthalmology
655 Beach St.
PO Box 7424
San Francisco, CA 94120-7424
Ph: (415)561-8500
Fax: (415)561-8533
E-mail: aaoe@aao.org
URL: http://www.aao.org

Annual. Primary Exhibits: Ophthalmic equipment and instruments.

8984 ■ International Vision Expo and Conference/East
Reed Exhibitions Contemporary Forums
11900 Silvergate Dr.
Dublin, CA 94568
Ph: (925)828-7100
Fax: 800-329-9923
E-mail: info@cforums.com
URL: http://www.contemporaryforums.com

Annual. Primary Exhibits: Equipment, supplies and services for the vision industry.

8985 ■ The OLA
Optical Laboratories Association
225 Reinekers Ln., Ste. 700
Alexandria, VA 22314
Ph: (703)548-6619
Fax: (703)548-4580
E-mail: ola@ola-labs.org
URL: http://www.ola-labs.org

Annual. Primary Exhibits: Ophthalmic laboratory equipment, supplies, and services.

8986 ■ Symposium of the New Orleans Academy of Ophthalmology
New Orleans Academy of Ophthalmology
7733 Maple St.
New Orleans, LA 70118
Ph: (504)861-2550
Fax: (504)861-2549
E-mail: web@noao.org
URL: http://www.noao.org

Annual. Primary Exhibits: Medical instruments, drug companies, and medical publishers. Dates and Locations: 2012 Feb 10-12; New Orleans, LA; Sheraton New Orleans Hotel.

OTHER SOURCES

8987 ■ American Academy of Optometry (AAO)
6110 Executive Blvd., Ste. 506
Rockville, MD 20852

Ph: (301)984-1441
Fax: (301)984-4737
E-mail: aaoptom@aaoptom.org
URL: http://www.aaopt.org

Description: Represents optometrists, educators, and scientists interested in optometric education, and standards of care in visual problems. Conducts continuing education for optometrists and visual scientists. Sponsors 4-day annual meeting.

8988 ■ American Society of Cataract and Refractive Surgery
4000 Legato Rd., Ste. 700
Fairfax, VA 22033
Ph: (703)591-2220
Fax: (703)591-0614
E-mail: cford@ascrs.org
URL: http://www.ascrs.org

Description: Aims to advance the art and science of ophthalmic surgery and the knowledge and skills of ophthalmic surgeons. Provides clinical and practice management education and promotes the delivery of quality eye care.

8989 ■ Association for Research in Vision and Ophthalmology (ARVO)
1801 Rockville Pike, Ste. 400
Rockville, MD 20852-5622
Ph: (240)221-2900
Fax: (240)221-0370
E-mail: arvo@arvo.org
URL: http://www.arvo.org

Description: Professional society of researchers in vision and ophthalmology. Encourages ophthalmic research in the field of blinding eye disease. Operates placement service. Maintains 13 scientific sections.

8990 ■ Association of Technical Personnel in Ophthalmology (ATPO)
2025 Woodlane Dr.
St. Paul, MN 55125-2998
Fax: (651)731-0410
Fr: 800-482-4858
E-mail: atpomembership@jcahpo.org
URL: http://www.atpo.org

Description: Ophthalmic assistants, technicians, technologists, surgical and keratorefractive techs, photographers, nurses, and orthoptists. Promotes high standards and professional ethics dedicated to quality ophthalmic medical care under the direction of an ophthalmologist. Recognizes the utilization of ophthalmic medical personnel to perform certain nonmedical procedures or tests as a means of enhancing the productivity of ophthalmologists and thereby increasing the availability of ophthalmologists to provide the highest level of medical service and comprehensive vision care to their patients.

8991 ■ Association of University Professors of Ophthalmology (AUPO)
PO Box 193030
San Francisco, CA 94119
Ph: (415)561-8548
Fax: (415)561-8531
E-mail: aupo@aao.org
URL: http://www.aupo.org

Description: Heads of departments or divisions of ophthalmology in accredited medical schools throughout the U.S. and Canada; directors of ophthalmology residency programs in institutions not connected to medical schools. Promotes medical education, research, and patient care relating to ophthalmology. Operates Ophthalmology Matching Program and faculty placement service, which aids ophthalmologists interested in being associated with university ophthalmology programs to locate such programs.

Optometrists

Sources of Help-Wanted Ads

8992 ■ American Optician
Opticians Association of America
4064 E Fir Hill Dr.
Lakeland, TN 38002
Ph: (901)388-2423
Fax: (901)388-2348
URL: http://www.oaa.org

Quarterly. Included in membership. Professional journal covering optometry.

8993 ■ AOSA Foresight
American Optometric Student Association
243 N Lindbergh Blvd.
St. Louis, MO 63141
Ph: (314)983-4231
Fax: (314)991-4101
Fr: 800-365-2219
URL: http://www.theaosa.org/x18850.xml

Description: Biannual. Reports news of AOSA and allied organizations and provides information concerning scholarships, grants, internships, and other educational issues related to the study of optometry. Recurring features include a calendar of events, news of research, editorials, and a President's Column.

8994 ■ EyeNet
American Academy of Ophthalmology
PO Box 7424
San Francisco, CA 94120-7424
Ph: (415)561-8500
Fax: (415)561-8533
E-mail: eyenet@aao.org
URL: http://www.eyenetmagazine.org

Monthly. $128.00/year for nonmembers, within U.S.; $180.00/year for nonmembers, outside US; $76.00/year for members, international; $20.00/year for individuals, inactive member. Professional magazine of the American Academy of Ophthalmology covering clinical, socioeconomic and political trends affecting their practice for members.

8995 ■ Eyewitness
Contact Lens Society of America
441 Carlisle Dr.
Herndon, VA 20170
Ph: (703)437-5100
Fax: (703)437-0727
Fr: 800-296-9776
E-mail: clsa@clsa.info
URL: http://www.clsa.info/join-clsa

Description: Quarterly. Informs members of developments in the contact lens industry. Also reports on related educational information and technical papers. Recurring features include news of research, calendar of events, reports of meetings, and associate member listing.

8996 ■ Investigative Ophthalmology & Visual Science
Association for Research in Vision and Ophthalmology
1801 Rockville Pike, Ste. 400
Rockville, MD 20852-1606
Ph: (240)221-2900
Fax: (240)221-0370
E-mail: iovs@arvo.org
URL: http://www.iovs.org

Monthly. $880.00/year for institutions, online only; $550.00/year for individuals, online only; $400.00/year for students, online only. Peer-reviewed journal dealing with all aspects of vision and ophthalmology.

8997 ■ Journal of Electronic Imaging
SPIE
1000 20th St.
PO Box 10
Bellingham, WA 98227-0010
Ph: (360)676-3290
Fax: (360)647-1445
Fr: 888-504-8171
URL: http://spie.org/x620.xml

Quarterly. $45.00/year for individuals, online; $70.00/year for individuals, print; $510.00/year for institutions, print and online; $550.00/year for institutions, other countries, print & online; $395.00/year for institutions, online. Journal covering issues in optical engineering.

8998 ■ Journal of Optical Communications and Networking
Optical Societyof America
2010 Massachusetts Ave. NW
Washington, DC 20036
Ph: (202)223-8130
Fax: (202)223-1096
E-mail: jocn@osa.org
URL: http://www.osa-jon.org/journal/jon/about.cfm

Monthly. $80.00/year for members, print & online; $56.00/year for members, online only; $180.00/year for other countries, members, print & online; $28.00/year for students, online only. Online journal covering for the optical networking community.

8999 ■ Newslink
Newsletters Ink
450 N Prince St.
PO Box 4008
Lancaster, PA 17604-4008
Ph: (717)393-1000
Fax: (717)393-4702
Fr: 800-379-5585
E-mail: info@newslettersink.com
URL: http://www.newslettersink.com

Description: Quarterly. Carries patient-oriented articles on vision and eye health topics such as prevention and detection of eye disease, new vision products and technologies, and eye safety. May be customized to include the name of the optometrist or practice on the masthead; space is available for articles by the practice.

9000 ■ Ophthalmology
Mosby Inc.
11830 Westline Industrial Dr.
St. Louis, MO 63146-3326
Ph: (314)872-8370
Fax: (314)432-1380
Fr: 800-325-4177
URL: http://www.elsevier.com/wps/find/journaldescription.cws_home

Monthly. $385.00/year for individuals; $636.00/year for institutions; $385.00/year for Canada; $636.00/year for institutions, Canada. Journal publishing original, peer-reviewed reports of research in ophthalmology, including basic science investigations and clinical studies.

9001 ■ Optometric Management
Lippincott Williams & Wilkins VisionCare Group
323 Norristown Rd., Ste. 200
Ambler, PA 19002
Ph: (215)646-8700
E-mail: om@boucher1.com
URL: http://www.optometric.com

Monthly. $42.00/year for individuals; $51.00/year for Canada; $90.00/year for other countries; $75.00/year for two years; $91.00/year for Canada, 2 years; $162.00/year for other countries, 2 years. Medical professional journal.

9002 ■ Optometry
American Optometric Association
243 N Lindbergh Blvd.
St. Louis, MO 63141
Ph: (314)983-4133
Fax: (314)991-4101
Fr: 800-365-2219
URL: http://www.optometryjaoa.com/

Monthly. $193.00/year for individuals; $95.00/year for students; $256.00/year for Canada; $153.00/year for students, other countries; $307.00/year for other countries; $153.00/year for students, other countries. Peer-reviewed clinical journal for members of the American Optometric Association.

9003 ■ Optometry and Vision Science
Lippincott Williams & Wilkins
351 W Camden St.
Baltimore, MD 21201
Ph: (410)528-4000
Fr: 800-638-3030
E-mail: ovs@osu.edu
URL: http://journals.lww.com/optvissci/pages/default.aspx

Monthly. $420.00/year for individuals; $619.00/year for institutions; $567.30/year for other countries; $841.30/year for institutions, other countries. Peer-reviewed journal providing the current developments and research in optometry, physiological optics, and vision science.

9004 ■ RETINA
Lippincott Williams & Wilkins
530 Walnut St.
Philadelphia, PA 19106-3619
Ph: (215)521-8300
Fax: (215)521-8902
Fr: 800-638-3030
E-mail: retina@retinajournal.com
URL: http://journals.lww.com/retinajournal/pages/default.aspx

$391.00/year for individuals; $924.00/year for institutions; $188.00/year for individuals, in-training; $540.50/year for other countries; $1,036.50/year for institutions, other countries; $204.50/year for other countries, in-training. Journal publishing clinically oriented articles for the general ophthalmologist and vitreoretinal specialist.

9005 ■ Review of Optometry
Jobson Professional Publications Group
11 Campus Blvd., Ste. 100
Newtown Square, PA 19073
Ph: (610)492-1000
Fax: (610)492-1039
URL: http://www.revoptom.com/

Monthly. Journal for the optometric profession and optical industry.

EMPLOYER DIRECTORIES AND NETWORKING LISTS

9006 ■ College of Optometrists in Vision Development—Membership Directory
College of Optometrists in Vision Development
215 W Garfield Rd., Ste. 210
Aurora, OH 44202
Ph: (330)995-0718
Fax: (330)995-0719
Fr: 888-268-3770
URL: http://www.covd.org

Annual, April. Covers: About 1500 members. Entries include: Name, address, phone, fax, e-mail. Arrangement: Geographical.

9007 ■ Eye Care Sourcebook
Omnigraphics Inc.
PO Box 31-1640
Detroit, MI 48231
Fr: 800-234-1340
URL: http://www.omnigraphics.com

latest edition 3rd, 2008. $85.00 for individuals. Publication includes: List of eye care organizations. Principal content of publication is information on various eye-related problems and solutions. Indexes: Alphabetical.

9008 ■ HMO/PPO Directory
Grey House Publishing
4919 Rte. 22
PO Box 56
Amenia, NY 12501
Ph: (518)789-8700
Fax: (518)789-0556
Fr: 800-562-2139
URL: http://www.greyhouse.com/hmo_ppo.htm

Annual, Latest edition 2011. $325.00 for individuals. Covers: Over 1,000 health maintenance organizations (HMOs) and preferred provider organizations (PPOs). Entries include: Name of organization, address, phone, number of members, names of officers, employer references, geographical area served, parent company, average fees and co-payments, financial data, and cost control procedures. Arrangement: Geographical. Indexes: Organization name, personnel name, HMOs and PPOs by state, and number of members enrolled.

9009 ■ Medical and Health Information Directory
Gale
PO Box 6904
Florence, KY 41022-6904

Fr: 800-354-9706
URL: http://www.gale.cengage.com

Annual, Latest edition April 2011. $1190.00 for individuals; $501.00 for individuals. Covers: In volume 1, more than 33,000 medical and health oriented associations, organizations, institutions, and government agencies, including health maintenance organizations (HMOs), preferred provider organizations (PPOs), insurance companies, pharmaceutical companies, research centers, and medical and allied health schools. In Volume 2, over 20,000 medical book publishers; medical periodicals, directories, audiovisual producers and services, medical libraries and information centers, electronic resources, and health-related internet search engines. In Volume 3, more than 40,500 clinics, treatment centers, care programs, and counseling/diagnostic services for 34 subject areas. Entries include: Institution, service, or firm name, address, phone, fax, email and URL; many include names of key personnel and, when pertinent, descriptive annotation. Volume 3 was formerly listed separately as Health Services Directory. Arrangement: Classified by organization activity, service, etc. Indexes: Each volume has a complete alphabetical name and keyword index.

9010 ■ Optometry and Vision Science—Geographical Directory, American Academy of Optometry Issue
American Academy of Optometry
6110 Executive Blvd., Ste. 506
Rockville, MD 20852
Ph: (301)984-1441
Fax: (301)984-4737
URL: http://www.aaopt.org/section/ovs

Biennial, odd years. $25.00. Publication includes: List of 3,400 members; international coverage. Entries include: Name, title, affiliation; office address, phone, fax, email. Arrangement: Geographical and alphabetical. Indexes: Name, specialty.

HANDBOOKS AND MANUALS

9011 ■ Expert Resumes for Health Care Careers
Jist Works
875 Montreal Way
St. Paul, MN 55102
Fr: 800-648-5478
E-mail: educate@emcp.com
URL: http://www.jist.com

Wendy S. Enelow and Louise M. Kursmark. 2010. $16.95. 288 pages.

9012 ■ Health Careers Today
Elsevier
11830 Westline Industrial Dr.
St. Louis, MO 63146
Ph: (314)453-7010
Fax: (314)453-7095
Fr: 800-545-2522
E-mail: usbkinfo@elsevier.com
URL: http://www.elsevier.com

Gerdin, Judith. Fourth edition. 2007. $74.95. 496 pages. Covers more than 45 health careers. Discusses the roles and responsibilities of various occupations and provides a solid foundation in the skills needed for all health careers.

9013 ■ Resumes for Health and Medical Careers
The McGraw-Hill Companies
PO Box 182604
Columbus, OH 43272
Fax: (614)759-3749
Fr: 877-883-5524
E-mail: customer.service@mcgraw-hill.com
URL: http://www.mhprofessional.com/product.php?isbn=0071545352

Third edition, 2008. $12.95 (paper). 144 pages.

EMPLOYMENT AGENCIES AND SEARCH FIRMS

9014 ■ Retail Recruiters
2189 Silas Deane Hwy.
Rocky Hill, CT 06067
Ph: (860)721-9550
Fax: (860)257-8813
E-mail: careers@retailrecruitersusa.com
URL: http://www.retailrecruitersusa.com

Employment agency. Affiliate offices in many locations across the country.

ONLINE JOB SOURCES AND SERVICES

9015 ■ American Academy of Ophthalmology Professional Choices Career Center
American Academy of Ophthalmology
655 Beach St.
PO Box 7424
San Francisco, CA 94120-7424
Ph: (415)561-8500
Fax: (415)561-8533
E-mail: pchoices@aao.org
URL: http://www.aao.org/careers

Description: A site providing regularly updated ophthalmology positions. Applicants for jobs contact the AAO with resume, cover letter, and listing reference number. Job hunters may post resumes for free. Employers may post 90-day job listings at the rate of $335 for members, $535 for nonmembers.

9016 ■ EyeCareProfessions.com
E-mail: contact@eyecareprofessions.com
URL: http://www.eyecareprofessions.com

Description: Provides career resources for eye care professionals. Features a job board for optometrists, ophthalmologists, and opticians.

9017 ■ HEALTHeCAREERS Network
Fr: 888-884-8242
E-mail: info@healthecareers.com
URL: http://www.healthecareers.com

Description: Career search site for jobs in all health care specialties; educational resources; visa and licensing information for relocation; interesting articles; relocation tools; links to professional organizations and general resources.

9018 ■ iHireOptometry
URL: http://www.ihireoptometry.com

Description: Offers nationwide career opportunities for candidates as well as posting options for employers.

9019 ■ Optometry.com
URL: http://optometry.com/index.php

Description: Features a job board which allows employers and job seekers to quickly and efficiently find one another. Connects thousands of applicants with potential employers for a wide variety of ophthalmic jobs.

9020 ■ ProHealthJobs.com
Ph: (484)443-8545
Fax: (484)443-8549
E-mail: info@prohealthjobs.com
URL: http://prohealthjobs.com/jobboard

Description: Career resources site for the medical and health care field. Lists professional opportunities, product information, continuing education and open positions.

TRADESHOWS

9021 ■ American Academy of Optometry
American Academy of Optometry
6110 Exec. Blvd., Ste. 506
Rockville, MD 20852

Ph: (301)984-1441
Fax: (301)984-4737
E-mail: aaoptom@aaoptom.org
URL: http://www.aaopt.org

Annual. Primary Exhibits: Exhibits focusing on the latest research and patient treatments relating to clinical practice standards, optometric education, and experimental research in visual problems. Dates and Locations: 2012 Oct 24-27; Phoenix, AZ; 2013 Oct 23-26; Seattle, WA; 2014 Nov 12-15; Denver, CO; 2015 Oct 14-17; New Orleans, LA.

9022 ■ College of Optometrists in Vision Development Annual Meeting
College of Optometrists in Vision Development
215 W. Garfield Rd., Ste. 200
Aurora, OH 44202
Ph: (330)995-1718
Fax: (330)995-0719
Fr: 888-268-3770
E-mail: info@covd.org
URL: http://www.covd.org

Annual. Primary Exhibits: Exhibits relating to orthoptics and optometric vision therapy with emphasis on visual information processing in visually related learning problems. Dates and Locations: 2012 Oct 16-20; Fort Worth, TX; Omni Fort Worth Hotel.

9023 ■ International Vision Expo and Conference/East
Reed Exhibitions Contemporary Forums
11900 Silvergate Dr.
Dublin, CA 94568
Ph: (925)828-7100
Fax: 800-329-9923
E-mail: info@cforums.com
URL: http://www.contemporaryforums.com

Annual. Primary Exhibits: Equipment, supplies and services for the vision industry.

9024 ■ Pan-American Congress of Ophthalmology
Pan-American Association of Ophthalmology
1301 S. Bowen Rd., Ste. 365
Arlington, TX 76013
Ph: (817)275-7553
Fax: (817)275-3961
E-mail: info@paao.org
URL: http://www.paao.org

Biennial. Primary Exhibits: Ophthalmology equipment, supplies, and services. Dates and Locations: 2013 Aug; Rio de Janeiro, Brazil.

9025 ■ Southern Council of Optometrists International
SECO International, LLC
4661 N. Shallowford Rd.
Atlanta, GA 30338
Ph: (770)451-8206
Fax: (770)451-3156
URL: http://www.secointernational.com

Annual. Primary Exhibits: Ophthalmic supplies, diagnostic equipment, reference books, frames for glasses, office equipment, computers, contact lenses,

and ophthalmic pharmaceuticals. Dates and Locations: 2012 Feb 29 - Mar 04; 2013 Feb 27 - Mar 03; 2014 Feb 12-16.

OTHER SOURCES

9026 ■ American Academy of Optometry (AAO)
6110 Executive Blvd., Ste. 506
Rockville, MD 20852
Ph: (301)984-1441
Fax: (301)984-4737
E-mail: aaoptom@aaoptom.org
URL: http://www.aaopt.org

Description: Represents optometrists, educators, and scientists interested in optometric education, and standards of care in visual problems. Conducts continuing education for optometrists and visual scientists. Sponsors 4-day annual meeting.

9027 ■ American Optometric Association (AOA)
243 N Lindbergh Blvd.
St. Louis, MO 63141
Ph: (314)991-4100
Fax: (314)991-4101
Fr: 800-365-2219
E-mail: dmcarlson@aoa.org
URL: http://www.aoa.org

Description: Professional association of optometrists, students of optometry, and paraoptometric assistants and technicians. Purposes are: to improve the quality, availability, and accessibility of eye and vision care; to represent the optometric profession; to help members conduct their practices; to promote the highest standards of patient care. Monitors and promotes legislation concerning the scope of optometric practice, alternate health care delivery systems, health care cost containment, Medicare, and other issues relevant to eye/vision care. Supports the International Library, Archives and Museum of Optometry which includes references on ophthalmic and related sciences with emphasis on the history and socioeconomic aspects of optometry. Operates Vision U.S.A. program, which provides free eye care to the working poor, and the InfantSEE program, which provides free vision assessments for infants between six and twelve months of age. Conducts specialized education programs; operates placement service; compiles statistics. Maintains museum. Conducts Seal of Acceptance Program.

9028 ■ American Optometric Student Association (AOSA)
243 N Lindbergh Blvd.
St. Louis, MO 63141
Ph: (314)983-4321
E-mail: mburle@theaosa.org
URL: http://www.theaosa.org

Description: Optometric students, state optometric associations, and family members of optometric students. Collects updated information on progress in the optometry field. Provides members with op-

portunities to work in areas of health care need such as local community health projects, school curriculum changes, and health manpower legislation. Works to improve optometric education and health care for the general population. Maintains active liaison with other optometric associations. Conducts communications program.

9029 ■ American Public Health Association (APHA)
800 I St. NW
Washington, DC 20001
Ph: (202)777-2742
Fax: (202)777-2534
E-mail: comments@apha.org
URL: http://www.apha.org

Description: Professional organization of physicians, nurses, educators, academicians, environmentalists, epidemiologists, new professionals, social workers, health administrators, optometrists, podiatrists, pharmacists, dentists, nutritionists, health planners, other community and mental health specialists, and interested consumers. Seeks to protect and promote personal, mental, and environmental health. Services include: promulgation of standards; establishment of uniform practices and procedures; development of the etiology of communicable diseases; research in public health; exploration of medical care programs and their relationships to public health. Sponsors job placement service.

9030 ■ American Society of Cataract and Refractive Surgery
4000 Legato Rd., Ste. 700
Fairfax, VA 22033
Ph: (703)591-2220
Fax: (703)591-0614
E-mail: cford@ascrs.org
URL: http://www.ascrs.org

Description: Aims to advance the art and science of ophthalmic surgery and the knowledge and skills of ophthalmic surgeons. Provides clinical and practice management education and promotes the delivery of quality eye care.

9031 ■ National Optometric Association (NOA)
PO Box 198959
Chicago, IL 60619-8959
Fax: (773)721-7351
Fr: 877-394-2020
E-mail: info@nationaloptometricassociation.com
URL: http://www.natoptassoc.org

Description: Represents optometrists dedicated to increasing awareness of the status of eye/vision health in the minority community and the national community at-large. Strives to make known the impact of the eye/vision dysfunction on the effectiveness and productivity of citizens and the academic proficiency of students. Conducts national minority recruiting programs, job placement, assistance programs for graduates, practitioners, and optometric organizations, and the promotion of delivery of care. Maintains speakers' bureau. Offers specialized education program.

SOURCES OF HELP-WANTED ADS

9032 ■ Ethics in Biology, Engineering and Medicine
Begell House Inc.
50 Cross Hwy.
Redding, CT 06896
Ph: (203)938-1300
Fax: (203)938-1304
URL: http://www.begellhouse.com/journals/
6ed509641f7324e6

$650.00/year for institutions. Peer-reviewed journal covering ethical issues on biomedical research and the development of new biomaterials, implants, devices and treatments.

9033 ■ The Journal of Arthroplasty
Elsevier
1600 John F. Kennedy Blvd., Ste. 1800
Philadelphia, PA 19103-2822
Ph: (215)239-3900
Fax: (215)238-7883
E-mail: elspcs@elsevier.com
URL: http://www.us.elsevierhealth.com/
product.jsp?isbn=08835403

$494.00/year for individuals; $802.00/year for institutions; $217.00/year for students. Peer-reviewed medical journal for orthopaedic surgeons. Covering clinical and basic science research on arthroplasty including surgical techniques, prosthetic design, biomechanics, biomaterials, and metallurgy.

9034 ■ Journal of Prosthetics and Orthotics
Lippincott Williams & Wilkins
Two Commerce Sq.
2001 Market St.
Philadelphia, PA 19103
Ph: (215)521-8300
Fax: (215)521-8902
Fr: 800-638-3030
E-mail: orders@lww.com
URL: http://journals.lww.com/pages/
default.aspx?filter=J

Four issues/year. $159 for individuals. Industry publication provides information concerning the latest research and clinical thinking in orthotics and prosthetics, including information on new devices, fitting techniques and patient management experiences.

9035 ■ O&P Business News
SLACK Incorporated
6900 Grove Rd.
Thorofare, NJ 08086-9447
Ph: (856)848-1000
Fax: (856)848-6091
E-mail: oandp@slackinc.com
URL: http://www.oandpbiznews.com

$149.00/year for individuals; $239.00/year for institutions; $298.00/year for two years; $478.00/year for institutions, two years; $74.00/year for individuals, resident; $39.00/year for single issue. Professional

magazine covering technical, business, professional and reimbursement activities of the orthotics and prosthetics industry.

9036 ■ The O&P Edge
Western Media LLC
11154 Huron St., Ste. 104
Northglenn, CO 80234
Ph: (303)255-0843
Fax: (303)255-0844
Fr: (866)613-0257
E-mail: edge@oandp.com
URL: http://www.oandp.com

Monthly. Free to individuals in the United States; $36/year in Canada; $96/year in other countries. Magazine covers news and cutting edge technology in the orthotics and prosthetics industry.

HANDBOOKS AND MANUALS

9037 ■ Careers in Medicine
The McGraw-Hill Companies
PO Box 182604
Columbus, OH 43272
Fax: (614)759-3749
Fr: 877-883-5524
E-mail: customer.service@mcgraw-hill.com
URL: http://www.mhprofessional.com/
product.php?isbn=0071458743

Terence J. Sacks. Third edition, 2006. $15.95 (paper). 192 pages. Examines the many paths open to M.D.s, D.O.s, and M.D./Ph.D.s, including clinical private or group practice, hospitals, public health organizations, the armed forces, emergency rooms, research institutions, medical schools, pharmaceutical companies and private industry, and research/advocacy groups like the World Health Organization. A special chapter on osteopathy and chiropractic explores this branch of medicine.

9038 ■ Pocket Orthopaedics:
Evidence-Based Survival Guide
Jones & Bartlett Learning
5 Wall St.
Burlington, MA 01803
Fax: (978)443-8000
Fr: 800-832-0034
E-mail: info@jblearning.com
URL: http://www.jblearning.com

Michael S. Wong. 2011. $41.95 (spiral/paperback). 412 pages. Serves as learning aide in evidence-based practice for both students and clinicians.

EMPLOYMENT AGENCIES AND SEARCH FIRMS

9039 ■ Jordan Medical Consultants
129 Park Ridge Dr.
O'Fallon, MO 63366

Ph: (636)294-6081
Fax: (636)294-6083
Fr: (866)750-7231
E-mail: info@jordanmc.com
URL: http://www.jordanmc.com

Employment agency serving medical professionals, particularly orthotic and prosthetic technicians; aims to match recruits with geographic and practical preferences such as family needs.

ONLINE JOB SOURCES AND SERVICES

9040 ■ GuideToHealthcareSchools.com
E-mail: privacy@degreepages.com
URL: http://www.guidetohealthcareschools.com

Online resource lists education and training in the healthcare industry.

9041 ■ O&P Digital Technologies:
OandP.com
E-mail: info@oandp.com
URL: http://www.oandp.com

Online resource provides comprehensive information and services to the orthotics and prosthetics profession including news, articles, job listings, a calendar of events and a directory of products and services.

9042 ■ Pedorthic Footwear Association
2025 M St. NW, Ste. 800
Washington, DC 20036
Ph: (202)367-1145
Fax: (202)367-2145
Fr: 800-673-8447
E-mail: info@pedorthics.org
URL: http://www.pedorthics.org

Represents the interests of certified and/or licensed pedorthists, the design, manufacture, modification, and fit of shoes and foot orthoses to alleviate problems caused by disease, congenital condition, overuse or injury. Website provides listings of help wanted classified for individuals in the pedorthic industry.

TRADESHOWS

9043 ■ National Association of Orthopaedic
Technologists Clinical Symposium
National Association of Orthopaedic Technologists
8365 Keystone Crossing, Ste. 107
Indianapolis, IN 46240
Ph: (317)205-9484
Fax: (317)205-9481
E-mail: naot@hp-assoc.com
URL: http://www.naot.org

Annual. Features sessions and hands-on workshops. 2012 August 1-4; San Diego, CA; Sheraton San Diego Hotel & Marina.

OTHER SOURCES

9044 ■ American Academy of Orthotists and Prosthetists
1331 H St. NW, Ste. 501
Washington, DC 20005
Ph: (202)380-3663
Fax: (202)380-3447
E-mail: prosenstein@oandp.org
URL: http://www.oandp.org

Promotes professionalism of orthotists and prosthetists and works to advance the standards of patient care through education, literature, research, advocacy and collaboration. Memberships include Active: practitioners in orthotics and/or prosthetics; Associate: practitioners not meeting the criteria for Active; Affiliate: technicians, fitters, assistants and CPeds; Professional: individuals in other professional fields related to orthotics and prosthetics; International Affiliate: international practitioners; Candidate: individuals in orthotics and/or prosthetics who have completed an NCOPE-accredited program; Resident: individuals currently enrolled in an NCOPE-accredited residency program; Student: individuals currently enrolled in a AAHEP accredited practitioner program; Emeritus: members awarded the title; Honorary: individuals in recognition of their contribution to the profession of orthotics and/or prosthetics. Membership benefits include access to the Academy's Member Directory, newsletters and journals, as well as papers from the Thranhardt Lecture Series and discounts on meetings and publications.

9045 ■ American Orthotic and Prosthetic Association
330 John Carlyle St., Ste. 200
Alexandria, VA 22314
Ph: (571)431-0876
Fax: (571)431-0899
E-mail: info@aopanet.org
URL: http://www.aopanet.org

Association web site acts as an online membership directory, searchable by name, city, state or zip code.

9046 ■ California Orthotics and Prosthetics Association
1231 I St., Ste. 203
Sacramento, CA 95814
Ph: (916)769-0573
URL: http://www.californiaoandp.com

Represents orthodists and prosthetists as well as orthotic and prosthetic companies in the State of California; offers annual newsletter to members.

9047 ■ Florida Association of Orthotists and Prosthetists
PO Box 340507
Tampa, FL 33694
Ph: (813)265-3267
E-mail: faopoffice@verizon.net
URL: http://www.faop.org

Aims to ensure the highest standard of orthotic and prosthetic care for persons with disabilities by actively promoting the professional development of members and supporting excellence in business practices. Also provides educational opportunities and sponsors seminars relating to the advancement of the field.

9048 ■ Midwest Chapter of the American Academy of Orthotists and Prosthetists
2551 N Clark St., Ste. 200
Chicago, IL 60614
Ph: (773)472-3663
Fax: (773)472-3668
E-mail: eric.neufeld@scheckandsiress.com
URL: http://www.oandp.org/membership/chapters/
   midwest/

Promotes professionalism of orthotists and prosthetists in Wisconsin, Illinois and Indiana; also works to advance the standards of patient care through education, literature, research, advocacy and collaboration.

Members must be in good standing with the American Academy of Orthotists and Prosthetists.

9049 ■ National Association of Orthopaedic Technologists
8365 Keystone Crossing, Ste. 107
Indianapolis, IN 46240
Ph: (317)205-9484
Fax: (317)205-9481
E-mail: naot@hp-assoc.com
URL: http://www.naot.org

Description: Represents orthopaedic technologists and other related allied health care professionals. Promotes educational development of orthopaedic allied health care professionals. Offers certification programs for orthopaedic technologists.

9050 ■ National Commission on Orthotic and Prosthetic Education
330 John Carlyle St., Ste. 200
Alexandria, VA 22314
Ph: (703)836-7114
Fax: (703)836-0838
E-mail: info@ncope.org
URL: http://www.ncope.org

Aims to promote education in the field of orthotics and prosthetics and raise the standards of education in the field; establish accreditation and evaluation procedures; aid in the development of new programs and ensure people entering the field receive formal preparation related to current requirements for professional practice.

9051 ■ New England Chapter of the American Academy of Orthotists and Prosthetists
2 Centennial Dr., Ste. 6A
Peabody, MA 01960
Ph: (781)820-0401
Fax: (781)942-2992
E-mail: jckndk@comcast.net
URL: http://www.oandp.org/membership/chapters/
   new_england/

Promotes professionalism of orthotists and prosthetists in Massachusetts, Maine, New Hampshire, Vermont, Connecticut, and Rhode Island; also works to advance the standards of patient care through education, literature, research, advocacy and collaboration. Members must be within the geographical boundaries and in good standing with the American Academy of Orthotists and Prosthetists.

9052 ■ North Carolina Chapter of the American Academy of Orthotists and Prosthetists
120 William Penn Plaza, 2nd Fl.
Durham, NC 27704
Ph: (919)281-1814
Fax: (919)281-1877
E-mail: hphillips@triangleortho.com
URL: http://www.oandp.org/membership/chapters/
   north_carolina/

Promotes professionalism of orthotists and prosthetists in North Carolina; also works to advance the standards of patient care through education, literature, research, advocacy and collaboration. Members must be within the geographical boundaries and in good standing with the American Academy of Orthotists and Prosthetists.

9053 ■ Northern Plains Chapter of the American Academy of Orthotists and Prosthetists
Winkley Orthopedic Labs, Inc.
910 E 26th St., Ste. 323
Minneapolis, MN 55404
Ph: (612)863-8963
Fax: (612)863-8962
E-mail: janderson@winkley.com
URL: http://www.oandp.org/membership/chapters/
   northern_plains/

Promotes professionalism of orthotists and prosthetists in North Dakota, South Dakota, Minnesota and

Iowa; also works to advance the standards of patient care through education, literature, research, advocacy and collaboration.

9054 ■ Northwest Chapter of the American Academy of Orthotists and Prosthetists
UW Bioengineering
7022 Palatine Ave., N
Seattle, WA 98103-5013
Ph: (206)390-0228
Fax: (206)324-0943
E-mail: kate@prs-research.org
URL: http://www.oandp.org/membership/chapters/
   northwest/

Promotes professionalism of orthotists and prosthetists in Alaska, Washington, Montana, Oregon and Idaho; also works to advance the standards of patient care through education, literature, research, advocacy and collaboration. Members receive discounted registration fees for Northwest Chapter meetings.

9055 ■ Ohio Chapter of the American Academy of Orthotists and Prosthetists
Shamp Bionics
2656 S Arlington Rd.
Akron, OH 44319
Ph: (330)644-4201
Fax: (330)644-4202
E-mail: mark@shampbionics.com
URL: http://www.oandp.org/membership/chapters/
   ohio/

Promotes professionalism of orthotists and prosthetists in Ohio, Michigan, Kentucky and West Virginia; also works to advance the standards of patient care through education, literature, research, advocacy and collaboration. Members must be within the geographical boundaries and in good standing with the American Academy of Orthotists and Prosthetists.

9056 ■ Pennsylvania/MD/DC/VA Chapter of the American Academy of Orthotists and Prosthetists
33 S 19th St.
Pittsburgh, PA 15203
Ph: (412)431-3553
Fax: (417)431-3493
E-mail: auggiedc@verizon.net
URL: http://www.oandp.org/membership/chapters/
   maryland/

Promotes professionalism of orthotists and prosthetists in Pennsylvania, Maryland, Virginia and the District of Columbia; also works to advance the standards of patient care through education, literature, research, advocacy and collaboration; 93 members. Dues are $45 annually. Members must practice within the geographical boundaries and be in good standing with the American Academy of Orthotists and Prosthetists.

9057 ■ Southwest Chapter of the American Academy of Orthotists and Prosthetists
3737 Moraga Ave., Ste. B107
San Diego, CA 92117
Ph: (858)270-9972
Fax: (858)270-6560
E-mail: bionics@utm.net
URL: http://www.oandp.org/membership/chapters/
   southwest_regional/

Promotes professionalism of orthotists and prosthetists in California, Nevada, Arizona, Utah, New Mexico and Hawaii; also works to advance the standards of patient care through education, literature, research, advocacy and collaboration.

9058 ■ Texas Chapter of the American Academy of Orthotists and Prosthetists
1936 N Story Rd.
Irving, TX 75061
E-mail: dtelfordcpo@aol.com
URL: http://www.txaaop.org

Promotes professionalism of orthotists and prosthetists in Texas; also works to advance the standards of patient care through education, literature, research, advocacy and collaboration.

SOURCES OF HELP-WANTED ADS

9059 ■ *Tourism, Culture & Communication*
Cognizant Communications Corp.
3 Hartsdale Rd.
Elmsford, NY 10523-3701
Ph: (914)592-7720
Fax: (914)592-8981
URL: http://www.cognizantcommunication.com/journal-titles/touris

$360.00/year for institutions, online only; $390.00/year for institutions, online & hard copy; $55.00/year for individuals, professional; $45.00/year for single issue. Journal covering tourism, culture, and communication.

9060 ■ *Workamper News*
709 W Searcy St.
Heber Springs, AR 72543-3761
Ph: (501)362-2637
Fax: (501)362-6769
E-mail: info@workamper.com
URL: http://www.workamper.com

Description: Bimonthly. Provides a list of information on seasonal and full-time job openings at campgrounds, forests, public and private resort areas, and motorsports events.

EMPLOYER DIRECTORIES AND NETWORKING LISTS

9061 ■ *AlaskaGuidesDirectory.com*
Kenai River Professional Guide Association
PO Box 3667
Homer, AK 99603
Fr: 800-478-7777
URL: http://alaskaguidesdirectory.com

Online directory lists guides and lodges throughout Alaska.

9062 ■ *Discovering Careers for Your Future—Adventure*
Facts On File Inc.
132 W 31st St., 17th Fl.
New York, NY 10001
Ph: (212)967-8800
Fax: 800-678-3633
Fr: 800-322-8755
URL: http://factsonfile.infobasepublishing.com

Latest edition 2nd, 2008. $21.95 for individuals. Covers: Adventure travel specialists, astronauts, detectives, police officers, and spies; links career education to curriculum, helping children investigate the subjects they are interested in, and the careers those subjects might lead to.

HANDBOOKS AND MANUALS

9063 ■ *A Career with Meaning*
Sagamore Publishing LLC
1807 N Federal Dr.
Urbana, IL 61801
Ph: (217)359-5940
Fax: (217)359-5975
Fr: 800-327-5557
URL: http://www.sagamorepub.com
Cheryl A. Stevens, James F. Murphy, Lawrence R. Allen, and Emilyn A. Sheffield. 2010. $53.96. 425 pages (paperback). Guides individuals to find professional opportunities within the leisure industry, such as recreation, parks, sport management, hospitality and tourism.

9064 ■ *Careers for Health Nuts and Others Who Like to Stay Fit*
The McGraw-Hill Companies
PO Box 182604
Columbus, OH 43272
Fax: (614)759-3749
Fr: 877-883-5524
E-mail: customer.service@mcgraw-hill.com
URL: http://www.mhprofessional.com
Blythe Camenson. Second edition. $13.95 (paper). 208 pages.

9065 ■ *Outdoor Careers*
Ferguson Publishing
132 W 31st St., 17th Fl.
New York, NY 10001
Fr: 800-322-8755
E-mail: custserv@factsonfile.com
URL: http://factsonfile.infobasepublishing.com
Amanda Kirk. 2009. $39.95. Provides a comprehensive review of outdoor careers as well as useful information on navigating career goals.

TRADESHOWS

9066 ■ Adventures in Travel Expos
Unicomm, LLC
284-C Quarry Rd.
PO Box 5010
Milford, CT 06460
Ph: (203)878-2577
Fax: (203)878-2154
E-mail: info@adventureexpo.com
URL: http://www.adventureexpo.com

Primary Exhibits: Adventure, active travel, eco, nature, cultural, and outdoor travel.

OTHER SOURCES

9067 ■ Acadia Mountain Guides
PO Box 121
92 Main St.
Orono, ME 04473

Ph: (207)288-8186
Fax: (207)866-7562
Fr: 888-232-9559
E-mail: climb@acadiamountainguides.com
URL: http://www.acadiamountainguides.com

Activities: Operates the Acadia Mountain Guides Climbing School that provides career development for professional guides. Offers a variety of courses for professional guides and is accredited by the American Mountain Guides Association for its certification program.

9068 ■ Adventure Travel Trade Association (ATTA)
601 Union St., 42nd Fl.
Seattle, WA 98101
Ph: (360)805-3131
Fax: (360)805-0649
E-mail: info@adventuretravel.biz
URL: http://www.adventuretravel.biz

Description: Serves the adventure travel industry. Aims to grow the adventure travel industry overall and to help build up its member organizations. Provides exposure, marketing expertise, education, research, and discount to its members.

9069 ■ American Mountain Guides Association
PO Box 1739
Boulder, CO 80306
Ph: (303)271-0984
Fax: (303)271-1377
URL: http://amga.com

Members: Professional mountain guides. **Purpose:** Provides support, education, and standards to its membership. **Activities:** Establishes and maintains certification guidelines for professional guides, sponsors educational opportunities, provides a guide finding service to the public, and offers scholarships and grants.

9070 ■ Idaho Outfitters and Guides Association
PO Box 95
Boise, ID 83701
Ph: (208)342-1438
Fax: (208)338-7830
Fr: 800-49I-DAHO
E-mail: gsimonds@cableone.net
URL: http://www.ioga.org

Members: Full-time licensed outfitters and guides. **Activities:** Disseminates information on the licensing requirements of guides. Maintains an outfitter directory listing its members.

9071 ■ Maine Professional Guides Association
55 Morrison Hill Rd.
Wilton, ME 04294
E-mail: info@maineguides.org
URL: http://www.maineguides.org

Members: Registered Maine guides. **Purpose:**

Promotes a quality, ethical, and legal outdoor experience for all. **Activities:** Monitors new and proposed legislation that affects the guiding industry. Issues guide licenses. Provides an online searchable database of members.

9072 ■ Montana Outfitters and Guides Association (MOGA)
5 Microwave Hill Rd.
Montana City, MT 59634
Ph: (406)449-3578
Fax: (406)449-9769
E-mail: moga@mt.net
URL: http://www.montanaoutfitters.org

Description: Represents outfitters and guides who operate outdoor trips in Montana for hunting, fishing, float boating, and sightseeing parties using saddle and pack animals, boats, and motorized equipment; operators of dude ranches, wagon trains, and cattle drives. Supports standards of service to be provided by members set by licensing board; encourages preservation of back country and wise use of resources, fish, and game. Maintains speaker's bureau.

9073 ■ New York State Outdoor Guides Association
1936 Saranac Ave., Ste. 2-150
Lake Placid, NY 12946

Fr: (866)469-7642
E-mail: info@nysoga.org
URL: http://www.nysoga.com

Members: Professional guides. **Activities:** Maintains a searchable membership list. Provides outdoor training and licensing information for its members.

9074 ■ Oregon Guides and Packers
PO Box 817
Bend, OR 97709
Ph: (541)385-5947
Fr: 800-788-7238
E-mail: info@ogpa.org
URL: http://www.ogpa.org

Members: Professional outdoor recreation service providers. **Purpose:** Assist outdoor enthusiasts from all walks-of-life to have a safe and rewarding outdoor experience. **Activities:** Provides a listing of member guides.

9075 ■ Rogue River Guides Association
PO Box 449
Phoenix, OR 97535
Ph: (541)840-3663
E-mail: meenusa@earthlink.net
URL: http://www.rogueriverguides.com

Members: Professional guides. **Purpose:** Works to

upgrade guiding standards and the quality of service offered to clients. **Activities:** Maintains a membership list, publishes a newsletter, and posts classified advertisements.

9076 ■ Vermont Outdoor Guide Association
PO Box 10
North Ferrisburg, VT 05473
Ph: (802)425-6211
Fr: 800-425-8747
E-mail: info@voga.org
URL: http://www.voga.org

Members: Outdoor leaders, educators, guides, and related services. **Purpose:** Provides support and promotion for outdoor travel services, including guides and outfitters. **Activities:** Maintains a membership directory and provides a forum for networking.

9077 ■ Western Montana School for Guides
PO Box 733
Darby, MT 59829
Fr: 800-946-6778
URL: http://www.guidetraining.com

Purpose: Offers training in every aspect of the guide and outfitter profession. **Activities:** Provides information on starting a guide business and offers job placement services.

SOURCES OF HELP-WANTED ADS

9078 ■ *ACM Transactions on Internet Technology*
Association for Computing Machinery
PO Box 30777
New York, NY 10087
Ph: (212)626-0500
Fax: (212)944-1318
Fr: 800-342-6626
URL: http://toit.acm.org

Quarterly. $190.00/year for nonmembers, print only; $152.00/year for nonmembers, online only; $228.00/year for nonmembers, online and print. Publication of the Association for Computing Machinery. Brings together many computing disciplines including computer software engineering, computer programming languages, middleware, database management, security, knowledge discovery and data mining, networking and distributed systems, communications, performance and scalability, and more. Covers the results and roles of the individual disciplines and the relationships among them.

9079 ■ *AVIOS Journal*
Applied Voice Input/Output Society
PO Box 20817
San Jose, CA 95160
Ph: (408)323-1783
Fax: (408)323-1782
URL: http://www.avios.com/

Annual. Journal covering issues in computer science.

9080 ■ *Computers and Composition*
Elsevier Science Inc.
360 Park Ave. S
New York, NY 10010-1710
Ph: (212)989-5800
Fax: (212)633-3990
Fr: 888-437-4636
URL: http://www.elsevier.com/wps/find/ journaldescription.cws_home

$454.00/year for institutions, all countries except Europe, Japan and Iran; $405.00/year for institutions, European countries and Iran; $53,500.00/year for institutions, Japan; $82.00/year for individuals, all countries except Europe, Japan and Iran; $62.00/year for individuals, European countries and Iran; $8,900.00/year for individuals, Japan. Journal covering computers in writing classes, programs, and research.

9081 ■ *Computers Programs/PC World*
IDG Communications Inc.
3 Speen St.
Framingham, MA 01701
Ph: (508)875-5000
URL: http://www.idg.com

Magazine devoted to IT specialists, covering practical questions of computing including purchase and us-age of the computer technology, software, computer components and peripherals.

9082 ■ *Computerworld/Correio Informatico*
IDG Communications Inc.
3 Speen St.
Framingham, MA 01701
Ph: (508)875-5000
URL: http://www.idg.com/www/IDGProducts.nsf/0/ B1E40F5ABD0169AB852

Weekly. Magazine providing news on latest developments in computer industry.

9083 ■ *Computerworld Top 100*
IDG Communications Inc.
3 Speen St.
Framingham, MA 01701
Ph: (508)875-5000
URL: http://www.idg.com/www/IDGProducts.nsf/0/ E7EDD4EC98463F2C852

Annual. Magazine for analyzing trends and events of information technology business.

9084 ■ *Computing SA*
IDG Communications Inc.
3 Speen St.
Framingham, MA 01701
Ph: (508)875-5000
URL: http://www.idg.com/www/IDGProducts.nsf/0/ 12C44C74D05A07DF852

Monthly. Newspaper focusing computer hardware, software, networking, telecommunications, channel management and online computing.

9085 ■ *CXO*
IDG Communications Inc.
3 Speen St.
Framingham, MA 01701
Ph: (508)875-5000
URL: http://www.idg.com/www/IDGProducts.nsf/0/ 022796185EED5984852

Monthly. Magazine providing technology information for chief officers and managers.

9086 ■ *Eclipse Review*
BZ Media L.L.C.
7 High St., Ste. 407
Huntington, NY 11743
Ph: (631)421-4158
Fax: (631)421-4130
URL: http://www.eclipsesource.com/contact.htm

Magazine for IT professionals.

9087 ■ *Foundations and Trends in Networking*
Now Publishers
PO Box 1024
Hanover, MA 02339-1001
Ph: (781)871-0245
URL: http://www.nowpublishers.com/ product.aspx?product=NET

$390.00/year for individuals, online only; $450.00/year for individuals, print and online; $390.00/year for other countries, online only; $450.00/year for other countries, print and online. Academic journal publishing new research in computer networking.

9088 ■ *Government Computer News*
PostNewsweek Tech Media
10 G St. NE, Ste. 500
Washington, DC 20002-4228
Ph: (202)772-2500
Fax: (202)772-2511
Fr: (866)447-6864
URL: http://gcn.com/

Semimonthly. Magazine for professionals interested in government IT.

9089 ■ *IEEE Security & Privacy Magazine*
IEEE Computer Society
10662 Los Vaqueros Cir.
PO Box 3014
Los Alamitos, CA 90720-1314
Ph: (714)821-8380
Fax: (714)821-4010
Fr: 800-272-6657
URL: http://www.computer.org/portal/site/security/

Bimonthly. $735.00/year for individuals, online; $770.00/year for individuals, print; $965.00/year for individuals, print and online. Journal that aims to explore role and importance of networked infrastructure and developing lasting security solutions.

9090 ■ *Information Security*
TechTarget
117 Kendrick St., Ste. 800
Needham, MA 02494
Ph: (781)657-1000
Fax: (781)657-1100
Fr: 888-274-4111
URL: http://searchsecurity.techtarget.com/

Monthly. Free to qualified subscribers. Magazine covering information security topics.

9091 ■ *IT Solutions Guide*
SYS-CON Media
577 Chestnut Ridge Rd.
Woodcliff Lake, NJ 07677
Ph: (201)802-3000
Fax: (201)782-9601
URL: http://itsolutions.sys-con.com/

Quarterly. Magazine for IT professionals.

9092 ■ *Journal of Computer Science*
Science Publications
Vails Gate Heights Dr.
PO Box 879
Vails Gate, NY 12584-0879
URL: http://thescipub.com/jcs.toc

Scholarly journal covering many areas of computer science, including: concurrent, parallel and distributed processing; artificial intelligence; image and voice processing; quality software and metrics; computer-aided education; wireless communication; real time processing; evaluative computation; and data bases and information recovery and neural networks.

9093 ■ Journal of Computer Systems, Networks, and Communications
Hindawi Publishing Corp.
410 Park Ave., 15th Fl.
287 PMB
New York, NY 10022-4407
Fax: (215)893-4392
E-mail: jcsnc@hindawi.com
URL: http://www.hindawi.com/journals/jcsnc/

$195.00/year for individuals, print & online. Journal covering important areas of information technology.

9094 ■ Monitor
Capital PC User Group
19209 Mt. Airey Rd.
Brookeville, MD 20833
Ph: (301)560-6442
Fax: (301)760-3303
E-mail: editor@cpcug.org
URL: http://monitor.cpcug.org/index.html

Quarterly. Magazine covering computer hardware and software reviews, special interest user group news, advertisers and author/subject index, and calendar of events.

9095 ■ PC Today
Sandhills Publishing
120 W Harvest Dr.
Lincoln, NE 68521
Ph: (402)479-2181
Fax: (402)479-2195
Fr: 800-331-1978
E-mail: editor@pctoday.com
URL: http://www.pctoday.com/

Monthly. $29.00/year for individuals; $37.00/year for Canada; $64.00/year for Canada, 2 years; $2.42/year for individuals, print; $17.00/year for individuals, online only; $69.00/year for other countries; $48.00/year for individuals, 2 years; $64.00/year for individuals, 3 years; $82.00/year for Canada, 3 years; $64.00/year for Canada, 2 years. Magazine for personal computer users.

9096 ■ PC WORLD
101 Communications
9121 Oakdale Ave., Ste. 101
Chatsworth, CA 91311
Ph: (818)814-5200
Fax: (818)734-1522
E-mail: pcwletters@pcworld.com
URL: http://www.pcworld.com

Quarterly. $19.97/year for individuals; $29.97/year for two years. Technology or business magazine meeting the informational needs of tech-savvy managers, both at work and at home.

9097 ■ Queue
Association for Computing Machinery
PO Box 30777
New York, NY 10087
Ph: (212)626-0500
Fax: (212)944-1318
Fr: 800-342-6626
E-mail: queue@acm.org
URL: http://queue.acm.org/

Monthly. Free, U.S./Canadian residents and all members. Online magazine aimed at the computer professional. Magazine editorial does not provide solutions for the "here-and-now", but instead helps decision-makers plan future projects by examining the challenges and problems they are most likely to face.

9098 ■ Revenue
Montgomery Media International
55 New Montgomery St., Ste. 617
San Francisco, CA 94105
Ph: (415)371-8800
URL: http://www.revenuetoday.com/

Free to qualified subscribers. Magazine covering internet marketing strategies.

9099 ■ Ubiquity
Association for Computing Machinery
PO Box 30777
New York, NY 10087
Ph: (212)626-0500
Fax: (212)944-1318
Fr: 800-342-6626
URL: http://ubiquity.acm.org

Weekly. Free. Web-based magazine of the Association for Computing Machinery dedicated to fostering critical analysis and in-depth commentary, including book reviews, on issues relating to the nature, constitution, structure, science, engineering, cognition, technology, practices and paradigms of the IT profession.

9100 ■ WITI FastTrack
United business Media L.L.C
240 W 35th St.
New York, NY 10001
Ph: (516)562-5000
URL: http://www.witi.com/corporate/fasttrack.php

Semiannual. Semiannual publication featuring in-depth content on the issues facing today's women professionals in technology.

Employer Directories and Networking Lists

9101 ■ Career Opportunities in Computers and Cyberspace
Facts On File Inc.
132 W 31st St., 17th Fl.
New York, NY 10001
Ph: (212)967-8800
Fax: 800-678-3633
Fr: 800-322-8755
URL: http://www.infobasepublishing.com

Published March, 2004. Covers: Nearly 200 professions, clustering them by skill, objectives, and work conditions. Entries include: Education, salaries, employment prospects.

9102 ■ Computer Directory
Computer Directories Inc.
23815 Nichols Sawmill Rd.
Hockley, TX 77447
Ph: (281)259-5959
Fax: (281)259-5959
Fr: 800-234-4353
URL: http://www.compdirinc.com

Annual, fall. Covers: Approximately 130,000 computer installations; 19 separate volumes for Alaska/Hawaii, Connecticut/New Jersey, Dallas/Ft. Worth, Eastern Seaboard, Far Midwest, Houston, Illinois, Midatlantic, Midcentral, Mideast, Minnesota/Wisconsin, North Central, New England, New York Metro, Northwest, Ohio, Pennsylvania/West Virginia, Southeast, and Southwest Texas. Entries include: Company name, address, phone, fax, email, name and title of contact, hardware used, software application, operating system, programming language, computer graphics, networking system. Arrangement: Geographical. Indexes: Alphabetical, industry, hardware.

Employment Agencies and Search Firms

9103 ■ Access Staffing
360 Lexington Ave., 8th Fl.
New York, NY 10017
Ph: (212)687-5440
Fax: (212)557-2544
URL: http://www.accessstaffingco.com

Serves as a staffing firm covering accounting/financial, advertising, bilingual Japanese, creative,

event planning, fashion/retail, healthcare/ human services, human resources, information technology, insurance, legal, light industrial and office support.

9104 ■ Computer Management
7982 Honeygo Blvd., No. 23
Baltimore, MD 21236
Ph: (410)679-7000
E-mail: info@technicaljobs.com
URL: http://www.technicaljobs.com

Search firm focusing on filling jobs for database administration, network administration, web development, and software.

9105 ■ Conselium
14850 Montfort Dr., Ste. 106
Dallas, TX 75254
Ph: (972)934-8444
E-mail: maurice@conselium.com
URL: http://www.conselium.com

Executive search firm with a core expertise in corporate compliance, audit and information technology security.

9106 ■ O'Keefe and Partners
4 Corporate Dr., Ste 490
Shelton, CT 06484
Ph: (203)929-4222
E-mail: smoore@okeefepartners.com
URL: http://www.okeefepartners.com

Executive search firm.

9107 ■ Recruiting Partners
3494 Camino Tassajara Rd., No. 404
Danville, CA 94506
Ph: (925)964-0249
E-mail: info@recruitingpartners.com
URL: http://www.recruitingpartners.com

Description: Serves as an executive and technical recruiting firm that specializes in accounting, legal, information technology, engineering, executive management and technical writing.

9108 ■ Sullivan and Cogliano
230 2nd Ave.
Waltham, MA 02451
Ph: (781)890-7890
Fax: (781)906-7801
Fr: 888-785-2641
E-mail: jobs@sullivancogliano.com
URL: http://www.sullivancogliano.com

Technical staffing firm.

9109 ■ Technical Talent Locators Ltd.
5570 Sterrett Pl., Ste. 208
Columbia, MD 21044
Ph: (410)740-0091
E-mail: steve@ttlgroup.com
URL: http://www.ttlgroup.com

Permanent employment agency working within the following fields: software and database engineering; computer, communication, and telecommunication system engineering; and other computer-related disciplines.

9110 ■ Worlco Computer Resources, Inc.
901 Rte. 38
Cherry Hill, NJ 08002
Ph: (610)293-9070
Fax: (856)665-8903
E-mail: recruiter@worlco.com
URL: http://www.worlco.com

Employment agency and executive search firm. Second location in Cherry Hill, New Jersey.

Online Job Sources and Services

9111 ■ ComputerWork.com
Fr: 800-691-8413
URL: http://www.computerwork.com

Description: Job search and resume submission service for professionals in information technology.

9112 ■ Computerworld Careers
URL: http://www.computerworld.com/careertopics/careers

Description: Offers career opportunities for IT (information technology) professionals. Job seekers may search the jobs database, register at the site, and read about job surveys and employment trends. Employers may post jobs.

9113 ■ Computing Research Association Job Announcements
1828 L St. NW, Ste. 800
Washington, DC 20036-4632
Ph: (202)234-2111
Fax: (202)667-1066
E-mail: info@cra.org
URL: http://www.cra.org/ads

Description: Contains dated links to national college and university computer technology positions.

9114 ■ Dice.com
URL: http://www.dice.com

Description: Job search database for computer consultants and high-tech professionals, listing thousands of high tech permanent contract and consulting jobs for programmers, software engineers, systems administrators, web developers, and hardware engineers. Also free career advice e-mail newsletter and job posting e-alerts.

9115 ■ ItJobs.com
E-mail: comments@itjobsllc.com
URL: http://www.itjobs.com

Description: Provides information technology employment opportunities for the following categories: internet/intranet/extranet, network systems, open systems, client/server, software engineering and development, software QA and testing, ERP applications and management consulting, and legacy systems.

9116 ■ Jobs4IT.com
URL: http://www.jobs4it.com

Description: Features information technology job

opportunities, job fairs, business opportunities, news, events, continuing education guide, resume database, distribution services and other career resources.

9117 ■ NetworkEngineer.com
URL: http://www.networkengineer.com

Description: Provides lists of job and career opportunities for network engineers.

9118 ■ TechCareers
URL: http://www.techcareers.com

Description: Features career-related resources, news, and job postings for information technology and engineering professionals.

9119 ■ ZDNet Tech Jobs
URL: http://www.zdnet.com

Description: Site houses a listing of national employment opportunities for professionals in high tech fields. Also contains resume building tips and relocation resources.

SOURCES OF HELP-WANTED ADS

9120 ▪ *CRM Buyer*
NewsFactor Network
23679 Calabasas Rd.
Calabasas, CA 91302
Ph: (818)713-2500
Fax: (818)713-2502
URL: http://www.crmbuyer.com/
Monthly. Magazine covering customer relationship management solutions.

9121 ▪ *Service Revenue*
Center for Services Marketing Inc.
300 Hess Ave., Bldg. II
Golden, CO 80401
Ph: (720)746-1900
Fax: (720)746-0599
URL: http://www.csmhub.com/
Bimonthly. $149.00/year for members. Newsletter giving information on marketing and sales knowledge for the service industry.

9122 ▪ *Today's Caregiver*
Caregiver Media Group
3350 Griffin Rd.
Fort Lauderdale, FL 33312
Ph: (954)893-0550
Fax: (954)893-1779
Fr: 800-829-2734
URL: http://www.caregiver.com/
Bimonthly. Magazine providing information, support, and guidance for family and professional caregivers.

EMPLOYER DIRECTORIES AND NETWORKING LISTS

9123 ▪ *Careers in Focus—Personal Services*
Facts On File Inc.
132 W 31st St., 17th Fl.
New York, NY 10001
Ph: (212)967-8800
Fax: 800-678-3633
Fr: 800-322-8755
URL: http://www.infobasepublishing.com
Latest edition 2nd; Published April, 2007. $32.95 for individuals. Covers: An overview of personal services, followed by a selection of jobs profiled in detail, including the nature of the job, earnings, prospects for employment, what kind of training and skills it requires, and sources for further information.

HANDBOOKS AND MANUALS

9124 ▪ *Career Information Center: Consumer, Homemaking, and Personal Services*
Cengage Learning
PO Box 6904
Florence, KY 41022
Fax: 800-487-8488
Fr: 800-354-9706
URL: http://www.cengage.com
Darryl Kestler.

TRADESHOWS

9125 ▪ National Association of Professional Pet Sitters - NAPPS Annual Conference & Small Business Forum
National Association of Professional Pet Sitters
15000 Commerce Parkway, Ste. C
Mount Laurel, NJ 08054
Ph: (856)439-0324
Fax: (856)439-0525
E-mail: napps@petsitters.org
URL: http://www.petsitters.org
Annual. Primary Exhibits: Exhibits relating to pet behavior, pet sitting, alternative care, pricing theory, and pet products. Dates and Locations: 2012 Jan 27-29; Las Vegas, NV; Flamingo Resort.

OTHER SOURCES

9126 ▪ American Association of Service Coordinators (AASC)
PO Box 1178
Powell, OH 43065-1178
Ph: (614)848-5958
Fax: (614)848-5954
E-mail: info@servicecoordinator.org
URL: http://www.servicecoordinator.org
Description: Advances the interests of the service coordinator profession. Increases awareness and understanding of service coordination and service-enriched housing. Provides guidance to members in the creation and maintenance of service-enhanced housing to families, the elderly and persons with disabilities. Strives to enhance the professionalism of its constituents through leadership, education, training, networking, and advocacy.

9127 ▪ Association of Residential Cleaning Services International
c/o Ernie Hartong, Exec.Dir.
7870 Olentangy River Rd., Ste. 300
Columbus, OH 43235
Ph: (614)547-0887
Fax: (614)888-9240
E-mail: ernie@arcsi.org
URL: http://www.arcsi.org
Description: Assists residential cleaning service owners and professionals in starting, promoting, building, and expanding their businesses.

9128 ▪ International Nanny Association (INA)
PO Box 1299
Hyannis, MA 02601
Ph: (713)526-2670
Fax: (508)638-6462
Fr: 888-878-1477
E-mail: info@nanny.org
URL: http://www.nanny.org
Description: An educational association for nannies and those who educate, place, employ, and support professional in-home child care. Membership is open to those who are directly involved with the in-home child care profession, including nannies, nanny employers, nanny placement agency owners (and staff), nanny educators, and providers of special services related to the nanny profession.

9129 ▪ National Association of Professional Pet Sitters (NAPPS)
15000 Commerce Pkwy., Ste. C
Mount Laurel, NJ 08054
Ph: (856)439-0324
Fax: (856)439-0525
E-mail: napps@ahint.com
URL: http://www.petsitters.org
Description: Owners or employees of pet-sitting services; professionals or businesses in related fields. Promotes professional and ethical standards in pet sitting and fosters cooperation among members of the pet-care industry. Serves as a network for the exchange of ideas and information on pet sitting and current industry practices. Disseminates information educating the pet-owning public on the advantages of leaving pets in a home environment and how to choose a reliable sitter.

9130 ▪ Pet Sitters International (PSI)
201 E King St.
King, NC 27021
Ph: (336)983-9222
Fax: (336)983-5266
E-mail: info@petsit.com
URL: http://www.petsit.com
Description: Represents professional pet sitters. Serves as an educational organization for professional pet sitters and advocates of at-home pet care. Promotes, recognizes and supports excellence in pet sitting. Provides a forum of communication for members who share a common vision of excellence in at-home pet care.

9131 ▪ United States Personal Chef Association
7680 Universal Blvd., Ste. 550
Orlando, FL 32819
Fr: 800-995-2138
URL: http://www.uspca.com
Description: Strives to set standards and create guidelines for the industry. Promotes ongoing education.

9132 ▪ Vacation Rental Housekeeping Professionals (VRHP)
5380 Gulf of Mexico Dr., Ste. 105
Longboat Key, FL 34228
Ph: (850)303-1358

Fax: 800-741-6988
Fr: (866)457-2582
URL: http://www.vrhp.org

Description: Strives to increase the quality, service level, and professionalism of housekeeping to both rental unit owners and rental guests. Provides educational opportunities for its members through networking and seminars. Grants certification to vacation rental housekeeping professionals, housekeepers, and inspectors.

SOURCES OF HELP-WANTED ADS

9133 ■ Business Insurance
Crain Communications Inc.
1155 Gratiot Ave.
Detroit, MI 48207-2997
Ph: (313)446-6000
URL: http://www.businessinsurance.com

Weekly. $399.00/year for individuals, print; $149.00/year for individuals, print & digital; $69.00/year for individuals, digital edition. International newsweekly reporting on corporate risk and employee benefit management news.

9134 ■ Human Resource Executive
LRP Publications
747 Dresher Rd., Ste. 500
PO Box 980
Horsham, PA 19044-0980
Ph: (215)784-0860
Fax: (215)784-9639
Fr: 800-341-7874
URL: http://www.hrexecutive.com

Business magazine (tabloid) for human resource executives in corporations, non-profit organizations, and government agencies.

9135 ■ Pensions & Investments
Crain Communications Inc.
1155 Gratiot Ave.
Detroit, MI 48207-2997
Ph: (313)446-6000
URL: http://www.pionline.com

Biweekly. $279.00/year for individuals, print; $995.00/year for individuals, daily email; $1,149.00/year for individuals, combo. Magazine containing news and features on investment management, pension management, corporate finance, and cash management.

9136 ■ Talent Management Magazine
MediaTec Publishing
111 E Wacker, Ste. 1290
Chicago, IL 60601
Ph: (312)676-9900
Fax: (312)676-9910
URL: http://www.talentmgt.com/

Monthly. Free to qualified subscribers. Magazine covering workplace performance and effectiveness.

9137 ■ T+D Magazine
American Society for Training & Development
1640 King St.
PO Box 1443
Alexandria, VA 22313-2043
Ph: (703)683-8100
Fax: (703)683-1523
Fr: 800-628-2783
URL: http://www.astd.org/content/publications/

Monthly. $89.00/year for members; $150.00/year for nonmembers, outside US; for Included in member-

ship; $300.00/year for institutions. Magazine on training and development.

9138 ■ Workforce Management
Crain Communications, Inc.
1155 Gratiot Ave.
Detroit, MI 48207-2997
Ph: (313)446-6000
URL: http://www.workforceonline.com

Biweekly. $79.00/year for individuals; $129.00/year for Canada and Mexico; $199.00/year for other countries. A Business magazine for human resources management leaders.

EMPLOYER DIRECTORIES AND NETWORKING LISTS

9139 ■ College and University Professional Association—Membership Directory
College and University Professional Association for Human Resources
1811 Commons Point Dr.
Knoxville, TN 37932
Ph: (865)637-7673
Fax: (865)637-7674
Fr: 877-287-2474
E-mail: memberservice@cupahr.org
URL: http://www.cupahr.org

Online continually updated; access restricted to members. Covers: More than 7,000 members interested in college and university human resource administration; over 1,700 institutions. Entries include: For members—Personal name, title, affiliation, address, fax, e-mail, phone. For institutions—Organization name, address, phone, and names/titles of representatives. Arrangement: Members are alphabetical; institutions are geographical.

HANDBOOKS AND MANUALS

9140 ■ Handbook of Employee Benefits and Administration
CRC Press
c/o Taylor & Francis Group LLC
6000 Broken Sound Pkwy. NW
Boca Raton, FL 33487
Fax: (561)989-9732
Fr: 800-272-7737
E-mail: orders@taylorandfrancis.com
URL: http://www.crcpress.com

Christopher G. Reddick. 2008. $93 (hardback). 448 pages. Provides human resource managers, consultants, students, and scholars in public administration with an overview of the employee benefit component. Contains analysis and insights on areas concerning public employee benefits, health and retirement benefits, financial management, and contemporary benefits.

9141 ■ Opportunities in Hospital Administration Careers
The McGraw-Hill Companies
PO Box 182604
Columbus, OH 43272
Fax: (614)759-3749
Fr: 877-883-5524
E-mail: customer.service@mcgraw-hill.com
URL: http://www.mhprofessional.com/product.php?isbn=0071467688

I. Donald Snook. 2006. $13.95. 160 pages. Discusses opportunities for administrators in a variety of management settings: hospital, department, clinic, group practice, HMO, mental health, and extended care facilities.

9142 ■ Opportunities in Insurance Careers
The McGraw-Hill Companies
PO Box 182604
Columbus, OH 43272
Fax: (614)759-3749
Fr: 877-883-5524
E-mail: customer.service@mcgraw-hill.com
URL: http://www.mhprofessional.com/product.php?isbn=0071482075

Robert M. Schrayer. Revised, 2007. $14.95 (paper). 160 pages. A guide to planning for and seeking opportunities in the field. Contains bibliography and illustrations.

EMPLOYMENT AGENCIES AND SEARCH FIRMS

9143 ■ Abbott Smith Associates, Inc.
11697 W Grand Ave.
Northlake, IL 60164
Ph: (708)223-1191
E-mail: contactus@abbottsmith.com
URL: http://www.abbottsmith.com

Human Resources executive search firm.

9144 ■ Action Employment Services
121 SW Morrison St., Ste. 425
Portland, OR 97204
Ph: (503)275-9011
Fax: (503)241-8772
Fr: (866)208-1643
E-mail: inquiry@actionemployment.net
URL: http://www.actionemployment.net

Description: Provides administrative, office, accounting, and human resource positions.

9145 ■ The Alexander Group
2700 Post Oak Blvd., Ste. 2400
Houston, TX 77056
Ph: (713)993-7900
URL: http://www.thealexandergroup.com

Executive search firm. Second location in San Francisco.

9146 ■ Apple and Associates
PO Box 996
Chapin, SC 29036
Ph: (803)932-2000
E-mail: info@appleassoc.com
URL: http://www.appleassoc.com

Provides staffing services to medical device, plastics,
pharmaceutical and performance materials industries.

9147 ■ Arlington Resources, Inc.
4902 Tollview Dr.
Rolling Meadows, IL 60008
Ph: (224)232-5900
Fr: (866)647-3091
E-mail: information@arlingtonresources.com
URL: http://www.arlingtonresources.com

Specializes in the placement of human resources
professionals for direct hire, contract and temporary
services.

9148 ■ The Aspire Group
711 Boylston St.
Boston, MA 02116-2616
Fax: (617)500-7284
Fr: 800-487-2967
URL: http://www.bmanet.com/Aspire/index.html

Employment agency.

9149 ■ Brindisi Search
10020 Baltimore National Pike., Ste. 100
PO Box 6034
Ellicott City, MD 21042
Ph: (410)489-6699
Fax: (410)823-0146
E-mail: tbrindisi@aol.com
URL: http://www.brindisisearch.com

Specializes in contemporary human resource and
select strategic leadership assignments, ranging from
manager to senior vice president level.

9150 ■ Career Advocates International
1539 Ave. A
Katy, TX 77493
Ph: (281)395-9848
Fax: (281)574-3949
URL: http://www.careeradvocates.org

Provides permanent placement and temporary staffing for executive and staff level positions. Specializes
in multiple niches including: sales and marketing, accounting and financial services, banking, communications, human resources, chemicals, oil and gas, medical and dental, legal, information technology, energy,
technology, engineering, manufacturing, construction,
and light industrial.

9151 ■ Centennial, Inc.
8044 Montgomery Rd., Ste. 260
Cincinnati, OH 45236
Ph: (513)366-3760
Fax: (513)366-3761
E-mail: info@centennialinc.com
URL: http://www.centennialinc.com

Serves as an executive search firm specializing in
the areas of executive and general management, accounting and finance, human resources, information
technology, manufacturing, engineering, marketing
and advertising, not-for-profit, sales and business
development, and supply chain and logistics. Performs executive coaching as well as career coaching
for clients.

9152 ■ Charleston Partners
2 Bellevue Ave.
Rumson, NJ 07760
Ph: (732)842-5015
E-mail: info@charlestonpartners.com
URL: http://www.charlestonpartners.com/human-
capital-partners.html

Executive search firm concentrated on human resource services.

9153 ■ Dankowski and Associates, Inc.
13089 Root Rd.
The Woods, Ste. 200 SE
Columbia Station, OH 44028
Ph: (216)973-0556
E-mail: info@dankowskiassocites.com
URL: http://www.dankowskiassociates.com

Executive search firm.

9154 ■ Daubenspeck and Associates Ltd.
Two Prudential Plaza
180 N Stetson Ave., Ste. 1935
Chicago, IL 60601
Ph: (312)297-4100
E-mail: rd@daubenspeck.com
URL: http://www.daubenspeck.com

Executive search firm specializing in team building.

9155 ■ Elinvar
1804 Hillsborough St.
Raleigh, NC 27605
Ph: (919)878-4454
E-mail: careers@elinvar.com
URL: http://www.elinvar.com

Executive search firm.

9156 ■ The Esquire Staffing Group Ltd.
1 S Wacker Dr., Ste. 1616
Chicago, IL 60606-4616
Ph: (312)795-4300
URL: http://www.esquirestaffing.com

Employment agency. Fills permanent as well as
temporary openings.

9157 ■ ExecuGroup Inc.
142 S Main St.
PO Box 5040
Grenada, MS 38901
Ph: (662)226-9025
Fax: (662)226-9090
E-mail: tray@execugroup.com
URL: http://www.execugroup.com

Executive search firm. Second location in Bethlehem,
PA.

9158 ■ Houser Martin Morris
110th Ave. NE, 110 Atrium Pl., Ste. 580
Bellevue, WA 98004
Ph: (425)453-2700
Fax: (425)453-8726
E-mail: info@houser.com
URL: http://www.houser.com

Focus is in the areas of retained executive search,
professional and technical recruiting. Areas of
specialization include software engineering, sales
and marketing, information technology, legal, human
resources, accounting and finance, manufacturing,
factory automation, and engineering.

9159 ■ HR Personnel Services
9800 Bren Rd. E, Ste. 290
Minnetonka, MN 55343
Ph: (952)929-3000
Fax: (952)927-4313
Fr: 800-476-1663
E-mail: hrps@hrpersonnelservices.com
URL: http://www.hrpersonnelservices.com

Offers customized recruitment and executive search
solutions for nationwide companies in all industries.
Specializes exclusively in the placement of human
resource professionals for businesses.

9160 ■ HR Solutions
2355 Northside Dr., Ste. 180
San Diego, CA 92108
Ph: (619)260-2036
E-mail: sandiego@hr-solutions.com
URL: http://www.hr-solutions.com

Provides human resource job search, specializing in
staffing and recruiting candidates handling temporary
jobs, temp-to-hire, and direct placement human
resource careers.

9161 ■ HRD Consultants Inc.
1812 Front St.
Scotch Plains, NJ 07076
Ph: (908)228-5500
Fax: (908)228-7415
E-mail: hrd@aol.com
URL: http://www.hrdconsultants.com

Focuses exclusively on the placement of executive
level human resource professionals. Services include:
acting as an advisor by identifying and addressing
key issues that effect talent acquisition and retention;
assessing internal human resource professionals on
their career readiness and participating in the on-
boarding process and candidate assimilation providing research reports which can be used for benchmarking and market research.

9162 ■ James Farris Associates
909 NW 63rd St.
Oklahoma City, OK 73116
Ph: (405)525-5061
Fax: (405)525-5069
E-mail: james@jamesfarris.com
URL: http://www.jamesfarris.com

Executive search firm.

9163 ■ OfficeTeam.com
2884 Sand Hill Rd.
Menlo Park, CA 94025
Fr: 800-804-8367
URL: http://www.officeteam.com

Serves as a specialized temporary staffing service
for administrative professionals including executive
assistant, administrative assistant, office manager,
project coordinator, receptionist, human resource assistant, marketing assistant, customer service representative, and data entry specialist.

9164 ■ Protocol Agency Inc.
27001 Agoura Rd., Ste. 210
Calabasas, CA 91301
Fr: 877-371-0069
E-mail: corp@protocolexec.com
URL: http://www.protocolagency.com

Executive search firm focusing on a variety of
placements.

9165 ■ R.A. Clark Consulting Ltd.
3101 Tower Creek Pky., Ste. 420
Atlanta, GA 30339
Ph: (770)857-0002
Fax: (770)857-0007
Fr: 800-251-0041
E-mail: resume@hrdracc.com
URL: http://www.raclark.com

National and international executive search focusing
exclusively in the human resource field. Also contracts
human resource executives for temporary
assignments.

9166 ■ Scion Staffing
576 Sacramento St., 2nd Fl.
San Francisco, CA 94111
Ph: (415)392-7500
E-mail: info@scionstaffing.com
URL: http://scionstaffing.com

Serves as an executive search firm and temporary
agency for professional candidates.

9167 ■ Techtronix Technical Search
4805 N 24th Pl.
PO Box 17713
Milwaukee, WI 53217-0173
Ph: (414)466-3100
Fax: (414)466-3598

Firm specializes in recruiting executives for the
engineering, information systems, manufacturing,
marketing, finance, and human resources industries.
Industries include electronic, manufacturing and
finance.

9168 ■ Tower Consultants, Ltd.
943 Central Pkwy.
Stuart, FL 34994
Ph: (772)288-3590
E-mail: contact@towerconsultants.com
URL: http://www.towerconsultants.com

Description: Specializes in the recruitment of human resources professionals.

9169 ■ Willmott and Associates, Inc.
922 Waltham St., Ste. 103
Lexington, MA 02421
Ph: (781)863-5400
Fax: (781)863-8000
E-mail: info@willmott.com
URL: http://www.willmott.com

Executive search firm and permanent employment agency. Also fills some temporary placements.

ONLINE JOB SOURCES AND SERVICES

9170 ■ HRCrossing.com
URL: http://www.hrcrossing.com

Description: Provides job listings and other resources related to human resources employment opportunities.

9171 ■ HumanResourcesCentral.com
URL: http://www.humanresourcescentral.com

Description: Provides job opportunities for human resource professionals.

9172 ■ iHireHR
URL: http://www.ihirehr.com

Description: Provides job listings and services to facilitate job searches in the field of human resources.

9173 ■ Instructional Design Central
URL: http://www.instructionaldesigncentral.com

Description: Provides instructional design related information, career and learning opportunities, and other resources to instructional design professionals, educators, and students.

9174 ■ Jobs4HR.com
URL: http://www.jobs4hr.com

Description: Provides job opportunities for human resource professionals.

9175 ■ RecruitingJobs.com
URL: http://www.recruitingjobs.com

Description: Serves as clearinghouse for human resource managers, employment and staffing professionals, and recruiters. Features a jobs database, career email notifiers, resume database and distribution services, calendar of career events, and continuing education guides.

9176 ■ WorkforceHRjobs.com
URL: http://www.workforcehrjobs.com/a/all-jobs/list

Description: Provides job opportunities for human resource professionals.

TRADESHOWS

9177 ■ Annual Employee Benefits Conference
International Foundation of Employee Benefit Plans
18700 W. Bluemound Rd.
Brookfield, WI 53045
Ph: (262)373-7701
Fax: (262)786-6115
URL: http://www.ifebp.org

Annual. Primary Exhibits: Products and services relating to accounting services, alternative medicine, banking/financial, communication, computer software, consulting services, health services, insurance, investments, legal services, preretirement planning.

9178 ■ Annual World EAP Conference
Employee Assistance Professionals Association
4350 N. Fairfax Dr., Ste. 410
Arlington, VA 22203
Ph: (703)387-1000
Fax: (703)522-4585
URL: http://www.eapassn.org/i4a/pages/
    index.cfm?pageid=1

Annual. Primary Exhibits: Exhibits geared toward persons employed full-time in the development or operation of employee assistance programs (EAPs) as administrators, consultants, or motivational counselors. Dates and Locations: 2012 Oct 17-20; Baltimore, MD; Hilton Baltimore.

9179 ■ Boston HR Leadership Summit
Evanta
KOIN Tower
222 SW Columbia, Ste. 1020
Portland, OR 97201
Ph: (503)443-6600
E-mail: info@evanta.com
URL: http://www.evanta.com/

Annual. Primary Exhibits: The latest in human resources. Dates and Locations: 2013 Mar; Boston, MA; Westin Waterfront Hotel.

9180 ■ Boston HR Leadership Summit
Evanta
KOIN Tower
222 SW Columbia, Ste. 1020
Portland, OR 97201
Ph: (503)443-6600
E-mail: info@evanta.com
URL: http://www.evanta.com/

Annual. Primary Exhibits: The latest in human resources. Dates and Locations: 2013 Mar; Boston, MA; Westin Waterfront Hotel.

9181 ■ DirectEmployers Annual Meeting & Conference
DirectEmployers Association
9002 Purdue Rd., Ste. 100
Indianapolis, IN 46268
Ph: (317)874-9000
Fax: (317)874-9100
Fr: (866)268-6206
URL: http://www.directemployers.org

Annual. Provides sessions and panels presented by industry experts, partners, and staff covering technology, trends, techniques, and practices.

9182 ■ Education Technology
Society for Applied Learning Technology
50 Culpeper St.
Warrenton, VA 20186
Ph: (540)347-0055
Fax: (540)349-3169
E-mail: info@salt.org
URL: http://www.salt.org

Annual. Primary Exhibits: Distance learning, web-based training systems, knowledge management systems, instructional systems design, and e-learning technology.

9183 ■ Training Magazine's Training Conference and Expo
VNU Expositions
14685 Avion Pkwy., Ste. 400
Chantilly, VA 20151
Ph: (703)488-2700
Fax: (703)488-2725
Fr: 800-765-7615
URL: http://www.vnuexpo.com

Annual. Primary Exhibits: Training and personnel materials, equipment, and services.

OTHER SOURCES

9184 ■ American Society for Healthcare Human Resources Administration (ASHHRA)
American Hospital Association
155 N Wacker Dr., Ste. 400
Chicago, IL 60606

Ph: (312)422-3720
Fax: (312)422-4577
E-mail: ashhra@aha.org
URL: http://www.ashhra.org

Description: Provides effective and continuous leadership in the field of health care human resources administration. Promotes cooperation with hospitals and allied associations in matters pertaining to hospital human resources administration. Works to further the professional and educational development of members. Encourages and assists local groups in chapter formation through regular programs and institutes on health care human resources issues. Offers placement service.

9185 ■ American Society of Pension Professionals and Actuaries (ASPPA)
4245 N Fairfax Dr., Ste. 750
Arlington, VA 22203
Ph: (703)516-9300
Fax: (703)516-9308
E-mail: asppa@asppa.org
URL: http://www.asppa.org

Description: Aims to educate pension actuaries, consultants, administrators, and other benefits professionals. Seeks to preserve and enhance the private pension system as part of the development of a cohesive and coherent national retirement income policy.

9186 ■ American Staffing Association (ASA)
277 S Washington St., Ste. 200
Alexandria, VA 22314-3675
Ph: (703)253-2020
Fax: (703)253-2053
E-mail: asa@americanstaffing.net
URL: http://www.americanstaffing.net

Description: Promotes and represents the staffing industry through legal and legislative advocacy, public relations, education, and the establishment of high standards of ethical conduct.

9187 ■ ASTD
Box 1443
Alexandria, VA 22313-1443
Ph: (703)683-8100
Fax: (703)683-8103
Fr: 800-628-2783
E-mail: customercare@astd.org
URL: http://www.astd.org

Description: Represents workplace learning and performance professionals.

9188 ■ College and University Professional Association for Human Resources (CUPA-HR)
1811 Commons Point Dr.
Knoxville, TN 37932
Ph: (865)637-7673
Fax: (865)637-7674
Fr: 877-287-2474
E-mail: abrantley@cupahr.org
URL: http://www.cupahr.org

Description: Professional organization made up of colleges and universities interested in the improvement of campus Human Resource administration. Carries out special research projects and surveys, including annual administrative compensation survey for higher education. Sponsors training seminars to meet members' technical, professional, and developmental needs in human resource management. Disseminates information to members regarding federal legislation and regulations affecting higher education institutions. Compiles statistics.

9189 ■ DirectEmployers Association
9002 Purdue Rd., Ste. 100
Indianapolis, IN 46268
Ph: (317)874-9000
Fax: (317)874-9100
Fr: (866)268-6206
URL: http://www.directemployers.org

Description: Serves as a human resource consortium of U.S. employers. Aims to improve labor market efficiency through the sharing of practices, research, and the development of technology.

9190 ■ Employee Assistance Society of North America (EASNA)
2001 Jefferson Davis Hwy., Ste. 1004
Arlington, VA 22202-3617
Ph: (703)416-0060
Fax: (703)416-0014
E-mail: bmclean@easna.org
URL: http://www.easna.org

Description: Individuals in the field of employee assistance, including psychiatrists, psychologists, and managers. Facilitates communication among members; provides resource information; serves as a network for employee assistance programs nationwide. Conducts research.

9191 ■ Human Resource Certification Institute (HRCI)
1800 Duke St.
Alexandria, VA 22314
Ph: (703)548-3440
Fax: (703)535-6474
Fr: (866)898-4724
E-mail: info@hrci.org
URL: http://www.hrci.org

Description: Promotes the establishment of standards for the profession. Recognizes human resource professionals who have met, through demonstrated professional experience and the passing of a comprehensive written examination, the Institute's requirements for mastering the codified HR body of knowledge. Offers three professional certifications: Professional in Human Resources (PHR), Senior Professional in Human Resources (SPHR), and Global Professional in Human Resources (GPHR).

9192 ■ Human Resource Planning Society (HRPS)
401 N Michigan Ave., Ste. 2200
Chicago, IL 60611
Ph: (312)321-6805
Fax: (312)673-6944
E-mail: info@hrps.org
URL: http://www.hrps.org

Description: Human resource planning professionals representing 160 corporations and 3,000 individual members, including strategic human resources planning and development specialists, staffing analysts, business planners, line managers, and others who function as business partners in the application of strategic human resource management practices. Seeks to increase the impact of human resource planning and management on business and organizational performance. Sponsors program of professional development in human resource planning concepts, techniques, and practices. Offers networking opportunities.

9193 ■ International Association for Human Resource Information Management (IHRIM)
PO Box 1086
Burlington, MA 01803
Ph: (781)791-9488
Fax: (781)998-8011
Fr: 800-804-3983
E-mail: information@ihrim.org
URL: http://www.ihrim.org

Description: Represents practitioners, vendors, consultants, students and faculty. Works to provide valuable knowledge through educational courses and webinars, CORE (member generated online community), professional certification, networking, publications and annual conference.

9194 ■ International Public Management Association for Human Resources (IPMA-HR)
1617 Duke St.
Alexandria, VA 22314
Ph: (703)549-7100
Fax: (703)684-0948
E-mail: nreichenberg@ipma-hr.org
URL: http://www.ipma-hr.org

Description: Seeks to improve human resource practices in government through provision of testing services, advisory service, conferences, professional development programs, research, and publications. Sponsors seminars, conferences, and workshops on various phases of public personnel administration. Compiles statistics.

9195 ■ International Society for Organization Development
11234 Walnut Ridge Rd.
Chesterland, OH 44026
Ph: (440)729-7419
Fax: (440)729-9319
E-mail: info@theisod.org
URL: http://www.theisod.org

Description: Professionals, students, and individuals interested in organization development. Disseminates information on and promotes a better understanding of organization development worldwide. Conducts specialized education programs. Develops the International O.D. Code of Ethics and a competency test for individuals wishing to qualify as a Registered Organization Development Consultant and a statement on the knowledge and skill necessary to be competent in organization development and criteria for the accreditation of OD/OB academic programs. Maintains job and consultant information service. Sponsors International Registry of Organization Development Professionals and Research/Study Team on Nonviolent Large Systems Change. Maintains 18 committees including an International Advisory Board.

9196 ■ Labor and Employment Relations Association (LERA)
University of Illinois
121 Labor and Employment Relations Bldg.
504 E Armory Ave.
Champaign, IL 61820
Ph: (217)333-0072
Fax: (217)265-5130
E-mail: leraoffice@illinois.edu
URL: http://www.leraweb.org

Description: Businesspersons, union leaders, government officials, lawyers, arbitrators, academics, and others interested in research and exchange of ideas on social, political, economic, legal, and psychological aspects of labor and employment relations.

9197 ■ National Public Employer Labor Relations Association
1012 S Coast Hwy., Ste. M
Oceanside, CA 92054
Ph: (760)433-1686
Fax: (760)433-1687
Fr: 877-673-5721
URL: http://www.npelra.org

Description: Consists of labor relations professionals working for special districts and federal, state, county, and city governments. Strives to provide high-quality, progressive labor relations advice that balances the needs of management, employees, and the public. Promotes the interests of public sector management in the judicial and legislative arenas. Provides opportunities for networking among mem-

bers by establishing state and regional organizations throughout the country.

9198 ■ Organization Development Network (ODN)
401 N Michigan Ave., Ste. 2200
Chicago, IL 60611
Ph: (312)321-5136
Fax: (973)763-7488
URL: http://www.odnetwork.org

Description: Represents practitioners, academics, managers and students employed or interested in organization development. Works to enhance and provide opportunities for colleagueship and professional development.

9199 ■ Professionals in Human Resources Association
360 N Sepulveda Blvd., Ste. 2020
El Segundo, CA 90245
Ph: (310)416-1210
Fax: (310)416-9055
URL: http://www.pihra.org

Description: Provides opportunities for members' interaction and professional development to enhance and enrich their profession. Serves as an advocate and source of information on human resource legislative information. Contributes to the body of human resource knowledge and promotes professional ethics.

9200 ■ Society for Human Resource Management (SHRM)
1800 Duke St.
Alexandria, VA 22314-3499
Ph: (703)548-3440
Fax: (703)535-6490
Fr: 800-283-7476
E-mail: board@shrm.org
URL: http://www.shrm.org

Description: Professional organization of human resource, personnel and industrial relations professionals and executives. Promotes the advancement of human resource management. Sponsors SHRM Foundation. Offers certification through the Human Resource Certification Institute.

9201 ■ Team and Workplace Excellence Forum
PO Box 3005
Milwaukee, WI 53201-3005
Ph: (414)272-1734
Fax: (414)272-1734
Fr: 800-248-1946
E-mail: help@asq.org
URL: http://www.asq.org/teamwork

Description: Works to promote the ideas of involvement, empowerment and workplace democracy. Disseminates information to members through the internet, publications, conferences and educational events.

9202 ■ WorldatWork
14040 N Northsight Blvd.
Scottsdale, AZ 85260
Ph: (480)951-9191
Fax: (480)483-8352
Fr: 877-951-9191
E-mail: customerrelations@worldatwork.org
URL: http://www.worldatwork.org

Description: Dedicated to knowledge leadership in compensation, benefits and total rewards, focusing on disciplines associated with attracting, retaining and motivating employees. Offers CCP, CBP and GRP certification and education programs, conducts surveys, research and provides networking opportunities.

SOURCES OF HELP-WANTED ADS

9203 ■ AMCA Newsletter
American Mosquito Control Association Inc.
15000 Commerce Pkwy., Ste. C
Mount Laurel, NJ 08054
Ph: (856)439-9222
Fax: (856)439-0525
E-mail: amca@mosquito.org
URL: http://www.mosquito.org/

Description: Four issues/year. Reports new products and developments in the mosquito control industry. Recurring features include Association news, listings of job openings and of new publications, and a calendar of events.

9204 ■ Common Sense Pest Control Quarterly
Bio-Integral Resource Center
PO Box 7414
Berkeley, CA 94707
Ph: (510)524-2567
Fax: (510)524-1758
E-mail: birc@igc.org
URL: http://www.birc.org

Features descriptions of the latest research, products, resources, and book reviews.

9205 ■ Home, Yard & Garden Pest Newsletter
University of Illinois at Urbana-Champaign
1408 W Green St.
Urbana, IL 61801
Ph: (217)333-2290
Fr: 800-345-6087
E-mail: acesnews@aces.illinois.edu
URL: http://hyg.ipm.illinois.edu

Description: 20/year. Discusses insect, weed, and plant disease pests of the yard and garden. Covers current pest controls, application equipment and methods, and storage and disposal of pesticides for the yard and garden.

9206 ■ Hort Notes
UMass Extension
French Hall
230 Stockbridge Rd.
University of Massachusetts
Amherst, MA 01003-9316
Ph: (413)545-0895
Fax: (413)577-1620
E-mail: kcarroll@umext.umass.edu
URL: http://extension.umass.edu/landscape/
   publications-resources/newsletters

Description: Biweekly, March-October. $20. Contains information highlighting new approaches in integrated pest management and plant maintenance. Includes updates on pest outbreaks, a calendar of educational programs, and insect/disease monitoring checklists.

9207 ■ The IPM Practitioner
Bio-Integral Resource Center
PO Box 7414
Berkeley, CA 94707
Ph: (510)524-2567
Fax: (510)524-1758
E-mail: birc@igc.org
URL: http://www.birc.org

Description: Ten issues/year. Supports the Center in its efforts to publish information "on all aspects of environmentally-sound pest control." Investigates the least-toxic methods of controlling pests in agriculture, urban landscapes and structures, greenhouse and general horticulture, forestry, medical/veterinary, range, and other settings. Recurring features include letters to the editor, interviews, news of research, reports of meetings, news of educational opportunities and job listings, notices and reviews of publications available, and a calendar of events. Contains yearly listings of products and services in the area of integrated pest management; listings of suppliers of beneficial insects.

9208 ■ Pest Control Technology
GIE Media
4020 Kinross Lakes Pkwy., Ste. 201
Richfield, OH 44286
Ph: (330)523-5323
Fax: (330)659-0823
Fr: 800-456-0707
E-mail: bharbison@gie.net
URL: http://www.pctonline.com

Industry news.

9209 ■ Techletter
Pinto & Associates Inc.
29839 Oak Rd.
Mechanicsville, CA 20659-2201
Ph: (301)884-3020
E-mail: techletter@techletter.com
URL: http://www.techletter.com

Description: Biweekly. $55/year. Covers topics of interest to pest control technicians.

HANDBOOKS AND MANUALS

9210 ■ Insect Pest Management: Field and Protected Crops
Springer-Verlag New York, Inc.
233 Spring St.
New York, NY 10013
Ph: (212)460-1500
Fax: (212)460-1575
URL: http://www.springer.com/life+sci/agriculture/
   book/978-3-540-20755-9

A. Rami Horowitz, I. Ishaaya. May 2004. $319.00. Illustrated. 344 pages.

9211 ■ Pest Control Aide
National Learning Corporation
212 Michael Dr.
Syosset, NY 11791
Fr: 800-632-8888
URL: http://www.passbooks.com

2009. $29.95 (paper). Serves as an exam preparation guide for pest control aides.

9212 ■ Pests of Landscape Trees and Shrubs: An Integrated Pest Management Guide
University of California Statewide Integrated Pest Management Program
One Shields Ave.
Davis, CA 95616-8621
Ph: (530)752-8350
Fax: (530)752-6004
URL: http://www.ipm.ucdavis.edu/IPMPROJECT/
   ADS/manual_landscape.html

Steve H. Dreistadt. 2004, Second Edition. $42.00. 501 pages. Compiled by scientists at the University of California's Statewide Integrated Pest Management Project, this guide is aimed at homeowners and gardeners as well as landscape and pest management professionals.

TRADESHOWS

9213 ■ Association of Applied IPM Ecologists Annual Conference
Association of Applied IPM Ecologists
PO Box 1119
Coarsegold, CA 93614
Ph: (559)761-1064
E-mail: director@aaie.net
URL: http://www.aaie.net

Annual. Primary Exhibits: Exhibits relating to the latest developments in integrated pest management. Dates and Locations: 2012 Feb 05-05; Oxnard, CA; Embassy Suites.

9214 ■ Florida Pest and Lawn Care Expo
Associated Food Dealers of Michigan
30415 W. Thirteen Mile Rd.
Farmington Hills, MI 48334
Ph: (248)671-9600
E-mail: info@afpdonline.org
URL: http://www.afdom.org/page.cfm/100/

Annual. Primary Exhibits: Exhibits relating to environment conservation, including disaster relief, fumigation, and turf management.

9215 ■ Pest Control Operators of California Convention
Pest Control Operators of California
3031 Beacon Blvd.
West Sacramento, CA 95691
Ph: (916)372-4363

Fax: (916)372-5437
URL: http://www.pcoc.org

Annual. Primary Exhibits: Equipment, supplies, and services for owners and operators of structural pest control companies in California. Dates and Locations: 2012 Jun 21-23; San Diego, CA; Catamaran Resort.

OTHER SOURCES

9216 ■ American Mosquito Control Association (AMCA)
15000 Commerce Pkwy., Ste. C
Mount Laurel, NJ 08054
Ph: (856)439-9222
Fax: (856)439-0525
E-mail: amca@mosquito.org
URL: http://www.mosquito.org

Description: Entomologists, biologists, medical personnel, engineers, public health officials, military personnel, and others interested in mosquito control and related work.

9217 ■ Association of American Pesticide Control Officials (AAPCO)
PO Box 466
Milford, DE 19963
Ph: (302)422-8152
Fax: (302)422-2435
E-mail: aapco-sfireg@comcast.net
URL: http://aapco.ceris.purdue.edu

Description: State agencies controlling the sale, use, and distribution of pesticides. Promotes uniform laws, regulations, and policies of enforcement.

9218 ■ Association of Applied IPM Ecologists (AAIE)
PO Box 1119
Coarsegold, CA 93614
Ph: (559)761-1064
E-mail: director@aaie.net
URL: http://www.aaie.net

Description: Professional agricultural pest management consultants, entomologists, and field personnel. Promotes the implementation of integrated pest management in agricultural and urban environments. Provides a forum for the exchange of technical information on pest control. Offers placement service.

9219 ■ Bio-Integral Resource Center (BIRC)
PO Box 7414
Berkeley, CA 94707
Ph: (510)524-2567
Fax: (510)524-1758
E-mail: birc@igc.org
URL: http://www.birc.org

Description: Provides publications and consultations

for pest management professionals, farmers, foresters, park service resource managers, environmentalists, and interested individuals. Provides practical information on methods of managing pests and land resource problems. Evaluates and disseminates information on the least toxic method of managing weed, vertebrate, insect, and microbe pests in urban, agricultural, forestall, and veterinary environments. Develops integrated pest management programs for community groups, public agencies, and private institutions. (IPM involves integrating biological, horticultural, mechanical, and chemical strategies to suppress pest populations below levels causing economic, medical, or aesthetic damage.) Areas of technical assistance include: consultation of community pest problems; identification of pests and their natural enemies; pest control program evaluation; development of contract specifications; landscape design and design plan review; integration of IPM methods and sustainable agriculture. Reports on educational opportunities; sponsors workshops and lectures.

9220 ■ Biopesticide Industry Alliance (BPIA)
PO Box 465
McFarland, WI 53558
Ph: (202)536-4602
E-mail: bstoneman@biopesticideindustryalliance.org
URL: http://www.biopesticideindustryalliance.org

Description: Fosters the use of biopesticide technology. Increases awareness of biopesticides as effective products. Develops and promotes industry standards for biopesticides. Provides networking opportunities for members and affiliates.

9221 ■ National Entomology Scent Detection Canine Association (NESDCA)
PO Box 3840
Seminole, FL 33775
E-mail: nesdca@nesdca.com
URL: http://www.nesdca.com

Description: Unites and assists entomology scent detection canine teams in the training and continued improvement. Strives to improve the image of the entomology scent-detecting canine teams. Educates consumers about the benefits of using trained entomology scent detecting dog teams in the process of locating and eradicating pest problems.

9222 ■ National Pest Management Association International (NPMA)
10460 N St.
Fairfax, VA 22030
Ph: (703)352-6762
Fax: (703)352-3031
Fr: 800-678-6722
E-mail: info@pestworld.org
URL: http://www.pestworld.org

Description: Represents firms engaged in control of

insects, rodents, birds, and other pests, in or around structures, through use of insecticides, rodenticides, miticides, fumigants, and non-chemical methods. Provides advisory services on control procedures, new products, and safety and business administration practices. Promotes June as National Pest Control Month. Sponsors research, periodic technical and management seminars.

9223 ■ Pesticide Applicators Professional Association (PAPA)
PO Box 80095
Salinas, CA 93912-0095
Ph: (831)442-3536
Fax: (831)442-2351
E-mail: stephanie@papaseminars.com
URL: http://www.papaseminars.com

Description: Purpose: Seeks to provide continuing education for members to be able to renew state licenses.

9224 ■ Responsible Industry for a Sound Environment (RISE)
1156 15th St. NW, Ste. 400
Washington, DC 20005
Ph: (202)872-3860
Fax: (202)355-1467
E-mail: kreardon@pestfacts.org
URL: http://www.pestfacts.org

Description: Manufacturers, formulators, distributors, and representatives of the specialty pesticides industry. Promotes the environmental, health, and safety benefits of the proper use of specialty pesticides.

9225 ■ Safer Pest Control Project
4611 N Ravenswood Ave., Ste. 107
Chicago, IL 60640
Ph: (773)878-7378
Fax: (773)878-8250
E-mail: general@spcpweb.org
URL: http://www.spcpweb.org

Description: Non-profit organization dedicated to reducing the public health risks and environmental impacts of pesticide use and promoting safer alternatives.

9226 ■ The Structural Pest Control Board
2005 Evergreen St., Ste. 1500
Sacramento, CA 95815
Ph: (916)561-8700
Fax: (916)263-2469
Fr: 800-737-8188
E-mail: pestboard@dca.ca.gov
URL: http://www.pestboard.ca.gov

Description: Strives to be the national leader in creating an environment where the public is fully protected and well informed, and where structural pest control industry operates without unreasonable restraint.

Sources of Help-Wanted Ads

9227 ■ *AEG News*
Association of Environmental & Engineering Geologists
PO Box 460518
Denver, CO 80246
Ph: (303)757-2926
E-mail: aeg@aegweb.org
URL: http://www.aegweb.org

Description: Bimonthly. $40 per year for nonmember. Covers news of the engineering geology profession and the Association, whose members are engineering geologists and geological engineers worldwide. Recurring features include letters to the editor, a calendar of events, news of research, and short articles of technical interest.

9228 ■ *Diesel & Gas Turbine Worldwide*
Diesel & Gas Turbine Publications
20855 Watertown Rd., Ste. 220
Waukesha, WI 53189
Ph: (262)754-4100
Fax: (262)754-4175
Fr: 800-558-4322
URL: http://www.dieselpub.com/ers/rdr_
    login.asp?magradio=WW

Monthly. $65.00/year for individuals; free to qualified subscribers. International magazine covering the design, application, and operation of diesel, natural gas, and gas turbine engine systems.

9229 ■ *Engineering*
Scientific Research Publishing
PO Box 54821
Irvine, CA 92619-4821
E-mail: eng@scirp.org
URL: http://www.scirp.org/journal/eng/

Monthly. $708.00/year for individuals. Peer-reviewed journal publishing articles on the latest advancements in engineering.

9230 ■ *Engineering Economist*
Taylor & Francis Group
270 Madison Ave.
New York, NY 10016
Fax: (212)244-4561
URL: http://www.tandf.co.uk/journals/titles/
    0013791x.asp

Quarterly. $89.00/year for individuals, print; $153.00/year for institutions, online only; $170.00/year for institutions, print & online. Publication covering business issues in the energy, petroleum and mining industries.

9231 ■ *ENR: Engineering News-Record*
McGraw-Hill Inc.
PO Box 182604
Columbus, OH 43218
Ph: (614)430-4000
Fax: (614)759-3749

Fr: 877-833-5524
URL: http://enr.construction.com/Default.asp

Weekly. $49.00/year for individuals, print; $89.00/year for Canada, print; $125.00/year for other countries, print. Magazine focusing on engineering and construction.

9232 ■ *Graduating Engineer & Computer Careers*
Career Recruitment Media
2 LAN Dr., Ste. 100
Westford, MA 01886
Ph: (978)692-5092
Fax: (978)692-4174
URL: http://www.graduatingengineer.com

Quarterly. $16.95/year for individuals. Magazine focusing on employment, education, and career development for entry-level engineers and computer scientists.

9233 ■ *High Technology Careers Magazine*
HTC
4701 Patrick Henry Dr., No. 1901
Santa Clara, CA 95054
Fax: (408)567-0242
URL: http://www.hightechcareers.com

Bimonthly. $29.00/year; $35.00/year for Canada; $85.00/year for out of country. Magazine (tabloid) containing employment opportunity information for the engineering and technical community.

9234 ■ *Journal of Women and Minorities in Science and Engineering*
Begell House Inc.
50 Cross Hwy.
Redding, CT 06896
Ph: (203)938-1300
Fax: (203)938-1304
URL: http://www.begellhouse.com/journals/
    00551c876cc2f027

$248.00/year for institutions. Peer-reviewed journal featuring innovative ideas and programs for classroom teachers, scientific studies, and formulation of concepts related to the education, recruitment, and retention of under-represented groups in science and engineering.

9235 ■ *NSBE Magazine*
NSBE Publications
205 Daingerfield Rd.
Alexandria, VA 22314
Ph: (703)549-2207
Fax: (703)683-5312
URL: http://www.nsbe.org/News-Media/Magazines/
    About-NSBE-Magazine

$20.00/year for individuals; $35.00/year for other countries; $15.00/year for students. Journal providing information on engineering careers, self-development, and cultural issues for recent graduates with technical majors.

9236 ■ *Offshore*
PennWell Publishing Co.
1455 W Loop S, Ste. 400
Houston, TX 77027
Ph: (713)621-9720
Fr: 800-736-6935
URL: http://www.offshore-mag.com/index.cfm

Monthly. Magazine for petroleum industry covering offshore operations, engineering, and technology.

9237 ■ *Oil & Gas Journal*
PennWell Publishing Co.
1455 W Loop S, Ste. 400
Houston, TX 77027
Ph: (713)621-9720
Fr: 800-736-6935
URL: http://www.ogj.com/index.html

Weekly. $69.00/year for individuals, print; $49.00/year for individuals, online; $73.00/year for other countries, Canada and Latin America; $108.00/year for other countries. Trade magazine serving engineers and managers in international petroleum operations.

9238 ■ *PE*
National Society of Professional Engineers
1420 King St.
Alexandria, VA 22314
Ph: (703)684-2800
Fax: (703)684-4875
URL: http://www.nspe.org/PEmagazine/index.html

Monthly. Magazine (tabloid) covering professional, legislative, and techology issues for an engineering audience.

9239 ■ *Sustainable Facility*
BNP Media
2401 W Big Beaver Rd., Ste. 700
Troy, MI 48084-3333
Ph: (847)763-9534
Fax: (847)763-9538
URL: http://www.sustainablefacility.com/

Monthly. Magazine reporting on the energy management market as it relates to commercial, industrial, and institutional facilities.

9240 ■ *SWE, Magazine of the Society of Women Engineers*
Society of Women Engineers
120 S La Salle St., Ste. 1515
Chicago, IL 60603
Ph: (312)596-5223
Fr: 877-793-4636
URL: http://societyofwomenengineers.swe.org/
    index.php

Quarterly. $30.00/year for nonmembers. Magazine for engineering students and for women and men working in the engineering and technology fields. Covers career guidance, continuing development and topical issues.

9241 ■ WEPANEWS
Women in Engineering Programs & Advocates
Network
1901 E Asbury Ave., Ste. 220
Denver, CO 80208
Ph: (303)871-4643
Fax: (303)871-4628
E-mail: dmatt@wepan.org
URL: http://www.wepan.org

Description: 2/year. Seeks to provide greater access for women to careers in engineering. Includes news of graduate, undergraduate, freshmen, precollege, and re-entry engineering programs for women. Recurring features include job listings, faculty, grant, and conference news, international engineering program news, action group news, notices of publications available, and a column titled Kudos.

9242 ■ Woman Engineer
Equal Opportunity Publications, Inc.
445 Broadhollow Rd., Ste. 425
Melville, NY 11747
Ph: (631)421-9421
Fax: (631)421-1352
E-mail: info@eop.com
URL: http://www.eop.com

Annual. Magazine that is offered at no charge to qualified female engineering, computer-science, and information-technology students and professionals seeking to find employment and advancement in their careers.

9243 ■ World Oil
Gulf Publishing Co.
2 Greenway Plz., Ste. 1020
PO Box 2608
Houston, TX 77046
Ph: (713)529-4301
Fax: (713)520-4433
Fr: 800-231-6275
E-mail: editorial@worldoil.com
URL: http://www.worldoil.com

Monthly. $149.00/year for individuals, domestic; $345.00/year for individuals, domestic, three years; free, qualifiers; $261.00/year for two years. Trade magazine on oil and gas exploration, drilling, and production.

EMPLOYER DIRECTORIES AND NETWORKING LISTS

9244 ■ American Men and Women of Science
Gale
PO Box 6904
Florence, KY 41022-6904
Fr: 800-354-9706
URL: http://www.gale.cengage.com

Biennial, even years; New edition expected 29th, June 2011. $1,368.00 for individuals. Covers: Over 135,000 U.S. and Canadian scientists active in the physical, biological, mathematical, computer science, and engineering fields; includes references to previous edition for deceased scientists and nonrespondents. Entries include: Name, address, education, personal and career data, memberships, honors and awards, research interest. Arrangement: Alphabetical. Indexes: Discipline (in separate volume).

9245 ■ Careers in Focus—Engineering
Facts On File Inc.
132 W 31st St., 17th Fl.
New York, NY 10001
Ph: (212)967-8800
Fax: 800-678-3633
Fr: 800-322-8755
URL: http://www.infobasepublishing.com

Latest edition 3rd; Published July, 2007. $32.95 for individuals. Covers: An overview of engineering, fol-

lowed by a selection of jobs profiled in detail, including the nature of the job, earnings, prospects for employment, what kind of training and skills it requires, and sources for further information.

9246 ■ Directory of Certified Petroleum Geologists
American Association of Petroleum Geologists
1444 S Boulder
Tulsa, OK 74119
Ph: (918)584-2555
Fax: (918)560-2665
Fr: 800-364-2274
URL: http://www.aapg.org/dpadirectory

Covers: About 3,400 members of the association. Entries include: Name, address; education and career data; whether available for consulting. Arrangement: Alphabetical. Indexes: Geographical.

9247 ■ Directory of Contract Staffing Firms
C.E. Publications Inc.
PO Box 3006
Bothell, WA 98041-3006
Ph: (425)806-5200
Fax: (425)806-5585
URL: http://www.cjhunter.com/dcsf/overview.html

Annual. Covers: Nearly 1,300 contract firms actively engaged in the employment of engineering, IT/IS, and technical personnel for 'temporary' contract assignments throughout the world. Entries include: Company name, address, phone, name of contact, email, web address. Arrangement: Alphabetical. Indexes: Geographical.

9248 ■ The Geophysical Directory
Geophysical Directory Inc.
PO Box 130508
Houston, TX 77219
Ph: (713)529-8789
Fax: (713)529-3646
Fr: 800-929-2462
E-mail: info@geophysicaldirectory.com
URL: http://www.geophysicaldirectory.com

Annual, Latest edition 66th; 2011. $150.00 for individuals; $165.00 for individuals. Covers: About 4,581 companies that provide geophysical equipment, supplies, or services, and mining and petroleum companies that use geophysical techniques; international coverage. Entries include: Company name, address, phone, fax, names of principal executives, operations, and 9,719 key personnel; similar information for branch locations. Arrangement: Classified by product or service. Indexes: Company name, personal name.

9249 ■ Indiana Society of Professional Engineers—Directory
Indiana Society of Professional Engineers
PO Box 20806
Indianapolis, IN 46220
Ph: (317)255-2267
Fax: (317)255-2530
URL: http://www.indspe.org

Annual, fall. Covers: Member registered engineers, land surveyors, engineering students, and engineers in training. Entries include: Member name, address, phone, type of membership, business information, specialty. Arrangement: Alpha by chapter area.

9250 ■ The Oil & Gas Directory
Geophysical Directory Inc.
PO Box 130508
Houston, TX 77219
Ph: (713)529-8789
Fax: (713)529-3646
Fr: 800-929-2462
URL: http://www.geophysicaldirectory.com

Annual, Latest edition 2011. $140.00 for individuals; $150.00 for individuals. Covers: About 12,904 companies worldwide involved in petroleum exploration, drilling, and production, and suppliers to the industry. Entries include: Company name, address, phone, fax, names of principal personnel, branch office addresses, phone numbers, and 22,675 key personnel.

Arrangement: Classified by activity. Indexes: Company name, personal name and regional.

HANDBOOKS AND MANUALS

9251 ■ Opportunities in Petroleum Careers
The McGraw-Hill Companies
PO Box 182604
Columbus, OH 43272
Fax: (614)759-3749
Fr: 877-883-5524
E-mail: customer.service@mcgraw-hill.com
URL: http://www.mhprofessional.com/
 product.php?isbn=0071493077

Gretchen Krueger. 2008. $14.95 (paper). 160 pages. Outlines jobs in looking for oil; drilling and producing oil; and transporting, refining, and marketing oil. Discusses job seeking, opportunities for advancement, and employment outlook.

9252 ■ Resumes for Scientific and Technical Careers
The McGraw-Hill Companies
PO Box 182604
Columbus, OH 43272
Fax: (614)759-3749
Fr: 877-883-5524
E-mail: customer.service@mcgraw-hill.com
URL: http://www.mhprofessional.com/
 product.php?isbn=0071482199

Third edition, 2007. $12.95 (paper). 144 pages. Provides resume advice for individuals interested in working in scientific and technical careers. Includes sample resumes and cover letters.

EMPLOYMENT AGENCIES AND SEARCH FIRMS

9253 ■ Dunn Associates
229 Limberline Dr.
Greensburg, PA 15601
Ph: (724)832-9822
E-mail: maddunn@aol.com
URL: http://www.dunnassociatesinc.com

Executive search firm.

9254 ■ Engineer One, Inc.
PO Box 23037
Knoxville, TN 37933
Fax: (865)691-0110
E-mail: engineerone@engineerone.com
URL: http://www.engineerone.com

Engineering employment service specializing in engineering and management in the chemical process, power utilities, manufacturing, mechanical, electrical, and electronic industries. Maintains an Information Technology Division that works nationwide across all industries. Also provides systems analysis consulting services specializing in VAX based systems.

9255 ■ First Choice Search
PO Box 946
Danville, WA 94526
Ph: (925)552-9985
E-mail: info@firstchoicesearch.com
URL: http://www.firstchoicesearch.com

Executive search firm.

9256 ■ Global Employment Solutions
10375 Park Meadows Dr., Ste. 375
Littleton, CO 80124
Ph: (303)216-9500
Fax: (303)216-9533
URL: http://www.gesnetwork.com

Employment agency.

9257 ■ **International Staffing Consultants**
31655 2nd Ave.
Laguna Beach, CA 92651
Ph: (949)255-5857
Fax: (949)767-5959
E-mail: iscinc@iscworld.com
URL: http://www.iscworld.com

Employment agency. Provides placement on regular or temporary basis. Affiliate office in London.

9258 ■ **Preng and Associates**
2925 Briarpark Dr., Ste. 1111
Houston, TX 77042
Ph: (713)266-2600
Fax: (713)266-3070
E-mail: houston@preng.com
URL: http://www.preng.com

Serves as an executive search firm specializing exclusively in oil, gas, and energy industries worldwide.

9259 ■ **SPECTRA Associates**
PO Box 688
Stevensville, MT 59870
Ph: (406)369-1188
E-mail: engineering@spectra-assoc.com
URL: http://www.spectra-assoc.com

Description: Serves as an executive search firm specializing in recruitment for engineering markets including companies involved with manufacturing, production and engineering.

ONLINE JOB SOURCES AND SERVICES

9260 ■ **BiomassEngineerJobs.com**
URL: http://www.biomassengineerjobs.com

Description: Serves as clearinghouse for individuals seeking positions in the biomass engineering field. Features salary reviews, resume postings, and other career development opportunities.

9261 ■ **EnergyCentralJobs.com**
E-mail: service@energycentral.com
URL: http://www.energycentraljobs.com

Description: Serves as an on-line job resource for candidates and power companies worldwide. Maintains a job search database dedicated to the power, nuclear, oil and gas career fields.

9262 ■ **EngineerJobs.com**
URL: http://www.engineerjobs.com

Description: Provides job opportunities for engineering professionals in the following disciplines: aerospace, agricultural, biomedical, chemical, civil, electrical, environmental, industrial, manufacturing, marine, materials, mechanical, mining, nuclear, petroleum, process, project, quality, sales, software, solar, systems, and structural.

9263 ■ **Engineer.net**
URL: http://www.engineer.net

Description: Provides engineering employment tools such as job search, job posting, and engineering resumes.

9264 ■ **Oil Jobs 411**
E-mail: info@oiljobs411.com
URL: http://www.oiljobs411.com

Description: Provides online resource and information to the oil and gas industry. Features job opportunities and job search advice.

9265 ■ **PetroleumEngineer.com**
URL: http://www.petroleumengineer.com

Description: Provides a forum where petroleum engineering employers can showcase their open jobs and products to petroleum engineers and to the petroleum engineering community.

9266 ■ **ThinkEnergyGroup.com**
E-mail: resumes@thinkjobs.com
URL: http://www.thinkenergygroup.com

Description: Serves as a job board for professionals looking for positions in engineering, power plant, energy, and technical fields. Contains advice and tips on interviews, job searching, resume writing, hiring, and management. Provides choices of work location, pay rates in the field of expertise and contract, temp-to-hire, and direct hiring options.

TRADESHOWS

9267 ■ **International Thermal and Heavy Oil Symposium**
Society of Petroleum Engineers (Richardson, Texas)
222 Palisades Creek Dr.
PO Box 833836
Richardson, TX 75080-2040
Ph: (972)952-9494
Fax: (972)952-9435
E-mail: service@otcnet.org
URL: http://www.otcnet.org

Biennial. Primary Exhibits: Equipment, supplies, and services for thermal operations, new recovery techniques, cold pumping, and application of horizontal drilling.

OTHER SOURCES

9268 ■ **American Association of Blacks in Energy (AABE)**
1625 K St. NW, Ste. 405
Washington, DC 20006
Ph: (202)371-9530
Fax: (202)371-9218
Fr: 800-466-0204
E-mail: info@aabe.org
URL: http://www.aabe.org

Description: Seeks to increase the knowledge, understanding, and awareness of the minority community in energy issues by serving as an energy information source for policymakers, recommending blacks and other minorities to appropriate energy officials and executives, encouraging students to pursue professional careers in the energy industry, and advocating the participation of blacks and other minorities in energy programs and policymaking activities. Updates members on key legislation and regulations being developed by the Department of Energy, the Department of Interior, the Department of Commerce, the Small Business Administration, and other federal and state agencies.

9269 ■ **American Association of Engineering Societies (AAES)**
1801 Alexander Bell Dr.
Reston, VA 20191
Ph: (202)296-2237
Fax: (202)296-1151
Fr: 888-400-2237
E-mail: dbateson@aaes.org
URL: http://www.aaes.org

Description: Coordinates the efforts of the member societies in the provision of reliable and objective information to the general public concerning issues which affect the engineering profession and the field of engineering as a whole; collects, analyzes, documents, and disseminates data which will inform the general public of the relationship between engineering and the national welfare; provides a forum for the engineering societies to exchange and discuss their views on matters of common interest; and represents the U.S. engineering community abroad through representation in WFEO and UPADI.

9270 ■ **American Indian Science and Engineering Society (AISES)**
PO Box 9828
Albuquerque, NM 87119-9828

Ph: (505)765-1052
Fax: (505)765-5608
E-mail: info@aises.org
URL: http://www.aises.org

Description: Represents American Indian and non-Indian students and professionals in science, technology, and engineering fields; corporations representing energy, mining, aerospace, electronic, and computer fields. Seeks to motivate and encourage students to pursue undergraduate and graduate studies in science, engineering, and technology. Sponsors science fairs in grade schools, teacher training workshops, summer math/science sessions for 8th-12th graders, professional chapters, and student chapters in colleges. Offers scholarships. Adult members serve as role models, advisers, and mentors for students. Operates placement service.

9271 ■ **Association for International Practical Training (AIPT)**
10400 Little Patuxent Pkwy., Ste. 250
Columbia, MD 21044-3519
Ph: (410)997-2200
Fax: (410)992-3924
E-mail: aipt@aipt.org
URL: http://www.aipt.org

Description: Provides worldwide of on-the-job training programs for students and professionals seeking international career development and life-changing experiences. Arranges workplace exchanges in hundreds of professional fields, bringing employers and trainees together from around the world. Client list ranges from small farming communities to Fortune 500 companies.

9272 ■ **Association for Women Geoscientists (AWG)**
12000 N Washington St., Ste. 285
Thornton, CO 80241
Ph: (303)412-6219
Fax: (303)253-9220
E-mail: office@awg.org
URL: http://www.awg.org

Description: Represents men and women geologists, geophysicists, petroleum engineers, geological engineers, hydrogeologists, paleontologists, geochemists, and other geoscientists. Aims to encourage the participation of women in the geosciences. Exchanges educational, technical, and professional information. Enhances the professional growth and advancement of women in the geosciences. Provides information through web site on opportunities and careers available to women in the geosciences. Sponsors educational booths and programs at geological society conventions. Operates charitable program. Maintains speaker's bureau, and Association for Women Geoscientists Foundation.

9273 ■ **Engineering Society of Detroit (ESD)**
20700 Civic Center Dr., Ste. 450
Southfield, MI 48076
Ph: (248)353-0735
Fax: (248)353-0736
E-mail: esd@esd.org
URL: http://ww2.esd.org/home.htm

Description: Engineers from all disciplines; scientists and technologists. Conducts technical programs and engineering refresher courses; sponsors conferences and expositions. Maintains speakers' bureau; offers placement services; although based in Detroit, MI, society membership is international.

9274 ■ **Korean-American Scientists and Engineers Association (KSEA)**
1952 Gallows Rd., Ste. 300
Vienna, VA 22182
Ph: (703)748-1221
Fax: (703)748-1331
E-mail: sejong@ksea.org
URL: http://www.ksea.org

Description: Represents scientists and engineers holding single or advanced degrees. Promotes friendship and mutuality among Korean and American scientists and engineers; contributes to Korea's scientific, technological, industrial, and economic developments; strengthens the scientific, technological, and cultural bonds between Korea and the U.S. Sponsors symposium. Maintains speakers' bureau, placement service, and biographical archives. Compiles statistics.

9275 ■ National Action Council for Minorities in Engineering (NACME)
440 Hamilton Ave., Ste. 302
White Plains, NY 10601-1813
Ph: (914)539-4010
Fax: (914)539-4032
E-mail: info@nacme.org
URL: http://www.nacme.org

Description: Leads the national effort to increase access to careers in engineering and other science-based disciplines. Conducts research and public policy analysis, develops and operates national demonstration programs at precollege and university levels, and disseminates information through publications, conferences and electronic media. Serves as a privately funded source of scholarships for minority students in engineering.

9276 ■ National Society of Professional Engineers (NSPE)
1420 King St.
Alexandria, VA 22314-2794
Ph: (703)684-2800
Fax: (703)836-4875
Fr: 888-285-6773
E-mail: memserv@nspe.org
URL: http://www.nspe.org

Description: Represents professional engineers and engineers-in-training in all fields registered in accordance with the laws of states or territories of the U.S. or provinces of Canada; qualified graduate engineers, student members, and registered land surveyors. Is concerned with social, professional, ethical, and economic considerations of engineering as a profession; encompasses programs in public relations, employment practices, ethical considerations, education, and career guidance. Monitors legislative and regulatory actions of interest to the engineering profession.

9277 ■ Society of Hispanic Professional Engineers (SHPE)
13181 Crossroads Pkwy. N, Ste. 450
City of Industry, CA 91746-3496
Ph: (323)725-3970
Fax: (323)725-0316
E-mail: shpenational@shpe.org
URL: http://oneshpe.shpe.org/wps/portal/national

Description: Represents engineers, student engineers, and scientists. Aims to increase the number of Hispanic engineers by providing motivation and support to students. Sponsors competitions and educational programs. Maintains placement service and speakers' bureau; compiles statistics.

9278 ■ Society of Petroleum Engineers (SPE)
222 Palisades Creek Dr.
PO Box 833836
Richardson, TX 75083-3836
Ph: (972)952-9393
Fax: (972)952-9435
Fr: 800-456-6863
E-mail: spedal@spe.org
URL: http://www.spe.org

Description: Worldwide technical society of engineers, scientists, managers, and operating personnel in the upstream petroleum industry. Offers distance learning, continuing education short courses, and distinguished lecturer program; sponsors contests; offers placement service and Internet Career Center.

9279 ■ Society of Women Engineers (SWE)
203 N La Salle St., Ste. 1675
Chicago, IL 60601
Ph: (312)596-5223
Fax: (312)596-5252
Fr: 877-SWE-INFO
E-mail: hq@swe.org
URL: http://societyofwomenengineers.swe.org

Description: Educational and service organization representing both students and professional women in engineering and technical fields.

SOURCES OF HELP-WANTED ADS

9280 ■ AACP E-lert
American Association of Colleges of Pharmacy
1727 King St.
Alexandria, VA 22314
Ph: (703)739-2330
Fax: (703)836-8982
E-mail: mail@aacp.org
URL: http://www.aacp.org/news/Pages/default.aspx

Description: Bi-weekly. Discusses issues relating to pharmaceutical education. Carries legislative information, feature stories on award winners, and Association news. Recurring features include news of research, notices of continuing education and employment opportunities, and listings of publications.

9281 ■ AAPS Newsmagazine
American Association of Pharmaceutical Scientists
2107 Wilson Blvd., Ste. 700
Arlington, VA 22201-3042
Ph: (703)243-2800
Fax: (703)243-9650
URL: http://www.aaps.org/Publications/AAPS_
Newsmagazine/

Monthly. Included in membership. Professional magazine covering issues of interest to pharmaceutical scientists.

9282 ■ AAPS PharmSciTech
Springer-Verlag New York Inc.
233 Spring St.
New York, NY 10013-1578
Ph: (212)460-1500
Fax: (212)460-1575
Fr: 800-777-4643
URL: http://www.springer.com/biomed/
pharmaceutical+science/journa

Quarterly. $355.00/year for institutions, print or online. Journal covering pharmaceuticals in health care, with particular emphasis on drug marketing and management.

9283 ■ American College of Apothecaries Newsletter
American College of Apothecaries
Research & Education Resource Center
2830 Summer Oaks Dr.
Bartlett, TN 38184
Ph: (901)383-8119
Fax: (901)383-8882
Fr: 800-828-5933
E-mail: aca@acainfo.org
URL: http://www.americancollegeofapothecaries.com

Description: Monthly. Presents national pharmacy news designed to assist Association members in their professional practices. Covers Association news, including items on membership, chapters, committees, elections, and conferences. Recurring features include book reviews and a necrology.

9284 ■ American Journal of Health-System Pharmacy
American Society of Health-System Pharmacists
7272 Wisconsin Ave.
Bethesda, MD 20814-4836
Ph: (301)657-3000
Fax: (301)664-8877
Fr: (866)279-0681
E-mail: ajhp@ashp.org
URL: http://www.ajhp.org

Semimonthly. $278.00/year for individuals. Journal for pharmacists practicing in health-systems (acute care, ambulatory care, homecare, long term care, HMO's, PPOs, & PBMs).

9285 ■ The Annals of Pharmacotherapy
Harvey Whitney Books Co.
8044 Montgomery Rd., Ste. 415
PO Box 42696
Cincinnati, OH 45236-2919
Ph: (513)793-3555
Fax: (513)793-3600
Fr: 877-742-7631
URL: http://www.theannals.com

Monthly. $574.00/year for U.S., Canada, and Mexico, institution; online or print; $597.00/year for U.S., Canada, and Mexico, institution; online & print; $574.00/year for institutions, other countries, online only; $636.00/year for institutions, other countries, online & print; $610.00/year for institutions, other countries, print only; $95.00/year for U.S., Canada, and Mexico, online or print; student; $99.00/year for U.S., Canada, and Mexico, online & print; student; $95.00/year for other countries, online only; student; $135.00/year for other countries, print only; student; $140.00/year for other countries, online & print; student. Peer-reviewed medical journal focusing on the advances of pharmacotherapy throughout the world.

9286 ■ BioPharm International
Advanstar Communications, Inc.
6200 Canoga Ave., 2nd Fl.
Woodland Hills, CA 91367
Ph: (818)593-5000
Fax: (818)593-5020
URL: http://biopharminternational.findpharma.com/

Monthly. $70.00/year for individuals; $95.00/year for Canada and Mexico; $135.00/year for other countries; $7.00/year for single issue; $9.00/year for Canada and Mexico, single copies; $9.00/year for other countries, single copies. Periodical publishing professional practice news and care reports, research development and manufacturing.

9287 ■ Christian Pharmacists Fellowship International-Newsletter
Christian Pharmacists Fellowship International
PO Box 24708
West Palm Beach, FL 33416-4708
Ph: (561)803-2737
Fax: (561)803-2738

Fr: 888-253-6885
E-mail: info@cpfi.org
URL: http://www.cpfi.org

Description: Bimonthly. Reports on the activities of members and the fellowship, as well as Christian events in pharmacy. Includes book reviews and directory.

9288 ■ Community Pharmacist
ELF Publications Inc.
5285 W Louisiana Ave.
Lakewood, CO 80232-5976
Ph: (303)975-0075
Fr: 800-922-8513
URL: http://www.elfpublications.com

Bimonthly. National magazine addressing the professional and business needs, concerns and continuing education of retail pharmacists practicing in independent, chain and supermarket pharmacies.

9289 ■ Current Opinion in Pharmacology
Elsevier Science Inc.
360 Park Ave. S
New York, NY 10010-1710
Ph: (212)989-5800
Fax: (212)633-3990
Fr: 888-437-4636
URL: http://www.elsevier.com/wps/find/
journaldescription.cws_home

$2,102.00/year for institutions, all countries except Europe, Japan and Iran; $260,800.00/year for institutions, Japan; $1,881.00/year for institutions, European countries and Iran; $386.00/year for individuals, all countries except Europe, Japan and Iran; $43,200.00/year for individuals, Japan; $355.00/year for individuals, European countries and Iran. Journal covering current advances in pharmacology.

9290 ■ Currents in Pharmacy Teaching and Learning
Reed Elsevier
125 Park Ave., 23rd Fl.
New York, NY 10017
Ph: (212)309-8100
Fax: (212)309-8187
URL: http://www.elsevier.com/wps/find/
journaldescription.cws_home

Quarterly. $584.00/year for institutions, other countries; $69.00/year for other countries; $87.00/year for students, other countries; $467.00/year for institutions, U.S., Canada, and Mexico; $69.00/year for students, Canada and Mexico; $69.00/year for students; $137.00/year for U.S., Canada, and Mexico, individual. Peer-reviewed journal covering all areas of pharmacy education.

9291 ■ Drug Topics
Advanstar Communications Inc.
641 Lexington Ave., 8th Fl.
New York, NY 10022
Ph: (212)951-6600
Fax: (212)951-6793

Fr: 800-346-0085
E-mail: fulfill@superfill.com
URL: http://drugtopics.modernmedicine.com

Bimonthly. $61.00/year for individuals; $30.50/year for students; $109.00/year for out of country; $10.00/year for single issue; $10.00/year for Canada and Mexico, for single issue; $15.00/year for other countries, for single issue. Newsmagazine for pharmacists.

9292 ■ Journal of the American Pharmacists Association

American Pharmacists Association
2215 Constitution Ave. NW
Washington, DC 20005-1707
Ph: (202)628-4410
Fax: (202)783-2351
Fr: 800-237-2742
URL: http://www.aphanet.org/

Bimonthly. $495.00/year for institutions, print and online; $395.00/year for institutions, online only. Peer-reviewed journal for pharmacy professionals.

9293 ■ The Journal of Pharmacy Technology

Harvey Whitney Books
PO Box 42696
Cincinnati, OH 45242
Ph: (513)793-3555
Fax: (513)793-3600
URL: http://www.jpharmtechnol.com

Bimonthly. $40.00/year for student; $181.00/year for institution. Covers articles of interest to pharmacists and pharmacy technicians. Includes new drugs, products, equipment and therapeutic trends, organizational, legal and educational activities, drug distribution and administration, plus continuing education.

9294 ■ MAPS Bulletin

Multidisciplinary Association for Psychedelic Studies
309 Cedar St., No. 2323
Santa Cruz, CA 95060-9989
Ph: (831)429-6362
Fax: (831)429-6370
URL: http://www.maps.org/news-letters/

Professional magazine covering issues in drugs and pharmacy for association members.

9295 ■ McKnight's Long-Term Care News

McKnight's Long-Term Care News
1 Northfield Plz., Ste. 521
Northfield, IL 60093-1216
Ph: (847)784-8706
Fax: (847)784-9346
Fr: 800-558-1703
URL: http://www.mcknightsonline.com/home

$60.00/year for individuals; $108.00/year for two years; $75.00/year for Canada; $135.00/year for Canada, two years; $75.00/year for other countries; $135.00/year for other countries, two years. Professional magazine.

9296 ■ Med Ad News

UBM Canon
11444 W Olympic Blvd.
Los Angeles, CA 90064
Fax: (310)445-4200
URL: http://www.pharmalive.com/magazines/medad/

Monthly. $190.00/year for individuals. Pharmaceutical business and marketing magazine.

9297 ■ NCPA Newsletter

National Community Pharmacists Association
100 Daingerfield Rd.
Alexandria, VA 22314
Ph: (703)683-8200
Fax: (703)683-3619
Fr: 800-544-7447
E-mail: info@ncpanet.org
URL: http://www.ncpanet.org

Description: Semimonthly. Reports on topics affecting independents, including developments within the pharmaceutical industry, regulatory and legislative activity, and pricing and import information. Recurring features include reports of meetings, news of educational opportunities, notices of publications available, and news of NARD activities and events.

9298 ■ The Nurse Practitioner

Lippincott Williams & Wilkins
530 Walnut St.
Philadelphia, PA 19106-3619
Ph: (215)521-8300
Fax: (215)521-8902
Fr: 800-638-3030
E-mail: npedit@wolterskluwer.com
URL: http://journals.lww.com/tnpj/pages/default.aspx

Monthly. $86.76/year for individuals; $401.76/year for institutions; $52.72/year for U.S., in-training; $176.49/year for other countries, individual; $620.49/year for institutions. Magazine presenting clinical information to nurses in advanced primary care practice. Also covers legal, business, economic, ethical, research, and pharmaceutical issues.

9299 ■ NYCPS-Newsletter

New York City Pharmacists Society
111 Broadway, Ste. 2002
New York, NY 10006
Ph: (212)616-7086
Fax: (646)300-6682
URL: http://www.nycps.org

Description: Bimonthly. Provides news, research, and developments relating to pharmacists and pharmaceutical products. Includes information on the New York City Pharmacists Society. Recurring features include letters to the editor, news of research, and lists of job opportunities.

9300 ■ Ohio Society of Health System Pharmacists-Bulletin

Ohio Society of Health-System Pharmacists
50 Greenwood Cir.
Marietta, OH 45750
Ph: (740)373-8595
Fax: (740)452-2552
E-mail: ohioshp@ohioshp.org
URL: http://www.ohioshp.org

Description: Six issues/year. Presents news of the Society and information on pharmacy rulings from the state board. Recurring features include news of research, a calendar of events, reports of meetings, news of educational opportunities, job listings, notices of publications available, a column titled News from Members, and clinical articles.

9301 ■ The PDA Journal of Pharmaceutical Science & Technology

Parenteral Drug Association Inc.
Bethesda Towers, 4350 E West Hwy., Ste. 150
Bethesda, MD 20814
Ph: (301)656-5900
Fax: (301)986-1093
E-mail: pda-journal@uiowa.edu
URL: http://journal.pda.org/

Bimonthly. Included in membership. Peer-reviewed professional journal covering pharmaceutical science.

9302 ■ Pharmaceutical Engineering

International Society for Pharmaceutical Engineering Inc.
600 N Westshore Blvd., Ste. 900
Tampa, FL 33609
Ph: (813)960-2105
Fax: (813)264-2816
URL: http://www.ispe.org/cs/publications_section/pharmaceutical_e

Bimonthly. Included in membership. Magazine on the health care manufacturing industry.

9303 ■ Pharmaceutical Technology

Advanstar Communications
485 Rte. 1 S
Bldg. F, 1st Fl.
Iselin, NJ 08830
Ph: (732)596-0276
Fax: (732)596-0003
URL: http://pharmtech.findpharma.com/

Monthly. $185.00/year for individuals; $331.00/year for two years; $263.00/year for individuals, Canada and Mexico; $458.00/year for two years, Canada and Mexico; $55.00/year for individuals, back issue; $85.00/year for two years, Canada/international, back issue. Magazine on applied technology for pharmaceutical firms.

9304 ■ Pharmacology and Pharmacy

Scientific Research Publishing
PO Box 54821
Irvine, CA 92619-4821
E-mail: pp@scirp.org
URL: http://www.scirp.org/journal/pp/

Quarterly. $156.00/year for individuals. Peer-reviewed journal publishing articles on pharmacology and pharmacy.

9305 ■ Pharmacy Now

Now Publishing Inc.
c/o Zachary Rolnik
PO Box 1024
Hanover, MA 02339
Ph: (781)871-0245
URL: http://www.pharmacynow.com

Continuous. Free, online. Online resource for pharmaceutical professionals. Features career advice and employment listings.

9306 ■ Pharmacy Times

Ascend Integrated Media
7015 College Blvd., Ste. 600
Overland Park, KS 66211
Ph: (913)469-1110
Fax: (913)469-0806
URL: http://www.pharmacytimes.com

Monthly. Journal providing information on health items (including prescription and over-the-counter drugs and surgical supplies) to independent, chain, and hospital pharmacists.

9307 ■ Pharmacy Today

American Pharmacists Association
2215 Constitution Ave. NW
Washington, DC 20005-1707
Ph: (202)628-4410
Fax: (202)783-2351
Fr: 800-237-2742
E-mail: pt@aphanet.org
URL: http://www.pharmacytoday.org/index.htm

Monthly. $200.00/year for individuals; $250.00/year for other countries. Reports on current news and opinions for pharmacists.

9308 ■ Pharmacy Week

7780 Elmwood Ave., Ste. 210
Middleton, WI 53562
Ph: (608)828-4400
Fax: (608)828-4401
E-mail: info@pharmacyweek.com
URL: http://www.pharmacyweek.com

Description: Weekly. Employment newsletter for pharmacists.

9309 ■ Voice of the Pharmacist Newsletter

American College of Apothecaries
Research & Education Resource Center
2830 Summer Oaks Dr.
Bartlett, TN 38184
Ph: (901)383-8119
Fax: (901)383-8882
Fr: 800-828-5933
E-mail: aca@acainfo.org
URL: http://www.americancollegeofapothecaries.com

Description: Quarterly. Examines current issues and opportunities affecting the retail, hospital, and consultant practices of pharmacy. Discusses controversial issues, often with commentary by pharmacists. Recurring features include editorials, news of research, and letters to the editor.

PLACEMENT AND JOB REFERRAL SERVICES

9310 ■ Pace Rx Recruiters
205 SE Wilson Ave., Ste. 1
Bend, OR 97702
Ph: (541)312-5849
Fax: (541)312-0077
Fr: (866)718-2923
E-mail: ryan@pacerxrecruiters.com
URL: http://pacerxrecruiters.com

Placement firm for pharmacy careers.

EMPLOYER DIRECTORIES AND NETWORKING LISTS

9311 ■ Crain's List—Chicago's Largest Hospitals
Crain Communications Inc.
360 N Michigan Ave.
Chicago, IL 60601
Ph: (312)649-5200
URL: http://www.chicagobusiness.com/section/lists

Published November, 2010. $25.00 for individuals; $45.00 for individuals. Covers: 25 hospitals in Chicago area ranked by net patient revenues. Entries include: Name, address, phone number, fax, web address, corporate e-mail, hospital administrator, network affiliation, 2009 net patient revenue, percentage change from 2008, 2009 net profits, percentage change from 2008, inpatient days, available beds, daily occupancy rate, number of hospital employees as of December 31, 2009, fiscal year end, Chairman, President, CEO, Chief Financial Officer, Human Resources Manager, Media Relations/Public Relations Director, and Hospital Administrator.

9312 ■ Directory of Drug Store & HBC Chains
Chain Store Guide
3922 Coconut Palm Dr.
Tampa, FL 33619
Ph: (813)627-6800
Fax: (813)627-6888
Fr: 800-927-9292
URL: http://www.chainstoreguide.com/

Annual, latest edition 2010. $395.00 for individuals; $445.00 for individuals; $1,375.00 for individuals; $1,075.00 for individuals. Covers: More than 1,200 drug store chains operation two or more units, including mass merchants and grocers with pharmacies; 215 wholesale drug companies in the United States and Canada. Entries include: For retailers—company name; phone and fax numbers; physical and mailing addresses; company e-mail and web addresses; listing type; number of stores; product lines; percentage of sales by product line; total sales; prescription drug sales; percentage of prescriptions filled with generic drugs; number of prescriptions filled daily; percentage of prescriptions filled with private third party, cash, and Medicaid; number of stores by type; mail order pharmacy indicator; managed care division indicator; projected openings and remodeling; store prototype sizes; total selling square footage; trading area; franchise group headquarters' name and location; distribution center and primary wholesaler names and locations; number of specialty departments; packaged liquor indicators; private label indicators; computerized pharmacy indicator; average number of checkouts; year founded; public company indicator; parent company name and location; regional and divisional office locations; headquarters personnel with titles. For wholesalers—company name, address, phone, and fax; e-mail and web addresses; listing type; product lines; percentage of sales by product line; total sales; percentage of sales by customer type; total stores served; number of member and non-member stores served; trading area; group store trading names; wholesaler type; distribution center locations; private label indica-

tor; year founded; public company indicator; headquarters personnel with titles. Arrangement: Separate geographical sections for retailers and wholesalers. Indexes: Alphabetical, exclusions.

9313 ■ Directory of Hospital Personnel
Grey House Publishing
4919 Rte. 22
PO Box 56
Amenia, NY 12501
Ph: (518)789-8700
Fax: (518)789-0556
Fr: 800-562-2139
URL: http://www.greyhouse.com/hospital_personnel.htm

Annual, Latest edition 2011. $325.00 for individuals. Covers: 200,000 executives at 6,000 U.S. Hospitals. Entries include: Name of hospital, address, phone, number of beds, type and JCAHO status of hospital, names and titles of key department heads and staff, medical and nursing school affiliations; number of residents, interns, and nursing students. Arrangement: Geographical. Indexes: Hospital name, personnel, hospital size.

9314 ■ Federation of American Societies for Experimental Biology—Directory of Members
Federation of American Societies for Experimental Biology
9650 Rockville Pike
Bethesda, MD 20814-3998
Ph: (301)634-7000
Fax: (301)634-7001
Fr: 800-433-2732
E-mail: directoryinfo@faseb.org
URL: http://www.faseb.org

Annual, Latest edition 2009-2010. $70.00 for individuals; $55.00 for individuals. Covers: About 63,000 members of The American Physiological Society, American Society for Biochemistry and Molecular Biology, American Society for Pharmacology and Experimental Therapeutics, American Society for Investigative Pathology, American Society for Nutritional Sciences, The American Association of Immunologists, Biophysical Society, American Association of Anatomists, The Protein Society, The American Society for Bone and Mineral Research, American Society for Clinical Investigation, The Endocrine Society, The American Society of Human Genetics, Society for Developmental Biology, American Peptide Society, Society for the Study of Reproduction and Radiation Research Society. Entries include: Name, address, title, affiliation, memberships in federation societies, highest degree, year elected to membership, phone, fax and electronic mail address. Membership directories of the Biophysical Society, The Protein Society, The American Society for Bone and Mineral Research, and American Society for Clinical Investigation are also available separately. Arrangement: Alphabetical. Indexes: Geographical.

9315 ■ Hospital Blue Book
Billian Publishing Inc. and Trans World Publishing Inc.
2100 River Edge Pky.
Atlanta, GA 30328
Ph: (770)955-5656
Fax: (770)952-0669
Fr: 800-800-5668
E-mail: blu-book@billian.com
URL: http://www.billianshealthdata.com/Products/bluebook.html

Annual, Latest edition 2010. $575.00 for individuals; $575.00 for individuals. Covers: More than 6,500 hospitals; some listings also appear in a separate southern edition of this publication. Entries include: Name of hospital, accreditation, mailing address, phone, fax, number of beds, type of facility (nonprofit, general, state, etc.); list of administrative personnel and chiefs of medical services, with specific titles. Arrangement: Geographical.

9316 ■ Medical and Health Information Directory
Gale
PO Box 6904
Florence, KY 41022-6904
Fr: 800-354-9706
URL: http://www.gale.cengage.com

Annual, Latest edition April 2011. $1190.00 for individuals; $501.00 for individuals. Covers: In volume 1, more than 33,000 medical and health oriented associations, organizations, institutions, and government agencies, including health maintenance organizations (HMOs), preferred provider organizations (PPOs), insurance companies, pharmaceutical companies, research centers, and medical and allied health schools. In Volume 2, over 20,000 medical book publishers; medical periodicals, directories, audiovisual producers and services, medical libraries and information centers, electronic resources, and health-related internet search engines. In Volume 3, more than 40,500 clinics, treatment centers, care programs, and counseling/diagnostic services for 34 subject areas. Entries include: Institution, service, or firm name, address, phone, fax, email and URL; many include names of key personnel and, when pertinent, descriptive annotation. Volume 3 was formerly listed separately as Health Services Directory. Arrangement: Classified by organization activity, service, etc. Indexes: Each volume has a complete alphabetical name and keyword index.

9317 ■ Vault Guide to the Top Pharmaceuticals & Biotech Employers
Vault.com Inc.
150 W 22nd St., 5th Fl.
New York, NY 10011
Ph: (212)366-4212
Fax: (212)366-6117
Fr: 888-562-8285
URL: http://www.vault.com/store/book_preview.jsp?product_id=34273

Latest edition 2009. $19.95 for individuals; $19.95 for members. Covers: Pharmaceuticals and biotech employers. Entries include: Name, address, phone, fax, website, branch office location, and major departments. Also include company overviews, recent company news, information on the hiring process, key competitors, and employment contact. Arrangement: Alphabetical by company name.

HANDBOOKS AND MANUALS

9318 ■ Careers in Health Care
The McGraw-Hill Companies
PO Box 182604
Columbus, OH 43272
Fax: (614)759-3749
Fr: 877-883-5524
E-mail: customer.service@mcgraw-hill.com
URL: http://www.mhprofessional.com/product.php?isbn=0071466533

Barbara M. Swanson. Fifth edition, 2005. $19.95 (paper). 192 pages. Describes job duties, work settings, salaries, licensing and certification requirements, educational preparation, and future outlook. Gives ideas on how to secure a job.

9319 ■ Comprehensive Pharmacy Review
Lippincott Williams & Wilkins
2 Commerce Sq.
2001 Market St.
Philadelphia, PA 19103
Ph: (215)521-8300
Fax: (215)521-8902
URL: http://www.lww.com

Leon Shargel, Alan Mutnick, Paul Souney and Larry Swanson. 2009. $55.95. 1472 pages. Helps applicants prepare for the North American Pharmacist Licensure Examination (NAPLEX). Includes topics central to the study of pharmacy such as pharmacology, chemistry, pharmacy practice and drug therapy.

9320 ■ Expert Resumes for Health Care Careers
Jist Works
875 Montreal Way
St. Paul, MN 55102
Fr: 800-648-5478
E-mail: educate@emcp.com
URL: http://www.jist.com
Wendy S. Enelow and Louise M. Kursmark. 2010. $16.95. 288 pages.

9321 ■ From Student to Pharmacist: Making the Transition
American Pharmacists Association
2215 Constitution Ave. NW
Washington, DC 20037
Ph: (202)628-4410
Fax: (202)783-2351
URL: http://www.pharmacist.com
Jennifer P. Askew. 2010. $24.00 for member; $29.95 for nonmember. 195 pages. Provides resource for student pharmacists and practitioners new to the profession of pharmacy. Examines the many career options available to new pharmacy professionals, provides practical information about the job interview process, offers tips about workplace responsibility and the adjustment from student life to the work environment and addresses the need for balancing work and professional life.

9322 ■ Get Into Pharmacy School: Rx for Success!
Kaplan Publishing
395 Hudson St.
New York, NY 10014
Ph: (212)492-5800
URL: http://store.kaptest.com
William D. Figg and Cindy H. Chau. $20.00. Contains advice on how to prepare an application, write persuasive personal essays, obtain the best recommendations, and sail through interviews.

9323 ■ Getting Started as a Pharmacy Faculty Member
American Pharmacists Association
2215 Constitution Ave., NW
Washington, DC 20037
Ph: (202)628-4410
Fax: (202)783-2351
Fr: 800-237-2742
URL: http://www.pharmacist.com
David P. Zgarrick. 2010. $29.95/non-member; $24.00/member (softcover). 136 pages. Informs readers about the types of academic positions available, how colleges and universities operate, how to obtain a position and succeed in academia.

9324 ■ Health Careers Today
Elsevier
11830 Westline Industrial Dr.
St. Louis, MO 63146
Ph: (314)453-7010
Fax: (314)453-7095
Fr: 800-545-2522
E-mail: usbkinfo@elsevier.com
URL: http://www.elsevier.com
Gerdin, Judith. Fourth edition. 2007. $74.95. 496 pages. Covers more than 45 health careers. Discusses the roles and responsibilities of various occupations and provides a solid foundation in the skills needed for all health careers.

9325 ■ Introduction to Public Health in Pharmacy
Jones & Bartlett Publishers, Inc.
5 Wall St.
Burlington, MA 01803
Ph: (978)443-5000
Fax: (978)443-8000
Fr: 800-832-0034
URL: http://www.jblearning.com/catalog/
   9780763735395
Lubotsky Levin, Peter D. Hurd, and Artis Hanson.

2008. $83.95. 356 pages. Two-part introduction to public health from a pharmacy perspective.

9326 ■ Opportunities in Health and Medical Careers
The McGraw-Hill Companies
PO Box 182604
Columbus, OH 43272
Fax: (614)759-3749
Fr: 877-883-5524
E-mail: customer.service@mcgraw-hill.com
URL: http://www.mhprofessional.com/
   product.php?isbn=0071437274
I. Donald Snook, Jr. and Leo D'Orazio. 2004. $14.95 (paper). 157 pages. Covers the full range of medical and health occupations. Illustrated.

9327 ■ Pharmacy Professional's Guide to Resumes, CVs, and Interviewing
American Pharmacists Association
2215 Constitution Ave. NW
Washington, DC 20037
Ph: (202)628-4410
Fax: (202)783-2351
URL: http://www.pharmacist.com
Thomas P. Reinders. 3rd Edition, 2011. $39.50 for member; 49.00 for nonmember. 175 pages. Offers valuable resource for student pharmacists and pharmacy professionals seeking employment in the pharmacy field. Provides step-by-step instructions on preparing the resume, the CV and cover letters and preparing for the interview.

9328 ■ Resumes for Health and Medical Careers
The McGraw-Hill Companies
PO Box 182604
Columbus, OH 43272
Fax: (614)759-3749
Fr: 877-883-5524
E-mail: customer.service@mcgraw-hill.com
URL: http://www.mhprofessional.com/
   product.php?isbn=0071545352
Third edition, 2008. $12.95 (paper). 144 pages.

9329 ■ Senior Pharmacist
National Learning Corporation
212 Michael Dr.
Syosset, NY 11791
Fr: 800-632-8888
URL: http://www.passbooks.com
2009. $39.95 (paper). Serves as an exam preparation guide for senior pharmacists.

EMPLOYMENT AGENCIES AND SEARCH FIRMS

9330 ■ AHR Pharmacy Solutions
27042 Towne Centre Dr., Ste. 150
Foothill Ranch, CA 92610
Fax: (949)457-7605
Fr: 800-873-3611
URL: http://www.ahrpharmacyjobs.com
Exists as a staffing firm providing both temporary and permanent pharmacy jobs.

9331 ■ Allerton Heneghan & O'Neill
1415 W 22nd St., Tower Fl.
Oak Brook, IL 60523
Ph: (630)645-2294
Fax: (630)645-2298
E-mail: info@ahosearch.com
URL: http://www.ahosearch.com
Executive search firm.

9332 ■ BioQuest
100 Spear St., Ste. 1125
San Francisco, CA 94105-1526

Ph: (415)777-2422
E-mail: resumes@bioquestinc.com
URL: http://www.bioquestinc.com
Executive search firm focused in healthcare and life sciences.

9333 ■ Brandywine Consulting Group
1398 Morstein Rd.
West Chester, PA 19380
Ph: (610)696-5872
Fax: (610)429-1954
URL: http://www.brandywineconsulting.com
Executive search firm. An Affiliate of Brandywine Management Group in Berlin, MD.

9334 ■ Break the Box Career Group
36 Unity Ave.
Belmont, MA 02478
Ph: (617)489-8706
E-mail: info@btbcareergroup.com
URL: http://www.btbcareergroup.com
Serves as a national recruiting and placement specializing in healthcare Features pharmacy jobs, physician jobs and radiology jobs.

9335 ■ CareerStaff RX
19401 40th Ave. W, Ste. 330
Lynnwood, WA 98036
Fax: (866)835-5848
Fr: 800-766-0122
URL: http://www.careerstaffrx.com
Provides job opportunities among qualified pharmacy professionals.

9336 ■ CareerTrax, Inc.
500 Foothills S, Ste. 2
Sedona, AZ 86336
Ph: (928)274-2266
Fax: 888-802-7407
E-mail: service@careertrax.com
URL: http://www.careertrax.com
Offers recruitment and career development services for biotechnology and pharmaceutical industry professionals.

9337 ■ Clark Executive Search Inc.
135 N Ferry Rd.
PO Box 560
Shelter Island, NY 11964
Ph: (631)749-3540
Fax: (631)749-3539
E-mail: mail@clarksearch.com
URL: http://www.clarksearch.com
Executive search firm.

9338 ■ CNR Search & Services
30752 Via Conquista
San Juan Capistrano, CA 92675
Ph: (949)488-0065
Fax: (775)851-4514
E-mail: cnrkenmiller@juno.com
URL: http://www.cnrsearch.com
Provides staffing services of permanent and temporary employees. Works primarily on a retained basis. Contingency on a limited basis. Services include human resources consulting, mergers and acquisitions in high technology firms. Industries served: computer; information services; insurance, pharmaceutical and health care. Provides staffing services of permanent and temporary employees. Works primarily on a retained basis. Contingency on a limited basis. Services include human resources consulting, mergers and acquisitions in high technology firms. Industries served: computer; information services; insurance, pharmaceutical and health care.

9339 ■ CompHealth
PO Box 713100
Salt Lake City, UT 84171-3100
Ph: (801)930-3000
Fax: (801)930-4517

Fr: 800-453-3030
E-mail: info@comphealth.com
URL: http://www.comphealth.com

Provides healthcare staffing and recruiting services covering certified registered nurse anesthetist, dosimetrist, imaging and radiation therapy, laboratory technology, medical physicist, nurse practitioner, nursing, pharmacy, physician, physician assistant, rehab therapy and respiratory therapy.

9340 ■ Complete Pharmacy Resources
3100 S Gessner Rd., Ste. 640
Houston, TX 77063
Ph: (713)821-1114
Fax: (713)337-9660
Fr: 800-635-9033
E-mail: info@completerx.com
URL: http://completepharmacyresources.com

Provides specialized pharmacy staffing services. Maintains a large active pool of pharmacists, pharmacy technicians and pharmacy specialists.

9341 ■ Conyngham Partners LLC
PO Box 94
Ridgewood, NJ 07451
Ph: (201)652-3444
E-mail: info@conynghampartners.com
URL: http://www.conynghampartners.com

Executive search firm.

9342 ■ Courtright & Associates Inc.
PO Box 236
Scranton, PA 18504
E-mail: rjcx@comcast.net
URL: http://www.courtrightassoc.com

Executive search firm.

9343 ■ Day & Associates
577 Airport Blvd., Ste. 130
Burlingame, CA 94010
Ph: (650)343-2660
Fax: (650)344-8460
E-mail: info@dayassociates.net
URL: http://www.dayassociates.net

Executive search firm.

9344 ■ Doleman Enterprises
11160-F S Lakes Dr., Ste. 326
Reston, VA 22091
Ph: (703)742-5454
Fax: (703)708-6992
E-mail: doleman@patriot.net

Human resources firm specializes in recruiting for the high-tech, data and computer engineering and pharmaceutical industries.

9345 ■ Healthcare Consultants Pharmacy Staffing
PO Box 915726
Longwood, FL 32791
Fax: 800-439-4160
Fr: 800-642-1652
E-mail: info@pharmacy-staffing.com
URL: http://www.pharmacy-staffing.com

Description: Works through a staffing personnel who have experience in all types of pharmacy. Offers placement service specializing in placing pharmacists and technicians in the Southeastern and Southwestern United States. Serves pharmacies looking to a fill a staff as well as pharmacists and technicians looking for placement.

9346 ■ JPM International
26034 Acero
Mission Viejo, CA 92691
Ph: (949)699-4300
Fax: (949)699-4333
Fr: 800-685-7856
E-mail: qtek37@yahoo.com
URL: http://www.jpmintl.com/pages/qss.html

Executive search firm and employment agency.

9347 ■ Ken Clark International
2000 Lenox Dr., Ste. 200
Lawrenceville, NJ 08648
Ph: (609)308-5200
Fax: (609)308-5250
E-mail: info-princeton@kenclark.com
URL: http://www.kenclark.com

Executive search firm. Branches in Newport Beach, CA; Deerfield, IL; Waltham, MA; and Wayne, PA.

9348 ■ Med Exec International
100 N Brand Blvd., Ste. 306-308
Glendale, CA 91203-2614
Ph: (818)552-2036
Fax: (818)552-2475
Fr: 800-507-5277
E-mail: info@medexecintl.com
URL: http://www.medexecintl.com

Firm provides customized executive recruitment services in a rapidly growing competitive pharmaceutical, medical device, biologics, diagnostics, and bio tech market. Expertise includes clinical research, regulatory affairs, quality assurance and compliance, medical affairs.

9349 ■ MedPro Healthcare Staffing
1580 Sawgrass Corporate Pkwy., Ste. 100
Sunrise, FL 33323
Ph: (954)739-4247
Fax: 800-370-0755
Fr: 800-886-8108
E-mail: medprogeneralinquiries@medprostaffing.com
URL: http://www.medprostaffing.com

Provides temporary and contract staffing services to healthcare facilities.

9350 ■ Meticulum, LLC
PO Box 451
Vinalhaven, ME 04863-0451
Ph: (207)470-0447
Fax: 877-773-0447
E-mail: meticulum@meticulum.com
URL: http://www.meticulum.com

Specializes in the identification, recruitment and strategic placement of professionals within the environmental health, biotechnology and pharmaceutical industries.

9351 ■ Pharmaceutical Strategies, LLC
PO Box 249
Wakefield, MA 01880
Fax: (781)279-2977
Fr: (866)352-3337
URL: http://pharmaceuticalstrategies.com

Helps candidates fulfill their career in a pharmacy field.

9352 ■ Pharmacy Staffing Partners
1220 Nicholson St.
Houston, TX 77008
Ph: (713)880-0585
Fax: 888-688-7905
URL: http://www.pharmacystaffingpartners.com

Provides PRN pharmacists and pharmacy technicians for short term and long term assignments.

9353 ■ PharmPro
Back Bldg., Ste. 1
3605 Edgmont Ave.
Brookhaven, PA 19015
Ph: (610)499-9040
Fax: (610)499-9112
Fr: 800-659-7440
URL: http://www.pharmpro-inc.com

Offers staffing services for all pharmacy practice settings. Provides both temporary and permanent staffing of pharmacy professionals.

9354 ■ PRS Pharmacy Staffing Services
201 Depot St., Ste. 200
PO Box 852
Latrobe, PA 15650
Ph: (724)539-7820

Fax: (724)539-1388
Fr: 800-338-3688
URL: http://www.prspharmacystaffing.com

Provides pharmacy staffing services to retail, hospital and specialty pharmacies. Offers pharmacy consulting services.

9355 ■ Sierra Staffing
5 Division St.
East Greenwich, RI 02818
Ph: (401)499-3175
Fr: 800-466-4555
E-mail: jobs@sierrastaffing.com
URL: http://www.sierrastaffing.com

Description: Serves as national pharmacy executive search firm specializing exclusively in health system recruitment.

9356 ■ Stat Group, LLC
PO Box 1674
Owensboro, KY 42302-1674
Ph: (270)663-8020
Fax: 877-998-9940
Fr: 877-998-9930
E-mail: info@statgroupllc.com
URL: http://www.statgroupllc.com

Description: Serves as a healthcare staffing firm which provides healthcare facilities with a workforce pool. Attracts and retains medical professionals to assist healthcare facilities throughout the United States.

9357 ■ United Pharmacy Staffing
1699 Wall St., Ste. 506
Mount Prospect, IL 60056
Ph: (847)228-0050
Fax: (847)228-0060
Fr: (866)321-7747
URL: http://www.upstaffing.com

Serves as a pharmacy recruitment firm that provides interim and permanent placement services.

ONLINE JOB SOURCES AND SERVICES

9358 ■ allpharmacistjobs.com
URL: http://www.allpharmacistjobs.com

Description: Provides pharmacy employment resource and career opportunities. Features pharmacy job listings around the United States.

9359 ■ CareerPharm.com
URL: http://www.careerpharm.com

Description: Exclusively serves the hospital and health system markets. Offers three ways for job seekers and advertisers to connect: online, in print or at a recruiting event.

9360 ■ CareerVitals.com
URL: http://www.careervitals.com

Description: Serves as a job board for healthcare professionals in different specializations.

9361 ■ ElitePharmacyJobs.com
URL: http://www.elitepharmacyjobs.com

Description: Provides job seekers with a relevant, current and comprehensive list of pharmacy industry employment opportunities on the internet. Serves as a resource for job seekers, employers and recruiters.

9362 ■ GreatPharmacyJobs.com
URL: http://www.greatpharmacyjobs.com

Description: Presents employment opportunities across the United States and North America. Uses a distributed advertising system that provides unique content and unique jobs.

9363 ■ GreatPharmaJobs.com
URL: http://greatpharmajobs.com

Description: Offers job vacancies in healthcare industry.

9364 ■ HEALTHeCAREERS Network
Fr: 888-884-8242
E-mail: info@healthcareers.com
URL: http://www.healthcareers.com

Description: Career search site for jobs in all health care specialties; educational resources; visa and licensing information for relocation; interesting articles; relocation tools; links to professional organizations and general resources.

9365 ■ HireRx.com
URL: http://www.hirerx.com

Description: E-recruiting and training company that is focused on solving workforce issues for biotechnology and pharmaceutical firms. Provides access to job openings, online training courses, and communities in their scientific or functional concentration.

9366 ■ HospitalPharmacyJobs.com
URL: http://www.hospitalpharmacyjobs.com/Public/Index.aspx

Description: Exists as an online job site focused entirely and exclusively on pharmacists interested in beginning or expanding their careers in hospital pharmacy. Provides a database of available hospital pharmacy positions located nationwide by location and positions of interest.

9367 ■ iHirePharmacy.com
URL: http://www.ihirepharmacy.com

Description: Provides pharmacy jobs from job postings, internet job boards, newspapers and classified ads.

9368 ■ JobPharm.com
URL: http://www.jobpharm.com

Description: Features a "JobGarden" that lists various pharmacy jobs and other career service facilities. Uses a database where users can either browse through the listings or search to narrow down job choices.

9369 ■ MedExplorer.com
E-mail: medmaster@medexplorer.com
URL: http://www.medexplorer.com

Description: Employment postings make up one module of this general medical site. Other sections contain: Newsletter, Classifieds, and Discussion Forum.

9370 ■ PharmaceuticalCrossing.com
URL: http://www.pharmaceuticalcrossing.com

Description: Consolidates pharmaceutical job openings from various Internet sites.

9371 ■ PharmacistJobsHelp.com
URL: http://www.pharmacistjobshelp.com

Description: Offers employment opportunities and career information for pharmacists. Features listings of pharmacist jobs.

9372 ■ Pharmacy Career Network
URL: http://www.pharmacycareernetwork.com

Description: Connects employers and job seekers to online job boards provided by pharmacy associations.

9373 ■ PharmacyCareerCentral.com
URL: http://www.pharmacycareercentral.com

Description: Features pharmacy jobs and products to the healthcare industry.

9374 ■ pharmacyjob.com
URL: http://www.pharmacyjob.com

Description: Features pharmacy jobs tailored to pharmacists, pharmacy technicians, pharmacy assistants and other pharmacy-related practitioners.

9375 ■ PharmacyJobsNationwide.com
URL: http://www.pharmacyjobsnationwide.com

Description: Provides jobs for pharmacists, phar-

macy technicians, pharmacy managers and pharmacy administration professionals.

9376 ■ PharmacyJobsOnly.com
URL: http://www.pharmacyjobsonly.com

Description: Provides pharmacist career opportunities throughout the United States. Features pharmacy jobs available in every state.

9377 ■ PharmacyPostings.com
E-mail: info@pharmacypostings.com
URL: http://www.pharmacypostings.com

Description: Offers pharmacy jobs including pharmacist jobs and other traditional and non-traditional positions. Provides a job search database by category, state or type of position.

9378 ■ Pharmiweb.com
URL: http://www.pharmiweb.com

Description: Serves as a pharmaceutical portal featuring news, press releases, product announcements, events, pharmaceutical jobs, resume postings, and other related information.

9379 ■ ProHealthJobs.com
Ph: (484)443-8545
Fax: (484)443-8549
E-mail: info@prohealthjobs.com
URL: http://prohealthjobs.com/jobboard

Description: Career resources site for the medical and health care field. Lists professional opportunities, product information, continuing education and open positions.

9380 ■ Rx Career Center
URL: http://www.rxcareercenter.com

Description: Serves as a job board on the internet for the pharmacist, pharmacy technician and pharmaceutical industry professional. Provides candidates with current opportunities in a variety of settings that include retail, hospital, clinical, and industry positions.

9381 ■ RxJobPostings.com
URL: http://rxjobpostings.com

Description: Functions as a pharmacy job board. Specializes in retail pharmacist jobs, clinical pharmacist jobs, and other related professions.

TRADESHOWS

9382 ■ Academy of Managed Care Pharmacy Annual Meeting and Expo
Academy of Managed Care Pharmacy
100 N Pitt St., Ste. 400
Alexandria, VA 22314
Fax: (703)683-8416
Fr: 800-827-2627
URL: http://www.amcp.org

Annual. Provides networking opportunities for managed care pharmacy professionals. 2013 April 3-5; San Diego, CA; San Diego Convention Center.

9383 ■ American Association of Pharmaceutical Scientists Annual Meeting and Exposition
American Association of Pharmaceutical Scientists
2107 Wilson Blvd., Ste. 700
Arlington, VA 22201-3042
Ph: (703)243-2800
Fax: (703)243-9650
URL: http://www.aaps.org

Annual. Primary Exhibits: Raw materials, supplies, equipment, contract research & contract service labs, computer software, packaging, and other suppliers to pharmaceutical scientists.

9384 ■ American Society of Consultant Pharmacists Annual Meeting and Exhibition
American Society of Consultant Pharmacists
1321 Duke St.
Alexandria, VA 22314-3563

Ph: (703)739-1300
Fax: (703)739-1321
Fr: 800-355-2727
E-mail: info@ascp.com
URL: http://www.ascp.com

Annual. Primary Exhibits: Pharmaceuticals, drug distribution systems, packaging equipment, computers, durable medical equipment, and medical supplies. Dates and Locations: 2012 Nov 07-10; National Harbor, MD; Gaylord National Resort and Convention Center.

9385 ■ Drug Development Summit
Canon Communications LLC
11444 W. Olympic Blvd., Ste. 900
Los Angeles, CA 90064-1549
Ph: (310)445-4200
Fax: (310)445-4299
E-mail: info@cancom.com
URL: http://www.cancom.com

Annual. Primary Exhibits: Exhibits relating to pharmaceuticals.

9386 ■ NCPA Convention and Trade Exposition
National Community Pharmacists Association
100 Daingerfield Rd.
Alexandria, VA 22314
Ph: (703)683-8200
Fax: (703)683-3619
Fr: 800-544-7447
E-mail: info@ncpanet.org
URL: http://www.ncpanet.org

Annual. Features exhibits, networking, and entertainment along with continuing education that enables independent community pharmacists to sharpen their patient care skills and improve business performance.

9387 ■ NPhA Convention
National Pharmaceutical Association
107 Kilmayne Dr., Ste. C
Cary, NC 27511
Fax: (919)469-5870
Fr: 877-215-2091
E-mail: npha@npha.net
URL: http://www.npha.net

Advances standards of pharmaceutical care to all practitioners. Discusses issues affecting healthcare and pharmacy. 2012 July 20-23; Las Vegas, NV; Renaissance Hotel.

9388 ■ PharmaMed Marketing and Media Conference
Canon Communications LLC
11444 W. Olympic Blvd., Ste. 900
Los Angeles, CA 90064-1549
Ph: (310)445-4200
Fax: (310)445-4299
E-mail: info@cancom.com
URL: http://www.cancom.com

Annual. Primary Exhibits: Exhibits relating to pharmaceuticals.

9389 ■ Texas Pharmacy Association Annual Meeting and Exhibit
Texas Pharmacy Association
12007 Research Blvd., Ste. 201
Austin, TX 78759
Ph: (512)836-8350
Fax: (512)836-0308
Fr: 800-505-5463
URL: http://www.txpharmacy.com

Annual. Primary Exhibits: Pharmaceuticals and various services provided to pharmacists.

OTHER SOURCES

9390 ■ Academy of Managed Care Pharmacy
100 N Pitt St., Ste. 400
Alexandria, VA 22314
Fax: (703)683-8416

Fr: 800-827-2627
URL: http://www.amcp.org

Description: Represents pharmacists and other health care practitioners who serve society by the application of sound medication management principles and strategies to improve health care for all. Develops and provides a diversified range of clinical, educational and business management services and strategies.

9391 ■ Academy of Pharmacy Practice and Management (APhA-APPM)
American Pharmacists Association
APhA-APPM Nominating Community
2215 Constitution Ave., NW
Washington, DC 20037
Ph: (202)628-4410
Fax: (202)783-2351
Fr: 800-237-APHA
E-mail: mnelson@aphanet.org
URL: http://www.pharmacist.com/AM/
Template.cfm?Section=Practitioners

Description: Pharmacists concerned with rendering professional services directly to the public, without regard for status of employment or environment of practice. Aims to provide a forum and mechanism whereby pharmacists may meet to discuss and implement programs and activities relevant and helpful to the practitioner of pharmacy; to recommend programs and courses of action which should be undertaken or implemented by the profession; to coordinate academy efforts so as to be an asset to the progress of the profession. Provides and co-sponsors continuing education meetings, seminars, and workshops; produces audiovisual materials.

9392 ■ American Academy of Clinical Toxicology (AACT)
110 W Lancaster Ave., Ste. 230
Wayne, PA 19087
Ph: (703)556-9222
Fax: (703)556-8729
E-mail: admin@clintox.org
URL: http://www.clintox.org

Description: Physicians, veterinarians, pharmacists, nurses research scientists, and analytical chemists. Seeks to unite medical scientists and facilitate the exchange of information. Encourages the development of therapeutic methods and technology. Conducts professional training in poison information and emergency service personnel.

9393 ■ American Association of Colleges of Pharmacy
1727 King St.
Alexandria, VA 22314
Ph: (703)739-2330
Fax: (703)836-8982
E-mail: mail@aacp.org
URL: http://www.aacp.org

Description: Represents the interests of pharmacy education in the United States. Promotes professional and graduate education through effective use of policy, information, advocacy, and programming.

9394 ■ American Association of Pharmaceutical Scientists (AAPS)
2107 Wilson Blvd., Ste. 700
Arlington, VA 22201-3042
Ph: (703)243-2800
Fax: (703)243-9650
E-mail: mays@aaps.org
URL: http://www.aapspharmaceutica.com

Description: Works to provide a forum for exchange of scientific information; serves as a resource in forming public policies to regulate pharmaceutical sciences and related issues of public concern. Promotes pharmaceutical sciences and provides for recognition of individual achievement; works to foster career growth and the development of members. Offers placement service.

9395 ■ American College of Clinical Pharmacy (ACCP)
13000 W 87th St. Pkwy.
Lenexa, KS 66215-4530
Ph: (913)492-3311
Fax: (913)492-0088
E-mail: accp@accp.com
URL: http://www.accp.com

Description: Clinical pharmacists dedicated to: promoting rational use of drugs in society; advancing the practice of clinical pharmacy and interdisciplinary health care; assuring high quality clinical pharmacy by establishing and maintaining standards in education and training at advanced levels. Encourages research and recognizes excellence in clinical pharmacy. Offers educational programs, symposia, research forums, fellowship training, and college-funded grants through competitions. Maintains placement service.

9396 ■ American Hospital Association (AHA)
155 N Wacker Dr.
Chicago, IL 60606
Ph: (312)422-3000
Fax: (312)422-4796
E-mail: rich@aha.org
URL: http://www.aha.org

Description: Represents health care provider organizations. Seeks to advance the health of individuals and communities. Leads, represents, and serves health care provider organizations that are accountable to the community and committed to health improvement.

9397 ■ American Public Health Association (APHA)
800 I St. NW
Washington, DC 20001
Ph: (202)777-2742
Fax: (202)777-2534
E-mail: comments@apha.org
URL: http://www.apha.org

Description: Professional organization of physicians, nurses, educators, academicians, environmentalists, epidemiologists, new professionals, social workers, health administrators, optometrists, podiatrists, pharmacists, dentists, nutritionists, health planners, other community and mental health specialists, and interested consumers. Seeks to protect and promote personal, mental, and environmental health. Services include: promulgation of standards; establishment of uniform practices and procedures; development of the etiology of communicable diseases; research in public health; exploration of medical care programs and their relationships to public health. Sponsors job placement service.

9398 ■ American Society of Consultant Pharmacists (ASCP)
1321 Duke St.
Alexandria, VA 22314-3563
Ph: (703)739-1300
Fax: (703)739-1321
Fr: 800-355-2727
E-mail: info@ascp.com
URL: http://www.ascp.com

Description: Provides leadership, education, advocacy and resources enabling consultant and senior care pharmacists to enhance quality of care and quality of life for older individuals through the provision of pharmaceutical care and the promotion of healthy aging. Excels in the areas of: knowledge and skills in geriatric pharmacotherapy; expertise in long-term care settings for the frail at-risk elderly and other residents; and patient-centered advocate for seniors at-risk for medication related problems. Improves drug therapy and quality of life of geriatric patients and other individuals residing in a variety of environments, including nursing facilities, subacute care and assisted living facilities, psychiatric hospitals, hospice programs, and in home and community settings.

9399 ■ American Society of Health System Pharmacists (ASHP)
7272 Wisconsin Ave.
Bethesda, MD 20814
Ph: (301)657-3000
Fax: (301)664-8867
Fr: (866)279-0681
E-mail: custserv@ashp.org
URL: http://www.ashp.org

Description: Professional society of pharmacists employed by hospitals, HMOs, clinics, and other health systems. Provides personnel placement service for members; sponsors professional and personal liability program. Conducts educational and exhibit programs. Maintains 30 practice interest areas, special sections for home care practitioners and clinical specialists, and research and education foundation.

9400 ■ American Society of Medication Safety Officers (ASMSO)
200 Lakeside Dr., Ste. 200
Horsham, PA 19044
Ph: (508)499-3043
Fax: (215)914-1492
E-mail: info@asmso.org
URL: http://www.asmso.org

Description: Seeks to advance and encourage excellence in safe medication by providing communication, leadership, direction and education among members. Promotes information sharing and collaboration among medication safety officers.

9401 ■ American Society of Pharmacognosy
3149 Dundee Rd., No. 260
Northbrook, IL 60062
Ph: (773)995-3748
Fax: (847)656-2800
E-mail: asphcog@aol.com
URL: http://www.phcog.org

Description: Represents professional pharmacognosists, graduate students, and other professionals with allied interests. Promotes the growth and development of pharmacognosy. Provides opportunities for association among workers in the pharmacognosy field.

9402 ■ Bangladeshi-American Pharmacists' Association (BAPA)
1596 Dale Ave.
East Meadow, NY 11554
Ph: (646)325-5441
Fax: (718)278-2716
E-mail: bapapresident@gmail.com
URL: http://www.bapainfo.org

Description: Represents and protects the professional interests of Bangladeshi-American pharmacists. Encourages and supports the development of Pharmaceutical Science in Bangladesh. Fosters cooperation and collaboration among Bangladeshi pharmacists residing in North America.

9403 ■ National Association of Boards of Pharmacy (NABP)
1600 Feehanville Dr.
Mount Prospect, IL 60056
Ph: (847)391-4406
Fax: (847)391-4502
E-mail: custserv@nabp.net
URL: http://www.nabp.net

Description: Pharmacy boards of several states, District of Columbia, Puerto Rico, Virgin Islands, several Canadian provinces, the states of Victoria, Australia, and New South Wales, the Pharmaceutical Society of New Zealand, and the South African Pharmacy Council. Provides for inter-state reciprocity in pharmaceutic licensure based upon a uniform minimum standard of pharmaceutic education and uniform legislation; improves the standards of pharmaceutical education licensure and practice. Provides legislative information; sponsors uniform licensure examination; also provides information on accredited school and college requirements. Maintains pharmacy and drug law statistics.

9404 ■ National Association of Chain Drug Stores (NACDS)
413 N Lee St.
Alexandria, VA 22314
Ph: (703)549-3001
Fax: (703)683-1451
URL: http://www.nacds.org
Description: Represents the concerns of community pharmacies in Washington, in state capitals, and across the country. Members are more than 210 chain community pharmacy companies. Collectively, community pharmacy comprises the largest component of pharmacy practice with over 107,000 FTE pharmacists.

9405 ■ National Pharmaceutical Association (NPhA)
107 Kilmayne Dr., Ste. C
Cary, NC 27511
Fax: (919)469-5870
Fr: 877-215-2091
E-mail: npha@npha.net
URL: http://npha.net
Description: State and local associations of professional minority pharmacists. Provides a means whereby members may "contribute to their common improvement, share their experiences, and contribute to the public good".

9406 ■ Pharmaceutical Care Management Association (PCMA)
601 Pennsylvania Ave. NW, Ste. 740 S
Washington, DC 20004
Ph: (202)207-3610
E-mail: kpumphrey@pcmanet.org
URL: http://www.pcmanet.org

Description: Represents managed care pharmacy, Pharmaceutical Benefits Management companies (PBMs) and their healthcare partners in pharmaceutical care. Promotes education, legislation, practice standards, and research to foster quality, affordable pharmaceutical care.

SOURCES OF HELP-WANTED ADS

9407 ■ AACP E-lert
American Association of Colleges of Pharmacy
1727 King St.
Alexandria, VA 22314
Ph: (703)739-2330
Fax: (703)836-8982
E-mail: mail@aacp.org
URL: http://www.aacp.org/news/Pages/default.aspx
Description: Bi-weekly. Discusses issues relating to pharmaceutical education. Carries legislative information, feature stories on award winners, and Association news. Recurring features include news of research, notices of continuing education and employment opportunities, and listings of publications.

9408 ■ AAPS Newsmagazine
American Association of Pharmaceutical Scientists
2107 Wilson Blvd., Ste. 700
Arlington, VA 22201-3042
Ph: (703)243-2800
Fax: (703)243-9650
URL: http://www.aaps.org/Publications/AAPS_Newsmagazine/
Monthly. Included in membership. Professional magazine covering issues of interest to pharmaceutical scientists.

9409 ■ American College of Apothecaries Newsletter
American College of Apothecaries
Research & Education Resource Center
2830 Summer Oaks Dr.
Bartlett, TN 38184
Ph: (901)383-8119
Fax: (901)383-8882
Fr: 800-828-5933
E-mail: aca@acainfo.org
URL: http://www.americancollegeofapothecaries.com
Description: Monthly. Presents national pharmacy news designed to assist Association members in their professional practices. Covers Association news, including items on membership, chapters, committees, elections, and conferences. Recurring features include book reviews and a necrology.

9410 ■ American Journal of Health-System Pharmacy
American Society of Health-System Pharmacists
7272 Wisconsin Ave.
Bethesda, MD 20814-4836
Ph: (301)657-3000
Fax: (301)664-8877
Fr: (866)279-0681
E-mail: ajhp@ashp.org
URL: http://www.ajhp.org
Semimonthly. $278.00/year for individuals. Journal for pharmacists practicing in health-systems (acute care, ambulatory care, homecare, long term care, HMO's, PPOs, & PBMs).

9411 ■ The Annals of Pharmacotherapy
Harvey Whitney Books Co.
8044 Montgomery Rd., Ste. 415
PO Box 42696
Cincinnati, OH 45236-2919
Ph: (513)793-3555
Fax: (513)793-3600
Fr: 877-742-7631
URL: http://www.theannals.com
Monthly. $574.00/year for U.S., Canada, and Mexico, institution; online or print; $597.00/year for U.S., Canada, and Mexico, institution; online & print; $574.00/year for institutions, other countries, online only; $636.00/year for institutions, other countries, online & print; $610.00/year for institutions, other countries, print only; $95.00/year for U.S., Canada, and Mexico, online or print; student; $99.00/year for U.S., Canada, and Mexico, online & print; student; $95.00/year for other countries, online only; student; $135.00/year for other countries, print only; student; $140.00/year for other countries, online & print; student. Peer-reviewed medical journal focusing on the advances of pharmacotherapy throughout the world.

9412 ■ BioPharm International
Advanstar Communications, Inc.
6200 Canoga Ave., 2nd Fl.
Woodland Hills, CA 91367
Ph: (818)593-5000
Fax: (818)593-5020
URL: http://biopharminternational.findpharma.com/
Monthly. $70.00/year for individuals; $95.00/year for Canada and Mexico; $135.00/year for other countries; $7.00/year for single issue; $9.00/year for Canada and Mexico, single copies; $9.00/year for other countries, single copies. Periodical publishing professional practice news and care reports, research development and manufacturing.

9413 ■ Community Pharmacist
ELF Publications Inc.
5285 W Louisiana Ave.
Lakewood, CO 80232-5976
Ph: (303)975-0075
Fr: 800-922-8513
URL: http://www.elfpublications.com
Bimonthly. National magazine addressing the professional and business needs, concerns and continuing education of retail pharmacists practicing in independent, chain and supermarket pharmacies.

9414 ■ Journal of the American Pharmacists Association
American Pharmacists Association
2215 Constitution Ave. NW
Washington, DC 20005-1707
Ph: (202)628-4410
Fax: (202)783-2351
Fr: 800-237-2742
URL: http://www.aphanet.org/
Bimonthly. $495.00/year for institutions, print and on-

line; $395.00/year for institutions, online only. Peer-reviewed journal for pharmacy professionals.

9415 ■ The Journal of Pharmacy Technology
Harvey Whitney Books
PO Box 42696
Cincinnati, OH 45242
Ph: (513)793-3555
Fax: (513)793-3600
URL: http://www.jpharmtechnol.com
Bimonthly. $40.00/year for student; $181.00/year for institution. Covers articles of interest to pharmacists and pharmacy technicians. Includes new drugs, products, equipment and therapeutic trends, organizational, legal and educational activities, drug distribution and administration, plus continuing education.

9416 ■ MAPS Bulletin
Multidisciplinary Association for Psychedelic Studies
309 Cedar St., No. 2323
Santa Cruz, CA 95060-9989
Ph: (831)429-6362
Fax: (831)429-6370
URL: http://www.maps.org/news-letters/
Professional magazine covering issues in drugs and pharmacy for association members.

9417 ■ Med Ad News
UBM Canon
11444 W Olympic Blvd.
Los Angeles, CA 90064
Fax: (310)445-4200
URL: http://www.pharmalive.com/magazines/medad/
Monthly. $190.00/year for individuals. Pharmaceutical business and marketing magazine.

9418 ■ NCPA Newsletter
National Community Pharmacists Association
100 Daingerfield Rd.
Alexandria, VA 22314
Ph: (703)683-8200
Fax: (703)683-3619
Fr: 800-544-7447
E-mail: info@ncpanet.org
URL: http://www.ncpanet.org
Description: Semimonthly. Reports on topics affecting independents, including developments within the pharmaceutical industry, regulatory and legislative activity, and pricing and import information. Recurring features include reports of meetings, news of educational opportunities, notices of publications available, and news of NARD activities and events.

9419 ■ NYCPS-Newsletter
New York City Pharmacists Society
111 Broadway, Ste. 2002
New York, NY 10006
Ph: (212)616-7086
Fax: (646)300-6682
URL: http://www.nycps.org
Description: Bimonthly. Provides news, research,

and developments relating to pharmacists and pharmaceutical products. Includes information on the New York City Pharmacists Society. Recurring features include letters to the editor, news of research, and lists of job opportunities.

9420 ■ The PDA Journal of Pharmaceutical Science & Technology

Parenteral Drug Association Inc.
Bethesda Towers, 4350 E West Hwy., Ste. 150
Bethesda, MD 20814
Ph: (301)656-5900
Fax: (301)986-1093
E-mail: pda-journal@uiowa.edu
URL: http://journal.pda.org/

Bimonthly. Included in membership. Peer-reviewed professional journal covering pharmaceutical science.

9421 ■ Pharmaceutical Engineering

International Society for Pharmaceutical Engineering Inc.
600 N Westshore Blvd., Ste. 900
Tampa, FL 33609
Ph: (813)960-2105
Fax: (813)264-2816
URL: http://www.ispe.org/cs/publications_section/pharmaceutical_e

Bimonthly. Included in membership. Magazine on the health care manufacturing industry.

9422 ■ Pharmacy Now

Now Publishing Inc.
c/o Zachary Rolnik
PO Box 1024
Hanover, MA 02339
Ph: (781)871-0245
URL: http://www.pharmacynow.com

Continuous. Free, online. Online resource for pharmaceutical professionals. Features career advice and employment listings.

9423 ■ Pharmacy Times

Ascend Integrated Media
7015 College Blvd., Ste. 600
Overland Park, KS 66211
Ph: (913)469-1110
Fax: (913)469-0806
URL: http://www.pharmacytimes.com

Monthly. Journal providing information on health items (including prescription and over-the-counter drugs and surgical supplies) to independent, chain, and hospital pharmacists.

9424 ■ Pharmacy Today

American Pharmacists Association
2215 Constitution Ave. NW
Washington, DC 20005-1707
Ph: (202)628-4410
Fax: (202)783-2351
Fr: 800-237-2742
E-mail: pt@aphanet.org
URL: http://www.pharmacytoday.org/index.htm

Monthly. $200.00/year for individuals; $250.00/year for other countries. Reports on current news and opinions for pharmacists.

9425 ■ Pharmacy Week

7780 Elmwood Ave., Ste. 210
Middleton, WI 53562
Ph: (608)828-4400
Fax: (608)828-4401
E-mail: info@pharmacyweek.com
URL: http://www.pharmacyweek.com

Description: Weekly. Employment newsletter for pharmacists.

9426 ■ Voice of the Pharmacist Newsletter

American College of Apothecaries
Research & Education Resource Center
2830 Summer Oaks Dr.
Bartlett, TN 38184
Ph: (901)383-8119

Fax: (901)383-8882
Fr: 800-828-5933
E-mail: aca@acainfo.org
URL: http://www.americancollegeofapothecaries.com

Description: Quarterly. Examines current issues and opportunities affecting the retail, hospital, and consultant practices of pharmacy. Discusses controversial issues, often with commentary by pharmacists. Recurring features include editorials, news of research, and letters to the editor.

EMPLOYER DIRECTORIES AND NETWORKING LISTS

9427 ■ Crain's List—Chicago's Largest Hospitals

Crain Communications Inc.
360 N Michigan Ave.
Chicago, IL 60601
Ph: (312)649-5200
URL: http://www.chicagobusiness.com/section/lists

Published November, 2010. $25.00 for individuals; $45.00 for individuals. Covers: 25 hospitals in Chicago area ranked by net patient revenues. Entries include: Name, address, phone number, fax, web address, corporate e-mail, hospital administrator, network affiliation, 2009 net patient revenue, percentage change from 2008, 2009 net profits, percentage change from 2008, inpatient days, available beds, daily occupancy rate, number of hospital employees as of December 31, 2009, fiscal year end, Chairman, President, CEO, Chief Financial Officer, Human Resources Manager, Media Relations/Public Relations Director, and Hospital Administrator.

9428 ■ Directory of Drug Store & HBC Chains

Chain Store Guide
3922 Coconut Palm Dr.
Tampa, FL 33619
Ph: (813)627-6800
Fax: (813)627-6888
Fr: 800-927-9292
URL: http://www.chainstoreguide.com/

Annual, latest edition 2010. $395.00 for individuals; $445.00 for individuals; $1,375.00 for individuals; $1,075.00 for individuals. Covers: More than 1,200 drug store chains operation two or more units, including mass merchants and grocers with pharmacies; 215 wholesale drug companies in the United States and Canada. Entries include: For retailers—company name; phone and fax numbers; physical and mailing addresses; company e-mail and web addresses; listing type; number of stores; product lines; percentage of sales by product line; total sales; prescription drug sales; percentage of prescriptions filled with generic drugs; number of prescriptions filled daily; percentage of prescriptions filled with private third party, cash, and Medicaid; number of stores by type; mail order pharmacy indicator; managed care division indicator; projected openings and remodeling; store prototype sizes; total selling square footage; trading area; franchise group headquarters' name and location; distribution center and primary wholesaler names and locations; number of specialty departments; packaged liquor indicators; private label indicators; computerized pharmacy indicator; average number of checkouts; year founded; public company indicator; parent company name and location; regional and divisional office locations; headquarters personnel with titles. For wholesalers—company name, address, phone, and fax; e-mail and web addresses; listing type; product lines; percentage of sales by product line; total sales; percentage of sales by customer type; total stores served; number of member and non-member stores served; trading area; group store trading names; wholesaler type; distribution center locations; private label indicator; year founded; public company indicator; headquarters personnel with titles. Arrangement: Separate geographical sections for retailers and wholesalers. Indexes: Alphabetical, exclusions.

9429 ■ Directory of Hospital Personnel

Grey House Publishing
4919 Rte. 22
PO Box 56
Amenia, NY 12501
Ph: (518)789-8700
Fax: (518)789-0556
Fr: 800-562-2139
URL: http://www.greyhouse.com/hospital_personnel.htm

Annual, Latest edition 2011. $325.00 for individuals. Covers: 200,000 executives at 6,000 U.S. Hospitals. Entries include: Name of hospital, address, phone, number of beds, type and JCAHO status of hospital, names and titles of key department heads and staff, medical and nursing school affiliations; number of residents, interns, and nursing students. Arrangement: Geographical. Indexes: Hospital name, personnel, hospital size.

9430 ■ Hospital Blue Book

Billian Publishing Inc. and Trans World Publishing Inc.
2100 River Edge Pky.
Atlanta, GA 30328
Ph: (770)955-5656
Fax: (770)952-0669
Fr: 800-800-5668
E-mail: blu-book@billian.com
URL: http://www.billianshealthdata.com/Products/bluebook.html

Annual, Latest edition 2010. $575.00 for individuals; $575.00 for individuals. Covers: More than 6,500 hospitals; some listings also appear in a separate southern edition of this publication. Entries include: Name of hospital, accreditation, mailing address, phone, fax, number of beds, type of facility (nonprofit, general, state, etc.); list of administrative personnel and chiefs of medical services, with specific titles. Arrangement: Geographical.

9431 ■ Medical and Health Information Directory

Gale
PO Box 6904
Florence, KY 41022-6904
Fr: 800-354-9706
URL: http://www.gale.cengage.com

Annual, Latest edition April 2011. $1190.00 for individuals; $501.00 for individuals. Covers: In volume 1, more than 33,000 medical and health oriented associations, organizations, institutions, and government agencies, including health maintenance organizations (HMOs), preferred provider organizations (PPOs), insurance companies, pharmaceutical companies, research centers, and medical and allied health schools. In Volume 2, over 20,000 medical book publishers; medical periodicals, directories, audiovisual producers and services, medical libraries and information centers, electronic resources, and health-related internet search engines. In Volume 3, more than 40,500 clinics, treatment centers, care programs, and counseling/diagnostic services for 34 subject areas. Entries include: Institution, service, or firm name, address, phone, fax, email and URL; many include names of key personnel and, when pertinent, descriptive annotation. Volume 3 was formerly listed separately as Health Services Directory. Arrangement: Classified by organization activity, service, etc. Indexes: Each volume has a complete alphabetical name and keyword index.

HANDBOOKS AND MANUALS

9432 ■ Expert Resumes for Health Care Careers

Jist Works
875 Montreal Way
St. Paul, MN 55102
Fr: 800-648-5478
E-mail: educate@emcp.com
URL: http://www.jist.com

Wendy S. Enelow and Louise M. Kursmark. 2010. $16.95. 288 pages.

9433 ■ *Health Careers Today*
Elsevier
11830 Westline Industrial Dr.
St. Louis, MO 63146
Ph: (314)453-7010
Fax: (314)453-7095
Fr: 800-545-2522
E-mail: usbkinfo@elsevier.com
URL: http://www.elsevier.com

Gerdin, Judith. Fourth edition. 2007. $74.95. 496 pages. Covers more than 45 health careers. Discusses the roles and responsibilities of various occupations and provides a solid foundation in the skills needed for all health careers.

9434 ■ *Pharmacy Professional's Guide to Resumes, CVs, and Interviewing*
American Pharmacists Association
2215 Constitution Ave. NW
Washington, DC 20037
Ph: (202)628-4410
Fax: (202)783-2351
URL: http://www.pharmacist.com

Thomas P. Reinders. 3rd Edition, 2011. $39.50 for member; 49.00 for nonmember. 175 pages. Offers valuable resource for student pharmacists and pharmacy professionals seeking employment in the pharmacy field. Provides step-by-step instructions on preparing the resume, the CV and cover letters and preparing for the interview.

9435 ■ *Resumes for Health and Medical Careers*
The McGraw-Hill Companies
PO Box 182604
Columbus, OH 43272
Fax: (614)759-3749
Fr: 877-883-5524
E-mail: customer.service@mcgraw-hill.com
URL: http://www.mhprofessional.com/product.php?isbn=0071545352

Third edition, 2008. $12.95 (paper). 144 pages.

EMPLOYMENT AGENCIES AND SEARCH FIRMS

9436 ■ AHR Pharmacy Solutions
27042 Towne Centre Dr., Ste. 150
Foothill Ranch, CA 92610
Fax: (949)457-7605
Fr: 800-873-3611
URL: http://www.ahrpharmacyjobs.com

Exists as a staffing firm providing both temporary and permanent pharmacy jobs.

9437 ■ CompHealth
PO Box 713100
Salt Lake City, UT 84171-3100
Ph: (801)930-3000
Fax: (801)930-4517
Fr: 800-453-3030
E-mail: info@comphealth.com
URL: http://www.comphealth.com

Provides healthcare staffing and recruiting services covering certified registered nurse anesthetist, dosimetrist, imaging and radiation therapy, laboratory technology, medical physicist, nurse practitioner, nursing, pharmacy, physician, physician assistant, rehab therapy and respiratory therapy.

9438 ■ PharmPro
Back Bldg., Ste. 1
3605 Edgmont Ave.
Brookhaven, PA 19015
Ph: (610)499-9040
Fax: (610)499-9112
Fr: 800-659-7440
URL: http://www.pharmpro-inc.com

Offers staffing services for all pharmacy practice settings. Provides both temporary and permanent staffing of pharmacy professionals.

9439 ■ Sierra Staffing
5 Division St.
East Greenwich, RI 02818
Ph: (401)499-3175
Fr: 800-466-4555
E-mail: jobs@sierrastaffing.com
URL: http://www.sierrastaffing.com

Description: Serves as national pharmacy executive search firm specializing exclusively in health system recruitment.

ONLINE JOB SOURCES AND SERVICES

9440 ■ allpharmacistjobs.com
URL: http://www.allpharmacistjobs.com

Description: Provides pharmacy employment resource and career opportunities. Features pharmacy job listings around the United States.

9441 ■ CareerPharm.com
URL: http://www.careerpharm.com

Description: Exclusively serves the hospital and health system markets. Offers three ways for job seekers and advertisers to connect: online, in print or at a recruiting event.

9442 ■ HireRx.com
URL: http://www.hirerx.com

Description: E-recruiting and training company that is focused on solving workforce issues for biotechnology and pharmaceutical firms. Provides access to job openings, online training courses, and communities in their scientific or functional concentration.

9443 ■ HospitalPharmacyJobs.com
URL: http://www.hospitalpharmacyjobs.com/Public/Index.aspx

Description: Exists as an online job site focused entirely and exclusively on pharmacists interested in beginning or expanding their careers in hospital pharmacy. Provides a database of available hospital pharmacy positions located nationwide by location and positions of interest.

9444 ■ iHirePharmacy.com
URL: http://www.ihirepharmacy.com

Description: Provides pharmacy jobs from job postings, internet job boards, newspapers and classified ads.

9445 ■ JobPharm.com
URL: http://www.jobpharm.com

Description: Features a "JobGarden" that lists various pharmacy jobs and other career service facilities. Uses a database where users can either browse through the listings or search to narrow down job choices.

9446 ■ PharmaceuticalCrossing.com
URL: http://www.pharmaceuticalcrossing.com

Description: Consolidates pharmaceutical job openings from various Internet sites.

9447 ■ pharmacyjob.com
URL: http://www.pharmacyjob.com

Description: Features pharmacy jobs tailored to pharmacists, pharmacy technicians, pharmacy assistants and other pharmacy-related practitioners.

9448 ■ Pharmiweb.com
URL: http://www.pharmiweb.com

Description: Serves as a pharmaceutical portal featuring news, press releases, product announcements, events, pharmaceutical jobs, resume postings, and other related information.

9449 ■ Rx Career Center
URL: http://www.rxcareercenter.com

Description: Serves as a job board on the internet for the pharmacist, pharmacy technician and pharmaceutical industry professional. Provides candidates with current opportunities in a variety of settings that include retail, hospital, clinical, and industry positions.

9450 ■ RxJobPostings.com
URL: http://rxjobpostings.com

Description: Functions as a pharmacy job board. Specializes in retail pharmacist jobs, clinical pharmacist jobs, and other related professions.

TRADESHOWS

9451 ■ Drug Development Summit
Canon Communications LLC
11444 W. Olympic Blvd., Ste. 900
Los Angeles, CA 90064-1549
Ph: (310)445-4200
Fax: (310)445-4299
E-mail: info@cancom.com
URL: http://www.cancom.com

Annual. Primary Exhibits: Exhibits relating to pharmaceuticals.

9452 ■ PharmaMed Marketing and Media Conference
Canon Communications LLC
11444 W. Olympic Blvd., Ste. 900
Los Angeles, CA 90064-1549
Ph: (310)445-4200
Fax: (310)445-4299
E-mail: info@cancom.com
URL: http://www.cancom.com

Annual. Primary Exhibits: Exhibits relating to pharmaceuticals.

OTHER SOURCES

9453 ■ American Association of Colleges of Pharmacy
1727 King St.
Alexandria, VA 22314
Ph: (703)739-2330
Fax: (703)836-8982
E-mail: mail@aacp.org
URL: http://www.aacp.org

Description: Represents the interests of pharmacy education in the United States. Promotes professional and graduate education through effective use of policy, information, advocacy, and programming.

9454 ■ American Association of Pharmacy Technicians
PO Box 1447
Greensboro, NC 27402
Ph: (336)333-9356
Fax: (336)333-9068
Fr: 877-368-4771
E-mail: aapt@pharmacytechnician.com
URL: http://www.pharmacytechnician.com

Description: Represents pharmacy technicians. Promotes the safe, efficacious, and cost effective dispensing, distribution, and use of medications. Provides leadership and continuing education programs and services to help technicians in updating their skills to keep pace with changes in pharmacy services.

9455 ■ American Public Health Association (APHA)
800 I St. NW
Washington, DC 20001
Ph: (202)777-2742
Fax: (202)777-2534
E-mail: comments@apha.org
URL: http://www.apha.org

Description: Professional organization of physicians, nurses, educators, academicians, environmentalists, epidemiologists, new professionals, social workers, health administrators, optometrists, podiatrists, pharmacists, dentists, nutritionists, health planners, other community and mental health specialists, and interested consumers. Seeks to protect and promote personal, mental, and environmental health. Services include: promulgation of standards; establishment of uniform practices and procedures; development of the etiology of communicable diseases; research in public health; exploration of medical care programs and their relationships to public health. Sponsors job placement service.

9456 ■ American Society of Consultant Pharmacists (ASCP)

1321 Duke St.
Alexandria, VA 22314-3563
Ph: (703)739-1300
Fax: (703)739-1321
Fr: 800-355-2727
E-mail: info@ascp.com
URL: http://www.ascp.com

Description: Provides leadership, education, advocacy and resources enabling consultant and senior care pharmacists to enhance quality of care and quality of life for older individuals through the provision of pharmaceutical care and the promotion of healthy aging. Excels in the areas of: knowledge and skills in geriatric pharmacotherapy; expertise in long-term care settings for the frail at-risk elderly and other residents; and patient-centered advocate for seniors at-risk for medication related problems. Improves drug therapy and quality of life of geriatric patients and other individuals residing in a variety of environments, including nursing facilities, subacute care and assisted living facilities, psychiatric hospitals, hospice programs, and in home and community settings.

9457 ■ National Association of Boards of Pharmacy (NABP)

1600 Feehanville Dr.
Mount Prospect, IL 60056
Ph: (847)391-4406
Fax: (847)391-4502
E-mail: custserv@nabp.net
URL: http://www.nabp.net

Description: Pharmacy boards of several states, District of Columbia, Puerto Rico, Virgin Islands, several Canadian provinces, the states of Victoria, Australia, and New South Wales, the Pharmaceutical Society of New Zealand, and the South African Pharmacy Council. Provides for inter-state reciprocity in pharmaceutic licensure based upon a uniform minimum standard of pharmaceutical education and uniform legislation; improves the standards of pharmaceutical education licensure and practice. Provides legislative information; sponsors uniform licensure examination; also provides information on accredited school and college requirements. Maintains pharmacy and drug law statistics.

9458 ■ National Association of Chain Drug Stores (NACDS)

413 N Lee St.
Alexandria, VA 22314
Ph: (703)549-3001
Fax: (703)683-1451
URL: http://www.nacds.org

Description: Represents the concerns of community pharmacies in Washington, in state capitals, and across the country. Members are more than 210 chain community pharmacy companies. Collectively, community pharmacy comprises the largest component of pharmacy practice with over 107,000 FTE pharmacists.

9459 ■ National Pharmaceutical Association (NPhA)

107 Kilmayne Dr., Ste. C
Cary, NC 27511
Fax: (919)469-5870

Fr: 877-215-2091
E-mail: npha@npha.net
URL: http://npha.net

Description: State and local associations of professional minority pharmacists. Provides a means whereby members may "contribute to their common improvement, share their experiences, and contribute to the public good".

9460 ■ National Pharmacy Technician Association

PO Box 683148
Houston, TX 77268
Fax: (281)895-7320
Fr: 888-247-8700
URL: http://www.pharmacytechnician.org

Description: Aims to advance pharmaceutical care by providing education, advocacy and support to, or for, pharmacy technicians in all practice settings. Provides leadership in continuing education, technician specialization programs and pharmacy technician training programs. Acts as a national advocate, representing members in issues pertaining to pharmacy technicians, the pharmacy profession, and the healthcare industry.

9461 ■ Pharmaceutical Care Management Association (PCMA)

601 Pennsylvania Ave. NW, Ste. 740 S
Washington, DC 20004
Ph: (202)207-3610
E-mail: kpumphrey@pcmanet.org
URL: http://www.pcmanet.org

Description: Represents managed care pharmacy, Pharmaceutical Benefits Management companies (PBMs) and their healthcare partners in pharmaceutical care. Promotes education, legislation, practice standards, and research to foster quality, affordable pharmaceutical care.

SOURCES OF HELP-WANTED ADS

9462 ■ *The Journal of Pharmacy Technology*
Harvey Whitney Books
PO Box 42696
Cincinnati, OH 45242
Ph: (513)793-3555
Fax: (513)793-3600
URL: http://www.jpharmtechnol.com
Bimonthly. $40.00/year for student; $181.00/year for institution. Covers articles of interest to pharmacists and pharmacy technicians. Includes new drugs, products, equipment and therapeutic trends, organizational, legal and educational activities, drug distribution and administration, plus continuing education.

PLACEMENT AND JOB REFERRAL SERVICES

9463 ■ Pace Rx Recruiters
205 SE Wilson Ave., Ste. 1
Bend, OR 97702
Ph: (541)312-5849
Fax: (541)312-0077
Fr: (866)718-2923
E-mail: ryan@pacerxrecruiters.com
URL: http://pacerxrecruiters.com
Placement firm for pharmacy careers.

EMPLOYER DIRECTORIES AND NETWORKING LISTS

9464 ■ *Crain's List—Chicago's Largest Hospitals*
Crain Communications Inc.
360 N Michigan Ave.
Chicago, IL 60601
Ph: (312)649-5200
URL: http://www.chicagobusiness.com/section/lists
Published November, 2010. $25.00 for individuals; $45.00 for individuals. Covers: 25 hospitals in Chicago area ranked by net patient revenues. Entries include: Name, address, phone number, fax, web address, corporate e-mail, hospital administrator, network affiliation, 2009 net patient revenue, percentage change from 2008, 2009 net profits, percentage change from 2008, inpatient days, available beds, daily occupancy rate, number of hospital employees as of December 31, 2009, fiscal year end, Chairman, President, CEO, Chief Financial Officer, Human Resources Manager, Media Relations/Public Relations Director, and Hospital Administrator.

HANDBOOKS AND MANUALS

9465 ■ *The 21st Century Pharmacy Technician*
Jones & Bartlett Learning
5 Wall St.
Burlington, MA 01803

Ph: (978)443-5000
Fax: (978)443-8000
Fr: 800-832-0034
E-mail: info@jblearning.com
URL: http://www.jblearning.com
Brinda Shah, Jennifer L. Gibson and Nick L. Tex. 2011. $86.95 (hardcover). 690 pages. Covers foundations and principles that students need to know in order to become a pharmacy tehnician. Provides an introduction to all aspects of the profession.

9466 ■ *Certification Exam Review for Pharmacy Technicians*
Paradigm Publishing
875 Montreal Way
St. Paul, MN 55102
Fax: 800-328-4564
Fr: 800-535-6865
E-mail: educate@emcp.com
URL: http://paradigm.emcpublishingllc.com/page/paradigm
Cheryl Aiken and Robert Anderson. 2011. $51.92. 200 pages. Provides study tips for passing the national certification exam.

9467 ■ *Certification Exam Review for The Pharmacy Technician*
Prentice Hall
c/o Pearson Education, Inc.
1 Lake St.
Upper Saddle River, NJ 07458-1813
URL: http://www.pearsonhighered.com
Mike Johnston and Jeff Gricar. 2010. $56.80 (paper bound with CD-ROM). 216 pages. Serves as a study guide for the pharmacy technician certification exam. Contains complete practice exams and classification tests.

9468 ■ *Certification Review for Pharmacy Technicians*
AuthorHouse
1663 Liberty Dr.
Bloomington, IN 47403
Fr: 888-519-5121
E-mail: authorsupport@authorhouse.com
URL: http://www.authorhouse.com
Noah Reifman. 2011. $59.95. 308 pages. Helps pharmacy technicians prepare for and pass the PTCB (Pharmacy Technician Certification Board) national certification exam.

9469 ■ *Clerical and Data Management for the Pharmacy Technician*
Cengage Learning
PO Box 6904
Florence, KY 41022
Fax: 800-487-8488
Fr: 800-354-9706
URL: http://www.cengage.com
Linda Quiett. 2012. $65.00 (paperback). 208 pages. Covers the day-to-day operations of pharmacy, from entering prescription data to third party insurance bill-

ing and other clerical processes. Includes examples of forms, prescriptions, and invoices.

9470 ■ *Complete Math Review for the Pharmacy Technician*
American Pharmacists Association
2215 Constitution Ave., NW
Washington, DC 20037
Ph: (202)628-4410
Fax: (202)783-2351
URL: http://www.pharmacist.com
William A. Hopkins, Jr. 2010. $42.95 (non-member); $33.95 (member). Serves as a training resoure for classroom, the National Pharmacy Technician Certification Examination, or the pharmacy practice setting. Contains topics related to pharmacy calculations with practice-problems, challenging questions, test readers' chapter and 101-question.

9471 ■ *Comprehensive Exam Review for the Pharmacy Technician*
Delmar Cengage Learning
5 Maxwell Dr.
Clifton Park, NY 12065
Fr: 800-648-7450
URL: http://www.cengage.com
Jahangir Moini. 2012. $72.95 (paper). 400 pages. Aims to prepare students who are about to take the Pharmacy Technician National Certification Exam. Covers key areas of pharmacology science, drug classifications, pharmaceutical calculation, and hospital and retail pharmacy. Includes a free CD-ROM that offers additional multiple choice questions not found in the book.

9472 ■ *Drug Information: A Guide for Pharmacists*
McGraw-Hill
1221 Avenue of the Americas
New York, NY 10020
Ph: (212)904-2000
URL: http://www.mhprofessional.com
Patrick Malone, Karen Kier and John Stanovich. 2011. $65.00 (paperback). 1,192 pages. 4th edition. Teaches students and professionals in the field how to research, interpret, evaluate, collate and disseminate drug information. Covers topics such as medication and patient safety, investigational drugs, and adverse drug reactions.

9473 ■ *Essentials of Law and Ethics for Pharmacy Technicians*
CRC Press
6000 Broken Sound Pkwy. NW, Ste. 300
Boca Raton, FL 33487
Fax: 800-374-3401
Fr: 800-272-7737
URL: http://www.crcpress.com
Kenneth M. Strandberg. 2011. Third Edition. $52.95. 186 pages. Provides legal and ethical information relevant to the pharmacy technicians' practice.

9474 ■ Lab Experiences for the Pharmacy Technician
Lippincott Williams & Wilkins
2 Commerce Sq.
2001 Market St.
Philadelphia, PA 19103
Ph: (215)521-8300
Fax: (215)521-8902
URL: http://www.lww.com

Mary E. Mohr. 2012. $52.95 (spiralbound). 224 pages. 2nd edition. Contains step-by-step, hands-on laboratory exercises. Covers skills needed by pharmacy technicians to dispense retail prescriptions, inpatient prescription orders, IV mixtures and extemporaneous compounds.

9475 ■ Manual for Pharmacy Technicians
American Society of Health-System Pharmacists
7272 Wisconsin Ave.
Bethesda, MD 20814
Fr: (866)279-0681
E-mail: custserv@ashp.org
URL: http://www.ashp.org

Bonnie S. Bachenheimer. 2010. $64.00 for member; $70.00 for non-member. 500 pages. Provides information on knowledge and skills that pharmacy technicians need in order to excel in the field.

9476 ■ Math Calculations for Pharmacy Technicians
Saunders
c/o Elsevier Health
1600 John F. Kennedy Blvd., Ste. 1800
Philadelphia, PA 19103
Ph: (215)239-3900
Fax: (215)239-3990
Fr: 800-523-1649
URL: http://www.us.elsevierhealth.com

Robert M. Fulcher and Eugenia M. Fulcher. 2013. $64.95 (paperback). 656 pages. 2nd edition. Helps pharmacy technicians calculate drug doses safely and accurately. Covers basic math skills, and reading and interpreting labels and physicians' orders. Includes prescription and practice exercises.

9477 ■ Math for Pharmacy Technicians
Jones & Bartlett Learning
5 Wall St.
Burlington, MA 01803
Fax: (978)443-8000
Fr: 800-832-0034
E-mail: info@jblearning.com
URL: http://www.jblearning.com

Lorraine Zentz. 2009. $52.95. 142 pages (paper). Covers the key Mathematical skills necessary for pharmacy technicians. Includes practice problems with answers, written procedures, tips, exercises and chapter quizzes.

9478 ■ Medication Safety: Dispensing Drugs Without Error
Cengage Learning
PO Box 6904
Florence, KY 41022
Fax: 800-487-8488
Fr: 800-354-9706
URL: http://www.cengage.com

Kenneth R. Baker. 2012. $39.95 (paperback). 256 pages. Serves as guide for aspiring pharmacy technicians. Focuses on continuous quality improvement (CQI) and reducing medication errors. Includes discussion of the newest tools in pharmacy, such as robots and spectrographic technology.

9479 ■ Pharmaceutical Care Practice: The Patient-Centered Approach to Medication Management
McGraw-Hill
1221 Avenue of the Americas
New York, NY 10020
Ph: (212)904-2000
URL: http://www.mhprofessional.com

Linda Strand, Robert Cipolle, Robert J. Cipolle and

Peter Morley. 2012. $79.00 (paperback). 704 pages. 3rd edition. Provides information on establishing, supporting, delivering and maintaining medication management services.

9480 ■ Pharmacy Management Software for Pharmacy Technicians: A Worktext
Mosby
1600 John F. Kennedy Blvd., Ste. 1800
Philadelphia, PA 19103
Ph: (215)239-3900
Fax: (215)239-3990
Fr: 800-523-1649
URL: http://www.us.elsevierhealth.com

DAA Enterprises, Inc. 2011. $96.95 (paper). 177 pages. Incorporates the full version of real pharmacy management software. Contains easy-to-follow, step-by-step instructions on how to perform the day-to-day tasks of a pharmacy technician, engaging readers to acquire the skills and experience for professional success.

9481 ■ Pharmacy Professional's Guide to Resumes, CVs, and Interviewing
American Pharmacists Association
2215 Constitution Ave. NW
Washington, DC 20037
Ph: (202)628-4410
Fax: (202)783-2351
URL: http://www.pharmacist.com

Thomas P. Reinders. 3rd Edition, 2011. $39.50 for member; 49.00 for nonmember. 175 pages. Offers valuable resource for student pharmacists and pharmacy professionals seeking employment in the pharmacy field. Provides step-by-step instructions on preparing the resume, the CV and cover letters and preparing for the interview.

9482 ■ Pharmacy Technician
National Learning Corporation
212 Michael Dr.
Syosset, NY 11791
Ph: (516)921-8888
Fr: 800-632-8888
URL: http://www.passbooks.com

2009. $29.95 (paper). Serves as a study guide to assist candidates in preparing for the pharmacy technician examination.

9483 ■ The Pharmacy Technician
Morton Publishing Company
925 W Kenyon Ave., Unit 12
Englewood, CO 80110
Ph: (303)761-4805
Fax: (303)762-9923
Fr: 800-348-3777
URL: http://www.morton-pub.com

Perspective Press. 2010. $66.95 (paper). 544 pages. Contains information on the principles, career concepts and pharmacy skills needed to be a successful pharmacy technician.

9484 ■ The Pharmacy Technician: A Comprehensive Approach
Delmar Cengage Learning
5 Maxwell Dr.
Clifton Park, NY 12065
Fr: 800-648-7450
URL: http://www.cengage.com

Jahangir Moini. 2011. $133.95 (paper). 807 pages. Offers resources to beginning pharmacy technicians, as well as practicing pharmacy technicians looking to hone their skills and seek national certification. Provides coverage of both hospital and retail pharmacy, laying the foundation for the reader to apply their skills in a variety of pharmacy practice settings.

9485 ■ Pharmacy Technician Certification Exam Review
Delmar Cengage Learning
5 Maxwell Dr.
Clifton Park, NY 12065

Fr: 800-648-7450
URL: http://www.cengage.com

Lorraine C. Zentz. 2012. $78.95 (paper). 608 pages. Serves as a comprehensive, all inclusive study tool to help prepare students become certified pharmacy technicians on a national level. Features expanded chapters on pharmacology, updated end-of-chapter practice questions, two cumulative tests at the end of the book, and solutions to all chapter review questions and practice exams. Includes additional back-of-book CD containing 600 review questions that simulate the PTCE for extended practice.

9486 ■ Pharmacy Technician Certification Review and Practice Exam
American Society of Health-System Pharmacists
7272 Wisconsin Ave.
Bethesda, MD 20814
Fr: (866)279-0681
E-mail: custserv@ashp.org
URL: http://www.ashp.org

Barbara Lacher. 2010. $40.00 for member; $44.00 for non-member (softbound). 150 pages. Contains review questions to help readers prepare for national technician certification exams. Includes chapter on test-taking tips and strategies for success.

9487 ■ Pharmacy Technician Certified Board Preparation: Comprehensive Review Manual
Xlibris Corporation
1663 Liberty Dr., Ste. 200
Bloomington, IN 47403
Fr: 888-795-4274
URL: http://www2.xlibris.com

Anne Nguyen, Thanh Nguyen and Christina Pham. $58.99 (casebound hardcover), $49.99 (perfect bound softcover). 130 pages. Serves as a review manual for the pharmacy technician certification board examination.

9488 ■ Pharmacy Technician Exam Review Guide and Online JBTest Prep
Jones & Bartlett Learning
5 Wall St.
Burlington, MA 01803
Ph: (978)443-5000
Fax: (978)443-8000
Fr: 800-832-0034
URL: http://www.jblearning.com

Judy Neville. 2012. $49.95. 275 pages. Serves as a study tool for the pharmacy technician certification exams (PTCE and ExCPT). Includes review questions at the end of each chapter, a checklist for skills assessment, practice tests to help students reach a comfort level, detailed answer keys to accompany practice tests and task sheets.

9489 ■ Pharmacy Technician Laboratory Manual
Jones & Bartlett Learning
5 Wall St.
Burlington, MA 01803
Fax: (978)443-8000
Fr: 800-832-0034
E-mail: info@jblearning.com
URL: http://www.jblearning.com

Sandeep Bansal. 2009. $60.95 (paper). 288 pages. Covers topics on terminology, law and ethics, reading and writing prescriptions, basic mathematical conversions, compounding, pharmacy technician job description, and other vital information. Contains various laboratory exercises pertaining to didactic learning. Includes questions and answers relating to the exercises, and an answer key available for instructors.

9490 ■ Pharmacy Technician National Certification Exam Preparation Manual
CreateSpace
7290 B. Investment Dr.
Charleston, SC 29418
E-mail: info@createspace.com
URL: http://www.createspace.com

Kenosha Dale Chastang. 2010. $38.00 (paper). 192 pages. Serves as a desciptive review guide for pharmacy technicians who will take the National Pharmacy Technician Examination. Includes sample exam questions, an assessment, drug flash cards, common conversions and pharmacy information, organization information as well as information for all state boards of pharmacy.

9491 ■ Pharmacy Technician: Practice and Procedures

McGraw-Hill Higher Education
1333 Burr Ridge Pkwy.
Burr Ridge, IL 60527
URL: http://catalogs.mhhe.com/mhhe/home.do

Gail Orum-Alexander and James Mizner. 2011. $93.39 - publisher's retail, $70.04 - bookstore's wholesale (softcover with CD-ROM). 640 pages. Provides a comprehensive approach to the training of a pharmacy technician. Focuses on customer service and communication, critical thinking and problem solving, and emphasizes hands-on lab work.

9492 ■ The Pharmacy Technician Workbook and Certification Review

American Pharmacists Association
2215 Constitution Ave., NW
Washington, DC 20037
Ph: (202)628-4410
Fax: (202)783-2351
Fr: 800-237-2742
E-mail: infocenter@aphanet.org
URL: http://www.pharmacist.com

2010. $35.95 (non-member). $32.50 (member). Includes question-practice test, calculation practice, key terms and concepts and list of the top brand names and generic drugs that help individuals prepare for the National Pharmacy Technician Certification Board examination.

9493 ■ Pharmacy Technician's Reference Guide

Lippincott Williams & Wilkins
2 Commerce Sq.
2001 Market St.
Philadelphia, PA 19103
Ph: (215)521-8300
Fax: (215)521-8902
URL: http://www.lww.com

Cristina Kaiser. 2009. $17.95. 96 pages. Serves as a quick reference for the national certification or as a review for current pharmacy technicians. Contains important terminology and abbreviations, common medications, drug classifications and formulas.

9494 ■ Reference Guide For Pharmacy Technician Exam

Krishna Publications, Inc.
c/o Pharmacy Exam
5012 Taylor Ln.
Ellicott City, MD 21043-6869
Fr: 888-325-2928
URL: http://www.pharmacyexam.com/RGFTE.cfm

Manan H. Shroff. 2010-2011, Second Edition. $45.00. Includes exercises on commonly asked pharmaceutical calculations examination.

9495 ■ Standards of Practice for the Pharmacy Technician

Lippincott Williams & Wilkins
2 Commerce Sq.
2001 Market St.
Philadelphia, PA 19103
Ph: (215)521-8300
Fax: (215)521-8902
URL: http://www.lww.com

Mary E. Mohr. 2009. $74.95. 448 pages. Discusses standards of practice, scope of practice, and projections for emerging pharmacy technicians. Includes case studies.

9496 ■ Workbook and Lab Manual for Mosby's Pharmacy Technician

Saunders
c/o Reed Elsevier
1600 John F. Kennedy Blvd., Ste. 1800
Philadelphia, PA 19103-2899
Ph: (215)239-3900
Fax: (215)239-3990
Fr: 800-523-1649
URL: http://www.us.elsevierhealth.com

Teresa Hopper. 2011. $44.95 (paperback). 400 pages. Includes review questions, exercises and activities that help become effective and apply the knowledge for success on the job.

EMPLOYMENT AGENCIES AND SEARCH FIRMS

9497 ■ CareerStaff RX

19401 40th Ave. W, Ste. 330
Lynnwood, WA 98036
Fax: (866)835-5848
Fr: 800-766-0122
URL: http://www.careerstaffrx.com

Provides job opportunities among qualified pharmacy professionals.

9498 ■ Complete Pharmacy Resources

3100 S Gessner Rd., Ste. 640
Houston, TX 77063
Ph: (713)821-1114
Fax: (713)337-9660
Fr: 800-635-9033
E-mail: info@completerx.com
URL: http://completepharmacyresources.com

Provides specialized pharmacy staffing services. Maintains a large active pool of pharmacists, pharmacy technicians and pharmacy specialists.

9499 ■ MedPro Healthcare Staffing

1580 Sawgrass Corporate Pkwy., Ste. 100
Sunrise, FL 33323
Ph: (954)739-4247
Fax: 800-370-0755
Fr: 800-886-8108
E-mail: medprogeneralinquiries@medprostaffing.com
URL: http://www.medprostaffing.com

Provides temporary and contract staffing services to healthcare facilities.

9500 ■ Pharmaceutical Strategies, LLC

PO Box 249
Wakefield, MA 01880
Fax: (781)279-2977
Fr: (866)352-3337
URL: http://pharmaceuticalstrategies.com

Helps candidates fulfill their career in a pharmacy field.

9501 ■ Pharmacy Staffing Partners

1220 Nicholson St.
Houston, TX 77008
Ph: (713)880-0585
Fax: 888-688-7905
URL: http://www.pharmacystaffingpartners.com

Provides PRN pharmacists and pharmacy technicians for short term and long term assignments.

9502 ■ PharmPro

Back Bldg., Ste. 1
3605 Edgmont Ave.
Brookhaven, PA 19015
Ph: (610)499-9040
Fax: (610)499-9112
Fr: 800-659-7440
URL: http://www.pharmpro-inc.com

Offers staffing services for all pharmacy practice settings. Provides both temporary and permanent staffing of pharmacy professionals.

9503 ■ PRS Pharmacy Staffing Services

201 Depot St., Ste. 200
PO Box 852
Latrobe, PA 15650
Ph: (724)539-7820
Fax: (724)539-1388
Fr: 800-338-3688
URL: http://www.prspharmacystaffing.com

Provides pharmacy staffing services to retail, hospital and specialty pharmacies. Offers pharmacy consulting services.

9504 ■ United Pharmacy Staffing

1699 Wall St., Ste. 506
Mount Prospect, IL 60056
Ph: (847)228-0050
Fax: (847)228-0060
Fr: (866)321-7747
URL: http://www.upstaffing.com

Serves as a pharmacy recruitment firm that provides interim and permanent placement services.

ONLINE JOB SOURCES AND SERVICES

9505 ■ allpharmacistjobs.com

URL: http://www.allpharmacistjobs.com

Description: Provides pharmacy employment resource and career opportunities. Features pharmacy job listings around the United States.

9506 ■ Get Pharmacy Technician Jobs

URL: http://www.getpharmacytechnicianjobs.com

Description: Serves as a one-stop resource for finding and filling pharmacy technician positions. Offers free pharmacy technician job postings and career opportunities.

9507 ■ GreatPharmaJobs.com

URL: http://greatpharmajobs.com

Description: Offers job vacancies in healthcare industry.

9508 ■ iHirePharmacy.com

URL: http://www.ihirepharmacy.com

Description: Provides pharmacy jobs from job postings, internet job boards, newspapers and classified ads.

9509 ■ Medjobsdata.com

URL: http://www.medjobsdata.com

Description: Helps jobseekers find a health profession from clinical to administrative.

9510 ■ PharmacistJobsHelp.com

URL: http://www.pharmacistjobshelp.com

Description: Offers employment opportunities and career information for pharmacists. Features listings of pharmacist jobs.

9511 ■ Pharmacy Technician Jobs Finder

URL: http://pharmacytechnicianjobsfinder.com

Description: Helps job seekers find the best and high paying pharmacy technician jobs.

9512 ■ pharmacyjob.com

URL: http://www.pharmacyjob.com

Description: Features pharmacy jobs tailored to pharmacists, pharmacy technicians, pharmacy assistants and other pharmacy-related practitioners.

9513 ■ PharmacyJobsNationwide.com

URL: http://www.pharmacyjobsnationwide.com

Description: Provides jobs for pharmacists, pharmacy technicians, pharmacy managers and pharmacy administration professionals.

9514 ■ PharmacyJobsOnly.com

URL: http://www.pharmacyjobsonly.com

Description: Provides pharmacist career opportunities throughout the United States. Features pharmacy jobs available in every state.

9515 ■ PharmacyTechnicianJobsHelp.com
URL: http://www.pharmacytechnicianjobshelp.com
Description: Provides job listings for pharmacy technicians. Features pharmacy technician career opportunities and details about pharmacy technician job requirements.

9516 ■ pharmacytechnicianjobs.us
URL: http://www.pharmacytechnicianjobs.us
Description: Assists job seekers in finding the best pharmacy technician career opportunities with the best companies. Helps employers and recruiters further their recruiting goals by matching qualified candidates with open positions in an efficient and cost-effective way.

9517 ■ PharmacyTechs.org
URL: http://pharmacytechs.org
Description: Features employment and career opportunities for pharmacy technicians.

TRADESHOWS

9518 ■ NPhA Convention
National Pharmaceutical Association
107 Kilmayne Dr., Ste. C
Cary, NC 27511
Fax: (919)469-5870
Fr: 877-215-2091
E-mail: npha@npha.net
URL: http://www.npha.net
Advances standards of pharmaceutical care to all practictioners. Discusses issues affecting healthcare and pharmacy. 2012 July 20-23; Las Vegas, NV; Renaissance Hotel.

9519 ■ Pharmacy Technician Educators Council Annual Conference
Pharmacy Technician Educators Council
7366 FM 672
Dale, TX 78616
URL: http://www.rxptec.org
Annual. 2012 July 12-15; Charleston, SC.

OTHER SOURCES

9520 ■ Virtual Pharmacy Externship for Technicians (CD-ROM)
Delmar Cengage Learning
PO Box 6904
Florence, KY 41022
Fax: 800-487-8488
Fr: 800-354-9706
URL: http://www.cengage.com

Description: CD-ROM. Provides virtual simulation of a retail pharmacy. Includes dynamic video, scenarios, and interactive tasks with emphasis on critical thinking and problem-solving.

SOURCES OF HELP-WANTED ADS

9521 ■ *Advanced Imaging*
Cygnus Business Media Inc.
3 Huntington Quadrangle, Ste. 301 N
Melville, NY 11747
Ph: (631)845-2700
Fax: (631)845-7109
Fr: 800-308-6397
URL: http://www.advancedimagingpro.com/
  magazine.jsp
Magazine covering the full range of electronic imaging technology and its uses.

9522 ■ *Adweek*
Nielsen Business Media
770 Broadway
New York, NY 10003-9595
URL: http://www.adweek.com/
Weekly. $299.00/year for individuals, print & online; $24.95/year for individuals, print & online per month; $19.95/year for individuals, online per month; $149.95/year for individuals, digital edition access. Advertising news magazine.

9523 ■ *AeroSpaceNews.com*
AeroSpaceNews.com
PO Box 1748
Ojai, CA 93024-1748
Ph: (805)985-2320
URL: http://www.aerospacenews.com/content/view/
  41/33/
Monthly. $19.95/year for individuals, private. Journal reporting on the insights, impressions and images of tomorrow's technological wonders in the field of aerospace.

9524 ■ *Afterimage*
Visual Studies Workshop
31 Prince St.
Rochester, NY 14607
Ph: (585)442-8676
Fax: (585)442-1992
E-mail: afterimage@vsw.org
URL: http://www.vsw.org/ai
Bimonthly. $33.00/year for individuals; $20.00/year for students; $100.00/year for institutions, library; $90.00/year for other countries; $165.00/year for institutions, other countries, libraries. Publication providing independent critical commentary on issues in media arts, including scholarly research, in-depth reviews, investigative journalism, interviews, and the largest list of exhibitions, festivals, position announcements and calls for work of its kind.

9525 ■ *AV Video & Multimedia Producer*
Access Intelligence L.L.C.
4 Choke Cherry Rd., 2nd Fl.
Rockville, MD 20850-4024
Ph: (301)354-2000
Fax: (301)309-3847
Fr: 800-777-5006
URL: http://www.accessintel.com/
Monthly. Magazine covering audio-visual, video and multimedia production, presentation, people, technology and techniques.

9526 ■ *Broadcasting & Cable*
Reed Business Information (New York, New York)
360 Park Ave. S
New York, NY 10010
Ph: (646)746-6400
Fax: (646)746-7431
Fr: 800-446-6551
URL: http://www.reedbusiness.com
$199.00/year for individuals; $249.99/year for Canada; $360.99/year for other countries. News magazine covering The Fifth Estate (radio, TV, cable, and satellite), and the regulatory commissions involved.

9527 ■ *Columbia Journalism Review*
Columbia Journalism Review
2950 Broadway, Journalism Bldg.
Columbia University
New York, NY 10027
Ph: (212)854-1881
Fax: (212)854-8367
URL: http://www.cjr.org/
Bimonthly. $19.95/year for individuals; $27.95/year for other countries. Magazine focusing on journalism.

9528 ■ *Digital Content Producer*
NewBay Media, LLC
28 E 28th St., 12th Fl.
New York, NY 10016
Ph: (212)378-0400
Fax: (917)281-4704
URL: http://digitalcontentproducer.com
Monthly. Magazine for users of professional video equipment.

9529 ■ *Editor & Publisher*
Editor & Publisher Magazine
17782 Cowan, Ste. A
Irvine, CA 92614
Ph: (949)660-6150
Fax: (949)660-6172
URL: http://www.editorandpublisher.com/
Weekly (Mon.). $65.00/year for individuals, print and online; $125.00/year for two years, print and online; $85.00/year for other countries; $49.00/year for individuals, digital only. Magazine focusing on newspaper journalism, advertising, printing equipment and interactive services.

9530 ■ *Entertainment Employment Journal*
Studiolot Publishing
5632 Van Nuys Blvd., Ste. 320
Van Nuys, CA 91401-4600
Ph: (818)776-2800
Fr: 800-640-4836
E-mail: support@eejonline.com
URL: http://www.eej.com
Semimonthly. $109.00/year for individuals; $67.00/year for individuals, 6 months; $39.00/year for individuals, 3 months. Trade magazine covering business and technical careers in broadcast, electronic media, and motion pictures.

9531 ■ *Film History*
Indiana University Press
601 N Morton St.
Bloomington, IN 47404-3778
Ph: (812)855-8817
Fax: (812)855-8507
Fr: 800-842-6796
E-mail: filmhist@aol.com
URL: http://inscribe.iupress.org/loi/fil
Quarterly. $82.50/year for individuals, print and online; $75.00/year for individuals, print only; $67.50/year for individuals, online only; $273.50/year for institutions, print and online; $199.50/year for institutions, print only; $179.50/year for institutions, online only. Journal tracing the history of the motion picture with reference to social, technological, and economic aspects, covering various aspects of motion pictures such as production, distribution, exhibition, and reception.

9532 ■ *News Photographer*
National Press Photographers Association
3200 Croasdaile Dr., Ste. 306
Durham, NC 27705
Ph: (919)383-7246
Fax: (919)383-7261
E-mail: magazine@nppa.org
URL: http://www.nppa.org./news_and_events/
  magazine/
Monthly. $60.00/year for nonmembers, Canada; $65.00/year for nonmembers, international; $48.00/year for nonmembers. Magazine featuring still and television photojournalism.

9533 ■ *Photo District News (PDN)*
Nielsen Business Media
770 Broadway
New York, NY 10003-9595
URL: http://www.pdnonline.com/pdn/index.jsp
Monthly. $45.00/year for individuals, digital edition; $65.00/year for individuals, print & online; $105.00/year for two years, print & online. Monthly magazine for professional photographers emphasizing the business aspects of advertising, corporate, editorial, fine-art and stock photography.

9534 ■ *Photo Trade News*
Cygnus Business Media Inc.
3 Huntington Quadrangle, Ste. 301 N
Melville, NY 11747
Ph: (631)845-2700
Fax: (631)845-7109

Fr: 800-308-6397
URL: http://www.cygnusb2b.com

Monthly. Trade publication covering the photography business.

9535 ■ Producers Masterguide
Producers Masterguide
60 E 8th St., 34th Fl.
New York, NY 10003-6514
Ph: (212)777-4002
Fax: (212)777-4101
URL: http://www.producers.masterguide.com/cover.html

Annual. $185.00/year for U.S.; $175.00/year for Canada; $205.00/year for other countries. An international film and TV production directory and guide for the professional motion picture, broadcast television, feature film, TV commercial, cable/satellite, digital and videotape industries in the U.S., Canada, the UK, the Caribbean Islands, Mexico, Australia, New Zealand, Europe, Israel, Morocco, the Far East, and South America.

9536 ■ Professional Photographer
Professional Photographers of America Inc.
229 Peachtree St. NE, Ste. 2200
Atlanta, GA 30303
Ph: (404)522-8600
Fax: (404)614-6400
Fr: 800-786-6277
E-mail: cbishopp@ppa.com
URL: http://www.ppa.com/ppmag/

Monthly. $19.95/year for individuals, print (U.S.); $35.95/year for individuals, print (Canada). Magazine for photographers.

9537 ■ The Rangefinder
The Rangefinder Publishing Company Inc.
6059 Bristol Pky., Ste. 100
Culver City, CA 90230
Ph: (310)846-4770
Fax: (310)846-5995
URL: http://www.rangefindermag.com

Monthly. $18.00/year for individuals; free to qualified subscribers. Trade publication for portrait, commercial and wedding photographers.

9538 ■ SMPTE Motion Imaging Journal
Society of Motion Picture and Television Engineers
3 Barker Ave., 5th Fl.
White Plains, NY 10601
Ph: (914)761-1100
Fax: (914)761-3115
URL: http://www.smpte.org

Monthly. $130.00/year for individuals. Peer-reviewed journal containing articles pertaining to new developments in motion picture and television technology; standards and recommended practices; general news of the industry.

9539 ■ Studio Photography & Design Magazine (SP & D)
Cygnus Business Media Inc.
3 Huntington Quadrangle, Ste. 301 N
Melville, NY 11747
Ph: (631)845-2700
Fax: (631)845-7109
Fr: 800-308-6397
URL: http://www.imaginginfo.com

Monthly. Magazine for the professional photographer. Highlights industry professionals working in today's photographic applications. Showcases portrait, wedding, commercial, digital, and travel photographers supported by a monthly selection of supplementary guides, tech tips, tutorials, and product round-ups.

9540 ■ TelevisionWeek
Crain Communications Inc. (Detroit, Michigan)
1155 Gratiot Ave.
Detroit, MI 48207-2997
Ph: (313)446-6000
Fax: (313)567-7681
URL: http://www.tvweek.com/

Weekly. $119.00/year for individuals; $171.00/year for Canada, incl. GST; $309.00/year for other countries, airmail. Newspaper covering management, programming, cable and trends in the television and the media industry.

EMPLOYER DIRECTORIES AND NETWORKING LISTS

9541 ■ American Society of Media Photographers—Membership Directory
American Society of Media Photographers Inc.
150 N 2nd St.
Philadelphia, PA 19106-1912
Ph: (215)451-2767
Fax: (215)451-0880
URL: http://www.asmp.org/tips

Covers: 5,000 professional photographers for publications. Entries include: Name, address, phone, fax, e-mail address, specialty.

9542 ■ Black Book Photography
Black Book Marketing Group
740 Broadway, Ste. 202
New York, NY 10003
Ph: (212)979-6700
Fax: (212)673-4321
Fr: 800-841-1246
URL: http://www.BlackBook.com

Annual, Latest edition 2008. $60.00 for individuals. Publication includes: Over 19,000 art directors, creative directors, photographers and photographic services, design firms, advertising agencies, and other firms whose products or services are used in advertising.

9543 ■ Bowker's News Media Directory
R.R. Bowker L.L.C.
630 Central Ave.
New Providence, NJ 07974
Ph: (908)286-1090
Fr: 888-269-5372
E-mail: wpn@bowker.com
URL: http://www.bowker.com

Annual, Latest edition 2009. $668.00 for individuals. Covers: In three separate volumes, syndicates and over 8,500 daily and weekly newspapers; 1,750 newsletters; over 16,800 radio and television stations; 5,500 magazines; 1,000 internal publications. Entries include: Name of publication or station, address, phone, fax, e-mail and URL, names of executives, editors, writers, etc., as appropriate. Broadcasting and magazine volumes include data on kinds of material accepted. Technical and mechanical requirements for publications are given. Arrangement: Magazines are classified by subject; newspapers and broadcasting stations geographical. Indexes: Newspaper department/editor by interest, metro area, feature syndicate subject; magazine subject, publication title; television director/personnel by subject, radio personnel and director by subject.

9544 ■ Broadcasting & Cable Yearbook
R.R. Bowker L.L.C.
630 Central Ave.
New Providence, NJ 07974
Ph: (908)286-1090
Fr: 888-269-5372
URL: http://www.bowker.com

Annual, latest edition 2010. $395.00 for individuals. Covers: Over 17,000 television and radio stations in the United States, its territories, and Canada; cable MSOs and their individual systems; television and radio networks, broadcast and cable group owners, station representatives, satellite networks and services, film companies, advertising agencies, government agencies, trade associations, schools, and suppliers of professional and technical services, including books, serials, and videos; communications lawyers. Entries include: Company name, address, phone, fax, names of executives. Station listings include broadcast power, other operating details. Ar-

rangement: Stations and systems are geographical, others are alphabetical. Indexes: Alphabetical.

9545 ■ Careers in Focus—Photography
Facts On File Inc.
132 W 31st St., 17th Fl.
New York, NY 10001
Ph: (212)967-8800
Fax: 800-678-3633
Fr: 800-322-8755
URL: http://www.infobasepublishing.com

Latest edition 2009; Published July, 2009. $32.95 for individuals. Covers: An overview of photography, followed by a selection of jobs profiled in detail, including the nature of the job, earnings, prospects for employment, what kind of training and skills it requires, and sources for further information.

9546 ■ Chicago Creative Directory
Chicago Creative Directory
4149 N Leamington Ave.
Chicago, IL 60601
Ph: (773)427-7777
Fax: (773)427-7771
URL: http://creativedir.com

Annual, March. Covers: Over 6,000 advertising agencies, photographers, sound studios, talent agencies, audiovisual services, and others offering creative and production services. Entries include: For most listings—Company name, address, phone, list of officers, description of services. For freelance listings—Name, talent, address, phone. Arrangement: Classified by specialty.

9547 ■ CPB Public Broadcasting Directory
Corporation for Public Broadcasting
401 9th St. NW
Washington, DC 20004-2129
Ph: (202)879-9600
Fax: (202)879-9699
Fr: 800-272-2190
URL: http://www.cpb.org/stations/isis

Annual. Covers: Public television and radio stations, national and regional public broadcasting organizations and networks, state government agencies and commissions, and other related organizations. Entries include: For radio and television stations—Station call letters, frequency or channel, address, phone, licensee name, licensee type, date on air, antenna height, area covered, names and titles of key personnel. For organizations—Name, address, phone, name and title of key personnel. Arrangement: National and regional listings are alphabetical; state groups and the public radio and television stations are each geographical; other organizations and agencies are alphabetical. Indexes: Geographical, personnel, call letter, licensee type (all in separate indexes for radio and television).

9548 ■ Fashion & Print Directory
Peter Glenn Publications
235 SE 5th Ave., Ste. R
Delray Beach, FL 33483
Ph: (561)404-4685
Fax: (561)279-4672
Fr: 888-332-6700
URL: http://www.pgdirect.com/fpintro.asp

Annual, November; latest edition 47th. $39.95 for individuals. Covers: Advertising agencies, PR firms, marketing companies, 1,000 client brand companies and related services in the U.S. and Canada. Includes photographers, marketing agency, suppliers, sources of props and rentals, fashion houses, beauty services, locations. Entries include: Company name, address, phone; paid listings numbering 5,000 include description of products or services, key personnel. Arrangement: Classified by line of business.

9549 ■ The Guide to Photography, Film & New Media Schools
ShawGuides Inc., Educational Publishers
1499 NW 79th Ave.
Miami, FL 33126

Ph: (305)532-9775
URL: http://photoschools.shawguides.com

Continuously updated. Free. Covers: Listings for more than 245 educational programs for photography, film and new media in the U.S. and abroad, searchable by date, state or country, or by type. Entries include: Name of school or program, description of educational offerings, fees, locations, enrollment details, degrees conferred, contact name, address, phone, fax, e-mail, web site.

9550 ■ The Guide to Photography, Film & New Media Workshops

ShawGuides Inc., Educational Publishers
1499 NW 79th Ave.
Miami, FL 33126
Ph: (305)532-9775
URL: http://photoworkshops.shawguides.com

Continuously updated. Free. Covers: Listings for more than 2,400 photography, film and new media educational workshops in the U.S. and abroad, searchable by date, state or country, or by type. Entries include: Name of workshop, description of programs, fees, locations, contact name, address, phone, fax, e-mail, web site.

9551 ■ International Television and Video Almanac

Quigley Publishing Company Inc.
64 Wintergreen Ln.
Groton, MA 01450-4129
Ph: (978)448-0272
Fax: (978)448-9325
Fr: 800-231-8239
URL: http://quigleypublishing.com/

Annual, January; latest edition 2011. $235.00 for individuals. Covers: "Who's Who in Motion Pictures and Television and Home Video," television networks, major program producers, major group station owners, cable television companies, distributors, firms serving the television and home video industry, equipment manufacturers, casting agencies, literary agencies, advertising and publicity representatives, television stations, associations, list of feature films produced for television; statistics, industry's year in review, award winners, satellite and wireless cable provider, primetime programming, video producers, distributors, wholesalers. Entries include: Generally, company name, address, phone; manufacturer and service listings may include description of products and services and name of contact; producing, distributing, and station listings include additional detail, and contacts for cable and broadcast networks. Arrangement: Classified by service or activity. Indexes: Full.

9552 ■ National Directory of Arts Internships

National Network for Artist Placement
935 West Ave. 37
Los Angeles, CA 90065
Ph: (323)222-4035
E-mail: info@artistplacement.com
URL: http://www.artistplacement.com

Biennial, odd years; latest edition 11th. $95.00 for individuals. Covers: Over 5,000 internship opportunities in dance, music, theater, art, design, film, and video & over 1,250 host organizations Entries include: Name of sponsoring organization, address, name of contact; description of positions available, eligibility requirements, stipend or salary (if any), application procedures. Arrangement: Classified by discipline, then geographical.

9553 ■ National Directory of Magazines

Oxbridge Communications Inc.
186 5th Ave.
New York, NY 10010-5202
Ph: (212)741-0231
Fax: (212)633-2938
Fr: 800-955-0231
URL: http://www.oxbridge.com

latest edition 2011. $995.00 for individuals; $1,195.00 for individuals; $1,995.00 for individuals. Covers: Over 20,000 magazines; coverage includes Canada.

Entries include: Title, publisher name, address, phone, fax number, names and titles of contact and key personnel, financial data, editorial and advertising information, circulation. Arrangement: Classified by subject. Indexes: Title, geographical, publisher.

9554 ■ Photographer's Market

Writer's Digest Books
4700 E Galbraith Rd.
Cincinnati, OH 45236
Ph: (715)445-4612
Fr: 800-258-0929
E-mail: photomarket@fwpubs.com
URL: http://www.writersdigest.com

Annual, Latest edition 2009. $14.99 for individuals. Covers: 2,000 companies and publications that purchase original photographs, including advertising agencies, public relations agencies, book and periodical publishers, stock photo agencies, photographic workshops, galleries, and competitions. Entries include: Name of buyer, address, phone, payment rates, requirements, reporting time, how to break in. Arrangement: Classified by type of market. Indexes: Digital markets, subject.

9555 ■ PhotoSource Book

PhotoSource International
Pine Lake Farm
1910 35th Rd.
Osceola, WI 54020-5602
Ph: (715)248-3800
Fax: (715)248-7394
Fr: 800-624-0266
E-mail: web@photosource.com
URL: http://www.photosource.com

Bimonthly, and weekly. Covers: Magazine and book publishers, public relations firms, advertising and government agencies currently soliciting photographs for publication; 6-12 listings per issue. Entries include: Company name, name of contact, address, phone, project title, and nature of photos sought. Indexes: CD-ROM editors.

9556 ■ Television & Cable Factbook

Warren Communications News
2115 Ward Ct. NW
Washington, DC 20037-1209
Ph: (202)872-9200
Fax: (202)318-8350
Fr: 800-771-9202
URL: http://www.warren-news.com/factbook.htm

Annual, Latest edition 2012. $945.00 for individuals; $295.00 for individuals; $195.00 for individuals; $995.00 for individuals. Covers: Commercial and noncommercial television stations and networks, including educational, low-power and instructional TV stations, and translators; United States cable television systems; cable and television group owners; program and service suppliers; and brokerage and financing companies. Entries include: For stations—Call letters, licensee name and address, studio address and phone; identification of owners, sales and legal representatives and chief station personnel; rates, technical data, map of service area, and Nielsen circulation data. For cable systems—Name, address, basic and pay subscribers, programming and fees, physical plant; names of personnel and ownership. Ownership. Arrangement: Geographical by state, province, city, county, or country. Indexes: Call letters, product/service, name, general subject.

9557 ■ Who's Who in Professional Imaging

Professional Photographers of America Inc.
229 Peachtree St. NE, Ste. 2200
Atlanta, GA 30303
Ph: (404)522-8600
Fax: (404)614-6400
Fr: 800-786-6277
URL: http://www.ppa.com/splash.cfm

Annual. Covers: Over 18,000 members, including portrait, commercial, wedding, and industrial photographers; also includes guide to photographic equipment and supply manufacturers and distributors. Entries include: For members—Name, office address,

phone, show specialties; listings for members available for assignments. For suppliers—Company name, address, phone, product/service. Arrangement: Geographical.

9558 ■ The Workbook

Scott & Daughters Publishing Inc.
6762 Lexington Ave.
Los Angeles, CA 90038
Ph: (323)856-0008
Fax: (323)856-4368
Fr: 800-547-2688
URL: http://www.workbook.com

Annual, Latest edition 2011. $60.00 for individuals; $30.00 for individuals; $35.00 for individuals. Covers: 55,000 advertising agencies, art directors, photographers, freelance illustrators and designers, artists' representatives, interactive designers, pre-press services, and other graphic arts services in the U.S. Entries include: Company or individual name, address, phone, specialty. National in scope. Arrangement: Classified by product or service.

HANDBOOKS AND MANUALS

9559 ■ ASMP Professional Business Practices in Photography

Watson-Guptill Publications
1745 Broadway
New York, NY 10019
Ph: (212)782-9000
Fax: (212)572-6066
E-mail: info@watsonguptill.com
URL: http://www.randomhouse.com

American Society of Media Photographers Seventh edition. 2008. $35.00. 480 pages.

9560 ■ Careers in Communications

The McGraw-Hill Companies
PO Box 182604
Columbus, OH 43272
Fax: (614)759-3749
Fr: 877-883-5524
E-mail: customer.service@mcgraw-hill.com
URL: http://www.mhprofessional.com/product.php?isbn=0071454764

Shonan Noronha. Fourth edition, 2004. $15.95 (paper). 192 pages. Examines the fields of journalism, photography, radio, television, film, public relations, and advertising. Gives concrete details on job locations and how to secure a job. Suggests many resources for job hunting.

9561 ■ Careers in Health Care

The McGraw-Hill Companies
PO Box 182604
Columbus, OH 43272
Fax: (614)759-3749
Fr: 877-883-5524
E-mail: customer.service@mcgraw-hill.com
URL: http://www.mhprofessional.com/product.php?isbn=0071466533

Barbara M. Swanson. Fifth edition, 2005. $19.95 (paper). 192 pages. Describes job duties, work settings, salaries, licensing and certification requirements, educational preparation, and future outlook. Gives ideas on how to secure a job.

9562 ■ Creative Careers in Photography

Allworth Press
307 W 36th St., 11th Fl.
New York, NY 10018
Ph: (212)643-6816
Fax: (212)643-6819
URL: http://www.allworth.com

Michal Heron. 2007. $19.95 (paper). 272 pages. Provides an overview of the many career opportunities in the field of photography. Contains a list of subspecialties and professions in photography, a detailed list of institutions providing photographic education, and a list of professional organizations for photographers.

9563 ■ *FabJob Guide to Become a Professional Photographer*
FabJob Inc.
4616 - 25th Ave. NE, No. 224
Seattle, WA 98105
Ph: (403)949-4980
Fr: 888-322-5621
URL: http://www.fabjob.com/photographer.asp

Jennifer James. $29.97(e-book). 127 pages. Provides information on becoming a professional portrait photographer or professional wedding photographer and starting a photography business.

9564 ■ *Going Pro: How to Make the Leap from Aspiring to Professional Photographer*
Amphoto Books
1745 Broadway
New York, NY 10019
Ph: (212)782-9000
URL: http://www.randomhouse.com/crown/amphoto.html

Scott Bourne and Skip Cohen. 2011. $29.99 (paper). 240 pages. Features advice on putting together a portfolio, pricing and showing a photographer's work, marketing, brand positioning, and building an online social media platform.

9565 ■ *Master Guide for Professional Photographers*
Amherst Media, Inc.
175 Rano St., Ste. 200
Buffalo, NY 14207
Ph: (716)874-4450
Fax: (716)874-4508
URL: http://www.amherstmedia.com

Patrick Rice. $34.95. Comprehensive guide for photographers, covering techniques from shooting basics to image editing.

9566 ■ *On Being a Photographer: A Practical Guide*
Lenswork Publishing
909 Third St.
Anacortes, OR 98221-1502
Fax: (503)905-6111
Fr: 800-659-2130
URL: http://www.lenswork.com/obp.htm

David Hurn and Bill Jay. Third Edition, 2007. $12.95 (paper). 136 pages.

9567 ■ *Opportunities in Film Careers*
The McGraw-Hill Companies
PO Box 182604
Columbus, OH 43272
Fax: (614)759-3749
Fr: 877-883-5524
E-mail: customer.service@mcgraw-hill.com
URL: http://www.mhprofessional.com/product.php?isbn=0071442472

Jan Bone and Ana Fernandez. 2004. $19.95 (paper). 160 pages. Provides advice on obtaining a job in film and in corporate non-broadcast film/video production. Illustrated.

9568 ■ *Opportunities in Visual Arts Careers*
The McGraw-Hill Companies
PO Box 182604
Columbus, OH 43272
Fax: (614)759-3749
Fr: 877-883-5524
E-mail: customer.service@mcgraw-hill.com
URL: http://www.mhprofessional.com/product.php?isbn=0071545298

Mark Salmon. 2008. $14.95 (paper). 160 pages. Points the way to a career in the visual arts, examining opportunities for designers, painters, sculptors, illustrators, animators, photographers, art therapists, educators, and others. Offers a view of the pros and cons of working for an art or design company or on your own.

9569 ■ *Photographer*
National Learning Corporation
212 Michael Dr.
Syosset, NY 11791
Fr: 800-632-8888
URL: http://www.passbooks.com

2009. $29.95 (paper). Serves as an exam preparation guide for photographers.

9570 ■ *Photography Your Way: A Career Guide to Satisfaction and Success*
Allworth Press
307 W 36th St., 11th Fl.
New York, NY 10018
Ph: (212)643-6816
Fax: (212)643-6819
URL: http://www.allworth.com/book/?GCOI=58115100833510

Chuck Delaney. Second edition, 2005. $24.95 (paper). 304 pages.

9571 ■ *Photos That Sell: The Art of Successful Freelance Photography*
Watson-Guptill Publications
1745 Broadway
New York, NY 10019
Ph: (212)782-9000
Fax: (212)940-7868
Fr: 800-733-3000
E-mail: info@watsonguptill.com
URL: http://www.randomhouse.com/crown/watsonguptill

Lee Frost. 2004. $27.95 (paper). 192 pages.

9572 ■ *Starting Your Career as an Artist: A Guide for Painters, Sculptors, Photographers, and Other Visual Artists*
Allworth Press
307 W 36th St., 11th Fl.
New York, NY 10018
Ph: (212)643-6816
Fax: (212)643-6819
URL: http://www.allworth.com

Angie Wojak and Stacy Miller. 2011. $19.95 (paper). 256 pages. Guides artists seeking professional careers. Covers topics essential to emerging artists such as networking, finding a mentor, setting up a studio, writing the best resume, and refining career aspirations.

ONLINE JOB SOURCES AND SERVICES

9573 ■ **BackstageJobs.com**
URL: http://www.backstagejobs.com

Description: Lists behind-the-scenes jobs in the live entertainment industry. Also features backstage related news and information.

9574 ■ **Cyber-Sierra.com**
E-mail: mtnplanner@cyber-sierra.com
URL: http://www.cyber-sierra.com

Description: Offers employment listings in natural resource occupations, ecology and environmental disciples.

9575 ■ **FreelancePhotoJobs.com**
URL: http://www.freelancephotojobs.com

Description: Offers daily freelance photography jobs to help freelance photographers.

9576 ■ **GetGigs.com**
URL: http://www.getgigs.com

Description: Seeks to provide an on-line experience for creative types, performing artists, and musicians around the world by integrating internet technologies into a one-stop information resource. Also functions as a creative directory and talent network.

9577 ■ **GetPhotographyJobs.com**
URL: http://www.getphotographyjobs.com

Description: Offers online photography job postings and employment services.

9578 ■ **PhotographerJobs.org**
URL: http://photographerjobs.org

Description: Features job sites, company career pages and associations for photographer jobs.

9579 ■ **ProductionHub.com**
URL: http://www.productionhub.com

Description: Serves as an online resource and industry directory for film, television, video, live event and digital media production. Features job opportunities, events, directory and other resources for the production industry.

TRADESHOWS

9580 ■ **Photo Marketing Association International Annual Convention and Trade Show**
Photo Marketing Association International
3000 Picture Pl.
Jackson, MI 49201
Ph: (517)788-8100
Fax: (517)788-8371
Fr: 800-762-9287
E-mail: pma_trade_exhibits@pmai.org
URL: http://www.pmai.org

Annual. Primary Exhibits: Profile of exhibitors: film, cameras and photo accessory manufacturers and distributors; photo processing equipment and materials suppliers; digital imaging hardware and software marketers; studio imaging equipment distributors; and original equipment manufacturers (OEMs).

9581 ■ **Photohistory**
Photographic Historical Society
One Lomb Memorial Dr.
Rochester, NY 14623-5603
Ph: (585)475-2411
URL: http://www.rit.edu

Triennial. Primary Exhibits: Cameras and photographic images.

OTHER SOURCES

9582 ■ **American Professional Wedding Photographers Association (APWPA)**
1155 Sherman St., No. 203
Denver, CO 80203
Fr: 800-725-1650
E-mail: info@apwpa.com
URL: http://www.apwpa.com

Description: Represents the interests of professional wedding photographers in the United States. Promotes high artistic and technical standards in wedding photography. Works for the further development of its members' craft.

9583 ■ **American Society of Media Photographers (ASMP)**
150 N 2nd St.
Philadelphia, PA 19106
Ph: (215)451-2767
Fax: (215)451-0880
E-mail: mopsik@asmp.org
URL: http://www.asmp.org

Description: Professional society of freelance photographers. Works to evolve trade practices for photographers in communications fields. Provides business information to photographers and their potential clients; promotes ethics and rights of members. Holds educational programs and seminars. Compiles statistics.

9584 ■ **American Society of Picture Professionals**
217 Palos Verdes Blvd., No. 700
Redondo Beach, CA 90277
Ph: (424)247-9944
Fax: (424)247-9844
E-mail: cathy@aspp.com
URL: http://www.aspp.com

Description: Represents image experts committed to sharing their experience and knowledge throughout the industry. Provides professional networking and educational opportunities for individuals who create, edit, research, license, manage or publish pictures. Conducts educational programs and chapter meetings.

9585 ■ **Art Directors Club (ADC)**
106 W 29th St.
New York, NY 10001
Ph: (212)643-1440
Fax: (212)643-4266
E-mail: info@adcglobal.org
URL: http://www.adcglobal.org

Description: Art directors of advertising magazines and agencies, visual information specialists, and graphic designers; associate members are artists, cinematographers, photographers, copywriters, educators, journalists, and critics. Promotes and stimulates interest in the practice of art direction. Sponsors Annual Exhibition of Advertising, Editorial and Television Art and Design; International Traveling Exhibition. Provides educational, professional, and entertainment programs; on-premise art exhibitions; portfolio review program. Conducts panels for students and faculty.

9586 ■ **BioCommunications Association (BCA)**
220 Southwind Ln.
Hillsborough, NC 27278
Ph: (919)245-0906
Fax: (919)245-0906
E-mail: office@bca.org
URL: http://www.bca.org

Description: Photographers, technicians, doctors, scientists, educators, and individuals concerned with photography in the health sciences and related fields. Seeks to advance the techniques of biophotography and biomedical communications through meetings, seminars, and workshops.

9587 ■ **Corporation for Public Broadcasting (CPB)**
401 9th St. NW
Washington, DC 20004-2129
Ph: (202)879-9600
Fr: 800-272-2190
URL: http://www.cpb.org

Description: Promotes and finances the growth and development of noncommercial radio and television. Makes grants to local public television and radio stations, program producers, and program distribution networks; studies emerging technologies; works to provide adequate long-range financing from the U.S. government and other sources for public broadcasting. Supports children's services; compiles statistics; sponsors training programs.

9588 ■ **Editorial Photographers (EP)**
PO Box 51192
Seattle, WA 98115
E-mail: info@editorialphoto.com
URL: http://www.editorialphoto.com

Description: Aims to improve the health and profitability of editorial photography. Seeks to educate photographers and photography buyers about business issues affecting the industry, and to raise the level of business practices in the profession. Promotes healthy relationships between photographers and publishers.

9589 ■ **Health Science Communications Association (HeSCA)**
39 Wedgewood Dr., Ste. A
Jewett City, CT 06351-2420
Ph: (860)376-5915
Fax: (860)376-6621
E-mail: hescaone@sbcglobal.net
URL: http://www.hesca.org

Description: Represents media managers, graphic artists, biomedical librarians, producers, faculty members of health science and veterinary medicine schools, health professional organizations, and industry representatives. Acts as a clearinghouse for information used by professionals engaged in health science communications. Coordinates Media Festivals Program that recognizes outstanding media productions in the health sciences. Offers placement service.

9590 ■ **Institute of American Indian Arts (IAIA)**
83 Avan Nu Po Rd.
Santa Fe, NM 87508
Ph: (505)424-2300
Fax: (505)424-3900
Fr: 800-804-6423
E-mail: setzel@iaia.edu
URL: http://www.iaia.edu

Description: Federally chartered private institution. Offers 4-year degrees in Creative Writing, New Media Arts, Museum Studies, Indigenous Studies and Studio arts primarily to Native American and Alaska Natives (but school is open enrollment). Emphasis is placed upon Indian traditions as the basis for creative expression in fine arts including painting, sculpture, museum studies, creative writing, printmaking, photography, communications, design, and dance, as well as training in metal crafts, jewelry, ceramics, textiles, and various traditional crafts. Students are encouraged to identify with their heritage and to be aware of themselves as members of a culture rich in architecture, the fine arts, music, pageantry, and the humanities. All programs are based on elements of the Native American cultural heritage that emphasizes differences between Native American and non-Native American cultures. Sponsors Indian arts-oriented junior college offering Associate of Fine Arts degrees in various fields as well as seminars, an exhibition program, and traveling exhibits. Maintains extensive library, museum, and biographical archives. Provides placement service. Conventions/Meetings: varies.

9591 ■ **Media Alliance (MA)**
1904 Franklin St., Ste. 500
Oakland, CA 94612
Ph: (510)832-9000
Fax: (510)238-8557
E-mail: information@media-alliance.org
URL: http://www.media-alliance.org

Description: Writers, photographers, editors, broadcast workers, public relations practitioners, videographers, filmmakers, commercial artists and other media workers and aspiring media workers. Supports free press and independent, alternative journalism that services progressive politics and social justice.

9592 ■ **National Association of Broadcasters (NAB)**
1771 N St. NW
Washington, DC 20036
Ph: (202)429-5300
Fax: (202)429-4199
E-mail: nab@nab.org
URL: http://www.nab.org

Description: Serves as the voice for the nation's radio and television broadcasters. Advances the interests of members in federal government, industry and public affairs; improves the quality and profitability of broadcasting; encourages content and technology innovation; and spotlights the important and unique ways stations serve their communities. Delivers value to its members through advocacy, education and innovation. Relies on the grassroots strength of its television and radio members and state broadcast associations. Helps broadcasters seize opportunities in the digital age. Offers broadcasters a variety of programs to help them grow in their careers, promote diversity in the workplace and strengthen their businesses.

9593 ■ **National Press Photographers Association (NPPA)**
3200 Croasdaile Dr., Ste. 306
Durham, NC 27705-2588
Ph: (919)383-7246
Fax: (919)383-7261
E-mail: info@nppa.org
URL: http://www.nppa.org

Description: Professional news photographers and others whose occupation has a direct professional relationship with photojournalism, the art of news communication by photographic image through publication, television film, or theater screen. Sponsors annual television-news film workshop and annual cross-country (five locations) short course. Conducts annual competition for news photos and for television-news film, and monthly contest for still clipping and television-news film.

9594 ■ **Professional Photographers of America (PPA)**
229 Peachtree St. NE, Ste. 2200
Atlanta, GA 30303-1608
Ph: (404)522-8600
Fr: 800-786-6277
E-mail: csc@ppa.com
URL: http://www.ppa.com

Description: Strives to create a global perspective that promotes business, creativity and excellence. Aims to be the leader in the dissemination of knowledge in the areas of professional business practices and creative image-making and to define and maintain the industry's standards of excellence. Represents portrait, wedding, commercial, industrial and specialized photographers. Sponsors PPA International School of Professional Photography. Maintains speakers' bureau.

9595 ■ **Professional School Photographers Association International (PSPA)**
11000 Viking Dr., 5th Fl.
Eden Prairie, MN 55344
Ph: (952)826-4278
Fax: (952)826-4373
URL: http://www.pmai.org/pspa

Description: A section of the Photo Marketing Association International. Firms engaged in the photographing and/or processing of school photographs. Purposes are: to encourage the exchange of production ideas and economies; to cooperate in the overall promotion of photography; to work for better relations and understanding with schools; to act as a group in making manufacturers of sensitized goods and photographic equipment aware of the specialized needs of school photography; to maintain a close watch on any legislation that may affect school photography; to promote career possibilities and personnel training and recruitment for school photography; to foster the well-being of the member firms by providing some of the advantages of a large-scale operation.

9596 ■ **University Photographers Association of America (UPAA)**
Community College
9000 W College Pkwy.
Palos Hills, IL 60465
E-mail: carpenter@morainevalley.edu
URL: http://www.upaa.org

Description: College and university personnel engaged professionally in photography, audiovisual work, or journalism for universities. Seeks to advance applied photography and the profession through the exchange of thoughts and opinions among its members. Awards fellowship for exceptional work in the advancement of photography. Provides a medium for exchange of ideas and technical information on photography, especially university photographic work.

Sponsors exhibits. Provides placement service for members.

9597 ■ Wedding and Portrait Photographers International (WPPI)
6059 Bristol Pkwy., Ste. 100
Culver City, CA 90230
Ph: (310)846-4770
Fax: (310)846-5995
URL: http://www.wppionline.com

Description: Represents wedding portrait and digital photographers and photographers employed at general photography studios. Promotes high artistic and technical standards in wedding photography. Serves as a forum for the exchange of technical knowledge and experience; makes available the expertise of top professionals in the field of photographic arts and technology, advertising, sales promotion, marketing, public relations, accounting, business management, tax, and profit planning. Members are offered the opportunity to purchase special products and services.

9598 ■ Women in Cable Telecommunications (WICT)
14555 Avion Pkwy., Ste. 250
Chantilly, VA 20151
Ph: (703)234-9810
Fax: (703)817-1595
E-mail: mbrennan@wict.org
URL: http://www.wict.org

Description: Empowers and educates women to achieve their professional goals by providing opportunities for leadership, networking and advocacy.

SOURCES OF HELP-WANTED ADS

9599 ■ ADVANCE for Physical Therapists and PT Assistants
Merion Publications Inc.
2900 Horizon Dr.
PO Box 61556
King of Prussia, PA 19406-0956
Ph: (610)278-1400
Fr: 800-355-5627
URL: http://physical-therapy.advanceweb.com/
main.aspx

Biweekly. Free to qualified subscribers. Reaches active, qualified physical therapists, physical therapist assistants, and senior students in PT and PTA programs.

9600 ■ The American Journal of Orthopedics
Quadrant Healthcom
7 Century Dr., Ste. 302
Parsippany, NJ 07054-4603
Ph: (973)206-3434
Fax: (973)206-9378
URL: http://www.quadranthealth.com

Monthly. $128.00/year for individuals; $184.00/year for institutions; $165.00/year for Canada and Mexico; $185.00/year for other countries; $266.00/year for individuals. Medical journal.

9601 ■ American Journal of Physical Medicine and Rehabilitation
Lippincott Williams & Wilkins
530 Walnut St.
Philadelphia, PA 19106-3619
Ph: (215)521-8300
Fax: (215)521-8902
Fr: 800-638-3030
URL: http://journals.lww.com/ajpmr/pages/
default.aspx

Monthly. $343.00/year for individuals; $579.00/year for institutions; $210.00/year for individuals, in-training; $498.00/year for other countries; $768.00/year for institutions, other countries; $358.00/year for other countries, in-training. Medical journal.

9602 ■ Critical Care Medicine
Society of Critical Care Medicine
500 Midway Dr.
Mount Prospect, IL 60056-9969
Ph: (847)827-6869
Fax: (847)827-6886
URL: http://journals.lww.com/ccmjournal/pages/
default.aspx

Monthly. $402.00/year for individuals; $711.00/year for institutions; $538.00/year for other countries; $848.00/year for institutions, other countries; $258.00/year for individuals, in-training. Interdisciplinary journal for ICU and CCU specialists.

9603 ■ Global Change, Peace & Security
Routledge
711 3 Ave., 8 Fl.
New York, NY 10016
Ph: (212)216-7800
Fax: (212)563-2269
Fr: 800-634-7064
URL: http://www.tandfonline.com/toc/cpar20/current

$160.00/year for individuals, print; $602.00/year for individuals, online only; $669.00/year for individuals, print & online. Journal promoting physical therapy and integration.

9604 ■ Journal of Applied Physiology
The American Physiological Society
9650 Rockville Pike
Bethesda, MD 20814-3991
Ph: (301)634-7164
Fax: (301)634-7241
URL: http://jap.physiology.org/

Monthly. $940.00/year for nonmembers, print only; $1,005.00/year for Canada and Mexico, print only; $1,035.00/year for other countries, print only; $425.00/year for members, print only; $485.00/year for members, Canada and Mexico, print only; $510.00/year for members, other Countries, print only; $1,425.00/year for institutions, print only; $1,485.00/year for institutions, Canada and Mexico, print only; $1,510.00/year for institutions, other countries, print only; $1,455.00/year for institutions, print and online. Journal covering respiratory, environmental, and exercise physiology.

9605 ■ Journal of Learning Disabilities
Sage Publications Inc.
2455 Teller Rd.
Thousand Oaks, CA 91320-2218
Ph: (805)499-9774
Fax: (805)583-2665
Fr: 800-818-7243
URL: http://www.sagepub.com/
journalsProdDesc.nav?ct_p=boardsΠ

Bimonthly. $77.00/year for individuals, print & e-access; $260.00/year for institutions, print & e-access; $255.00/year for institutions, print only; $234.00/year for institutions, e-access. Special education journal.

9606 ■ The Journal of Orthopaedic and Sports Physical Therapy
Lippincott Williams & Wilkins
530 Walnut St.
Philadelphia, PA 19106-3619
Ph: (215)521-8300
Fax: (215)521-8902
Fr: 800-638-3030
E-mail: jospt@jospt.org
URL: http://www.jospt.org/

Monthly. $440.00/year for individuals, print & online; $405.00/year for institutions, online only; $135.00/year for students, print & online; $315.00/year for other countries, print & online; $530.00/year for

institutions, other countries, print & online; $220.00/year for students, other countries, print & online. Peer-reviewed journal for physical therapists and others in the healthcare and research communities to advance musculoskeletal and sports-related best practice.

9607 ■ Massage Therapy Journal
American Massage Therapy Association
500 Davis St., Ste. 900
Evanston, IL 60201-4695
Ph: (847)864-0123
Fax: (847)864-5196
Fr: 877-905-2700
URL: http://www.amtamassage.org/

Annual. $25.00/year for U.S. and Canada; $45.00/year for U.S. and Canada, 2 years; $70.00/year for other countries; $120.00/year for other countries, 2 years. Magazine focusing on professional massage therapy benefits, techniques, research, news, and practitioners.

9608 ■ Pediatric Physical Therapy
Lippincott Williams & Wilkins
530 Walnut St.
Philadelphia, PA 19106-3619
Ph: (215)521-8300
Fax: (215)521-8902
Fr: 800-638-3030
URL: http://journals.lww.com/pedpt/pages/
default.aspx

Quarterly. $167.48/year for individuals; $350.00/year for institutions; $114.49/year for individuals, in-training; $270.73/year for other countries; $457.73/year for institutions, other countries. Peer-reviewed journal reporting on new clinical care for pediatric patients.

9609 ■ Physical & Occupational Therapy in Geriatrics
Informa Healthcare
52 Vanderbilt Ave., 7th Fl.
New York, NY 10017-3846
Ph: (212)520-2777
URL: http://informahealthcare.com/pog

Quarterly. $520.00/year for institutions; $920.00/year for institutions; $685.00/year for institutions. Journal for allied health professionals focusing on current practice and emerging issues in the health care of and rehabilitation of the older client.

9610 ■ Physical and Occupational Therapy in Pediatrics
Informa Healthcare
52 Vanderbilt Ave., 7th Fl.
New York, NY 10017-3846
Ph: (212)520-2777
URL: http://informahealthcare.com/loi/pop

Quarterly. $945.00/year for institutions; $1,900.00/year for institutions, corporate; $700.00/year for institutions; $530.00/year for institutions; $1,065.00/year corporate; $1,410.00/year corporate. Journal for therapists involved in developmental and physical rehabilitation of infants and children.

9611 ■ Physical Therapy
American Physical Therapy Association
1111 N Fairfax St.
Alexandria, VA 22314-1488
Ph: (703)684-2782
Fax: (703)684-6748
Fr: 800-999-2782
URL: http://ptjournal.apta.org

Monthly. Included in membership. Journal of the American Physical Therapy Association.

9612 ■ Physical Therapy Products
Novicom Inc.
6100 Center Dr., Ste. 1000
Los Angeles, CA 90045
Ph: (310)642-4400
Fax: (310)641-4444
URL: http://www.ptproductsonline.com/

Monthly. Free to qualified subscribers. Magazine featuring new products and services available in the physical therapy field.

9613 ■ PT in Motion
American Physical Therapy Association
1111 N Fairfax St.
Alexandria, VA 22314-1488
Ph: (703)684-2782
Fax: (703)684-6748
Fr: 800-999-2782
URL: http://www.apta.org/PTinMotion

Monthly. $119.00/year for institutions, non-members; $139.00/year for institutions, other countries, non-members. Magazine for physical therapy professionals.

9614 ■ Teaching Exceptional Children
Council for Exceptional Children
2900 Crystal Dr., Ste. 1000
Arlington, VA 22202
Ph: (703)620-3660
Fax: (703)264-9494
Fr: 888-232-7733
URL: http://www.cec.sped.org/Content/
   NavigationMenu/Publications2

$90.00/year for individuals, print; $152.00/year for two years, print; $101.00/year for Canada, print; $169.00/year for two years, Canada; $197.00/year for institutions, print; $332.00/year for two years, print; $208.00/year for institutions, Canada, print; $236.00/year for institutions, other countries, print; $399.00/year for two years, institutional (print); $225.00/year for institutions, Canada, print and online. Peer-reviewed journal exploring practical methods for teaching students who have exceptionalities and those who are gifted and talented.

EMPLOYER DIRECTORIES AND NETWORKING LISTS

9615 ■ Crain's List—Chicago's Largest Hospitals
Crain Communications Inc.
360 N Michigan Ave.
Chicago, IL 60601
Ph: (312)649-5200
URL: http://www.chicagobusiness.com/section/lists

Published November, 2010. $25.00 for individuals; $45.00 for individuals. Covers: 25 hospitals in Chicago area ranked by net patient revenues. Entries include: Name, address, phone number, fax, web address, corporate e-mail, hospital administrator, network affiliation, 2009 net patient revenue, percentage change from 2008, 2009 net profits, percentage change from 2008, inpatient days, available beds, daily occupancy rate, number of hospital employees as of December 31, 2009, fiscal year end, Chairman, President, CEO, Chief Financial Officer, Human

Resources Manager, Media Relations/Public Relations Director, and Hospital Administrator.

9616 ■ Directory of Hospital Personnel
Grey House Publishing
4919 Rte. 22
PO Box 56
Amenia, NY 12501
Ph: (518)789-8700
Fax: (518)789-0556
Fr: 800-562-2139
URL: http://www.greyhouse.com/hospital_
   personnel.htm

Annual, Latest edition 2011. $325.00 for individuals. Covers: 200,000 executives at 6,000 U.S. Hospitals. Entries include: Name of hospital, address, phone, number of beds, type and JCAHO status of hospital, names and titles of key department heads and staff, medical and nursing school affiliations; number of residents, interns, and nursing students. Arrangement: Geographical. Indexes: Hospital name, personnel, hospital size.

9617 ■ Hospital Blue Book
Billian Publishing Inc. and Trans World Publishing Inc.
2100 River Edge Pky.
Atlanta, GA 30328
Ph: (770)955-5656
Fax: (770)952-0669
Fr: 800-800-5668
E-mail: blu-book@billian.com
URL: http://www.billianshealthdata.com/Products/
   bluebook.html

Annual, Latest edition 2010. $575.00 for individuals; $575.00 for individuals. Covers: More than 6,500 hospitals; some listings also appear in a separate southern edition of this publication. Entries include: Name of hospital, accreditation, mailing address, phone, fax, number of beds, type of facility (nonprofit, general, state, etc.); list of administrative personnel and chiefs of medical services, with specific titles. Arrangement: Geographical.

9618 ■ Medical and Health Information Directory
Gale
PO Box 6904
Florence, KY 41022-6904
Fr: 800-354-9706
URL: http://www.gale.cengage.com

Annual, Latest edition April 2011. $1190.00 for individuals; $501.00 for individuals. Covers: In volume 1, more than 33,000 medical and health oriented associations, organizations, institutions, and government agencies, including health maintenance organizations (HMOs), preferred provider organizations (PPOs), insurance companies, pharmaceutical companies, research centers, and medical and allied health schools. In Volume 2, over 20,000 medical book publishers; medical periodicals, directories, audiovisual producers and services, medical libraries and information centers, electronic resources, and health-related internet search engines. In Volume 3, more than 40,500 clinics, treatment centers, care programs, and counseling/diagnostic services for 34 subject areas. Entries include: Institution, service, or firm name, address, phone, fax, email and URL; many include names of key personnel and, when pertinent, descriptive annotation. Volume 3 was formerly listed separately as Health Services Directory. Arrangement: Classified by organization activity, service, etc. Indexes: Each volume has a complete alphabetical name and keyword index.

9619 ■ Private Practice Section of the American Physical Therapy Association—Membership Directory
American Physical Therapy Association
1055 N Fairfax St., Ste. 100
Alexandria, VA 22314-1488
Ph: (703)299-2410
Fax: (703)299-2411
URL: http://www.ppsapta.org

Biennial, fall; even years. Covers: About 4,700 member physical therapists in private practice. Entries include: Firm name, home address, business address and phone, fax, names and titles of key personnel, specialty, type of practice, congressional district. Arrangement: Same information is listed alphabetically and geographically. Indexes: Geographical, personal name.

HANDBOOKS AND MANUALS

9620 ■ Athletic Footwer and Orthoses in Sports Medicine
Springer Science+Business Media LLC
233 Spring St.
New York, NY 10013
Ph: (212)460-1500
Fax: (212)460-1575
URL: http://www.springer.com

Matthew B. Werd and Leslie E. Knight. 2010. $29.95 (softcover). 400 pages. Guides sports medicine physicians, podiatrists, physical therapists, and athletic trainers in prescribing footwear to maximize performance and minimize injury in athletes.

9621 ■ Careers in Health Care
The McGraw-Hill Companies
PO Box 182604
Columbus, OH 43272
Fax: (614)759-3749
Fr: 877-883-5524
E-mail: customer.service@mcgraw-hill.com
URL: http://www.mhprofessional.com/
   product.php?isbn=0071466533

Barbara M. Swanson. Fifth edition, 2005. $19.95 (paper). 192 pages. Describes job duties, work settings, salaries, licensing and certification requirements, educational preparation, and future outlook. Gives ideas on how to secure a job.

9622 ■ Careers for Health Nuts and Others Who Like to Stay Fit
The McGraw-Hill Companies
PO Box 182604
Columbus, OH 43272
Fax: (614)759-3749
Fr: 877-883-5524
E-mail: customer.service@mcgraw-hill.com
URL: http://www.mhprofessional.com

Blythe Camenson. Second edition. $13.95 (paper). 208 pages.

9623 ■ Careers in Medicine
The McGraw-Hill Companies
PO Box 182604
Columbus, OH 43272
Fax: (614)759-3749
Fr: 877-883-5524
E-mail: customer.service@mcgraw-hill.com
URL: http://www.mhprofessional.com/
   product.php?isbn=0071458743

Terence J. Sacks. Third edition, 2006. $15.95 (paper). 192 pages. Examines the many paths open to M.D.s, D.O.s, and M.D./Ph.D.s, including clinical private or group practice, hospitals, public health organizations, the armed forces, emergency rooms, research institutions, medical schools, pharmaceutical companies and private industry, and research/advocacy groups like the World Health Organization. A special chapter on osteopathy and chiropractic explores this branch of medicine.

9624 ■ Careers in Social and Rehabilitation Services
The McGraw-Hill Companies
PO Box 182604
Columbus, OH 43272
Fax: (614)759-3749

Fr: 877-883-5524
E-mail: customer.service@mcgraw-hill.com
URL: http://www.mhprofessional.com/
  product.php?isbn=0071641955
Geraldine O. Garner. 2008. $16.95. 192 pages.

9625 ■ Core Assessment and Training
Human Kinetics
PO Box 5076
Champaign, IL 61825-5076
Fax: (217)351-1549
Fr: 800-747-4457
E-mail: info@hkusa.com
URL: http://www.humankinetics.com

2010. $42.00 (DVD and paper). 160 pages. Serves as reference for coaches, athletic and personal trainers, and physical therapists. Covers all aspects of core training, from basic to advanced core exercises, stretches, and pylometrics. Includes photos, illustrations and instructions for more than 120 exercises. Accompanying DVD features demontrations of proper exercise techniques and protocols for review. Helps professionals in the field assess clients' needs and design customized training programs.

9626 ■ Expert Resumes for Health Care Careers
Jist Works
875 Montreal Way
St. Paul, MN 55102
Fr: 800-648-5478
E-mail: educate@emcp.com
URL: http://www.jist.com

Wendy S. Enelow and Louise M. Kursmark. 2010. $16.95. 288 pages.

9627 ■ Functional Testing in Human Performance
Human Kinetics
PO Box 5076
Champaign, IL 61825-5076
Fax: (217)351-1549
Fr: 800-747-4457
E-mail: info@hkusa.com
URL: http://www.humankinetics.com

Michael Reiman and Robert Manske. 2009. $79.00 (DVD and cloth). 328 pages. Serves as resource for the accurate assessment of an individual's functional abilities. Offers clinicians the compilation of information on clinical and data-based functional testing for sport, exercise and occupational settings. Accompanying DVD features live-action demonstrations of 40 of the most advanced tests.

9628 ■ Health Careers Today
Elsevier
11830 Westline Industrial Dr.
St. Louis, MO 63146
Ph: (314)453-7010
Fax: (314)453-7095
Fr: 800-545-2522
E-mail: usbkinfo@elsevier.com
URL: http://www.elsevier.com

Gerdin, Judith. Fourth edition. 2007. $74.95. 496 pages. Covers more than 45 health careers. Discusses the roles and responsibilities of various occupations and provides a solid foundation in the skills needed for all health careers.

9629 ■ Opportunities in Health and Medical Careers
The McGraw-Hill Companies
PO Box 182604
Columbus, OH 43272
Fax: (614)759-3749
Fr: 877-883-5524
E-mail: customer.service@mcgraw-hill.com
URL: http://www.mhprofessional.com/
  product.php?isbn=0071437274

I. Donald Snook, Jr. and Leo D'Orazio. 2004. $14.95 (paper). 157 pages. Covers the full range of medical and health occupations. Illustrated.

9630 ■ Opportunities in Physical Therapy Careers
The McGraw-Hill Companies
PO Box 182604
Columbus, OH 43272
Fax: (614)759-3749
Fr: 877-883-5524
E-mail: customer.service@mcgraw-hill.com
URL: http://www.mhprofessional.com/
  product.php?isbn=0071389504

Bernice R. Krumhansl. $11.95. 160 pages. Defines what the jobs are, where they are, and how to pursue them. Contains bibliography and illustrations.

9631 ■ Physical Therapist
National Learning Corporation
212 Michael Dr.
Syosset, NY 11791
Fr: 800-632-8888
URL: http://www.passbooks.com

2009. $34.95 (paper). Serves as an exam preparation guide for physical therapists.

9632 ■ Pocket Orthopaedics: Evidence-Based Survival Guide
Jones & Bartlett Learning
5 Wall St.
Burlington, MA 01803
Fax: (978)443-8000
Fr: 800-832-0034
E-mail: info@jblearning.com
URL: http://www.jblearning.com

Michael S. Wong. 2011. $41.95 (spiral/paperback). 412 pages. Serves as learning aide in evidence-based practice for both students and clinicians.

9633 ■ Resumes for Health and Medical Careers
The McGraw-Hill Companies
PO Box 182604
Columbus, OH 43272
Fax: (614)759-3749
Fr: 877-883-5524
E-mail: customer.service@mcgraw-hill.com
URL: http://www.mhprofessional.com/
  product.php?isbn=0071545352

Third edition, 2008. $12.95 (paper). 144 pages.

EMPLOYMENT AGENCIES AND SEARCH FIRMS

9634 ■ Access Staffing
360 Lexington Ave., 8th Fl.
New York, NY 10017
Ph: (212)687-5440
Fax: (212)557-2544
URL: http://www.accessstaffingco.com

Serves as a staffing firm covering accounting/financial, advertising, bilingual Japanese, creative, event planning, fashion/retail, healthcare/human services, human resources, information technology, insurance, legal, light industrial and office support.

9635 ■ Advanced Medical Personnel Services
5535 S Williamson Blvd., Ste. 774
Port Orange, FL 32128
Ph: (386)756-4395
Fr: 800-330-7711
URL: http://www.advanced-medical.net

Specializes in the placement of physical therapists, physical therapy assistants, occupational therapists, certified occupational therapy assistants and speech-language pathologists in assignments across the United States.

9636 ■ Cobb Pediatric Therapy Services
3104 Creekside Village Dr., Ste. 404
Kennesaw, GA 30144
Ph: (770)218-6274
Fax: (770)218-8568

Fr: 888-288-1048
E-mail: info@cobbpediatric.com
URL: http://www.cobbpediatric.com

Description: Staffing company that works primarily with school systems to match them with qualified speech language pathologists, occupational therapists, and physical therapists.

9637 ■ CompHealth
PO Box 713100
Salt Lake City, UT 84171-3100
Ph: (801)930-3000
Fax: (801)930-4517
Fr: 800-453-3030
E-mail: info@comphealth.com
URL: http://www.comphealth.com

Provides healthcare staffing and recruiting services covering certified registered nurse anesthetist, dosimetrist, imaging and radiation therapy, laboratory technology, medical physicist, nurse practitioner, nursing, pharmacy, physician, physician assistant, rehab therapy and respiratory therapy.

9638 ■ Cross Country TravCorps
6551 Park of Commerce Blvd.
Boca Raton, FL 33487-8247
Fax: (561)998-8533
Fr: 800-530-6125
E-mail: sms@cctc.com
URL: http://www.crosscountrytravcorps.com/cctc/

Places traveling nurses in assignments nationwide.

9639 ■ Foundation Rehab Staffing
416 W 15th St., Bldg. 600
Edmond, OK 73013
Fax: 800-774-9252
Fr: (866)337-6113
URL: http://www.foundationrehabstaffing.com

Provides staffing services; specializes in rehabilitation therapy.

9640 ■ Harper Associates
31000 NW Hwy., Ste. 240
Farmington Hills, MI 48334
Ph: (248)932-1170
Fax: (248)932-1214
E-mail: info@harperjobs.com
URL: http://www.harperjobs.com

Executive search firm and employment agency.

9641 ■ Jackson Therapy Partners
11315 Corporate Blvd., Ste. 100
Orlando, FL 32817
Fr: 800-774-7785
URL: http://www.jacksontherapy.com

Serves as a therapy recruiting firm. Features therapy jobs available across the United States including permanent and travel opportunities.

9642 ■ JPM International
26034 Acero
Mission Viejo, CA 92691
Ph: (949)699-4300
Fax: (949)699-4333
Fr: 800-685-7856
E-mail: qtek37@yahoo.com
URL: http://www.jpmintl.com/pages/qss.html

Executive search firm and employment agency.

9643 ■ Professional Placement Associates, Inc.
287 Bowman Ave.
Purchase, NY 10577-2517
Ph: (914)251-1000
Fax: (914)251-1055
E-mail: careers@ppasearch.com
URL: http://www.ppasearch.com

Executive search firm specializing in the health and medical field.

9644 ■ Stat Group, LLC
PO Box 1674
Owensboro, KY 42302-1674
Ph: (270)663-8020
Fax: 877-998-9940
Fr: 877-998-9930
E-mail: info@statgroupllc.com
URL: http://www.statgroupllc.com

Description: Serves as a healthcare staffing firm
which provides healthcare facilities with a workforce
pool. Attracts and retains medical professionals to
assist healthcare facilities throughout the United
States.

9645 ■ Team Placement Service, Inc.
1414 Prince St., Ste. 202
Alexandria, VA 22314
Ph: (703)820-8618
Fax: (703)820-3368
Fr: 800-495-6767
E-mail: 4jobs@teamplace.com
URL: http://www.teamplace.com

Full-service personnel consultants provide placement
for healthcare staff, physician and dentist, private
practice, and hospitals. Conduct interviews, tests,
and reference checks to select the top 20% of
applicants. Survey applicants' skill levels, provide
backup information on each candidate, select compatible candidates for consideration, and insure the hiring process minimizes potential legal liability. Industries served: healthcare and government agencies
providing medical, dental, biotech, laboratory, hospitals, and physician search.

9646 ■ TheraKare
8596 E 101st St., Ste. H
Tulsa, OK 74146
Ph: (918)251-5982
Fax: (918)251-6047
Fr: 800-258-1036
E-mail: info@therakare.com
URL: http://www.therakare.com

Description: Specializes in providing temporary and
permanent placement options for rehabilitation
therapy professionals, including physical therapists,
occupational therapists and speech language
pathologists.

ONLINE JOB SOURCES AND SERVICES

9647 ■ ExploreHealthCareers.org
E-mail: feedback@explorehealthcareers.org
URL: http://explorehealthcareers.org/en/home

Description: Provides employment information in
health professions. Includes links to health-related
education/training programs, financial aid resources,
specialized learning opportunities, and current issues
in health care.

9648 ■ HEALTHeCAREERS Network
Fr: 888-884-8242
E-mail: info@healthecareers.com
URL: http://www.healthecareers.com

Description: Career search site for jobs in all health
care specialties; educational resources; visa and
licensing information for relocation; interesting
articles; relocation tools; links to professional organizations and general resources.

9649 ■ Hospital Jobs OnLine
E-mail: support@hospitaljobsonline.com
URL: http://www.hospitaljobsonline.com

Description: Serves as a niche healthcare job board
designed exclusively for hospitals, healthcare companies, and healthcare job seekers.

9650 ■ JobsInLTC.com
URL: http://www.jobsinltc.com

Description: Serves as a job board for long-term
care jobs for nursing home administrators, assisted

living staff, directors of nursing, MDS coordinators,
and other related fields.

9651 ■ nurse-recruiter.com
URL: http://www.nurse-recruiter.com

Description: Serves as a resource of jobs for the
nursing and allied health fields.

9652 ■ PhysicalTherapist.com
URL: http://www.physicaltherapist.com

Description: Exists as a collaborative informational
website designed for the physical therapy community.
Provides listings of job opportunities and features
physical therapy resources, associations, school
search, library search and more.

9653 ■ PhysicalTherapyCrossing.com
URL: http://www.physicaltherapycrossing.com

Description: Provides a collection of researched job
openings in the physical therapy field.

9654 ■ ProHealthJobs.com
Ph: (484)443-8545
Fax: (484)443-8549
E-mail: info@prohealthjobs.com
URL: http://prohealthjobs.com/jobboard

Description: Career resources site for the medical
and health care field. Lists professional opportunities,
product information, continuing education and open
positions.

9655 ■ PTJobs.com
URL: http://www.ptjobs.com

Description: Serves as a job board dedicated to
physical therapists, physical therapist assistants,
clinic directors, instructors, and other physical therapy
communities.

9656 ■ PTJungle.com
URL: http://www.ptjungle.com

Description: Serves as job board built specifically
for physical therapists and physical therapist
assistants.

9657 ■ RehabCareer.com
URL: http://www.rehabcareer.com

Description: Serves as a job site for physical, occupational and speech therapy.

9658 ■ RehabJobs Online
E-mail: support@atsrehabjobs.com
URL: http://www.rehabjobsonline.com

Description: Resource center for the professional
therapist. Main files include: Therapists Only, Therapy
Forums, Nationwide Job Search (database), Therapy
Job Outlook, Therapy Job Search Utilities, Therapy
Links, Information for Employers and Recruiters.

9659 ■ RehabWorld.com
URL: http://www.rehabworld.com

Description: Site for rehabilitation professionals to
learn about the profession and locate jobs. Includes
user groups, salary surveys, and chat capabilities.
Main files include: Physical Therapy, Occupational
Therapy, Speech Therapy, Mental Health, Employer
World, Student World, International World, Forum.

9660 ■ TherapistsCentral.com
URL: http://www.therapistscentral.com

Description: Provides lists of job and career opportunities to physical therapists, speech therapists
and occupational therapists.

9661 ■ TherapyJobBoard.com
URL: http://www.therapyjobboard.com

Description: Serves as an employment resource for
job seekers and employers in the physical therapy,
occupational therapy, speech therapy and respiratory
therapy professions.

9662 ■ TherapyJobs.com
URL: http://www.therapyjobs.com

Description: Serves as an online career center
bringing therapy employers and candidates together.

TRADESHOWS

**9663 ■ American Physical Therapy
Association Annual Conference**
American Physical Therapy Association
1111 N. Fairfax St.
Alexandria, VA 22314-1488
Ph: (703)684-2782
Fax: (703)684-7343
Fr: 800-999-2782
URL: http://www.apta.org

Annual. Primary Exhibits: Physical therapy products,
equipment, and services. Dates and Locations: 2012
Jun 06-09; Tampa, FL.

**9664 ■ American Society of Hand Therapists
Annual Meeting**
Smith, Bucklin and Associates, Inc. (Chicago, Illinois)
401 N Michigan Ave.
Chicago, IL 60611-4267
Ph: (312)321-6610
Fax: (312)673-6670
Fr: 800-289-NAON
E-mail: info@smithbucklin.com
URL: http://www.smithbucklin.com

Annual. Primary Exhibits: Hand therapy equipment
and products. Dates and Locations: 2012 Sep 18-21;
San Diego, CA; Sheraton San Diego Hotel & Marina.

OTHER SOURCES

**9665 ■ American Health Care Association
(AHCA)**
1201 L St. NW
Washington, DC 20005
Ph: (202)842-4444
Fax: (202)842-3860
E-mail: hr@ahca.org
URL: http://www.ahcancal.org/Pages/Default.aspx

Description: Federation of state associations of long-
term health care facilities. Promotes standards for
professionals in long-term health care delivery and
quality care for patients and residents in a safe
environment. Focuses on issues of availability, quality, affordability, and fair payment. Operates as liaison
with governmental agencies, Congress, and professional associations. Compiles statistics.

**9666 ■ American Kinesiotherapy Association
(AKTA)**
118 College Dr., No. 5142
Hattiesburg, MS 39406
Fr: 800-296-2582
E-mail: info@akta.org
URL: http://www.akta.org

Description: Professional society of kinesiotherapists, associate and student members with interest in
therapeutic exercise and education. Kinesiotherapy is
the application of scientifically-based exercise
principles adapted to enhance the strength, endurance and mobility of individuals with functional limitations of those requiring extended physical
reconditioning. Seeks to serve the interest of members and represent the profession to the public
through the promotion of continuing competency and
continuing educational opportunities.

**9667 ■ American Physical Therapy
Association (APTA)**
1111 N Fairfax St.
Alexandria, VA 22314-1488
Ph: (703)684-2782
Fax: (703)684-7343

Fr: 800-999-2782
E-mail: memberservices@apta.org
URL: http://www.apta.org

Description: Professional organization of physical therapists and physical therapist assistants and students. Fosters the development and improvement of physical therapy service, education, and research; evaluates the organization and administration of curricula; directs the maintenance of standards and promotes scientific research. Acts as an accrediting body for educational programs in physical therapy. Establishes standards. Offers advisory and consultation services to schools of physical therapy and facilities offering physical therapy services; provides placement services at conference.

9668 ■ American Public Health Association (APHA)
800 I St. NW
Washington, DC 20001
Ph: (202)777-2742
Fax: (202)777-2534
E-mail: comments@apha.org
URL: http://www.apha.org

Description: Professional organization of physicians, nurses, educators, academicians, environmentalists, epidemiologists, new professionals, social workers, health administrators, optometrists, podiatrists, pharmacists, dentists, nutritionists, health planners, other community and mental health specialists, and interested consumers. Seeks to protect and promote personal, mental, and environmental health. Services include: promulgation of standards; establishment of uniform practices and procedures; development of the etiology of communicable diseases; research in public health; exploration of medical care programs and their relationships to public health. Sponsors job placement service.

9669 ■ American Society of Hand Therapists (ASHT)
15000 Commerce Pkwy., Ste. C
Mount Laurel, NJ 08054
Ph: (856)380-6856
Fax: (856)439-0525
E-mail: asht@asht.org
URL: http://www.asht.org

Description: Registered and licensed occupational and physical therapists specializing in hand therapy and committed to excellence and professionalism in hand rehabilitation. Works to promote research, publish information, improve treatment techniques, and standardize hand evaluation and care. Fosters education and communication between therapists in the U.S. and abroad. Compiles statistics; conducts research and education programs and continuing education seminars.

9670 ■ Association on Higher Education and Disability (AHEAD)
107 Commerce Center Dr., Ste. 204
Huntersville, NC 28078
Ph: (704)947-7779
Fax: (704)948-7779
E-mail: ahead@ahead.org
URL: http://www.ahead.org

Description: Individuals interested in promoting the equal rights and opportunities of disabled postsecondary students, staff, faculty, and graduates. Provides an exchange of communication for those professionally involved with disabled students; collects, evaluates, and disseminates information; encourages and supports legislation for the benefit of disabled students. Conducts surveys on issues pertinent to college students with disabilities; offers resource referral system and employment exchange for positions in disability student services. Conducts research programs; compiles statistics.

9671 ■ Foundation for Physical Therapy (FPT)
1111 N Fairfax St.
Alexandria, VA 22314-1488
Ph: (703)684-2782
Fax: (703)706-8587
Fr: 800-875-1378
E-mail: info@foundation4pt.org
URL: http://foundation4pt.org

Description: Supports the physical therapy profession's research needs by funding scientific and clinically-relevant physical therapy research.

9672 ■ Holistic Dental Association (HDA)
1825 Ponce de Leon Blvd., No. 148
Coral Gables, FL 33134
Ph: (305)356-7338
Fax: (305)468-6359
E-mail: director@holisticdental.org
URL: http://www.holisticdental.org

Description: Represents dentists, chiropractors, dental hygienists, physical therapists, and medical doctors. Aims to provide a holistic approach to better dental care for patients, and to expand techniques, medications, and philosophies that pertain to extractions, anesthetics, fillings, crowns, and orthodontics. Encourages the use of homeopathic medications, acupuncture, cranial osteopathy, nutritional techniques, and physical therapy in treating patients in addition to conventional treatments. Sponsors training and educational seminars.

9673 ■ Inter-American Conductive Education Association (IACEA)
PO Box 3169
Toms River, NJ 08756-3169
Ph: (732)797-2566
Fax: (732)797-2599
Fr: 800-824-2232
E-mail: info@iacea.org
URL: http://www.iacea.org

Description: Promotes and disseminates the principles of conductive education using the services of parents, conductors, therapists, teachers, and other related health care professionals. Qualifies trained conductors as new professionals to obtain health care, Medicare, Medicaid, and private health insurance reimbursement. Trains and certifies conductive education practitioners working in the United States and Canada.

9674 ■ National Rehabilitation Association (NRA)
633 S Washington St.
Alexandria, VA 22314
Ph: (703)836-0850
Fax: (703)836-0848
E-mail: info@nationalrehab.org
URL: http://www.nationalrehab.org

Description: Provides opportunities through knowledge and diversity for professionals in the fields of rehabilitation of people with disabilities.

9675 ■ National Strength and Conditioning Association (NSCA)
1885 Bob Johnson Dr.
Colorado Springs, CO 80906
Ph: (719)632-6722
Fax: (719)632-6367
Fr: 800-815-6826
E-mail: nsca@nsca-lift.org
URL: http://www.nsca-lift.org

Description: Represents professionals in the sports science, athletic, and fitness industries. Promotes the total conditioning of athletes to a level of optimum performance, with the belief that a better conditioned athlete not only performs better but is less prone to injury. Gathers and disseminates information on strength and conditioning techniques and benefits. Conducts national, regional, state, and local clinics and workshops. Operates professional certification program.

SOURCES OF HELP-WANTED ADS

9676 ■ *ADVANCE for Physical Therapists and PT Assistants*
Merion Publications Inc.
2900 Horizon Dr.
PO Box 61556
King of Prussia, PA 19406-0956
Ph: (610)278-1400
Fr: 800-355-5627
URL: http://physical-therapy.advanceweb.com/main.aspx

Biweekly. Free to qualified subscribers. Reaches active, qualified physical therapists, physical therapist assistants, and senior students in PT and PTA programs.

9677 ■ *American Journal of Physical Medicine and Rehabilitation*
Lippincott Williams & Wilkins
530 Walnut St.
Philadelphia, PA 19106-3619
Ph: (215)521-8300
Fax: (215)521-8902
Fr: 800-638-3030
URL: http://journals.lww.com/ajpmr/pages/default.aspx

Monthly. $343.00/year for individuals; $579.00/year for institutions; $210.00/year for individuals, in-training; $498.00/year for other countries; $768.00/year for institutions, other countries; $358.00/year for other countries, in-training. Medical journal.

9678 ■ *The Journal of Orthopaedic and Sports Physical Therapy*
Lippincott Williams & Wilkins
530 Walnut St.
Philadelphia, PA 19106-3619
Ph: (215)521-8300
Fax: (215)521-8902
Fr: 800-638-3030
E-mail: jospt@jospt.org
URL: http://www.jospt.org/

Monthly. $440.00/year for individuals, print & online; $405.00/year for institutions, online only; $135.00/year for students, print & online; $315.00/year for other countries, print & online; $530.00/year for institutions, other countries, print & online; $220.00/year for students, other countries, print & online. Peer-reviewed journal for physical therapists and others in the healthcare and research communities to advance musculoskeletal and sports-related best practice.

9679 ■ *Massage Therapy Journal*
American Massage Therapy Association
500 Davis St., Ste. 900
Evanston, IL 60201-4695
Ph: (847)864-0123
Fax: (847)864-5196
Fr: 877-905-2700
URL: http://www.amtamassage.org/

Annual. $25.00/year for U.S. and Canada; $45.00/year for U.S. and Canada, 2 years; $70.00/year for other countries; $120.00/year for other countries, 2 years. Magazine focusing on professional massage therapy benefits, techniques, research, news, and practitioners.

9680 ■ *Pediatric Physical Therapy*
Lippincott Williams & Wilkins
530 Walnut St.
Philadelphia, PA 19106-3619
Ph: (215)521-8300
Fax: (215)521-8902
Fr: 800-638-3030
URL: http://journals.lww.com/pedpt/pages/default.aspx

Quarterly. $167.48/year for individuals; $350.00/year for institutions; $114.49/year for individuals, in-training; $270.73/year for other countries; $457.73/year for institutions, other countries. Peer-reviewed journal reporting on new clinical care for pediatric patients.

9681 ■ *Physical & Occupational Therapy in Geriatrics*
Informa Healthcare
52 Vanderbilt Ave., 7th Fl.
New York, NY 10017-3846
Ph: (212)520-2777
URL: http://informahealthcare.com/pog

Quarterly. $520.00/year for institutions; $920.00/year for institutions; $685.00/year for institutions. Journal for allied health professionals focusing on current practice and emerging issues in the health care of and rehabilitation of the older client.

9682 ■ *Physical and Occupational Therapy in Pediatrics*
Informa Healthcare
52 Vanderbilt Ave., 7th Fl.
New York, NY 10017-3846
Ph: (212)520-2777
URL: http://informahealthcare.com/loi/pop

Quarterly. $945.00/year for institutions; $1,900.00/year for institutions, corporate; $700.00/year for institutions; $530.00/year for institutions; $1,065.00/year corporate; $1,410.00/year corporate. Journal for therapists involved in developmental and physical rehabilitation of infants and children.

9683 ■ *Physical Therapy*
American Physical Therapy Association
1111 N Fairfax St.
Alexandria, VA 22314-1488
Ph: (703)684-2782
Fax: (703)684-6748
Fr: 800-999-2782
URL: http://ptjournal.apta.org

Monthly. Included in membership. Journal of the American Physical Therapy Association.

9684 ■ *Physical Therapy Products*
Novicom Inc.
6100 Center Dr., Ste. 1000
Los Angeles, CA 90045
Ph: (310)642-4400
Fax: (310)641-4444
URL: http://www.ptproductsonline.com/

Monthly. Free to qualified subscribers. Magazine featuring new products and services available in the physical therapy field.

9685 ■ *PT in Motion*
American Physical Therapy Association
1111 N Fairfax St.
Alexandria, VA 22314-1488
Ph: (703)684-2782
Fax: (703)684-6748
Fr: 800-999-2782
URL: http://www.apta.org/PTinMotion

Monthly. $119.00/year for institutions, non-members; $139.00/year for institutions, other countries, non-members. Magazine for physical therapy professionals.

EMPLOYER DIRECTORIES AND NETWORKING LISTS

9686 ■ *Crain's List—Chicago's Largest Hospitals*
Crain Communications Inc.
360 N Michigan Ave.
Chicago, IL 60601
Ph: (312)649-5200
URL: http://www.chicagobusiness.com/section/lists

Published November, 2010. $25.00 for individuals; $45.00 for individuals. Covers: 25 hospitals in Chicago area ranked by net patient revenues. Entries include: Name, address, phone number, fax, web address, corporate e-mail, hospital administrator, network affiliation, 2009 net patient revenue, percentage change from 2008, 2009 net profits, percentage change from 2008, inpatient days, available beds, daily occupancy rate, number of hospital employees as of December 31, 2009, fiscal year end, Chairman, President, CEO, Chief Financial Officer, Human Resources Manager, Media Relations/Public Relations Director, and Hospital Administrator.

HANDBOOKS AND MANUALS

9687 ■ *Careers for Health Nuts and Others Who Like to Stay Fit*
The McGraw-Hill Companies
PO Box 182604
Columbus, OH 43272
Fax: (614)759-3749

Fr: 877-883-5524
E-mail: customer.service@mcgraw-hill.com
URL: http://www.mhprofessional.com
Blythe Camenson. Second edition. $13.95 (paper). 208 pages.

9688 ■ Careers in Medicine
The McGraw-Hill Companies
PO Box 182604
Columbus, OH 43272
Fax: (614)759-3749
Fr: 877-883-5524
E-mail: customer.service@mcgraw-hill.com
URL: http://www.mhprofessional.com/product.php?isbn=0071458743
Terence J. Sacks. Third edition, 2006. $15.95 (paper). 192 pages. Examines the many paths open to M.D.s, D.O.s, and M.D./Ph.D.s, including clinical private or group practice, hospitals, public health organizations, the armed forces, emergency rooms, research institutions, medical schools, pharmaceutical companies and private industry, and research/advocacy groups like the World Health Organization. A special chapter on osteopathy and chiropractic explores this branch of medicine.

9689 ■ Careers in Social and Rehabilitation Services
The McGraw-Hill Companies
PO Box 182604
Columbus, OH 43272
Fax: (614)759-3749
Fr: 877-883-5524
E-mail: customer.service@mcgraw-hill.com
URL: http://www.mhprofessional.com/product.php?isbn=0071641955
Geraldine O. Garner. 2008. $16.95. 192 pages.

9690 ■ Expert Resumes for Health Care Careers
Jist Works
875 Montreal Way
St. Paul, MN 55102
Fr: 800-648-5478
E-mail: educate@emcp.com
URL: http://www.jist.com
Wendy S. Enelow and Louise M. Kursmark. 2010. $16.95. 288 pages.

9691 ■ Health Careers Today
Elsevier
11830 Westline Industrial Dr.
St. Louis, MO 63146
Ph: (314)453-7010
Fax: (314)453-7095
Fr: 800-545-2522
E-mail: usbkinfo@elsevier.com
URL: http://www.elsevier.com
Gerdin, Judith. Fourth edition. 2007. $74.95. 496 pages. Covers more than 45 health careers. Discusses the roles and responsibilities of various occupations and provides a solid foundation in the skills needed for all health careers.

9692 ■ Opportunities in Health and Medical Careers
The McGraw-Hill Companies
PO Box 182604
Columbus, OH 43272
Fax: (614)759-3749
Fr: 877-883-5524
E-mail: customer.service@mcgraw-hill.com
URL: http://www.mhprofessional.com/product.php?isbn=0071437274
I. Donald Snook, Jr. and Leo D'Orazio. 2004. $14.95 (paper). 157 pages. Covers the full range of medical and health occupations. Illustrated.

9693 ■ Opportunities in Physical Therapy Careers
The McGraw-Hill Companies
PO Box 182604
Columbus, OH 43272

Fax: (614)759-3749
Fr: 877-883-5524
E-mail: customer.service@mcgraw-hill.com
URL: http://www.mhprofessional.com/product.php?isbn=0071389504
Bernice R. Krumhansl. $11.95. 160 pages. Defines what the jobs are, where they are, and how to pursue them. Contains bibliography and illustrations.

9694 ■ Pocket Orthopaedics: Evidence-Based Survival Guide
Jones & Bartlett Learning
5 Wall St.
Burlington, MA 01803
Fax: (978)443-8000
Fr: 800-832-0034
E-mail: info@jblearning.com
URL: http://www.jblearning.com
Michael S. Wong. 2011. $41.95 (spiral/paperback). 412 pages. Serves as learning aide in evidence-based practice for both students and clinicians.

9695 ■ The Role of the Physical Therapist Assistant: Regulations and Responsibilities
F.A. Davis Company
404 N 2nd St.
Philadelphia, PA 19123
Ph: (215)440-3001
Fax: (215)440-3016
Fr: 800-323-3555
E-mail: orders@fadavis.com
URL: http://www.fadavis.com
Holly Clynch. 2011. $41.95 (paper). 234 pages. Presents an introduction to the history of physical therapist assistants and their responsibilities today. Addresses issues of role delineation, teamwork, professionalism and leadership development. Includes a discussion of the relationship between the physical therapist and physical therapist assistant. Features a workbook-like design with perforated, tear-out pages.

EMPLOYMENT AGENCIES AND SEARCH FIRMS

9696 ■ Advanced Medical Personnel Services
5535 S Williamson Blvd., Ste. 774
Port Orange, FL 32128
Ph: (386)756-4395
Fr: 800-330-7711
URL: http://www.advanced-medical.net
Specializes in the placement of physical therapists, physical therapy assistants, occupational therapists, certified occupational therapy assistants and speech-language pathologists in assignments across the United States.

9697 ■ Cross Country TravCorps
6551 Park of Commerce Blvd.
Boca Raton, FL 33487-8247
Fax: (561)998-8533
Fr: 800-530-6125
E-mail: sms@cctc.com
URL: http://www.crosscountrytravcorps.com/cctc/
Places traveling nurses in assignments nationwide.

9698 ■ Jackson Therapy Partners
11315 Corporate Blvd., Ste. 100
Orlando, FL 32817
Fr: 800-774-7785
URL: http://www.jacksontherapy.com
Serves as a therapy recruiting firm. Features therapy jobs available across the United States including permanent and travel opportunities.

9699 ■ Team Placement Service, Inc.
1414 Prince St., Ste. 202
Alexandria, VA 22314
Ph: (703)820-8618
Fax: (703)820-3368

Fr: 800-495-6767
E-mail: 4jobs@teamplace.com
URL: http://www.teamplace.com
Full-service personnel consultants provide placement for healthcare staff, physician and dentist, private practice, and hospitals. Conduct interviews, tests, and reference checks to select the top 20% of applicants. Survey applicants' skill levels, provide backup information on each candidate, select compatible candidates for consideration, and insure the hiring process minimizes potential legal liability. Industries served: healthcare and government agencies providing medical, dental, biotech, laboratory, hospitals, and physician search.

ONLINE JOB SOURCES AND SERVICES

9700 ■ HEALTHeCAREERS Network
Fr: 888-884-8242
E-mail: info@healthecareers.com
URL: http://www.healthecareers.com
Description: Career search site for jobs in all health care specialties; educational resources; visa and licensing information for relocation; interesting articles; relocation tools; links to professional organizations and general resources.

9701 ■ Hospital Jobs OnLine
E-mail: support@hospitaljobsonline.com
URL: http://www.hospitaljobsonline.com
Description: Serves as a niche healthcare job board designed exclusively for hospitals, healthcare companies, and healthcare job seekers.

9702 ■ ProHealthJobs.com
Ph: (484)443-8545
Fax: (484)443-8549
E-mail: info@prohealthjobs.com
URL: http://prohealthjobs.com/jobboard
Description: Career resources site for the medical and health care field. Lists professional opportunities, product information, continuing education and open positions.

9703 ■ PTJobs.com
URL: http://www.ptjobs.com
Description: Serves as a job board dedicated to physical therapists, physical therapist assistants, clinic directors, instructors, and other physical therapy communities.

9704 ■ PTJungle.com
URL: http://www.ptjungle.com
Description: Serves as job board built specifically for physical therapists and physical therapist assistants.

9705 ■ RehabJobs Online
E-mail: support@atsrehabjobs.com
URL: http://www.rehabjobsonline.com
Description: Resource center for the professional therapist. Main files include: Therapists Only, Therapy Forums, Nationwide Job Search (database), Therapy Job Outlook, Therapy Job Search Utilities, Therapy Links, Information for Employers and Recruiters.

9706 ■ RehabWorld.com
URL: http://www.rehabworld.com
Description: Site for rehabilitation professionals to learn about the profession and locate jobs. Includes user groups, salary surveys, and chat capabilities. Main files include: Physical Therapy, Occupational Therapy, Speech Therapy, Mental Health, Employer World, Student World, International World, Forum.

9707 ■ TherapyJobBoard.com
URL: http://www.therapyjobboard.com
Description: Serves as an employment resource for job seekers and employers in the physical therapy,

■ 9708 ■   Physical Therapy Assistants and Aides

occupational therapy, speech therapy and respiratory therapy professions.

OTHER SOURCES

9708 ■ American Physical Therapy Association (APTA)
1111 N Fairfax St.
Alexandria, VA 22314-1488
Ph: (703)684-2782
Fax: (703)684-7343
Fr: 800-999-2782
E-mail: memberservices@apta.org
URL: http://www.apta.org

Description: Professional organization of physical therapists and physical therapist assistants and students. Fosters the development and improvement of physical therapy service, education, and research; evaluates the organization and administration of curricula; directs the maintenance of standards and promotes scientific research. Acts as an accrediting body for educational programs in physical therapy. Establishes standards. Offers advisory and consultation services to schools of physical therapy and facilities offering physical therapy services; provides placement services at conference.

9709 ■ Foundation for Physical Therapy (FPT)
1111 N Fairfax St.
Alexandria, VA 22314-1488
Ph: (703)684-2782
Fax: (703)706-8587
Fr: 800-875-1378
E-mail: info@foundation4pt.org
URL: http://foundation4pt.org

Description: Supports the physical therapy profession's research needs by funding scientific and clinically-relevant physical therapy research.

9710 ■ National Association of Rehabilitation Providers and Agencies (NARA)
701 8th St. NW, Ste. 500
Washington, DC 20001
Fax: 800-716-1847
Fr: (866)839-7710
E-mail: nara.admin@naranet.org
URL: http://www.naranet.org

Description: Members are rehabilitation companies servicing patients (including Medicare recipients) with physical therapy, occupational therapy and speech pathology services in outpatient and long-term care settings. Associate members are rehabilitation vendors.

686   Job Hunter's Sourcebook, 12th Edition

SOURCES OF HELP-WANTED ADS

9711 ■ *AAPA News*
American Academy of Physician Assistants
2318 Mill Rd., Ste. 1300
Alexandria, VA 22314
Ph: (703)836-2272
Fax: (703)684-1924
E-mail: aapa@aapa.org
URL: http://www.aapa.org

Description: Biweekly. Updates physician assistants on professional, legislative, and academy issues. Profiles members. Recurring features include news of research, a calendar of events, news of educational opportunities, available resource materials, and news affecting physician profession and practice.

9712 ■ *ADVANCE for Physician Assistants*
Merion Publications Inc.
2900 Horizon Dr.
PO Box 61556
King of Prussia, PA 19406-0956
Ph: (610)278-1400
Fr: 800-355-5627
URL: http://nurse-practitioners-and-physician-assistants.advancew

Monthly. Free to qualified subscribers. Targets practicing physician assistants and physician assistant students with senior status.

9713 ■ *AJP Reports*
Thieme Medical Publishers Inc.
333 7th Ave.
New York, NY 10001
Ph: (212)760-0888
Fax: (212)947-1112
Fr: 800-782-3488
URL: http://www.thieme.com/index.php?option=com_content&view=arti

Peer-reviewed journal publishing information in the fields of neonatology, maternal and fetal medicine.

9714 ■ *American Family Physician*
American Academy of Family Physicians
11400 Tomahawk Creek Pky.
PO Box 11210
Leawood, KS 66211-2680
Ph: (913)906-6000
Fax: (913)906-6075
Fr: 800-274-2237
E-mail: afpedit@aafp.org
URL: http://www.aafp.org/online/en/home/publications/journals/afp

Semimonthly. $101.00/year for individuals, healthcare professionals; $164.00/year for Canada, healthcare professionals; $227.00/year for other countries, healthcare professionals; $173.00/year for individuals, physicians and other individuals; $240.00/year for Canada, physicians and other individuals; $299.00/year for other countries, physicians and other individuals; $236.00/year for institutions; $299.00/year for institutions, Canada; $362.00/year for institutions, other countries. Peer-reviewed clinical journal for family physicians and others in primary care. Review articles detail the latest diagnostic and therapeutic techniques in the medical field. Department features in each issue include 'Tips from other Journals,' CME credit opportunities and course calendar.

9715 ■ *American Journal of Emergency Medicine*
Mosby Inc.
11830 Westline Industrial Dr.
St. Louis, MO 63146-3326
Ph: (314)872-8370
Fax: (314)432-1380
Fr: 800-325-4177
URL: http://www.elsevier.com/wps/find/journaldescription.cws_home

$340.00/year for individuals; $529.00/year for institutions; $159.00/year for students; $523.00/year for other countries; $711.00/year for institutions, other countries; $261.00/year for students, other countries. Journal reporting on emergency medicine.

9716 ■ *Annals of Medicine*
Informa Healthcare
52 Vanderbilt Ave., 7th Fl.
New York, NY 10017-3846
Ph: (212)520-2777
URL: http://informahealthcare.com/ann

$595.00/year for institutions; $980.00/year for institutions; $780.00/year for institutions. Journal covering health science and medical education.

9717 ■ *Cardiac Cath Lab Director*
Sage Publications Inc.
2455 Teller Rd.
Thousand Oaks, CA 91320-2218
Ph: (805)499-9774
Fax: (805)583-2665
Fr: 800-818-7243
URL: http://www.sagepub.com/journalsProdDesc.nav?prodId=Journal20

Bimonthly. $315.00/year for institutions, print and e-access; $284.00/year for institutions, e-access. Peer-reviewed journal publishing research on cardiac catheterization procedures.

9718 ■ *Clinical Medicine & Research*
Marshfield Clinic
1000 N Oak Ave.
Marshfield, WI 54449
Ph: (715)387-5511
Fax: (715)389-3808
Fr: 800-782-8581
E-mail: clinmedres@mcrf.mfldclin.edu
URL: http://www.clinmedres.org/

Quarterly. Free within the U.S. Peer-reviewed journal that publishes scientific medical research that is relevant to a broad audience of medical researchers and healthcare professionals.

9719 ■ *The CMA Today*
American Association of Medical Assistants
20 N Wacker Dr., Ste. 1575
Chicago, IL 60606
Ph: (312)899-1500
Fax: (312)899-1259
URL: http://www.aama-ntl.org/cmatoday/about.aspx

Bimonthly. $30.00/year free to members; $60.00/year for nonmembers. Professional health journal.

9720 ■ *CME Supplement to Emergency Medicine Clinics of North America*
Elsevier Science Inc.
360 Park Ave. S
New York, NY 10010-1710
Ph: (212)989-5800
Fax: (212)633-3990
Fr: 888-437-4636
URL: http://www.elsevier.com/wps/find/journaldescription.cws_home

$209.00/year for individuals. Journal covering emergency medicine clinics.

9721 ■ *Discovery Medicine*
Discovery Medicine
10 Gerard Ave., Ste. 201
Timonium, MD 21093
Ph: (410)773-9938
Fax: 888-833-0526
URL: http://www.discoverymedicine.com

Bimonthly. $599.00/year for institutions, digital edition; $99.95/year for individuals, digital edition. Online journal that publishes articles on diseases, biology, new diagnostics, and treatments for medical professionals.

9722 ■ *Education & Treatment of Children*
West Virginia University Press
139 Stansbury Hall
PO Box 6295
Morgantown, WV 26506
Ph: (304)293-8400
Fax: (304)293-6585
URL: http://www.educationandtreatmentofchildren.net

Quarterly. $85.00/year for institutions; $45.00/year for individuals; $100.00/year for institutions, elsewhere; $60.00/year for individuals, elsewhere. Periodical featuring information concerning the development of services for children and youth. Includes reports written for educators and other child care and mental health providers focused on teaching, training, and treatment effectiveness.

9723 ■ *Forum on Immunopathological Diseases and Therapeutics*
Begell House Inc.
50 Cross Hwy.
Redding, CT 06896
Ph: (203)938-1300
Fax: (203)938-1304
URL: http://www.begellhouse.com/journals/1a654bf03faf67ac.html

$748.00/year for institutions. Journal publishing articles on immunopathological diseases and therapeutics.

9724 ■ Genes and Nutrition
New Century Health Publishers L.L.C.
PO Box 175
Coppell, TX 75019
Fax: (940)565-8148
URL: http://www.newcenturyhealthpublishers.com/ genes_and_nutritio

Quarterly. $428.00/year for institutions; $228.00/year for individuals. International, interdisciplinary peer reviewed scientific journal for critical evaluation of research on the relationship between genetics & nutrition with the goal of improving human health.

9725 ■ Global Change, Peace & Security
Routledge
711 3 Ave., 8 Fl.
New York, NY 10016
Ph: (212)216-7800
Fax: (212)563-2269
Fr: 800-634-7064
URL: http://www.tandfonline.com/toc/cpar20/current

$160.00/year for individuals, print; $602.00/year for individuals, online only; $669.00/year for individuals, print & online. Journal promoting physical therapy and integration.

9726 ■ Hospitals & Health Networks
Health Forum L.L.C.
155 N Wacker Dr., Ste. 400
Chicago, IL 60606
Ph: (312)893-6800
Fax: (312)422-4500
Fr: 800-821-2039
URL: http://www.hhnmag.com

Weekly. Free. Publication covering the health care industry.

9727 ■ The IHS Primary Care Provider
Indian Health Service
The Reyes Bldg.
801 Thompson Ave., Ste. 400
Rockville, MD 20852-1627
Ph: (301)443-1011
URL: http://www.ihs.gov/provider

Monthly. Journal for health care professionals, physicians, nurses, pharmacists, dentists, and dietitians.

9728 ■ Injury
Mosby Inc.
11830 Westline Industrial Dr.
St. Louis, MO 63146-3326
Ph: (314)872-8370
Fax: (314)432-1380
Fr: 800-325-4177
URL: http://www.elsevier.com/wps/find/ journaldescription.cws_home

Monthly. $200.00/year for individuals, European countries and Iran; $224.00/year for individuals, all countries except Europe, Japan and Iran; $26,500.00/ year for individuals; $1,381.00/year for institutions, European countries and Iran; $1,543.00/year for institutions, all Countries except Europe, Japan and Iran; $183,200.00/year for institutions. Journal publishing articles and research related to the treatment of injuries such as trauma systems and management; surgical procedures; epidemiological studies; surgery (of all tissues); resuscitation; biomechanics; rehabilitation; anaesthesia; radiology and wound management.

9729 ■ ISRN Cardiology
Hindawi Publishing Corporation
410 Park Ave., 15th Fl.
287 PMB
New York, NY 10022
E-mail: cardiology@isrn.com
URL: http://www.isrn.com/journals/cardiology

Peer-reviewed journal publishing research and studies in all areas of cardiology.

9730 ■ ISRN Dermatology
Hindawi Publishing Corporation
410 Park Ave., 15th Fl.
287 PMB
New York, NY 10022
E-mail: dermatology@isrn.com
URL: http://www.isrn.com/journals/dermatology

Peer-reviewed and open access journal publishing original research articles, review articles, and clinical studies in all areas of dermatology.

9731 ■ ISRN Endocrinology
Hindawi Publishing Corporation
410 Park Ave., 15th Fl.
287 PMB
New York, NY 10022
E-mail: endocrinology@isrn.com
URL: http://www.isrn.com/journals/endocrinology

Peer-reviewed, open access journal publishing original research articles, review articles, case reports, and clinical studies in all areas of endocrinology.

9732 ■ ISRN Hematology
Hindawi Publishing Corporation
410 Park Ave., 15th Fl.
287 PMB
New York, NY 10022
E-mail: hematology@isrn.com
URL: http://www.isrn.com/journals/hematology

Peer-reviewed journal covering research in all areas of hematology.

9733 ■ ISRN Neurology
Hindawi Publishing Corporation
410 Park Ave., 15th Fl.
287 PMB
New York, NY 10022
E-mail: neurology@isrn.com
URL: http://www.isrn.com/journals/neurology

Peer-reviewed journal publishing research in all areas of neurology.

9734 ■ ISRN Obstetrics and Gynecology
Hindawi Publishing Corporation
410 Park Ave., 15th Fl.
287 PMB
New York, NY 10022
E-mail: obgyn@isrn.com
URL: http://www.isrn.com/journals/obgyn

Peer-reviewed, open access journal publishing original research articles, review articles, case reports, and clinical studies in all areas of obstetrics and gynecology.

9735 ■ ISRN Oncology
Hindawi Publishing Corporation
410 Park Ave., 15th Fl.
287 PMB
New York, NY 10022
E-mail: oncology@isrn.com
URL: http://www.isrn.com/journals/oncology

Peer-reviewed journal publishing research articles in all areas of oncology.

9736 ■ ISRN Pharmacology
Hindawi Publishing Corporation
410 Park Ave., 15th Fl.
287 PMB
New York, NY 10022
E-mail: pharmacology@isrn.com
URL: http://www.isrn.com/journals/pharmacology

Peer-reviewed journal publishing articles in all areas of pharmacology.

9737 ■ ISRN Rheumatology
Hindawi Publishing Corporation
410 Park Ave., 15th Fl.
287 PMB
New York, NY 10022
E-mail: rheumatology@isrn.com
URL: http://www.isrn.com/journals/rheumatology

Peer-reviewed journal publishing information in all areas of rheumatology.

9738 ■ ISRN Surgery
Hindawi Publishing Corporation
410 Park Ave., 15th Fl.
287 PMB
New York, NY 10022
E-mail: surgery@isrn.com
URL: http://www.isrn.com/journals/surgery

Peer-reviewed journal publishing research in all areas of surgery.

9739 ■ ISRN Urology
Hindawi Publishing Corporation
410 Park Ave., 15th Fl.
287 PMB
New York, NY 10022
E-mail: urology@isrn.com
URL: http://www.isrn.com/journals/urology

Peer-reviewed journal publishing research in all areas of urology.

9740 ■ Journal of Adolescent and Young Adult Oncology
Mary Ann Liebert Inc., Publishers
140 Huguenot St., 3rd Fl.
New Rochelle, NY 10801-5215
Ph: (914)740-2100
Fax: (914)740-2101
Fr: 800-654-3237
URL: http://www.liebertpub.com/products/ product.aspx?pid=387

Quarterly. $336.00/year for individuals, print and online; $758.00/year for institutions, print and online. Peer-reviewed journal focusing on research, education, communication and collaboration between health professionals in adolescent and young adult oncology.

9741 ■ Journal of the American Society of Podiatric Medical Assistants
American Society of Podiatric Medical Assistants
1616 N 78th Ct.
Elmwood Park, IL 60707
Fr: 888-882-7762
URL: http://www.aspma.org

Quarterly. Included in membership. Professional journal covering issues in podiatry.

9742 ■ Journal of Diabetes Mellitus
Scientific Research Publishing
PO Box 54821
Irvine, CA 92619-4821
E-mail: jdm@scirp.org
URL: http://www.scirp.org/journal/jdm/

Quarterly. $156.00/year for individuals. Peer-reviewed journal publishing research on diabetes mellitus.

9743 ■ Journal of Environmental Pathology, Toxicology and Oncology
Begell House Inc.
50 Cross Hwy.
Redding, CT 06896
Ph: (203)938-1300
Fax: (203)938-1304
URL: http://www.begellhouse.com/journals/ 0ff459a57a4c08d0

$940.00/year for institutions. Journal covering research and reviews of factors and conditions that affect human and animal carcinogenesis.

9744 ■ Journal of Health and Life Sciences Law
American Health Lawyers Association
1620 Eye St. NW, 6th Fl.
Washington, DC 20006-4010
Ph: (202)833-1100
Fax: (202)833-1105
URL: http://www.healthlawyers.org

Quarterly. $149.00/year for individuals. Professional journal covering healthcare issues and cases and their impact on the health care arena.

9745 ■ Journal of Hospital Medicine
John Wiley & Sons Inc.
111 River St.
Hoboken, NJ 07030-5773
Ph: (201)748-6000
Fax: (201)748-6088
Fr: 800-825-7550
URL: http://onlinelibrary.wiley.com/journal/10.1002/ (ISSN)1553-56

$827.00/year for U.S., Canada, and Mexico, print only; $827.00/year for institutions, other countries, print only. Journal on hospital medicine.

9746 ■ Journal of Skin Cancer
Hindawi Publishing Corp.
410 Park Ave., 15th Fl.
287 PMB
New York, NY 10022-4407
Fax: (215)893-4392
E-mail: jsc@hindawi.com
URL: http://www.hindawi.com/journals/jsc/

$195.00/year for individuals. Peer-reviewed journal publishing original research and review articles, case reports and clinical studies related to all aspects of skin cancer.

9747 ■ Laboratory Medicine
American Society for Clinical Pathology
33 W Monroe, Ste. 1600
Chicago, IL 60603
Ph: (312)541-4999
Fax: (312)541-4998
Fr: 800-267-2727
E-mail: labmed@ascp.org
URL: http://labmed.ascpjournals.org/

Monthly. $95.00/year for individuals, online; $120.00/ year for individuals, print and online; $120.00/year for institutions, online; $145.00/year for institutions, print and online. Professional journal covering medical technology and pathology.

9748 ■ Leukemia Supplements
Nature Publishing Group
75 Varick St., 9th Fl.
New York, NY 10013-1917
Ph: (212)726-9200
Fax: (212)696-9006
Fr: 888-331-6288
URL: http://www.nature.com/leusup/marketing/ index.html

Peer-reviewed journal covering all aspects of the research and treatment of leukemia and allied diseases.

9749 ■ Minnesota Medicine
Minnesota Medical Association
1300 Godward St. NE, Ste. 2500
Minneapolis, MN 55413
Ph: (612)378-1875
Fax: (612)378-3875
Fr: 800-342-5662
URL: http://www.minnesotamedicine.com/

Monthly. $45.00/year for individuals; $81.00/year for two years; $80.00/year for other countries; $144.00/ year for other countries, 2 years. Magazine on medical, socioeconomic, public health, medical-legal, and biomedical ethics issues of interest to physicians.

9750 ■ Narrative Inquiry in Bioethics
The Johns Hopkins University Press
2715 N Charles St.
Baltimore, MD 21218-4319
Ph: (410)516-6900
Fax: (410)516-6968
URL: http://www.press.jhu.edu/journals/narrative_ inquiry_in_bioet

$175.00/year for institutions, print; $50.00/year for individuals, print. Journal publishing information on bioethics.

9751 ■ The Neurohospitalist
Sage Publications Inc.
2455 Teller Rd.
Thousand Oaks, CA 91320-2218
Ph: (805)499-9774
Fax: (805)583-2665
Fr: 800-818-7243
URL: http://www.sagepub.com/ journalsProdDesc.nav?prodId=Journal20

Quarterly. $387.00/year for institutions, print and e-access; $348.00/year for institutions, e-access; $379.00/year for institutions, print; $102.00/year for individuals, print and e-access. Peer-reviewed journal focusing on practice and performance of neurohospitalist medicine.

9752 ■ Neuroscience and Medicine
Scientific Research Publishing
PO Box 54821
Irvine, CA 92619-4821
E-mail: nm@scirp.org
URL: http://www.scirp.org/journal/nm/

Quarterly. $156.00/year for individuals. Peer-reviewed journal publishing the latest advancements in neuroscience.

9753 ■ PAEA Networker
Physician Assistant Education Association
300 N Washington St., Ste. 710
Alexandria, VA 22314-2544
Ph: (703)548-5538
Fax: (703)548-5539
E-mail: info@paeaonline.org
URL: http://www.paeaonline.org/index.php?ht=d/sp/i/ 253/pid/253

Description: Monthly. Presents news of interest to members. Recurring features include interviews, a calendar of events, job listings, news of recent events and meetings, articles on APAP award winners, updates on member services.

9754 ■ Pharmacology and Pharmacy
Scientific Research Publishing
PO Box 54821
Irvine, CA 92619-4821
E-mail: pp@scirp.org
URL: http://www.scirp.org/journal/pp/

Quarterly. $156.00/year for individuals. Peer-reviewed journal publishing articles on pharmacology and pharmacy.

9755 ■ Practical Radiation Oncology
Elsevier
1600 John F. Kennedy Blvd., Ste. 1800
Philadelphia, PA 19103-2822
Ph: (215)239-3900
Fax: (215)238-7883
E-mail: pro@astro.org
URL: http://www.practicalradonc.org/

Peer-reviewed journal featuring information about radiation oncology practice.

9756 ■ Surgical Science
Scientific Research Publishing
PO Box 54821
Irvine, CA 92619-4821
E-mail: ss@scirp.org
URL: http://www.scirp.org/journal/ss/

$390.00/year for individuals. Peer-reviewed journal publishing articles on the latest developments in surgery.

9757 ■ Therapeutic Advances in Drug Safety
Sage Publications Inc.
2455 Teller Rd.
Thousand Oaks, CA 91320-2218
Ph: (805)499-9774
Fax: (805)583-2665
Fr: 800-818-7243
URL: http://www.sagepub.com/ journalsProdDesc.nav?prodId=Journal20

Bimonthly. $1,125.00/year for institutions, print and e-access; $1,013.00/year for institutions, e-access; $1,103.00/year for institutions, print. Peer-reviewed journal covering novel and controversial aspects pertaining to the safe use of drugs in different age and ethnic patient groups.

9758 ■ USA Body Psychotherapy Journal
United States Association for Body Psychotherapy
8639 B 16th St., Ste. 119
Silver Spring, MD 20910
Ph: (202)466-1619
E-mail: admin@usabp.org
URL: http://www.usabp.org/ displaycommon.cfm?an=4

Semiannual. Academic journal that seeks to support, promote and stimulate the exchange of ideas, scholarship and research within the field of body psychotherapy as well as an interdisciplinary exchange with related fields of clinical practice and inquiry.

9759 ■ World Journal of AIDS
Scientific Research Publishing
PO Box 54821
Irvine, CA 92619-4821
E-mail: wja@scirp.org
URL: http://www.scirp.org/journal/wja/

Quarterly. $156.00/year for individuals. Peer-reviewed journal publishing articles on research data and education in all aspects of HIV and AIDS.

9760 ■ World Journal of Vaccines
Scientific Research Publishing
PO Box 54821
Irvine, CA 92619-4821
E-mail: wjv@scirp.org
URL: http://www.scirp.org/journal/wjv/

Quarterly. $156.00/year for individuals. Peer-reviewed journal publishing articles on the latest advancements in vaccine.

9761 ■ Year Book of Critical Care Medicine
Elsevier Science Inc.
360 Park Ave. S
New York, NY 10010-1710
Ph: (212)989-5800
Fax: (212)633-3990
Fr: 888-437-4636
URL: http://www.elsevier.com/wps/find/ journaldescription.cws_home

Annual. $271.00/year for institutions, other countries; $197.00/year for other countries; $103.00/year for students, other countries; $250.00/year for institutions, other countries; $167.00/year for individuals; $81.00/year for students. Journal focused on treatment of severe sepsis and septic shock, echocardiography in the evaluation of hemo-dynamically unstable patients & mechanical ventilation of acute respiratory distress syndrome.

EMPLOYER DIRECTORIES AND NETWORKING LISTS

9762 ■ Association of Physician's Assistants in Cardiovascular Surgery—Membership Directory
Association of Physician's Assistants in Cardiovascular Surgery
PO Box 4834
Englewood, CA 80155
Ph: (303)221-5651
Fax: (303)771-2550
Fr: 877-221-5651
URL: http://www.apacvs.org

Annual. Covers: About 800 physician's assistants who work with cardiovascular surgeons. Entries include: Name, address, phone. Arrangement: Alphabetical.

9763 ■ Crain's List—Chicago's Largest Hospitals
Crain Communications Inc.
360 N Michigan Ave.
Chicago, IL 60601
Ph: (312)649-5200
URL: http://www.chicagobusiness.com/section/lists

Published November, 2010. $25.00 for individuals; $45.00 for individuals. Covers: 25 hospitals in Chicago area ranked by net patient revenues. Entries include: Name, address, phone number, fax, web address, corporate e-mail, hospital administrator, network affiliation, 2009 net patient revenue, percentage change from 2008, 2009 net profits, percentage change from 2008, inpatient days, available beds, daily occupancy rate, number of hospital employees as of December 31, 2009, fiscal year end, Chairman, President, CEO, Chief Financial Officer, Human Resources Manager, Media Relations/Public Relations Director, and Hospital Administrator.

9764 ■ Directory of Hospital Personnel
Grey House Publishing
4919 Rte. 22
PO Box 56
Amenia, NY 12501
Ph: (518)789-8700
Fax: (518)789-0556
Fr: 800-562-2139
URL: http://www.greyhouse.com/hospital_personnel.htm

Annual, Latest edition 2011. $325.00 for individuals. Covers: 200,000 executives at 6,000 U.S. Hospitals. Entries include: Name of hospital, address, phone, number of beds, type and JCAHO status of hospital, names and titles of key department heads and staff, medical and nursing school affiliations; number of residents, interns, and nursing students. Arrangement: Geographical. Indexes: Hospital name, personnel, hospital size.

9765 ■ Hospital Blue Book
Billian Publishing Inc. and Trans World Publishing Inc.
2100 River Edge Pky.
Atlanta, GA 30328
Ph: (770)955-5656
Fax: (770)952-0669
Fr: 800-800-5668
E-mail: blu-book@billian.com
URL: http://www.billianshealthdata.com/Products/bluebook.html

Annual, Latest edition 2010. $575.00 for individuals; $575.00 for individuals. Covers: More than 6,500 hospitals; some listings also appear in a separate southern edition of this publication. Entries include: Name of hospital, accreditation, mailing address, phone, fax, number of beds, type of facility (nonprofit, general, state, etc.); list of administrative personnel and chiefs of medical services, with specific titles. Arrangement: Geographical.

9766 ■ Medical and Health Information Directory
Gale
PO Box 6904
Florence, KY 41022-6904
Fr: 800-354-9706
URL: http://www.gale.cengage.com

Annual, Latest edition April 2011. $1190.00 for individuals; $501.00 for individuals. Covers: In volume 1, more than 33,000 medical and health oriented associations, organizations, institutions, and government agencies, including health maintenance organizations (HMOs), preferred provider organizations (PPOs), insurance companies, pharmaceutical companies, research centers, and medical and allied health schools. In Volume 2, over 20,000 medical book publishers; medical periodicals, directories, audiovisual producers and services, medical libraries and information centers, electronic resources, and health-related internet search engines. In Volume 3, more than 40,500 clinics, treatment centers, care programs, and counseling/diagnostic services for 34

subject areas. Entries include: Institution, service, or firm name, address, phone, fax, email and URL; many include names of key personnel and, when pertinent, descriptive annotation. Volume 3 was formerly listed separately as Health Services Directory. Arrangement: Classified by organization activity, service, etc. Indexes: Each volume has a complete alphabetical name and keyword index.

9767 ■ Physician Assistant Programs Directory
Association of Physician Assistant Programs
950 N Washington St.
Alexandria, VA 22314-1552
Ph: (703)836-2272
Fax: (703)684-1924
URL: http://www.aapa.org

Annual. $35.00. Covers: Over 100 accredited programs that educate physician assistants. Entries include: Program name, institution name, address, phone; description of program, including curriculum, selection criteria, degrees of certificates offered. Arrangement: Geographical.

HANDBOOKS AND MANUALS

9768 ■ Career Opportunities in Health Care (Career Opportunities)
Facts On File Inc.
132 W 31st St., 17th Fl.
New York, NY 10001-2006
Fax: 800-678-3633
Fr: 800-322-8755
E-mail: custserv@factsonfile.com
URL: http://www.infobasepublishing.com

Shelly Field. 2007. Third Edition. $49.50. 304 pages. Part of the Career Opportunities Series.

9769 ■ Careers in Health Care
The McGraw-Hill Companies
PO Box 182604
Columbus, OH 43272
Fax: (614)759-3749
Fr: 877-883-5524
E-mail: customer.service@mcgraw-hill.com
URL: http://www.mhprofessional.com/product.php?isbn=0071466533

Barbara M. Swanson. Fifth edition, 2005. $19.95 (paper). 192 pages. Describes job duties, work settings, salaries, licensing and certification requirements, educational preparation, and future outlook. Gives ideas on how to secure a job.

9770 ■ Careers in Medicine
The McGraw-Hill Companies
PO Box 182604
Columbus, OH 43272
Fax: (614)759-3749
Fr: 877-883-5524
E-mail: customer.service@mcgraw-hill.com
URL: http://www.mhprofessional.com/product.php?isbn=0071458743

Terence J. Sacks. Third edition, 2006. $15.95 (paper). 192 pages. Examines the many paths open to M.D.s, D.O.s, and M.D./Ph.D.s, including clinical private or group practice, hospitals, public health organizations, the armed forces, emergency rooms, research institutions, medical schools, pharmaceutical companies and private industry, and research/advocacy groups like the World Health Organization. A special chapter on osteopathy and chiropractic explores this branch of medicine.

9771 ■ Expert Resumes for Health Care Careers
Jist Works
875 Montreal Way
St. Paul, MN 55102
Fr: 800-648-5478
E-mail: educate@emcp.com
URL: http://www.jist.com

Wendy S. Enelow and Louise M. Kursmark. 2010. $16.95. 288 pages.

9772 ■ Health Careers Today
Elsevier
11830 Westline Industrial Dr.
St. Louis, MO 63146
Ph: (314)453-7010
Fax: (314)453-7095
Fr: 800-545-2522
E-mail: usbkinfo@elsevier.com
URL: http://www.elsevier.com

Gerdin, Judith. Fourth edition. 2007. $74.95. 496 pages. Covers more than 45 health careers. Discusses the roles and responsibilities of various occupations and provides a solid foundation in the skills needed for all health careers.

9773 ■ How To Get a Job in Health Care
Cengage Learning
PO Box 6904
Florence, KY 41022-6904
Fax: 800-487-8488
Fr: 800-354-9706
URL: http://www.cengage.com

Robert H. Zedlitz. 2012. $58.00. 144 pages (paperback). Serves as a preparatory reference tool for job seekers, includes job research, writing resumes, completing applications, and preparing for interviews.

9774 ■ Opportunities in Health and Medical Careers
The McGraw-Hill Companies
PO Box 182604
Columbus, OH 43272
Fax: (614)759-3749
Fr: 877-883-5524
E-mail: customer.service@mcgraw-hill.com
URL: http://www.mhprofessional.com/product.php?isbn=0071437274

I. Donald Snook, Jr. and Leo D'Orazio. 2004. $14.95 (paper). 157 pages. Covers the full range of medical and health occupations. Illustrated.

9775 ■ Opportunities in Physician Assistant Careers
The McGraw-Hill Companies
PO Box 182604
Columbus, OH 43272
Fax: (614)759-3749
Fr: 877-883-5524
E-mail: customer.service@mcgraw-hill.com
URL: http://www.mhprofessional.com/product.php?isbn=0071400613

Terence J. Sacks. $15.95. 160 pages.

9776 ■ Physician Assistant: A Guide to Clinical Practice
W. B. Saunders Co.
6277 Sea Harbor Dr.
Orlando, FL 32887
Fr: 800-654-2452
URL: http://www.elsevier.com

Ruth Ballweg, Edward M. Sullivan, Darwin Brown and Daniel Vetrosky. Fourth edition, 2008. $99.95. 960 pages. The first and only comprehensive physician assistant text, this up-to-date edition covers all aspects of the physician assistant profession, the PA curriculum, and the PA's role in practice.

9777 ■ Physician Assistant's Business Practice and Legal Guide
Jones & Bartlett Publishers, Inc.
5 Wall St.
Burlington, MA 01803
Ph: (978)443-5000
Fax: (978)443-8000
Fr: 800-832-0034
E-mail: info@jblearning.com
URL: http://www.jblearning.com/catalog/9780763726744

Michele Roth-Kauffman. 2006. $128.95. 549 pages.

Medical resource for physician assistants, covering the role the physician assistant plays in patient care.

9778 ■ *Resumes for Health and Medical Careers*
The McGraw-Hill Companies
PO Box 182604
Columbus, OH 43272
Fax: (614)759-3749
Fr: 877-883-5524
E-mail: customer.service@mcgraw-hill.com
URL: http://www.mhprofessional.com/
    product.php?isbn=0071545352
Third edition, 2008. $12.95 (paper). 144 pages.

EMPLOYMENT AGENCIES AND SEARCH FIRMS

9779 ■ Advanced Care Providers
PO Box 972
Minocqua, WI 54548
Ph: (715)661-0030
Fax: (323)375-3290
URL: http://www.acpstaff.com

Specializes in the placement of physician assistants and nurse practitioners. Matches qualified providers with healthcare facilities in need of temporary or permanent staffing.

9780 ■ CompHealth
PO Box 713100
Salt Lake City, UT 84171-3100
Ph: (801)930-3000
Fax: (801)930-4517
Fr: 800-453-3030
E-mail: info@comphealth.com
URL: http://www.comphealth.com

Provides healthcare staffing and recruiting services covering certified registered nurse anesthetist, dosimetrist, imaging and radiation therapy, laboratory technology, medical physicist, nurse practitioner, nursing, pharmacy, physician, physician assistant, rehab therapy and respiratory therapy.

9781 ■ Davis-Smith, Inc.
27656 Franklin Rd.
Southfield, MI 48034
Ph: (248)354-4100
Fax: (248)354-6702
E-mail: info@davissmith.com
URL: http://www.davissmith.com

Healthcare staffing agency. Executive search firm.

9782 ■ Harris Brand Recruiting
4 Avis Dr., Ste. 1
Latham, NY 12110
Ph: (518)782-5250
Fr: 800-288-1730
E-mail: info@harrisbrand.com
URL: http://www.harrisbrand.com

Offers resource for physician jobs and practice opportunities for primary care and specialty doctors, physician assistants, nurse practitioners and certified nurse midwives.

9783 ■ MEDCareerNET
23072 Lake Center Dr., Ste. 210
Lake Forest, CA 92630
Ph: (949)380-4800
Fax: (949)380-7477
E-mail: vic@medcareernet.com
URL: http://www.medcareernet.com

Firm provides medical career professionals with a choice of career alternatives that extend their reach within their respective disciplines.

9784 ■ Professional Placement Associates, Inc.
287 Bowman Ave.
Purchase, NY 10577-2517
Ph: (914)251-1000

Fax: (914)251-1055
E-mail: careers@ppasearch.com
URL: http://www.ppasearch.com

Executive search firm specializing in the health and medical field.

9785 ■ Weatherby Locums
6451 N Federal Hwy., Ste. 800
Fort Lauderdale, FL 33308
Ph: (954)343-3050
Fax: (866)588-0085
Fr: (866)906-1637
E-mail: jobs@weatherbylocums.com
URL: http://www.weatherbylocums.com

Executive search firm for physicians. Branch office in Fairfax, VA.

9786 ■ Whitaker Medical
1200 Enclave Pkwy., Ste. 200
Houston, TX 77077
Ph: (281)870-1000
Fax: (866)513-0183
Fr: 800-444-5628
URL: http://www.whitakermedical.com

Exists as a healthcare recruitment firm that provides staffing solutions for healthcare professionals and facilities across the nation.

ONLINE JOB SOURCES AND SERVICES

9787 ■ American Academy of Physician Assistants Career Opportunities
2318 Mill Rd., Ste. 1300
Alexandria, VA 22314-1352
Ph: (703)836-2272
Fax: (703)684-1924
E-mail: aapa@aapa.org
URL: http://www.aapa.org/your_pa_career.aspx

Description: Online newsletter of the AAPA. Job opportunities may be searched by state or type. Members may also post position wanted on AAPA website.

9788 ■ DocCafe.com
URL: http://www.doccafe.com

Description: Provides physician employment opportunities and services. Offers physician hiring service and job listings.

9789 ■ EmployMED: Healthcare Job Listings
E-mail: customerservice@evalumed.com
URL: http://www.evalumed.com/EmployMed.aspx

Description: Lists practice opportunities throughout North America for all medical specialties. Contains job listings directory. Posting option is available for those who wish to advertise jobs. Fee: $25 per month per posting for minimum of two months.

9790 ■ ExploreHealthCareers.org
E-mail: feedback@explorehealthcareers.org
URL: http://explorehealthcareers.org/en/home

Description: Provides employment information in health professions. Includes links to health-related education/training programs, financial aid resources, specialized learning opportunities, and current issues in health care.

9791 ■ Health Care Recruitment Online
E-mail: info@healthcarerecruitment.com
URL: http://healthcarerecruitment.com

Description: Helps seekers find healthcare positions through on-line postings with national staffing companies and hospital partners. Main files include: Featured Employers, Job Search, Immediate Openings, Relocating, Career Management, State boards, and more.

9792 ■ HEALTHeCAREERS Network
Fr: 888-884-8242
E-mail: info@healthecareers.com
URL: http://www.healthecareers.com

Description: Career search site for jobs in all health care specialties; educational resources; visa and licensing information for relocation; interesting articles; relocation tools; links to professional organizations and general resources.

9793 ■ Hospital Jobs OnLine
E-mail: support@hospitaljobsonline.com
URL: http://www.hospitaljobsonline.com

Description: Serves as a niche healthcare job board designed exclusively for hospitals, healthcare companies, and healthcare job seekers.

9794 ■ Monster Healthcare
URL: http://healthcare.monster.com

Description: Delivers nationwide access to healthcare recruiting. Employers can post job listings or ads. Job seekers can post and code resumes, and search over 150,000 healthcare job listings, healthcare career advice columns, career resources information, and member employer profiles and services.

9795 ■ ProHealthJobs.com
Ph: (484)443-8545
Fax: (484)443-8549
E-mail: info@prohealthjobs.com
URL: http://prohealthjobs.com/jobboard

Description: Career resources site for the medical and health care field. Lists professional opportunities, product information, continuing education and open positions.

9796 ■ United Search Associates: Health Network USA
PO Box 342
Vinita, OK 74301
Ph: (918)323-4165
E-mail: jobs@hnusa.com
URL: http://homepage.mac.com/hnusa

Description: Visitors may explore healthcare positions, submit an electronic resume, or advertise with the site.

TRADESHOWS

9797 ■ American Academy of Physician Assistants Annual PA Conference
American Academy of Physician Assistants
2318 Mill Rd., Ste. 1300
Alexandria, VA 22314
Ph: (703)836-2272
Fax: (703)684-1924
URL: http://www.aapa.org

Primary Exhibits: Pharmaceuticals, medical equipment and supplies, medical books, and medical software. Dates and Locations: 2013 May 25-30; Washington, DC; 2014 May 24-29; Boston, MA; 2015 May 23-24; San Francisco, CA.

9798 ■ California Academy of Physician Assistants Convention
California Academy of Physician Assistants
3100 W. Warner Ave., Ste. 3
Santa Ana, CA 92704-5331
Ph: (714)427-0321
Fax: (714)427-0324
E-mail: capa@capanet.org
URL: http://www.capanet.org

Semiannual. Primary Exhibits: Medical equipment, supplies, and services, including pharmaceuticals and employment recruitment services. Dates and Locations: 2012 Oct 04-07; Palm Springs, CA; Renaissance Palm Springs Hotel.

OTHER SOURCES

9799 ■ American Academy of Physician Assistants (AAPA)
2318 Mill Rd., Ste. 1300
Alexandria, VA 22314-6868

Ph: (703)836-2272
Fax: (703)684-1924
E-mail: aapa@aapa.org
URL: http://www.aapa.org

Description: Physician assistants and other interested parties. Seeks to promote quality, cost-effective, and accessible healthcare, and the professional and personal development of PAs. Provides services for members. Organizes annual National PA Day. Develops research and education programs; compiles statistics.

9800 ■ American Association of Pathologists' Assistants (AAPA)

2345 Rice St., Ste. 220
St. Paul, MN 55113
Ph: (651)697-9264
Fax: (651)317-8048
Fr: 800-532-AAPA
E-mail: info@pathassist.org
URL: http://www.pathassist.org

Description: Pathologists' assistants and individuals qualified by academic and practical training to provide service in anatomic pathology under the direction of a qualified pathologist who is responsible for the performance of the assistant. Promotes the mutual association of trained pathologists' assistants and informs the public and the medical profession concerning the goals of this profession. Compiles statistics on salaries, geographic distribution, and duties of pathologists' assistants. Sponsors a continuing medical education program; offers a job hotline for members only.

9801 ■ American Association of Surgical Physician Assistants

PO Box 781688
Sebastian, FL 32978
Ph: (772)388-0498
Fax: (772)388-3457
Fr: 888-882-2772
E-mail: aaspa@aaspa.com
URL: http://www.aaspa.com

Description: Represents surgical physician assistants and students in accredited physician assistant programs. Promotes academic and clinical excellence among surgical physician assistants and addresses the needs of members. Creates an awareness of the role of surgical physician assistants in health care.

9802 ■ American Society of Anesthesia Technologists and Technicians

7044 S 13th St.
Oak Creek, WI 53154
Ph: (414)908-4942
Fax: (414)768-8001
E-mail: customercare@asatt.org
URL: http://www.asatt.org

Description: Consists of anesthesia technicians and technologists, medical technology students, and other individuals, organizations, and corporations with an interest in the field of anesthesiology. Provides professional development and continuing educational programs for anesthesiology technicians and technologists. Maintains certification programs and develops standards of ethics and practice among members.

9803 ■ Association of Operating Room Nurses

2170 S Parker Rd., Ste. 400
Denver, CO 80231
Ph: (303)755-6304
Fax: (303)750-3212
Fr: 800-755-2676
E-mail: custsvc@aorn.org
URL: http://www.aorn.org

Description: Represents registered professional nurses, individuals pursuing education leading to eligibility to sit for the registered nurse licensing exam, and registered professional nurses who are retired from the health care industry. Aims to promote safety and optimal outcomes for patients undergoing operative and other invasive procedures by providing practice support and professional development opportunities to perioperative nurses. Advocates for excellence in perioperative practice and healthcare.

9804 ■ Association of Physician Assistants in Cardiology (APAC)

401 W 15th St.
Austin, TX 78701
Fax: (703)684-1924
Fr: (866)970-2272
E-mail: jtpaphd@aol.com
URL: http://www.cardiologypa.org

Description: Represents physician assistants who practice in cardiology. Provides resources for cardiology physician assistants. Offers information on jobs in cardiology, cardiology physician assistants, scope of practice, compensation, and the results of the practice survey.

9805 ■ Association of Physician Assistants in Cardiovascular Surgery (APACVS)

PO Box 674867
Marietta, GA 30006
Fax: (770)509-0027
Fr: 877-221-5651
E-mail: admin@apacvs.org
URL: http://www.apacvs.org

Description: Represents physician assistants who work with cardiovascular surgeons. Assists in defining the role of physician assistants in the field of cardiovascular surgery through educational forums.

9806 ■ Association of Physician Assistants in Obstetrics and Gynecology (APAOG)

563 Carter Ct., Ste. B
Kimberly, WI 54136
Fax: (920)882-3655
Fr: 800-545-0636
E-mail: apaog@paobgyn.org
URL: http://www.paobgyn.org

Description: Comprised of physician assistants, students and other individuals dedicated to women's health. Aims to improve the health care of women by supporting physician/PA teams who provide care to female patients. Provides a network of communication and education on women's health.

9807 ■ Association of Plastic Surgery Physician Assistants (APSPA)

1050 Pittsford-Victor Rd., Bldg. B
Pittsford, NY 14534
Ph: (585)314-8921
E-mail: chrysapac@gmail.com
URL: http://www.apspa.net

Description: Promotes the profession of plastic surgery physician assistants. Seeks to enhance the skills of members. Creates an awareness in the medical community and the public about the role of plastic surgery physician assistants in health care.

9808 ■ Commission on Accreditation of Allied Health Education Programs (CAAHEP)

1361 Park St.
Clearwater, FL 33756
Ph: (727)210-2350
Fax: (727)210-2354
E-mail: megivern@caahep.org
URL: http://www.caahep.org

Description: Serves as a nationally recognized accrediting agency for allied health programs in 23 occupational areas.

9809 ■ Gastroenterology Physician Assistants (GIPA)

PO Box 82511
Tampa, FL 33682
Ph: (813)988-7795
Fax: (813)988-7796
E-mail: gipa@focus-ed.net
URL: http://www.gipas.org

Description: Provides professional support to Physician Assistants (PAs) practicing in the fields of Gastroenterology and Hepatology. Seeks to educate other health care professionals about the role of PAs in Gastroenterology and Hepatology. Promotes patient education to the public pertaining to diseases and social issues related to Gastroenterology and Hepatology. Provides a forum for discussion of issues affecting Gastrointestinal Physician Assistants.

9810 ■ Joint Council of Allergy, Asthma and Immunology (JCAAI)

50 N Brockway, Ste. 3-3
Palatine, IL 60067
Ph: (847)934-1918
Fax: (847)934-1820
E-mail: info@jcaai.org
URL: http://www.jcaai.org

Description: Physicians specializing in allergy or clinical immunology. Members must belong to the American Academy of Allergy and Immunology or the American College of Allergy and Immunology. Serves as political and socioeconomic advocate for these sponsoring organizations.

9811 ■ National Association of Physician Assistants (NAPA)

2375 E Tropicana Ave., Ste. 8, No. 213
Las Vegas, NV 89119-6563
Ph: (702)939-4788
Fr: 800-229-6172
E-mail: president@nationalassociationpa.com
URL: http://www.nationalassociationpa.com

Description: Promotes the physician assistant profession to the public, physicians, health care administrators and other healthcare personnel. Advances the profession through television, magazines and other means of communication. Conducts education and professional promotion through PR and marketing.

9812 ■ National Commission on Certification of Physician Assistants (NCCPA)

12000 Findley Rd., Ste. 100
Johns Creek, GA 30097
Ph: (678)417-8100
Fax: (678)417-8135
E-mail: nccpa@nccpa.net
URL: http://www.nccpa.net

Description: Certifies physician assistants at the entry level and for continued competence; has certified 22,750 physician assistants.

9813 ■ National Rural Health Association (NRHA)

Administrative Office
521 E 63rd St.
Kansas City, MO 64110-3329
Ph: (816)756-3140
Fax: (816)756-3144
E-mail: mail@nrharural.org
URL: http://www.ruralhealthweb.org

Description: Administrators, physicians, nurses, physician assistants, health planners, academicians, and others interested or involved in rural health care. Creates a better understanding of health care problems unique to rural areas; utilizes a collective approach in finding positive solutions; articulates and represents the health care needs of rural America; supplies current information to rural health care providers; serves as a liaison between rural health care programs throughout the country. Offers continuing education credits for medical, dental, nursing, and management courses.

9814 ■ Physician Assistant Education Association (PAEA)

300 N Washington St., Ste. 710
Alexandria, VA 22314-2544
Ph: (703)548-5538
Fax: (703)548-5539
E-mail: info@paeaonline.org
URL: http://www.paeaonline.org

Description: Represents physician assistant (PA)

educational programs in the United States. Assists PA educational programs-institutions with training programs for physician assistants to primary care and surgical physicians. Assists in the development and organization of educational curricula for PA programs to assure the public of competent PA's. Contributes to defining the roles of PA's in the field of medicine to maximize their benefit to the public; serves as a public information center on the profession; coordinates program logistics such as admissions and career placements; and is currently initiat-

ing a centralized application service for PA applicants. Sponsors the Annual Survey of Physician Assistant Educational Programs in the United States. Conducts and sponsors research projects; compiles statistics; offers ongoing training for PA leadership and faculty.

9815 ■ Visiting Nurse Associations of America (VNAA)
900 19th St. NW, Ste. 200
Washington, DC 20006
Ph: (202)384-1420

Fax: (202)384-1444
Fr: 888-866-8773
E-mail: vnaa@vnaa.org
URL: http://www.vnaa.org

Description: Home health care agencies. Develops competitive strength among community-based nonprofit visiting nurse organizations; works to strengthen business resources and economic programs through contracting, marketing, governmental affairs and publications.

Sources of Help-Wanted Ads

9816 ■ AARC Times
Daedalus Enterprises Inc.
11030 Ables Ln.
PO Box 29686
Dallas, TX 75229
Ph: (972)243-2272
Fax: (972)484-2720
URL: http://www.aarc.org/resources/

Monthly. $85.00/year for individuals. Professional magazine for respiratory therapists and other cardiopulmonary specialists.

9817 ■ ACP Internist
American College of Physicians
190 N Independence Mall W
Philadelphia, PA 19106-1572
Ph: (215)351-2400
Fr: 800-523-1546
URL: http://www.acpinternist.org

Free to members. Official membership tabloid of the American College of Physicians.

9818 ■ AJP Reports
Thieme Medical Publishers Inc.
333 7th Ave.
New York, NY 10001
Ph: (212)760-0888
Fax: (212)947-1112
Fr: 800-782-3488
URL: http://www.thieme.com/index.php?option=com_ content&view=arti

Peer-reviewed journal publishing information in the fields of neonatology, maternal and fetal medicine.

9819 ■ American Family Physician
American Academy of Family Physicians
11400 Tomahawk Creek Pky.
PO Box 11210
Leawood, KS 66211-2680
Ph: (913)906-6000
Fax: (913)906-6075
Fr: 800-274-2237
E-mail: afpedit@aafp.org
URL: http://www.aafp.org/online/en/home/ publications/journals/afp

Semimonthly. $101.00/year for individuals, healthcare professionals; $164.00/year for Canada, healthcare professionals; $227.00/year for other countries, healthcare professionals; $173.00/year for individuals, physicians and other individuals; $240.00/year for Canada, physicians and other individuals; $299.00/year for other countries, physicians and other individuals; $236.00/year for institutions; $299.00/year for institutions, Canada; $362.00/year for institutions, other countries. Peer-reviewed clinical journal for family physicians and others in primary care. Review articles detail the latest diagnostic and therapeutic techniques in the medical field. Department features in each issue include 'Tips from other

Journals,' CME credit opportunities and course calendar.

9820 ■ American Heart Journal
Mosby
1600 John F. Kennedy Blvd., Ste. 1800
Philadelphia, PA 19103-2899
Ph: (215)239-3275
Fax: (215)239-3286
URL: http://www.ahjonline.com/

Monthly. $298.00/year for individuals; $142.00/year for students; $395.00/year for other countries; $188.00/year for students, other countries. Medical journal serving practicing cardiologists, university-affiliated clinicians, and physicians keeping abreast of developments in the diagnosis and management of cardiovascular disease.

9821 ■ The American Journal of Cardiology
Excerpta Medica Inc.
685 US-202
Bridgewater, NJ 08807
Ph: (908)547-2100
Fax: (908)547-2200
URL: http://www.ajconline.org/

Semimonthly. $162.00/year for U.S. and Canada; $414.00/year for other countries; $88.00/year for students; $94.00/year for students, other countries. Peer-reviewed journal publishing information on cardiovascular disease.

9822 ■ American Journal of Clinical Nutrition
American Society for Nutrition
9650 Rockville Pike
Bethesda, MD 20814
Ph: (301)634-7050
Fax: (301)634-7892
E-mail: ajcn@nutrition.org
URL: http://www.nutrition.org/publications/the-american-journal-o

Monthly. $555.00/year for institutions, print and online U.S.; $515.00/year for institutions, online U.S.; $215.00/year for individuals, print and online U.S.; $180.00/year for individuals, online U.S.; $585.00/year for institutions, Canada and Mexico, print and online; $515.00/year for institutions, Canada and Mexico, online only; $610.00/year for other countries, print and online; $515.00/year for other countries, online only. Peer-reviewed journal publishing basic and clinical studies relevant to human nutrition.

9823 ■ American Journal of Emergency Medicine
Mosby Inc.
11830 Westline Industrial Dr.
St. Louis, MO 63146-3326
Ph: (314)872-8370
Fax: (314)432-1380
Fr: 800-325-4177
URL: http://www.elsevier.com/wps/find/ journaldescription.cws_home

$340.00/year for individuals; $529.00/year for institu-

tions; $159.00/year for students; $523.00/year for other countries; $711.00/year for institutions, other countries; $261.00/year for students, other countries. Journal reporting on emergency medicine.

9824 ■ American Journal of Epidemiology
Oxford University Press
2001 Evans Rd.
Cary, NC 27513-2009
Ph: (919)677-0977
Fax: (919)677-1714
Fr: 800-852-7323
URL: http://aje.oupjournals.org

Semimonthly. $508.00/year for institutions, print & online; $762.00/year for institutions, print & online; $762.00/year for institutions, print & online; $237.00/year for individuals, online; $355.00/year for individuals, online; $355.00/year for individuals, online; $483.00/year for institutions, print; $724.00/year for institutions, print; $724.00/year for institutions, print. Science research and medical journal.

9825 ■ American Journal of Medical Genetics
John Wiley & Sons Inc.
111 River St.
Hoboken, NJ 07030-5773
Ph: (201)748-6000
Fax: (201)748-6088
Fr: 800-825-7550
URL: http://onlinelibrary.wiley.com/journal/10.1002/ (ISSN)1552-48

Monthly. $130.00/year for individuals, print; $130.00/year for Canada, in Canada, add 5% GST, print; $1,137.00/year for other countries, print; $14,339.00/year for institutions, print; $14,843.00/year for institutions, Canada, print, in Canada add 5% GST; $15,095.00/year for institutions, other countries, print. Medical research journal.

9826 ■ American Journal of Medicine
Excerpta Medica Inc.
685 US-202
Bridgewater, NJ 08807
Ph: (908)547-2100
Fax: (908)547-2200
URL: http://www.amjmed.com/

Monthly. $373.00/year for other countries; $145.00/year for U.S. and Canada; $80.00/year for students, other countries; $84.00/year for students. Medical journal.

9827 ■ American Journal of Obstetrics and Gynecology
Mosby Inc.
11830 Westline Industrial Dr.
St. Louis, MO 63146-3326
Ph: (314)872-8370
Fax: (314)432-1380
Fr: 800-325-4177
E-mail: usjcs@elsevier.com
URL: http://www.ajog.org

Monthly. $296.00/year for individuals; $744.00/year for institutions; $150.00/year for students; $393.00/year for other countries; $850.00/year for institutions, other countries; $196.00/year for other countries, student; $187.00/year for Canada and Mexico, student. Journal for specialists in obstetrics and gynecology and for general practitioners. Official Journal of the American Gynecological and Obstetrical Society, American Board of Obstetrics and Gynecology, Society of Gynecologic Surgeons, and Society of Maternal-Fetal Medicine.

9828 ■ The American Journal of Orthopedics
Quadrant Healthcom
7 Century Dr., Ste. 302
Parsippany, NJ 07054-4603
Ph: (973)206-3434
Fax: (973)206-9378
URL: http://www.quadranthealth.com

Monthly. $128.00/year for individuals; $184.00/year for institutions; $165.00/year for Canada and Mexico; $185.00/year for other countries; $266.00/year for individuals. Medical journal.

9829 ■ The American Journal of Pathology
The American Journal of Pathology
9650 Rockville Pike, Ste. E133
Bethesda, MD 20814-3993
Ph: (301)634-7130
Fax: (301)634-7990
E-mail: asip@asip.org
URL: http://ajp.amjpathol.org

Monthly. $195.00/year for members, U.S.; $270.00/year for members, Canada & Mexico; $290.00/year for members, elsewhere; $320.00/year for nonmembers, U.S.; $425.00/year for nonmembers, Canada & Mexico; $425.00/year for nonmembers, elsewhere; $685.00/year for institutions, U.S.; $775.00/year for institutions, Canada & Mexico; $800.00/year for institutions, elsewhere. Journal publishing original experimental and clinical studies in diagnostic and experimental pathology.

9830 ■ American Journal of Psychiatry
American Psychiatric Publishing Inc.
1000 Wilson Blvd., Ste. 1825
Arlington, VA 22209-3924
Ph: (703)907-7322
Fax: (703)907-1091
Fr: 800-368-5777
E-mail: ajp@psych.org
URL: http://www.appi.org/SearchCenter/Pages/
   Journal.aspx?ItemId=A

Monthly. $244.00/year for nonmembers, print + online; $244.00/year for members, print + online, international; $368.00/year for nonmembers, print + online, international; $440.00/year for nonmembers, 2 years, print + online; $440.00/year for members, 2 years, print + online, international; $662.00/year for nonmembers, 2 years, print + online, international. Psychiatry journal.

9831 ■ American Journal of Respiratory Cell and Molecular Biology
American Thoracic Society
25 Broadway
New York, NY 10006-2755
Ph: (212)315-8600
Fax: (212)315-6498
E-mail: atsinfo@thoracic.org
URL: http://www.thoracic.org

Monthly. Contains original and basic research in the area of pulmonary biology including cellular, biochemical, molecular, development, genetic, and immunologic studies of lung cells and molecules. Displays professional recruitment and announcement advertising.

9832 ■ American Journal of Respiratory and Critical Care Medicine
American Thoracic Society
25 Broadway
New York, NY 10006-2755
Ph: (212)315-8600

Fax: (212)315-6498
E-mail: atsinfo@thoracic.org
URL: http://www.thoracic.org

Focuses on human biology and disease as well as animal studies that contribute to the understanding of pathophysiology and treatment of diseases that affect the respiratory system and critically ill patients. Displays professional recruitment and announcement advertising.

9833 ■ The American Journal of Sports Medicine
The American Orthopaedic Society for Sports Medicine
6300 N River Rd., Ste. 500
Rosemont, IL 60018
Ph: (847)292-4900
Fax: (847)292-4905
URL: http://ajs.sagepub.com/

$521.00/year for institutions, print & e-access; $117.00/year for individuals, print & e-access; $47.00/year for institutions, single print issue; $13.00/year for single issue, print. Medical journal.

9834 ■ American Journal of Surgery
Excerpta Medica Inc.
685 US-202
Bridgewater, NJ 08807
Ph: (908)547-2100
Fax: (908)547-2200
URL: http://americanjournalofsurgery.com/

Monthly. $247.00/year for individuals; $99.00/year for students; $247.00/year for Canada; $481.00/year for other countries; $105.00/year for students, other countries. Surgical journal.

9835 ■ The American Journal of Surgical Pathology (AJSP)
Lippincott Williams & Wilkins
351 W Camden St.
Baltimore, MD 21201
Ph: (410)528-4000
Fr: 800-638-3030
URL: http://journals.lww.com/ajsp/pages/default.aspx

Monthly. $599.00/year for individuals; $1,484.00/year for institutions; $302.00/year for individuals, in-training; $770.00/year for other countries; $1,714.00/year for institutions, other countries; $329.10/year for other countries, in-training. Peer-reviewed medical journal covering issues concerning diagnostic problems.

9836 ■ Anesthesia & Analgesia
Lippincott Williams & Wilkins
530 Walnut St.
Philadelphia, PA 19106-3619
Ph: (215)521-8300
Fax: (215)521-8902
Fr: 800-638-3030
URL: http://www.anesthesia-analgesia.org/

Monthly. $600.00/year for individuals; $897.00/year for institutions; $291.00/year for U.S., In-training; $1,091.00/year for institutions, other countries; $803.00/year for other countries; $482.00/year for other countries, In-training. Medical journal.

9837 ■ Anesthesiology
Lippincott Williams & Wilkins
530 Walnut St.
Philadelphia, PA 19106-3619
Ph: (215)521-8300
Fax: (215)521-8902
Fr: 800-638-3030
URL: http://journals.lww.com/anesthesiology/pages/
   default.aspx

Monthly. $655.00/year for individuals; $1,086.00/year for institutions; $725.00/year for other countries; $1,281.00/year for institutions, other countries; $256.00/year for individuals, in-training; $306.60/year for other countries, in-training. Medical journal publishing original manuscripts and brief abstracts from current literature on anesthesiology.

9838 ■ Annals of Emergency Medicine
Mosby Inc.
11830 Westline Industrial Dr.
St. Louis, MO 63146-3326
Ph: (314)872-8370
Fax: (314)432-1380
Fr: 800-325-4177
E-mail: eic@acep.org
URL: http://www.annemergmed.com

Monthly. $240.00/year for individuals; $456.00/year for institutions; $119.00/year for students; $335.00/year for other countries; $556.00/year for institutions, other countries; $207.00/year for students, other countries. Peer-reviewed journal publishing the highest quality science for emergency medicine and related medical specialties.

9839 ■ Annals of Medicine
Informa Healthcare
52 Vanderbilt Ave., 7th Fl.
New York, NY 10017-3846
Ph: (212)520-2777
URL: http://informahealthcare.com/ann

$595.00/year for institutions; $980.00/year for institutions; $780.00/year for institutions. Journal covering health science and medical education.

9840 ■ Annals of Neurology
John Wiley & Sons Inc.
111 River St.
Hoboken, NJ 07030-5773
Ph: (201)748-6000
Fax: (201)748-6088
Fr: 800-825-7550
URL: http://onlinelibrary.wiley.com/journal/10.1002/
   (ISSN)1531-82

Monthly. $852.00/year for institutions, print; $1,020.00/year for institutions, Canada and Mexico, print; $1,104.00/year for institutions, other countries, print; $1,148.00/year for institutions, Canada and Mexico, print and online; $1,232.00/year for institutions, other countries, print and online; $980.00/year for institutions, print and online. Articles of scientific and clinical merit for neurologists.

9841 ■ Annals of Plastic Surgery
Lippincott Williams & Wilkins
530 Walnut St.
Philadelphia, PA 19106-3619
Ph: (215)521-8300
Fax: (215)521-8902
Fr: 800-638-3030
URL: http://www.lww.com/product/?0148-7043

Monthly. $547.00/year for individuals; $1,007.00/year for institutions; $275.00/year for individuals, in-training; $739.00/year for other countries; $1,296.00/year for institutions, other countries; $299.20/year for other countries, in-training. Medical journal for the plastic surgeon.

9842 ■ Annals of Surgery
Lippincott Williams & Wilkins
530 Walnut St.
Philadelphia, PA 19106-3619
Ph: (215)521-8300
Fax: (215)521-8902
Fr: 800-638-3030
URL: http://journals.lww.com/annalsofsurgery/pages/
   default.aspx

Monthly. $326.00/year for individuals; $929.00/year for institutions; $133.00/year for individuals, in-training; $539.50/year for individuals, international; $1,244.50/year for institutions, other countries; $160.50/year for other countries, in-training. Medical journal publishing original manuscripts promoting the advancement of surgical knowledge and practice.

9843 ■ Applied Radiology
Anderson Publishing Ltd.
180 Glenside Ave.
Scotch Plains, NJ 07076
Ph: (908)301-1995
Fax: (908)301-1997
URL: http://www.appliedradiology.com

Monthly. $115.00/year for individuals; $210.00/year for two years; $215.00/year for other countries. Magazine for radiologists, chief radiologic technologists, radiology department administrators and key managers in HMOs. Presents articles written by radiologic professionals on all aspects of general diagnostic radiology, the diagnostic radiologic subspecialties, radiation therapy and the socioeconomics of imaging.

9844 ■ *Archives of Dermatology*
American Medical Association
515 N State St.
Chicago, IL 60654
Fr: 800-621-8335
URL: http://archderm.ama-assn.org

Monthly. $145.00/year for members, print and online; $540.00/year for institutions, print and online. Peer-reviewed educational/clinical journal for dermatologists.

9845 ■ *Archives of General Psychiatry*
American Medical Association
515 N State St.
Chicago, IL 60610
Fr: 800-621-8335
E-mail: archgenpsychiatry@jama-archives.org
URL: http://archpsyc.ama-assn.org/

Monthly. $745.00/year for institutions, print and online; $135.00/year for members, print and online; $199.00/year for nonmembers, print and online. Educational/clinical journal for psychiatrists.

9846 ■ *Archives of Neurology*
American Medical Association
515 N State St.
Chicago, IL 60654
Fr: 800-621-8335
E-mail: archneurol@mednet.swmed.edu
URL: http://archneur.ama-assn.org

Monthly. $150.00/year for individuals, print and online; $535.00/year for institutions, print and online. Peer-reviewed educational/clinical journal for neurologists.

9847 ■ *Archives of Surgery*
American Medical Association
515 N State St.
Chicago, IL 60654
Fr: 800-621-8335
E-mail: archsurg@jama-archives.org
URL: http://archsurg.ama-assn.org/

Monthly. $125.00/year for members, print and online; $485.00/year for institutions, print and online. Peer-reviewed educational/clinical journal for general surgeons and surgical specialists.

9848 ■ *Brain Connectivity*
Mary Ann Liebert Inc., Publishers
140 Huguenot St., 3rd Fl.
New Rochelle, NY 10801-5215
Ph: (914)740-2100
Fax: (914)740-2101
Fr: 800-654-3237
URL: http://www.liebertpub.com/products/
    product.aspx?pid=389

Bimonthly. Peer-reviewed journal publishing research on neurological disorders.

9849 ■ *Cardiac Cath Lab Director*
Sage Publications Inc.
2455 Teller Rd.
Thousand Oaks, CA 91320-2218
Ph: (805)499-9774
Fax: (805)583-2665
Fr: 800-818-7243
URL: http://www.sagepub.com/
    journalsProdDesc.nav?prodId=Journal20

Bimonthly. $315.00/year for institutions, print and e-access; $284.00/year for institutions, e-access. Peer-reviewed journal publishing research on cardiac catheterization procedures.

9850 ■ *Chinese American Medical Society Newsletter*
Chinese American Medical Society
41 Elizabeth St., Ste. 403
New York, NY 10013
Ph: (212)334-4760
Fax: (212)965-1876
E-mail: jseto@camsociety.org
URL: http://www.camsociety.org

Description: Two issues/year. Publishes Society news. Recurring features include recent activities of the Society, upcoming scientific meetings, excerpts of presentations at the scientific meeting, new members, job listings and a calendar of events.

9851 ■ *Clinical Cardiology*
Wiley InterScience
111 River St.
Hoboken, NJ 07030-5774
Ph: (201)748-6000
Fax: (201)748-6088
E-mail: clinicalcardiology@fams.org
URL: http://onlinelibrary.wiley.com/journal/10.1002/
    (ISSN)1932-87

Monthly. $128.00/year for individuals; $128.00/year for Canada and Mexico; $128.00/year for other countries. Peer-reviewed indexed medical journal.

9852 ■ *Clinical Medicine & Research*
Marshfield Clinic
1000 N Oak Ave.
Marshfield, WI 54449
Ph: (715)387-5511
Fax: (715)389-3808
Fr: 800-782-8581
E-mail: clinmedres@mcrf.mfldclin.edu
URL: http://www.clinmedres.org

Quarterly. Free within the U.S. Peer-reviewed journal that publishes scientific medical research that is relevant to a broad audience of medical researchers and healthcare professionals.

9853 ■ *Clinical Pediatrics*
Sage Publications Inc.
2455 Teller Rd.
Thousand Oaks, CA 91320-2218
Ph: (805)499-9774
Fax: (805)583-2665
Fr: 800-818-7243
URL: http://www.sagepub.com/
    journalsProdDesc.nav?prodId=Journal20

Monthly. $943.00/year for institutions, print and e-access; $849.00/year for institutions, e-access; $943.00/year for institutions, all online content; $613.00/year for U.S., hospital, print and e-access; $325.00/year for individuals, print and e-access; $85.00/year for institutions, single print; $35.00/year for individuals, single print. Professional journal for pediatric practitioners.

9854 ■ *Clinical Psychiatry News*
International Medical News Group
60 Columbia Rd., Bldg. B
Morristown, NJ 07960
Ph: (973)290-8200
Fax: (973)290-8250
E-mail: cpnews@elsevier.com
URL: http://journals.elsevierhealth.com/periodicals/
    cpnews

Monthly. $109.00/year for individuals; $173.00/year for other countries. Medical and psychiatry tabloid.

9855 ■ *CME Supplement to Emergency Medicine Clinics of North America*
Elsevier Science Inc.
360 Park Ave. S
New York, NY 10010-1710
Ph: (212)989-5800
Fax: (212)633-3990
Fr: 888-437-4636
URL: http://www.elsevier.com/wps/find/
    journaldescription.cws_home

$209.00/year for individuals. Journal covering emergency medicine clinics.

9856 ■ *Contemporary OB/GYN*
Advanstar Communications Inc.
641 Lexington Ave., 8th Fl.
New York, NY 10022
Ph: (212)951-6600
Fax: (212)951-6793
Fr: 800-346-0085
URL: http://www.modernmedicine.com/
    modernmedicine/Obstetrics/Gyne

Monthly. $109.20/year for individuals, U.S.; $139.65/year for individuals, Canada and foreign; $10.50/year for individuals, single copy U.S.; $15.75/year for individuals, Canada and foreign. Magazine covering clinical, investigative, and socioeconomic aspects of obstetrics and gynecology for specialists.

9857 ■ *Contemporary Pediatrics*
Advanstar Communications Inc.
641 Lexington Ave., 8th Fl.
New York, NY 10022
Ph: (212)951-6600
Fax: (212)951-6793
Fr: 800-346-0085
URL: http://www.modernmedicine.com/
    modernmedicine/Pediatrics/home

Monthly. $89.00/year for individuals; $105.00/year for Canada and Mexico; $105.00/year for other countries. Peer-reviewed journal to help pediatricians diagnose, treat, and prevent illness in infants, children, adolescents, and young adults.

9858 ■ *Contemporary Urology*
Advanstar Communications Inc.
641 Lexington Ave., 8th Fl.
New York, NY 10022
Ph: (212)951-6600
Fax: (212)951-6793
Fr: 800-346-0085
URL: http://www.contemporaryurology.com/conturo

Monthly. Clinical magazine for urologists.

9859 ■ *Critical Care Medicine*
Society of Critical Care Medicine
500 Midway Dr.
Mount Prospect, IL 60056-9969
Ph: (847)827-6869
Fax: (847)827-6886
URL: http://journals.lww.com/ccmjournal/pages/
    default.aspx

Monthly. $402.00/year for individuals; $711.00/year for institutions; $538.00/year for other countries; $848.00/year for institutions, other countries; $380.00/year for other countries, in-training; $258.00/year for individuals, in-training. Interdisciplinary journal for ICU and CCU specialists.

9860 ■ *Diagnostic Imaging*
United business Media L.L.C
240 W 35th St.
New York, NY 10001
Ph: (516)562-5000
URL: http://www.diagnosticimaging.com/

Monthly. News and analysis on clinical and economic developments in medical imaging.

9861 ■ *Dialysis & Transplantation*
John Wiley & Sons Inc.
111 River St.
Hoboken, NJ 07030-5773
Ph: (201)748-6000
Fax: (201)748-6088
Fr: 800-825-7550
URL: http://onlinelibrary.wiley.com/journal/10.1002/
    (ISSN)1932-69

Monthly. $128.00/year for U.S. and other countries, institution; print only; $65.00/year for institutions, print only; $82.00/year for institutions, print only. Multidisciplinary, peer-reviewed journal on clinical applications in dialysis, transplantation and nephrology for renal-care team.

9862 ■ *Discovery Medicine*
Discovery Medicine
10 Gerard Ave., Ste. 201
Timonium, MD 21093
Ph: (410)773-9938
Fax: 888-833-0526
URL: http://www.discoverymedicine.com

Bimonthly. $599.00/year for institutions, digital edition; $99.95/year for individuals, digital edition. Online journal that publishes articles on diseases, biology, new diagnostics, and treatments for medical professionals.

9863 ■ *Diseases of the Colon and Rectum*
Lippincott Williams & Wilkins
530 Walnut St.
Philadelphia, PA 19106-3619
Ph: (215)521-8300
Fax: (215)521-8902
Fr: 800-638-3030
URL: http://www.fascrs.org/dcr/

Monthly. $477.00/year for individuals; $861.00/year for institutions; $570.50/year for other countries; $1,095.50/year for institutions, other countries. Medical journal.

9864 ■ *The DO*
American Osteopathic Association
142 E Ontario St.
Chicago, IL 60611
Ph: (312)202-8000
Fax: (312)202-8200
Fr: 800-621-1773
URL: http://www.do-online.org/TheDO/

Monthly. $100.00/year for individuals; $170.00/year for other countries; $15.00/year for single issue. Osteopathic medical magazine.

9865 ■ *Ear, Nose & Throat Journal*
Vendome Group L.L.C.
6 E 32nd St.
New York, NY 10016
Ph: (212)812-8420
E-mail: entjournal@phillyent.com
URL: http://www.entjournal.com

Monthly. $220.00/year for individuals, print; $255.00/year for other countries, print; $400.00/year for two years, print; $470.00/year for other countries, 2 years. Journal on otorhinolaryugology, head and neck surgery, and allergies.

9866 ■ *Education & Treatment of Children*
West Virginia University Press
139 Stansbury Hall
PO Box 6295
Morgantown, WV 26506
Ph: (304)293-8400
Fax: (304)293-6585
URL: http://www.educationandtreatmentofchildren.net

Quarterly. $85.00/year for institutions; $45.00/year for individuals; $100.00/year for institutions, elsewhere; $60.00/year for individuals, elsewhere. Periodical featuring information concerning the development of services for children and youth. Includes reports written for educators and other child care and mental health providers focused on teaching, training, and treatment effectiveness.

9867 ■ *Emergency Medical Services*
Cygnus Business Media
1233 Janesville Ave.
Fort Atkinson, WI 53538
Ph: (920)563-6388
Fax: (920)563-1702
Fr: 800-547-7377
URL: http://www.emsworld.com

Monthly. Magazine covering emergency care, rescue and transportation.

9868 ■ *Endocrine News*
Endocrine Society
8401 Connecticut Ave., Ste. 900
Chevy Chase, MD 20815

Ph: (301)941-0200
Fax: (301)941-0259
Fr: 888-363-6274
E-mail: societyservices@endo-society.org
URL: http://www.endo-society.org

Monthly. $125.00/year for institutions; 60.00/year for individuals. Covers the discipline of endocrinology. Provides practicing endocrinologists with the latest information about new drugs and therapies to improve patient health and quality of life.

9869 ■ *Endocrine Practice*
American Association of Clinical Endocrinologists
245 Riverside Ave., Ste. 200
Jacksonville, FL 32202
Ph: (904)353-7878
Fax: (904)353-8185
Fr: 800-838-2223
E-mail: segan@aace.com
URL: http://www.aace.com

Nine times a year. $300 for domestic non-member; $625 for domestic institution. Enhances the health care of patients with endocrine diseases through continuing education of practicing endocrinologist. Contains classified and recruitment advertising.

9870 ■ *Epigenetics*
Landes Bioscience
1806 Rio Grande St.
Austin, TX 78701
Ph: (512)637-6050
Fax: (512)637-6079
URL: http://www.landesbioscience.com/journals/
 epigenetics/

$129.00/year for individuals, online; $350.00/year for individuals, print and online; $450.00/year for other countries, print and online; $1,500.00/year for institutions, online; $1,850.00/year for institutions, print and online; $1,950.00/year for institutions, other countries, print and online. Journal devoted to practicing physicians, residents and students.

9871 ■ *Ethics in Biology, Engineering and Medicine*
Begell House Inc.
50 Cross Hwy.
Redding, CT 06896
Ph: (203)938-1300
Fax: (203)938-1304
URL: http://www.begellhouse.com/journals/
 6ed509641f7324e6

$650.00/year for institutions. Peer-reviewed journal covering ethical issues on biomedical research and the development of new biomaterials, implants, devices and treatments.

9872 ■ *Family Practice Management*
American Academy of Family Physicians
11400 Tomahawk Creek Pky.
PO Box 11210
Leawood, KS 66211-2680
Ph: (913)906-6000
Fax: (913)906-6075
Fr: 800-274-2237
E-mail: fpmedit@aafp.org
URL: http://www.aafp.org/fpm

Bimonthly. $93.00/year for institutions; $107.00/year for institutions, Canada; $118.00/year for institutions, other countries; $68.00/year for U.S., physicians and other individuals; $81.00/year for Canada, physicians and other individuals; $93.00/year for other countries, physicians and other individuals; $50.00/year for U.S., health care professionals; $63.00/year for Canada, health care professionals; $76.00/year for other countries, health care professionals. Magazine covering socio-economic and management topics concerning family physicians.

9873 ■ *Family Practice News*
International Medical News Group
60 Columbia Rd., Bldg. B
Morristown, NJ 07960
Ph: (973)290-8200

Fax: (973)290-8250
E-mail: fpnews@elsevier.com
URL: http://www.efamilypracticenews.com

$139.00/year for individuals; $278.00/year for other countries. Family physician medical tabloid.

9874 ■ *The Federal Physician*
Federal Physicians Association
12427 Hedges Run Dr., Ste. 104
Lake Ridge, VA 22192
Fax: (703)426-8400
Fr: 800-528-3492
E-mail: info@fedphy.com
URL: http://www.fedphy.org

Description: Bimonthly. Covers issues affecting physicians in the federal government. Recurring features include news of research, reports of meetings, and job listings.

9875 ■ *Fertility and Sterility*
The American Society for Reproductive Medicine
1209 Montgomery Hwy.
Birmingham, AL 35216-2809
Ph: (205)978-5000
Fax: (205)978-5005
URL: http://www.asrm.org/FertilityAndSterility/

Monthly. Included in membership. Medical journal covering all aspects of reproductive medicine.

9876 ■ *Forensic Science, Medicine and Pathology*
Humana Press Inc.
233 Spring St.
New York, NY 10013-1578
Ph: (973)256-1699
Fax: (973)256-8341
Fr: 800-777-4643
URL: http://www.springer.com/humana+press/
 pathology+%26+laborator

$541.00/year for institutions, print and electronic; $649.00/year for institutions, print and enchanced access. Journal focusing on forensic science, medicine, and pathology.

9877 ■ *Forum on Immunopathological Diseases and Therapeutics*
Begell House Inc.
50 Cross Hwy.
Redding, CT 06896
Ph: (203)938-1300
Fax: (203)938-1304
URL: http://www.begellhouse.com/journals/
 1a654bf03faf67ac.html

$748.00/year for institutions. Journal publishing articles on immunopathological diseases and therapeutics.

9878 ■ *Genes and Nutrition*
New Century Health Publishers L.L.C.
PO Box 175
Coppell, TX 75019
Fax: (940)565-8148
URL: http://www.newcenturyhealthpublishers.com/
 genes_and_nutritio

Quarterly. $428.00/year for institutions; $228.00/year for individuals. International, interdisciplinary peer reviewed scientific journal for critical evaluation of research on the relationship between genetics & nutrition with the goal of improving human health.

9879 ■ *Global Change, Peace & Security*
Routledge
711 3 Ave., 8 Fl.
New York, NY 10016
Ph: (212)216-7800
Fax: (212)563-2269
Fr: 800-634-7064
URL: http://www.tandfonline.com/toc/cpar20/current

$160.00/year for individuals, print; $602.00/year for individuals, online only; $669.00/year for individuals, print & online. Journal promoting physical therapy and integration.

9880 ■ Head & Neck Surgery
John Wiley & Sons Inc.
111 River St.
Hoboken, NJ 07030-5773
Ph: (201)748-6000
Fax: (201)748-6088
Fr: 800-825-7550
URL: http://onlinelibrary.wiley.com/journal/10.1002/
   (ISSN)1097-03

Monthly. $1,950.00/year for institutions, print only;
$2,118.00/year for institutions, Canada and Mexico,
print only; $2,202.00/year for institutions, other
countries, print only; $276.00/year for individuals,
print; $2,495.00/year for institutions, other countries,
print with online; $2,243.00/year for institutions, print
with online; $2,411.00/year for institutions, Canada
and Mexico, print with online. International, multidisciplinary publication of original contributions concerning diagnosis and surgical management of diseases
of the head and neck. Publishes articles of interest to
several medical and surgical specialists including
general surgeons, neurosurgeons, otolaryngologists,
and plastic surgeons.

9881 ■ Heart and Lung
Mosby
1600 John F. Kennedy Blvd., Ste. 1800
Philadelphia, PA 19103-2899
Ph: (215)239-3275
Fax: (215)239-3286
URL: http://www.elsevier.com/wps/find/
   journaldescription.cws_home

Bimonthly. $103.00/year for individuals; $445.00/year
for institutions; $524.00/year for institutions, other
countries; $153.00/year for other countries. Journal
offering articles prepared by nurse and physician
members of the critical care team, recognizing the
nurse's role in the care and management of major
organ-system conditions in critically ill patients.

9882 ■ Hematology
American Society of Hematology
2021 L St. NW, Ste. 900
Washington, DC 20036
Ph: (202)776-0544
Fax: (202)776-0545
URL: http://asheducationbook.hematologylibrary.org

Annual. $75.00/year for members; $125.00/year for
nonmembers. Journal providing continuing medical
education for physicians.

9883 ■ Hospitals & Health Networks
Health Forum L.L.C.
155 N Wacker Dr., Ste. 400
Chicago, IL 60606
Ph: (312)893-6800
Fax: (312)422-4500
Fr: 800-821-2039
URL: http://www.hhnmag.com

Weekly. Free. Publication covering the health care
industry.

9884 ■ The IHS Primary Care Provider
Indian Health Service
The Reyes Bldg.
801 Thompson Ave., Ste. 400
Rockville, MD 20852-1627
Ph: (301)443-1011
URL: http://www.ihs.gov/provider

Monthly. Journal for health care professionals, physicians, nurses, pharmacists, dentists, and dietitians.

9885 ■ Infectious Disease News
SLACK Incorporated
6900 Grove Rd.
Thorofare, NJ 08086-9447
Ph: (856)848-1000
Fax: (856)848-6091
E-mail: idn@slackinc.com
URL: http://infectiousdiseasenews.com

Monthly. $299.00/year for individuals; $598.00/year
for individuals, two years; $897.00/year for individu-
als, three years; $479.00/year for institutions;

$958.00/year for institutions, two years; $1,437.00/
year for institutions, three years; $149.00/year for
individuals, resident; $39.00/year for single issue;
$65.00/year for other countries. Newspaper for infec-
tious disease specialists.

9886 ■ Infectious Diseases in Children
SLACK Incorporated
6900 Grove Rd.
Thorofare, NJ 08086-9447
Ph: (856)848-1000
Fax: (856)848-6091
E-mail: idc@slackinc.com
URL: http://www.idinchildren.com

Monthly. $299.00/year for individuals; $598.00/year
for individuals, two years; $897.00/year for individu-
als, three years; $479.00/year for institutions;
$958.00/year for institutions, two years; $1,437.00/
year for institutions, three years; $149.00/year for
individuals, resident; $39.00/year for single issue;
$65.00/year for other countries. Newspapers for
physician.

9887 ■ Injury
Mosby Inc.
11830 Westline Industrial Dr.
St. Louis, MO 63146-3326
Ph: (314)872-8370
Fax: (314)432-1380
Fr: 800-325-4177
URL: http://www.elsevier.com/wps/find/
   journaldescription.cws_home

Monthly. $200.00/year for individuals, European
countries and Iran; $224.00/year for individuals, all
countries except Europe, Japan and Iran; $26,500.00/
year for individuals; $1,381.00/year for institutions,
European countries and Iran; $1,543.00/year for
institutions, all Countries except Europe, Japan and
Iran; $183,200.00/year for institutions. Journal
publishing articles and research related to the treatment of injuries such as trauma systems and management; surgical procedures; epidemiological studies;
surgery (of all tissues); resuscitation; biomechanics;
rehabilitation; anaesthesia; radiology and wound
management.

9888 ■ ISRN Cardiology
Hindawi Publishing Corporation
410 Park Ave., 15th Fl.
287 PMB
New York, NY 10022
E-mail: cardiology@isrn.com
URL: http://www.isrn.com/journals/cardiology

Peer-reviewed journal publishing research and studies in all areas of cardiology.

9889 ■ ISRN Dermatology
Hindawi Publishing Corporation
410 Park Ave., 15th Fl.
287 PMB
New York, NY 10022
E-mail: dermatology@isrn.com
URL: http://www.isrn.com/journals/dermatology

Peer-reviewed and open access journal publishing
original research articles, review articles, and clinical
studies in all areas of dermatology.

9890 ■ ISRN Endocrinology
Hindawi Publishing Corporation
410 Park Ave., 15th Fl.
287 PMB
New York, NY 10022
E-mail: endocrinology@isrn.com
URL: http://www.isrn.com/journals/endocrinology

Peer-reviewed, open access journal publishing
original research articles, review articles, case
reports, and clinical studies in all areas of
endocrinology.

9891 ■ ISRN Hematology
Hindawi Publishing Corporation
410 Park Ave., 15th Fl.
287 PMB
New York, NY 10022
E-mail: hematology@isrn.com
URL: http://www.isrn.com/journals/hematology

Peer-reviewed journal covering research in all areas
of hematology.

9892 ■ ISRN Neurology
Hindawi Publishing Corporation
410 Park Ave., 15th Fl.
287 PMB
New York, NY 10022
E-mail: neurology@isrn.com
URL: http://www.isrn.com/journals/neurology

Peer-reviewed journal publishing research in all areas
of neurology.

9893 ■ ISRN Obstetrics and Gynecology
Hindawi Publishing Corporation
410 Park Ave., 15th Fl.
287 PMB
New York, NY 10022
E-mail: obgyn@isrn.com
URL: http://www.isrn.com/journals/obgyn

Peer-reviewed, open access journal publishing
original research articles, review articles, case
reports, and clinical studies in all areas of obstetrics
and gynecology.

9894 ■ ISRN Oncology
Hindawi Publishing Corporation
410 Park Ave., 15th Fl.
287 PMB
New York, NY 10022
E-mail: oncology@isrn.com
URL: http://www.isrn.com/journals/oncology

Peer-reviewed journal publishing research articles in
all areas of oncology.

9895 ■ ISRN Pharmacology
Hindawi Publishing Corporation
410 Park Ave., 15th Fl.
287 PMB
New York, NY 10022
E-mail: pharmacology@isrn.com
URL: http://www.isrn.com/journals/pharmacology

Peer-reviewed journal publishing articles in all areas
of pharmacology.

9896 ■ ISRN Rheumatology
Hindawi Publishing Corporation
410 Park Ave., 15th Fl.
287 PMB
New York, NY 10022
E-mail: rheumatology@isrn.com
URL: http://www.isrn.com/journals/rheumatology

Peer-reviewed journal publishing information in all
areas of rheumatology.

9897 ■ ISRN Surgery
Hindawi Publishing Corporation
410 Park Ave., 15th Fl.
287 PMB
New York, NY 10022
E-mail: surgery@isrn.com
URL: http://www.isrn.com/journals/surgery

Peer-reviewed journal publishing research in all areas
of surgery.

9898 ■ ISRN Urology
Hindawi Publishing Corporation
410 Park Ave., 15th Fl.
287 PMB
New York, NY 10022
E-mail: urology@isrn.com
URL: http://www.isrn.com/journals/urology

Peer-reviewed journal publishing research in all areas
of urology.

**9899 ■ Journal of Adolescent and Young
   Adult Oncology**
Mary Ann Liebert Inc., Publishers
140 Huguenot St., 3rd Fl.
New Rochelle, NY 10801-5215
Ph: (914)740-2100
Fax: (914)740-2101

Fr: 800-654-3237
URL: http://www.liebertpub.com/products/
product.aspx?pid=387

Quarterly. $336.00/year for individuals, print and on-line; $758.00/year for institutions, print and online. Peer-reviewed journal focusing on research, educa-tion, communication and collaboration between health professionals in adolescent and young adult oncology.

9900 ■ The Journal of Allergy and Clinical Immunology
Mosby Inc.
11830 Westline Industrial Dr.
St. Louis, MO 63146-3326
Ph: (314)872-8370
Fax: (314)432-1380
Fr: 800-325-4177
URL: http://www.jacionline.org

Monthly. $342.00/year for individuals; $172.00/year for students; $467.00/year for other countries; $234.00/year for students, other countries. Journal for clinical allergists and immunologists, as well as dermatologists, internists, general practitioners, pediatricians, and otolaryngologists (ENT physicians) concerned with clinical manifestations of allergies in their practice.

9901 ■ Journal of the American Academy of Child and Adolescent Psychiatry
Lippincott Williams & Wilkins
530 Walnut St.
Philadelphia, PA 19106-3619
Ph: (215)521-8300
Fax: (215)521-8902
Fr: 800-638-3030
URL: http://www.jaacap.com/

Monthly. $249.00/year for individuals; $163.00/year for students; $354.00/year for Canada; $261.00/year for students, Canada; $354.00/year for individuals, Mexico; $261.00/year for students, Mexico; $354.00/year for other countries; $261.00/year for students, other countries. Child psychiatry journal.

9902 ■ Journal of the American Academy of Dermatology
Mosby Inc.
11830 Westline Industrial Dr.
St. Louis, MO 63146-3326
Ph: (314)872-8370
Fax: (314)432-1380
Fr: 800-325-4177
E-mail: mderby@aad.org
URL: http://www.us.elsevierhealth.com/
product.jsp?isbn=01909622

Monthly. $738.00/year for institutions; $852.00/year for institutions, other countries; $343.00/year for individuals; $98.00/year for students; $449.00/year for other countries; $98.00/year for students, other countries. Journal for dermatologists and for family practitioners, pediatricians, and internists who are concerned with clinical manifestations of skin disease in their practice.

9903 ■ Journal of the American Medical Association
American Medical Association
PO Box 10946
Chicago, IL 60610
Ph: (312)670-7827
Fr: 800-262-2350
E-mail: ama-subs@ama-assn.org
URL: http://jama.ama-assn.org

Weekly. Promotes the science and art of medicine and the betterment of public health. Features job op-portunities for physicians, career related news and articles.

9904 ■ Journal of the American Osteopathic Association
American Osteopathic Association
142 E Ontario St.
Chicago, IL 60611
Ph: (312)202-8000

Fax: (312)202-8200
Fr: 800-621-1773
URL: http://www.osteopathic.org

Monthly. $160.00/year for nonmembers; $270.00/year for other countries, non-members. Osteopathic clini-cal journal.

9905 ■ Journal of the American Society of Echocardiography
Mosby
1600 John F. Kennedy Blvd., Ste. 1800
Philadelphia, PA 19103-2899
Ph: (215)239-3275
Fax: (215)239-3286
URL: http://www.elsevier.com/wps/find/
journalbibliographicinfo.cw

$408.00/year for other countries, print; $613.00/year for institutions, other countries, print; $298.00/year for individuals, print; $499.00/year for institutions, print; $196.00/year for students, other countries; $143.00/year for students. Official journal of the American Society of Echocardiography serving as a source of information on the technical basis and clini-cal application of echocardiography. Peer-reviewed publication featuring research, reviews, and case studies.

9906 ■ Journal of the American Society of Podiatric Medical Assistants
American Society of Podiatric Medical Assistants
1616 N 78th Ct.
Elmwood Park, IL 60707
Fr: 888-882-7762
URL: http://www.aspma.org

Quarterly. Included in membership. Professional journal covering issues in podiatry.

9907 ■ The Journal of Arthroplasty
Elsevier
1600 John F. Kennedy Blvd., Ste. 1800
Philadelphia, PA 19103-2822
Ph: (215)239-3900
Fax: (215)238-7883
E-mail: elspcs@elsevier.com
URL: http://www.us.elsevierhealth.com/
product.jsp?isbn=08835403

$494.00/year for individuals; $802.00/year for institu-tions; $217.00/year for students. Peer-reviewed medi-cal journal for orthopaedic surgeons. Covering clini-cal and basic science research on arthroplasty including surgical techniques, prosthetic design, bio-mechanics, biomaterials, and metallurgy.

9908 ■ Journal of Behavioral and Brain Science
Scientific Research Publishing
PO Box 54821
Irvine, CA 92619-4821
E-mail: jbbs@scirp.org
URL: http://www.scirp.org/journal/jbbs/

Peer-reviewed journal publishing original research articles and reviews in the field of behavioral and brain function.

9909 ■ Journal of Clinical Oncology
American Society of Clinical Oncology
2318 Mill Rd., Ste. 800
Alexandria, VA 22314
Ph: (571)483-1300
Fr: 888-282-2552
E-mail: membermail@asco.org
URL: http://www.asco.org

Provides manuscripts dedicated to clinical oncology. Contains commercial display, banner advertising, and oncology career/classified advertising.

9910 ■ Journal of Clinical Psychiatry
Physicians Postgraduate Press Inc.
PO Box 752870
Memphis, TN 38175
Ph: (901)751-3800

Fax: (901)751-3444
E-mail: mwaters@psychiatrist.com
URL: http://www.psychiatrist.com

Monthly. $156.00/year for individuals, print & online; $207.00/year for other countries, print & online; $86.00/year for individuals, online. Journal containing original papers about practical and clinical psychiatry.

9911 ■ Journal of Diabetes Mellitus
Scientific Research Publishing
PO Box 54821
Irvine, CA 92619-4821
E-mail: jdm@scirp.org
URL: http://www.scirp.org/journal/jdm/

Quarterly. $156.00/year for individuals. Peer-reviewed journal publishing research on diabetes mellitus.

9912 ■ Journal of Environmental Pathology, Toxicology and Oncology
Begell House Inc.
50 Cross Hwy.
Redding, CT 06896
Ph: (203)938-1300
Fax: (203)938-1304
URL: http://www.begellhouse.com/journals/
0ff459a57a4c08d0

$940.00/year for institutions. Journal covering re-search and reviews of factors and conditions that af-fect human and animal carcinogenesis.

9913 ■ Journal of Health and Life Sciences Law
American Health Lawyers Association
1620 Eye St. NW, 6th Fl.
Washington, DC 20006-4010
Ph: (202)833-1100
Fax: (202)833-1105
URL: http://www.healthlawyers.org

Quarterly. $149.00/year for individuals. Professional journal covering healthcare issues and cases and their impact on the health care arena.

9914 ■ Journal of Hospital Medicine
John Wiley & Sons Inc.
111 River St.
Hoboken, NJ 07030-5773
Ph: (201)748-6000
Fax: (201)748-6088
Fr: 800-825-7550
URL: http://onlinelibrary.wiley.com/journal/10.1002/
(ISSN)1553-56

$827.00/year for U.S., Canada, and Mexico, print only; $827.00/year for institutions, other countries, print only. Journal on hospital medicine.

9915 ■ Journal of Long-Term Effects of Medical Implants
Begell House Inc.
50 Cross Hwy.
Redding, CT 06896
Ph: (203)938-1300
Fax: (203)938-1304
URL: http://www.begellhouse.com/journals/
1bef42082d7a0fdf

$1,072.00/year for institutions. Peer-reviewed journal covering medical implants.

9916 ■ Journal of the National Medical Association
National Medical Association
8403 Colesville Rd., Ste. 920
Silver Spring, MD 20910
Ph: (202)347-1895
Fax: (202)898-2510
E-mail: aredd@nmanet.org
URL: http://www.nmanet.org/index.php?option=com_
content&view=arti

Monthly. $125.00/year for individuals; $275.00/year for institutions; $50.00/year for individuals, intern, resident, fellow, student; $22.00/year for single issue. Journal on specialized clinical research related to the health problems of African-Americans and other minorities. Recognizes significant contributions by black physicians and others involved with minority health issues and health disparities.

9917 ■ Journal of Occupational and Environmental Medicine
Lippincott Williams & Wilkins
530 Walnut St.
Philadelphia, PA 19106-3619
Ph: (215)521-8300
Fax: (215)521-8902
Fr: 800-638-3030
URL: http://www.lww.com/product/?1076-2752

Monthly. $422.00/year for individuals; $758.00/year for institutions; $615.00/year for other countries; $998.00/year for institutions, other countries; $394.00/year for other countries, in-training; $265.00/year for individuals, in-training. Occupational and environmental medicine journal.

9918 ■ Journal of Pediatric Hematology/Oncology
Lippincott Williams & Wilkins
351 W Camden St.
Baltimore, MD 21201
Ph: (410)528-4000
Fr: 800-638-3030
E-mail: jpho@ymail.com
URL: http://journals.lww.com/jpho-online/pages/default.aspx

$510.00/year for individuals; $1,211.00/year for institutions; $189.00/year for individuals, in-training; $623.40/year for individuals, international; $1,441.40/year for institutions, other countries; $204.40/year for other countries, in-training. Peer-reviewed journal containing reports on major advances in the diagnosis and treatment of cancer and blood diseases in children.

9919 ■ The Journal of Pediatrics
Mosby Inc.
11830 Westline Industrial Dr.
St. Louis, MO 63146-3326
Ph: (314)872-8370
Fax: (314)432-1380
Fr: 800-325-4177
E-mail: journal.pediatrics@cchmc.org
URL: http://journals.elsevierhealth.com/periodicals/ympd

Monthly. $234.00/year for individuals; $116.00/year for students; $310.00/year for other countries; $124.00/year for students, other countries; $767.00/year for institutions; $870.00/year for institutions, other countries. Journal for physicians who diagnose and treat disorders in infants and children.

9920 ■ Journal of Skin Cancer
Hindawi Publishing Corp.
410 Park Ave., 15th Fl.
287 PMB
New York, NY 10022-4407
Fax: (215)893-4392
E-mail: jsc@hindawi.com
URL: http://www.hindawi.com/journals/jsc/

$195.00/year for individuals. Peer-reviewed journal publishing original research and review articles, case reports and clinical studies related to all aspects of skin cancer.

9921 ■ Journal of Trauma
Lippincott Williams & Wilkins
530 Walnut St.
Philadelphia, PA 19106-3619
Ph: (215)521-8300
Fax: (215)521-8902
Fr: 800-638-3030
URL: http://journals.lww.com/jtrauma/pages/default.aspx

Monthly. $487.00/year for individuals; $855.00/year for institutions; $282.00/year for other countries, in-training; $658.00/year for other countries; $1,058.00/year for institutions, other countries; $426.00/year for other countries, in-training. Surgery journal.

9922 ■ Journal of Urology
Elsevier Science
PO Box 945
New York, NY 10159-0945
Ph: (212)989-5800
Fax: (212)633-3680
Fr: 888-615-4500
E-mail: publications@auanet.org
URL: http://www.jurology.com/

Monthly. $865.00/year for individuals; $1,158.00/year for Canada and Mexico; $689.00/year for students, other countries; $369.00/year for students. Medical journal.

9923 ■ Journal of Vascular Surgery
Mosby
1600 John F. Kennedy Blvd., Ste. 1800
Philadelphia, PA 19103-2899
Ph: (215)239-3275
Fax: (215)239-3286
E-mail: elspcs@elsevier.com
URL: http://us.elsevierhealth.com/product.jsp?isbn=07415214#descr

Monthly. $403.00/year for individuals; $842.00/year for institutions; $208.00/year for students, residents; $513.00/year for other countries; $965.00/year for institutions, other countries; $272.00/year for students, other countries, residents. Journal providing a forum for the advances in knowledge of the peripheral vascular system. Publishes peer-reviewed original articles on all aspects of disease and injury to the arterial and venous systems.

9924 ■ Laboratory Medicine
American Society for Clinical Pathology
33 W Monroe, Ste. 1600
Chicago, IL 60603
Ph: (312)541-4999
Fax: (312)541-4998
Fr: 800-267-2727
E-mail: labmed@ascp.org
URL: http://labmed.ascpjournals.org/

Monthly. $95.00/year for individuals, online; $120.00/year for individuals, print and online; $120.00/year for institutions, online; $145.00/year for institutions, print and online. Professional journal covering medical technology and pathology.

9925 ■ The Lancet North American Edition
Elsevier
1600 John F. Kennedy Blvd., Ste. 1800
Philadelphia, PA 19103-2822
Ph: (215)239-3900
Fax: (215)238-7883
E-mail: editorial@lancet.com
URL: http://www.us.elsevierhealth.com/product.jsp?isbn=01406736

Weekly. $279.00/year for individuals; $1,565.00/year for institutions; $111.00/year for students. Medical journal. Contents identical to British edition.

9926 ■ Leukemia Supplements
Nature Publishing Group
75 Varick St., 9th Fl.
New York, NY 10013-1917
Ph: (212)726-9200
Fax: (212)696-9006
Fr: 888-331-6288
URL: http://www.nature.com/leusup/marketing/index.html

Peer-reviewed journal covering all aspects of the research and treatment of leukemia and allied diseases.

9927 ■ Medical Economics
Advanstar Communications Inc.
641 Lexington Ave., 8th Fl.
New York, NY 10022
Ph: (212)951-6600
Fax: (212)951-6793
Fr: 800-346-0085
URL: http://www.modernmedicine.com/modernmedicine/Practice+Manage

Semimonthly. $95.00/year for individuals; $150.00/year for Canada and Mexico; $150.00/year for other countries. Magazine covering physicians practice management, professional relations, and financial affairs.

9928 ■ Medical Society of Milwaukee County-Membership Newsletter(MSMC)
Medical Society of Milwaukee County
210 Green Bay Rd.
Thiensville, WI 53092
Ph: (414)475-4750
Fax: (262)242-1862
E-mail: office@medicalsocietymilwaukee.org
URL: http://www.medicalsocietymilwaukee.org/

Description: Monthly. Serves as an informational newsletter for physicians. Contains IOCU medical business notes and practice announcements. Recurring features include letters to the editor, a calendar of events, reports of meetings, news of educational opportunities, job listings, and columns titled President's Letter.

9929 ■ Military Medicine
AMSUS - The Society of the Federal Health Agencies
9320 Old Georgetown Rd.
Bethesda, MD 20814
Ph: (301)897-8800
Fax: (301)503-5446
Fr: 800-761-9320
URL: http://www.amsus.org/index.php/journal

Monthly. $170.00/year for individuals, print and online; $225.00/year for other countries. Journal for professional personnel affiliated with the Federal medical services.

9930 ■ Minnesota Medicine
Minnesota Medical Association
1300 Godward St. NE, Ste. 2500
Minneapolis, MN 55413
Ph: (612)378-1875
Fax: (612)378-3875
Fr: 800-342-5662
URL: http://www.minnesotamedicine.com/

Monthly. $45.00/year for individuals; $81.00/year for two years; $80.00/year for other countries; $144.00/year for other countries, 2 years. Magazine on medical, socioeconomic, public health, medical-legal, and biomedical ethics issues of interest to physicians.

9931 ■ Narrative Inquiry in Bioethics
The Johns Hopkins University Press
2715 N Charles St.
Baltimore, MD 21218-4319
Ph: (410)516-6900
Fax: (410)516-6968
URL: http://www.press.jhu.edu/journals/narrative_inquiry_in_bioet

$175.00/year for institutions, print; $50.00/year for individuals, print. Journal publishing information on bioethics.

9932 ■ The Neurohospitalist
Sage Publications Inc.
2455 Teller Rd.
Thousand Oaks, CA 91320-2218
Ph: (805)499-9774
Fax: (805)583-2665
Fr: 800-818-7243
URL: http://www.sagepub.com/journalsProdDesc.nav?prodId=Journal20

Quarterly. $387.00/year for institutions, print and e-access; $348.00/year for institutions, e-access; $379.00/year for institutions, print; $102.00/year for individuals, print and e-access. Peer-reviewed journal focusing on practice and performance of neurohospitalist medicine.

9933 ■ Neuroscience and Medicine
Scientific Research Publishing
PO Box 54821
Irvine, CA 92619-4821
E-mail: nm@scirp.org
URL: http://www.scirp.org/journal/nm/

Quarterly. $156.00/year for individuals. Peer-reviewed journal publishing the latest advancements in neuroscience.

9934 ■ *Neuroscience Quarterly*

Society for Neuroscience
1121 14th St., Ste. 1010
Washington, DC 20005
Ph: (202)962-4000
Fax: (202)962-4941
E-mail: info@sfn.org
URL: http://www.sfn.org/index.aspx?pagename=nq

Description: Quarterly. Covers developments in neuroscience, with attention to research findings and funding, education, and interdisciplinary programs. Carries summaries or text of talks, papers, and of the prepared testimony of the Society's representatives before congressional committees. Recurring features include announcements of meetings and symposia, reports of foreign neuroscience societies, and Society news.

9935 ■ *The New England Journal of Medicine*

Massachusetts Medical Society
Waltham Woods Corporate Ctr.
860 Winter St.
Waltham, MA 02451-1413
Ph: (781)893-3800
Fax: (781)893-8009
URL: http://content.nejm.org/

Weekly. $139.00/year for individuals, online only; $169.00/year for individuals, print & online. Journal for the medical profession.

9936 ■ *Ob.Gyn. News*

International Medical News Group
60 Columbia Rd., Bldg. B
Morristown, NJ 07960
Ph: (973)290-8200
Fax: (973)290-8250
E-mail: obnews@elsevier.com
URL: http://www.obgynnews.com/

Semimonthly. $109.00/year for individuals; $173.00/year for other countries. Obstetrics and gynecology tabloid distributed to obstetricians and gynecologists.

9937 ■ *Ocular Surgery News*

SLACK Incorporated
6900 Grove Rd.
Thorofare, NJ 08086-9447
Ph: (856)848-1000
Fax: (856)848-6091
URL: http://www.osnsupersite.com

Semimonthly. $399.00/year for individuals; $798.00/year for two years; $1,197.00/year for individuals, three years; $199.00/year for individuals, resident with letter from academic organization; $48.00/year for single issue; $519.00/year for institutions; $1,038.00/year for institutions, two years; $1,557.00/year for institutions, three years. Medical newspaper for ophthalmologists. Covering scientific meetings and events, with emphasis on cataract/IOL, glaucoma treatment, refractive therapy, general ophthalmic topics, and legislative/ regulatory developments, and industry news.

9938 ■ *Oncology*

S. Karger Publishers Inc.
26 W Avon Rd.
PO Box 529
Unionville, CT 06085-1162
Ph: (860)675-7834
Fax: (203)675-7302
Fr: 800-828-5479
URL: http://content.karger.com/ProdukteDB/produkte.asp?Aktion=Jou

$2,972.00/year for institutions, print or online; $2,202.00/year for institutions, in Germany; print or online; $2,778.00/year for institutions, print or online; $3,270.00/year for institutions, combined print and online; $2,422.00/year for institutions, in Germany; combined print and online; $3,056.00/year for institutions, combined print and online. Peer-reviewed

medical journal presenting experimental and clinical findings on cancer.

9939 ■ *Ophthalmic Surgery Lasers and Imaging*

SLACK Incorporated
6900 Grove Rd.
Thorofare, NJ 08086-9447
Ph: (856)848-1000
Fax: (856)848-6091
E-mail: osli@slackinc.com
URL: http://www.slackjournals.com/osli

Bimonthly. $169.00/year for individuals; $338.00/year for individuals, two years; $499.00/year for institutions; $998.00/year for individuals, two years; $79.00/year for single issue. Peer-reviewed journal publishing articles on ophthalmic surgery, lasers, research, and clinical approaches.

9940 ■ *Optometric Management*

Lippincott Williams & Wilkins VisionCare Group
323 Norristown Rd., Ste. 200
Ambler, PA 19002
Ph: (215)646-8700
E-mail: om@boucher1.com
URL: http://www.optometric.com

Monthly. $42.00/year for individuals; $51.00/year for Canada; $90.00/year for other countries; $75.00/year for two years; $91.00/year for Canada, 2 years; $162.00/year for other countries, 2 years. Medical professional journal.

9941 ■ *Orthopedics Today*

SLACK Incorporated
6900 Grove Rd.
Thorofare, NJ 08086-9447
Ph: (856)848-1000
Fax: (856)848-6091
E-mail: ortoday@slackinc.com
URL: http://www.orthosupersite.com/iContent.aspx?pid=ot

Monthly. $288.00/year for individuals; $576.00/year for two years; $864.00/year for individuals, 3 years; $455.00/year for institutions; $910.00/year for two years; $1,365.00/year for institutions, 3 years; $144.00/year for individuals, resident; $48.00/year for single issue; $65.00/year for out of country. Newspaper covering orthopedic meetings, courses, and symposia.

9942 ■ *Patient Care*

Advanstar Communications Inc.
641 Lexington Ave., 8th Fl.
New York, NY 10022
Ph: (212)951-6600
Fax: (212)951-6793
Fr: 800-346-0085
URL: http://patientcare.modernmedicine.com/patcare/issue/issueLis

Monthly. $57.00/year for individuals; $72.00/year for Canada and Mexico; $72.00/year for other countries. Medical journal publishing today's best clinical practices.

9943 ■ *Pediatric Annals*

SLACK Incorporated
6900 Grove Rd.
Thorofare, NJ 08086-9447
Ph: (856)848-1000
Fax: (856)848-6091
URL: http://www.pediatricsupersite.com/issue.aspx?pubid=pedann

Monthly. $229.00/year for individuals; $379.00/year for institutions; $458.00/year for two years; $758.00/year for institutions, two years; $687.00/year for individuals, three years; $1,137.00/year for institutions, three years; $114.00/year for individuals, resident with letter from school; $39.00/year for single issue. Scholarly journal.

9944 ■ *Pediatric News*

International Medical News Group
60 Columbia Rd., Bldg. B
Morristown, NJ 07960
Ph: (973)290-8200
Fax: (973)290-8250
E-mail: rhnews@elsevier.com
URL: http://www.epediatricnews.com

Monthly. $109.00/year for individuals; $173.00/year for other countries. Tabloid covering pediatric medicine and distributed to pediatricians.

9945 ■ *Pediatrics*

American Academy of Pediatrics
141 NW Point Blvd.
Elk Grove Village, IL 60007-1098
Ph: (847)434-4000
Fax: (847)434-8000
Fr: 800-433-9016
E-mail: journals@aap.org
URL: http://pediatrics.aappublications.org/

Monthly. $179.00/year for nonmembers, physician, print & online; $136.00/year for nonmembers, physician, online; $96.00/year for nonmembers, student/allied, online; $128.00/year for nonmembers, student/allied, print & online. Medical journal reporting on pediatrics.

9946 ■ *Pharmacology and Pharmacy*

Scientific Research Publishing
PO Box 54821
Irvine, CA 92619-4821
E-mail: pp@scirp.org
URL: http://www.scirp.org/journal/pp/

Quarterly. $156.00/year for individuals. Peer-reviewed journal publishing articles on pharmacology and pharmacy.

9947 ■ *Plastic Surgery International*

Hindawi Publishing Corp.
410 Park Ave., 15th Fl.
287 PMB
New York, NY 10022-4407
Fax: (215)893-4392
URL: http://www.hindawi.com/journals/psi/

$195.00/year for individuals. Peer-reviewed journal focusing on clinical studies in all areas of plastic surgery.

9948 ■ *Practical Radiation Oncology*

Elsevier
1600 John F. Kennedy Blvd., Ste. 1800
Philadelphia, PA 19103-2822
Ph: (215)239-3900
Fax: (215)238-7883
E-mail: pro@astro.org
URL: http://www.practicalradonc.org/

Peer-reviewed journal featuring information about radiation oncology practice.

9949 ■ *Proceedings of the American Thoracic Society*

American Thoracic Society
25 Broadway
New York, NY 10004
Ph: (212)315-8600
Fax: (212)315-6498
E-mail: atsinfo@thoracic.org
URL: http://www.thoracic.org

Periodical. Features reviews of clinical or basic science resulting from conferences or workshops organized or sponsored by the ATS and/or other organizations. Provides understanding of diseases within respiratory and critical care medicine. Displays professional recruitment and announcement advertising.

9950 ■ *Psychiatric Annals*

SLACK Incorporated
6900 Grove Rd.
Thorofare, NJ 08086-9447
Ph: (856)848-1000

Fax: (856)848-6091
E-mail: psyann@slackinc.com
URL: http://www.psychiatricannalsonline.com/

Monthly. $229.00/year for individuals; $458.00/year for two years; $687.00/year for individuals, three years; $379.00/year for institutions; $758.00/year for institutions, two years; $1,137.00/year for institutions, three years; $114.00/year for individuals, resident; $53.00/year for individuals, outside the U.S.; $39.00/year for single issue. Peer-reviewed journal analyzing concepts and practices in every area of psychiatry.

9951 ■ Psychiatric News
American Psychiatric Publishing Inc.
1000 Wilson Blvd., Ste. 1825
Arlington, VA 22209-3924
Ph: (703)907-7322
Fax: (703)907-1091
Fr: 800-368-5777
URL: http://pn.psychiatryonline.org/

Semimonthly. $111.00/year for nonmembers, print and online; $151.00/year for members, international, print & online; $167.00/year for nonmembers, international, print & online; $22.00/year for single issue, United States; $37.00/year for single issue, international. Professional magazine of the American Psychiatric Assn.

9952 ■ Psychiatric Times
United Business Media
600 Harrison St., 6th Fl.
San Francisco, CA 94107
Ph: (415)947-6000
Fax: (415)947-6055
URL: http://www.psychiatrictimes.com/home

$55.00/year for individuals; $90.00/year for two years; $120.00/year for libraries, institution; $120.00/year for other countries. Newspaper (tabloid) on psychiatric disorders and issues.

9953 ■ Psychology of Violence
American Psychological Association
750 1st St. NE
Washington, DC 20002-4242
Ph: (202)336-5500
Fax: (202)336-5549
Fr: 800-374-2721
URL: http://www.apa.org/pubs/journals/vio/index.aspx

Quarterly. $65.00/year for members; $89.00/year for other countries, members; $65.00/year for students; $110.00/year for nonmembers; $139.00/year for other countries, nonmembers; $441.00/year for institutions; $490.00/year for institutions, other countries. Multidisciplinary research journal concerning topics on the psychology of violence and extreme aggression.

9954 ■ Resident & Staff Physician
Ascend Integrated Media
7015 College Blvd., Ste. 600
Overland Park, KS 66211
Ph: (913)469-1110
Fax: (913)469-0806
URL: http://www.residentandstaff.com

Monthly. Free to qualified subscribers. Peer-reviewed medical journal.

9955 ■ RETINA
Lippincott Williams & Wilkins
530 Walnut St.
Philadelphia, PA 19106-3619
Ph: (215)521-8300
Fax: (215)521-8902
Fr: 800-638-3030
E-mail: retina@retinajournal.com
URL: http://journals.lww.com/retinajournal/pages/default.aspx

$391.00/year for individuals; $924.00/year for institutions; $188.00/year for individuals, in-training; $540.50/year for other countries; $1,036.50/year for institutions, other countries; $204.50/year for other countries, in-training. Journal publishing clinically oriented articles for the general ophthalmologist and vitreoretinal specialist.

9956 ■ Same-Day Surgery
American Health Consultants Inc.
3525 Piedmont Rd. NE, Bldg. 6-400
Atlanta, GA 30305
Ph: (404)262-5476
Fax: (404)262-5560
Fr: 800-688-2421
E-mail: editorial_questions@ahcmedia.com
URL: http://www.ahcmedia.com/public

Description: Monthly. $499. Focuses on the management, structure, and legal and medical aspects of ambulatory surgery. Carries expert opinions and recommendations on policies and procedures.

9957 ■ Skin & Allergy News
International Medical News Group
60 Columbia Rd., Bldg. B
Morristown, NJ 07960
Ph: (973)290-8200
Fax: (973)290-8250
E-mail: sknews@elsevier.com
URL: http://www.skinandallergynews.com

Monthly. $109.00/year for individuals; $173.00/year for other countries. Dermatology/allergy tabloid.

9958 ■ Surgical Rounds
Ascend Integrated Media
7015 College Blvd., Ste. 600
Overland Park, KS 66211
Ph: (913)469-1110
Fax: (913)469-0806
URL: http://www.hcplive.com/publications/surgical-rounds

Monthly. Free to qualified subscribers. Peer-reviewed journal featuring clinical articles of interest to office-based and hospital-based surgeons, including residents, full-time staff, and surgical faculty.

9959 ■ Surgical Science
Scientific Research Publishing
PO Box 54821
Irvine, CA 92619-4821
E-mail: ss@scirp.org
URL: http://www.scirp.org/journal/ss/

$390.00/year for individuals. Peer-reviewed journal publishing articles on the latest developments in surgery.

9960 ■ Therapeutic Advances in Drug Safety
Sage Publications Inc.
2455 Teller Rd.
Thousand Oaks, CA 91320-2218
Ph: (805)499-9774
Fax: (805)583-2665
Fr: 800-818-7243
URL: http://www.sagepub.com/journalsProdDesc.nav?prodId=Journal20

Bimonthly. $1,125.00/year for institutions, print and e-access; $1,013.00/year for institutions, e-access; $1,103.00/year for institutions, print. Peer-reviewed journal covering novel and controversial aspects pertaining to the safe use of drugs in different age and ethnic patient groups.

9961 ■ USA Body Psychotherapy Journal
United States Association for Body Psychotherapy
8639 B 16th St., Ste. 119
Silver Spring, MD 20910
Ph: (202)466-1619
E-mail: admin@usabp.org
URL: http://www.usabp.org/displaycommon.cfm?an=4

Semiannual. Academic journal that seeks to support, promote and stimulate the exchange of ideas, scholarship and research within the field of body psychotherapy as well as an interdisciplinary exchange with related fields of clinical practice and inquiry.

9962 ■ World Journal of AIDS
Scientific Research Publishing
PO Box 54821
Irvine, CA 92619-4821
E-mail: wja@scirp.org
URL: http://www.scirp.org/journal/wja/

Quarterly. $156.00/year for individuals. Peer-reviewed journal publishing articles on research data and education in all aspects of HIV and AIDS.

9963 ■ World Journal of Vaccines
Scientific Research Publishing
PO Box 54821
Irvine, CA 92619-4821
E-mail: wjv@scirp.org
URL: http://www.scirp.org/journal/wjv/

Quarterly. $156.00/year for individuals. Peer-reviewed journal publishing articles on the latest advancements in vaccine.

9964 ■ Year Book of Critical Care Medicine
Elsevier Science Inc.
360 Park Ave. S
New York, NY 10010-1710
Ph: (212)989-5800
Fax: (212)633-3990
Fr: 888-437-4636
URL: http://www.elsevier.com/wps/find/journaldescription.cws_home

Annual. $271.00/year for institutions, other countries; $197.00/year for other countries; $103.00/year for students, other countries; $250.00/year for institutions; $167.00/year for individuals; $81.00/year for students. Journal focused on treatment of severe sepsis and septic shock, echocardiography in the evaluation of hemo-dynamically unstable patients & mechanical ventilation of acute respiratory distress syndrome.

PLACEMENT AND JOB REFERRAL SERVICES

9965 ■ eMatchPhysicians.com
27134 A Paseo Espada, Ste. 323
San Juan Capistrano, CA 92675
Ph: (949)215-0501
Fax: (949)215-0982
Fr: 877-362-8247
E-mail: support@ematchphysicians.com
URL: http://www.ematchphysicians.com

Description: Exists as an online physician matching service that helps connects practice seeking physicians to hospitals and medical groups. Works to simplify the physician recruitment process by merging the efforts = of in-house physician recruiters and a search firm with today's sophisticated web-based technology.

9966 ■ Jackson and Coker
3000 Old Alabama Rd., Ste. 119-608
Alpharetta, GA 30022
Fax: 800-936-4562
Fr: 800-272-2707
E-mail: connect@jacksoncoker.com
URL: http://www.jacksoncoker.com

Description: Serves as a permanent physician recruitment firm with experience identifying physician jobs. Provides information technology and human resources solutions to hospitals and healthcare organizations across the country.

9967 ■ National Association of Physician Recruiters
c/o Willard S. Kautter, Exec. VP
222 S Westmonte Dr., Ste. 101
Altamonte Springs, FL 32714
Ph: (407)774-7880
Fax: (407)774-6440
Fr: 800-726-5613
E-mail: napr@napr.org
URL: http://www.napr.org

Comprised of physician recruiting organizations, hospitals, medical groups, individuals and vendor organizations. Provides healthcare recruiting and consulting services to the growing healthcare industry. Commits to providing continuous and dynamic educational forums to insure the ability of its membership to respond to the changes in the healthcare industry.

EMPLOYER DIRECTORIES AND NETWORKING LISTS

9968 ■ American Association of Public Health Physicians—Membership Roster
American Association of Public Health Physicians
1605 Pebble Beach Blvd.
Green Cove Springs, FL 32043-8077
Ph: (904)860-9208
Fax: (904)529-7761
URL: http://www.aaphp.org

Annual. Covers: 200 physicians. Entries include: Name, address, professional affiliation. Arrangement: Available in alphabetical or geographical arrangement.

9969 ■ American Group Psychotherapy Association—Membership Directory
American Group Psychotherapy Association Inc.
25 E 21st St., 6th Fl.
New York, NY 10010
Ph: (212)477-2677
Fax: (212)979-6627
Fr: 877-668-2472
URL: http://www.agpa.org

Covers: 4,500 physicians, psychologists, clinical social workers, psychiatric nurses, and other mental health professionals interested in treatment of emotional problems by group methods. Entries include: Name, office or home address, highest degree held, office or home phone number. Arrangement: Alphabetical. Indexes: Geographical.

9970 ■ Crain's List—Chicago's Largest Hospitals
Crain Communications Inc.
360 N Michigan Ave.
Chicago, IL 60601
Ph: (312)649-5200
URL: http://www.chicagobusiness.com/section/lists

Published November, 2010. $25.00 for individuals; $45.00 for individuals. Covers: 25 hospitals in Chicago area ranked by net patient revenues. Entries include: Name, address, phone number, fax, web address, corporate e-mail, hospital administrator, network affiliation, 2009 net patient revenue, percentage change from 2008, 2009 net profits, percentage change from 2008, inpatient days, available beds, daily occupancy rate, number of hospital employees as of December 31, 2009, fiscal year end, Chairman, President, CEO, Chief Financial Officer, Human Resources Manager, Media Relations/Public Relations Director, and Hospital Administrator.

9971 ■ Directory of Child Life Programs
Child Life Council Inc.
11821 Parklawn Dr., Ste. 310
Rockville, MD 20852-2539
Ph: (301)881-7090
Fax: (301)881-7092
URL: http://www.childlife.org

Biennial, latest edition 14th, 2006. Covers: Over 400 child life programs. Entries include: Facility name, address, phone, name of child life department and director, reporting structure, staff statistics, educational requirements for employment, and internship or educational opportunities. Arrangement: Geographical. Indexes: Speciality areas, internship sessions, program size, fellowships.

9972 ■ Directory of Hospital Personnel
Grey House Publishing
4919 Rte. 22
PO Box 56
Amenia, NY 12501
Ph: (518)789-8700
Fax: (518)789-0556
Fr: 800-562-2139
URL: http://www.greyhouse.com/hospital_personnel.htm

Annual, Latest edition 2011. $325.00 for individuals. Covers: 200,000 executives at 6,000 U.S. Hospitals. Entries include: Name of hospital, address, phone, number of beds, type and JCAHO status of hospital, names and titles of key department heads and staff, medical and nursing school affiliations; number of residents, interns, and nursing students. Arrangement: Geographical. Indexes: Hospital name, personnel, hospital size.

9973 ■ Directory of Physicians in the United States
American Medical Association
515 N State St.
Chicago, IL 60654
Fr: 800-621-8335
URL: http://www.directoryofphysicians.org

Biennial, latest edition 2010. $775.00 for individuals; $750.00 for individuals. Covers: In four volume set, more than 978,000 physicians in the United States, Puerto Rico, Virgin Islands, and certain Pacific Islands. Entries include: Name, address, year licensed in mailing address state, medical school, type of practice, primary and secondary specialties, board certifications, and Physician's Recognition award status. Both print and CD-ROM versions are available. Arrangement: Geographical by city; federal service separate section. Indexes: Alphabetical (constitutes Volume 1 of set); geographical.

9974 ■ Health & Wellness Resource Center
Gale
PO Box 6904
Florence, KY 41022-6904
Fr: 800-354-9706
E-mail: gale.galeord@cengage.com
URL: http://www.gale.cengage.com

Database includes: Located in the Health Organization Directory component: listings of agencies, schools and organizations; journals, newsletters, and publishers websites; hospitals, health care facilities, programs and special care. Data is derived from the Medical and Health Information Directory. Entries include: Contact information. Principal content of database is a medical encyclopedia, drug and herb locator, health assessment tools, medical dictionary, links to other sites, and health news. Indexes: Searchable by key term along with city and state.

9975 ■ Health & Wellness Resource Center—Alternative Health Module
Gale
PO Box 6904
Florence, KY 41022-6904
Fr: 800-354-9706
E-mail: gale.galeord@cengage.com
URL: http://www.gale.cengage.com

Database includes: Focused upon alternative medicine topics this information is located in the Health Organization Directory component: listings of agencies, schools and organizations; journals, newsletters, and publishers websites; hospitals, health care facilities, programs and special care. Data is derived from the Medical and Health Information Directory. Entries include: Contact information. Principal content of database is a medical encyclopedia, drug and herb locator, health assessment tools, medical dictionary, links to other sites, and health news and includes references to homeopathic treatments, yoga, massage therapy, etc.

9976 ■ HMO/PPO Directory
Grey House Publishing
4919 Rte. 22
PO Box 56
Amenia, NY 12501

Ph: (518)789-8700
Fax: (518)789-0556
Fr: 800-562-2139
URL: http://www.greyhouse.com/hmo_ppo.htm

Annual, Latest edition 2011. $325.00 for individuals. Covers: Over 1,000 health maintenance organizations (HMOs) and preferred provider organizations (PPOs). Entries include: Name of organization, address, phone, number of members, names of officers, employer references, geographical area served, parent company, average fees and co-payments, financial data, and cost control procedures. Arrangement: Geographical. Indexes: Organization name, personnel name, HMOs and PPOs by state, and number of members enrolled.

9977 ■ Hospital Blue Book
Billian Publishing Inc. and Trans World Publishing Inc.
2100 River Edge Pky.
Atlanta, GA 30328
Ph: (770)955-5656
Fax: (770)952-0669
Fr: 800-800-5668
E-mail: blu-book@billian.com
URL: http://www.billianshealthdata.com/Products/bluebook.html

Annual, Latest edition 2010. $575.00 for individuals; $575.00 for individuals. Covers: More than 6,500 hospitals; some listings also appear in a separate southern edition of this publication. Entries include: Name of hospital, accreditation, mailing address, phone, fax, number of beds, type of facility (nonprofit, general, state, etc.); list of administrative personnel and chiefs of medical services, with specific titles. Arrangement: Geographical.

9978 ■ Medical and Health Information Directory
Gale
PO Box 6904
Florence, KY 41022-6904
Fr: 800-354-9706
URL: http://www.gale.cengage.com

Annual, Latest edition April 2011. $1190.00 for individuals; $501.00 for individuals. Covers: In volume 1, more than 33,000 medical and health oriented associations, organizations, institutions, and government agencies, including health maintenance organizations (HMOs), preferred provider organizations (PPOs), insurance companies, pharmaceutical companies, research centers, and medical and allied health schools. In Volume 2, over 20,000 medical book publishers; medical periodicals, directories, audiovisual producers and services, medical libraries and information centers, electronic resources, and health-related internet search engines. In Volume 3, more than 40,500 clinics, treatment centers, care programs, and counseling/diagnostic services for 34 subject areas. Entries include: Institution, service, or firm name, address, phone, fax, email and URL; many include names of key personnel and, when pertinent, descriptive annotation. Volume 3 was formerly listed separately as Health Services Directory. Arrangement: Classified by organization activity, service, etc. Indexes: Each volume has a complete alphabetical name and keyword index.

9979 ■ Society of Gynecologic Oncologists—Membership Directory
Society of Gynecologic Oncologists
230 W Monroe St., Ste. 710
Chicago, IL 60606
Ph: (312)235-4060
Fax: (312)235-4059
URL: http://www.sgo.org

Annual. $35.00 for individuals. Publication includes: Contact information of all SGO members and staff, SGO committees and networks, governance and Bylaws information, and details about the Gynecologic Cancer Foundation.

9980 ■ Student Resource Center—Health Module
Gale
PO Box 6904
Florence, KY 41022-6904
Fr: 800-354-9706
E-mail: gale.galeord@cengage.com
URL: http://www.gale.cengage.com

Database includes: Listing of individuals who have "made significant contributions to the world of health." Entries include: Biographical data. Principal content of database is approximately 1,200 essays on all aspects of major health issues along with events, definitions, pamphlets and links to reviewed websites.

Handbooks and Manuals

9981 ■ AMAA Journal
American Medical Athletic Association
4405 East-West Hwy., Ste. 405
Bethesda, MD 20814
Ph: (301)913-9517
Fax: (301)913-9520
Fr: 800-776-2732
E-mail: amaa@americanrunning.org
URL: http://www.amaasportsmed.org

Three issues/year. Presents essential topics related to the medical aspects of sports, exercise, and fitness that assist physicians and other healthcare professionals in caring for active patients.

9982 ■ Barron's Guide to Medical and Dental Schools
Barron's Educational Series, Inc.
250 Wireless Blvd.
Hauppauge, NY 11788-3917
Ph: (631)434-3311
Fax: (631)434-3723
Fr: 800-645-3476
E-mail: fbrown@barronseduc.com
URL: http://barronseduc.com

Sol Wischnitzer and Edith Wischnitzer. Twelve edition, 2009. $17.09. 768 pages. Updated with the latest facts and figures, this school directory and guidance manual presents profiles of all accredited medical, dental, and osteopathic schools in the United States and Canada.

9983 ■ Career Opportunities in Health Care (Career Opportunities)
Facts On File Inc.
132 W 31st St., 17th Fl.
New York, NY 10001-2006
Fax: 800-678-3633
Fr: 800-322-8755
E-mail: custserv@factsonfile.com
URL: http://www.infobasepublishing.com

Shelly Field. 2007. Third Edition. $49.50. 304 pages. Part of the Career Opportunities Series.

9984 ■ Careers in Health Care
The McGraw-Hill Companies
PO Box 182604
Columbus, OH 43272
Fax: (614)759-3749
Fr: 877-883-5524
E-mail: customer.service@mcgraw-hill.com
URL: http://www.mhprofessional.com/ product.php?isbn=0071466533

Barbara M. Swanson. Fifth edition, 2005. $19.95 (paper). 192 pages. Describes job duties, work settings, salaries, licensing and certification requirements, educational preparation, and future outlook. Gives ideas on how to secure a job.

9985 ■ Careers in Medicine
The McGraw-Hill Companies
PO Box 182604
Columbus, OH 43272
Fax: (614)759-3749

Fr: 877-883-5524
E-mail: customer.service@mcgraw-hill.com
URL: http://www.mhprofessional.com/ product?isbn=0071458743

Terence J. Sacks. Third edition, 2006. $15.95 (paper). 192 pages. Examines the many paths open to M.D.s, D.O.s, and M.D./Ph.D.s, including clinical private or group practice, hospitals, public health organizations, the armed forces, emergency rooms, research institutions, medical schools, pharmaceutical companies and private industry, and research/advocacy groups like the World Health Organization. A special chapter on osteopathy and chiropractic explores this branch of medicine.

9986 ■ Clinical Journal of Sport Medicine
Lippincott Williams & Wilkins
2001 Market St.
Philadelphia, PA 19103
Ph: (215)521-8300
Fax: (215)521-8902
URL: http://journals.lww.com/cjsportsmed

Bimonthly. $390.00/year (individuals); $729.00/year (institutions). Journal covering research and review articles on diagnostics, therapeutics, and rehabilitation of healthy and physically-challenged individuals engaged in all levels of sports and exercise activities.

9987 ■ Essential Guide to Becoming a Doctor
Wiley-Blackwell
111 River St.
Hoboken, NJ 07030-5774
Ph: (201)748-6000
Fax: (201)748-6088
E-mail: info@wiley.com
URL: http://as.wiley.com/WileyCDA

Adrian Blundell, Richard Harrison, and Benjamin W. Turney. 2010. $36.95 (paper). 296 pages. Provides comprehensive resources on the stages of becoming a doctor. Includes current information on admission tests and an admission table with practical details about each medical school.

9988 ■ Expert Resumes for Health Care Careers
Jist Works
875 Montreal Way
St. Paul, MN 55102
Fr: 800-648-5478
E-mail: educate@emcp.com
URL: http://www.jist.com

Wendy S. Enelow and Louise M. Kursmark. 2010. $16.95. 288 pages.

9989 ■ Exploring Health Careers
Delmar Cengage Learning
5 Maxwell Dr.
Clifton Park, NY 12065
Fr: 800-648-7450
URL: http://www.delmarlearning.com/about/ contact.aspx

Maureen McCutcheon, Mary Phillips. 2006. $98.95. Provides an overview of the many career opportunities available within the health care field. Covers career descriptions, including educational requirements, salary information, skills and procedures performed within the various careers and more.

9990 ■ Functional Testing in Human Performance
Human Kinetics
PO Box 5076
Champaign, IL 61825-5076
Fax: (217)351-1549
Fr: 800-747-4457
E-mail: info@hkusa.com
URL: http://www.humankinetics.com

Michael Reiman and Robert Manske. 2009. $79.00 (DVD and cloth). 328 pages. Serves as resource for the accurate assessment of an individual's functional abilities. Offers clinicians the compilation of information on clinical and data-based functional testing for

sport, exercise and occupational settings. Accompanying DVD features live-action demonstrations of 40 of the most advanced tests.

9991 ■ Getting that Medical Job: Secrets for Success, Third Edition
John Wiley & Sons, Inc.
111 River St.
Hoboken, NJ 07030-5774
Ph: (201)748-6000
Fax: (201)748-6088
E-mail: info@wiley.com
URL: http://as.wiley.com/WileyCDA

Colin J. Mumford and Suvankar Pal. 2011. $27.95 (paper). 168 pages. Assists job seekers in planning an effective strategy to land their ideal medical job.

9992 ■ Health Care Job Explosion! High Growth Health Care Careers and Job Locator
Bookhaven Press LLC
249 Field Club Cir.
McKees Rocks, PA 15136
Ph: (412)494-6926
Fax: (412)494-5749
Fr: 800-782-7424
E-mail: bookhaven@aol.com
URL: http://www.bookhavenpress.com

Dennis V. Damp. Fourth edition, 2006. 320 pages. $19.95.

9993 ■ Health Careers Today
Elsevier
11830 Westline Industrial Dr.
St. Louis, MO 63146
Ph: (314)453-7010
Fax: (314)453-7095
Fr: 800-545-2522
E-mail: usbkinfo@elsevier.com
URL: http://www.elsevier.com

Gerdin, Judith. Fourth edition. 2007. $74.95. 496 pages. Covers more than 45 health careers. Discusses the roles and responsibilities of various occupations and provides a solid foundation in the skills needed for all health careers.

9994 ■ How to Start a Private Practice
Yvonne Mart Fox
PO Box 620291
Middleton, WI 53562-0291
Ph: (608)831-3390
Fax: (608)831-2635
E-mail: yvonne@yvonnemartfox.com
URL: http://www.yvonnemartfox.com/how_to_ start.html

Yvonne Mart Fox. Revised edition, 2008. $36.00 (paper). 149 pages.

9995 ■ How To Get a Job in Health Care
Cengage Learning
PO Box 6904
Florence, KY 41022-6904
Fax: 800-487-8488
Fr: 800-354-9706
URL: http://www.cengage.com

Robert H. Zedlitz. 2012. $58.00. 144 pages (paperback). Serves as a preparatory reference tool for job seekers, includes job research, writing resumes, completing applications, and preparing for interviews.

9996 ■ The Medical Job Interview
Blackwell Science, Incorporated
Commerce Pl.
350 Main St.
Malden, MA 02148-5018
Ph: (781)388-8200
Fax: (781)388-8210
URL: http://www.blackwellpublishing.com

Colin Mumford. Second edition, 2005. $27.95 (paper). 88 pages.

9997 ■ *On Becoming a Doctor*
Sourcebooks, Inc.
1935 Brookdale Rd., Ste. 139
Naperville, IL 60563
Ph: (630)961-3900
Fax: (630)961-2168
Fr: 800-432-7444
E-mail: info@sourcebooks.com
URL: http://www.sourcebooks.com

Tania Heller. 2009. $16.99 (paper). 224 pages. Contains guidelines for pursuing a successful career in medicine. Includes interviews with different specialists to help the reader choose a medical path that fits his/her preferences and career goals.

9998 ■ *Opportunities in Health and Medical Careers*
The McGraw-Hill Companies
PO Box 182604
Columbus, OH 43272
Fax: (614)759-3749
Fr: 877-883-5524
E-mail: customer.service@mcgraw-hill.com
URL: http://www.mhprofessional.com/
   product.php?isbn=0071437274

I. Donald Snook, Jr. and Leo D'Orazio. 2004. $14.95 (paper). 157 pages. Covers the full range of medical and health occupations. Illustrated.

9999 ■ *Physician's Pathways to Non-Traditional Careers and Leadership Opportunities*
Springer Science+Business Media LLC
233 Spring St.
New York, NY 10013-1578
Ph: (212)460-1500
Fax: (212)460-1575
URL: http://www.springer.com

Richard D. Urman and Jesse M. Ehrenfeld. 2012. $39.95. 385 pages (softcover). Serves as a guide for medical professionals and medical students considering additional or new career outside of their field.

10000 ■ *Pocket Orthopaedics: Evidence-Based Survival Guide*
Jones & Bartlett Learning
5 Wall St.
Burlington, MA 01803
Fax: (978)443-8000
Fr: 800-832-0034
E-mail: info@jblearning.com
URL: http://www.jblearning.com

Michael S. Wong. 2011. $41.95 (spiral/paperback). 412 pages. Serves as learning aide in evidence-based practice for both students and clinicians.

10001 ■ *Resumes for Health and Medical Careers*
The McGraw-Hill Companies
PO Box 182604
Columbus, OH 43272
Fax: (614)759-3749
Fr: 877-883-5524
E-mail: customer.service@mcgraw-hill.com
URL: http://www.mhprofessional.com/
   product.php?isbn=0071545352

Third edition, 2008. $12.95 (paper). 144 pages.

Employment Agencies and Search Firms

10002 ■ **A. Berendt Associates**
PO Box 31054
Charleston, SC 29417
Ph: (843)766-3105
Fax: (843)766-3144
Fr: 888-273-4628
E-mail: berendtmed@aol.com
URL: http://www.berendtmedical.com

Physician and mid-level practitioner recruitment firm.

Offers physician jobs, cardiology jobs and cardiology positions.

10003 ■ **Alan Darling Consulting**
374 Dover Rd.
South Newfane, VT 05351-7901
Ph: (802)348-6365
Fax: (802)348-7826
URL: http://www.alandarling.com

Executive search firm focused on the healthcare industry.

10004 ■ **Alliance Recruiting Resources**
900 Rockmead Dr., Ste. 274
Kingwood, TX 77339
Fax: (866)706-4959
Fr: 800-759-8203
URL: http://www.alliancerr.com

Provides job listings, job search assistance, and recruitment services to medical professionals in the healthcare industry.

10005 ■ **B. E. Smith**
9777 Ridge Dr.
Lenexa, KS 66219
Fr: 800-467-9117
URL: http://www.besmith.com

Serves as an executive search to healthcare organizations across the nation. Offers permanent and interim placements.

10006 ■ **The Bauman Group**
1514 Redwood Dr.
Los Altos, CA 94022
Ph: (650)941-0800
Fax: (650)941-1729
E-mail: info@thebaumangroup.com
URL: http://www.thebaumangroup.com

Executive search firm.

10007 ■ **Beck-Field and Associates**
9330 Corporate Dr., Ste. 103
Selma, TX 78154
Ph: (210)651-4337
Fax: (210)651-4338
Fr: 800-304-3095
URL: http://www.beck-field.com

Recruitment firm specializing in the permanent placement of registered nurses, physicians, and other healthcare related staff.

10008 ■ **BeechTree Partners LLC**
875 N Michigan Ave., Ste. 3100
Chicago, IL 60611
Ph: (312)794-7808
E-mail: brad@beechtreepartners.com
URL: http://www.beechtreepartners.com

Executive search firm.

10009 ■ **Born and Bicknell**
Hillsboro Executive Park
4855 W Hillsboro Blvd., Ste. B10
Coconut Creek, FL 33073
Fr: 800-376-2676
E-mail: info@bornbicknell.com
URL: http://www.bornbicknell.com

Serves as a national physician opportunity placement agency. Offers staffing needs for physicians and those looking to hire physicians. Search methodology includes profile generation, recruitment and selection, screening and reference checking, interviews, contract negotiations, as well as follow-up through transition and guarantee periods.

10010 ■ **Break the Box Career Group**
36 Unity Ave.
Belmont, MA 02478
Ph: (617)489-8706
E-mail: info@btbcareergroup.com
URL: http://www.btbcareergroup.com

Serves as a national recruiting and placement

specializing in healthcare Features pharmacy jobs, physician jobs and radiology jobs.

10011 ■ **Breitner Transcription Services, Inc.**
1017 Turnpike St., Ste. 22A
Canton, MA 02021
Ph: (781)828-6411
Fax: (781)828-6431
Fr: 800-331-7004
E-mail: info@breitner.com
URL: http://www.breitner.com

Executive search firm focused on the healthcare industry.

10012 ■ **Carson Kolb Healthcare Group Inc.**
27201 Puerta Real, Ste. 420
Mission Viejo, CA 92691
Fax: (949)272-1483
Fr: 800-606-9439
E-mail: info@carsonkolb.com
URL: http://www.carsonkolb.com

Executive search firm focused on the healthcare industry.

10013 ■ **Cejka Search**
4 CityPlace Dr., Ste. 300
St. Louis, MO 63141
Fr: 800-678-7858
E-mail: info@cejkasearch.com
URL: http://www.cejkasearch.com

Executive search firm for the healthcare industry. Branch in Norcross, GA.

10014 ■ **CompHealth**
PO Box 713100
Salt Lake City, UT 84171-3100
Ph: (801)930-3000
Fax: (801)930-4517
Fr: 800-453-3030
E-mail: info@comphealth.com
URL: http://www.comphealth.com

Provides healthcare staffing and recruiting services covering certified registered nurse anesthetist, dosimetrist, imaging and radiation therapy, laboratory technology, medical physicist, nurse practitioner, nursing, pharmacy, physician, physician assistant, rehab therapy and respiratory therapy.

10015 ■ **DDS Resources**
16020 Swingley Ridge Rd., Ste. 340
Chesterfield, MO 63017
Ph: (636)536-6656
Fax: (636)536-6667
Fr: 877-337-0563
E-mail: info@mdr-inc.com
URL: http://www.mdr-inc.com/dentists.aspx

Serves as a dental recruitment agency in the United States. Specializes in matching qualified dentists with dental employers.

10016 ■ **The Energists**
10260 Westheimer Blvd., Ste. 300
Houston, TX 77042
Ph: (713)781-6881
Fax: (713)781-2998
E-mail: search@energists.com
URL: http://www.energists.com

Executive search firm.

10017 ■ **Enterprise Medical Services**
714 Spirit 40 Park Dr., No. 125
Chesterfield, MO 63005
Ph: (636)449-4100
Fax: (314)966-8833
Fr: 800-467-3737
E-mail: info@enterprisemed.com
URL: http://www.enterprisemed.com

Description: Covers recruiting and consulting organizations in the United States, connecting the most progressive hospitals, clinics and medical group with the most qualified physicians.

10018 ■ Foley Proctor Yoskowitz LLC
1 Cattano Ave.
Morristown, NJ 07960
Ph: (973)605-1000
Fax: (973)605-1020
Fr: 800-238-1123
E-mail: resumes@fpysearch.com
URL: http://www.fpysearch.com
Executive search firm for the healthcare industry.
Second location in New York, NY.

10019 ■ Global Medical Staffing
2450 Ft. Union Blvd.
Salt Lake, UT 84121
Ph: (801)449-3237
Fax: (801)449-3237
Fr: (866)858-6269
URL: http://www.gmedical.com
International and domestic physician recruitment firm.
Offers United States licensed physicians jobs in
emergency medicine, hospitalist/internal medicine,
primary care/family practice and psychiatry.

10020 ■ Harper Associates
31000 NW Hwy., Ste. 240
Farmington Hills, MI 48334
Ph: (248)932-1170
Fax: (248)932-1214
E-mail: info@harperjobs.com
URL: http://www.harperjobs.com
Executive search firm and employment agency.

10021 ■ Harris Brand Recruiting
4 Avis Dr., Ste. 1
Latham, NY 12110
Ph: (518)782-5250
Fr: 800-288-1730
E-mail: info@harrisbrand.com
URL: http://www.harrisbrand.com
Offers resource for physician jobs and practice op-
portunities for primary care and specialty doctors,
physician assistants, nurse practitioners and certified
nurse midwives.

10022 ■ Integrity Healthcare
2944 Needham Ct.
Delray Beach, FL 33445
Fr: 800-479-5028
URL: http://www.ihcrecruiting.com
Offers physician and healthcare staffing services
nationwide. Features physician job search according
to specialty and state.

10023 ■ Kendall and Davis
3668 S Geyer Rd. Ste. 100
St. Louis, MO 63127
Fax: 877-371-9976
Fr: (866)675-3755
E-mail: info@kendallanddavis.com
URL: http://www.kendallanddavis.com
Specializes in recruitment and placement of doctors
in physician jobs nationwide.

10024 ■ Keystone Healthcare Management
6075 Poplar Ave., Ste. 727
Memphis, TN 38119
Ph: (901)795-3600
Fax: (901)795-6060
Fr: (866)291-8600
E-mail: scross@keystonehealthcare.com
URL: http://www.keystonehealthcare.com
Specializes in the organization and management of
emergency physician groups, offering support ser-
vices in emergency department management, emer-
gency medicine and physician placement.

10025 ■ Lee Calhoon & Company Inc.
1621 Birchrun Rd.
PO Box 201
Birchrunville, PA 19421
Ph: (610)469-9000
Fax: (610)469-0398

Fr: 800-469-0896
E-mail: info@leecalhoon.com
URL: http://www.leecalhoon.com
Executive search firm.

10026 ■ Medical Search Consultants
2012 Otter Valley Ln.
Nashville, TN 37215
Fax: (615)665-8811
Fr: 800-991-1344
E-mail: medsearch@bellsouth.net
URL: http://www.medicalsearchconsultants.com
Specializes in recruiting physicians and other health-
care professionals to clinical practices across the
United States.

10027 ■ Medicorp
1421 Triad Center Dr., Ste. A
St. Peters, MO 63376
Ph: (636)278-1700
Fax: (636)278-6080
Fr: 877-295-7778
URL: http://www.medicorpinc.com
Offers physician employment opportunities available
in many specialties throughout the United States in
private practice or hospitals.

10028 ■ MedPlan Recruiting, Inc
3940 Montclair Rd., Ste. 202
Birmingham, AL 35213
Ph: (205)870-7068
E-mail: medplankab@aol.com
URL: http://www.medplanrecruiting.com
Serves as a recruiting firm for physicians and medi-
cal staff.

10029 ■ Merritt Hawkins & Associates
5001 Statesman Dr.
Irving, TX 75063
Ph: (469)524-1400
Fax: (469)524-1421
Fr: 800-876-0500
E-mail: info@merritthawkins.com
URL: http://www.merritthawkins.com
Physician recruitment firm. Provides physician search
and consulting services. Industries served: health
care.

10030 ■ O'Shea System of Employment Inc.
PO Box 2134
Aston, PA 19014
Ph: (610)364-3964
Fax: (610)364-3962
Fr: 800-220-5203
E-mail: osheasys@aol.com
Offers personnel staff recruiting nationally in the fol-
lowing fields: insurance, health care, financial,
information technology, administration, human re-
source, manufacturing and sales.

10031 ■ Pate Resources Group Inc.
505 Orleans St., Ste. 300
Beaumont, TX 77701
Ph: (409)833-4514
Fax: (409)833-4646
Fr: 800-669-4514
E-mail: opportunities@pateresourcesgroup.com
URL: http://www.pateresourcesgroup.com
Offers executive search and recruiting services to
professionals who include physicians, healthcare
administrators, engineers, accounting and financial
disciplines, legal, outplacement, sales and marketing.
Industries served: healthcare, petrochemicals, ac-
counting, utility, legal, and municipalities.

10032 ■ Physician Executive Management Center
3403 W Fletcher Ave.
Tampa, FL 33618-2813
Ph: (813)963-1800
Fax: (813)963-0569
E-mail: info@physicianexecutive.com
URL: http://www.physicianexecutive.com

Specialists in physician executive search for health
care delivery organizations such as health systems,
hospitals, group practice and managed care.

10033 ■ P.J. Murphy & Associates Inc.
735 N Water St.
Milwaukee, WI 53202
Ph: (414)277-9777
Fax: (414)277-7626
E-mail: info@pjmurphy.com
URL: http://www.pjmurphy.com
Management consulting firm which specializes in
retained executive search. Industries served: all
industries, to include healthcare and physician
recruiting.

10034 ■ Professional Placement Associates, Inc.
287 Bowman Ave.
Purchase, NY 10577-2517
Ph: (914)251-1000
Fax: (914)251-1055
E-mail: careers@ppasearch.com
URL: http://www.ppasearch.com
Executive search firm specializing in the health and
medical field.

10035 ■ Team Placement Service, Inc.
1414 Prince St., Ste. 202
Alexandria, VA 22314
Ph: (703)820-8618
Fax: (703)820-3368
Fr: 800-495-6767
E-mail: 4jobs@teamplace.com
URL: http://www.teamplace.com
Full-service personnel consultants provide placement
for healthcare staff, physician and dentist, private
practice, and hospitals. Conduct interviews, tests,
and reference checks to select the top 20% of
applicants. Survey applicants' skill levels, provide
backup information on each candidate, select compatible candidates for consideration, and insure the hiring process minimizes potential legal liability. Industries served: healthcare and government agencies
providing medical, dental, biotech, laboratory, hospitals, and physician search.

10036 ■ Weatherby Locums
6451 N Federal Hwy., Ste. 800
Fort Lauderdale, FL 33308
Ph: (954)343-3050
Fax: (866)588-0085
Fr: (866)906-1637
E-mail: jobs@weatherbylocums.com
URL: http://www.weatherbylocums.com
Executive search firm for physicians. Branch office in
Fairfax, VA.

10037 ■ Whitaker Medical
1200 Enclave Pkwy., Ste. 200
Houston, TX 77077
Ph: (281)870-1000
Fax: (866)513-0183
Fr: 800-444-5628
URL: http://www.whitakermedical.com
Exists as a healthcare recruitment firm that provides
staffing solutions for healthcare professionals and
facilities across the nation.

ONLINE JOB SOURCES AND SERVICES

10038 ■ American Association of Anatomists Career Center
9650 Rockville Pike
Bethesda, MD 20814-3998
Ph: (301)634-7910
Fax: (301)634-7965
E-mail: exec@anatomy.org
URL: http://aaatoday.org/content/career-center
Description: Job advertisers include academic sites
in the U.S. and Canada. Job seekers may review

these posted jobs through "Positions Offered" or post their own needs under "Positions Wanted." Offerings for Postdoctoral Positions also available. Contains Career Resources sections and links to online career resources.

10039 ■ American Medical Athletic Association
4405 East-West Hwy., Ste. 405
Bethesda, MD 20814
Ph: (301)913-9517
Fax: (301)913-9520
Fr: 800-776-2732
E-mail: amaa@americanrunning.org
URL: http://www.amaasportsmed.org

Description: Provides information on training, diet, injury prevention, and sports medicine to physicians and other healthcare professionals as leaders of active and healthy lifestyles. Hosts a sports medicine professional referral service made up of doctors, nutritionists, and other sports-oriented professionals.

10040 ■ CareerVitals.com
URL: http://www.careervitals.com

Description: Serves as a job board for healthcare professionals in different specializations.

10041 ■ DocCafe.com
URL: http://www.doccafe.com

Description: Provides physician employment opportunities and services. Offers physician hiring service and job listings.

10042 ■ DocJungle.com
URL: http://www.docjungle.com

Description: Serves as job board built specifically for physicians, doctors, and surgeons. Provides CV posting, job search and career development resources for physicians.

10043 ■ EmployMED: Healthcare Job Listings
E-mail: customerservice@evalumed.com
URL: http://www.evalumed.com/EmployMed.aspx

Description: Lists practice opportunities throughout North America for all medical specialties. Contains job listings directory. Posting option is available for those who wish to advertise jobs. Fee: $25 per month per posting for minimum of two months.

10044 ■ Employment for Physicians.com
URL: http://www.employmentforphysicians.com

Description: Provides physician employment in various specialties such as cardiology, anesthesiology, radiology, plastic surgery, family practice and psychiatry.

10045 ■ FCS - The 1st Choice in Psychiatric Recruitment
1711 Ashley Cir., Ste. 6
Bowling Green, KY 42104-5801
Fax: (270)782-1055
Fr: 800-783-9152
E-mail: admin@fcspsy.com
URL: http://www.fcspsy.com

Description: Physician search firm specializing in the recruitment of psychiatrists. After the applicant fills out an interest survey, a tailored search is run on the jobs database. Confidential and free.

10046 ■ Health Care Job Store
395 South End Ave., Ste. 15-D
New York, NY 10280
Ph: (561)630-5201
E-mail: jobs@healthcarejobstore.com
URL: http://www.healthcarejobstore.com

Description: Job sites include every job title in the healthcare industry, every healthcare industry and every geographic location in the U.S.

10047 ■ Health Care Recruitment Online
E-mail: info@healthcarerecruitment.com
URL: http://healthcarerecruitment.com

Description: Helps seekers find healthcare positions through on-line postings with national staffing companies and hospital partners. Main files include: Featured Employers, Job Search, Immediate Openings, Relocating, Career Management, State boards, and more.

10048 ■ Health Search USA
Fax: (602)650-0664
Fr: 800-899-2200
E-mail: info@healthsearchusa.com
URL: http://www.healthsearchusa.com

Description: A site for national physician recruitment. Offers job postings classified by region and salary comparison.

10049 ■ HEALTHeCAREERS Network
Fr: 888-884-8242
E-mail: info@healthecareers.com
URL: http://www.healthecareers.com

Description: Career search site for jobs in all health care specialties; educational resources; visa and licensing information for relocation; interesting articles; relocation tools; links to professional organizations and general resources.

10050 ■ Hospital Jobs OnLine
E-mail: support@hospitaljobsonline.com
URL: http://www.hospitaljobsonline.com

Description: Serves as a niche healthcare job board designed exclusively for hospitals, healthcare companies, and healthcare job seekers.

10051 ■ iHirePhysicians.com
URL: http://www.ihirephysicians.com

Description: Serves as a job site network that lists physician jobs from job postings, internet job boards, newspapers and classified ads.

10052 ■ IMcareer.com
URL: http://www.imcareer.com

Description: Serves as a job board for internal medicine physicians and jobs for sub-specialty of internal medicine.

10053 ■ Mdsearch.com
URL: http://www.mdsearch.com

Description: Provides resources for physicians who wish to advance their careers. Keeps users updated on industry news and information. Allows users to browse physician jobs by specialty.

10054 ■ MDSPots.com
E-mail: info@mdspots.com
URL: http://www.mdspots.com

Description: Helps physicians locate new practice and job opportunities. Offers free access to physician employment opportunities, free CV posting, customized job search capabilities and real time e-mail notifications of new physician employment opportunities.

10055 ■ MedExplorer.com
E-mail: medmaster@medexplorer.com
URL: http://www.medexplorer.com

Description: Employment postings make up one module of this general medical site. Other sections contain: Newsletter, Classifieds, and Discussion Forum.

10056 ■ MedSourceConsultants.com
300 Main St., 7th Fl.
Stamford, CT 06901
Fax: (203)324-0555
Fr: 800-575-2880
E-mail: dpascale@medsourceconsultants.com
URL: http://www.medsourceconsultants.com

Description: Site houses a physician search and consulting company for psychiatrists. Consultants at-

tempt to match job seekers to positions according to the individual's personal and professional needs. This page also aids institutions looking to recruit psychiatrists.

10057 ■ Medzilla.com
URL: http://www.medzilla.com

Description: General medical website which matches employers and job hunters to their ideal employees and jobs through search capabilities. Main files include: Post Jobs, Search Resumes, Post Resumes, Search Jobs, Head Hunters, Articles, Salary Survey.

10058 ■ Monster Healthcare
URL: http://healthcare.monster.com

Description: Delivers nationwide access to healthcare recruiting. Employers can post job listings or ads. Job seekers can post and code resumes, and search over 150,000 healthcare job listings, healthcare career advice columns, career resources information, and member employer profiles and services.

10059 ■ NEJM CareerCenter
URL: http://www.nejmjobs.org

Description: Offers physician job searching tools with search functionalities that include specialty and geography. Provides physician-employment articles in the resource center as well as articles on physician careers, physician job-hunting tips, and physician employment.

10060 ■ Neonatology on the Web
URL: http://www.neonatology.org

Description: Features clinical resources, career information, job directory, and internet resources for neonatal-perinatal medicine.

10061 ■ PhysEmp.com
URL: http://www.physemp.com

Description: Provides listings of physician jobs for all specialties. Features online physician jobs, job search, and physician employment opportunities and recruitment.

10062 ■ Physician-Employments.com
URL: http://www.physician-employments.com

Description: Exists as an employment opportunities resource center for physicians and others in the healthcare industry.

10063 ■ PhysicianCrossroads.com
E-mail: info@physiciancrossroads.com
URL: http://physiciancrossroads.com

Description: Consists of physicians within their professional specialties and a multitude of physician advocate professionals who are intent and passionate about helping colleagues be more successful in their medical practices.

10064 ■ PhysicianDepot.com
URL: http://www.physiciandepot.com

Description: Provides a one-stop source for physician positions. Offers physician employment listings nationwide, in all specialties, and both permanent and local positions.

10065 ■ PhysicianRecruiting.com
Fr: 800-880-2028
E-mail: info@physicianrecruiting.com
URL: http://www.physicianrecruiting.com

Description: Provides listings of job opportunities for physicians. Lists jobs according to specialty and state.

10066 ■ PhysiciansCentral.com
URL: http://www.physicianscentral.com

Description: Provides physician jobs and products in the healthcare industry.

10067 ■ PracticeLink.com
E-mail: physicianhelpdesk@practicelink.com
URL: http://www.practicelink.com

Description: Provides listings of job opportunities for physicians.

10068 ■ United Search Associates: Health Network USA
PO Box 342
Vinita, OK 74301
Ph: (918)323-4165
E-mail: jobs@hnusa.com
URL: http://homepage.mac.com/hnusa

Description: Visitors may explore healthcare positions, submit an electronic resume, or advertise with the site.

TRADESHOWS

10069 ■ AACE Annual Meeting and Clinical Congress
American Association of Clinical Endocrinologists
245 Riverside Ave., Ste. 200
Jacksonville, FL 32202
Ph: (904)353-7878
Fax: (904)353-8185
Fr: 800-838-2223
E-mail: segan@aace.com
URL: http://www.aace.com

Annual. Includes exhibits of diagnostic equipment, educational materials, publications, electronic medical records, laboratory services, patient support or services, pharmaceutical, recruitment, professional placement, and others. 2013 May 1-5; New York, NY; Sheraton Phoenix Downtown and the Phoenix Convention Center.

10070 ■ American Academy of Pediatrics National Conference and Exhibition
American Academy of Pediatrics
141 Northwest Point Blvd.
PO Box 927
Elk Grove Village, IL 60007-1098
Ph: (847)434-4000
Fax: (847)434-8000
E-mail: commun@aap.org
URL: http://www.aap.org

Annual. Primary Exhibits: Prescription and over-the-counter drugs, infant formulas and baby foods, medical equipment, developmental toys, and publications. Dates and Locations: 2012 Oct 20-23; New Orleans, LA; Ernest N. Morial Convention Center; 2013 Oct 26-29; Orlando, FL; Orange County Convention Center; 2014 Oct 10-14; San Diego, CA; San Diego Convention Center.

10071 ■ American Academy of Physical Medicine and Rehabilitation Annual Assembly
American Academy of Physical Medicine and Rehabilitation
9700 W. Bryn Mawr Ave., Ste. 200
Rosemont, IL 60018-5701
Ph: (847)737-6000
Fax: (847)737-6001
E-mail: info@aapmr.org
URL: http://www.aapmr.org

Annual. Primary Exhibits: Pharmaceuticals, electrodiagnostic equipment, wheelchairs, and related equipment, supplies, and services. Dates and Locations: 2012 Nov 15-18; Atlanta, GA; World Congress Center; 2013 Oct 03-06; Washington, DC; Marriott Convention Center; 2014 Nov 13-16; San Diego, CA; Marriott Convention Center.

10072 ■ American College of Osteopathic Obstetricians and Gynecologists Annual Convention
American College of Osteopathic Obstetricians and Gynecologists
8851 Camp Bowie W., Ste. 120
Fort Worth, TX 76116

Ph: (817)377-0421
Fax: (817)377-0439
Fr: 800-875-6360
E-mail: info@acoog.com
URL: http://www.acoog.com

Annual. Primary Exhibits: Pharmaceuticals and medical supplies pertaining to Ob/Gyn. Clothing, vitamins, personal toiletries (all relating to healthcare for women).

10073 ■ American College of Sports Medicine Annual Meeting
American College of Sports Medicine
401 W. Michigan St.
PO Box 1440
Indianapolis, IN 46202-3233
Ph: (317)637-9200
Fax: (317)634-7817
Fr: 800-486-5643
E-mail: publicinfo@acsm.org
URL: http://www.acsm.org

Annual. Primary Exhibits: Exercise equipment, physiological monitoring equipment, ergometers, treadmills, scientific publications, sports medicine monitoring software, and pharmaceuticals. Dates and Locations: 2012 May 30 - Jun 02; San Francisco, CA; 2013 May 29 - Jun 01; Indianapolis, IN; 2014 May 28-31; Orlando, FL; 2015 May 27-30; San Diego, CA.

10074 ■ American College of Surgeons Annual Clinical Congress
American College of Surgeons
633 N. St. Clair St.
Chicago, IL 60611-3211
Ph: (312)202-5000
Fax: (312)202-5001
Fr: 800-621-4111
E-mail: postmaster@facs.org
URL: http://www.facs.org

Annual. Primary Exhibits: Medical products, patent care, practice management and educational services and products. Dates and Locations: 2012 Sep 30 - Oct 04; Chicago, IL; 2013 Oct 06-10; Washington, DC; 2014 Oct 26-30; San Francisco, CA; 2015 Oct 04-08; Chicago, IL; 2016 Oct 16-20; Washington, DC; 2017 Oct 22-26; San Diego, CA; 2018 Oct 21-25; Boston, MA; 2019 Oct 27-31; San Francisco, CA.

10075 ■ American Heart Association Scientific Sessions
American Heart Association
7272 Greenville Ave.
Dallas, TX 75231-4596
Ph: 800-242-8721
URL: http://www.americanheart.org

Annual. Primary Exhibits: Equipment, books, pharmaceuticals, exercise equipment, heart-healthy food, and services relevant to cardiological research or physician practice.

10076 ■ American Medical Women's Association Annual Meeting
American Medical Women's Association
100 N. 20th St., 4th Fl.
Philadelphia, PA 19103
Ph: (215)320-3716
Fax: (215)564-2175
E-mail: info@amwa-doc.org
URL: http://www.amwa-doc.org

Annual. Primary Exhibits: Medical equipment, supplies, pharmaceuticals, and services. Dates and Locations: 2012 Apr 13-15; Miami, FL; Sofitel Miami.

10077 ■ American Pain Society Scientific Meeting
American Pain Society
4700 W. Lake Ave.
Glenview, IL 60025
Ph: (847)375-4715
Fax: (866)574-2654
E-mail: info@ampainsoc.org
URL: http://www.ampainsoc.org

Annual. Primary Exhibits: Pharmaceutical and medical instruments, medical equipment, products, supplies, services and alternative delivery systems (homecare, hospice). Dates and Locations: 2012 May 16-19; Honolulu, HI.

10078 ■ American Society for Laser Medicine and Surgery Conference
American Society for Laser Medicine and Surgery
2100 Stewart Ave., Ste. 240
Wausau, WI 54401
Ph: (715)845-9283
Fax: (715)848-2493
Fr: 877-258-6028
E-mail: information@aslms.org
URL: http://www.aslms.org

Annual. Primary Exhibits: Laser medicine equipment, supplies, and services. Dates and Locations: 2012 Apr 18-22; Kissimmee, FL; Gaylord Palms Resort & Convention Center ; 2013 Apr 03-07; Boston, MA; Sheraton Boston Hotel/Hynes Convention Center; 2014 Apr 02-06; Phoenix, AZ; Phoenix Convention Center/Sheraton Phoenix Downtown Hotel; 2015 Apr 22-26; Kissimmee, FL; Gaylord Palms Resort & Convention Center.

10079 ■ American Thoracic Society International Conference
American Thoracic Society
25 Broadway
New York, NY 10006-2755
Ph: (212)315-8600
Fax: (212)315-6498
E-mail: atsinfo@thoracic.org
URL: http://www.thoracic.org

Annual. Includes exhibits of pharmaceutical products, medical equipment, publications, and research services.

10080 ■ Annual Regional Anesthesia Meeting and Workshops
American Society of Regional Anesthesia and Pain Medicine
520 N Northwest Hwy.
Park Ridge, IL 60068
Ph: (847)825-7246
Fax: (847)825-5658
E-mail: j.kahlfeldt@asahq.org
URL: http://www.asra.com

Annual. Features refresher courses, general sessions, parallel sessions, cadaver workshops, intensive lower back pain workshops, problem-based learning discussions, poster presentations, and a technical exhibition.

10081 ■ ASCPT Annual Meeting
American Society for Clinical Pharmacology and Therapeutics
528 N Washington St.
Alexandria, VA 22314
Ph: (703)836-6981
Fax: (703)836-5223
E-mail: info@ascpt.org
URL: http://www.ascpt.org

Annual. Includes exhibits of products or services in the field of clinical pharmacology such as pharmaceuticals, contract research, software developers, clinical research equipment supplies, books, and others. Provides networking and career enhancement opportunities for attendees. 2013 March 6-9; Indianapolis, IN; JW Marriott Indianapolis. 2014 March 19-22; Atlanta, GA; Atlanta Marriott Marquis.

10082 ■ National Medical Association Annual Convention and Scientific Assembly
National Medical Association
8403 Colesville Rd., Ste. 920
Silver Spring, MD 20910
Ph: (202)347-1895
Fax: (202)347-0722
URL: http://www.nmanet.org

Annual. Primary Exhibits: Medical equipment, supplies, and services. Dates and Locations: 2012 Jul 28 - Aug 01; New Orleans, LA.

OTHER SOURCES

10083 ■ American Academy of Allergy Asthma & Immunology
555 E Wells St., Ste. 1100
Milwaukee, WI 53202-3823
Ph: (414)272-6071
Fax: (414)272-6070
E-mail: info@aaaai.org
URL: http://www.aaaai.org

Description: Represents asthma specialists, clinical immunologists, allied health professionals, and others with a special interest in the research and treatment of allergic disease. Strives for advancement of the knowledge and practice of allergy, asthma, and immunology for optimal patient care.

10084 ■ American Academy of Clinical Toxicology (AACT)
110 W Lancaster Ave., Ste. 230
Wayne, PA 19087
Ph: (703)556-9222
Fax: (703)556-8729
E-mail: admin@clintox.org
URL: http://www.clintox.org

Description: Physicians, veterinarians, pharmacists, nurses research scientists, and analytical chemists. Seeks to unite medical scientists and facilitate the exchange of information. Encourages the development of therapeutic methods and technology. Conducts professional training in poison information and emergency service personnel.

10085 ■ American Academy of Craniofacial Pain (AACP)
12100 Sunset Hills Rd., Ste. 130
Reston, VA 20190-3221
Ph: (703)234-4142
Fax: (703)435-4390
Fr: 800-322-8651
E-mail: central@aacfp.org
URL: http://www.aacfp.org

Description: Health Care Practitioners who treat head, facial, and neck pain. Functions as a referral service for patients suffering from head, facial, and neck pain worldwide. Plans to establish computerized medical procedures and insurance database.

10086 ■ American Academy of Dermatology (AAD)
PO Box 4014
Schaumburg, IL 60168
Ph: (847)240-1280
Fax: (847)240-1859
Fr: (866)503-SKIN
E-mail: tsmith@aad.org
URL: http://www.aad.org

Description: Serves as professional society of medical doctors specializing in skin diseases. Provides educational opportunities through meetings and publications. Provides support to members' practices. Promotes dermatologists as experts in treating skin, hair, and nail conditions. Maintains liaison with Congress, Federal agencies, State legislatures and State agencies.

10087 ■ American Academy of Emergency Medicine
555 E Wells St., Ste. 1100
Milwaukee, WI 53202-3800
Fax: (414)276-3349
Fr: 800-884-2236
URL: http://www.aaem.org

Description: Physicians specializing in emergency medicine or pediatric emergency medicine, medical students and residents. Aims to advance the study and profession of emergency medicine and to represent members' economic and professional interests. Supports growth of medical residency and graduate medical education programs and works to create a professional and legal environment conducive to the delivery of quality emergency medical care.

10088 ■ American Academy of Facial Plastic and Reconstructive Surgery
310 S Henry St.
Alexandria, VA 22314
Ph: (703)299-9291
Fax: (703)299-8898
E-mail: info@aafprs.org
URL: http://www.aafprs.org

Description: Represents facial plastic and reconstructive surgeons throughout the world. Promotes quality facial plastic surgery through education, dissemination of professional information, and the establishment of professional standards. Serves as the public's information source on facial plastic surgery.

10089 ■ American Academy of Family Physicians (AAFP)
PO Box 11210
Shawnee Mission, KS 66207-1210
Ph: (913)906-6000
Fax: (913)906-6075
Fr: 800-274-2237
E-mail: contactcenter@aafp.org
URL: http://www.aafp.org

Description: Serves as a professional society of family physicians who provide continuing comprehensive care to patients.

10090 ■ American Academy of Medical Acupuncture (AAMA)
1970 E Grand Ave., Ste. 330
El Segundo, CA 90245
Ph: (310)364-0193
Fax: (310)364-0196
E-mail: administrator@medicalacupuncture.org
URL: http://www.medicalacupuncture.org

Description: Professional society of physicians and osteopaths who utilize acupuncture in their practices. Provides ongoing training and information related to the Chinese practice of puncturing the body at specific points to cure disease or relieve pain. Offers educational and research programs.

10091 ■ American Academy of Neurology (AAN)
1080 Montreal Ave.
St. Paul, MN 55116
Ph: (651)695-2717
Fax: (651)695-2791
Fr: 800-879-1960
E-mail: memberservices@aan.com
URL: http://www.aan.com

Description: Professional society of medical doctors specializing in brain and nervous system diseases. Maintains placement service. Sponsors research and educational programs. Compiles statistics. Publishes scientific journal.

10092 ■ American Academy of Otolaryngology - Head and Neck Surgery (AAO-HNS)
1650 Diagonal Rd.
Alexandria, VA 22314
Ph: (703)836-4444
E-mail: membersservices@entnet.org
URL: http://www.entnet.org

Description: Professional society of medical doctors specializing in otolaryngology (diseases of the ear, nose, and throat) and head and neck surgery. Represents otolaryngology in governmental and socioeconomic areas and provides high-quality medical education for otolaryngologists. Coordinates Combined Otolaryngological Spring Meetings for ten national otolaryngological societies. Operates job information exchange service and museum.

10093 ■ American Association of Acupuncture and Oriental Medicine (AAAOM)
PO Box 96503
Washington, DC 20090-6503
Fax: (916)443-4766

Fr: (866)455-7999
E-mail: jeannie@goodki.com
URL: http://www.aaaomonline.org

Description: Professional acupuncturists and Oriental Medicine Practitioners. Seeks to: elevate the standards of education and practice of acupuncture and oriental medicine; establish laws governing acupuncture; provide a forum to share information on acupuncture techniques; increase public awareness of acupuncture; support research in the field. Conducts educational programs; compiles statistics. Operates speakers' bureau.

10094 ■ American Association of Certified Orthoptists (AACO)
3914 Nakoma Rd.
Madison, WI 53711
Ph: (608)233-5383
Fax: (608)263-4247
E-mail: bfurr@umich.edu
URL: http://www.orthoptics.org

Description: Orthoptists certified by the American Orthoptic Council, after completing a minimum of 24 months' special training, to treat defects in binocular function. Assists in postgraduate instruction courses; conducts programs and courses at international, national, and regional meetings; helps individual orthoptists with special or unusual problem cases; trains new orthoptists. Operates a placement listing.

10095 ■ American Association of Clinical Endocrinologists
245 Riverside Ave., Ste. 200
Jacksonville, FL 32202
Ph: (904)353-7878
Fax: (904)353-8185
Fr: 800-838-2223
E-mail: segan@aace.com
URL: http://www.aace.com

Description: Represents physicians with special education, training, and interests in the practice of clinical endocrinology. Seeks to enhance the quality of patient care. Provides practicing clinical endocrinologists with an avenue for the study of the scientific, social, political, and economic aspects of endocrinology.

10096 ■ American Association for Geriatric Psychiatry (AAGP)
7910 Woodmont Ave., Ste. 1050
Bethesda, MD 20814-3004
Ph: (301)654-7850
Fax: (301)654-4137
E-mail: main@aagponline.org
URL: http://www.aagponline.org

Description: Psychiatrists interested in promoting better mental health care for the elderly. Maintains placement service and speakers' bureau.

10097 ■ American Association of Immunologists (AAI)
9650 Rockville Pike
Bethesda, MD 20814-3998
Ph: (301)634-7178
Fax: (301)634-7887
E-mail: infoaai@aai.org
URL: http://www.aai.org

Description: Represents scientists engaged in immunological research including aspects of virology, bacteriology, biochemistry, genetics, and related disciplines. Advances knowledge of immunology and related disciplines and facilitate the interchange of information among investigators in various fields. Promotes interaction between laboratory investigators and clinicians. Conducts training courses, symposia, workshop, and lectures. Compiles statistics.

10098 ■ American Association of Neuropathologists (AANP)
Case Western Reserve University
2103 Cornell Rd., WRB 5101
Cleveland, OH 44106

Ph: (216)368-3671
Fax: (216)368-8964
E-mail: aanp@case.edu
URL: http://www.neuropath.org

Description: Promotes neuropathology, especially the study of diverse aspects of diseases of the nervous system including changes at tissue, cellular, subcellular, and molecular levels with consideration of etiology and pathophysiology, genetics, epidemiology and clinical manifestations of such diseases.

10099 ■ American Association of Physician Specialists (AAPS)
5550 W Executive Dr., Ste. 400
Tampa, FL 33609
Ph: (813)433-2277
Fax: (813)830-6599
E-mail: wcarbone@aapsus.org
URL: http://www.aapsus.org

Description: Represents twelve major specialties and twelve sub-specialties of medicine. Accepts qualified physicians into membership with either an allopathic (MD) or osteopathic (DO) degree. Serves as the official headquarters for 15 academies of medicine and boards of certification in the following specialties: anesthesiology, dermatology, disaster medicine, emergency medicine, family practice, internal medicine, geriatric medicine, neurology/psychiatry, obstetrics/gynecology, orthopedic surgery, plastic/reconstructive surgery, radiology, surgery.

10100 ■ American College of Chest Physicians (ACCP)
3300 Dundee Rd.
Northbrook, IL 60062
Ph: (847)498-1400
Fax: (847)498-5460
Fr: 800-343-2227
E-mail: accp@chestnet.org
URL: http://www.chestnet.org/accp

Description: Serves as a professional society of physicians and surgeons specializing in diseases of the chest (heart and lungs). Promotes undergraduate and postgraduate medical education and research in the field. Sponsors forums. Maintains placement service; conducts educational programs.

10101 ■ American College of Emergency Physicians (ACEP)
PO Box 619911
Irving, TX 75038-2522
Ph: (972)550-0911
Fax: (972)580-2816
Fr: 800-798-1822
E-mail: execdirector@acep.org
URL: http://www.acep.org

Description: Supports quality emergency medical care and promotes the interests of emergency physicians. Represents more than 22,000 members and is the emergency medicine specialty society recognized by organized medicine.

10102 ■ American College Health Association (ACHA)
891 Elkridge Landing Rd., Ste. 100
Linthicum, MD 21090
Ph: (410)859-1500
Fax: (410)859-1510
E-mail: contact@acha.org
URL: http://www.acha.org

Description: Provides an organization in which institutions of higher education and interested individuals may work together to promote health in its broadest aspects for students and all other members of the college community. Offers continuing education programs for health professionals. Maintains placement listings for physicians and other personnel seeking positions in college health. Compiles statistics. Conducts seminars and training programs.

10103 ■ American College of Medical Quality (ACMQ)
5272 River Rd., Ste. 630
Bethesda, MD 20816

Ph: (301)718-6516
Fax: (301)656-0989
Fr: 800-924-2149
E-mail: krumholz.alan@mayo.edu
URL: http://www.acmq.org

Description: Physicians, affiliates, and institutions. Seeks to educate and set standards of competence in the field of quality improvement and management. Offers a core curriculum in quality. Maintains speakers' bureau.

10104 ■ American College of Occupational and Environmental Medicine (ACOEM)
25 NW Point Blvd., Ste. 700
Elk Grove Village, IL 60007-1030
Ph: (847)818-1800
Fax: (847)818-9266
E-mail: memberinfo@acoem.org
URL: http://www.acoem.org

Description: Represents physicians specializing in occupational and environmental medicine. Promotes maintenance and improvement of the health of workers; works to increase awareness of occupational medicine as a medical specialty. Sponsors educational programs; maintains placement service.

10105 ■ American College of Osteopathic Internists (ACOI)
3 Bethesda Metro Ctr., Ste. 508
Bethesda, MD 20814
Ph: (301)656-8877
Fax: (301)656-7133
Fr: 800-327-5183
E-mail: bjd@acoi.org
URL: http://www.acoi.org

Description: Osteopathic doctors who limit their practice to internal medicine and various subspecialties and who intend, through postdoctoral education, to qualify as certified specialists in the field. Aims to provide educational programs and to improve educational standards in the field of osteopathic internal medicine. Sponsors competitions. Compiles statistics; offers placement service.

10106 ■ American College of Osteopathic Surgeons (ACOS)
123 N Henry St.
Alexandria, VA 22314-2903
Ph: (703)684-0416
Fax: (703)684-3280
Fr: 800-888-1312
E-mail: info@facos.org
URL: http://www.facos.org

Description: Professional society of osteopathic physicians specializing in surgery and surgical specialties. Maintains placement service; conducts seminars in continuing surgical education.

10107 ■ American College of Physician Executives (ACPE)
400 N Ashley Dr., Ste. 400
Tampa, FL 33602
Ph: (813)287-2000
Fax: (813)287-8993
Fr: 800-562-8088
E-mail: acpe@acpe.org
URL: http://www.acpe.org

Description: Physicians whose primary professional responsibility is in management. Provides for continuing education and certification of the physician executive and the advancement and recognition of the physician executive and the profession. Offers specialized career planning, counseling, recruitment and placement services, and research and information data on physician executives.

10108 ■ American College of Preventive Medicine
455 Massachusetts Ave. NW, Ste. 200
Washington, DC 20001-2621
Ph: (202)466-2044

Fax: (202)466-2662
E-mail: info@acpm.org
URL: http://www.acpm.org

Description: Represents specialists in preventive medicine. Focuses on disease prevention and health promotion. Represents preventive medicine in national forums that contribute to the organization's role as a national resource of expertise in disease prevention and health promotion.

10109 ■ American College of Radiology (ACR)
1891 Preston White Dr.
Reston, VA 20191
Ph: (703)648-8900
Fax: (703)264-2093
Fr: 800-227-5463
E-mail: info@acr.org
URL: http://www.acr.org

Description: Principal organization serving radiologists with programs that focus on the practice of radiology and the delivery of comprehensive radiological health services. These programs in medical sciences, education, and in practice management, serve the public interest and the interests of the medical community in which radiologists serve in both diagnostic and therapeutic roles. Seeks to "advance the science of radiology, improve radiologic service to the patient, study the economic aspects of the practice of radiology, and encourage improved and continuing education for radiologists and allied professional fields".

10110 ■ American College of Sports Medicine (ACSM)
401 W Michigan St.
Indianapolis, IN 46202-3233
Ph: (317)637-9200
Fax: (317)634-7817
E-mail: publicinfo@acsm.org
URL: http://www.acsm.org

Description: Promotes and integrates scientific research, education, and practical applications of sports medicine and exercise science to maintain and enhance physical performance, fitness, health, and quality of life. Certifies fitness leaders, fitness instructors, exercise test technologists, exercise specialists, health/fitness program directors, and U.S. military fitness personnel. Grants Continuing Medical Education (CME) and Continuing Education Credits (CEC). Operates more than 50 committees.

10111 ■ American Gastroenterological Association (AGA)
4930 Del Ray Ave.
Bethesda, MD 20814
Ph: (301)654-2055
Fax: (301)654-5920
E-mail: member@gastro.org
URL: http://www.gastro.org

Description: Physicians of internal medicine certified in gastroenterology; radiologists, pathologists, surgeons, and physiologists with special interest and competency in gastroenterology. Studies normal and abnormal conditions of the digestive organs and problems connected with their metabolism; conducts scientific research; offers placement services.

10112 ■ American Health Quality Association (AHQA)
1776 I St. NW, 9th Fl.
Washington, DC 20036
Ph: (202)331-5790
Fax: (202)331-9334
E-mail: info@ahqa.org
URL: http://www.ahqa.org

Description: Institutions and individuals. Develops communication programs for physicians, institutions, and others interested in peer review organizations (PROs). Provides a national forum for the interchange of ideas, techniques, and information relating to medical quality assessment. Conducts courses and on-site educational programs to increase physicians' involvement and leadership in PROs, improve practice patterns through review, understand and use PRO data to improve service delivery, pre-admission review, profile analysis, retrospective review, and organizational development. Sponsors placement service; maintains a speakers' bureau and a library.

10113 ■ American Hospital Association (AHA)
155 N Wacker Dr.
Chicago, IL 60606
Ph: (312)422-3000
Fax: (312)422-4796
E-mail: rich@aha.org
URL: http://www.aha.org

Description: Represents health care provider organizations. Seeks to advance the health of individuals and communities. Leads, represents, and serves health care provider organizations that are accountable to the community and committed to health improvement.

10114 ■ American Medical Association (AMA)
515 N State St.
Chicago, IL 60654
Ph: (312)464-5262
Fr: 800-621-8335
E-mail: msc-amermedassn@ama-assn.org
URL: http://www.ama-assn.org

Description: Represents county medical societies and physicians. Disseminates scientific information to members and the public. Informs members on significant medical and health legislation on state and national levels and represents the profession before Congress and governmental agencies. Cooperates in setting standards for medical schools, hospitals, residency programs, and continuing medical education courses. Offers physician placement service and counseling on practice management problems. Operates library that lends material and provides specific medical information to physicians. Maintains Ad-hoc committees for such topics as health care planning and principles of medical ethics.

10115 ■ American Medical Group Association (AMGA)
One Prince St.
Alexandria, VA 22314-3318
Ph: (703)838-0033
Fax: (703)548-1890
E-mail: dfisher@amga.org
URL: http://www.amga.org

Description: Represents the interests of medical groups. Advocates for the medical groups and patients through innovation and information sharing, benchmarking, developing leadership, and improving patient care. Provides political advocacy, educational and networking programs and publications, benchmarking data services, and financial and operations assistance.

10116 ■ American Mental Health Alliance (AMHA)
PO Box 4075
Portland, OR 97208-4075
Ph: (503)227-2027
Fr: 888-826-3682
E-mail: memberinfo@americanmentalhealth.com
URL: http://www.americanmentalhealth.com

Description: Represents mental health professionals licensed or certified for independent practice. Creates a professional community that provides therapy of the highest quality and ethical standards. Supports and markets competent, ethical mental health services that preserve privacy and confidentiality. Supports education, supervision, and research opportunities for members. Opposes legislation and regulations that invade patent privacy and confidentiality.

10117 ■ American Mental Health Counselors Association (AMHCA)
801 N Fairfax St., Ste. 304
Alexandria, VA 22314
Ph: (703)548-6002

Fax: (703)548-4775
Fr: 800-326-2642
E-mail: mhamilton@amhca.org
URL: http://www.amhca.org

Description: Professional counselors employed in mental health services; students. Aims to: deliver quality mental health services to children, youth, adults, families, and organizations; improve the availability and quality of counseling services through licensure and certification, training standards, and consumer advocacy. Supports specialty and special interest networks. Fosters communication among members. A division of the American Counseling Association.

10118 ■ American Muslim Women Physicians Association (AMWPA)
6300 Stonewood Dr., Ste. 412
Plano, TX 75024
Ph: (817)938-0792
E-mail: info@amwpa.org
URL: http://amwpa.org

Description: Promotes health, welfare and education of women. Improves the condition of women's health through medical resources. Provides a platform for Muslim women in medicine and raises awareness of issues regarding community welfare.

10119 ■ American Osteopathic Association (AOA)
142 E Ontario St.
Chicago, IL 60611
Ph: (312)202-8000
Fax: (312)202-8200
Fr: 800-621-1773
E-mail: info@osteopathic.org
URL: http://www.osteopathic.org

Description: Osteopathic physicians, surgeons, and graduates of approved colleges of osteopathic medicine. Associate members include teaching, research, administrative, and executive employees of approved colleges, hospitals, divisional societies, and affiliated organizations. Forms (with its affiliates) an officially recognized structure of the osteopathic profession. Promotes the public health to encourage scientific research, and to maintain and improve high standards of medical education in osteopathic colleges. Inspects and accredits colleges and hospitals; conducts a specialty certification program; sponsors a national examining board satisfactory to state licensing agencies; maintains mandatory program of continuing medical education for members.

10120 ■ American Osteopathic Association of Medical Informatics (AOAMI)
142 E Ontario St.
Chicago, IL 60611
Ph: (312)202-8142
Fr: 800-621-1773
E-mail: agippe@osteotech.org
URL: http://www.aoami.org

Description: Promotes expertise in the use of technology in the practice of osteopathic medicine. Fosters the integration of osteopathic principles and practices in the use of medical informatics. Encourages research and education in the field of medical informatics.

10121 ■ American Public Health Association (APHA)
800 I St. NW
Washington, DC 20001
Ph: (202)777-2742
Fax: (202)777-2534
E-mail: comments@apha.org
URL: http://www.apha.org

Description: Professional organization of physicians, nurses, educators, academicians, environmentalists, epidemiologists, new professionals, social workers, health administrators, optometrists, podiatrists, pharmacists, dentists, nutritionists, health planners, other community and mental health specialists, and interested consumers. Seeks to protect and promote personal, mental, and environmental health. Services

include: promulgation of standards; establishment of uniform practices and procedures; development of the etiology of communicable diseases; research in public health; exploration of medical care programs and their relationships to public health. Sponsors job placement service.

10122 ■ American School Health Association (ASHA)
4340 East West Hwy., Ste. 403
Bethesda, MD 20814
Ph: (301)652-8072
Fax: (301)652-8077
Fr: 800-445-2742
E-mail: info@ashaweb.org
URL: http://www.ashaweb.org

Description: School physicians, school nurses, counselors, nutritionists, psychologists, social workers, administrators, school health coordinators, health educators, and physical educators working in schools, professional preparation programs, public health, and community-based organizations. Promotes coordinated school health programs that include health education, health services, a healthful school environment, physical education, nutrition services, and psycho-social health services offered in schools collaboratively with families and other members of the community. Offers professional reference materials and professional development opportunities. Conducts pilot programs that inform materials development, provides technical assistance to school professionals, advocates for school health.

10123 ■ American Society of Anesthesiologists (ASA)
520 N Northwest Hwy.
Park Ridge, IL 60068-2573
Ph: (847)825-5586
Fax: (847)825-1692
E-mail: mail@asahq.org
URL: http://www.asahq.org

Description: Professional society of physicians specializing or interested in anesthesiology. Seeks "to develop and further the specialty of anesthesiology for the general elevation of the standards of medical practice". Encourages education, research, and scientific progress in anesthesiology. Conducts refresher courses and other postgraduate educational activities. Maintains placement service.

10124 ■ American Society of Clinical Oncology
2318 Mill Rd., Ste. 800
Alexandria, VA 22314
Ph: (571)483-1300
Fr: 888-282-2552
E-mail: membermail@asco.org
URL: http://www.asco.org

Description: Represents the interests of clinical oncologists. Sets the standards for patient care worldwide and carries out clinical research aimed at improving the prevention, diagnosis, and treatment of cancer. Advocates for policies that provide access to high-quality care for all patients with cancer and increased funding for clinical and translational research.

10125 ■ American Society for Clinical Pharmacology and Therapeutics
528 N Washington St.
Alexandria, VA 22314
Ph: (703)836-6981
E-mail: info@ascpt.org
URL: http://www.ascpt.org

Description: Represents physicians and other professionals serving the discipline of clinical pharmacology. Aims to promote and advance the science of human pharmacology and therapeutics. Provides a forum for the exchange, development, and integration of translational science into the drug development continuum from discovery to safe and effective medication use.

10126 ■ American Society of Colon and Rectal Surgeons (ASCRS)
85 W Algonquin Rd., Ste. 550
Arlington Heights, IL 60005
Ph: (847)290-9184
Fax: (847)290-9203
E-mail: ascrs@fascrs.org
URL: http://www.fascrs.org

Description: Professional society of surgeons specializing in the diagnosis and treatment of diseases of the colon, rectum, and anus. Offers placement service; conducts research programs.

10127 ■ American Society of Extra-Corporeal Technology (AmSECT)
2209 Dickens Rd.
Richmond, VA 23230-2005
Ph: (804)565-6363
Fax: (804)282-0090
E-mail: stewart@amsect.org
URL: http://www.amsect.org

Description: Perfusionists, technologists, doctors, nurses, and others actively employed and using the applied skills relating to the practice of extracorporeal technology (involving heart-lung machines); student members. Disseminates information necessary to the proper practice of the technology. Conducts programs in continuing education and professional-public liaison and hands-on workshops. Maintains placement service.

10128 ■ American Society for Histocompatibility and Immunogenetics (ASHI)
15000 Commerce Pkwy., Ste. C
Mount Laurel, NJ 08054-2212
Ph: (856)638-0428
Fax: (856)439-0525
E-mail: info@ashi-hla.org
URL: http://www.ashi-hla.org

Description: Scientists, physicians, and technologists involved in research and clinical activities related to histocompatibility testing (a state of mutual tolerance that allows some tissues to be grafted effectively to others). Conducts proficiency testing and educational programs. Maintains liaison with regulatory agencies; offers placement services and laboratory accreditation. Has co-sponsored development of histocompatibility specialist and laboratory certification program.

10129 ■ American Society of Nephrology (ASN)
1510 H St. NW, Ste. 800
Washington, DC 20005-1003
Ph: (202)640-4660
Fax: (202)637-9793
E-mail: email@asn-online.org
URL: http://www.asn-online.org

Description: Nephrologists united for the exchange of scientific information. Seeks to contribute to the education of members and to improve the quality of patient care. Conducts educational courses. Maintains placement service.

10130 ■ American Society for Reproductive Medicine (ASRM)
1209 Montgomery Hwy.
Birmingham, AL 35216-2809
Ph: (205)978-5000
Fax: (205)978-5005
E-mail: asrm@asrm.org
URL: http://www.asrm.org

Description: Gynecologists, obstetricians, urologists, reproductive endocrinologists, veterinarians, research workers, and others interested in reproductive health in humans and animals. Seeks to extend knowledge of all aspects of fertility and problems of infertility and mammalian reproduction; provides a rostrum for the presentation of scientific studies dealing with these subjects. Offers patient resource information.

10131 ■ American Thoracic Society
25 Broadway
New York, NY 10006-2755
Ph: (212)315-8600
Fax: (212)315-6498
E-mail: atsinfo@thoracic.org
URL: http://www.thoracic.org

Description: Represents specialists in pulmonary or critical care medicine. Works for the prevention and treatment of respiratory disease through research, education, patient care, and advocacy.

10132 ■ American Urological Association (AUA)
1000 Corporate Blvd.
Linthicum, MD 21090
Ph: (410)689-3700
Fax: (410)689-3800
Fr: (866)746-4282
E-mail: aua@auanet.org
URL: http://www.auanet.org/content/homepage/homepage.cfm

Description: Serves as professional society of physicians specializing in urology. Provides education and formulation of health care policy for urologists.

10133 ■ Association for Academic Surgery (AAS)
11300 W Olympic Blvd., Ste. 600
Los Angeles, CA 90064
Ph: (310)437-1606
Fax: (310)437-0585
E-mail: aaron@aasurg.org
URL: http://www.aasurg.org

Description: Active and senior surgeons with backgrounds in all surgical specialties in academic surgical centers at chief resident level or above. Encourages young surgeons to pursue careers in academic surgery; supports them in establishing themselves as investigators and educators by providing a forum in which senior surgical residents and junior faculty members may present papers on subjects of clinical or laboratory investigations; promotes interchange of ideas between senior surgical residents, junior faculty, and established academic surgeons; facilitates communication among academic surgeons in all surgical fields. Maintains placement service.

10134 ■ Association for the Advancement of Medical Instrumentation (AAMI)
4301 N Fairfax Dr., Ste. 301
Arlington, VA 22203-1633
Ph: (703)525-4890
Fax: (703)276-0793
Fr: 800-332-2264
E-mail: mlogan@aami.org
URL: http://www.aami.org

Description: Clinical engineers, biomedical equipment technicians, physicians, hospital administrators, consultants, engineers, manufacturers of medical devices, nurses, researchers and others interested in medical instrumentation. Works to improve the quality of medical care through the application, development, and management of technology. Maintains placement service. Offers certification programs for biomedical equipment technicians and clinical engineers. Produces numerous standards and recommended practices on medical devices and procedures. Offers educational programs.

10135 ■ Association of American Indian Physicians
1225 Sovereign Row, Ste. 103
Oklahoma City, OK 73108
Ph: (405)946-7072
Fax: (405)946-7651
E-mail: mknight@aaip.org
URL: http://www.aaip.org

Description: Represents physicians who are American Indians or Alaskan Natives. Strives for excellence in Native American health care by promoting education in the medical disciplines, honoring traditional healing principles, and restoring the balance of mind, body, and spirit. Offers educational programs, services, and activities that motivate American Indian and Alaskan Native students to remain in the academic pipeline and to pursue a career in the health profession and/or biomedical research.

10136 ■ Association of Black Cardiologists
Heart House
2400 N St. NW, Ste. 604
Washington, DC 20037
Ph: (202)375-6618
Fax: (202)375-6801
Fr: 800-753-9222
URL: http://www.abcardio.org

Description: Represents physicians and other health professionals interested in lowering the high rate of cardiovascular disease. Member services include scholarships, fellowships, and access to a career center.

10137 ■ Association of Dermatology Administrators and Managers (ADAM)
1120 G St. NW, Ste. 1000
Washington, DC 20005
Fax: 800-671-3763
Fr: (866)480-3573
E-mail: adaminfo@shcare.net
URL: http://associationdatabase.com/aws/ADAM/pt/sp/Home_Page

Description: Aims to improve profitability and efficiency in the dermatology practice. Promotes responsible and progressive business practices in a quality healthcare environment. Provides education, professional recognition, growth and networking opportunities to members.

10138 ■ Association for Medical Ethics (AME)
UC Irvine Spine Center
101 The City Dr. S
Pavilion 3, 2nd Fl.
Orange, CA 92868
Ph: (215)322-6654
Fax: (949)315-3668
E-mail: drrosen@ethicaldoctor.com
URL: http://www.ethicaldoctor.org

Description: Consists of physicians from every specialty of medicine. Promotes the care of patients absent of any consideration of financial gain or loss based on choice of surgical equipment, implant, manufacturer, hospital or surgery center.

10139 ■ Association of Muslim Health Professionals (AMHP)
1284 S Vermont St.
Palatine, IL 60067
E-mail: contact@amhp.us
URL: http://www.amhp.us

Description: Represents Muslim health professionals and students. Seeks to increase awareness of the importance of public health as a means of improving the overall health status of Muslim communities. Strives to empower Muslim health professionals to improve the quality and delivery of health services and increase access to care in America.

10140 ■ Association for Research in Vision and Ophthalmology (ARVO)
1801 Rockville Pike, Ste. 400
Rockville, MD 20852-5622
Ph: (240)221-2900
Fax: (240)221-0370
E-mail: arvo@arvo.org
URL: http://www.arvo.org

Description: Professional society of researchers in vision and ophthalmology. Encourages ophthalmic research in the field of blinding eye disease. Operates placement service. Maintains 13 scientific sections.

10141 ■ Association of Staff Physician Recruiters (ASPR)
1000 Westgate Dr., Ste. 252
St. Paul, MN 55114

Ph: (651)290-7475
Fax: (651)290-2266
Fr: 800-830-2777
E-mail: admin@aspr.org
URL: http://www.aspr.org

Description: Recruits physicians and other health-care providers to staff hospitals, clinics and managed care organizations where the members are employed. Sponsors educational programs and meetings on various recruitment issues.

10142 ■ Chinese American Doctors Association (CADA)
8775 Centre Park Dr., No. 501
Columbia, MD 21045
Ph: (713)201-7928
E-mail: adzhang2000@yahoo.com
URL: http://www.chineseamericandoctors.org

Description: Facilitates education and professional development among licensed Chinese American physicians. Promotes and strengthens mutual understanding and collaboration among members, and with other medical professionals and health organizations. Promotes healthcare and provides opportunities for physicians to participate in the governance and decision-making of health care policies that affect the communities that they serve.

10143 ■ Chinese American Medical Society (CAMS)
41 Elizabeth St., Ste. 403
New York, NY 10013
Ph: (212)334-4760
Fax: (212)965-1876
E-mail: jseto@camsociety.org
URL: http://www.camsociety.org

Description: Physicians of Chinese origin residing in the U.S. and Canada. Seeks to advance medical knowledge, scientific research, and interchange of information among members and to promote the health status of Chinese Americans. Conducts educational meetings; supports research. Maintains placement service. Sponsors limited charitable program.

10144 ■ Chinese American Society Of Anesthesiology (CASA)
4 Hickory Ln.
Warren, NJ 07059
E-mail: chineseasa@yahoo.com
URL: http://www.chineseasa.org

Description: Represents physicians and scientists of Chinese descent in the United States who are engaged in the practice of, or research in, anesthesiology. Seeks to improve the standards of the specialty by fostering and encouraging education, research and scientific progress in anesthesiology. Enhances the professional communication and exchange of international physicians and scientists in the field of anesthesiology and related fields.

10145 ■ Chiropractic Orthopedists of North America (CONA)
2048 Montrose Ave.
Montrose, CA 91020
Ph: (818)249-8326
E-mail: rakechiro@ca.rr.com
URL: http://www.conanet.org

Description: Assists in the advancement of chiropractic using scientific and evidence-based research and information. Maintains highest standards of moral and ethical conduct among members. Promotes chiropractic orthopedics with other branches of the healing arts and professions.

10146 ■ College of American Pathologists (CAP)
325 Waukegan Rd.
Northfield, IL 60093-2750
Ph: (847)832-7000
Fax: (847)832-8000
Fr: 800-323-4040
URL: http://www.cap.org/apps/cap.portal

Description: Physicians practicing the specialty of pathology (diagnosis, treatment, observation, and understanding of the progress of disease or medical condition) obtained by morphologic, microscopic, chemical, microbiologic, serologic, or any other type of laboratory examination made on the patient. Fosters improvement of education, research, and medical laboratory service to physicians, hospitals, and the public. Provides job placement information for members. Conducts laboratory accreditation program and laboratory proficiency testing surveys. Maintains spokespersons' network; provides free health information to the public; compiles statistics; sponsors educational programs.

10147 ■ Community Oncology Alliance (COA)
1101 Pennsylvania Ave. NW, Ste. 700
Washington, DC 20004
Ph: (202)756-2258
E-mail: tokon@coacancer.org
URL: http://www.communityoncology.org

Description: Seeks to protect and foster the community oncology delivery system in the United States through public policy, advocacy and education. Enhances the effectiveness and efficiency of cancer care in the community by increasing awareness of community cancer care delivery systems.

10148 ■ Congress of Neurological Surgeons (CNS)
10 N Martingale Rd., Ste. 190
Schaumburg, IL 60173
Ph: (847)240-2500
Fax: (847)240-0804
Fr: 877-517-1267
E-mail: info@1cns.org
URL: http://www.cns.org

Description: Professional society of neurological surgeons in the United States and 55 other countries who meet annually to express their views on various aspects of the principles and practice of neurological surgery; to exchange technical information and experience; to join study of the developments in scientific fields allied to neurological surgery. Promotes interest of neurological surgeons in their practice; provides placement service; honors a living leader in the field of neurological surgery annually.

10149 ■ Emergency Medicine Residents' Association (EMRA)
1125 Executive Cir.
Irving, TX 75038-2522
Ph: (972)550-0920
Fax: (972)580-2829
Fr: (866)566-2492
E-mail: emra@emra.org
URL: http://www.emra.org

Description: Physicians enrolled in emergency medicine residency training programs; medical students. Aims to provide a unified voice for emergency medicine residents and encourage high standards in training and education for emergency physicians. Encourages research to improve emergency medicine education; promotes community, state, and national representation for emergency medicine in organized and academic medicine.

10150 ■ Endocrine Society
8401 Connecticut Ave., Ste. 900
Chevy Chase, MD 20815-5817
Ph: (301)941-0200
Fax: (301)941-0259
Fr: 888-363-6274
E-mail: societyservices@endo-society.org
URL: http://www.endo-society.org

Description: Promotes excellence in research, education, and clinical practice in endocrinology and related disciplines. Maintains placement service.

10151 ■ Holistic Dental Association (HDA)
1825 Ponce de Leon Blvd., No. 148
Coral Gables, FL 33134
Ph: (305)356-7338

Fax: (305)468-6359
E-mail: director@holisticdental.org
URL: http://www.holisticdental.org

Description: Represents dentists, chiropractors, dental hygienists, physical therapists, and medical doctors. Aims to provide a holistic approach to better dental care for patients, and to expand techniques, medications, and philosophies that pertain to extractions, anesthetics, fillings, crowns, and orthodontics. Encourages the use of homeopathic medications, acupuncture, cranial osteopathy, nutritional techniques, and physical therapy in treating patients in addition to conventional treatments. Sponsors training and educational seminars.

10152 ■ Institute on Psychiatric Services
American Psychiatric Association
1000 Wilson Blvd., Ste. 1825
Arlington, VA 22209-3901
Ph: (703)907-7300
Fax: (703)907-1085
Fr: 888-357-7924
E-mail: apa@psych.org
URL: http://www.psych.org

Description: Annual meeting sponsored by the American Psychiatric Association. Open to Physicians and all mental health professionals of all psychiatric and related health and educational facilities. Includes lectures by experts in the field and workshops and accredited courses on problems, programs, and trends. Offers on-site Job Bank, which lists opportunities for mental health professionals. Organized scientific exhibits.

10153 ■ Integrative Clinics International (ICI)
3871 Piedmont Ave., No. 34
Oakland, CA 94611
E-mail: contactici@yahoo.com
URL: http://www.icihealth.org

Description: Improves the healthcare of under-served communities. Facilitates the formation of medical teams who will travel to clinic sites to provide health care. Forms partnerships with local health providers and other relief agencies.

10154 ■ International Association of Hygienic Physicians (IAHP)
4620 Euclid Blvd.
Youngstown, OH 44512
Ph: (330)788-0526
Fax: (330)788-0093
E-mail: mhuberman@zoominternet.net
URL: http://www.iahp.net

Description: Doctors of medicine, osteopathy, chiropractic, and naturopathy who specialize in the supervision of therapeutic fasting as part of a natural hygiene regimen. Promotes clinical advancement and ethical responsibility. Works for the health freedom of members. Provides certification for professionals and accreditation for schools and training programs; offers internship programs. Funds research.

10155 ■ International Cellular Medicine Society (ICMS)
PO Box 4423
Salem, OR 97302
E-mail: info@cellmedicinesociety.org
URL: http://www.cellmedicinesociety.org

Description: Aims to advance the field of adult cell based medicine through developing international best practice standards that ensure patient safety, facilitate physician education, and provide peer oversight. Strives to provide unbiased, objective information regarding the medical use of autologous adult stem cells.

10156 ■ International Palestinian Cardiac Relief Organization (IPCRO)
PO Box 1926
Kent, OH 44240
Ph: (330)678-2645
Fax: (330)678-2661
E-mail: pcrf1@pcrf.net
URL: http://www.pcrf.net/?page_id=529

Description: Seeks to provide medical and humanitarian assistance to people in the Middle East. Sends volunteer teams of doctors and nurses to provide expert surgical treatment for sick children as well as training for local staff. Helps local institutions in the Middle East get the resources to further their medical services for poor and needy patients throughout the region.

10157 ■ International Psoriasis Council (IPC)
2626 Cole Ave., Ste. 400
Dallas, TX 75204
Ph: (214)369-0406
Fax: (214)242-3391
E-mail: info@psoriasiscouncil.org
URL: http://www.psoriasiscouncil.org

Description: Aims to advance research and treatment of psoriasis. Provides a forum for collaboration, innovation and education among health professionals and researchers. Implements programs to promote a better understanding of psoriasis.

10158 ■ International Society for Clinical Densitometry (ISCD)
306 Industrial Park Rd., Ste. 208
Middletown, CT 06457
Ph: (860)259-1000
Fax: (860)259-1030
E-mail: iscd@iscd.org
URL: http://www.iscd.org

Description: Raises awareness and understanding of the clinical application of bone mass measurement technology. Seeks to adopt an industry and technology neutral approach towards advances in the field. Encourages improvements in patient care through appropriate utilization of densitometry. Fosters continuing professional education and certification for clinicians and technologists.

10159 ■ International Society of Gastrointestinal Oncology (ISGIO)
200 Broadhollow Rd., Ste. 207
Melville, NY 11747
Ph: (631)390-8390
Fax: (631)393-5026
E-mail: willet@radonc.duke.edu
URL: http://www.isgio.org

Description: Facilitates gastrointestinal cancer research and education. Promotes dissemination of new gastrointestinal oncology-related knowledge and discovery. Provides a platform to build international and regional consensuses on therapy and research in gastrointestinal oncology.

10160 ■ Islamic Medical Association of North America (IMANA)
101 W 22nd St., Ste. 106
Lombard, IL 60148
Ph: (630)932-0000
Fax: (630)932-0005
E-mail: hq@imana.org
URL: http://www.imana.org

Description: Muslim physicians and allied health professionals. Unites Muslim physicians and allied health professionals in the U.S. and Canada for the improvement of professional and social contact; provides assistance to Muslim communities worldwide. Charitable programs include: donation of books, journals, and educational and research materials to medical institutions; donation of medical supplies and equipment to charity medical institutions in Muslim countries. Maintains speakers' bureau to present Islamic viewpoints on medical topics; sponsors placement service; offers assistance in orientation.

10161 ■ Joint Council of Allergy, Asthma and Immunology (JCAAI)
50 N Brockway, Ste. 3-3
Palatine, IL 60067
Ph: (847)934-1918
Fax: (847)934-1820
E-mail: info@jcaai.org
URL: http://www.jcaai.org

Description: Physicians specializing in allergy or clinical immunology. Members must belong to the American Academy of Allergy and Immunology or the American College of Allergy and Immunology. Serves as political and socioeconomic advocate for these sponsoring organizations.

10162 ■ Mental Health Challenges in the Athletic Training Room: A Team Physician's Perspective
American College of Sports Medicine
401 W Michigan St.
Indianapolis, IN 46202-3233
Ph: (317)637-9200
Fax: (317)634-7817
URL: http://www.acsmstore.org

Description: DVD. Focuses on the role of physicians as primary care providers in the field of athletic training. Provides basic overview of the clinical features, diagnostic criteria, and screening tools appropriate for mental health conditions diagnosed in primary care sports medicine clinics.

10163 ■ National Alliance of Wound Care
5464 N Port Washington Rd., No. 134
Glendale, WI 53217
Fax: 800-352-8339
Fr: 877-922-6292
E-mail: information@nawccb.org
URL: http://www.nawccb.org

Description: Represents the interests of wound care certified professionals. Provides resources and support to advance professional recognition of members.

10164 ■ National Association of Managed Care Physicians (NAMCP)
4435 Waterfront Dr., Ste. 101
Glen Allen, VA 23058
Ph: (804)527-1905
Fax: (804)747-5316
E-mail: info@namcp.com
URL: http://www.namcp.com

Description: Licensed physicians and allied health professionals working in managed health care programs; medical residents and students interested in managed health care; corporations or agencies providing services or goods to the industry; interested others. Enhances the ability of practicing physicians to proactively participate within the managed health care arena through research, communication, and education. Provides a forum for members to communicate their concerns about the changing health care environment, integrate into managed health care delivery systems, and assure continuous improvement in the quality of health care services provided. Develops practice criteria, quality assurance measures, and appropriate utilization management criteria. Offers educational programs; maintains speakers' bureau and placement services; conducts research programs; develops informational clearinghouse.

10165 ■ National Council of Certified Dementia Practitioners (NCCDP)
103 Valley View Trail
Sparta, NJ 07871
Fax: (973)860-2244
Fr: 877-729-5191
E-mail: nationalccdp@aol.com
URL: http://www.nccdp.org

Description: Represents professionals with varying work and personal experiences in the field of dementia care. Seeks to develop and encourage standards of excellence in the profession and delivery of dementia care. Promotes and enhances the knowledge, skills and practice of all persons who provide care and services to dementia clients.

10166 ■ National Medical Association (NMA)
8403 Colesville Rd., Ste. 920
Silver Spring, MD 20910
Ph: (202)347-1895

Fax: (202)347-0722
E-mail: publicaffairs@nmanet.org
URL: http://www.nmanet.org

Description: Serves as professional society of minority physicians.

10167 ■ National Rehabilitation Association (NRA)
633 S Washington St.
Alexandria, VA 22314
Ph: (703)836-0850
Fax: (703)836-0848
E-mail: info@nationalrehab.org
URL: http://www.nationalrehab.org

Description: Provides opportunities through knowledge and diversity for professionals in the fields of rehabilitation of people with disabilities.

10168 ■ National Rural Health Association (NRHA)
Administrative Office
521 E 63rd St.
Kansas City, MO 64110-3329
Ph: (816)756-3140
Fax: (816)756-3144
E-mail: mail@nrharural.org
URL: http://www.ruralhealthweb.org

Description: Administrators, physicians, nurses, physician assistants, health planners, academicians, and others interested or involved in rural health care. Creates a better understanding of health care problems unique to rural areas; utilizes a collective approach in finding positive solutions; articulates and represents the health care needs of rural America; supplies current information to rural health care providers; serves as a liaison between rural health care programs throughout the country. Offers continuing education credits for medical, dental, nursing, and management courses.

10169 ■ Neuro-Developmental Treatment Association (NDTA)
1540 S Coast Hwy., Ste. 203
Laguna Beach, CA 92651
Fax: (949)376-3456
Fr: 800-869-9295
E-mail: info@ndta.org
URL: http://www.ndta.org

Description: Physical and occupational therapists, speech pathologists, special educators, physicians, parents, and others interested in neurodevelopmental treatment. (NDT is a form of therapy for individuals who suffer from central nervous system disorders resulting in abnormal movement. Treatment attempts to initiate or refine normal stages and processes in the development of movement.) Informs members of new developments in the field and with ideas that will eventually improve fundamental independence. Locates articles related to NDT.

10170 ■ North American Sikh Medical and Dental Association (NASMDA)
4104 Old Vestal Rd., Ste. 108
Vestal, NY 13850
Ph: (607)729-0726
Fax: (607)729-1341
E-mail: nasmda@gmail.com
URL: http://nasmda.org

Description: Promotes the interests of Sikh physicians and dentists in the United States, Canada and elsewhere. Supports Sikh physicians, dentists and other Sikh professionals pursuing their careers in those fields or any other fields. Assists Sikh medical and dental graduates to establish practices and help them obtain adequate post-graduate training. Seeks to improve the medical education and delivery of medical care in the parent homeland. Compiles a comprehensive directory of Sikh physicians and dentists residing in North America.

10171 ■ Preimplantation Genetic Diagnosis International Society (PGDIS)
2825 N Halsted St.
Chicago, IL 60657

Ph: (773)472-4900
Fax: (773)871-5221
E-mail: anverkuliev@hotmail.com
URL: http://www.pgdis.org

Description: Encourages collaboration among obstetricians, fertility specialists, embryologists and human geneticists. Coordinates research, education and training in preimplantation genetic diagnosis. Ensures safety and accuracy in Preimplantation Genetics Diagnosis(PGD) and its application to clinical practice.

10172 ■ Ruth Jackson Orthopaedic Society (RJOS)
6300 N River Rd., Ste. 727
Rosemont, IL 60018-4226
Ph: (847)698-1626
Fax: (847)823-0536
E-mail: rjos@aaos.org
URL: http://www.rjos.org

Description: Women orthopaedic surgeons, residents, fellows, and medical students. Seeks to advance the science of orthopaedic surgery and to provide support for women orthopaedic surgeons. Named for practicing orthopaedic surgeon Dr. Ruth Jackson (1902-94), the first woman certified by the American Board of Orthopaedic Surgery and the first female member of the American Academy of Orthopaedic Surgeons. Conducts educational programs; operates placement service and speakers' bureau, holds biennial meeting, sponsors mentoring program,

offers traveling fellowship and resident research award.

10173 ■ Society of Hospital Medicine
1500 Spring Garden St., Ste. 501
Philadelphia, PA 19130
Fax: (267)702-2690
Fr: 800-843-3360
URL: http://www.hospitalmedicine.org

Description: Represents practicing hospitalists. Promotes excellence in the practice of hospital medicine through education, advocacy and research. Assists individuals' search for employment opportunities in hospital medicine.

10174 ■ Society of Plastic Surgical Skin Care Specialists (SPSSCS)
11262 Monarch St.
Garden Grove, CA 92841
Ph: (562)799-0466
Fax: (562)799-1098
Fr: 800-486-0611
E-mail: info@spsscs.org
URL: http://www.spsscs.org

Description: Seeks to promote and educate plastic surgical skin care professionals. Fosters the enhancement of professional skills and the delivery of safe and quality skin care provided to patients. Facilitates a forum and encourages collaboration and networking among plastic surgical skin care specialists.

10175 ■ Society for Translational Oncology (STC)
318 Blackwell St., Ste. 270
Durham, NC 27701
Ph: (919)433-0489
Fax: (919)680-4411
E-mail: admin@sto-online.org
URL: http://sto-online.org

Description: Aims to speed up the discovery and translation of treatments in the field of cancer medicine. Brings knowledge and strategies for critical new developments in cancer treatment to the practice of the community oncologist. Provides educational activities to improve physician competencies and strategies for screening, prevention, diagnosis, treatment and management of patients with cancer.

10176 ■ Ukrainian Medical Association of North America (UMANA)
2247 W Chicago Ave.
Chicago, IL 60622
Fax: (773)278-6962
Fr: 888-RXU-MANA
E-mail: umana@umana.org
URL: http://www.umana.org

Description: Physicians, surgeons, dentists, and persons in related professions who are of Ukrainian descent. Provides assistance to members; sponsors lectures. Maintains placement service, museum, biographical and medical archives.

Sources of Help-Wanted Ads

10177 ■ AACG Newsletter
American Association for Crystal Growth
6986 S Wadsworth Ct.
Littleton, CO 80128
Ph: (303)539-6907
Fax: (303)482-2775
Fr: 888-506-1271
E-mail: aacg@att.net
URL: http://www.crystalgrowth.org/publications.html

Description: Three issues/year. Contains news and features on developments in crystal growth and characterization, international research, and historical retrospectives. Recurring features include news from local AACG chapters, employment notices, coverage of meetings and conferences, letters to the editor, a calendar of events, and columns titled Crystal Growth News, Historical Perspectives, and The President's Corner.

10178 ■ Astronomy
Kalmbach Publishing Co.
21027 Crossroads Cir.
PO Box 1612
Waukesha, WI 53187-1612
Ph: (262)796-8776
Fax: (262)796-1615
Fr: 800-533-6644
URL: http://www.astronomy.com

Monthly. $50.95/year for Canada; $95.95/year for Canada, two years; $138.95/year for Canada, three years; $42.95/year for individuals; $79.95/year for two years; $114.95/year for individuals, three years; $58.95/year for other countries; $111.95/year for other countries, two years; $162.95/year for other countries, three years. Magazine for the "star gazing public."

10179 ■ Astronomy Education Review
National Optical Astronomy Observatory
950 N Cherry Ave.
Tucson, AZ 85719
Ph: (520)318-8000
Fax: (520)318-8360
E-mail: aer@noao.edu
URL: http://aer.noao.edu/cgi-bin/new.pl

Free, online. Scholarly journal publishing research and articles on astronomy.

10180 ■ Computational Thermal Sciences
Begell House Inc.
50 Cross Hwy.
Redding, CT 06896
Ph: (203)938-1300
Fax: (203)938-1304
URL: http://www.begellhouse.com/journals/648192910890cd0e

$672.00/year for institutions. Journal focusing on the fundamental methods of thermodynamics, fluid mechanics, heat transfer and combustion.

10181 ■ The Electrochemical Society Interface
Electrochemical Society Inc.
65 S Main St., Bldg. D
Pennington, NJ 08534-2839
Ph: (609)737-1902
Fax: (609)737-2743
E-mail: interface@electrochem.org
URL: http://www.electrochem.org/dl/interface/

Quarterly. $64.00/year for individuals, tier 1, print & online; $82.00/year for other countries, tier 1, print & online. Publication featuring news and articles of interest to members of the Electrochemical Society.

10182 ■ Heat Pipe Science and Technology
Begell House Inc.
50 Cross Hwy.
Redding, CT 06896
Ph: (203)938-1300
Fax: (203)938-1304
URL: http://www.begellhouse.com/journals/4b0844fc3a2ef17f

$650.00/year for institutions. Journal featuring the fundamentals, principles and technologies associated with the design and operation of heat pipes and thermosyphons.

10183 ■ International Journal of Astronomy and Astrophysics
Scientific Research Publishing
PO Box 54821
Irvine, CA 92619-4821
E-mail: ijaa@scirp.org
URL: http://www.scirp.org/journal/ijaa/

Quarterly. $156.00/year for individuals. Peer-reviewed journal publishing research on fields of astrophysics and space sciences.

10184 ■ International Journal of Energetic Materials and Chemical Propulsion
Begell House Inc.
50 Cross Hwy.
Redding, CT 06896
Ph: (203)938-1300
Fax: (203)938-1304
URL: http://www.begellhouse.com/journals/17bbb47e377ce023

$1,240.00/year for institutions. Journal promoting scientific investigation, technical advancements and information exchange on energetic materials and chemical propulsion.

10185 ■ International Journal of Fluid Mechanics Research
Begell House Inc.
50 Cross Hwy.
Redding, CT 06896
Ph: (203)938-1300
Fax: (203)938-1304
URL: http://www.begellhouse.com/journals/71cb29ca5b40f8f8

$1,811.00/year for institutions. Journal publishing articles on fluid mechanics.

10186 ■ ISRN Astronomy and Astrophysics
Hindawi Publishing Corporation
410 Park Ave., 15th Fl.
287 PMB
New York, NY 10022
E-mail: astro@isrn.com
URL: http://www.isrn.com/journals/astro

Peer-reviewed journal publishing research in all areas of astronomy and astrophysics.

10187 ■ Journal of Biomaterials and Nanobiotechnology
Scientific Research Publishing
PO Box 54821
Irvine, CA 92619-4821
URL: http://www.scirp.org/journal/jbnb/

Peer-reviewed journal covering the basic science and engineering aspects of biomaterials and nanotechnology.

10188 ■ Journal of Flow Visualization and Image Processing
Begell House Inc.
50 Cross Hwy.
Redding, CT 06896
Ph: (203)938-1300
Fax: (203)938-1304
URL: http://www.begellhouse.com/journals/52b74bd3689ab10b

Quarterly. $691.00/year for institutions. Peer-reviewed journal covering articles in the areas of flow visualization and image processing.

10189 ■ Journal of Nanomechanics and Micromechanics
American Society of Civil Engineers
1801 Alexander Bell Dr.
Reston, VA 20191-4400
Ph: (703)295-6300
Fax: (703)295-6333
Fr: 800-548-2723
URL: http://ascelibrary.org/nmo/

Quarterly. $373.00/year for institutions, print and online; $393.00/year for institutions, other countries, print and online. Peer-reviewed journal featuring articles on nanomechanics and micromechanics.

10190 ■ Journal of Vacuum Science and Technology A & B
American Institute of Physics
1 Physics Ellipse
College Park, MD 20740-3843
Ph: (301)209-3100
Fax: (301)209-0843
E-mail: jvst@mcnc.org
URL: http://www.virtualjournals.org/

Monthly. $1,840.00/year for individuals, print & online; $1,980.00/year for other countries, print & online (surface); $2,040.00/year for individuals, print & online (air). Journal containing research review articles in all areas of vacuum science.

10191 ■ Laser Focus World
PennWell Corp.
98 Spit Brook Rd.
Nashua, NH 03062-5737
Ph: (603)891-0123
Fax: (603)891-9294
Fr: 800-225-0556
URL: http://www.optoiq.com/index/photonics-technologies-applicati

Monthly. $162.00/year for individuals; $216.00/year for Canada; $60.00/year for individuals, digital distribution; $270.00/year for other countries. Magazine covering advances and applications in optoelectronics and photonics.

10192 ■ Lasers & Optronics
Reed Business Information (New York, New York)
360 Park Ave. S
New York, NY 10010
Ph: (646)746-6400
Fax: (646)746-7431
Fr: 800-446-6551
URL: http://www.lasersoptrmag.com

Monthly. $55.00/year for individuals. Magazine serving the laser and optoelectronic market.

10193 ■ Nanomechanics Science and Technology
Begell House Inc.
50 Cross Hwy.
Redding, CT 06896
Ph: (203)938-1300
Fax: (203)938-1304
URL: http://www.begellhouse.com/journals/11e12455066dab5d

$748.00/year for institutions. Journal covering the areas of nano- and micromechanics.

10194 ■ Nature International Weekly Journal of Science
Nature Publishing Group
75 Varick St., 9th Fl.
New York, NY 10013-1917
Ph: (212)726-9200
Fax: (212)696-9006
Fr: 888-331-6288
E-mail: nature@natureny.com
URL: http://www.nature.com/nature/index.html

Weekly. $199.00/year for individuals, print and online; $338.00/year for two years, print and online. Magazine covering science and technology, including the fields of biology, biochemistry, genetics, medicine, earth sciences, physics, pharmacology, and behavioral sciences.

10195 ■ Optics and Photonics Journal
Scientific Research Publishing
PO Box 54821
Irvine, CA 92619-4821
E-mail: opj@scirp.org
URL: http://www.scirp.org/journal/opj/

Quarterly. $156.00/year for individuals. Peer-reviewed journal publishing articles on all areas of optics and photonics.

10196 ■ PE & RS Photogrammetric Engineering & Remote Sensing
The Imaging and Geospatial Information Society
5410 Grosvenor Ln., Ste. 210
Bethesda, MD 20814-2160
Ph: (301)493-0290
Fax: (301)493-0208
URL: http://www.asprs.org/PE-RS-Journal/

Monthly. $410.00/year for individuals, first class mail; $426.00/year for Canada, airmail; $420.00/year for other countries, air standard. Peer-reviewed journal covering photogrammetry, remote sensing, geographic information systems, cartography, and surveying, global positioning systems, digital photogrammetry.

10197 ■ The Physics Teacher
American Association of Physics Teachers
1 Physics Ellipse
College Park, MD 20740-3845
Ph: (301)209-3311
Fax: (301)209-0845
URL: http://tpt.aapt.org

; $434.00/year for nonmembers, domestic; $469.00/year for nonmembers, international. Scientific education magazine.

10198 ■ Physics Today
American Institute of Physics
1 Physics Ellipse
College Park, MD 20740-3843
Ph: (301)209-3100
Fax: (301)209-0843
URL: http://www.aip.org

Monthly. $69.00/year for individuals; $59.00/year for members, in affiliated societies. Journal covering news of physics research and activities that affect physics.

10199 ■ Radio Physics and Radio Astronomy
Begell House Inc.
50 Cross Hwy.
Redding, CT 06896
Ph: (203)938-1300
Fax: (203)938-1304
URL: http://www.begellhouse.com/journals/6fd1549c0e2c05da

$708.00/year for institutions. Journal publishing articles on investigations in present-day radio physics and electronic engineering, radio astronomy and astrophysics.

10200 ■ The Scientist
The Scientist Inc.
121 W 27th St., Ste. 604
New York, NY 10001
Ph: (212)461-4470
Fax: (347)626-2385
URL: http://www.the-scientist.com

Monthly. $39.95/year for individuals, print only; $49.95/year for individuals, print & online; $64.95/year for other countries, print only; $74.95/year for other countries, print & online. News journal (tabloid) for life scientists featuring news, opinions, research, and professional section.

10201 ■ Sky & Telescope
Sky Publishing Corp.
90 Sherman St.
Cambridge, MA 02140-3264
Ph: (617)864-7360
Fax: (617)864-6117
Fr: 800-253-0245
URL: http://www.skyandtelescope.com/

Monthly. $37.95/year for individuals; $69.95/year for individuals, 2 years; $49.95/year for Canada; $89.95/year for Canada, 2 years; $61.95/year for other countries; $113.95/year for other countries, 2 years. Magazine on astronomy and space science.

10202 ■ Soft Nanoscience Letters
Scientific Research Publishing
PO Box 54821
Irvine, CA 92619-4821
E-mail: snl@scirp.org
URL: http://www.scirp.org/journal/snl/

Quarterly. $156.00/year for individuals. Peer-reviewed journal publishing articles in the field of soft nanoscience.

10203 ■ The SPS Observer
Society of Physics Students
1 Physics Ellipse
College Park, MD 20740
Ph: (301)209-3007
Fax: (301)209-0839
E-mail: sps@aip.org
URL: http://www.spsobserver.org

Description: Three issues/year and one issue per year online. Carries materials of interest to undergraduate and graduate-level physics students, including articles on employment, available fellowships, meetings, and Society news.

10204 ■ TsAGI Science Journal
Begell House Inc.
50 Cross Hwy.
Redding, CT 06896
Ph: (203)938-1300
Fax: (203)938-1304
URL: http://www.begellhouse.com/journals/58618e1439159b1f

Bimonthly. $999.00/year for institutions. Journal covering the areas of mechanics, aviation and cosmonautics, industrial aerodynamic and hydrodynamics of rapid motion.

10205 ■ World Journal of Nano Science and Engineering
Scientific Research Publishing
PO Box 54821
Irvine, CA 92619-4821
E-mail: wjnse@scirp.org
URL: http://www.scirp.org/journal/wjnse/

Quarterly. $156.00/year for individuals. Peer-reviewed journal publishing articles on applications of physical, chemical and biological sciences to engineering.

EMPLOYER DIRECTORIES AND NETWORKING LISTS

10206 ■ American Men and Women of Science
Gale
PO Box 6904
Florence, KY 41022-6904
Fr: 800-354-9706
URL: http://www.gale.cengage.com

Biennial, even years; New edition expected 29th, June 2011. $1,368.00 for individuals. Covers: Over 135,000 U.S. and Canadian scientists active in the physical, biological, mathematical, computer science, and engineering fields; includes references to previous edition for deceased scientists and nonrespondents. Entries include: Name, address, education, personal and career data, memberships, honors and awards, research interest. Arrangement: Alphabetical. Indexes: Discipline (in separate volume).

10207 ■ Directory of Physics, Astronomy, and Geophysics Staff
American Institute of Physics
1 Physics Ellipse
College Park, MD 20740-3843
Ph: (301)209-3100
Fax: (301)209-0843
URL: http://www.aip.org/pubs/books/dpags.html

Biennial, Latest edition 2006. $82.00 for individuals. Covers: 36,000 staff members at 2,600 colleges, universities, and laboratories throughout North America that employ physicists and astronomers; list of foreign organizations. Entries include: Name, address, phone, fax, electronic mail address. Arrangement: Separate alphabetical sections for individuals, academic institutions, and laboratories. Indexes: Academic institution location, type of laboratory.

10208 ■ Discovering Careers for Your Future—Science
Facts On File Inc.
132 W 31st St., 17th Fl.
New York, NY 10001
Ph: (212)967-8800
Fax: 800-678-3633
Fr: 800-322-8755
URL: http://factsonfile.infobasepublishing.com

Latest edition 2nd, 2004. $21.95 for individuals. Covers: Astronomers, biochemists, genetic scientists, marine biologists, pharmacologists, physicists, and zoologists; links career education to curriculum, helping children investigate the subjects they are interested in, and the careers those subjects might lead to.

HANDBOOKS AND MANUALS

10209 ■ *A Career in Theoretical Physics*
World Scientific Publishing Co. Inc.
27 Warren St., Ste., 401-402
Hackensack, NJ 07601
Ph: (201)487-9655
Fax: (201)487-9656
Fr: 800-227-7562
URL: http://www.worldscibooks.com/physics/
   2314.html
Philip W. Anderson. $138 (paper). 896 pages. Part of the Series in Twentieth Century Physics.

10210 ■ *Resumes for Scientific and Technical Careers*
The McGraw-Hill Companies
PO Box 182604
Columbus, OH 43272
Fax: (614)759-3749
Fr: 877-883-5524
E-mail: customer.service@mcgraw-hill.com
URL: http://www.mhprofessional.com/
   product.php?isbn=0071482199
Third edition, 2007. $12.95 (paper). 144 pages. Provides resume advice for individuals interested in working in scientific and technical careers. Includes sample resumes and cover letters.

EMPLOYMENT AGENCIES AND SEARCH FIRMS

10211 ■ International Staffing Consultants
31655 2nd Ave.
Laguna Beach, CA 92651
Ph: (949)255-5857
Fax: (949)767-5959
E-mail: iscinc@iscworld.com
URL: http://www.iscworld.com
Employment agency. Provides placement on regular or temporary basis. Affiliate office in London.

ONLINE JOB SOURCES AND SERVICES

10212 ■ AstronomerCareers.com
URL: http://www.astronomercareers.com
Description: Features job listings for astronomers across the United States.

TRADESHOWS

10213 ■ March Meeting of the American Physical Society
American Physical Society
1 Physics Ellipse
College Park, MD 20740-3844
Ph: (301)209-3200
Fax: (301)209-0865
E-mail: exoffice@aps.org
URL: http://www.aps.org
Annual. Primary Exhibits: Physics equipment. Dates and Locations: 2012 Feb 27 - Mar 02; Boston, MA; Boston Convention Center.

OTHER SOURCES

10214 ■ Acoustical Society of America
2 Huntington Quadrangle, Ste. 1NO1
Melville, NY 11747-4502
Ph: (516)576-2360
Fax: (516)576-2377
E-mail: asa@aip.org
URL: http://acousticalsociety.org
Description: Represents members from various fields related to sound including physics, electrical, mechanical and aeronautical engineering, oceanography, biology, physiology, psychology, architecture, speech, noise and noise control, and music. Aims to increase and diffuse the knowledge of acoustics and its practical applications. Organizes meetings, provides reprints of out-of-print classic texts in acoustics, and translation books.

10215 ■ American Association of Physicists in Medicine (AAPM)
1 Physics Ellipse
College Park, MD 20740
Ph: (301)209-3350
Fax: (301)209-0862
E-mail: 2011.aapm@aapm.org
URL: http://www.aapm.org
Description: Persons professionally engaged in application of physics to medicine and biology in medical research and educational institutions; encourages interest and training in medical physics and related fields; promotes high professional standards; disseminates technical information. Maintains placement service. Conducts research programs. Member society of American Institute of Physics.

10216 ■ American Astronomical Society (AAS)
2000 Florida Ave. NW, Ste. 400
Washington, DC 20009-1231
Ph: (202)328-2010
Fax: (202)234-2560
E-mail: aas@aas.org
URL: http://www.aas.org
Description: Represents astronomers, physicists, and scientists in related fields. Conducts Visiting Professor in Astronomy Program.

10217 ■ American Crystallographic Association (ACA)
PO Box 96 Ellicot Station
Buffalo, NY 14205-0096
Ph: (716)898-8692
Fax: (716)898-8695
E-mail: marcia@hwi.buffalo.edu
URL: http://aca.hwi.buffalo.edu
Description: Chemists, biochemists, physicists, mineralogists, and metallurgists interested in crystallography and in the application of X-ray, electron, and neutron diffraction. Promotes the study of the arrangement of atoms in matter, its causes, its nature, and its consequences, and of the tools and methods used in such studies. Maintains employment clearinghouse for members and employers.

10218 ■ American Institute of Physics (AIP)
1 Physics Ellipse
College Park, MD 20740
Ph: (301)209-3100
Fax: (301)209-0843
Fr: (866)773-2274
E-mail: aipinfo@aip.org
URL: http://www.aip.org
Description: Consists of ten national societies in the fields of physics, astronomy and related disciplines with a total of 100,000 members, 17 affiliated societies, 47 corporate associates and 7,500 student members. Seeks to assist in the advancement and diffusion of the knowledge of physics and its application to human welfare. Publishes scientific journals devoted to physics and related sciences; provides secondary information services and online electronic journals; serves the public by making available to the press and other channels of public information reliable communications on physics and its progress; carries on extensive career services activities; maintains projects directed toward providing information about physics education to students, physics teachers and physics departments; encourages and

assists in the documentation and study of the history of recent physics; cooperates with local, national and international organizations devoted to physics; and fosters the relations of the science of physics to other sciences and to the arts and industry. Provides placement service; compiles statistics; maintains biographical archives and Niels Bohr Library of History of Physics.

10219 ■ American Physical Society (APS)
One Physics Ellipse
College Park, MD 20740-3844
Ph: (301)209-3200
Fax: (301)209-0865
E-mail: exoffice@aps.org
URL: http://www.aps.org
Description: Scientists worldwide, dedicated to the advancement and the diffusion of the knowledge of physics. Publishes some of the leading international physics journals, organizes major scientific meetings and provides strong outreach programs in physics education and in international and public affairs.

10220 ■ American Society of Clinical Radiation Oncology (ASCRO)
9909 Le Grand Dr.
Wexford, PA 15090
Ph: (412)721-4311
Fax: (412)202-5612
E-mail: info@ascro.org
URL: http://www.ascro.org
Description: Seeks to achieve the quality of care for cancer patients by promoting clinical oncology physicists as health care professionals with provider status and medical staff status. Encourages interest in the field of radiation oncology physics and related fields. Facilitates close cooperation between therapy physicists and radiation oncologists.

10221 ■ ASPRS - The Imaging and Geospatial Information Society
5410 Grosvenor Ln., Ste. 210
Bethesda, MD 20814-2160
Ph: (301)493-0290
Fax: (301)493-0208
E-mail: asprs@asprs.org
URL: http://www.asprs.org
Description: Firms, individuals, government employees and academicians engaged in photogrammetry, photointerpretation, remote sensing, and geographic information systems and their application to such fields as archaeology, geographic information systems, military reconnaissance, urban planning, engineering, traffic surveys, meteorological observations, medicine, geology, forestry, agriculture, construction and topographic mapping. Seeks to advance knowledge and improve understanding of these sciences and promote responsible applications. Offers voluntary certification program open to persons associated with one or more functional area of photogrammetry, remote sensing and GIS. Surveys the profession of private firms in photogrammetry and remote sensing in the areas of products and services.

10222 ■ Association for International Practical Training (AIPT)
10400 Little Patuxent Pkwy., Ste. 250
Columbia, MD 21044-3519
Ph: (410)997-2200
Fax: (410)992-3924
E-mail: aipt@aipt.org
URL: http://www.aipt.org
Description: Providers worldwide of on-the-job training programs for students and professionals seeking international career development and life-changing experiences. Arranges workplace exchanges in hundreds of professional fields, bringing employers and trainees together from around the world. Client list ranges from small farming communities to Fortune 500 companies.

10223 ■ Astronomical League
9201 Ward Pkwy., Ste. 100
Kansas City, MO 64114

Ph: (816)333-7759
E-mail: leagueoffice@astroleague.org
URL: http://www.astroleague.org

Description: Members of 250 astronomical societies and other interested individuals. Promotes the science of astronomy; encourages and coordinates activities of amateur astronomical societies; fosters observational and computational work and craftsmanship in various fields of astronomy; correlates amateur activities with professional research. Sponsors educational programs.

10224 ■ Health Physics Society (HPS)
1313 Dolley Madison Blvd., Ste. 402
McLean, VA 22101
Ph: (703)790-1745
Fax: (703)790-2672
E-mail: hps@burkinc.com
URL: http://www.hps.org

Description: Persons engaged in some form of activity in the field of health physics (the profession devoted to radiation protection). Strives to improve public understanding of the problems and needs in radiation protection. Promotes health physics as a profession. Maintains Elda E. Anderson Memorial Fund to be used for teachers, researchers, and others. Provides placement service at annual meeting. Co-sponsors American Board of Health Physics for certification of health physicists.

10225 ■ International Lunar Observatory Association (ILOA)
65-1230 Mamalahoa Hwy., Ste. D20
Kamuela, HI 96743
Ph: (808)885-3474
Fax: (808)885-3475
E-mail: info@iloa.org
URL: http://www.iloa.org

Description: Seeks to expand human knowledge of the cosmos through observation from the moon and participating in a lunar base build-out. Aims to be a catalyst for human space exploration in the 21st century.

10226 ■ International Planetarium Society (IPS)
Imiloa Astronomy Center of Hawaii
600 Imiloa Pl.
Hilo, HI 96720
Ph: (808)969-9735
Fax: (808)969-9748
E-mail: slaatsch@imiloahawaii.org
URL: http://www.ips-planetarium.org

Description: Planetarium staff members; planetarium equipment suppliers; students in planetarium education and astronomy. Promotes astronomy and space education through the use of planetariums around the globe. Encourages exchange of ideas relating to planetariums and the profession. Operates placement service.

10227 ■ National Society of Black Physicists
1100 N Glebe Rd., Ste. 1010
Arlington, VA 22201
Ph: (703)536-4207
Fax: (703)536-4203
E-mail: headquarters@nsbp.org
URL: http://www.nsbp.org

Description: Promotes the professional well-being of African American physicists and physics students. Develops activities and programs to highlight the scientific contributions of African American physicists. Maintains a job board for African American physicists seeking employment.

10228 ■ PlanetQuest
PO Box 211
Sausalito, CA 94966
E-mail: info@planetquest.org
URL: http://www.planetquest.org

Description: Aims to inspire global participation in the discovery of planets. Works on the detection of other planets and for the development of citizen science.

10229 ■ Radiation Research Society (RRS)
PO Box 7050
Lawrence, KS 66044
Fax: (785)843-1274
Fr: 800-627-0326
E-mail: info@radres.org
URL: http://www.radres.org

Description: Professional society of biologists, physicists, chemists, and physicians contributing to knowledge of radiation and its effects. Promotes original research in the natural sciences relating to radiation; facilitates integration of different disciplines in the study of radiation effects.

10230 ■ Society for In Vitro Biology (SIVB)
514 Daniels St., Ste. 411
Raleigh, NC 27605-1317
Ph: (919)562-0600
Fax: (919)562-0608
E-mail: sivb@sivb.org
URL: http://www.sivb.org

Description: Fosters exchange of knowledge of in vitro biology of cells, tissues and organs from both plant and animals (including humans). Focuses on biological research, development, and applications of significance to science and society. Accomplishes its mission through the society's publications; national and local conferences, meetings and workshops; and through support of teaching initiatives in cooperation with educational institutions. Creates an environment of scientific exchange and interdisciplinary synergy with the goal of advancing current and future systems for in vitro biology.

Plumbers

Sources of Help-Wanted Ads

10231 ■ *Builder*
Hanley-Wood L.L.C.
1 Thomas Cir. NW, Ste. 600
Washington, DC 20005-5803
Ph: (202)452-0800
Fax: (202)785-1974
E-mail: builder@omeda.com
URL: http://www.hanleywood.com/
default.aspx?page=magazines

$29.95/year for U.S. and Canada; $54.95/year for U.S. and Canada, 2 years; $192.00/year for other countries. Magazine covering housing and construction industry.

10232 ■ *Constructor*
Associated General Contractors of America
2300 Wilson Blvd., Ste. 400
Arlington, VA 22201
Ph: (703)548-3118
Fax: (703)548-3119
Fr: 800-242-1767
URL: http://constructor.agc.org/

Bimonthly. $95.00/year for individuals. Management magazine for the Construction Industry.

10233 ■ *Contractor Magazine*
Penton Media Inc.
330 N Wabash Ave., Ste. 2300
Chicago, IL 60611
Ph: (312)840-8498
Fax: (312)595-0295
URL: http://contractormag.com/

Monthly. Free, USA/Canada; $110.00/year for other countries; $189.00/year for other countries, 2 years. Industry news and management how-to magazine for heating, plumbing, piping, fire sprinkler, and other mechanical specialties contracting firms.

10234 ■ *MCAA Reporter*
Mechanical Contractors Association of America Inc.
1385 Piccard Dr.
Rockville, MD 20850
Ph: (301)869-5800
Fax: (301)990-9690
Fr: 800-556-3653
E-mail: abreedlove@mcaa.org
URL: http://www.mcaa.org/reporter/

Description: Bimonthly. Covers labor issues and government affairs as they affect mechanical contractors in the plumbing, pipefitting, air conditioning, refrigeration, fire protection, and high-purity piping industries. Recurring features include reports on the activities of the Association and notices of pertinent seminars and meetings.

10235 ■ *Plumbing Business Owner*
Cahaba Media Group
1900 28th Ave. S
Birmingham, AL 35209

Ph: (205)212-9402
URL: http://www.pbomag.com/

Monthly. Free. Business magazine for plumbers.

10236 ■ *Plumbing Engineer*
TMB Publishing Inc.
1838 Techny Ct.
Northbrook, IL 60062
Ph: (847)564-1127
URL: http://www.plumbingengineer.com/

Monthly. Trade journal for consulting engineering, mechanical engineering, architecture, and contracting professionals.

10237 ■ *Professional Builder*
SGC Horizon LLC
3030 W Salt Creek Ln., Ste. 201
Arlington Heights, IL 60005
Ph: (847)391-1000
Fax: (847)390-0408
URL: http://www.housingzone.com/pb/pubhome/

Monthly. Free. The integrated engineering magazine of the building construction industry.

Employer Directories and Networking Lists

10238 ■ *ABC Today—Associated Builders and Contractors National Membership Directory Issue*
Associated Builders and Contractors Inc.
4250 N Fairfax Dr., 9th Fl.
Arlington, VA 22203-1607
Ph: (703)812-2000
Fax: (703)812-8235
URL: http://www.abc.org

Annual, December. $150.00. Publication includes: List of approximately 19,000 member construction contractors and suppliers.

10239 ■ *ENR—Top 400 Construction Contractors Issue*
McGraw-Hill Inc.
PO Box 182604
Columbus, OH 43218
Ph: (614)430-4000
Fax: (614)759-3749
Fr: 877-833-5524
URL: http://enr.construction.com/toplists/Contractors/001-100.asp

Annual, Latest edition 2011. $35.00 for individuals. Publication includes: List of 400 United States contractors receiving largest dollar volumes of contracts in preceding calendar year. Separate lists of 50 largest design/construct management firms; 50 largest program and construction managers; 25 building contractors; 25 heavy contractors.

10240 ■ *Minnesota P-H-C Contractor—Membership Directory Issue*
Minnesota Association of Plumbing-Heating-Cooling Contractors
6300 Shingle Creek Pky., No. 320
Brooklyn Center, MN 55430-2183
Ph: (763)569-0891
Fax: (763)569-0893
Fr: 800-646-6742
URL: http://www.minnesotaphcc.org

Annual, July. Publication includes: List of 450 member firms and associates. Entries include: Name of company, address, phone, fax, code indicating type of work, local association affiliation (chapter memberships and other), name and title of owner or officer. Arrangement: Alphabetical. Indexes: Alphabetical by business.

10241 ■ *Who's Who in the Plumbing-Heating-Cooling Contracting Business*
National Association of Plumbing, Heating, Cooling Contractors
180 S Washington St.
PO Box 6808
Falls Church, VA 22046
Ph: (703)237-8100
Fax: (703)237-7442
Fr: 800-533-7694
URL: http://www.phccweb.org

Annual. $75.00 for nonmembers; $25.00 for members. Covers: About 4,000 professional plumbing/heating/cooling contractors and member firms. Entries include: Name, address, phone, fax, contact. Arrangement: Geographical. Indexes: Individual member.

Handbooks and Manuals

10242 ■ *Plumber's Licensing Study Guide*
The McGraw-Hill Companies
PO Box 182604
Columbus, OH 43272
Fax: (614)759-3749
Fr: 877-883-5524
E-mail: customer.service@mcgraw-hill.com
URL: http://www.mcgraw-hill.com

R. Woodson. 2006. $39.95 (paper). 422 pages.

Employment Agencies and Search Firms

10243 ■ Plumbing Agent
203 Main St., Ste. 100
Lake Dallas, TX 75065
Fax: 800-446-9634

Fr: 800-396-4822
E-mail: info@myopenjobs.com
URL: http://www.plumbingagent.com

Description: Tracks down plumbing jobs, piping jobs, facilities maintenance jobs, and other industry related positions.

ONLINE JOB SOURCES AND SERVICES

10244 ■ Great Green Careers
URL: http://www.greatgreencareers.com

Description: Serves as online resource that connects employers and job seekers in the green jobs industries.

10245 ■ Locate Plumber Jobs
URL: http://www.locateplumbingjobs.com

Description: Serves as a career resource and job search site for plumber employment opportunities.

10246 ■ MEP Jobs
URL: http://www.mepjobs.com

Description: Serves as a job board and resume bank for professionals in the mechanical, electrical, and plumbing industries.

TRADESHOWS

10247 ■ American Society of Plumbing Engineers Convention
American Society of Plumbing Engineers
2980 S. River Rd.
Des Plaines, IL 60018
Ph: (847)296-0002
E-mail: info@aspe.org
URL: http://www.aspe.org

Biennial. Primary Exhibits: Exhibits for the plumbing engineering industry. Dates and Locations: 2012 Oct 27-31; Charlotte, NC.

10248 ■ Massachusetts Association of Plumbing/Heating/Cooling Contractors Convention and Tradeshow
Massachusetts Association of Plumbing/Heating/Cooling Contractors
400 Washington St., Ste. 401
Braintree, MA 02184-4767
Ph: (781)843-3800
Fax: (781)843-1178
Fr: 800-542-7422
E-mail: phcc.ma@verizon.net
URL: http://www.phccma.org

Annual. Primary Exhibits: Plumbing, heating and cooling equipment, supplies, and services. Dates and Locations: 2012 Mar 10.

10249 ■ PHCC/ACCA Convention
Ohio Association of Plumbing-Heating-Cooling Contractors
18961 River's Edge Dr.
Chagrin Falls, OH 44023
Ph: (440)543-4011
Fax: (440)543-1699
E-mail: info@phccohio.org
URL: http://www.phccohio.org

Annual. Primary Exhibits: Products, tools, and services used by plumbing and heating contractors.

10250 ■ Plumbing-Heating-Cooling Contractors Association Annual Convention
Plumbing-Heating-Cooling Contractors Association
PO Box 6808
Falls Church, VA 22046
Ph: (703)237-8100
Fax: (703)237-7442
Fr: 800-533-7694
E-mail: naphcc@naphcc.org
URL: http://www.phccweb.org

Annual. Primary Exhibits: Exhibits relating to plumbing and heating.

OTHER SOURCES

10251 ■ American Society of Plumbing Engineers (ASPE)
2980 S River Rd.
Des Plaines, IL 60018
Ph: (847)296-0002
E-mail: info@aspe.org
URL: http://aspe.org

Description: Represents engineers and designers involved in the design and specification of plumbing systems; manufacturers, governmental officials, and contractors related to the industry may become members on a limited basis. Seeks to resolve professional problems in plumbing engineering; advocates greater cooperation among members and plumbing officials, contractors, laborers, and the public. Code committees examine regulatory codes pertaining to the industry and submit proposed revisions to code writing authorities to simplify, standardize, and modernize all codes. Sponsors American Society of Plumbing Engineers Research Foundation; operates certification program.

10252 ■ American Society of Sanitary Engineering (ASSE)
901 Canterbury Rd., Ste. A
Westlake, OH 44145
Ph: (440)835-3040
Fax: (440)835-3488
E-mail: info@asse-plumbing.org
URL: http://www.asse-plumbing.org

Description: Plumbing officials, sanitary engineers, plumbers, plumbing contractors, building officials, architects, engineers, designing engineers, physicians, and others interested in health. Conducts research on plumbing and sanitation, and develops performance standards for components of the plumbing system. Sponsors disease research program and other studies of water-borne epidemics.

10253 ■ Associated Builders and Contractors (ABC)
4250 N Fairfax Dr., 9th Fl.
Arlington, VA 22203-1607
Ph: (703)812-2000
Fax: (703)812-8201
E-mail: gotquestions@abc.org
URL: http://www.abc.org

Description: Construction contractors, subcontractors, suppliers and associates. Aims to foster and perpetuate the principles of rewarding construction workers and management on the basis of merit. Sponsors management education programs and craft training; also sponsors apprenticeship and skill training programs. Disseminates technological and labor relations information.

10254 ■ Associated General Contractors of America (AGC)
2300 Wilson Blvd., Ste. 400
Arlington, VA 22201
Ph: (703)548-3118
Fax: (703)548-3119
Fr: 800-242-1767
E-mail: info@agc.org
URL: http://www.agc.org

Description: General construction contractors; subcontractors; industry suppliers; service firms. Provides market services through its divisions. Conducts special conferences and seminars designed specifically for construction firms. Compiles statistics on job accidents reported by member firms. Maintains 65 committees, including joint cooperative committees with other associations and liaison committees with federal agencies.

10255 ■ Associated Specialty Contractors (ASC)
3 Bethesda Metro Ctr., Ste. 1100
Bethesda, MD 20814
E-mail: dgw@necanet.org
URL: http://www.assoc-spec-con.org

Description: Works to promote efficient management and productivity. Coordinates the work of specialized branches of the industry in management information, research, public information, government relations and construction relations. Serves as a liaison among specialty trade associations in the areas of public relations, government relations, and with other organizations. Seeks to avoid unnecessary duplication of effort and expense or conflicting programs among affiliates. Identifies areas of interest and problems shared by members, and develops positions and approaches on such problems.

10256 ■ Mechanical Contractors Association of America (MCAA)
1385 Piccard Dr.
Rockville, MD 20850-4340
Ph: (301)869-5800
Fax: (301)990-9690
E-mail: mcaainfo@mcaa.org
URL: http://www.mcaa.org

Description: Represents firms involved in heating, air conditioning, refrigeration, plumbing, piping, and mechanical service. Provides educational materials and programs to help members attain the highest level of managerial and technical expertise.

10257 ■ National Association of Home Builders (NAHB)
1201 15th St. NW
Washington, DC 20005
Ph: (202)266-8200
Fax: (202)266-8400
Fr: 800-368-5242
E-mail: jhoward@nahb.com
URL: http://www.nahb.org

Description: Single and multifamily home builders, commercial builders, and others associated with the building industry. Lobbies on behalf of the housing industry and conducts public affairs activities to increase public understanding of housing and the economy. Collects and disseminates data on current developments in home building and home builders' plans through its Economics Department and nationwide Metropolitan Housing Forecast. Maintains NAHB Research Center, which functions as the research arm of the home building industry. Sponsors seminars and workshops on construction, mortgage credit, labor relations, cost reduction, land use, remodeling, and business management. Compiles statistics; offers charitable program, spokesman training, and placement service; maintains speakers' bureau, and Hall of Fame. Subsidiaries include the National Council of the Housing Industry. Maintains over 50 committees in many areas of construction; operates National Commercial Builders Council, National Council of the Multifamily Housing Industry, National Remodelers Council, and National Sales and Marketing Council.

10258 ■ National Association of Women in Construction (NAWIC)
327 S Adams St.
Fort Worth, TX 76104
Ph: (817)877-5551
Fax: (817)877-0324
Fr: 800-552-3506
E-mail: nawic@nawic.org
URL: http://www.nawic.org

Description: Seeks to enhance the success of women in the construction industry.

10259 ■ Plumbing-Heating-Cooling Contractors Association (PHCC)
PO Box 6808
Falls Church, VA 22046
Ph: (703)237-8100
Fax: (703)237-7442

Fr: 800-533-7694
E-mail: naphcc@naphcc.org
URL: http://www.phccweb.org

Description: Federation of state and local associations of plumbing, heating, and cooling contractors. Seeks to advance sanitation, encourage sanitary laws, and generally improve the plumbing, heating, ventilating, and air conditioning industries. Conducts apprenticeship training programs, workshops, seminars, political action committee, educational and research programs.

SOURCES OF HELP-WANTED ADS

10260 ■ APMA News
American Podiatric Medical Association
9312 Old Georgetown Rd.
Bethesda, MD 20814-1621
Ph: (301)581-9200
Fax: (301)530-2752
Fr: 800-275-2762
URL: http://www.wt-group.com/wtgroot/content/
journals/apma.htm

$75.00/year for individuals, U.S.; $100.00/year for
out of country. Non-scientific news for member
podiatrists.

**10261 ■ Journal of the Academy of
Ambulatory Foot Surgery**
Academy of Ambulatory Foot and Ankle Surgery
1601 Walnut St., Ste. 1005
Philadelphia, PA 19102
Ph: (215)569-3303
Fax: (215)569-3310
Fr: 800-433-4892
URL: http://www.academy-afs.org/

Periodic. Professional journal covering issues in
podiatry.

**10262 ■ Journal of the American Podiatric
Medical Association**
American Podiatric Medical Association
9312 Old Georgetown Rd.
Bethesda, MD 20814-1621
Ph: (301)581-9200
Fax: (301)530-2752
Fr: 800-275-2762
URL: http://www.japmaonline.org

$75.00/year for members, U.S. & other countries
including Canada; $195.00/year for institutions, print
+ online; $175.00/year for institutions, online;
$195.00/year for individuals, print + online; $145.00/
year for individuals, online; $40.00/year for single is-
sue, institutional & individual; $230.00/year for institu-
tions, print + online; other countries, Canada;
$210.00/year for institutions, online; other countries
including Canada; $230.00/year for individuals, print
+ online; other countries, Canada; $170.00/year for
individuals, online; other countries including Canada.
Peer-reviewed journal focusing on foot and ankle
medicine.

**10263 ■ Journal of the American Society of
Podiatric Medical Assistants**
American Society of Podiatric Medical Assistants
1616 N 78th Ct.
Elmwood Park, IL 60707
Fr: 888-882-7762
URL: http://www.aspma.org

Quarterly. Included in membership. Professional
journal covering issues in podiatry.

**10264 ■ The New England Journal of
Medicine**
Massachusetts Medical Society
Waltham Woods Corporate Ctr.
860 Winter St.
Waltham, MA 02451-1413
Ph: (781)893-3800
Fax: (781)893-8009
URL: http://content.nejm.org/

Weekly. $139.00/year for individuals, online only;
$169.00/year for individuals, print & online. Journal
for the medical profession.

10265 ■ Podiatry Management Magazine
Kane Communications Inc.
10 E Athens Ave., Ste. 208
Ardmore, PA 19003
Ph: (610)645-6940
Fax: (610)645-6943
URL: http://www.podiatrym.com/

$30.00/year for individuals; $49.00/year for two years.
Magazine serving as a medical and surgical management guide for podiatrists.

EMPLOYER DIRECTORIES AND
NETWORKING LISTS

10266 ■ Directory of Hospital Personnel
Grey House Publishing
4919 Rte. 22
PO Box 56
Amenia, NY 12501
Ph: (518)789-8700
Fax: (518)789-0556
Fr: 800-562-2139
URL: http://www.greyhouse.com/hospital_
personnel.htm

Annual, Latest edition 2011. $325.00 for individuals.
Covers: 200,000 executives at 6,000 U.S. Hospitals.
Entries include: Name of hospital, address, phone,
number of beds, type and JCAHO status of hospital,
names and titles of key department heads and staff,
medical and nursing school affiliations; number of
residents, interns, and nursing students. Arrangement: Geographical. Indexes: Hospital name, personnel, hospital size.

10267 ■ HMO/PPO Directory
Grey House Publishing
4919 Rte. 22
PO Box 56
Amenia, NY 12501
Ph: (518)789-8700
Fax: (518)789-0556
Fr: 800-562-2139
URL: http://www.greyhouse.com/hmo_ppo.htm

Annual, Latest edition 2011. $325.00 for individuals.
Covers: Over 1,000 health maintenance organiza-
tions (HMOs) and preferred provider organizations
(PPOs). Entries include: Name of organization, ad-

dress, phone, number of members, names of officers, employer references, geographical area served,
parent company, average fees and co-payments,
financial data, and cost control procedures. Arrangement: Geographical. Indexes: Organization name,
personnel name, HMOs and PPOs by state, and
number of members enrolled.

10268 ■ Hospital Blue Book
Billian Publishing Inc. and Trans World Publishing
Inc.
2100 River Edge Pky.
Atlanta, GA 30328
Ph: (770)955-5656
Fax: (770)952-0669
Fr: 800-800-5668
E-mail: blu-book@billian.com
URL: http://www.billianshealthdata.com/Products/
bluebook.html

Annual, Latest edition 2010. $575.00 for individuals;
$575.00 for individuals. Covers: More than 6,500
hospitals; some listings also appear in a separate
southern edition of this publication. Entries include:
Name of hospital, accreditation, mailing address,
phone, fax, number of beds, type of facility (nonprofit,
general, state, etc.); list of administrative personnel
and chiefs of medical services, with specific titles. Arrangement: Geographical.

**10269 ■ Medical and Health Information
Directory**
Gale
PO Box 6904
Florence, KY 41022-6904
Fr: 800-354-9706
URL: http://www.gale.cengage.com

Annual, Latest edition April 2011. $1190.00 for
individuals; $501.00 for individuals. Covers: In volume
1, more than 33,000 medical and health oriented associations, organizations, institutions, and government agencies, including health maintenance organizations (HMOs), preferred provider organizations
(PPOs), insurance companies, pharmaceutical
companies, research centers, and medical and allied
health schools. In Volume 2, over 20,000 medical
book publishers; medical periodicals, directories,
audiovisual producers and services, medical libraries
and information centers, electronic resources, and
health-related internet search engines. In Volume 3,
more than 40,500 clinics, treatment centers, care
programs, and counseling/diagnostic services for 34
subject areas. Entries include: Institution, service, or
firm name, address, phone, fax, email and URL;
many include names of key personnel and, when
pertinent, descriptive annotation. Volume 3 was
formerly listed separately as Health Services
Directory. Arrangement: Classified by organization
activity, service, etc. Indexes: Each volume has a
complete alphabetical name and keyword index.

HANDBOOKS AND MANUALS

**10270 ■ Athletic Footwer and Orthoses in
Sports Medicine**
Springer Science+Business Media LLC
233 Spring St.
New York, NY 10013

Ph: (212)460-1500
Fax: (212)460-1575
URL: http://www.springer.com

Matthew B. Werd and Leslie E. Knight. 2010. $29.95 (softcover). 400 pages. Guides sports medicine physicians, podiatrists, physical therapists, and athletic trainers in prescribing footwear to maximize performance and minimize injury in athletes.

10271 ■ Expert Resumes for Health Care Careers
Jist Works
875 Montreal Way
St. Paul, MN 55102
Fr: 800-648-5478
E-mail: educate@emcp.com
URL: http://www.jist.com

Wendy S. Enelow and Louise M. Kursmark. 2010. $16.95. 288 pages.

10272 ■ Health Careers Today
Elsevier
11830 Westline Industrial Dr.
St. Louis, MO 63146
Ph: (314)453-7010
Fax: (314)453-7095
Fr: 800-545-2522
E-mail: usbkinfo@elsevier.com
URL: http://www.elsevier.com

Gerdin, Judith. Fourth edition. 2007. $74.95. 496 pages. Covers more than 45 health careers. Discusses the roles and responsibilities of various occupations and provides a solid foundation in the skills needed for all health careers.

10273 ■ Opportunities in Health and Medical Careers
The McGraw-Hill Companies
PO Box 182604
Columbus, OH 43272
Fax: (614)759-3749
Fr: 877-883-5524
E-mail: customer.service@mcgraw-hill.com
URL: http://www.mhprofessional.com/product.php?isbn=0071437274

I. Donald Snook, Jr. and Leo D'Orazio. 2004. $14.95 (paper). 157 pages. Covers the full range of medical and health occupations. Illustrated.

10274 ■ Resumes for Health and Medical Careers
The McGraw-Hill Companies
PO Box 182604
Columbus, OH 43272
Fax: (614)759-3749
Fr: 877-883-5524
E-mail: customer.service@mcgraw-hill.com
URL: http://www.mhprofessional.com/product.php?isbn=0071545352

Third edition, 2008. $12.95 (paper). 144 pages.

EMPLOYMENT AGENCIES AND SEARCH FIRMS

10275 ■ Harper Associates
31000 NW Hwy., Ste. 240
Farmington Hills, MI 48334
Ph: (248)932-1170
Fax: (248)932-1214
E-mail: info@harperjobs.com
URL: http://www.harperjobs.com

Executive search firm and employment agency.

10276 ■ Professional Placement Associates, Inc.
287 Bowman Ave.
Purchase, NY 10577-2517
Ph: (914)251-1000
Fax: (914)251-1055
E-mail: careers@ppasearch.com
URL: http://www.ppasearch.com

Executive search firm specializing in the health and medical field.

10277 ■ Team Placement Service, Inc.
1414 Prince St., Ste. 202
Alexandria, VA 22314
Ph: (703)820-8618
Fax: (703)820-3368
Fr: 800-495-6767
E-mail: 4jobs@teamplace.com
URL: http://www.teamplace.com

Full-service personnel consultants provide placement for healthcare staff, physician and dentist, private practice, and hospitals. Conduct interviews, tests, and reference checks to select the top 20% of applicants. Survey applicants' skill levels, provide backup information on each candidate, select compatible candidates for consideration, and insure the hiring process minimizes potential legal liability. Industries served: healthcare and government agencies providing medical, dental, biotech, laboratory, hospitals, and physician search.

10278 ■ Weatherby Locums
6451 N Federal Hwy., Ste. 800
Fort Lauderdale, FL 33308
Ph: (954)343-3050
Fax: (866)588-0085
Fr: (866)906-1637
E-mail: jobs@weatherbylocums.com
URL: http://www.weatherbylocums.com

Executive search firm for physicians. Branch office in Fairfax, VA.

ONLINE JOB SOURCES AND SERVICES

10279 ■ HEALTHeCAREERS Network
Fr: 888-884-8242
E-mail: info@healthecareers.com
URL: http://www.healthecareers.com

Description: Career search site for jobs in all health care specialties; educational resources; visa and licensing information for relocation; interesting articles; relocation tools; links to professional organizations and general resources.

10280 ■ ProHealthJobs.com
Ph: (484)443-8545
Fax: (484)443-8549
E-mail: info@prohealthjobs.com
URL: http://prohealthjobs.com/jobboard

Description: Career resources site for the medical and health care field. Lists professional opportunities, product information, continuing education and open positions.

TRADESHOWS

10281 ■ American Podiatric Medical Association Annual Scientific Meeting
American Podiatric Medical Association
9312 Old Georgetown Rd.
Bethesda, MD 20814-1621
Ph: (301)581-9200
Fax: (301)530-2752
Fr: 800-FOOTCARE
E-mail: sbsaylor@apma.org
URL: http://www.apma.org

Annual. Primary Exhibits: Podiatric supplies and services. Dates and Locations: 2012 Aug 16-19; Washington, DC; Marriott Wardman Park; 2013 Jul 21-24; Las Vegas, NV; The Venetian/The Palazzo and Congress Center; 2014 Jul 24-27; Honolulu, HI; Hilton Hawaiian Village and Convention Center; 2015 Jul 23-26; Orlando, FL; Marriott Orlando World Center; 2016 Jul 14-17; Philadelphia, PA; Philadelphia Marriott and Convention Center.

OTHER SOURCES

10282 ■ American Association of Hospital and Healthcare Podiatrists (AAHHP)
8508 18th Ave.
Brooklyn, NY 11214
Ph: (718)259-1822
Fax: (718)259-4002
E-mail: info@hospitalpodiatrists.org
URL: http://www.hospitalpodiatrists.org

Description: A general specialty group of the American Podiatric Medical Association. Podiatrists (trained and certified persons dealing in the care and diseases of the foot) who are affiliated with hospitals. Seeks to: elevate the standards of podiatry practices in hospitals and health institutions; standardize hospital podiatry procedures, charting, recording forms, and methods; promote understanding among personnel in podiatry, medicine, and allied health professions; aid podiatrists in attaining institutional affiliations; assist in the educational and teaching programs of health institutions and hospitals; foster the development of podiatric internships and residencies in hospitals and institutions. Compiles statistics.

10283 ■ American Board of Podiatric Orthopedics and Primary Podiatric Medicine (ABPOPPM)
3812 Sepulveda Blvd., Ste. 530
Torrance, CA 90505
Ph: (310)375-0700
Fax: (310)375-1386
E-mail: admin@abpoppm.org
URL: http://www.abpoppm.org

Description: Podiatrists who have taken a competency exam prepared by the board. Offers certifying examinations in podiatric orthopedics and primary podiatric medicine aims at improving public health by encouraging and elevating standards for practicing podiatrics.

10284 ■ American Board of Podiatric Surgery (ABPS)
445 Fillmore St.
San Francisco, CA 94117-3404
Ph: (415)553-7800
Fax: (415)553-7801
E-mail: info@abps.org
URL: http://www.abps.org

Description: Podiatrists certified as diplomates. Protects and improves public health by advancing the science of foot surgery and by encouraging the study and evaluation of standards of foot surgery. Acts upon application for certification of legally licensed podiatrists to ascertain their competency in foot surgery. Grants certificates to candidates who have met all qualifications.

10285 ■ American Hospital Association (AHA)
155 N Wacker Dr.
Chicago, IL 60606
Ph: (312)422-3000
Fax: (312)422-4796
E-mail: rich@aha.org
URL: http://www.aha.org

Description: Represents health care provider organizations. Seeks to advance the health of individuals and communities. Leads, represents, and serves health care provider organizations that are accountable to the community and committed to health improvement.

10286 ■ American Medical Association (AMA)
515 N State St.
Chicago, IL 60654
Ph: (312)464-5262
Fr: 800-621-8335
E-mail: msc-amermedassn@ama-assn.org
URL: http://www.ama-assn.org

Description: Represents county medical societies

and physicians. Disseminates scientific information to members and the public. Informs members on significant medical and health legislation on state and national levels and represents the profession before Congress and governmental agencies. Cooperates in setting standards for medical schools, hospitals, residency programs, and continuing medical education courses. Offers physician placement service and counseling on practice management problems. Operates library that lends material and provides specific medical information to physicians. Maintains Ad-hoc committees for such topics as health care planning and principles of medical ethics.

10287 ■ American Podiatric Medical Association (APMA)
9312 Old Georgetown Rd.
Bethesda, MD 20814-1621
Ph: (301)581-9200

Fax: (301)530-2752
Fr: 800-FOOTCARE
E-mail: gbgastwirth@apma.org
URL: http://www.apma.org

Description: Serves as professional society of doctors of podiatric medicine.

10288 ■ American Public Health Association (APHA)
800 I St. NW
Washington, DC 20001
Ph: (202)777-2742
Fax: (202)777-2534
E-mail: comments@apha.org
URL: http://www.apha.org

Description: Professional organization of physicians, nurses, educators, academicians, environmentalists, epidemiologists, new professionals, social workers, health administrators, optometrists, podiatrists, pharmacists, dentists, nutritionists, health planners, other community and mental health specialists, and interested consumers. Seeks to protect and promote personal, mental, and environmental health. Services include: promulgation of standards; establishment of uniform practices and procedures; development of the etiology of communicable diseases; research in public health; exploration of medical care programs and their relationships to public health. Sponsors job placement service.

10289 ■ American Experiment Quarterly
Center of the American Experiment
12 S 6th St., Ste. 1024
Minneapolis, MN 55402
Ph: (612)338-3605
Fax: (612)338-3621
URL: http://www.americanexperiment.org/
publications/AEQ.php

Quarterly. Magazine covering political issues and politics.

10290 ■ Contemporary Politics
Routledge Journals
270 Madison Ave.
New York, NY 10016-0601
Ph: (212)216-7800
Fax: (212)563-2269
URL: http://www.tandf.co.uk/journals/titles/
13569775.asp

Quarterly. $672.00/year for institutions, online only; $404.00/year for institutions, online only; $747.00/year for institutions, print + online; $449.00/year for institutions, print + online; $136.00/year for individuals, print only; $83.00/year for individuals, print only. Journal covering social, economic, developmental, environmental and gender issues.

10291 ■ In These Times
Institute for Public Affairs Inc.
2040 N Milwaukee Ave.
Chicago, IL 60647
Ph: (773)772-0100
Fax: (773)772-4180
E-mail: itt@inthesetimes.com
URL: http://www.inthesetimes.com

Biweekly. $19.95/year for individuals; $34.95/year for two years; $34.95/year for Canada; $40.95/year for other countries. National political newsmagazine.

10292 ■ Presidential Studies Quarterly
John Wiley & Sons Inc.
350 Main St., Commerce Pl.
Malden, MA 02148-5089
Ph: (781)388-8200
Fax: (781)388-8210
URL: http://www.wiley.com/bw/journal.asp?ref=0360-
4918&site=1

Quarterly. $466.00/year for institutions, print & online; $405.00/year for institutions, print, online; $302.00/year for institutions, other countries, print & online; $262.00/year for institutions, other countries, print, online. Publication covering political science and history.

10293 ■ Theory and Research in Education
Sage Publications Inc.
2455 Teller Rd.
Thousand Oaks, CA 91320-2218
Ph: (805)499-9774
Fax: (805)583-2665
Fr: 800-818-7243
URL: http://www.sagepub.com/
journalsProdDesc.nav?prodId=Journal20

$546.00/year for institutions, print and e-access; $491.00/year for institutions, e-access; $535.00/year for institutions, print; $85.00/year for individuals, print; $196.00/year for single issue, institutional; $37.00/year for single issue, individual. Interdisciplinary journal covering normative and theoretical issues concerning education including multi-faceted philosophical analysis of moral, social, political and epistemological problems and issues arising from educational practice.

Employer Directories and Networking Lists

10294 ■ Carroll's Federal Directory
Carroll Publishing
4701 Sangamore Rd., Ste. S-155
Bethesda, MD 20816
Ph: (301)263-9800
Fax: (301)263-9801
Fr: 800-336-4240
URL: http://www.carrollpub.com

4x/yr. $450.00 for single issue. Covers: About 38,000 executive managers in federal government offices in Washington, DC, including executive, congressional and judicial branches; members of Congress and Congressional committees and staff. Entries include: Agency names, titles, office address (including room numbers), e-mail addresses, and telephone and fax numbers. Also available as part of a "library edition" titled "Federal Directory Annual". Arrangement: By cabinet department or administrative agency. Indexes: Keyword, personal name (with phone) and e-mail addresses.

10295 ■ Congressional Directory
Capitol Advantage
2751 Prosperity Ave., Ste. 600
Fairfax, VA 22031
Ph: (703)289-4670
Fax: (703)289-4678
Fr: 800-659-8708
URL: http://capitoladvantage.com/publishing/
products.html

Annual. $17.95 for individuals. Covers: 100 current senators and 440 House of Representative members. Entries include: Name, district office address, phone, fax; names and titles of key staff; committee and subcommittee assignments; biographical data, percentage of votes won, photo. Arrangement: Available in separate alphabetical, geographical, or condensed editions. Indexes: Name.

10296 ■ Congressional Yellow Book
Leadership Directories Inc.
104 5th Ave.
New York, NY 10011
Ph: (212)627-4140
Fax: (212)645-0931
URL: http://www.leadershipdirectories.com/
Products.aspx

Quarterly. Latest edition 2011. $550.00 for individuals; $385.00 for individuals; $523.00 for individuals; $366.00 for individuals. Covers: Members of Congress and their principal aides, Congressional committees, leadership, and congressional support arms. Entries include: For members of Congress—Name, Washington office address, party affiliation, state or district represented, year began service, reelection year; names, titles, and legislative responsibilities of principal aides, member's committee assignments and other responsibilities; photograph, biographical data, fax, and map of district; state and district office addresses and phone; ZIP codes by congressional district. For committees—Committee name, office address, phone, members' names and parties, description of committee jurisdiction, fax, key staff for full and subcommittees. Arrangement: Alphabetical by member of Congress or committee name. Indexes: Name, subject, organization.

10297 ■ United States Government Manual
Office of the Federal Register
c/o The National Archives & Records Administration
8601 Adelphi Rd.
College Park, MD 20740-6001
Ph: (301)837-0482
Fax: (301)837-0483
Fr: (866)272-6272
URL: http://www.archives.gov/federal-register/
publications/govern

Annual, latest edition 2009-2010. $29.00 for individuals. Provides information on the agencies of the executive, judicial, and legislative branches of the Federal government. Contains a section on terminated or transferred agencies. Arrangement: Classified by department and agency. Indexes: Personal name, agency/subject.

10298 ■ Washington
Columbia Books & Information Services
8120 Woodmont Ave., Ste. 110
Bethesda, MD 20814
Ph: (202)464-1662
Fax: (202)464-1775
Fr: 888-265-0600
URL: http://www.columbiabooks.com

Annual, May. $149.00; $150.00. Covers: over 5,000 federal and district government offices, businesses, associations, publications, radio and television stations, labor organizations, religious and cultural institutions, health care facilities and community organizations in the District of Columbia area. Entries include: Name, address, phone, names and titles of key personnel and board of directors. Arrangement: Classified by subject. Indexes: Individuals, organizations.

10299 ■ Washington Information Directory
CQ Press
2300 North St. NW, Ste. 800
Washington, DC 20037

Ph: (202)729-1900
Fax: 800-380-3810
Fr: (866)427-7737
URL: http://www.cqpress.com

Annual, Latest edition 2010-2011. $155.00 for individuals. Covers: 10,000 governmental agencies, congressional committees, and non-governmental associations considered competent sources of specialized information. Entries include: Name of agency, committee, or association; address, phone, fax, and Internet; annotation concerning function or activities of the office; and name of contact. Arrangement: Classified by activity or competence (economics and business, housing and urban affairs, etc.). Indexes: Subject, agency/organization name, contact name.

HANDBOOKS AND MANUALS

10300 ■ *The Book of US Government Jobs: Where They Are, What's Available and How to Write a Federal Resume*
Bookhaven Press LLC
249 Field Club Cir.
McKees Rocks, PA 15136
Ph: (412)494-6926
Fax: (412)494-5749
E-mail: bookhaven@aol.com
URL: http://federaljobs.net/us10.htm

Dennis Damp. 11th edition. 2011. $19.50.

OTHER SOURCES

10301 ■ American Political Science Association (APSA)
1527 New Hampshire Ave. NW
Washington, DC 20036-1206
Ph: (202)483-2512
Fax: (202)483-2657
E-mail: apsa@apsanet.org
URL: http://www.apsanet.org

Description: College and university teachers of political science, public officials, research workers, and businessmen. Encourages the impartial study and promotes the development of the art and science of government. Develops research projects of public interest and educational programs for political scientists and journalists; seeks to improve the knowledge of and increase citizen participation in political and governmental affairs. Serves as clearinghouse for teaching and research positions in colleges, universities, and research bureaus in the U.S. and abroad and for positions open to political scientists in government and private business; conducts Congressional Fellowship Program. Conducts Committee on Professional Ethic, and Rights and Freedom. Offers placement service.

10302 ■ Congressional Black Caucus (CBC)
1433 Longworth House Office Bldg.
Washington, DC 20515

Ph: (202)226-9776
Fax: (202)225-9817
E-mail: congressionalblackcaucus@mail.house.gov
URL: http://www.thecongressionalblackcaucus.com

Description: Black members of the U.S. House of Representatives. Addresses the legislative concerns of black and other underrepresented citizens and to formalize and strengthen the efforts of its members. Works to implement these objectives through personal contact with other House members, through the dissemination of information to individual black constituents, and by working closely with black elected officials in other levels of government. Establishes a yearly legislative agenda setting forth the issues which it supports: full employment, national health development, welfare reform, and international affairs.

10303 ■ National Conference of State Legislatures
7700 E First Pl.
Denver, CO 80230
Ph: (303)364-7700
URL: http://www.ncsl.org

Description: Serves the legislators and staffs of the nation's 50 states, its commonwealths and territories. Provides research, technical assistance and opportunities for policymakers to exchange ideas on the most pressing state issues. Promotes the interests of state governments before Congress and federal agencies.

Sources of Help-Wanted Ads

10304 ■ American Journal of Political Science
John Wiley & Sons Inc.
350 Main St., Commerce Pl.
Malden, MA 02148-5089
Ph: (781)388-8200
Fax: (781)388-8210
URL: http://www.ajps.org/

Quarterly. $600.00/year for institutions, print + online; $521.00/year for institutions, print or online; $467.00/year for institutions, other countries, print + online; $592.00/year for institutions, print & online; $406.00/year for institutions, other countries, print or online. Journal focusing on all major areas of political science including American politics, public policy, international relations, comparative politics, political methodology, and political theory.

10305 ■ BardPolitik
Bard College
PO Box 5000
Annandale-on-Hudson, NY 12504-5000
Ph: (845)758-6822
URL: http://bgia.bard.edu/bp.php?id=2

Semiannual. Free. Magazine that covers debate and discussion on global political and international affairs.

10306 ■ Federal Times
Gannett Government Media Corporation
6883 Commercial Dr.
Springfield, VA 22159-0500
Ph: (703)750-7400
Fr: 800-368-5718
URL: http://www.federaltimes.com/

Weekly (Mon.). Federal bureaucracy; technology in government.

10307 ■ In These Times
Institute for Public Affairs Inc.
2040 N Milwaukee Ave.
Chicago, IL 60647
Ph: (773)772-0100
Fax: (773)772-4180
E-mail: itt@inthesetimes.com
URL: http://www.inthesetimes.com

Biweekly. $19.95/year for individuals; $34.95/year for two years; $34.95/year for Canada; $40.95/year for other countries. National political newsmagazine.

10308 ■ Miller Center Report
Miller Center of Public Affairs
PO Box 400406
Charlottesville, VA 22904-4406
Ph: (434)924-7236
Fax: (434)982-2739
URL: http://millercenter.org

Description: Quarterly. Reports on the activities and programs of the Miller Center. Features information on the study of American governance and presidency. Recurring features include reports of meetings, and notices of publications available.

10309 ■ Political Science Education
American Political Science Association (APSA)
1527 New Hampshire Ave., NW
Washington, DC 20036-1206
Ph: (202)483-2512
Fax: (202)483-2657
E-mail: apsa@apsanet.org
URL: http://www.apsanet.org

Description: Quarterly. Provides information on The American Political Science Association. Includes news of meetings and conferences, and reviews of pertinent books.

10310 ■ Presidential Studies Quarterly
John Wiley & Sons Inc.
350 Main St., Commerce Pl.
Malden, MA 02148-5089
Ph: (781)388-8200
Fax: (781)388-8210
URL: http://www.wiley.com/bw/journal.asp?ref=0360-4918&site=1

Quarterly. $466.00/year for institutions, print & online; $405.00/year for institutions, print, online; $302.00/year for institutions, other countries, print & online; $262.00/year for institutions, other countries, print, online. Publication covering political science and history.

10311 ■ Quarterly Journal of Political Science
Now Publishers
PO Box 1024
Hanover, MA 02339-1001
Ph: (781)871-0245
URL: http://www.qjps.com

Quarterly. $360.00/year for institutions, plus shipping cost, North America; $360.00/year for institutions, plus shipping cost, outside North America; $410.00/year for institutions, print and online, plus shipping costs, North America; $410.00/year for institutions, print and online, outside North America; $75.00/year for individuals, print and online, plus $20 shipping fee; $50.00/year for individuals, online only. Journal focusing on positive political science and contemporary political economy.

10312 ■ State Politics & Policy Quarterly
Sage Publications Inc.
2455 Teller Rd.
Thousand Oaks, CA 91320-2218
Ph: (805)499-9774
Fax: (805)583-2665
Fr: 800-818-7243
URL: http://www.sagepub.com/home.nav

Quarterly. $50.00/year for individuals, print and e-access; $284.00/year for institutions, print and e-access. Official journal of the State Politics and Policy section of the American Political Science As-sociation covering studies that develop general hypotheses of the political behavior and policymaking and test those hypotheses using methodological advantages of the states.

10313 ■ White House Studies
Nova Science Publishers Inc.
400 Oser Ave., Ste. 1600
Hauppauge, NY 11788-3667
Ph: (631)231-7269
Fax: (631)231-8175
URL: http://www.novapublishers.com/catalog/product_info.php?cPath

Quarterly. $400.00/year for individuals. Publication covering political science and history.

Employer Directories and Networking Lists

10314 ■ American Political Science Association—Centennial Biographical Directory of Members
American Political Science Association
1527 New Hampshire Ave. NW
Washington, DC 20036-1206
Ph: (202)483-2512
Fax: (202)483-2657
URL: http://www.apsanet.org

Irregular. $50.00 for nonmembers; $30.00 for members; $65.00 for members. Number of listings: 13,000. Entries include: Name, address, affiliation, highest degree, fields of interest, phone, e-mail, URL, honors, employment history, publications. Arrangement: Alphabetical. Indexes: Women members, African American members, Asian American members, Latino/a members, Native American members, fields of interest, geographical.

10315 ■ Career Opportunities in Politics, Government, and Activism
Facts On File Inc.
132 W 31st St., 17th Fl.
New York, NY 10001
Ph: (212)967-8800
Fax: 800-678-3633
Fr: 800-322-8755
URL: http://www.infobasepublishing.com

Latest edition 2nd, Published July, 2008. $49.50 for individuals. Covers: 75 jobs from government, human services, and international relations, such as mayor, governor, political consultant, urban/regional planner, press secretary, foreign service officer, community organizer, and human rights advocate.

10316 ■ Carroll's Federal Directory
Carroll Publishing
4701 Sangamore Rd., Ste. S-155
Bethesda, MD 20816
Ph: (301)263-9800
Fax: (301)263-9801

Fr: 800-336-4240
URL: http://www.carrollpub.com

4x/yr. $450.00 for single issue. Covers: About 38,000 executive managers in federal government offices in Washington, DC, including executive, congressional and judicial branches; members of Congress and Congressional committees and staff. Entries include: Agency names, titles, office address (including room numbers), e-mail addresses, and telephone and fax numbers. Also available as part of a "library edition" titled "Federal Directory Annual". Arrangement: By cabinet department or administrative agency. Indexes: Keyword, personal name (with phone) and e-mail addresses.

10317 ■ Encyclopedia of Governmental Advisory Organizations
Gale
PO Box 6904
Florence, KY 41022-6904
Fr: 800-354-9706
URL: http://www.gale.cengage.com

Annual, Latest edition 26th; June, 2011. $1,073.00 for individuals. Covers: More than 7,300 boards, panels, commissions, committees, presidential conferences, and other groups that advise the President, Congress, and departments and agencies of federal government; includes interagency committees and federally sponsored conferences. Also includes historically significant organizations. Entries include: Unit name, address, phone, URL and email (if active), name of principal executive, legal basis for the unit, purpose, reports and publications, findings and recommendations, description of activities, members. Arrangement: Classified by general subject. Indexes: Alphabetical/keyword, personnel, publication, federal department/agency, presidential administration.

10318 ■ Federal Yellow Book
Leadership Directories Inc.
104 5th Ave.
New York, NY 10011
Ph: (212)627-4140
Fax: (212)645-0931
URL: http://www.leadershipdirectories.com/
   Products.aspx

Quarterly, Latest edition 2011. $550.00 for individuals; $385.00 for individuals; $523.00 for individuals; $366.00 for individuals. Covers: Federal departments, including the Executive Office of the President, the Office of the Vice President, the Office of Management and Budget, the Cabinet, and the National Security Council, and over 40,000 key personnel; over 85 independent federal agencies. Entries include: For personnel—Name, address, phone, fax, e-mails, titles. For departments and agencies—Office, or branch name and address; names and titles of principal personnel, with their room numbers, direct-dial phone numbers, and E-mails. Arrangement: Classified by department or agency. Indexes: Subject, organization, individuals' names.

10319 ■ United States Government Manual
Office of the Federal Register
c/o The National Archives & Records Administration
8601 Adelphi Rd.
College Park, MD 20740-6001
Ph: (301)837-0482
Fax: (301)837-0483
Fr: (866)272-6272
URL: http://www.archives.gov/federal-register/
   publications/govern

Annual, latest edition 2009-2010. $29.00 for individuals. Provides information on the agencies of the executive, judicial, and legislative branches of the Federal government. Contains a section on terminated or transferred agencies. Arrangement: Classified by department and agency. Indexes: Personal name, agency/subject.

10320 ■ Washington
Columbia Books & Information Services
8120 Woodmont Ave., Ste. 110
Bethesda, MD 20814

Ph: (202)464-1662
Fax: (202)464-1775
Fr: 888-265-0600
URL: http://www.columbiabooks.com

Annual, May. $149.00; $150.00. Covers: over 5,000 federal and district government offices, businesses, associations, publications, radio and television stations, labor organizations, religious and cultural institutions, health care facilities and community organizations in the District of Columbia area. Entries include: Name, address, phone, names and titles of key personnel and board of directors. Arrangement: Classified by subject. Indexes: Individuals, organizations.

10321 ■ Washington Information Directory
CQ Press
2300 North St. NW, Ste. 800
Washington, DC 20037
Ph: (202)729-1900
Fax: 800-380-3810
Fr: (866)427-7737
URL: http://www.cqpress.com

Annual, Latest edition 2010-2011. $155.00 for individuals. Covers: 10,000 governmental agencies, congressional committees, and non-governmental associations considered competent sources of specialized information. Entries include: Name of agency, committee, or association; address, phone, fax, and Internet; annotation concerning function or activities of the office; and name of contact. Arrangement: Classified by activity or competence (economics and business, housing and urban affairs, etc.). Indexes: Subject, agency/organization name, contact name.

HANDBOOKS AND MANUALS

10322 ■ The Book of US Government Jobs: Where They Are, What's Available and How to Write a Federal Resume
Bookhaven Press LLC
249 Field Club Cir.
McKees Rocks, PA 15136
Ph: (412)494-6926
Fax: (412)494-5749
E-mail: bookhaven@aol.com
URL: http://federaljobs.net/us10.htm

Dennis Damp. 11th edition. 2011. $19.50.

10323 ■ Careers in International Affairs
Georgetown University Press
3240 Prospect St., NW
Washington, DC 20007
Ph: (202)687-5889
Fax: (202)687-6340
Fr: 800-537-5487
E-mail: gupress@georgetown.edu
URL: http://www.press.georgetown.edu

Maria Carland and Candace Faber (editors). Eighth edition, 2008. $24.95 (paper). 432 pages. Includes index and bibliography.

10324 ■ Opportunities in Social Science Careers
The McGraw-Hill Companies
PO Box 182604
Columbus, OH 43272
Fax: (614)759-3749
Fr: 877-883-5524
E-mail: customer.service@mcgraw-hill.com
URL: http://www.mcgraw-hill.com

Rosanne J. Marek. 2004. $13.95. 160 Pages. VGM Opportunities Series.

TRADESHOWS

10325 ■ American Political Science Association Meeting and Exhibition
American Political Science Association
1527 New Hampshire Ave. NW
Washington, DC 20036-1206

Ph: (202)483-2512
Fax: (202)483-2657
E-mail: apsa@apsanet.org
URL: http://www.apsanet.org

Annual. Primary Exhibits: Publications and computer software.

OTHER SOURCES

10326 ■ Academy of Political Science (APS)
475 Riverside Dr., Ste. 1274
New York, NY 10115-1274
Ph: (212)870-2500
Fax: (212)870-2202
E-mail: aps@psqonline.org
URL: http://www.psqonline.org

Description: Individual members, libraries and institutions. Promotes the cultivation of political science and its application to the solution of political, social, and economic problems.

10327 ■ African Studies Association (ASA)
Rutgers University, Livingston Campus
54 Joyce Kilmer Ave.
Piscataway, NJ 08854-8045
Ph: (848)445-8173
Fax: (732)445-1366
E-mail: karen.jenkins@africanstudies.org
URL: http://www.africanstudies.org

Description: Persons specializing in teaching, writing, or research on Africa including political scientists, historians, geographers, anthropologists, economists, librarians, linguists, and government officials; persons who are studying African subjects; institutional members are universities, libraries, government agencies, and others interested in receiving information about Africa. Seeks to foster communication and to stimulate research among scholars on Africa. Sponsors placement service; conducts panels and discussion groups; presents exhibits and films.

10328 ■ American Academy of Political and Social Science (AAPSS)
Annenberg Policy Center
202 S 36th St.
Philadelphia, PA 19104-3806
Ph: (215)746-6500
Fax: (215)573-2667
E-mail: ewood@asc.upenn.edu
URL: http://www.aapss.org

Description: Professionals and laymen concerned with the political and social sciences and related fields. Promotes the progress of political and social science through publications and meetings. The academy does not take sides in controversial issues, but seeks to gather and present reliable information to assist the public in forming an intelligent and accurate judgment.

10329 ■ American Association of Political Consultants (AAPC)
8400 Westpark Dr., 2nd Fl.
Washington, DC 20003
Ph: (703)245-8020
Fax: (703)610-9005
E-mail: info@aapc.org
URL: http://www.theaapc.org

Description: Regular members are corporations and individuals who devote a major portion of their time to or earn a major portion of their livelihood from political counseling and related activities; associate members are persons who devote part of their time to or earn part of their living from political counseling, have an interest in the political process, are teachers of political science, or intend to become actively involved in political activities. Provides a vehicle for the exchange of information, resources, and ideas among persons involved in political activity. Arranges seminars and holds biennial updates on campaign techniques and professional advances.

10330 ■ American Political Science Association (APSA)
1527 New Hampshire Ave. NW
Washington, DC 20036-1206
Ph: (202)483-2512
Fax: (202)483-2657
E-mail: apsa@apsanet.org
URL: http://www.apsanet.org

Description: College and university teachers of political science, public officials, research workers, and businessmen. Encourages the impartial study and promotes the development of the art and science of government. Develops research projects of public interest and educational programs for political scientists and journalists; seeks to improve the knowledge of and increase citizen participation in political and governmental affairs. Serves as clearinghouse for teaching and research positions in colleges, universities, and research bureaus in the U.S. and abroad and for positions open to political scientists in government and private business; conducts Congressional Fellowship Program. Conducts Committee on Professional Ethic, and Rights and Freedom. Offers placement service.

10331 ■ Congressional Black Caucus (CBC)
1433 Longworth House Office Bldg.
Washington, DC 20515
Ph: (202)226-9776
Fax: (202)225-9817
E-mail: congressionalblackcaucus@mail.house.gov
URL: http://www.thecongressionalblackcaucus.com

Description: Black members of the U.S. House of Representatives. Addresses the legislative concerns of black and other underrepresented citizens and to formalize and strengthen the efforts of its members. Works to implement these objectives through personal contact with other House members, through the dissemination of information to individual black constituents, and by working closely with black elected officials in other levels of government. Establishes a yearly legislative agenda setting forth the issues which it supports: full employment, national health development, welfare reform, and international affairs.

10332 ■ International Studies Association (ISA)
University of Arizona
324 Social Sciences Bldg.
Tucson, AZ 85721
Ph: (520)621-7715
Fax: (520)621-5780
E-mail: isa@isanet.org
URL: http://www.isanet.org

Description: Social scientists and other scholars from a wide variety of disciplines who are specialists in international affairs and cross-cultural studies; academicians; government officials; officials in international organizations; business executives; students. Promotes research, improved teaching, and the orderly growth of knowledge in the field of international studies; emphasizes a multidisciplinary approach to problems. Conducts conventions, workshops and discussion groups.

SOURCES OF HELP-WANTED ADS

10333 ■ *The American Postal Worker*
American Postal Workers Union, AFL-CIO
1300 L St. NW
Washington, DC 20005
Ph: (202)842-4200
Fax: (202)842-4297
URL: http://www.apwu.org/index2.htm

Monthly. $3.00/year for individuals. AFL-CIO postal labor.

10334 ■ *Business Mailers Review*
PO Box 328
Boyds, MD 20841
Ph: (301)528-0011
Fax: (240)599-7679
E-mail: support@pnmsi.com
URL: http://www.businessmailersreview.com/

Description: Biweekly. Concerned with the monitoring of the U.S. Postal Service, private carriers, and suppliers. Offers volume mailers, traffic managers, parcel shippers, and operators of letter-shops news of current developments in the field of business mailings. Reports on new technologies and products, rate changes, metering alternatives, and relevant legislative activity. Recurring features include interviews and news of research.

10335 ■ *Postal Bulletin*
U.S. Government Printing Office and Superintendent of Documents
Mail Stop: IDCC
732 N Capitol St. NW
Washington, DC 20401
Ph: (202)512-1800
Fax: (202)512-2104
Fr: (866)512-1800
E-mail: pbulleti@usps.gov
URL: http://www.usps.com/cpim/ftp/bulletin/pb.htm

$163.00/year for individuals; $228.00/year for other countries. Bulletin reporting U.S. Postal Service news.

10336 ■ *Postal Record*
National Association of Letter Carriers
100 Indiana Ave. NW
Washington, DC 20001-2144
Ph: (202)393-4695
E-mail: postalrecord@nalc.org
URL: http://www.nalc.org/news/precord/index.html

Monthly. Magazine for active and retired letter carriers.

10337 ■ *Postal World*
United Communications Group
9737 Washingtonian Blvd., Ste. 100
Gaithersburg, MD 20878
Ph: (301)287-2700
Fax: (301)816-8945
Fr: 800-929-4824
URL: http://www.ucg.com

Description: Disseminates information to help readers run a more efficient mail operation. Discusses how to trim postage costs, speed delivery, improve mailroom productivity, and plan for rate increases. Recurring features include an annual salary survey and periodic special reports.

10338 ■ *Postmasters Advocate Express*
National League of Postmasters of the United States
5904 Richmond Hwy., Ste. 500
Alexandria, VA 22303-1864
Ph: (703)329-4550
Fax: (703)329-0466
E-mail: information@postmasters.org
URL: http://www.postmasters.org

Description: 5-9 issues/year. Monitors the advocacy activities of the League, which sponsors the Postmasters Benefit Plan and represents postmasters and other federal employees before Congress and provides liaison to USPS. Covers pertinent legislative developments and postal issues. Recurring features include items on members and information on League officer training programs.

10339 ■ *Postmasters Gazette*
National Association of Postmasters
8 Herbert St.
Alexandria, VA 22305-2600
Ph: (703)683-9027
Fax: (703)683-6820
URL: http://www.napus.org/membership-publications/

$18.00/year for nonmembers. Postal magazine.

EMPLOYER DIRECTORIES AND NETWORKING LISTS

10340 ■ *National Five-Digit Zip Code and Post Offices Directory*
United States Postal Service
6060 Primacy Pky., Ste. 201
Memphis, TN 38188-0001
Fax: (901)681-4409
Fr: 800-275-8777
URL: http://www.usps.com

Annual, January. Covers: post offices, named stations, named branches, community post offices, and place names of former post offices frequently used as delivery addresses. Also includes Postal Service regional offices, bulk mail centers, etc. Zip codes are given for cities, for buildings having their own zip codes, and for streets and blocks within zip code areas. Entries include: For post offices—Post office name, county, states, and zip code. For Postal Service installations—Office name, mailing address, areas served. Arrangement: Post offices are listed alphabetically and by zip code. Cities which have more than one zip code are listed separately by state, then city, with buildings and other installations with their own zip code listed first. Discontinued post of-

fices and military installation zip code lists are also provided separately.

10341 ■ *Who's Who—The MFSA Buyer's Guide to Blue Ribbon Mailing Services*
Mailing & Fulfillment Service Association
1421 Prince St., Ste. 410
Alexandria, VA 22314-2806
Ph: (703)836-9200
Fax: (703)548-8204
Fr: 800-333-6272
URL: http://www.mfsanet.org

Annual, Latest edition 2010. Covers: 650 member firms that provide printing, addressing, inserting, sorting, and other mailing services, and mailing list brokers. Entries include: Firm name; MFSA representative name and title, address, phone, coded list of services, gross business volume for latest year. Arrangement: Geographical. Indexes: Company name, personal name, geographical, product/service.

HANDBOOKS AND MANUALS

10342 ■ *Post Office Jobs: Explore and Find Jobs, Prepare for the 473 Postal Exam, and Locate All Job Opportunties*
Bookhaven Press LLC
249 Field Club Cir.
McKees Rocks, PA 15136
Ph: (412)494-6926
E-mail: info@bookhavenpress.com
URL: http://bookhavenpress.com

Dennis V. Damp. 2009. $24.95 (paperback). 256 pages. Includes a study guide for the new 473 and 473-C Postal exams, and covers the new eCareer Postal Service hiring process. Provides information on preparing for the exams, plus test-taking strategies. Also features details on locating job vacancies.

10343 ■ *Post Office Jobs: How to Get a Job With the U.S. Postal Service*
Bookhaven Press LLC
249 Field Club Cir.
McKees Rocks, PA 15136
Ph: (412)494-6926
Fax: (412)494-5749
E-mail: bookhaven@aol.com
URL: http://www.bookhavenpress.com/
reviews.htm#Post_Office_Jobs

Dennis V. Damp. Fifth edition. 2009. $24.95. 256 pages. Includes tips on how to identify job openings, preparing for interviews, and a study guide for exams.

ONLINE JOB SOURCES AND SERVICES

10344 ■ MailmanStuff.com
E-mail: mailman@rollanet.org
URL: http://www.mailmanstuff.com
Description: Shared resources for letter carriers.

10345 ■ Postal Work
URL: http://www.postalwork.net
Description: Provides information on post office job opportunities, application guidance, job descriptions, how to prepare for interviews, benefits and pay information.

TRADESHOWS

10346 ■ National Association of Postmasters of the United States Convention
National Association of Postmasters of the United States
8 Herbert St.
Alexandria, VA 22305-2600
Ph: (703)683-9027
Fax: (703)683-6820
E-mail: napusinfo@napus.org
URL: http://www.napus.org
Annual. Primary Exhibits: Office supplies and materials for the postal service. Dates and Locations: 2012 Sep 01-06; Oklahoma City, OK.

OTHER SOURCES

10347 ■ American Postal Workers Union (APWU)
1300 L St. NW
Washington, DC 20005
Ph: (202)842-4200
Fax: (202)842-4297
URL: http://www.apwu.org
Description: AFL-CIO. Works to advance the interest of members. Negotiates, interprets and enforces a national agreement with the U.S. Postal Service.

10348 ■ Association of Mailing, Shipping and Office Automation Specialists (AIMED)
11310 Wornall Rd.
Kansas City, MO 64114
Fax: 888-836-9561
Fr: 888-750-6245
E-mail: rick@aimedweb.org
URL: http://www.aimedweb.org
Description: Independent dealers of mail-related products and services; manufacturers of mailing equipment. Informs members about industry changes and new products. Maintains speakers' bureau, hall of fame; conducts educational programs.

10349 ■ Association for Postal Commerce (PostCom)
1421 Prince St., Ste. 410
Alexandria, VA 22314-2806
Ph: (703)524-0096
Fax: (703)997-2414
E-mail: info@postcom.org
URL: http://www.postcom.org
Description: Represents supporters and users of mail as an advertising, marketing, and fundraising medium. Seeks to protect interests of members with respect to postal rates and services before Congress, the U.S. Postal Service, and the Postal Rate Commission.

10350 ■ Mail Systems Management Association (MSMA)
PO Box 1145
North Riverside, IL 60546-0545

Ph: (708)442-8589
Fax: (708)853-0471
Fr: 800-714-6762
E-mail: karen.cornelius@pb.com
URL: http://www.msmanational.org
Description: Mail management executives. Provides training, through the development of management skills, in reducing costs, improving services and reducing employee turnover. Organizes meetings to discuss topics such as presort discounts, scheduling and recruiting and training personnel. Conducts certification program, training programs for mail distribution clerks and management programs for mail managers and supervisors. Maintains placement service. Conducts research; operates speakers' bureau and consulting service.

10351 ■ National Association of Letter Carriers of the U.S.A. (NALC)
100 Indiana Ave. NW
Washington, DC 20001-2144
Ph: (202)393-4695
Fax: (202)737-1540
Fr: 800-424-5186
E-mail: nalcinf@nalc.org
URL: http://www.nalc.org
Description: AFL-CIO. Provides Collective Bargaining representation for city delivery letter carriers employed by the U.S. Postal Service. Maintains information center.

10352 ■ National Association of Postal Supervisors (NAPS)
1727 King St., Ste. 400
Alexandria, VA 22314-2700
Ph: (703)836-9660
Fax: (703)836-9665
E-mail: napshq@naps.org
URL: http://www.naps.org
Description: Represents first-line supervisors who work both in facilities where postal employees process mail and where they deliver mail. Promotes and cooperates with USPS and other agencies of the federal government in a continuing effort to improve the service.

10353 ■ National Association of Postmasters of the United States (NAPUS)
8 Herbert St.
Alexandria, VA 22305-2600
Ph: (703)683-9027
Fax: (703)683-6820
E-mail: napusinfo@napus.org
URL: http://www.napus.org
Description: Purpose: Serves the professional interests of postmasters and promotes cooperation and interchange of ideas between members and officials of the U.S. Postal Service.

10354 ■ National League of Postmasters of the United States (NLPM)
1 Beltway Ctr.
5904 Richmond Hwy., Ste. 500
Alexandria, VA 22303-1864
Ph: (703)329-4550
Fax: (703)329-0466
E-mail: information@postmasters.org
URL: http://www.postmasters.org
Description: Independent. Sponsors the Postmasters Benefit Plan, an insurance program operated under the Federal Employees Health Benefit Program (FEHBP). Represents postmasters and other federal employees before Congress. Conducts annual league

forum and national convention for league officer training.

10355 ■ National Postal Forum (NPF)
3998 Fair Ridge Dr., Ste. 150
Fairfax, VA 22033-2907
Ph: (703)218-5015
Fax: (703)218-5020
E-mail: info@npf.org
URL: http://www.npf.org
Description: Postal authorities and businesses making use of the postal service. Seeks to ensure the most efficient use of postal services by businesses. Serves as a clearinghouse on products and services offered by the U.S. Postal Service; conducts educational and training programs for business mailers.

10356 ■ National Postal Mail Handlers Union (NPMHU)
1101 Connecticut Ave. NW, Ste. 500
Washington, DC 20036-4325
Ph: (202)833-9095
Fax: (202)833-0008
URL: http://www.npmhu.org
Description: AFL-CIO. Operates as a division of Laborers' International Union of North America. Aims to negotiate and enforce a National Agreement with the U.S. Postal Service, a contract that establishes wages, cost-of-living adjustments and other pay increases, working conditions, and fringe benefits for all workers within its jurisdiction.

10357 ■ National Rural Letter Carriers' Association (NRLCA)
1630 Duke St.
Alexandria, VA 22314-3465
Ph: (703)684-5545
E-mail: pswartz@nrlca.org
URL: http://www.nrlca.org
Description: Works to improve the methods used by rural letter carriers, to benefit their conditions of labor with the United States Postal Service (USPS), and to promote a fraternal spirit among its members.

10358 ■ National Star Route Mail Contractors Association (NSRMCA)
324 E Capitol St.
Washington, DC 20003-3897
Ph: (202)543-1661
Fax: (202)543-8863
E-mail: info@starroutecontractors.org
URL: http://www.starroutecontractors.org
Description: Highway mail contractors with the U.S. Postal Service transporting mail over the highway on authorized schedules.

10359 ■ Parcel Shippers Association (PSA)
1420 King St., Ste. 620
Alexandria, VA 22314
Ph: (571)257-7617
Fax: (571)257-7613
E-mail: psa@parcelshippers.org
URL: http://www.parcelshippers.org
Description: Wholesalers, retailers, mail order houses, and other firms using parcel post service for distribution of products. Promotes the efficient and economical distribution of small package shipments.

SOURCES OF HELP-WANTED ADS

10360 ■ About Campus
John Wiley & Sons Inc.
111 River St.
Hoboken, NJ 07030-5773
Ph: (201)748-6000
Fax: (201)748-6088
Fr: 800-825-7550
URL: http://onlinelibrary.wiley.com/journal/10.1002/
    (ISSN)1536-06

Bimonthly. $207.00/year for institutions, print only; $267.00/year for institutions, Canada and Mexico, print only; $318.00/year for institutions, other countries, print only; $60.00/year for U.S., Canada, and Mexico, print only; $96.00/year for other countries, print only. Journal focused on the critical issues faced by both student affairs and academic affairs staff as they work on helping students learn.

10361 ■ American Academic
American Federation of Teachers
555 New Jersey Ave. NW
Washington, DC 20001
Ph: (202)879-4400
URL: http://www.aft.org/pubs-reports/american_
    academic/index.htm

Higher education policy journal.

10362 ■ Annals of Medicine
Informa Healthcare
52 Vanderbilt Ave., 7th Fl.
New York, NY 10017-3846
Ph: (212)520-2777
URL: http://informahealthcare.com/ann

$595.00/year for institutions; $980.00/year for institutions; $780.00/year for institutions. Journal covering health science and medical education.

10363 ■ Assessment & Evaluation in Higher Education
Routledge Journals
270 Madison Ave.
New York, NY 10016-0601
Ph: (212)216-7800
Fax: (212)563-2269
URL: http://www.tandf.co.uk/journals/titles/
    02602938.asp

Bimonthly. $1,316.00/year for institutions, online only; $2,547.00/year for institutions, print + online; $1,462.00/year for individuals, print + online; $2,292.00/year for institutions, online only; $578.00/year for individuals, print only; $314.00/year for individuals, print only. Peer-reviewed journal focusing on publishing papers and reports on all aspects of assessment and evaluation within higher education.

10364 ■ Better
The Johns Hopkins University Press
2715 N Charles St.
Baltimore, MD 21218-4319

Ph: (410)516-6900
Fax: (410)516-6968
URL: http://www.press.jhu.edu/journals/better_
    evidence_based_educ

$29.50/year for individuals, print and electronic; $80.00/year for institutions, print and electronic. Magazine for educators and policy makers interested in evidence-based education reform.

10365 ■ Brookings Papers on Education Policy
Brookings Institution Press
1775 Massassusetts Ave. NW
Washington, DC 20036
Ph: (202)797-6000
URL: http://www.brookings.edu/press/Journals/2007/
    brookingspapers

$36.00/year for individuals. Journal dealing with all aspects of American education.

10366 ■ Creative Education
Scientific Research Publishing
PO Box 54821
Irvine, CA 92619-4821
E-mail: ce@scirp.org
URL: http://www.scirp.org/journal/ce/

$195.00/year for individuals. Peer-reviewed journal publishing articles on the latest advancements in creative education.

10367 ■ Education & Treatment of Children
West Virginia University Press
139 Stansbury Hall
PO Box 6295
Morgantown, WV 26506
Ph: (304)293-8400
Fax: (304)293-6585
URL: http://www.educationandtreatmentofchildren.net

Quarterly. $85.00/year for institutions; $45.00/year for individuals; $100.00/year for institutions, elsewhere; $60.00/year for individuals, elsewhere. Periodical featuring information concerning the development of services for children and youth. Includes reports written for educators and other child care and mental health providers focused on teaching, training, and treatment effectiveness.

10368 ■ Educational Research and Evaluation
Routledge Journals
270 Madison Ave.
New York, NY 10016-0601
Ph: (212)216-7800
Fax: (212)563-2269
URL: http://www.tandf.co.uk/journals/titles/
    13803611.asp

Bimonthly. $428.00/year for institutions, print + online; $385.00/year for institutions, online only; $165.00/year for individuals, print only; $731.00/year for institutions, print + online; $658.00/year for institutions, online only; $275.00/year for individuals, print only. Peer-reviewed journal on theory and practice.

10369 ■ Environmental Education Research
Routledge Journals
270 Madison Ave.
New York, NY 10016-0601
Ph: (212)216-7800
Fax: (212)563-2269
URL: http://www.tandf.co.uk/journals/titles/
    13504622.asp

Bimonthly. $1,373.00/year for institutions, print + online; $1,236.00/year for institutions, online only; $364.00/year for individuals, print only. Journal covering all aspects of environmental education.

10370 ■ Essays in Education
University of South Carolina
471 University Pky.
Aiken, SC 29801
Ph: (803)648-6851
URL: http://www.usca.edu/essays/

Monthly. Journal covering issues that impact and influence education.

10371 ■ Hematology
American Society of Hematology
2021 L St. NW, Ste. 900
Washington, DC 20036
Ph: (202)776-0544
Fax: (202)776-0545
URL: http://asheducationbook.hematologylibrary.org

Annual. $75.00/year for members; $125.00/year for nonmembers. Journal providing continuing medical education for physicians.

10372 ■ Interdisciplinary Journal of Teaching and Learning
Southern University at Baton Rouge
PO Box 9942
Baton Rouge, LA 70813
Ph: (225)711-4500
Fax: (225)771-4400
URL: http://www.subr.edu/CollegeofEducation/
    COE%20ONLINE%20Journa

Online academic journal that publishes research and scholarly articles in the field of education and learning.

10373 ■ The International Electronic Journal of Health Education
American Alliance for Health, Physical Education, Recreation & Dance
1900 Association Dr.
Reston, VA 20191-1598
Ph: (703)476-3400
Fax: (703)476-9527
Fr: 800-213-7193
URL: http://www.aahperd.org/aahe/publications/iejhe/

Annual. Free, health education professionals and students. Journal promoting health through education and other systematic strategies.

**10374 ■ *International Journal of Critical
Pedagogy***
University of North Carolina at Greensboro
1400 Spring Garden St.
Greensboro, NC 27412
Ph: (336)334-5000
URL: http://libjournal.uncg.edu/ojs/index.php/ijcp/
index

Peer-reviewed journal publishing innovative understandings and applications of critical pedagogy.

**10375 ■ *International Journal of Early Years
Education***
Routledge Journals
270 Madison Ave.
New York, NY 10016-0601
Ph: (212)216-7800
Fax: (212)563-2269
URL: http://www.tandf.co.uk/journals/titles/
09669760.asp

$705.00/year for institutions, online only; $783.00/
year for institutions, print + online; $271.00/year for
individuals, print only. Journal focusing on education
world-wide.

**10376 ■ *International Journal of Inclusive
Education***
Routledge Journals
270 Madison Ave.
New York, NY 10016-0601
Ph: (212)216-7800
Fax: (212)563-2269
URL: http://www.tandf.co.uk/journals/titles/
13603116.asp

$589.00/year for individuals, print only; $1,135.00/
year for institutions, online only; $1,261.00/year for
individuals, print + online; $355.00/year for individu-
als, print only; $694.00/year for institutions, online
only; $771.00/year for institutions, print + online.
Journal providing information on the nature of
schools, universities and technical colleges for the
educators and educational policy-makers.

**10377 ■ *International Journal of Leadership
in Education***
Routledge
711 3 Ave., 8 Fl.
New York, NY 10016
Ph: (212)216-7800
Fax: (212)563-2269
Fr: 800-634-7064
E-mail: ijle@txstate.edu
URL: http://www.tandf.co.uk/journals/tf/
13603124.html

Quarterly. $240.00/year for individuals, print only;
$612.00/year for institutions, online only; $680.00/
year for institutions, print and online; $408.00/year for
institutions, print and online; $367.00/year for institu-
tions, online only; $142.00/year for individuals, print
only. Journal dealing with leadership in education.

**10378 ■ *International Journal of Progressive
Education***
International Journal of Progressive Education
c/o Alex Jean-Charles, PhD, Asst. Mng. Ed.
320 Fitzelle Hall, Ravine Pky.
Oneonta, NY 13820
URL: http://www.inased.org/ijpe.htm

$35.00/year for members; $45.00/year for individuals;
$140.00/year for institutions, library; $35.00/year for
students; $25.00/year for single issue; $50.00/year
for students, other countries. Peer-reviewed online
journal that aims to create an open and continuing
dialogue about current educational issues and future
conceptions of educational theory.

**10379 ■ *International Journal of Whole
Schooling***
Whole Schooling Press
Wayne State University
217 Education
Detroit, MI 48202
URL: http://www.wholeschooling.net/Journal_of_
Whole_Schooling/IJW

Free. International, refereed academic journal dedicated to exploring ways to improve learning and
schooling for all children.

10380 ■ *Journal of Academic Leadership*
Academic Leadership
600 Park St.
Rarick Hall 219
Hays, KS 67601-4099
Ph: (785)628-4547
URL: http://www.academicleadership.org/

Journal focusing on the leadership issues in the
academic world.

**10381 ■ *Journal of Cases in Educational
Leadership***
Sage Publications Inc.
2455 Teller Rd.
Thousand Oaks, CA 91320-2218
Ph: (805)499-9774
Fax: (805)583-2665
Fr: 800-818-7243
URL: http://jel.sagepub.com

Quarterly. $411.00/year for institutions, e-access;
$94.00/year for individuals, e-access. Journal cover-
ing cases appropriate for use in programs that
prepare educational leaders.

**10382 ■ *Journal of Curriculum and
Supervision***
Association for Supervision and Curriculum Develop-
ment
1703 N Beauregard St.
Alexandria, VA 22311-1714
Ph: (703)578-9600
Fax: (703)575-5400
Fr: 800-933-2723
URL: http://www.ascd.org/publications/jcs/fall2002/
On_Community.a

Scholarly journal focusing on curriculum and
supervision.

10383 ■ *Journal of Direct Instruction*
Association for Direct Instruction
PO Box 10252
Eugene, OR 97440
Ph: (541)485-1293
Fax: (541)868-1397
Fr: 800-995-2464
URL: http://www.adihome.org/
index.php?option=com_content&view=art

Quarterly. Included in membership. Journal covering
education.

**10384 ■ *Journal of Language, Identity, and
Education***
Routledge Journals
270 Madison Ave.
New York, NY 10016-0601
Ph: (212)216-7800
Fax: (212)563-2269
URL: http://www.tandf.co.uk/journals/titles/
15348458.asp

$316.00/year for institutions, print + online; $284.00/
year for institutions, online; $43.00/year for individu-
als, print + online; $527.00/year for institutions, print
+ online; $474.00/year for institutions, online; $71.00/
year for individuals, print + online; $421.00/year for
institutions, print + online; $379.00/year for institu-
tions, online; $57.00/year for individuals, print +
online. Scholarly, interdisciplinary journal covering issues in language, identity and education worldwide
for academics, educators and policy specialists in a
variety of disciplines, and others.

10385 ■ *Journal of Latinos and Education*
Routledge Journals
270 Madison Ave.
New York, NY 10016-0601
Ph: (212)216-7800
Fax: (212)563-2269
URL: http://www.tandf.co.uk/journals/titles/
15348431.asp

Quarterly. $286.00/year for institutions, print + on-
line; $257.00/year for institutions, online; $38.00/year
for individuals, print + online; $480.00/year for institu-
tions, print + online; $432.00/year for institutions, on-
line; $63.00/year for individuals, print + online;
$331.00/year for institutions, print + online; $343.00/
year for institutions, online; $51.00/year for individu-
als, print + online. Scholarly, multidisciplinary journal
covering educational issues that impact Latinos for
researchers, teaching professionals, academics,
scholars, institutions, and others.

10386 ■ *Journal of STEM Education*
Auburn University
9088 Haley Ctr.
Auburn, AL 36849
Ph: (334)844-9088
Fax: (334)844-9027
URL: http://ojs.jstem.org/index.php?journal=JSTEM

Semiannual. Journal for educators in Science,
Technology, Engineering, and Mathematics (STEM)
education.

10387 ■ *Leadership and Policy in Schools*
Routledge Journals
270 Madison Ave.
New York, NY 10016-0601
Ph: (212)216-7800
Fax: (212)563-2269
URL: http://www.tandf.co.uk/journals/titles/
15700763.asp

Quarterly. $567.00/year for institutions, print and on-
line; $260.00/year for individuals, print only; $510.00/
year for institutions, online only. Journal providing
information about leadership and policy in primary
and secondary education.

10388 ■ *NJEA Review*
New Jersey Education Association
180 W State St.
PO Box 1211
Trenton, NJ 08607-1211
Ph: (609)599-4561
Fax: (609)392-6321
E-mail: njeareview@njea.org
URL: http://www.njea.org/page.aspx?z=1094&pz=8

Monthly. $250.00/year for nonmembers. Educational
journal for public school employees.

10389 ■ *Oxford Review of Education*
Routledge Journals
270 Madison Ave.
New York, NY 10016-0601
Ph: (212)216-7800
Fax: (212)563-2269
URL: http://www.tandf.co.uk/journals/titles/
03054985.asp

$709.00/year for institutions, print + online;
$1,224.00/year for institutions, print + online;
$249.00/year for individuals, print only; $454.00/year
for individuals, print only. Journal covering advance
study of education.

**10390 ■ *School Effectiveness and School
Improvement***
Routledge
711 3 Ave., 8 Fl.
New York, NY 10016
Ph: (212)216-7800
Fax: (212)563-2269
Fr: 800-634-7064
URL: http://www.tandf.co.uk/journals/titles/
09243453.asp

Quarterly. $387.00/year for institutions, print and on-
line; $348.00/year for institutions, online only;
$186.00/year for individuals, print only; $660.00/year
for institutions, print and online; $594.00/year for
institutions, online only; $312.00/year for individuals,
print only. Journal focusing on educational progress
of all students.

10391 ■ Teaching and Learning in Nursing
Elsevier Science Inc.
360 Park Ave. S
New York, NY 10010-1710
Ph: (212)989-5800
Fax: (212)633-3990
Fr: 888-437-4636
URL: http://www.elsevier.com/wps/find/
journaldescription.cws_home

Quarterly. $232.00/year for institutions, other countries; $134.00/year for other countries; $160.00/year for institutions; $91.00/year for individuals. Journal devoted to associate degree nursing education and practice.

10392 ■ Theory and Research in Education
Sage Publications Inc.
2455 Teller Rd.
Thousand Oaks, CA 91320-2218
Ph: (805)499-9774
Fax: (805)583-2665
Fr: 800-818-7243
URL: http://www.sagepub.com/
journalsProdDesc.nav?prodId=Journal20

$546.00/year for institutions, print and e-access; $491.00/year for institutions, e-access; $535.00/year for institutions, print; $85.00/year for individuals, print; $196.00/year for single issue, institutional; $37.00/year for single issue, individual. Interdisciplinary journal covering normative and theoretical issues concerning education including multi-faceted philosophical analysis of moral, social, political and epistemological problems and issues arising from educational practice.

EMPLOYER DIRECTORIES AND NETWORKING LISTS

10393 ■ Career Ideas for Teens in Education and Training
Facts On File Inc.
132 W 31st St., 17th Fl.
New York, NY 10001
Ph: (212)967-8800
Fax: 800-678-3633
Fr: 800-322-8755
URL: http://factsonfile.infobasepublishing.com

Published 2005. $40.00 for individuals. Covers: A multitude of career possibilities based on a teenager's specific interests and skills and links his/her talents to a wide variety of actual professions.

10394 ■ Discovering Careers for Your Future—Teaching
Facts On File Inc.
132 W 31st St., 17th Fl.
New York, NY 10001
Ph: (212)967-8800
Fax: 800-678-3633
Fr: 800-322-8755
URL: http://factsonfile.infobasepublishing.com

Latest edition 2nd, 2008. $21.95 for individuals. Covers: Athletic and fitness trainers, career counselors, college professors, elementary school teachers, ESL teachers, music teachers, and preschool teachers; links career education to curriculum, helping children investigate the subjects they are interested in, and the careers those subjects might lead to.

HANDBOOKS AND MANUALS

10395 ■ Ferguson Career Coach: Managing Your Career in Education
Facts On File
132 W 31st St., 17th Fl.
New York, NY 10001
Fax: 800-678-3633
Fr: 800-322-8755
E-mail: custserv@factsonfile.com
URL: http://factsonfile.infobasepublishing.com

Shelly Field. 2008. $39.95 (hardcover). 272 pages. Contains tips on achieving career success in the field of education. Provides students with advice on making contacts, interviewing, and career strategies.

10396 ■ Inside Secrets of Finding a Teaching Job, Third Edition: The Most Effective Search Methods for Both New and Experienced Educators
JIST Publishing
875 Montreal Way
St. Paul, MN 55102
Fax: 800-547-8329
Fr: 800-648-5478
E-mail: info@jist.com
URL: http://www.jist.com/shop/
product.php?productid=3423

Jack Warner and Clyde Bryan. 2006. $6.47. 208 pages. Covers researching job opportunities; preparing resumes, cover letters, mission statements, teacher portfolios, and demonstration videos; preparing for interviews; and finding the inside track.

10397 ■ Opportunities in Child Care Careers
The McGraw-Hill Companies
PO Box 182604
Columbus, OH 43272
Fax: (614)759-3749
Fr: 877-883-5524
E-mail: customer.service@mcgraw-hill.com
URL: http://www.mhprofessional.com/
product.php?isbn=0071467661

Renee Wittenberg. 2006. $13.95 (paper). 160 pages. Discusses various job opportunities and how to secure a position. Illustrated.

10398 ■ Skills for Preschool Teachers
Prentice Hall PTR
1 Lake St.
Upper Saddle River, NJ 07458
Ph: (201)236-7000
Fr: 800-922-0579
URL: http://www.pearsonhighered.com/educator

Janice J. Beaty. 2012. $66.40 (paper). 416 pages. Focuses on training students to help young children become independent and self-directed in their learning.

ONLINE JOB SOURCES AND SERVICES

10399 ■ Preschool Teacher Jobs
URL: http://www.preschoolteacherjobs.us

Description: Offers job search and recruiting resource for employment candidates and employers for preschool teacher jobs.

10400 ■ School-Jobs.net
URL: http://www.school-jobs.net/jobs

Description: Matches teachers, administrators, support staff, and other school employees to related jobs across the country. Features jobs by salary, location, and area of expertise.

10401 ■ SchoolSpring.com
E-mail: contact@schoolspring.com
URL: http://www.schoolspring.com

Description: Serves as an employment source for educators. Offers teaching jobs and other education job listings including complete archiving of all necessary documents and certifications, as well as access to all education jobs in a specific area.

10402 ■ WantToTeach.com
URL: http://www.wanttoteach.com

Description: Serves as an education website to search for administrative, instructional and support openings throughout the United States. Features job openings and job fairs and allows access to various education resources.

TRADESHOWS

10403 ■ Association for Childhood Education International Annual International Conference & Exhibition
Association for Childhood Education International
17904 Georgia Ave., Ste. 215
Olney, MD 20832
Ph: (301)570-2111
Fax: (301)570-2212
Fr: 800-423-3563
E-mail: headquarters@acei.org
URL: http://www.acei.org

Annual. Primary Exhibits: Commercial and educational exhibits of interest to teachers, teacher educators, college students, daycare personnel and other care givers.

10404 ■ National Art Education Association National Convention
National Art Education Association
1806 Robert Fulton Dr., Ste. 300
Reston, VA 20191
Ph: (703)860-8000
Fax: (703)860-2960
Fr: 800-299-8321
E-mail: info@arteducators.org
URL: http://www.naea-reston.org

Annual. Primary Exhibits: Art materials; art-related books and magazines; art career education information; arts and crafts supplies. Dates and Locations: 2012 Mar 01-04; New York, NY; 2013 Mar 07-10; Fort Worth, TX.

10405 ■ National Association for the Education of Young Children Annual Conference
National Association for the Education of Young Children
1313 L St. NW, Ste. 500
Washington, DC 20005
Ph: (202)232-8777
Fax: (202)328-1846
Fr: 800-424-2460
URL: http://www.naeyc.org

Annual. Primary Exhibits: Educational materials and equipment designed for children ages birth through eight years old. Dates and Locations: 2012 Nov 07-10; Atlanta, GA.

OTHER SOURCES

10406 ■ American Federation of Teachers (AFT)
555 New Jersey Ave. NW
Washington, DC 20001
Ph: (202)879-4400
E-mail: online@aft.org
URL: http://www.aft.org

Description: Affiliated with the AFL-CIO. Works with teachers and other educational employees at the state and local level in organizing, collective bargaining, research, educational issues, and public relations. Conducts research in areas such as educational reform, teacher certification, and national assessments and standards. Represents members' concerns through legislative action; offers technical assistance. Serves professionals with concerns similar to those of teachers, including state employees, healthcare workers, and paraprofessionals.

10407 ■ American Montessori Society (AMS)
281 Park Ave. S
New York, NY 10010-6102
Ph: (212)358-1250
Fax: (212)358-1256
E-mail: ams@amshq.org
URL: http://www.amshq.org

Description: School affiliates and teacher training affiliates; heads of schools, teachers, parents, non-

Montessori educators, and other interested individuals dedicated to stimulating the use of the Montessori teaching approach and promoting better education for all children. Seeks to meet demands of growing interest in the Montessori approach to early learning. Assists in establishing schools; supplies information and limited services to member schools in other countries. Maintains school consultation and accreditation service; provides information service; assists research and gathers statistical data; offers placement service. Maintains Montessori and related materials exhibit.

10408 ■ Association for Direct Instruction (ADI)
PO Box 10252
Eugene, OR 97440
Ph: (541)485-1293
Fax: (541)868-1397
Fr: 800-995-2464
E-mail: brywick@adihome.org
URL: http://www.adihome.org

Description: Public school regular and special education teachers and university instructors. Encourages, promotes, and engages in research aimed at improving educational methods. Promotes dissemination of developmental information and skills that facilitate the education of adults and children. Administers a preschool for developmentally delayed children. Offers educational training workshops for instructors. Maintains speaker's bureau and placement service.

10409 ■ National Association for the Education of Young Children (NAEYC)
PO Box 97156
Washington, DC 20090-7156
Ph: (202)232-8777
Fax: (202)328-1846
Fr: 800-424-2460
E-mail: naeyc@naeyc.org
URL: http://www.naeyc.org

Description: Teachers and directors of preschool and primary schools, kindergartens, child care centers, and early other learning programs for young childhood; early childhood education and child development educators, trainers, and researchers and other professionals dedicated to young children's healthy development.

10410 ■ *Overseas Employment Opportunities for Educators: Department of Defense Dependents Schools*
DIANE Publishing Co.
PO Box 617
Darby, PA 19023-0617
Fr: 800-782-3833
URL: http://www.dianepublishing.net

Barry Leonard, editor. $20.00. 52 pages. An introduction to teachings positions in the Dept. of Defense Dependents Schools (DoDDS), a worldwide school system, operated by the DoD in 14 countries.

SOURCES OF HELP-WANTED ADS

10411 ■ *American Printer*
Penton Media Inc.
9800 Metcalf Ave.
Overland Park, KS 66212
Ph: (913)341-1300
Fax: (913)967-1898
E-mail: apeditor@penton.com
URL: http://www.americanprinter.com

Monthly. Magazine covering the printing and publishing market.

10412 ■ *FLEXO*
Foundation of Flexographic Technical Association
900 Marconi Ave.
Ronkonkoma, NY 11779-7212
Ph: (631)737-6020
Fax: (631)737-6813
URL: http://www.flexography.org/flexo/index.cfm

Monthly. $55.00/year for U.S., Canada, and Mexico; $76.00/year for other countries; $30.00/year for individuals; $92.00/year for two years; $125.00/year for individuals, 3 years. Magazine covering the flexographic printing method.

10413 ■ *Guild of Book Workers Newsletter*
Guild of Book Workers Inc.
521 5th Ave.
New York, NY 10175-0038
E-mail: newsletter@guildofbookworkers.org
URL: http://www.guildofbookworkers.org

Description: Bimonthly. Covers issues in book arts, binding, book conservation, calligraphy, and printing. Recurring features include letters to the editor, interviews, news of research, a calendar of events, reports of meetings, news of educational opportunities, job listings, book reviews, and notices of publications available.

10414 ■ *Printing Impressions*
North American Publishing Co.
1500 Spring Garden St., Ste. 1200
Philadelphia, PA 19130-4069
Ph: (215)238-5300
Fax: (215)238-5412
Fr: 800-777-8074
URL: http://www.napco.com

Monthly. Free. Trade magazine.

10415 ■ *Quick Printing*
Cygnus Business Media Inc.
3 Huntington Quadrangle, Ste. 301 N
Melville, NY 11747
Ph: (631)845-2700
Fax: (631)845-7109
Fr: 800-308-6397
URL: http://www.myprintresource.com/magazine

Monthly. Free. For Quick and Small Commercial Printers.

EMPLOYER DIRECTORIES AND NETWORKING LISTS

10416 ■ *International Literary Market Place*
Information Today Inc.
143 Old Marlton Pike
Medford, NJ 08055-8750
Ph: (609)654-6266
Fax: (609)654-4309
Fr: 800-300-9868
URL: http://www.literarymarketplace.com

Annual, Latest edition 2012. $289.00 for individuals; $260.10 for individuals. Covers: Over 10,500 publishers in over 180 countries outside the United States and Canada, and about 1,499 trade and professional organizations related to publishing abroad; includes major printers, binders, typesetters, book manufacturers, book dealers, libraries, literary agencies, translators, book clubs, reference books and journals, periodicals, prizes, and international reference section. Entries include: For publishers—Name, address, phone, fax, telex, names and titles of key personnel, branches, type of publications, subjects, ISBN prefix. Listings for others include similar information but less detail. Arrangement: Classified by business activities, then geographical. Indexes: Company name, subject, type of publication.

10417 ■ *Literary Market Place*
Information Today Inc.
143 Old Marlton Pike
Medford, NJ 08055-8750
Ph: (609)654-6266
Fax: (609)654-4309
Fr: 800-300-9868
URL: http://books.infotoday.com

Annual, Latest edition 2012. $339.00 for individuals; $305.10 for individuals. Covers: Over 12,500 firms or organizations offering services related to the publishing industry, including book publishers in the United States and Canada who issued three or more books during the preceding year, plus a small press section of publishers who publish less than three titles per year or those who are self-published. Also included: book printers and binders; book clubs; book trade and literary associations; selected syndicates, newspapers, periodicals, and radio and TV programs that use book reviews or book publishing news; translators and literary agents. Entries include: For publishers—Company name, address, phone, address for orders, principal executives, editorial directors, and managers, date founded, number of titles in previous year, number of backlist titles in print, types of books published, ISBN prefixes, representatives, imprints, and affiliations. For suppliers, etc.—Listings usually show firm name, address, phone, executives, services, etc. Arrangement: Classified by line of business. Indexes: Principal index is 35,000-item combined index of publishers, publications, and personnel; several sections have geographical and/or subject indexes; translators are indexed by source and target language.

10418 ■ *Publishers Directory*
Gale
PO Box 6904
Florence, KY 41022-6904
Fr: 800-354-9706
URL: http://www.gale.cengage.com

Annual, Latest edition 36th; April, 2011. $720.00 for individuals. Covers: Over 20,000 new and established, commercial and nonprofit, private and alternative, corporate and association, government and institution publishing programs and their distributors; includes producers of books, classroom materials, prints, reports, and databases. Entries include: Firm name, address, phone, fax, company e-mail address, URL, year founded, ISBN prefix, Standard Address Number, whether firm participates in the Cataloging in Publication program of the Library of Congress, names of principal executives, personal e-mail addresses, number of titles in print, description of firm and its main subject interests, discount and returns policies, affiliated and parent companies, mergers and amalgamations, principal markets, imprints and divisions, alternate formats products are offered; distributors also list firms for which they distribute, special services, terms to publishers and regional offices. Arrangement: Alphabetical; distributors listed separately. Indexes: Subject, geographical, publisher, imprints, and distributor.

10419 ■ *Who's Who in SGIA*
Screenprinting and Graphic Imaging Association International
10015 Main St.
Fairfax, VA 22031-3489
Ph: (703)385-1335
Fax: (703)273-0456
Fr: 888-385-3588
URL: http://www.sgia.org

Annual, August. Covers: About 3,800 screen printers and graphic imaging companies, suppliers of screen printing equipment and graphic imaging materials, and investors in the Screen Printing Technical Foundation; international coverage. Entries include: Company name, address, phone, fax, e-mail, name of contact, products or services. Arrangement: Classified by type of business, then geographical. Indexes: Alphabetical by company, within state or country.

10420 ■ *The Workbook*
Scott & Daughters Publishing Inc.
6762 Lexington Ave.
Los Angeles, CA 90038
Ph: (323)856-0008
Fax: (323)856-4368
Fr: 800-547-2688
URL: http://www.workbook.com

Annual, Latest edition 2011. $60.00 for individuals; $30.00 for individuals; $35.00 for individuals. Covers: 55,000 advertising agencies, art directors, photographers, freelance illustrators and designers, artists' representatives, interactive designers, pre-press services, and other graphic arts services in the U.S. Entries include: Company or individual name, address, phone, specialty. National in scope. Arrangement: Classified by product or service.

EMPLOYMENT AGENCIES AND SEARCH FIRMS

10421 ■ Burton & Grove Executive Search.
1320 Tower Rd.
Schaumburg, IL 60173
Ph: (847)919-8880
E-mail: support@burtonandgrove.com
URL: http://www.burtonandgrove.com
Executive search firm.

10422 ■ Core Management Search LLC
PO Box 421042
Minneapolis, MN 55442
Ph: (763)559-0977
E-mail: jlentner@coremanage.com
URL: http://www.coremanage.com
Executive search firm.

10423 ■ Graphic Arts Employment Specialists, Inc.
409 Pacific Coast Hwy., Ste. 455
Redondo Beach, CA 90277
Fax: (310)937-3760
Fr: 888-499-9722
E-mail: info@gaes.com
URL: http://www.gaes.com

Employment agency specializing in the publishing and packaging industries.

10424 ■ LandaJob Advertising Staffing Specialists
222 W Gregory Blvd., Ste. 304
Kansas City, MO 64114
Ph: (816)523-1881
Fax: (816)523-1876
Fr: 800-931-8806
E-mail: adstaff@landajobnow.com
URL: http://www.landajobnow.com

Personnel consultants and recruiters for advertising, marketing, and communications positions. Industries served: advertising, communications, marketing, graphic arts, printing and publishing.

10425 ■ Printemps
18 Avery Pl.
Westport, CT 06880
Ph: (203)226-6869
Fax: (203)226-1594
E-mail: printemps7@aol.com

Specializes in providing temporary support for graphic design, document management and the electronic printing industry. Provides permanent placement for professionals and production personnel. Consults with printers and in-house print shops for greater production efficiency. Handles personnel management and policy programs as well. Industries served: printing, advertising, manufacturing, insurance, banking, and government agencies.

10426 ■ Zachary & Sanders Inc.
24 Linden Ln.
PO Box 32
East Norwich, NY 11732
Ph: (516)922-5500

Fax: (516)922-2286
Fr: 800-540-7919
E-mail: zacharyserch@earthlink.net

Serves the printing, packaging, publishing, advertising, direct marketing industries.

ONLINE JOB SOURCES AND SERVICES

10427 ■ PrintJobs.com
E-mail: printjobs@roadrunner.com
URL: http://www.printjobs.com

Description: Aims to find suitable graphic arts jobs for qualified candidates. Over a hundred jobs are maintained and updated on the site. Fee: Must be paid by employers using the site; no registration charge for job hunters.

TRADESHOWS

10428 ■ Binding Industries Association International Annual Convention
Binding Industries Association International
200 Deer Run Rd.
Sewickley, PA 15143
Ph: (412)741-6860
Fax: (412)259-1800
Fr: 800-910-4283
E-mail: printing@printing.org
URL: http://www.gain.net

Annual. Primary Exhibits: Exhibits relating to binding and printing.

OTHER SOURCES

10429 ■ Amalgamated Printers' Association (APA)
135 East Church St.
Clinton, MI 49236
E-mail: phil@phillipdriscoll.com
URL: http://www.apa-letterpress.com

Description: Active printers interested in furthering of the art and craft of printing. Encourages excellence of printing content, design and techniques among members. Sponsors competitions.

10430 ■ American Institute of Graphic Arts (AIGA)
164 5th Ave.
New York, NY 10010-5901
Ph: (212)807-1990
Fax: (212)807-1799
E-mail: grefe@aiga.org
URL: http://www.aiga.org

Description: Graphic designers, art directors, illustrators and packaging designers. Sponsors exhibits and projects in the public interest. Sponsors traveling exhibitions. Operates gallery. Maintains library of design books and periodicals; offers slide archives.

10431 ■ Binding Industries Association International (BIA)
200 Deer Run Rd.
Sewickley, PA 15143
Ph: (412)259-1802
Fax: (412)259-1800
E-mail: jgoldstein@printing.org
URL: http://www.gain.net

Description: Represents trade binders and loose-

leaf manufacturers united to conduct seminars, hold conventions, and formulate and maintain standards.

10432 ■ National Association for Printing Leadership (NAPL)
75 W Century Rd., Ste. 100
Paramus, NJ 07652-1408
Ph: (201)634-9600
Fax: (201)634-0324
Fr: 800-642-6275
E-mail: jtruncale@napl.org
URL: http://www.napl.org

Description: Represents commercial printers and suppliers to the commercial printing industry. Enables those in the industry to operate their businesses for maximum profitability. Offers following management products and services: sales and marketing, customer service, financial, human resources, operations and economic. Maintains Management Institute, which conducts Executive Certification Program. Compiles extensive economic statistics.

10433 ■ Printing Brokerage/Buyers Association (PB/BA)
PO Box 744
Palm Beach, FL 33480
Ph: (215)821-6581
Fax: (561)845-7130
Fr: 877-585-7141
URL: http://www.pbba.org

Description: Printing buyers/brokers/distributors, printers, typographers, binders, envelope and book manufacturers, packagers, color separation houses, pre-press service organizations, and related companies in the graphic arts industry. Promotes understanding, cooperation, and interaction among members while obtaining the highest standard of professionalism in the graphic arts industry. Gathers information on current technology in the graphic communications industry. Sponsors seminars for members to learn how to work with buyers, brokers and printers; also conducts technical and management seminars. Maintains referral service; compiles statistics. Conducts charitable programs.

10434 ■ Printing Industries of America (PIA)
200 Deer Run Rd.
Sewickley, PA 15143
Ph: (412)741-6860
Fax: (412)741-2311
Fr: 800-910-4283
E-mail: printing@printing.org
URL: http://www.printing.org

Description: Commercial printing firms (lithography, letterpress, gravure, platemakers, typographic houses); allied firms in the graphic arts. Provides extensive management services for member companies, including government relations, industry research and statistical information, technology information and assistance, and management education and publications. Compiles statistical and economic data, including annual ratio study that provides a benchmark for printers to compare profits as a basis for improving individual member company and industry profits. Provides reporting system on provisions, rates, and other matters relating to union contracts in effect throughout the industry. Sponsors annual Premier Print Awards Competition.

10435 ■ Typophiles
15 Gramercy Park S, No. 6C
New York, NY 10003
E-mail: info@typophiles.org
URL: http://www.typophiles.org

Description: Represents designers, printers, book collectors, artists, calligraphers, private press owners, wood engravers, librarians and others interested in graphic arts. Promotes the love and appreciation of fine graphic design and printing. Conducts quarterly meeting-luncheons and maintains publications.

SOURCES OF HELP-WANTED ADS

10436 ■ *The Legal Investigator*
National Association of Legal Investigators Inc.
235 N Pine St.
Lansing, MI 48933
Ph: (517)702-9835
Fax: (517)372-1501
Fr: (866)520-6254
E-mail: info@nalionline.org
URL: http://www.nalionline.org/publications.htm

Description: Six issues/year. Focuses on concerns of the legal investigator, especially on professionalization of the career through a certification program. Discusses issues and legal developments relating to the investigation of personal injury matters for the plaintiff and criminal defense.

EMPLOYER DIRECTORIES AND NETWORKING LISTS

10437 ■ *Investigator's International All-in-One Directory*
National Association of Investigative Specialists
PO Box 82148
Austin, TX 78708
Ph: (512)719-3595
Fax: (512)719-3594
URL: http://www.pimall.com/nais/dir.menu.html

Annual. Covers: Approximately 1,800 NAIS members; national, state, and foreign private investigative and related associations; online networks for private investigators; security associations; publications; information services; training programs and seminars; equipment sources; state investigative licensing agencies. Entries include: Company name or individual name, address, contact, investigative specialty, services provided, and geographic area covered. Arrangement: Geographical.

HANDBOOKS AND MANUALS

10438 ■ *Careers for Legal Eagles and Other Law-and-Order Types*
The McGraw-Hill Companies
PO Box 182604
Columbus, OH 43272
Fax: (614)759-3749
Fr: 877-883-5524
E-mail: customer.service@mcgraw-hill.com
URL: http://www.mhprofessional.com/
 product.php?isbn=0071466207

Blythe Camenson. Second edition, 2005. $13.95 (paper). 176 pages.

10439 ■ *Careers for Mystery Buffs and Other Snoops and Sleuths*
The McGraw-Hill Companies
PO Box 182604
Columbus, OH 43272
Fax: (614)759-3749
Fr: 877-883-5524
E-mail: customer.service@mcgraw-hill.com
URL: http://www.mhprofessional.com

Blythe Camenson. Second edition. $14.95 (hardback). 160 pages.

10440 ■ *Introduction to Private Investigation: Essential Knowledge and Procedures for the Private Investigator*
Charles C Thomas Publisher, Ltd.
2600 S 1st St.
PO Box 19265
Springfield, IL 62794-9265
Ph: (217)789-8980
Fax: (217)789-9130
Fr: 800-258-8980
E-mail: books@ccthomas.com
URL: http://www.ccthomas.com/details.cfm?P_
 ISBN13=9780398075613

Joseph A. Travers. Second edition, 2005. $41.95. 304 pages.

10441 ■ *Practical Handbook for Professional Investigators, 2nd Edition*
CRC Press
6000 Broken Sound Parkway NW, Ste. 300
Boca Raton, FL 33487
Ph: (561)994-0555
Fax: 800-374-3401
Fr: 800-272-7737
URL: http://www.crcpress.com/product/isbn/
 9780849370458

Rory J. McMahon, 2007. $63.99 (hardback). 440 pages. Includes information on certification programs, job descriptions, earning capabilities, and future outlook. Provides names and contact information for professional associations.

10442 ■ *Private Investigation and Security Science*
Charles C Thomas Publisher, LTD.
2600 S First St.
Springfield, IL 62704
Ph: (217)789-8980
Fr: 800-258-8980
E-mail: books@ccthomas.com
URL: http://www.ccthomas.com/details.cfm?P_
 ISBN13=9780398076672

Frank MacHovec, 2006. $32.95 (paper). 204 pages. Covers training materials, state exam preparation and skill-building exercises.

10443 ■ *Process of Investigation*
Elsevier Inc.
30 Corporate Dr.
4th Fl.
Burlington, MA 01803
Ph: (781)313-4700
Fax: (781)313-4880
URL: http://www.elsevierdirect.com/
 product.jsp?isbn=9780750679503

Charles A. Sennewald and John Tsukayama, 2006. $69.95 (hardcover). 344 pages. Covers investigative skills and techniques for both new private investigators, and those already in the field.

ONLINE JOB SOURCES AND SERVICES

10444 ■ Be-a-private-investigator.net
URL: http://www.be-a-private-investigator.net

Description: Provides news on private investigating, and tips for becoming a private investigator. Job links are available as well.

10445 ■ BeAPrivateEye.com
E-mail: scotth@compasspointpi.com
URL: http://www.beaprivateeye.com

Description: Offers a course for becoming a private investigator. Provides news via weblog and FAQ.

10446 ■ Einvestigator.com
URL: http://www.einvestigator.com

Description: Provides resources for private detectives. Investigation software is available, and users may join forums for discussion.

10447 ■ Pimagazine.com
URL: http://www.pimagazine.com

Description: Online magazine for private investigators. Provides news, information on educational conferences, and job postings.

10448 ■ PrivateDetectiveSource.com
URL: http://www.privatedetectivesource.com

Description: Provides information and tools for private investigating. Includes links for job searching.

OTHER SOURCES

10449 ■ American Association of Police Polygraphers
PO Box 657
Waynesville, OH 45068
Ph: (937)728-7827
Fax: (937)488-1046
Fr: 888-743-5479
URL: http://www.policepolygraph.org

Description: Encourages the application and utilization of accepted polygraph techniques among law enforcement organizations. Develops standards of proficiency in the polygraph profession by fostering scientific training and research through advanced study and progressive techniques. Provides an opportunity and forum for the exchange of information regarding polygraph experiences, studies, and research.

10450 ■ Council of International Investigators (CII)
2150 N 107th St., Ste. 205
Seattle, WA 98133-9009
Ph: (206)361-8869
Fax: (206)367-8777
Fr: 888-759-8884
E-mail: office@cii2.org
URL: http://www.cii2.org

Description: Represents licensed and accredited professional private investigators and detectives in 28 countries. Conducts seminars on investigation, security work, criminology and lie detection.

10451 ■ National Association of Investigative Specialists (NAIS)
PO Box 82148
Austin, TX 78708
Ph: (512)719-3595
Fax: (512)719-3594
E-mail: rthomas007@aol.com
URL: http://www.pimall.com/nais/dir.menu.html

Description: Private investigators, automobile repossessors, bounty hunters, and law enforcement officers. Promotes professionalism and provides for information exchange among private investigators. Lobbies for investigative regulations. Offers training programs and issues certificates of completion. Sponsors charitable programs; compiles statistics; maintains speakers' bureau and placement service. Operates Investigators' Hall of Fame of Private Investigators. Offers seminars on cassette tape.

10452 ■ National Association of Traffic Accident Reconstructionists and Investigators (NATARI)
PO Box 2588
West Chester, PA 19382
Ph: (610)696-1919
E-mail: natari@natari.org
URL: http://www.natari.org

Description: Represents engineers, attorneys, police officers, private investigators, medical examiners, and other individuals involved in the analysis of motor vehicle traffic accidents. Gathers and disseminates information on techniques and equipment of potential use to members; reviews literature in the field. Participating Organization of the Accreditation Commission for Traffic Accident Reconstruction.

SOURCES OF HELP-WANTED ADS

10453 ■ WorkingWorld.com
3600 Wilshire Blvd., Ste. 1526
Los Angeles, CA 90010
Ph: (213)385-4781
URL: http://www.workingworld.com

Monthly. Employment magazine that features a searchable jobs database and career-related articles, including information for professional organizers.

EMPLOYER DIRECTORIES AND NETWORKING LISTS

10454 ■ National Association of Professional Organizers—Directory
National Association of Professional Organizers
15000 Commerce Pkwy., Ste. C
Mount Laurel, NJ 08054
Ph: (856)380-6828
Fax: (856)439-0525
URL: http://www.napo.net

Annual. Covers: Over 500 member professionals involved with time management, information management, space planning, and productivity improvement in the workplace and in the home. Entries include: Name, company name, address, phone, description of services. Arrangement: Geographical, alphabetical, specialty.

HANDBOOKS AND MANUALS

10455 ■ Becoming a Professional Organizer
1563 Solano Ave, Ste. 306
Berkeley, CA 94707
URL: http://
www.becomingaprofessionalorganizer.com

$29.95 (kit). Offers a systematic guide that provides advice and practical guidance for starting a professional organizing business. Contains forms and business letters that will assist in starting the business.

10456 ■ FabJob Guide to Become a Professional Organizer
FabJob.com
4616 25th Ave. NE, Ste. 224
Seattle, WA 98105
Ph: (403)949-4980
Fr: 888-322-5621
URL: http://www.fabjob.com/Organizer.asp

Grace Jasmine and Jennifer James. 2009. $39.95 (paper). 297 pages. Includes sections on residential organizing, office organizing, and how to start a professional organizing business.

10457 ■ Newbie Pitfalls
Red Letter Day
Ph: (586)746-1428
E-mail: info@rldpo.com
URL: http://www.rldpo.com/ForOrganizers.htm

$29.95 (paper); $24.95 (PDF download). 50 pages. Includes lessons and tips from a veteran organizer to help those new to the profession avoid costly learning experiences.

10458 ■ Secrets of a Professional Organizer and How to Become One
OverHall Consulting
PO Box 263
Port Republic, MD 20676
Ph: (410)586-9440
Fr: 800-687-3040
E-mail: janet@soverhall.com
URL: http://www.overhall.com/become_an_organizer.htm

Janet L. Hall. $49.95 (download). Includes information on establishing an organizing business, including business skills needed, how to set fees, writing contracts, and proven systems and techniques.

EMPLOYMENT AGENCIES AND SEARCH FIRMS

10459 ■ America's Most Organized
441 Ski Lodge Rd.
McQueeney, TX 78123
Ph: (830)560-3248
E-mail: info@americasmostorganized.com
URL: http://americasmostorganized.com

Consults with individuals and businesses who seek professional organizing services and outsources services with a pool of freelance professional organizers and custom storage contractors.

ONLINE JOB SOURCES AND SERVICES

10460 ■ BlueSuitMom.com
E-mail: info@bluesuitmom.com
URL: http://www.bluesuitmom.com/career

Description: An online database containing over 300,000 searchable job postings, including those in professional organizing. Offers career advice for the professional organizer.

10461 ■ Clutterbug.net
URL: http://www.clutterbug.net

Description: Acts as an online clearinghouse of information for those interested in becoming professional organizers. Also maintains a directory of professional organizers.

10462 ■ OnlineOrganizing.com
URL: http://www.onlineorganizing.com

Description: Serves as an online source for organizing advice, products, and other information related to professional organizing. Maintains an online listing of professional organizers.

10463 ■ Organizing Network
PO Box 12312
Ogden, UT 84414-2312
Ph: (801)668-2410
Fax: (801)782-9832
E-mail: contact.info@organizingnetwork.com
URL: http://www.myorganizedlife.com

Description: Provides a searchable online list of professional organizers based on geographic location for those seeking professional organizing services.

10464 ■ Professional Organizers Web Ring
E-mail: ringmasters@organizerswebring.com
URL: http://www.organizerswebring.com

Description: Maintains a searchable member directory, as well as information on upcoming organizing events, seminars, workshops, and conferences. Provides an online collection of featured articles written by professional organizers and a section on frequently asked questions in the field of professional organizing.

10465 ■ Ryze Business Networking
E-mail: press@ryze.com
URL: http://www.ryze.com

Description: Provides an online classifieds section as well as networking services.

OTHER SOURCES

10466 ■ HG Training Academy
8209 Foothill Blvd., Ste. A-184
Sunland, CA 91040
Ph: (818)686-8888
URL: http://professional-organizers.com

Purpose: Provides online training for professional organizers. **Activities:** Offers courses in the basic principles of organization, as well as an apprenticeship program.

10467 ■ National Association of Professional Organizers (NAPO)
15000 Commerce Pkwy., Ste. C
Mount Laurel, NJ 08054
Ph: (856)380-6828
Fax: (856)439-0525
E-mail: napo@napo.net
URL: http://www.napo.net

Description: Professional organizers providing organization, time management, or productivity improvement services; persons in related fields such as organizational product sales and organizational development. Works to promote and educate the public about the profession and to offer support, education, and networking opportunities to members.

10468 ■ Organizing Resources
PO Box 7080
Plainville, CT 06062-0412
Ph: (860)747-8962
E-mail: judith@organizingresources.com
URL: http://www.organizingresources.com

Purpose: Offers resources, tips, and techniques for the professional organizer. **Activities:** Provides learning modules, a mentoring program, and teleclasses for the professional organizer.

10469 ■ The Professional Organizer
180 Worthington Dr., Ste. 1A
Marietta, GA 30068
Ph: (770)579-9866

Fax: (770)579-0314
E-mail: organizer@theprofessionalorganizer.com
URL: http://www.theprofessionalorganizer.com

Description: Provides advice, information, and products on organization. **Activities:** Administers Organizer U, a training, mentoring, and licensing program for professional organizers.

SOURCES OF HELP-WANTED ADS

10470 ■ Business Performance Management
Penton Media Inc.
249 W 17th St.
New York, NY 10011
Ph: (212)204-4200
URL: http://www.bpmmag.net/

Free to qualified subscribers. Magazine for business managers. Covers organizing, automating, and analyzing of business methodologies and processes.

10471 ■ CXO
IDG Communications Inc.
3 Speen St.
Framingham, MA 01701
Ph: (508)875-5000
URL: http://www.idg.com/www/IDGProducts.nsf/0/022796185EED5984852

Monthly. Magazine providing technology information for chief officers and managers.

10472 ■ D & O Advisor
American Lawyer Media L.P.
120 Broadway, 5th Fl.
New York, NY 10271
Ph: (212)457-9400
Fax: (646)417-7705
Fr: 800-603-6571
URL: http://www.alm.com

Quarterly. Magazine that offers advice and perspective on corporate oversight responsibilities for directors and officers.

10473 ■ E Journal of Organizational Learning and Leadership
WeLEAD Inc.
PO Box 202
Litchfield, OH 44253
Fr: 877-778-5494
URL: http://www.leadingtoday.org/weleadinlearning/

Semiannual. Free. Online academic journal about organizational leadership.

10474 ■ Event Management
Cognizant Communications Corp.
3 Hartsdale Rd.
Elmsford, NY 10523-3701
Ph: (914)592-7720
Fax: (914)592-8981
URL: http://www.cognizantcommunication.com/journal-titles/event-

Quarterly. $445.00/year for institutions, online only; $525.00/year for institutions, online & hard copy; $52.00/year for individuals, professional; $50.00/year for members, online & hard copy; $65.00/year for single issue. Peer-reviewed journal covering research and analytic needs of a rapidly growing profession focused on events.

10475 ■ Executive Legal Adviser
Incisive Media
120 Broadway, 5th Fl.
New York, NY 10271
Ph: (212)457-9400
Fax: (646)417-7705
URL: http://www.executivelegaladviser.com

Bimonthly. Free to qualified subscribers. Magazine that offers legal advice for corporate executives.

10476 ■ Forrester
Forrester Research Inc.
400 Technology Sq.
Cambridge, MA 02139
Ph: (617)613-5730
Fr: (866)367-7378
URL: http://www.forrester.com/mag

Free. Journal that aims to provide ideas and advice that is relevant to today's CEOs.

10477 ■ International Journal of Business Research
International Academy of Business and Economics
PO Box 2536
Ceres, CA 95307
Ph: (702)560-0653
Fax: (702)508-9166
URL: http://www.iabe.eu/domains/iabeX/journal.aspx?journalid=12

Peer-reviewed journal publishing theoretical, conceptual, and applied research on topics related to research, practice and teaching in all areas of business, management, and marketing.

10478 ■ Journal of Academic Leadership
Academic Leadership
600 Park St.
Rarick Hall 219
Hays, KS 67601-4099
Ph: (785)628-4547
URL: http://www.academicleadership.org/

Journal focusing on the leadership issues in the academic world.

10479 ■ Journal of Business and Psychology
Springer-Verlag New York Inc.
233 Spring St.
New York, NY 10013-1578
Ph: (212)460-1500
Fax: (212)460-1575
Fr: 800-777-4643
URL: http://www.springer.com/psychology/community+%26+environment

$904.00/year for institutions, print or online; $1,085.00/year for institutions, print & enchanced access. Journal covering all aspects of psychology that apply to the business segment. Includes topics such as personnel selection and training, organizational assessment and development, risk management and loss control, marketing and consumer behavior research.

10480 ■ Journal of International Business Strategy
International Academy of Business and Economics
PO Box 2536
Ceres, CA 95307
Ph: (702)560-0653
Fax: (702)508-9166
URL: http://www.iabe.eu/domains/iabeX/journal.aspx?journalid=7

Peer-reviewed journal publishing theoretical, conceptual, and applied research on topics related to strategy in international business.

10481 ■ Organization Management Journal
Eastern Academy of Management
c/o Vicki Fairbanks Taylor, VP
John I. Grove College of Business
45 Keefer Way
Mechanicsburg, PA 17011
Ph: (518)762-4651
Fax: (518)736-1716
E-mail: omj@palgrave.com
URL: http://www1.wnec.edu/omj

Free to qualified subscribers. Refereed, online journal focusing on organization management issues.

10482 ■ Project Management Journal
Project Management Institute
14 Campus Blvd.
Newtown Square, PA 19073-3299
Ph: (610)356-4600
Fax: (610)482-9971
URL: http://www.pmi.org/en/Knowledge-Center/Publications-Project-

Quarterly. Peer-reviewed professional journal devoted to theory and practice in the field of project management.

EMPLOYER DIRECTORIES AND NETWORKING LISTS

10483 ■ Harvard Business School Guide to Careers in Management Consulting
Harvard Business School Publishing
60 Harvard Way
Boston, MA 02163
Ph: (617)783-7400
Fax: (617)783-7489
Fr: 888-500-1016
URL: http://www.hbsp.harvard.edu

$10.83 for individuals. Publication includes: Well-known consulting firms, a mailing list of recruiting contacts, and a selective bibliography of relevant books and directories compiled by the Harvard Business School.

HANDBOOKS AND MANUALS

10484 ■ 90 Days to Success as a Project Manager
Course Technology PTR
20 Channel Center St.
Boston, MA 02210

Fr: 800-354-9706
URL: http://www.courseptr.com

Paul Sanghera. 2009. $19.99 (paper). 376 pages. Serves as a guide for first-time project managers. Provides readers with tips on how to achieve successful project management. Includes case studies and real work scenarios.

10485 ■ Essential People Skills for Project Managers
Management Concepts, Inc.
8230 Leesburg Pke., Ste. 800
Vienna, VA 22182
Ph: (703)790-9595
Fax: (703)790-1371
URL: http://www.managementconcepts.com

Steven Glannes and Ginger Levin. 2005. $32.00. 181 pages. People management skills for project managers are discussed.

10486 ■ PMP Project Management Professional Study Guide
The McGraw-Hill Companies
PO Box 182604
Columbus, OH 43272
Fax: (614)759-3749
Fr: 877-883-5524
E-mail: customer.service@mcgraw-hill.com
URL: http://www.mhprofessional.com/
product.php?isbn=0071626735

Joseph Phillips. 2009. $49.99 (paper). 576 pages. Includes complete coverage of all objectives of the PMP examination, hundreds of practice questions, and hands-on exercises.

10487 ■ PMP: Project Management Professional Workbook
Sybex
111 River St.
Hoboken, NJ 07030
Ph: (201)748-6000
Fax: (201)748-6088
Fr: 800-225-5945
E-mail: custserv@wiley.com
URL: http://as.wiley.com/WileyCDA/Brand/id-23.html

Kim Heldman, Patti M. Jansen, and Claudia M. Baca. 2005. $34.99 (paper). 816 pages. Offers hands-on experience in preparation for the PMP examination sponsored by the Project Management Institute.

10488 ■ Project Management: A Systems Approach to Planning, Scheduling, and Controlling
John Wiley & Sons, Inc.
1 Wiley Dr.
Somerset, NJ 08873
Fax: (732)302-2300
Fr: 800-225-5945
E-mail: custserv@wiley.com
URL: http://as.wiley.com/WileyCDA/WileyTitle/
productCd-0470278706.html

Harold Kerzner. Tenth edition, 2009. $98.95. 1120 pages. Focuses on the critical aspects of project management and includes expanded problems and exercises.

10489 ■ Project Management Workbook and PMP/CAPM Exam Study Guide
Sybex
111 River St.
Hoboken, NJ 07030
Ph: (201)748-6000
Fax: (201)748-6088
Fr: 800-225-5945
E-mail: custserv@wiley.com
URL: http://as.wiley.com

Harold Kerzner and Frank P. Saladis. Tenth Edition. 2009. $79.95. 480 pages. Provides problems and exercises to reinforce project management concepts. Prepares project managers for the Project Management Professional certification examination.

EMPLOYMENT AGENCIES AND SEARCH FIRMS

10490 ■ Access Staffing
360 Lexington Ave., 8th Fl.
New York, NY 10017
Ph: (212)687-5440
Fax: (212)557-2544
URL: http://www.accessstaffingco.com

Serves as a staffing firm covering accounting/financial, advertising, bilingual Japanese, creative, event planning, fashion/retail, healthcare/human services, human resources, information technology, insurance, legal, light industrial and office support.

10491 ■ Acuity
159 Samoset St.
Plymouth, MI 02360
Fax: (734)533-6606
Fr: (866)332-8489
URL: http://www.acuitybi.com

Provider of qualified project managers for various business needs.

10492 ■ Apple and Associates
PO Box 996
Chapin, SC 29036
Ph: (803)932-2000
E-mail: info@appleassoc.com
URL: http://www.appleassoc.com

Provides staffing services to medical device, plastics, pharmaceutical and performance materials industries.

10493 ■ EEG Recruiting
PO Box 803338-55448
Chicago, IL 60680
Fax: (866)847-2759
Fr: 800-819-1841
E-mail: info@eegrecruiting.com
URL: http://www.eegrecruiting.com

Executive recruiting firm with a focus on project management.

10494 ■ Kimmel & Associates
25 Page Ave.
Asheville, NC 28801
Ph: (828)251-9900
Fax: (828)251-9955
E-mail: kimmel@kimmel.com
URL: http://www.kimmel.com

Specializes in the construction, waste, architecture, engineering, logistics and supply chain industries.

10495 ■ ManpowerGroup
100 Manpower Pl.
Milwaukee, WI 53212
Ph: (414)961-1000
Fax: (414)906-7822
URL: http://us.manpower.com

Specializes in a wide range of employment services including permanent placement, recruitment process outsourcing, managed service programs, outplacement and human resources consulting. Provides companies with workforce solutions that help them increase productivity and improve efficiency.

10496 ■ Project Performance Corporation
1760 Old Meadow Rd.
McLean, VA 22102
Ph: (703)748-7000
Fax: (703)748-7001
E-mail: info@ppc.com
URL: http://www.ppc.com

Serves as a placement and recruiting firm for project management professionals.

10497 ■ Recruiting Partners
3494 Camino Tassajara Rd., No. 404
Danville, CA 94506

Ph: (925)964-0249
E-mail: info@recruitingpartners.com
URL: http://www.recruitingpartners.com

Description: Serves as an executive and technical recruiting firm that specializes in accounting, legal, information technology, engineering, executive management and technical writing.

10498 ■ Sherpa LLC
1001 Morehead Square Dr., Ste. 600
Charlotte, NC 28203
Ph: (704)374-0001
E-mail: info@sherpallc.com
URL: http://www.sherpallc.com

Specializes in recruiting, staffing and consulting services for accounting/finance, information technology and project management in direct hire, temporary and project-based consulting positions.

10499 ■ S.R. Clarke
105 Huntercombe
Williamburg, VA 23188
Ph: (703)934-4200
Fax: (703)344-0259
URL: http://www.srclarke.com/index.html

Serves as an executive search and recruitment firm specializing in commercial construction, commercial real estate development, residential asset management, residential construction and development, subcontractor trades, finance, accounting, administration, heavy construction, architectural design and engineering design.

10500 ■ Torch Group
30675 Solon Rd., Ste. 102
Cleveland, OH 44139
Ph: (440)519-1822
Fax: (440)519-1823
E-mail: info@torchgroup.com
URL: http://www.torchgroup.com

Professional employment services firm that supplies businesses with professional project managers.

10501 ■ TRS Staffing Solutions USA
3 Polaris Way
Aliso Viejo, CA 92656
Ph: (949)349-3630
Fax: (949)349-7196
Fr: 800-248-8774
E-mail: info-av@trsstaffing.com
URL: http://www.trsstaffing.com/us

Specializes in engineering recruitment. Maintains a pool of experienced technical, engineering and professional services personnel.

10502 ■ Woltcom, Inc.
650 San Benito St., Ste. 230
Hollister, CA 95023
Fax: (831)638-4944
Fr: 800-682-4949
E-mail: wci@woltcom.com
URL: http://www.woltcom.com

A national provider of contract and career staffing and management solutions for the telecommunications industry. Specializes in project management and telecommunications engineering.

ONLINE JOB SOURCES AND SERVICES

10503 ■ Construction Executive Online
URL: http://www.constructionexecutive.com

Description: Serves as a career management center for construction executives. Provides members access to a job board of executive construction jobs and to career counseling from top executive coaches.

10504 ■ CSC CareerSource
URL: http://www.csc.com/careersus

Description: Virtual recruiting site listing employment opportunities in the project management field.

10505 ■ Diversity Environmental Jobs
URL: http://www.diversityenvironmentaljobs.com

Description: Serves as a niche job board that provides diverse environmental career opportunities.

10506 ■ GeneralConstructionJobs.com
URL: http://www.generalconstructionjobs.com/JobSeeker/Jobs.aspx

Description: Serves as a job board for online employment advertising built exclusively for the general construction industry.

10507 ■ Justmeans - CSR JOBS
URL: http://www.justmeans.com

Description: Serves as online resource that provides available career opportunities for the sustainable business industry.

10508 ■ ProjectManagementCareers.net
URL: http://www.projectmanagementcareers.net

Description: Provides new job openings in addition to research into the management and business employment market. Also contains a career articles section which is written and frequented by industry professionals.

10509 ■ ProjectManagementCrossing.com
URL: http://www.projectmanagementcrossing.com

Description: Lists new job openings for project managers. Shows jobs from employer career pages, job websites, association websites, newspaper classifieds and recruiter sites.

10510 ■ ProjectManager.com
E-mail: support@projectmanager.com
URL: http://www.projectmanager.com

Description: Allows job seekers to create an online resume, browse available jobs, and use a career alert tool linking them with potential employers. Also maintains a knowledge section containing employment information and resources for project managers.

10511 ■ Projects@Work
E-mail: aaron@projectsatwork.com
URL: http://www.projectsatwork.com

Description: Online newsletter for project management professionals. Provides a forum for networking and examines trends in project management.

10512 ■ StartWright.com
URL: http://www.startwright.com

Description: Provides a comprehensive list of links to various sites on project management, project management methodology, and the project management profession.

10513 ■ ThinkEnergyGroup.com
E-mail: resumes@thinkjobs.com
URL: http://www.thinkenergygroup.com

Description: Serves as a job board for professionals looking for positions in engineering, power plant, energy, and technical fields. Contains advice and tips on interviews, job searching, resume writing, hiring, and management. Provides choices of work location, pay rates in the field of expertise and contract, temp-to-hire, and direct hiring options.

TRADESHOWS

10514 ■ Project Management Institute Annual Seminars and Symposium
Project Management Institute
14 Campus Blvd.
Newtown Square, PA 19073-3299
Ph: (610)356-4600
Fax: (610)356-4647
E-mail: customercare@pmi.org
URL: http://www.pmi.org

Annual. Primary Exhibits: Project management related exhibits.

OTHER SOURCES

10515 ■ 4PM
3547 S Ivanhoe St.
Denver, CO 80237
Ph: (303)596-0000
Fr: 800-942-4323
URL: http://www.4pm.com

Activities: Provides project management training and certification courses for professional project managers.

10516 ■ American Academy of Project Management
1670-F E Cheyenne Mountain Blvd., Ste. 293
Colorado Springs, CO 80906
E-mail: info@projectmanagementcertification.org
URL: http://projectmanagementcertification.org

Purpose: Acts as the global board of standards for project management professionals. **Activities:** Offers courses in conjunction with certification. Maintains a job board for certified project managers.

10517 ■ American Association of Service Coordinators (AASC)
PO Box 1178
Powell, OH 43065-1178
Ph: (614)848-5958
Fax: (614)848-5954
E-mail: info@servicecoordinator.org
URL: http://www.servicecoordinator.org

Description: Advances the interests of the service coordinator profession. Increases awareness and understanding of service coordination and service-enriched housing. Provides guidance to members in the creation and maintenance of service-enhanced housing to families, the elderly and persons with disabilities. Strives to enhance the professionalism of its constituents through leadership, education, training, networking, and advocacy.

10518 ■ American Road & Transportation Builders Association
1219 28th St., NW
Washington, DC 20007-3389
Ph: (202)289-4434
Fax: (202)289-4435
E-mail: general@artba.org
URL: http://www.artba.org

Description: Advances the interests of the transportation construction industry. Promotes the growth and protection of transportation infrastructure investment to meet the public and business demand for safe and efficient travel. Works to ensure its members' views and business concerns are addressed before Congress, the White House, federal agencies and news media.

10519 ■ American Society for the Advancement of Project Management (ASAPM)
6547 N Academy, No. 404
Colorado Springs, CO 80918
Ph: (719)488-3850
E-mail: info@asapm.org
URL: http://www.asapm.org

Description: Promotes the mainstreaming of project management as a profession and as a way to improve human welfare. Advances project management methods, standards, and practical application techniques. Seeks to improve understanding and practice of the profession. Offers certification of USA Project Managers, Senior Project Managers and Program Managers; also offers certification in PM for professionals in other disciplines related to project management, such as Architects and Engineers. Established and offers the aPRO Standard, the asapm Performance Rated Organization, that is used to assess (and certify) the performance effectiveness of project and program performing organizations.

10520 ■ International Association of Project and Program Management
2220 County Rd., 210 W
St. Johns, FL 32259
Fr: 800-571-0470
E-mail: info@iappm.org
URL: http://www.iappm.org

Members: Professional project managers. **Purpose:** Enhances and adds value to members and the project community and assists them in managing projects and programs successfully. **Activities:** Conducts a certification program. Offers members a forum in which they can network with other project managers.

10521 ■ Leading Edge Alliance (LEA)
621 Cedar St.
St. Charles, IL 60174
Ph: (630)513-9814
Fax: (630)524-9014
URL: http://www.leadingedgealliance.com

Description: Represents independently owned accounting and consulting firms. Provides business development, professional training and education, and peer-to-peer networking opportunities. Offers business advisory expertise and experience and conducts accounting, tax and consulting services.

10522 ■ Location Managers Guild of America (LMGA)
8033 Sunset Blvd., Ste. 1017
West Hollywood, CA 90046
Ph: (310)967-2007
Fax: (310)967-2013
E-mail: boardofdirectors@locationmanagers.org
URL: http://www.locationmanagers.org

Description: Enhances recognition and respect for members within the entertainment and related industries. Strengthens their ability to develop meaningful and credible careers. Strives to serve the public and the production industries through philanthropic and educational programs. Identifies, improves, exchanges and encourages the mutual benefits of location filming among the entertainment industries and the communities.

10523 ■ Management Education Alliance (MEA)
300 Cumnock Hall
Boston, MA 02163
Ph: (617)495-6494
Fax: (617)495-8736
URL: http://mgteducationalliance.org

Description: Seeks to help business schools that serve African-American and Hispanic-American students to provide the skills and knowledge that will lead to successful careers in management. Fosters the professional growth of faculty members, innovations in curriculum, and development of supporting institutional policies. Communicates and collaborates with business schools and U.S. business corporations.

10524 ■ Project Management Institute (PMI)
14 Campus Blvd.
Newtown Square, PA 19073-3299
Ph: (610)356-4600
Fax: (610)482-9971
E-mail: customercare@pmi.org
URL: http://www.pmi.org

Description: Corporations and individuals engaged in the practice of project management; project management students and educators. Seeks to advance the study, teaching and practice of project management. Establishes project management standards; conducts educational and professional certification courses; bestows Project Management Professional credential upon qualified individuals. Offers educational seminars and global congresses.

10525 ■ Schedule Associates International
2604 Elmwood Ave., No. 328
Rochester, NY 14618-2213
Ph: (585)271-1450

Fax: (585)244-1249
Fr: 800-606-1450
E-mail: info@scheduleassociates.net
URL: http://www.scheduleassociates.net

Activities: Offers training courses and seminars for professional project managers and those asked to fill that role. Courses can be applied towards CAPM or PMP project management certification.

SOURCES OF HELP-WANTED ADS

10526 ■ Buildings
Stamats Communications Inc.
615 5th St. SE
PO Box 1888
Cedar Rapids, IA 52406-1888
Ph: (319)364-6167
Fax: (319)365-5421
Fr: 800-553-8878
URL: http://www.buildings.com

Monthly. $125.00/year for other countries, surface mail; $150.00/year for other countries, air mail. The facilities construction and management magazine covering news, concepts and technologies related to commercial building ownership and facilities management.

10527 ■ The Caretaker Gazette
Gary C. Dunn
3 Estancia Lane
Boerne, TX 78006
Ph: (830)755-2300
E-mail: caretaker@caretaker.org
URL: http://www.caretaker.org

Description: Bimonthly. $34.95/year; $59.95 for two years; $84.95 for three years. Covers the property caretaking field. Recurring features include rent-free living opportunities, job listings, letters to the editor, interviews, and a column titled Caretaker Profile. Offers mailing labels.

10528 ■ Clayton-Fillmore Report
Clayton-Fillmore Ltd.
PO Box 480894
Denver, CO 80248
Ph: (303)663-0606
Fax: (303)663-1616

Monthly. $195.00/year for individuals. Periodical covering real estate and business.

10529 ■ Commercial Property News
Nielsen Business Media
770 Broadway
New York, NY 10003-9595
URL: http://www.commercialpropertynews.com/cpn/index.jsp

Semimonthly. $199.00/year for individuals. Twice-monthly magazine for senior level executive in the commercial real estate market, including brokers, developers, investors, lenders, property managers, owners, and corporate real estate executives.

10530 ■ eConnect
Women's Council of Realtors
430 N Michigan Ave.
Chicago, IL 60611
Ph: (312)329-5967
Fax: (312)329-3290

Fr: 800-245-8512
E-mail: wcr@wcr.org
URL: http://www.wcr.org

Description: Monthly. Carries articles on personal and career growth topics relating to women in real estate. Includes council news.

10531 ■ Innkeeping
Professional Association of Innkeepers International
207 White Horse Pike
Haddon Heights, NJ 08035
Ph: (856)310-1102
Fax: (856)895-0432
Fr: 800-468-7244
E-mail: membership@paii.org
URL: http://www.innkeeping.org

Description: Monthly. Addresses topics of interest to innkeepers who own and operate bed and breakfast operations. Recurring features include letters to the editor, news of research, news of educational opportunities, and notices of publications available.

10532 ■ Journal of Property Management
Institute of Real Estate Management
430 N Michigan Ave.
Chicago, IL 60611
Ph: (312)329-6000
Fax: 800-338-4736
Fr: 800-837-0706
E-mail: jpmsub@irem.org
URL: http://www.irem.org/sechome.cfm?sec=JPM

Bimonthly. $72.32/year for Canada; $62.95/year for individuals; $115.50/year for two years; $110.99/year for other countries, airmail; $169.10/year for individuals, 3 years. Magazine serving real estate managers.

10533 ■ Journal of Real Estate Literature
American Real Estate Society
Clemson University
314 Sirrine Hall
Clemson, SC 29634-1343
Ph: (864)656-1373
Fax: (864)656-3748
URL: http://cbeweb-1.fullerton.edu/finance/jrel/

Semiannual. Professional journal covering real estate issues.

10534 ■ Journal of Real Estate Portfolio Management
American Real Estate Society
Clemson University
314 Sirrine Hall
Clemson, SC 29634-1343
Ph: (864)656-1373
Fax: (864)656-3748
URL: http://realestate.fiu.edu/journals_jrepm.html

Quarterly. Journal for real estate professionals.

10535 ■ Journal of Real Estate Research
American Real Estate Society
Clemson University
314 Sirrine Hall
Clemson, SC 29634-1343

Ph: (864)656-1373
Fax: (864)656-3748
URL: http://aux.zicklin.baruch.cuny.edu/jrer
Journal focusing on scholarly real estate research.

10536 ■ Lives of Real Estate
REAL Trends Inc.
7501 Village Sq. Dr., Ste. 200
Castle Rock, CO 80108
Ph: (303)741-1000
Fax: (303)741-1070
URL: http://www.loremagazine.com/
Bimonthly. Free to qualified subscribers. Magazine that profiles personnel in the residential real estate industry.

10537 ■ New England Real Estate Journal
East Coast Publications
PO Box 55
Accord, MA 02018-0055
Ph: (781)878-4540
Fax: (781)871-1853
Fr: 800-654-4993
E-mail: nerej@rejournal.com
URL: http://www.rejournal.com/ne/homeNE.aspx
Weekly (Fri.). $139.00/year for individuals. Newspaper publishing commercial, industrial, and investment real estate news.

10538 ■ Property Management Association-Bulletin
Property Management Association
7508 Wisconsin Ave., 4th Fl.
Bethesda, MD 20814
Ph: (301)657-9200
Fax: (301)907-9326
E-mail: info@pma-dc.org
URL: http://www.pma-dc.org/content/38/pma-bulletin
Description: Monthly. Reports market trends and other information related to property management. Contains information on the Association and tips for members. Recurring features include news of research, a calendar of events, reports of meetings, news of educational opportunities, job listings, book reviews, and notices of publications available.

10539 ■ Real Estate Issues
The Counselors of Real Estate
430 N Michigan Ave.
Chicago, IL 60611-4089
Ph: (312)329-8427
Fax: (312)329-8881
E-mail: rei@cre.org
URL: http://www.cre.org/publications/rei.cfm
$48.00/year for individuals; $15.00/year for single issue. Trade publication covering the real estate industry.

EMPLOYER DIRECTORIES AND NETWORKING LISTS

10540 ■ National Association of Real Estate Companies—Membership Directory
National Association of Real Estate Cos.
216 W Jackson Blvd., Ste. 625
Chicago, IL 60606-6945

Ph: (312)263-1755
Fax: (312)750-1203
E-mail: cindy@narec.org
URL: http://www.narec.org

Quarterly. Covers: about 200 real estate development companies. Entries include: Company name, address, phone, name of contact.

HANDBOOKS AND MANUALS

10541 ■ *Be a Successful Property Manager*
McGraw-Hill
PO Box 182604
Columbus, OH 43272
Fax: (614)759-3749
Fr: 877-833-5524
E-mail: pbg.ecommerce_custserv@mcgraw-hill.com
URL: http://www.mhprofessional.com/
  product.php?isbn=0071473610

Roger Woodson. 2006. $29.95. 294 pages. Comprehensive guide offering information for managing rental properties.

10542 ■ *Careers in Focus: Real Estate*
Ferguson Publishing
132 W 31st St., 17th Fl.
New York, NY 10001
Fr: 800-322-8755
E-mail: custserv@factsonfile.com
URL: http://factsonfile.infobasepublishing.com

2006. $32.95. 160 pages. Provides jobs profiled in detail, including the nature of the job, earnings, prospects for employment, what kind of training and skills it requires and sources for further information.

**10543 ■ *Great Big Book for Landlords and
  Property Managers***
Entrepreneur Press
PO Box 432
Newburgh, NY 12551
Fax: (845)457-5029
Fr: 800-215-7814
E-mail: press@entrepreneur.com
URL: http://www.entrepreneurpress.com

Stuart Leland Rider. $29.95. 330 pages. Comprehensive guide for landlords that teaches how to find and retain quality tenants.

**10544 ■ *Opportunities in Property
  Management Careers***
McGraw-Hill
PO Box 182604
Columbus, OH 43272
Fax: (614)759-3749
Fr: 877-833-5524
E-mail: pbg.ecommerce_custserv@mcgraw-hill.com
URL: http://www.mhprofessional.com/
  product.php?cat=106&isbn=0071594124

Mariwyn Evans. 2007. $12.00 (e-book). 160 pages. Offers the latest information on a field of interest, training and educational requirements for each career, salary statistics for different positions within each field, and up-to-date professional and Internet resources.

**10545 ■ *Real Estate Blues: A Guide to Jump
  Start Your Real Estate Career***
PublishAmerica, Incorporated
PO Box 151
Frederick, MD 21705
Ph: (301)695-1707
Fax: (301)631-9073
URL: http://www.publishamerica.com

David H. Lawrence. May 2004. $19.95 (paper). 138 pages.

**10546 ■ *The Rental Property Manager's Tool
  Box: A Complete Guide Including
  Pre-Written Forms, Agreements, Letters,
  Legal Notices with Companion CD-ROM***
Atlantic Publishing Company
1210 SW 23rd Pl.
Ocala, FL 34474-7014

Ph: (352)622-1825
Fax: (352)622-1875
Fr: 800-814-1132
E-mail: sales@atlantic-pub.com
URL: http://www.atlantic-pub.com

Jamaine Burrell. $29.95. 288 pages. Complete guide for managing rental property covering advertising, tenant screening, managing tenants, legal rights, discrimination, vacancies, lease clauses, crime prevention, drugs, gangs, security, liability, eviction, maintenance, recordkeeping, and taxes; includes companion CD-ROM.

**10547 ■ *Your Successful Career as a
  Mortgage Broker***
AMACOM Publishing
c/o American Management Association
1601 Broadway
New York, NY 10019-7434
Ph: (212)586-8100
Fax: (518)891-0368
Fr: 800-714-6395
E-mail: pubs_cust_serv@amanet.org
URL: http://www.amacombooks.org

David Reed. 2007. $18.95 (paper/softback). 240 pages. Offers advice on licensing and educational requirements as well as guidance on the different career options available as a mortgage broker, mortgage banker, correspondent mortgage banker, and more. Provides tips on how to quote interest rates; get approved by wholesale lenders; negotiate the steps of the loan process; and market and prospect successfully.

EMPLOYMENT AGENCIES AND SEARCH FIRMS

10548 ■ The Alfus Group Inc.
353 Lexington Ave.
New York, NY 10016
Ph: (212)599-1000
Fax: (212)599-1523
E-mail: mail@thealfusgroup.com
URL: http://www.thealfusgroup.com

Executive search firm. Specializes in the hospitality industry.

10549 ■ Arlene Clapp Ltd.
4250 Park Glen Rd.
Minneapolis, MN 55416
Ph: (952)928-7474
E-mail: arlene@arleneclapp.com
URL: http://www.arleneclapp.com

Executive search firm.

10550 ■ Caruso & Associates Inc.
990 Stinson Way, Ste. 201
West Palm Beach, FL 33411
Ph: (561)683-2336
E-mail: info@carusoassociates.com
URL: http://www.carusoassociates.com

Executive search firm.

10551 ■ ChaseAmerica Inc.
300 Park Ave.
New York, NY 10022
Ph: (215)338-1952
Fr: 800-491-4980
E-mail: info@chaseamericainc.com
URL: http://www.chaseamericainc.com

Executive search firm.

10552 ■ Contractor Marketing
346 Dayton St.
Dayton, OH 45387-1704
Ph: (937)767-2876
Fax: (937)767-7281
E-mail: larry@contractormarketing.com
URL: http://www.contractormarketing.com

Executive search firm.

10553 ■ Crown Advisors Inc.
100 McKnight Park Dr., Ste. 110
Pittsburgh, PA 15237
Ph: (412)348-1540
E-mail: info@crownsearch.com
URL: http://www.crownsearch.com

Executive search firm.

10554 ■ DLG Associates Inc.
2210 Roswell Ave., No. 103
Charlotte, NC 28207
Ph: (704)372-2155
Fax: (704)372-2188
E-mail: dguilford@dlgassociates.com
URL: http://www.dlgassociates.com

Executive search firm.

10555 ■ Edward Dellon Associates Inc.
450 N Brand Blvd., Ste. 600
Glendale, CA 91203
Ph: (310)286-0625
E-mail: edward_dellon@yahoo.com
URL: http://edwarddellonassociatesinc.com

Executive search firm.

10556 ■ Franchise Recruiters Ltd.
Lincolnshire Country Club
3500 Innsbruck
Crete, IL 60417
Ph: (708)757-5595
Fax: (708)758-8222
Fr: 800-334-6257
E-mail: franchise@att.net
URL: http://www.franchiserecruiters.com

Executive search firm. Second location in Toronto, Canada.

10557 ■ Maison Group
7200 Wisconsin Ave., Ste. 402
Bethesda, MD 20814
Ph: (240)395-0480
Fax: (240)395-0481
E-mail: info@themaisongroup.com
URL: http://www.themaisongroup.com

Executive search firm focused exclusively within the real estate industry. Represents organizations involved in acquiring, developing, building, managing, owning, financing, and advising across every major asset class within the real estate industry.

10558 ■ MSB Resources
1425 Candlebrook Dr.
Dresher, PA 19025
Ph: (215)661-8834
Fax: (215)661-8831
URL: http://msbresources.com

Specializes exclusively in evaluating and placing professionals and management talent in commercial and residential property management, construction, development, and real estate.

10559 ■ Real Estate Executive Search, Inc.
225 E Dania Beach Blvd. Ste., 200
Dania Beach, FL 33004
Ph: (954)927-6000
Fax: (954)927-6003
E-mail: reesearch954@aol.com
URL: http://reesearchinc.com

Executive search firm for the real estate and finance fields.

10560 ■ S.R. Clarke
105 Huntercombe
Williamburg, VA 23188
Ph: (703)934-4200
Fax: (703)344-0259
URL: http://www.srclarke.com/index.html

Serves as an executive search and recruitment firm specializing in commercial construction, commercial real estate development, residential asset management, residential construction and development, subcontractor trades, finance, accounting, administration, heavy construction, architectural design and engineering design.

ONLINE JOB SOURCES AND SERVICES

10561 ■ Locate Real Estate Jobs
URL: http://www.locaterealestatejobs.com

Description: Serves as a job board for real estate professionals. Focuses on bringing together employers and employment candidates in the real estate field.

10562 ■ New Real Estate Jobs
URL: http://www.newrealestatejobs.com

Description: Provides an online listing of companies with available real estate jobs in all specialties.

10563 ■ Real Estate Job Store.com
E-mail: jobs@ejobstores.com
URL: http://www.realestatejobstore.com

Description: Features real estate job listings from all over the United States. Enables users to search for real estate salaries as well as resume posting.

10564 ■ Real Estate Manager Jobs
URL: http://www.realestatemanagerjobs.org

Description: Serves as a job board for real estate managers seeking career opportunities in real estate jobs.

10565 ■ Real-Jobs
URL: http://www.real-jobs.com

Description: Provides resumes and job listings for the commercial real estate industry. Focuses on general skills (sales management, sales, and communication) and also allows users to discuss selected experiences or unique skills.

10566 ■ RealEstateAndLandCrossing.com
URL: http://www.realestateandlandcrossing.com

Description: Provides job listings and other resources related to real estate employment opportunities.

10567 ■ RealEstateJobsite.com
URL: http://www.realestatejobsite.com

Description: Features real estate and building maintenance jobs. Offers online job listings and resume posting.

10568 ■ SelectLeaders.com
E-mail: support@selectleaders.com
URL: http://www.selectleaders.com

Description: Exists as a real estate job site focused on the real estate and finance industries. Serves as a source of information for real estate professionals and executives in managing their careers and networking.

TRADESHOWS

10569 ■ The Annual Meeting for Commercial Real Estate
National Association of Industrial and Office Properties
2201 Cooperative Way, Ste. 300
Herndon, VA 20171
Ph: (703)904-7100
Fax: (703)904-7942
URL: http://www.naiop.org

Annual. Features educational offerings and keynote speakers. Offers opportunities to see new markets and meet local partners, as well as explore products and services.

10570 ■ Building Owners and Managers Association International Annual Convention and The Office Building Show
Building Owners and Managers Association International
1101 15th St., N.W., Ste. 800
Washington, DC 20005
Ph: (202)408-2662
Fax: (202)682-5934
E-mail: meetings@boma.org
URL: http://www.bomaconvention.org

Annual. Primary Exhibits: Products, supplies and equipment for the office building industry, including architectural and building hardware, asbestos abatement, building automation, carpeting, control systems, doors, elevators and elevator maintenance, electrical and lighting, environmental services, financial services, fire protection, flooring and floor machines, hazardous waste removal, interior design, landscaping, locks, paper products, parking, pest control, plumbing and fixtures, recycling, renovation and restoration, roofing, security, signage, water treatment, windows. Dates and Locations: 2012 Jun 24-26; Seattle, WA.

10571 ■ IFMA's World Workplace Conference and Expo
International Facility Management Association
1 E Greenway Plaza, Ste. 1100
Houston, TX 77046
Ph: (713)623-4362
Fax: (713)623-6124
URL: http://www.ifma.org

Annual. Features special networking activities that provide participants with opportunities to make business contacts. Attendees include individuals in workplace-related industries such as technology, engineering, architecture, design, security, real estate, and facility management.

10572 ■ National Association of Residential Property Managers Convention and Trade Show
National Association of Residential Property Managers
638 Independence Pkwy., Ste. 100
Chesapeake, VA 23320
Fax: (866)466-2776
Fr: 800-782-3452
E-mail: info@narpm.org
URL: http://www.narpm.org

Annual. Features conferences, sessions, and networking opportunities. 2012 October 16-19; Arlington, VA; Crystal City Hyatt Regency. 2013 October 15-18; San Diego, CA; Hyatt Regency La Jolla.

OTHER SOURCES

10573 ■ Association of Green Property Owners and Managers (AGPOM)
3400 Capitol Blvd. SE, Ste. 101
Tumwater, WA 98501
Ph: (425)646-6425
Fax: (425)454-8233
URL: http://agpom.org

Description: Promotes environmental sustainability awareness and involvement among property owners and managers. Encourages the protection of the natural environment by promoting the benefits of going green. Offers financial incentives for property owners and managers to get involved in green practices.

10574 ■ Association of Real Estate Women
1201 Wakarusa Dr., Ste. C3
Lawrence, KS 66049
Ph: (212)599-6181
Fax: (785)832-1551
Fr: 888-329-2739
E-mail: info@arew.org
URL: http://www.arew.org

Description: Provides programs and networking op-

portunities that can contribute to the career growth of both men and women in all segments and all levels of the real estate industry. Helps members find new employment opportunities.

10575 ■ Building Owners and Managers Association International (BOMA)
1101 15th St. NW, Ste. 800
Washington, DC 20005
Ph: (202)408-2662
Fax: (202)326-6377
E-mail: info@boma.org
URL: http://www.boma.org

Description: Building owners, managers, developers, leasing professionals, facility managers, asset managers and the providers of goods and services. Represents all facets of the commercial real estate industry.

10576 ■ Certified Commercial Investment Member Institute
430 N Michigan Ave., Ste. 800
Chicago, IL 60611-4092
Ph: (312)321-4460
Fax: (312)321-4530
Fr: 800-621-7027
URL: http://www.ccim.com

Description: Offers web resources in the commercial real estate industry. Provides CCIM members with comprehensive site analysis, mapping software, demographic data, aerial photography, financial analysis tools, transaction management software, customized report options and a broad spectrum of other business services.

10577 ■ Coalition of Landlords, Homeowners and Merchants (CLHM)
656C N Wellwood Ave.
Lindenhurst, NY 11757
Ph: (631)376-2110
Fax: (631)376-2148
E-mail: paulcolham@aol.com
URL: http://www.clhm.org

Description: Strives to maintain and advance the principles of a free and democratic society. Offers economical assistance to landlords, merchants and residential property owners. Provides a registry of legal counsel. Assists in the acquisition, transfer and foreclosure of real property.

10578 ■ CoreNet Global
260 Peachtree St. NW, Ste. 1500
Atlanta, GA 30303
Ph: (404)589-3200
Fax: (404)589-3201
Fr: 800-726-8111
E-mail: acain@corenetglobal.org
URL: http://www.corenetglobal.org

Description: Executives, attorneys, real estate department heads, architects, engineers, analysts, researchers and anyone responsible for the management, administration and operation of national and regional real estate departments of national and international corporations. Encourages professionalism within corporate real estate through education and communication; protects the interests of corporate realty in dealing with adversaries, public or private; maintains contact with other real estate organizations; publicizes the availability of fully qualified members to the job market. Conducts seminars, including concentrated workshops on the corporate real estate field. Compiles statistics; sponsors competitions; maintains biographical archives and placement service.

10579 ■ Institute of Real Estate Management (IREM)
430 N Michigan Ave.
Chicago, IL 60611
Ph: (312)329-6000
Fax: 800-338-4736
Fr: 800-837-0706
E-mail: custserv@irem.org
URL: http://www.irem.org

Description: Professional organization of real property and asset managers. Awards professional designation Certified Property Manager (CPM) to qualifying individuals, Accredited Management Organization (AMO) to qualifying management firms and also awards Accredited Residential Manager (ARM) accreditation to qualifying individuals who are primarily residential site managers. Monitors legislation affecting real estate management. Offers management courses and seminars; conducts research and educational programs, publishes books and reports; maintains formal code of ethics; compiles statistics; maintains employment Website for real estate management industry.

10580 ■ International Facility Management Association
1 E Greenway Plaza, Ste. 1100
Houston, TX 77046
Ph: (713)623-4362
Fax: (713)623-6124
E-mail: ifma@ifma.org
URL: http://www.ifma.org

Description: Promotes excellence in the facility management profession. Provides educational programs and networking opportunities among members. Offers facility management certification programs.

10581 ■ National Apartment Association (NAA)
4300 Wilson Blvd., Ste. 400
Arlington, VA 22203
Ph: (703)518-6141
Fax: (703)248-9440
E-mail: info@naahq.org
URL: http://www.naahq.org

Description: Federation of 155 state and local associations of industry professionals engaged in all aspects of the multifamily housing industry, including owners, builders, investors, developers, managers, and allied service representatives. Provides education and certification for property management executives, on-site property managers, maintenance personnel, property supervisors, and leasing agents. Offers a nationwide legislative network concerned with governmental decisions at the federal, state, and local levels.

10582 ■ National Association of Industrial and Office Properties
2201 Cooperative Way, Ste. 300
Herndon, VA 20171
Ph: (703)904-7100
Fax: (703)904-7942
URL: http://www.naiop.org

Description: Represents developers, owners, and related professionals in office, industrial, and mixed-use real estate. Provides networking and education, and advocates for effective legislation on behalf of its members.

10583 ■ National Association of Realtors (NAR)
430 N Michigan Ave.
Chicago, IL 60611-4087
Fr: 800-874-6500
URL: http://www.realtor.org

Description: Federation of 54 state and territory associations and 1,860 local real estate boards whose members are real estate brokers and agents; terms are registered by the association in the U.S. Patent and Trademark Office and in the states. Promotes education, high professional standards and modern techniques in specialized real estate work such as brokerage, appraisal, property management, land development, industrial real estate, farm brokerage and counseling. Conducts research programs.

10584 ■ National Property Management Association (NPMA)
28100 U.S. Hwy. 19 N, Ste. 400
Clearwater, FL 33761
Ph: (727)736-3788
Fax: (727)736-6707
E-mail: hq@npma.org
URL: http://www.npma.org

Description: Aims to build leadership by educating, training and promoting standards of competency and ethical behavior in the asset management of personal property. Serves property professionals throughout the United States; members represent companies and organizations in both the public and private sectors, including scientific laboratories, universities, hospitals, public school systems, and local, state and federal government agencies.

10585 ■ Realtors Land Institute (RLI)
430 N Michigan Ave.
Chicago, IL 60611
Ph: (312)329-8446
Fax: (312)329-8633
Fr: 800-441-5263
E-mail: rli@realtors.org
URL: http://www.rliland.com

Description: Real estate brokers and salespersons selling, managing, appraising, or developing all types of land. Maintains educational programs for real estate brokers; promotes competence and accredits members. Sponsors courses for realtors and others seeking professional excellence on Land Brokerage, Agricultural Land Brokerage, Exchanging Properties, Estate Planning, Subdivision Development and Financial Analysis of Land Investment.

SOURCES OF HELP-WANTED ADS

10586 ■ AAAP News
American Academy of Addiction Psychiatry
400 Massasoit Ave., Ste. 307, 2nd Fl.
East Providence, RI 02914
Ph: (401)524-3076
Fax: (401)272-0922
URL: http://www2.aaap.org/advertising/newsletter-advertising

$45.00/year for individuals, per year; $15.00/year for individuals, per issue; $50.00/year for individuals, international; $20.00/year for individuals, per issue. Professional journal covering addiction psychiatry.

10587 ■ The ABA Newsletter
Association for Behavior Analysis (ABA)
550 W Centre Ave., Ste. 1
Portage, MI 49024
Ph: (269)492-9310
Fax: (269)492-9316
E-mail: mail@abainternational.org
URL: http://www.abainternational.org/aba/newsletter

Description: Three issues/year. Covers Association activities, with reports of committees and special interest groups, and news from regional, state, and local associations for behavior analysis. Recurring features include convention details and overview, news of research, and positions-available notices.

10588 ■ Academic Psychiatry
American Psychiatric Publishing Inc.
1000 Wilson Blvd., Ste. 1825
Arlington, VA 22209-3924
Ph: (703)907-7322
Fax: (703)907-1091
Fr: 800-368-5777
URL: http://ap.psychiatryonline.org/

$42.00/year for members, in-training; online only; $178.00/year for members, print + online; $223.00/year for nonmembers, print + online; $268.00/year for members, international; print + online; $335.00/year for nonmembers, international, print + online. Journal contributing to the efforts in furthering psychiatry as a profession and to knowledge pool of medicine.

10589 ■ Alcoholism
John Wiley & Sons Inc.
350 Main St., Commerce Pl.
Malden, MA 02148-5089
Ph: (781)388-8200
Fax: (781)388-8210
E-mail: mnewcomb-acer@earthlink.net
URL: http://www.wiley.com/bw/journal.asp?ref=0145-6008&site=1

Monthly. $506.00/year for individuals, print & online; $1,341.00/year for institutions, print & online; $1,166.00/year for institutions, print or online; $327.00/year for individuals, UK, print & online; $819.00/year for institutions, UK, print & online; $327.00/year for other countries, print & online; $1,041.00/year for institutions, Europe, print & online; $905.00/year for institutions, Europe, print or online; $712.00/year for institutions, UK, print or online. Publishing original clinical and research studies on alcoholism and alcohol-induced organ damage.

10590 ■ American Journal of Family Therapy
Routledge Journals
270 Madison Ave.
New York, NY 10016-0601
Ph: (212)216-7800
Fax: (212)563-2269
URL: http://www.tandf.co.uk/journals/titles/01926187.asp

$200.00/year for institutions, print + online; $180.00/year for individuals, online only; $92.00/year for individuals, print only; $332.00/year for institutions, print + online; $299.00/year for institutions, online only; $155.00/year for individuals, print only; $264.00/year for institutions, print + online; $238.00/year for institutions, online only; $123.00/year for individuals, print only. Periodical covering the techniques for treating families, theory on normal and dysfunctional family relationships, research on sexuality and intimacy, the effects of traditional and alternative family styles, and community approaches to family intervention. Also includes family measurement techniques, family behavioral medicine and health, family law issues in family therapy practice, and continuing education and training.

10591 ■ American Journal of Geriatric Psychiatry
American Association for Geriatric Psychiatry
7910 Woodmont Ave., Ste. 1050
Bethesda, MD 20814-3004
Ph: (301)654-7850
Fax: (301)654-4137
URL: http://journals.lww.com/ajgponline/pages/default.aspx

Monthly. $396.74/year for individuals; $1,157.40/year for institutions; $554.06/year for other countries; $1,457.12/year for institutions, other countries; $214.00/year for individuals, in-training; $238.00/year for other countries, in-training. Peer-reviewed professional journal covering geriatric psychiatry.

10592 ■ American Journal of Psychology
University of Illinois Press
1325 S Oak St.
Champaign, IL 61820-6903
Ph: (217)333-0950
Fax: (217)244-8082
E-mail: ajp@psych.purdue.edu
URL: http://www.press.uillinois.edu/journals/ajp.html

Quarterly. $74.00/year for individuals, print or online; $81.00/year for individuals, print + online; $236.00/year for institutions, print or online; $260.00/year for institutions, print + online; $30.00/year for students, online only; $60.00/year for single issue. Journal dealing with experimental psychology and basic principles of psychology.

10593 ■ American Psychologist
American Psychological Association
750 1st St. NE
Washington, DC 20002-4242
Ph: (202)336-5500
Fax: (202)336-5549
Fr: 800-374-2721
URL: http://www.apa.org/journals/amp.html

$12.00/year for members, domestic; $310.00/year for nonmembers, domestic; $12.00/year for students, domestic; $907.00/year for institutions, domestic; $1,009.00/year for institutions, other countries, foreign, surface mail; $87.00/year for members, foreign, air mail; $87.00/year for students, foreign, air mail; $1,037.00/year for institutions, other countries, foreign, air mail; $363.00/year for nonmembers, foreign, surface; $391.00/year for nonmembers, foreign, air mail. Official journal of the association. Publishes empirical, theoretical, and professional articles.

10594 ■ Annual Review of Psychology
Annual Reviews Inc.
4139 El Camino Way
Palo Alto, CA 94306
Ph: (650)493-4400
Fax: (650)424-0910
Fr: 800-523-8635
URL: http://www.annualreviews.org/journal/psych

Annual. $80.00/year for individuals, print and online; $202.00/year for institutions, print only; $202.00/year for institutions, online only; $242.00/year for institutions, print and online. Publication covering psychology and mental health issues.

10595 ■ APS Observer
Association for Psychological Science
1133 15th St., NW
Washington, DC 20005-4918
Ph: (202)293-9300
Fax: (202)293-9350
E-mail: apsobserver@aps.washington.dc.us
URL: http://www.psychologicalscience.org/

Description: Monthly. Provides information on issues of interest to members. Offers a monthly employment listing for academic and scientific psychologists.

10596 ■ Archives of General Psychiatry
American Medical Association
515 N State St.
Chicago, IL 60610
Fr: 800-621-8335
E-mail: archgenpsychiatry@jama-archives.org
URL: http://archpsyc.ama-assn.org/

Monthly. $745.00/year for institutions, print and online; $135.00/year for members, print and online; $199.00/year for nonmembers, print and online. Educational/clinical journal for psychiatrists.

10597 ■ Children & Society
John Wiley & Sons Inc.
111 River St.
Hoboken, NJ 07030-5773
Ph: (201)748-6000
Fax: (201)748-6088
Fr: 800-825-7550
URL: http://onlinelibrary.wiley.com/journal/10.1111/
(ISSN)1099-08

Bimonthly. $211.00/year for individuals, print & on-line; $171.00/year for individuals, print & online; $114.00/year for individuals, print & online; $126.00/year for other countries, print & online, rest of World; $756.00/year for institutions, print & online; $374.00/year for institutions, print & online; $475.00/year for institutions, print & online; $807.00/year for institutions, other countries, print & online. Journal focusing on children and services for children.

10598 ■ Clinical Psychiatry News
International Medical News Group
60 Columbia Rd., Bldg. B
Morristown, NJ 07960
Ph: (973)290-8200
Fax: (973)290-8250
E-mail: cpnews@elsevier.com
URL: http://journals.elsevierhealth.com/periodicals/
cpnews

Monthly. $109.00/year for individuals; $173.00/year for other countries. Medical and psychiatry tabloid.

10599 ■ Counselling Psychology Quarterly
Routledge Journals
270 Madison Ave.
New York, NY 10016-0601
Ph: (212)216-7800
Fax: (212)563-2269
URL: http://www.tandf.co.uk/journals/titles/
09515070.asp

Quarterly. $754.00/year for institutions, print + on-line; $1,266.00/year for institutions, print + online; $679.00/year for institutions, online only; $1,139.00/year for institutions, online only; $206.00/year for individuals, print only; $347.00/year for individuals, print only; $40.00/year for institutions, society; $66.00/year for institutions, society. Journal covering practical counseling, clinical, occupational and medical psychology.

10600 ■ EAP Digest
Performance Resource Press Inc.
1270 Rankin Dr., Ste. F
Troy, MI 48083-2843
Ph: (248)588-7733
Fax: (248)588-6633
Fr: 800-453-7733
URL: http://store.prponline.net/index.php/ea-
providers/eaprovider

Quarterly. $36.00/year for individuals; $60.00/year for two years; $72.00/year for individuals, 3years. Magazine covering planning, development, and administration of employee assistance programs.

10601 ■ Ethical Human Psychology and Psychiatry
Springer Publishing Co.
11 W 42nd St., 15th Fl.
New York, NY 10036
Ph: (212)431-4370
Fax: (212)941-7842
Fr: 877-687-7476
URL: http://www.springerpub.com/
journal.aspx?jid=1559-4343

$90.00/year for individuals, print; $125.00/year for individuals, print and online; $230.00/year for institutions, print; $275.00/year for institutions, print and online. Books on nursing, psychology, gerontology, geriatrics, social work, counseling, public health, rehabilitation and medical education.

10602 ■ GradPsych
American Psychoanalytic Association
309 E 49th St.
New York, NY 10017-1601

Ph: (212)752-0450
Fax: (212)593-0571
E-mail: gradpsych@apa.org
URL: http://www.apa.org/gradpsych

Quarterly. $17.50/year for members, domestic; $35.00/year for individuals, non-members; $70.00/year for institutions; $17.50/year for other countries, international affiliates; $17.50/year for individuals, high school teacher affiliates; $27.50/year for members, international surface; $50.00/year for individuals, international surface; $39.50/year for members, international air mail; $60.00/year for individuals, international air mail; $115.00/year for institutions, international air mail. Magazine that offers information about psychology careers, finance, and emerging trends in psychology practice, research, and education.

10603 ■ The Industrial-Organizational Psychologist
Society for Industrial and Organizational Psychology
440 E Poe Rd., Ste 101
Bowling Green, OH 43402
Ph: (419)353-0032
Fax: (419)352-2645
E-mail: siop@siop.org
URL: http://www.siop.org

Quarterly. $25.00/year for individuals; $35.00/year for institutions. Contains information about society activities and articles of interest to those in the field.

10604 ■ Intellectual and Developmental Disabilities
American Association on Intellectual and Developmental Disabilities
501 3rd St. NW, Ste. 200
Washington, DC 20001-2730
Ph: (202)387-1968
Fax: (202)387-2193
Fr: 800-424-3688
URL: http://www.aaiddjournals.org/

Bimonthly. $348.00/year for institutions, tier 1, print + online; $398.00/year for institutions, other countries, tier 1, print + online; $308.00/year for institutions, tier 1, online only. Magazine featuring articles on mental retardation for professionals and parents.

10605 ■ International Journal of Play Therapy
American Psychological Association
750 1st St. NE
Washington, DC 20002-4242
Ph: (202)336-5500
Fax: (202)336-5549
Fr: 800-374-2721
URL: http://www.apa.org/pubs/journals/pla/
index.aspx

Quarterly. $65.00/year for members; $89.00/year for other countries, members; $65.00/year for students; $454.00/year for institutions; $518.00/year for institutions, other countries, by mail; $120.00/year for nonmembers; $149.00/year for other countries, nonmembers. Journal for mental health professionals specializing on play therapy.

10606 ■ International Journal of Psychiatry in Clinical Practice
Informa Healthcare
52 Vanderbilt Ave., 7th Fl.
New York, NY 10017-3846
Ph: (212)520-2777
URL: http://informahealthcare.com/journal/jpc

Quarterly. $460.00/year for institutions; $765.00/year for institutions; $610.00/year for institutions. Journal for health professionals with clinical, academic, and research interests in psychiatry.

10607 ■ International Journal of Psychology
Psychology Press
270 Madison Ave.
New York, NY 10016-0601
Fax: 800-248-4724

Fr: 800-634-7064
URL: http://www.tandf.co.uk/journals/titles/
00207594.asp

$567.00/year for institutions, print + online; $510.00/year for institutions, online; $125.00/year for individuals, print; $938.00/year for institutions, print + online; $844.00/year for institutions, online; $210.00/year for individuals, print; $747.00/year for institutions, print + online; $672.00/year for institutions, online; $166.00/year for individuals, print. Journal dealing with all aspects of development of international psychological science.

10608 ■ Journal of the American Academy of Child and Adolescent Psychiatry
Lippincott Williams & Wilkins
530 Walnut St.
Philadelphia, PA 19106-3619
Ph: (215)521-8300
Fax: (215)521-8902
Fr: 800-638-3030
URL: http://www.jaacap.com/

Monthly. $249.00/year for individuals; $163.00/year for students; $354.00/year for Canada; $261.00/year for students, Canada; $354.00/year for individuals, Mexico; $261.00/year for students, Mexico; $354.00/year for other countries; $261.00/year for students, other countries. Child psychiatry journal.

10609 ■ Journal of Behavioral and Brain Science
Scientific Research Publishing
PO Box 54821
Irvine, CA 92619-4821
E-mail: jbbs@scirp.org
URL: http://www.scirp.org/journal/jbbs/

Peer-reviewed journal publishing original research articles and reviews in the field of behavioral and brain function.

10610 ■ Journal of Business and Psychology
Springer-Verlag New York Inc.
233 Spring St.
New York, NY 10013-1578
Ph: (212)460-1500
Fax: (212)460-1575
Fr: 800-777-4643
URL: http://www.springer.com/psychology/
community+%26+environment

$904.00/year for institutions, print or online; $1,085.00/year for institutions, print & enchanced access. Journal covering all aspects of psychology that apply to the business segment. Includes topics such as personnel selection and training, organizational assessment and development, risk management and loss control, marketing and consumer behavior research.

10611 ■ Journal of Clinical Psychology
John Wiley & Sons Inc.
111 River St.
Hoboken, NJ 07030-5773
Ph: (201)748-6000
Fax: (201)748-6088
Fr: 800-825-7550
URL: http://onlinelibrary.wiley.com/journal/10.1002/
(ISSN)1097-46

Monthly. $129.00/year for U.S., Canada, and Mexico, print only; $973.00/year for institutions, print only; $1,057.00/year for institutions, other countries, print only; $1,119.00/year for institutions, print with online; $1,203.00/year for institutions, other countries, print with online. Peer-reviewed journal for professionals in the field of psychology.

10612 ■ Journal of Counseling Psychology
American Psychological Association
750 1st St. NE
Washington, DC 20002-4242
Ph: (202)336-5500
Fax: (202)336-5549

Fr: 800-374-2721
E-mail: journals@apa.org
URL: http://www.apa.org/pubs/journals/cou/
index.aspx

Quarterly. $55.00/year for members, domestic; $77.00/year for members, foreign, surface; $89.00/year for members, foreign, air mail; $44.00/year for students, domestic; $66.00/year for students, foreign, surface; $78.00/year for students, foreign, air mail; $145.00/year for nonmembers, domestic; $172.00/year for nonmembers, foreign, surface; $183.00/year for nonmembers, foreign, air mail; $415.00/year for institutions, domestic. Journal presenting empirical studies about counseling processes and interventions, theoretical articles about counseling, and studies dealing with evaluation of counseling applications and programs.

10613 ■ Journal of Family Psychotherapy
Routledge Journals
270 Madison Ave.
New York, NY 10016-0601
Ph: (212)216-7800
Fax: (212)563-2269
URL: http://www.tandf.co.uk/journals/WJFP

Quarterly. $110.00/year for individuals, online only; $118.00/year for individuals, print + online; $624.00/year for institutions, online only; $693.00/year for institutions, print + online. Journal includes case studies, treatment reports, and strategies in clinical practice for psychotherapists.

10614 ■ Journal of Positive Behavior Interventions
PRO-ED Inc.
8700 Shoal Creek Blvd.
Austin, TX 78757-6897
Ph: (512)451-3246
Fax: (512)451-8542
Fr: 800-897-3202
URL: http://www.proedinc.com/customer/
content.aspx?redid=24

Quarterly. $164.00/year for institutions, print & e-access; $148.00/year for institutions, e-access; $161.00/year for institutions, print; $61.00/year for individuals, print & e-access; $44.00/year for institutions, single print; $20.00/year for single issue, print. Journal covering issues in mental health and psychology.

10615 ■ The Journal of Psychology
Routledge
711 3 Ave., 8 Fl.
New York, NY 10016
Ph: (212)216-7800
Fax: (212)563-2269
Fr: 800-634-7064
E-mail: jrl@heldref.org
URL: http://www.tandf.co.uk/journals/titles/
00223980.asp

Bimonthly. $330.00/year for institutions, online only; $141.00/year for individuals, print and online; $233.00/year for individuals, print and online; $367.00/year for institutions, print and online. Psychology journal which publishes a variety of research and theoretical articles.

10616 ■ Medical Economics
Advanstar Communications Inc.
641 Lexington Ave., 8th Fl.
New York, NY 10022
Ph: (212)951-6600
Fax: (212)951-6793
Fr: 800-346-0085
URL: http://www.modernmedicine.com/
modernmedicine/Practice+Manage

Semimonthly. $95.00/year for individuals; $150.00/year for Canada and Mexico; $150.00/year for other countries. Magazine covering physicians practice management, professional relations, and financial affairs.

10617 ■ Monitor on Psychology
American Psychological Association
750 1st St. NE
Washington, DC 20002-4242
Ph: (202)336-5500
Fax: (202)336-5549
Fr: 800-374-2721
E-mail: journals@apa.org
URL: http://www.apa.org/monitor/

$50.00/year for nonmembers; $99.00/year for individuals, foreign, surface freight; $126.00/year for individuals, foreign, air mail; $93.00/year for institutions; $190.00/year for institutions, surface freight; $217.00/year for institutions, air freight; $20.00/year for single issue. Magazine of the APA. Reports on the science, profession, and social responsibility of psychology, including latest legislative developments affecting mental health, education, and research support.

10618 ■ North American Society of Adlerian Psychology Newsletter (NASAP Newsletter)
North American Society of Adlerian Psychology
614 Old West Chocolate Ave.
Hershey, PA 17033
Ph: (717)579-8795
Fax: (717)533-8616
E-mail: info@alfredadler.org
URL: http://www.alfredadler.org/AboutUs.htm

Description: Bimonthly. Relates news and events of the North American Society of Adlerian Psychology and regional news of affiliated associations. Recurring features include lists of courses and workshops offered by affiliated associations, reviews of new publications in the field, professional employment opportunities, a calendar of events, and a column titled President's Message.

10619 ■ Patient Education and Counseling
Mosby Inc.
11830 Westline Industrial Dr.
St. Louis, MO 63146-3326
Ph: (314)872-8370
Fax: (314)432-1380
Fr: 800-325-4177
URL: http://www.elsevier.com/wps/find/
journaldescription.cws_home

Monthly. $284.00/year for individuals, all countries except Europe, Japan and Iran; $2,648.00/year for institutions, all countries except Europe, Japan and Iran; $314,200.00/year for institutions; $33,700.00/year for individuals. Journal publishing articles on patient education and health promotion researchers, managers, physicians, nurses and other health care provider.

10620 ■ Pediatrics
American Academy of Pediatrics
141 NW Point Blvd.
Elk Grove Village, IL 60007-1098
Ph: (847)434-4000
Fax: (847)434-8000
Fr: 800-433-9016
E-mail: journals@aap.org
URL: http://pediatrics.aappublications.org/

Monthly. $179.00/year for nonmembers, physician, print & online; $136.00/year for nonmembers, physician, online; $96.00/year for nonmembers, student/allied, online; $128.00/year for nonmembers, student/allied, print & online. Medical journal reporting on pediatrics.

10621 ■ Practice
Routledge Journals
270 Madison Ave.
New York, NY 10016-0601
Ph: (212)216-7800
Fax: (212)563-2269
URL: http://www.tandf.co.uk/journals/titles/
09503153.asp

$253.00/year for institutions, print + online; $228.00/year for institutions, online only; $83.00/year for individuals, print only; $409.00/year for institutions, print + online; $368.00/year for institutions, online

only; $135.00/year for individuals, print only. Journal for a strong base in social work practice.

10622 ■ PsycCRITIQUES
American Psychological Association
750 1st St. NE
Washington, DC 20002-4242
Ph: (202)336-5500
Fax: (202)336-5549
Fr: 800-374-2721
URL: http://www.apa.org/pubs/databases/
psyccritiques/index.aspx

Bimonthly. $20.00/year for single issue. Journal presenting critical reviews of books, films, tapes, and other media representing a cross section of psychological literature.

10623 ■ Psychiatric Annals
SLACK Incorporated
6900 Grove Rd.
Thorofare, NJ 08086-9447
Ph: (856)848-1000
Fax: (856)848-6091
E-mail: psyann@slackinc.com
URL: http://www.psychiatricannalsonline.com/

Monthly. $229.00/year for individuals; $458.00/year for two years; $687.00/year for individuals, three years; $379.00/year for institutions; $758.00/year for institutions, two years; $1,137.00/year for institutions, three years; $114.00/year for individuals, resident; $53.00/year for individuals, outside the U.S.; $39.00/year for single issue. Peer-reviewed journal analyzing concepts and practices in every area of psychiatry.

10624 ■ Psychiatric News
American Psychiatric Publishing Inc.
1000 Wilson Blvd., Ste. 1825
Arlington, VA 22209-3924
Ph: (703)907-7322
Fax: (703)907-1091
Fr: 800-368-5777
URL: http://pn.psychiatryonline.org/

Semimonthly. $111.00/year for nonmembers, print and online; $151.00/year for members, international, print & online; $167.00/year for nonmembers, international, print & online; $22.00/year for single issue, United States; $37.00/year for single issue, international. Professional magazine of the American Psychiatric Assn.

10625 ■ Psychiatric Times
United Business Media
600 Harrison St., 6th Fl.
San Francisco, CA 94107
Ph: (415)947-6000
Fax: (415)947-6055
URL: http://www.psychiatrictimes.com/home

$55.00/year for individuals; $90.00/year for two years; $120.00/year for libraries, institution; $120.00/year for other countries. Newspaper (tabloid) on psychiatric disorders and issues.

10626 ■ Psychological Bulletin
American Psychological Association
750 1st St. NE
Washington, DC 20002-4242
Ph: (202)336-5500
Fax: (202)336-5549
Fr: 800-374-2721
E-mail: journals@apa.org
URL: http://www.apa.org/pubs/journals/bul/
index.aspx

Bimonthly. $106.00/year for members, domestic; $130.00/year for members, foreign, surface; $149.00/year for members, foreign, air mail; $84.00/year for students, domestic; $108.00/year for students, foreign, surface; $127.00/year for students, foreign, air mail; $280.00/year for nonmembers, domestic; $312.00/year for nonmembers, foreign, surface; $327.00/year for nonmembers, foreign, air mail; $765.00/year for institutions, domestic. Journal presenting comprehensive and integrative reviews and interpretations of critical substantive and methodological issues and practical problems from all the diverse areas of psychology.

10627 ■ Psychological Services
American Psychological Association
750 1st St. NE
Washington, DC 20002-4242
Ph: (202)336-5500
Fax: (202)336-5549
Fr: 800-374-2721
URL: http://www.apa.org/pubs/journals/ser/
index.aspx

Quarterly. $63.00/year for members; $85.00/year for members, international surface; $97.00/year for members, international airmail; $63.00/year for students; $85.00/year for students, other countries, surface; $97.00/year for students, other countries, airmail; $98.00/year for nonmembers; $125.00/year for nonmembers, international surface; $136.00/year for nonmembers, international airmail; $403.00/year for institutions. Journal of the Division of Psychologists in Public Service, publishing data-based articles on the broad range of psychological services.

10628 ■ Psychology Journal
Psychological Publishing
PO Box 176
Natchitoches, LA 71458
E-mail: psychjournal@aol.com
URL: http://www.psychologicalpublishing.com/

Quarterly. $90.00/year for individuals; $175.00/year for institutions. Journal dedicated to all areas of the science and practice of counseling and clinical psychology.

10629 ■ Psychology of Violence
American Psychological Association
750 1st St. NE
Washington, DC 20002-4242
Ph: (202)336-5500
Fax: (202)336-5549
Fr: 800-374-2721
URL: http://www.apa.org/pubs/journals/vio/index.aspx

Quarterly. $65.00/year for members; $89.00/year for other countries, members; $65.00/year for students; $110.00/year for nonmembers; $139.00/year for other countries, nonmembers; $441.00/year for institutions; $490.00/year for institutions, other countries. Multidisciplinary research journal concerning topics on the psychology of violence and extreme aggression.

10630 ■ Review of General Psychology
American Psychological Association
750 1st St. NE
Washington, DC 20002-4242
Ph: (202)336-5500
Fax: (202)336-5549
Fr: 800-374-2721
URL: http://www.apa.org/pubs/journals/gpr/
index.aspx

Quarterly. $63.00/year for members; $63.00/year for students; $110.00/year for nonmembers; $415.00/year for institutions; $85.00/year for members, international, surface; $85.00/year for students, other countries, surface; $137.00/year for nonmembers, international, surface; $460.00/year for institutions, other countries, surface; $97.00/year for members, international, airmail; $97.00/year for students, other countries, airmail. Journal including a wide variety of psychological research-related articles.

10631 ■ Teaching Exceptional Children
Council for Exceptional Children
2900 Crystal Dr., Ste. 1000
Arlington, VA 22202
Ph: (703)620-3660
Fax: (703)264-9494
Fr: 888-232-7733
URL: http://www.cec.sped.org/Content/
NavigationMenu/Publications2

$90.00/year for individuals, print; $152.00/year for two years, print; $101.00/year for Canada, print; $169.00/year for two years, Canada; $197.00/year for institutions, print; $332.00/year for two years, print;

$208.00/year for institutions, Canada, print; $236.00/year for institutions, other countries, print; $399.00/year for two years, institutional (print); $225.00/year for institutions, Canada, print and online. Peer-reviewed journal exploring practical methods for teaching students who have exceptionalities and those who are gifted and talented.

10632 ■ USA Body Psychotherapy Journal
United States Association for Body Psychotherapy
8639 B 16th St., Ste. 119
Silver Spring, MD 20910
Ph: (202)466-1619
E-mail: admin@usabp.org
URL: http://www.usabp.org/
displaycommon.cfm?an=4

Semiannual. Academic journal that seeks to support, promote and stimulate the exchange of ideas, scholarship and research within the field of body psychotherapy as well as an interdisciplinary exchange with related fields of clinical practice and inquiry.

EMPLOYER DIRECTORIES AND NETWORKING LISTS

10633 ■ American Board of Professional Psychology—Directory of Diplomates
American Board of Professional Psychology
600 Market St., Ste. 300
Chapel Hill, NC 27516
Ph: (919)537-8031
Fax: (919)537-8034
URL: http://www.abpp.org

Biennial, odd years. Covers: 3,200 psychologists who have passed the board's examination. Entries include: Name, office address, highest degree held, date of certification, practice areas. Arrangement: Alphabetical. Indexes: Geographical; speciality.

10634 ■ American Group Psychotherapy Association—Membership Directory
American Group Psychotherapy Association Inc.
25 E 21st St., 6th Fl.
New York, NY 10010
Ph: (212)477-2677
Fax: (212)979-6627
Fr: 877-668-2472
URL: http://www.agpa.org

Covers: 4,500 physicians, psychologists, clinical social workers, psychiatric nurses, and other mental health professionals interested in treatment of emotional problems by group methods. Entries include: Name, office or home address, highest degree held, office or home phone number. Arrangement: Alphabetical. Indexes: Geographical.

10635 ■ American Psychological Association—APA Membership Directory
American Psychological Association
750 1st St. NE
Washington, DC 20002-4242
Ph: (202)336-5500
Fax: (202)336-5549
Fr: 800-374-2721
E-mail: regdir@apa.org
URL: http://www.apa.org/databases/mem_directory/
homepage.html

Annual, Latest edition 2010. Free. Covers: Over 83,000 members in the United States, Canada, and abroad; also includes membership rosters of American Board of Professional Psychology and American Board of Psychological Hypnosis. Entries include: Name, office or home address, phone, fax, degrees and universities where obtained, election date, membership and divisional affiliations. Arrangement: Alphabetical. Indexes: Association division.

10636 ■ American Society for Adolescent Psychiatry—Membership Directory
American Society for Adolescent Psychiatry
PO Box 570218
Dallas, TX 75357-0218

Ph: (972)613-0985
Fax: (972)613-5532
URL: http://www.adolpsych.org

Covers: 1,500 members. Entries include: Name, office address and phone, fax, home address and phone (when given). Arrangement: Alphabetical. Indexes: Geographical, chapter.

10637 ■ Christian Association for Psychological Studies International—Membership Directory
Christian Association for Psychological Studies
PO Box 365
Batavia, IL 60510-0365
Ph: (630)639-9478
Fax: (630)454-3799
URL: http://www.caps.net

Annual, June. $12.00 for Canada; $12.00 for other countries. Covers: 2,300 Christians involved in psychology, psychiatry, counseling, sociology, social work, ministry, and nursing. Entries include: Name, office address and phone number, highest degree held, area of occupational specialization, and career data. Arrangement: Geographical. Indexes: Alphabetical.

10638 ■ Directory of Accredited Counseling Services
International Association of Counseling Services
101 S Whiting St., Ste. 211
Alexandria, VA 22304-3416
Ph: (703)823-9840
Fax: (703)823-9843
URL: http://iacsinc.org/iacsmem.html

Annual, September. $50.00. Covers: About 200 accredited services in the United States and Canada concerned with psychological, educational, and vocational counseling, including those at colleges and universities, and public and private agencies. Entries include: Name, address, phone, hours of operation, director's name, service, clientele served. Arrangement: Geographical.

10639 ■ Directory of Child Life Programs
Child Life Council Inc.
11821 Parklawn Dr., Ste. 310
Rockville, MD 20852-2539
Ph: (301)881-7090
Fax: (301)881-7092
URL: http://www.childlife.org

Biennial, latest edition 14th, 2006. Covers: Over 400 child life programs. Entries include: Facility name, address, phone, name of child life department and director, reporting structure, staff statistics, educational requirements for employment, and internship or educational opportunities. Arrangement: Geographical. Indexes: Speciality areas, internship sessions, program size, fellowships.

10640 ■ Directory of Hospital Personnel
Grey House Publishing
4919 Rte. 22
PO Box 56
Amenia, NY 12501
Ph: (518)789-8700
Fax: (518)789-0556
Fr: 800-562-2139
URL: http://www.greyhouse.com/hospital_
personnel.htm

Annual, Latest edition 2011. $325.00 for individuals. Covers: 200,000 executives at 6,000 U.S. Hospitals. Entries include: Name of hospital, address, phone, number of beds, type and JCAHO status of hospital, names and titles of key department heads and staff, medical and nursing school affiliations; number of residents, interns, and nursing students. Arrangement: Geographical. Indexes: Hospital name, personnel, hospital size.

10641 ■ Hospital Blue Book
Billian Publishing Inc. and Trans World Publishing Inc.
2100 River Edge Pky.
Atlanta, GA 30328

Ph: (770)955-5656
Fax: (770)952-0669
Fr: 800-800-5668
E-mail: blu-book@billian.com
URL: http://www.billianshealthdata.com/Products/
bluebook.html

Annual, Latest edition 2010. $575.00 for individuals;
$575.00 for individuals. Covers: More than 6,500
hospitals; some listings also appear in a separate
southern edition of this publication. Entries include:
Name of hospital, accreditation, mailing address,
phone, fax, number of beds, type of facility (nonprofit,
general, state, etc.); list of administrative personnel
and chiefs of medical services, with specific titles. Arrangement: Geographical.

**10642 ■ Internship Programs in Professional
Psychology, Including Post-Doctoral
Training Programs**
Association of Psychology Postdoctoral and Intern-
ship Centers
10 G St. NE, Ste. 440
Washington, DC 20002
Ph: (202)589-0600
Fax: (202)589-0603
URL: http://www.appic.org/directory/search_dol_
internships.asp

Annual, September; Latest edition 2008. $37.05 for
members; $74.85 for nonmembers. Covers: institu-
tions offering PhD internship programs in professional
psychology. Entries include: Institution name, name
and address of contact, description of program,
theoretical orientation, number of interns, stipend,
admission requirements. Arrangement: Geographical.

**10643 ■ Legal and Ethical Dictionary for
Mental Health Professionals**
University Press of America Inc.
4501 Forbes Blvd., Ste. 200
Lanham, MD 20706
Ph: (301)459-3366
Fax: (301)429-5748
Fr: 800-462-6420
URL: http://www.univpress.com

Latest edition 2009. $61.99 for individuals; $29.99 for
individuals. Publication includes: Lists of state licensure boards and Web sites for mental health
organizations. Principal content of publication is a
dictionary of legal and ethical responsibilities for
mental health professionals.

**10644 ■ Medical and Health Information
Directory**
Gale
PO Box 6904
Florence, KY 41022-6904
Fr: 800-354-9706
URL: http://www.gale.cengage.com

Annual, Latest edition April 2011. $1190.00 for
individuals; $501.00 for individuals. Covers: In volume
1, more than 33,000 medical and health oriented associations, organizations, institutions, and government agencies, including health maintenance organizations (HMOs), preferred provider organizations
(PPOs), insurance companies, pharmaceutical
companies, research centers, and medical and allied
health schools. In Volume 2, over 20,000 medical
book publishers; medical periodicals, directories,
audiovisual producers and services, medical libraries
and information centers, electronic resources, and
health-related internet search engines. In Volume 3,
more than 40,500 clinics, treatment centers, care
programs, and counseling/diagnostic services for 34
subject areas. Entries include: Institution, service, or
firm name, address, phone, fax, email and URL;
many include names of key personnel and, when
pertinent, descriptive annotation. Volume 3 was
formerly listed separately as Health Services
Directory. Arrangement: Classified by organization
activity, service, etc. Indexes: Each volume has a
complete alphabetical name and keyword index.

Handbooks and Manuals

10645 ■ 101 Careers in Counseling
Springer Publishing Company
11 W 42nd St., 15th Fl.
New York, NY 10036
Ph: (212)431-4370
Fax: (212)941-7842
Fr: 877-687-7476
URL: http://www.springerpub.com

Shannon Hodges. 2012. $25.00 (paper). 332 pages.
Describes the many benefits of a counseling career
and explores a wealth of opportunities in both
traditional and non-traditional settings. Includes an
overview, salary range, employment prospects, best
and most challenging aspects of the job, and educational and licensing requirements.

10646 ■ 101 Careers in Psychology
Springer Publishing Company
11 W 42nd St., 15th Fl.
New York, NY 10036
Ph: (212)431-4370
Fax: (212)941-7842
Fr: 877-687-7476
URL: http://www.springerpub.com

Tracey Ryan. 2012. $25.00 (paper). 240 pages.
Provides an engaging and practical guide to the
diverse careers in psychology that will be most in
demand in the coming decade, along with guidance
for students and recent psychology graduates on how
to select a fulfilling career. Discusses careers requiring bachelor's, master's, and doctoral degrees,
including careers often overlooked by psychology
majors.

**10647 ■ Career Paths in Psychology: Where
Your Degree Can Take You**
American Psychological Association
750 1st St. NE
Washington, DC 20002-4242
Ph: (202)336-5500
Fax: (202)336-5620
Fr: 800-374-2721
URL: http://www.apa.org/pubs/books/4313008.aspx

Robert J. Sternberg. 2006. $29.95 (paper). 376
pages.

**10648 ■ Careers for Mystery Buffs and Other
Snoops and Sleuths**
The McGraw-Hill Companies
PO Box 182604
Columbus, OH 43272
Fax: (614)759-3749
Fr: 877-883-5524
E-mail: customer.service@mcgraw-hill.com
URL: http://www.mhprofessional.com

Blythe Camenson. Second edition. $14.95
(hardback). 160 pages.

**10649 ■ Careers in Social and Rehabilitation
Services**
The McGraw-Hill Companies
PO Box 182604
Columbus, OH 43272
Fax: (614)759-3749
Fr: 877-883-5524
E-mail: customer.service@mcgraw-hill.com
URL: http://www.mhprofessional.com/
product.php?isbn=0071641955

Geraldine O. Garner. 2008. $16.95. 192 pages.

10650 ■ Great Jobs for Liberal Arts Majors
The McGraw-Hill Companies
PO Box 182604
Columbus, OH 43272
Fax: (614)759-3749
Fr: 877-883-5524
E-mail: customer.service@mcgraw-hill.com
URL: http://www.mhprofessional.com/
product.php?isbn=0071482148

Blythe Camenson. Second edition, 2007. $16.95
(paper). 192 pages.

10651 ■ Great Jobs for Psychology Majors
McGraw-Hill
PO Box 182604
Columbus, OH 43272
Ph: (609)426-5793
Fax: (614)759-3749
Fr: 877-833-5524
E-mail: customer.service@mcgraw-hill.com
URL: http://www.mcgraw-hill.com

Julie DeGalan, Stephen Lambert. 2006. $15.95 (3rd.
ed. paperback). 192 pages. Helps readers explore
the possibilities that having a psychology major can
create. Provides guidance on how to present psychology major as a workplace asset during an interview.

10652 ■ Opportunities in Child Care Careers
The McGraw-Hill Companies
PO Box 182604
Columbus, OH 43272
Fax: (614)759-3749
Fr: 877-883-5524
E-mail: customer.service@mcgraw-hill.com
URL: http://www.mhprofessional.com/
product.php?isbn=0071467661

Renee Wittenberg. 2006. $13.95 (paper). 160 pages.
Discusses various job opportunities and how to
secure a position. Illustrated.

**10653 ■ Opportunities in Health and Medical
Careers**
The McGraw-Hill Companies
PO Box 182604
Columbus, OH 43272
Fax: (614)759-3749
Fr: 877-883-5524
E-mail: customer.service@mcgraw-hill.com
URL: http://www.mhprofessional.com/
product.php?isbn=0071437274

I. Donald Snook, Jr. and Leo D'Orazio. 2004. $14.95
(paper). 157 pages. Covers the full range of medical
and health occupations. Illustrated.

**10654 ■ Opportunities in Psychology
Careers**
McGraw-Hill
PO Box 182604
Columbus, OH 43272
Ph: (609)426-5793
Fax: (609)308-4480
Fr: 800-262-4729
E-mail: customer.service@mcgraw-hill.com
URL: http://www.mhprofessional.com/
product.php?isbn=0071392068

Donald E. Super. 2008. $14.95. 160 pages. Provides
job seekers with essential information about a variety
of careers in the field of psychology. Includes training
and education requirements, salary statistics and
professional and Internet resources.

**10655 ■ Opportunities in Social Science
Careers**
The McGraw-Hill Companies
PO Box 182604
Columbus, OH 43272
Fax: (614)759-3749
Fr: 877-883-5524
E-mail: customer.service@mcgraw-hill.com
URL: http://www.mcgraw-hill.com

Rosanne J. Marek. 2004. $13.95. 160 Pages. VGM
Opportunities Series.

**10656 ■ The Psychology Major: Career
Options and Strategies for Success**
Prentice Hall
1 Lake St.
Upper Saddle River, NJ 07458
Fr: 800-922-0579
URL: http://prenticehall.com

Stephen F. Davis, R. Eric Landrum. 2010. $28.40
(4th ed. paperback). 216 pages. Provides information

on a variety of career opportunities in the field of psychology.

10657 ■ The Role of Work in People's Lives: Applied Career Counseling & Vocational Psychology

Wadsworth Publishing
PO Box 6904
Florence, KY 41022
Fax: 800-487-8488
Fr: 800-354-9706
E-mail: esales@cengage.com
URL: http://www.cengage.com

Nadene Peterson and Roberto Cortez Gonzalez. 2005. Second edition. $117.99. 592 pages.

10658 ■ The School Psychologist's Survival Guide

Jossey-Bass
c/o John Wiley & Sons, Inc.
111 River St.
Hoboken, NJ 07030-5774
Ph: (201)748-6000
Fax: (201)748-6088
E-mail: info@wiley.com
URL: http://www.wiley.com

Rebecca Branstetter. 2012. $34.95 (paper). 368 pages. Offers advice and survival tips for school psychologists. Includes ideas and strategies for dealing with a diverse group of students, traveling to multiple school sites, meeting with concerned parents, and managing school crises.

ONLINE JOB SOURCES AND SERVICES

10659 ■ Delta T Group

E-mail: cfassl@deltatg.com
URL: http://www.delta-tgroup.com

Description: Specialized contract temporary staffing source for healthcare professionals in the fields of social service, psychiatry, mental health, and substance abuse. Organizations may request services and staffing; job seekers may view services provided, submit a resume, or peruse jobs available.

10660 ■ MedSourceConsultants.com

300 Main St., 7th Fl.
Stamford, CT 06901
Fax: (203)324-0555
Fr: 800-575-2880
E-mail: dpascale@medsourceconsultants.com
URL: http://www.medsourceconsultants.com

Description: Site houses a physician search and consulting company for psychiatrists. Consultants attempt to match job seekers to positions according to the individual's personal and professional needs. This page also aids institutions looking to recruit psychiatrists.

10661 ■ RehabWorld.com

URL: http://www.rehabworld.com

Description: Site for rehabilitation professionals to learn about the profession and locate jobs. Includes user groups, salary surveys, and chat capabilities. Main files include: Physical Therapy, Occupational Therapy, Speech Therapy, Mental Health, Employer World, Student World, International World, Forum.

TRADESHOWS

10662 ■ American Psychological Association Convention

American Psychological Association
750 1st St., N.E.
Washington, DC 20002-4242
Ph: (202)336-5500
Fr: 800-374-2721
E-mail: convention@apa.org
URL: http://www.apa.org

Annual. Primary Exhibits: Computers, publications, and related government services. Dates and Locations: 2012 Aug 02-05; Orlando, FL; 2013 Jul 21 - Aug 04; Honolulu, HI; 2014 Aug 06-09; Washington, DC; 2015 Aug 06-09; Toronto, ON, Canada; 2016 Aug 04-07; Denver, CO; 2017 Aug 03-06; Washington, DC; 2018 Aug 09-12; San Francisco, CA.

10663 ■ Association for Psychological Science Convention

Association for Psychological Science
1133 15th St. NW, Ste. 1000
Washington, DC 20005
Ph: (202)293-9300
Fax: (202)293-9350
URL: http://www.psychologicalscience.org

Annual. Features special theme programs addressing current issues in the field of psychological science. Incorporates a variety of invited guest speakers, a roundtable discussion and posters relating to the theme.

10664 ■ Society for Industrial and Organizational Psychology Annual Conference

Society for Industrial and Organizational Psychology
440 E Poe Rd., Ste 101
Bowling Green, OH 43402
Ph: (419)353-0032
Fax: (419)352-2645
E-mail: siop@siop.org
URL: http://www.siop.org

Annual. Includes workshops, seminars, theme tracks, and networking opportunities.

10665 ■ Society for Personality and Social Psychology Conference

Society for Personality and Social Psychology
c/o Christie Marvin, Exec. Asst.
Cornell University
Department of Psychology
239 Uris Hall
Ithaca, NY 14853
Ph: (607)254-5416
URL: http://www.spsp.org

Annual. Hosts symposia, poster sessions, publisher exhibits, and special events.

10666 ■ Southwestern Psychological Association Annual Convention

Southwestern Psychological Association
Tarleton State University
PO Box T-0820
Dr. Bob Newby
Stephenville, TX 76401
Ph: (785)827-5541
Fax: (254)968-9947
E-mail: russinr@kwu.edu
URL: http://www.swpsych.org

Annual. Primary Exhibits: Publications, films, and health products.

OTHER SOURCES

10667 ■ Academy of Psychosomatic Medicine

5272 River Rd., Ste. 630
Bethesda, MD 20816-1453
Ph: (301)718-6520
Fax: (301)656-0989
E-mail: apm@apm.org
URL: http://www.apm.org

Description: Psychiatrists engaged in psychosomatic medicine or consultation liaison psychiatry, physicians and medical students. Promotes the advancement of medical science, education, and healthcare for persons with comorbid psychiatric and general medical conditions. Provides national and international leadership by influencing direction and process of research and public policy and promoting interdisciplinary education.

10668 ■ American Association of Psychiatric Technicians (AAPT)

1220 S St., Ste. 100
Sacramento, CA 95811-7138
Fax: (916)329-9145
Fr: 800-391-7589
E-mail: aapt@psychtechs.net
URL: http://www.psychtechs.org

Description: Administers the Nationally Certified Psychiatric Technician examination to non-licensed direct-care workers in the fields of mental illness, developmental disabilities and substance abuse.

10669 ■ American Mental Health Alliance (AMHA)

PO Box 4075
Portland, OR 97208-4075
Ph: (503)227-2027
Fr: 888-826-3682
E-mail: memberinfo@americanmentalhealth.com
URL: http://www.americanmentalhealth.com

Description: Represents mental health professionals licensed or certified for independent practice. Creates a professional community that provides therapy of the highest quality and ethical standards. Supports and markets competent, ethical mental health services that preserve privacy and confidentiality. Supports education, supervision, and research opportunities for members. Opposes legislation and regulations that invade patent privacy and confidentiality.

10670 ■ American Psychological Association (APA)

750 First St. NE
Washington, DC 20002-4242
Ph: (202)336-5500
Fax: (202)336-6069
Fr: 800-374-2721
E-mail: president@apa.org
URL: http://www.apa.org

Description: Scientific and professional society of psychologists; students participate as affiliates. Advances psychology as a science, a profession, and as a means of promoting health, education and the human welfare.

10671 ■ American Public Health Association (APHA)

800 I St. NW
Washington, DC 20001
Ph: (202)777-2742
Fax: (202)777-2534
E-mail: comments@apha.org
URL: http://www.apha.org

Description: Professional organization of physicians, nurses, educators, academicians, environmentalists, epidemiologists, new professionals, social workers, health administrators, optometrists, podiatrists, pharmacists, dentists, nutritionists, health planners, other community and mental health specialists, and interested consumers. Seeks to protect and promote personal, mental, and environmental health. Services include: promulgation of standards; establishment of uniform practices and procedures; development of the etiology of communicable diseases; research in public health; exploration of medical care programs and their relationships to public health. Sponsors job placement service.

10672 ■ American Society of Criminology (ASC)

1314 Kinnear Rd., Ste. 212
Columbus, OH 43212-1156
Ph: (614)292-9207
Fax: (614)292-6767
E-mail: asc@asc41.com
URL: http://www.asc41.com

Description: Represents professional and academic criminologists, students of criminology in accredited universities, psychiatrists, psychologists, and sociologists. Develops criminology as a science and academic discipline. Aids in the construction of criminological curricula in accredited universities. Upgrades the practitioner in criminological fields (police, prisons, probation, parole, delinquency workers). Conducts research programs and sponsors three student paper competitions. Provides placement service at annual convention.

10673 ■ Association for Behavior Analysis (ABA)

550 W Centre Ave., Ste. 1
Portage, MI 49024
Ph: (269)492-9310
Fax: (269)492-9316
E-mail: mail@abainternational.org
URL: http://www.abainternational.org

Description: Professionals, paraprofessionals, and students interested in the applied, experimental, and theoretical analysis of behavior. Promotes the development of behavior analysis as a profession and science. Provides a forum for the discussion of issues; disseminates information on behavior analysis. Conducts workshops and seminars in 16 specialty areas including: Behavioral Pharmacology and Toxicology; Developmental Disabilities; Organizational Behavior Analysis. Offers continuing education credits for psychologists. Maintains archives of the association's publications; offers placement service.

10674 ■ Association of Black Psychologists (ABPsi)

PO Box 55999
Washington, DC 20040-5999
Ph: (202)722-0808
Fax: (202)722-5941
E-mail: info@abpsi.org
URL: http://www.abpsi.org

Description: Professional psychologists and others in associated disciplines. Aims to: enhance the psychological well being of black people in America; define mental health in consonance with newly established psychological concepts and standards; develop policies for local, state and national decision-making that have impact on the mental health of the black community; support established black sister organizations and aid in the development of new, independent black institutions to enhance the psychological, educational, cultural and economic situation. Offers training and information on AIDS. Conducts seminars, workshops and research.

10675 ■ Association for Humanistic Counseling

PO Box 791006
Baltimore, MD 21279-1006
Ph: (703)823-9800
Fax: 800-473-2329
Fr: 800-347-6647
E-mail: cmalchiodi@insightbb.com
URL: http://www.c-ahead.com

Description: A division of the American Counseling Association. Teachers, educational administrators, community agency workers, counselors, school social workers, and psychologists; others interested in the area of human development. Aims to assist individuals in improving their quality of life. Provides forum for the exchange of information about humanistically-oriented administrative and instructional practices.

Supports humanistic practices and research on instructional and organizational methods for facilitating humanistic education; encourages cooperation among related professional groups.

10676 ■ Association for Psychological Science

1133 15th St. NW, Ste. 1000
Washington, DC 20005
Ph: (202)293-9300
Fax: (202)293-9350
URL: http://www.psychologicalscience.org

Description: Serves psychological scientists and academics, clinicians, researchers, teachers and administrators. Promotes, protects and advances the interests of scientifically oriented psychology in research, application, teaching and the improvement of human welfare. Disseminates and advocates psychological research.

10677 ■ Association of Psychology Postdoctoral and Internship Centers (APPIC)

10 G St. NE, Ste. 440
Washington, DC 20002
Ph: (202)589-0600
Fax: (202)589-0603
E-mail: appic@aol.com
URL: http://www.appic.org

Description: Veterans administration hospitals, medical centers, state hospitals, university counseling centers, and other facilities that provide internship and postdoctoral programs in professional psychology. Promotes activities that assist in the development of professional psychology training programs. Serves as a clearinghouse to provide Ph.D. candidates with internship placement assistance at member facilities. Conducts workshops and seminars on training procedures in clinical psychology at the PhD level.

10678 ■ Council of Professional Geropsychology Training Programs (CoPGTP)

Center for Aging Resources
447 N El Molino Ave.
Pasadena, CA 91101
E-mail: jyang@wucfar1stl.org
URL: http://www.copgtp.org

Description: Aims to advance geropsychology training and provide resources for programs and individuals seeking training in the field. Supports the development of training programs in professional geropsychology at the graduate school, internship, postdoctoral fellowship and post-licensure levels. Provides opportunities for continued dialogue on training issues.

10679 ■ Employee Assistance Society of North America (EASNA)

2001 Jefferson Davis Hwy., Ste. 1004
Arlington, VA 22202-3617
Ph: (703)416-0060

Fax: (703)416-0014
E-mail: bmclean@easna.org
URL: http://www.easna.org

Description: Individuals in the field of employee assistance, including psychiatrists, psychologists, and managers. Facilitates communication among members; provides resource information; serves as a network for employee assistance programs nationwide. Conducts research.

10680 ■ International Association of Counselors and Therapists (IACT)

8852 SR 3001
Laceyville, PA 18623
Ph: (570)869-1021
Fax: (570)869-1249
Fr: 800-553-6886
E-mail: info@iact.org
URL: http://www.iact.org

Description: Mental health professionals, medical professionals, social workers, clergy, educators, hypnotherapists, counselors, and individuals interested in the helping professions. Promotes enhanced professional image and prestige for complementary therapy. Provides a forum for exchange of information and ideas among practitioners of traditional and nontraditional therapies and methodologies; fosters unity among "grassroots" practitioners and those with advanced academic credentials. Facilitates the development of new therapy programs. Conducts educational, research, and charitable programs. Awards credits for continuing education. Maintains speakers' bureau and library; operates referral and placement services; compiles statistics. Assists in the development of local chapters.

10681 ■ National Association of School Psychologists (NASP)

4340 E West Hwy., Ste. 402
Bethesda, MD 20814
Ph: (301)657-0270
Fax: (301)657-0275
Fr: (866)331-NASP
E-mail: membership@naspweb.org
URL: http://www.nasponline.org

Description: School psychologists. Serves the mental health and educational needs of all children and youth. Encourages and provides opportunities for professional growth of individual members. Informs the public on the services and practice of school psychology, and advances the standards of the profession. Operates national school psychologist certification system. Sponsors children's services.

10682 ■ Society for Industrial and Organizational Psychology

440 E Poe Rd., Ste 101
Bowling Green, OH 43402
Ph: (419)353-0032
Fax: (419)352-2645
E-mail: siop@siop.org
URL: http://www.siop.org

Description: Aims to enhance human well-being and performance in organizational and work settings by promoting the science, practice, and teaching of industrial-organizational psychology. Provides forums for industrial-organizational psychologists to exchange research, insights, and information.

Public Relations Specialists

10683 ■ Bulldog Reporter Business Media
Infocom Group
124 Linden St.
Oakland, CA 94607
Ph: (510)596-9300
Fr: 800-959-1059
URL: http://www.infocomgroup.com

Description: Semimonthly. Covers U.S. news media for public relations professionals. Recurring features include interviews, media contact lists, and media personnel changes.

10684 ■ Bulldog Reporter-Eastern Edition
Infocom Group
124 Linden St.
Oakland, CA 94607
Ph: (510)596-9300
Fr: 800-959-1059
URL: http://www.infocomgroup.com

Description: Semimonthly. Features information on effective ways to place stories in newspapers, magazines, and radio and/or television programs. Recurring features include interviews, media contact listings, and media personnel changes.

10685 ■ Communication Briefings
Briefings Publishing Group
2807 N Parham Rd., Ste. 200
Richmond, VA 23294
Ph: (570)567-1982
Fax: (804)217-8999
Fr: 800-791-8699
E-mail: citytreeseditor@gmail.com
URL: http://www.briefings.com

Description: Monthly. Provides communication ideas and techniques for a wide variety of areas, including public relations, advertising, fund raising, speeches, media relations, human resources, and employee/manager relations. Carries interviews with top communicators, business leaders, university experts, and research specialists. Recurring features include news of research, book reviews, and abstracts of articles from national publications.

10686 ■ Contacts: The Media Pipeline for PR People
Mercomm Inc.
500 Executive Blvd.
Ossining, NY 10562
Ph: (914)923-9400
Fax: (914)923-9484
E-mail: contacts@mercommawards.com
URL: http://www.mercommawards.com

Description: Weekly. Contains media placement opportunities for publicists and public relations professionals.

10687 ■ Editor & Publisher
Editor & Publisher Magazine
17782 Cowan, Ste. A
Irvine, CA 92614
Ph: (949)660-6150
Fax: (949)660-6172
URL: http://www.editorandpublisher.com/

Weekly (Mon.). $65.00/year for individuals, print and online; $125.00/year for two years, print and online; $85.00/year for other countries; $49.00/year for individuals, digital only. Magazine focusing on newspaper journalism, advertising, printing equipment and interactive services.

10688 ■ Healthcare Marketer's Executive Briefing
The E-Commerce Information Center
PO Box 456
Allenwood, NJ 08720
Ph: (732)292-1100
Fax: (732)292-1111
Fr: 800-516-4343
E-mail: info@healthresourcesonline.com
URL: http://www.healthresourcesonline.com/management/12nl.htm

Description: Monthly. $147/year. Designed to keep professionals abreast of the newest marketing and public relations techniques and strategies within the field of health care.

10689 ■ Jack O'Dwyer's Newsletter
J.R. O'Dwyer Company Inc.
271 Madison Ave., No. 600
New York, NY 10016
Ph: (212)679-2471
Fax: (212)683-2750
Fr: (866)395-7710
E-mail: john@odwyerpr.com
URL: http://www.odwyerpr.com

Description: Weekly. $295.00/year. Provides nationwide coverage of the public relations industry. Reports on executive and account changes, new public relations firms, and honors won in the field. Recurring features include a calendar of events, book reviews, lists of free pamphlets and other materials, new services available to public relations personnel, and media changes.

10690 ■ Media Relations Report
Lawrence Ragan Communications Inc.
111 E Wacker Dr., Ste. 500
Chicago, IL 60601
Ph: (312)960-4100
Fax: (312)861-3592
Fr: 800-878-5331
E-mail: cservice@ragan.com
URL: http://www.ragan.com

Description: Monthly. Covers advertising and public relations media placement. Topics include placement opportunities, media news, pitching media campaigns, targeting ads, press releases, and others.

10691 ■ Partyline Newsletter
Partyline Publishing Co.
35 Sutton Pl.
New York, NY 10022
Ph: (212)755-3487
Fax: (212)755-4859
E-mail: byarmon@ix.netcom.com
URL: http://www.partylinepublishing.com

Description: Weekly. Disseminates information about media placement opportunities for public relations professionals.

10692 ■ PR Intelligence Report
Lawrence Ragan Communications Inc.
111 E Wacker Dr., Ste. 500
Chicago, IL 60601
Ph: (312)960-4100
Fax: (312)861-3592
Fr: 800-878-5331
E-mail: cservice@ragan.com
URL: http://www.ragan.com

Description: Semimonthly. Internet newsletter providing news about the public relations industry, including tips for those in the industry.

10693 ■ PR News
Access Intelligence L.L.C.
4 Choke Cherry Rd.
Rockville, MD 20850
Ph: (301)354-2000
Fax: (301)309-3847
Fr: 800-777-5006
E-mail: info@accessintel.com
URL: http://info.accessintel.com/index.html?PRN

Description: Weekly. $797 per year. Carries public relations news and information of interest to high-level executives. Offers a two-page case study in each issue on an aspect of public relations within business, industry, and government. Recurring features include mention of awards and honors in the field, personnel and account changes, excerpts from major speeches, media insight chart, global PR and cyber PR.

10694 ■ The Ragan Report
Lawrence Ragan Communications Inc.
111 E Wacker Dr., Ste. 500
Chicago, IL 60601
Ph: (312)960-4100
Fax: (312)861-3592
Fr: 800-878-5331
E-mail: cservice@ragan.com
URL: http://www.ragan.com

Description: Monthly. $279 for non-members. $249 for members.Offers ideas and techniques for communications executives, especially the organizational press. Provides commentary; "how-to" advice on writing, photography, and design; plus examples of outstanding work in the field. Recurring features include editorials, news of research, letters to the editor, news of members, book reviews, a calendar of events, and columns titled The Typochondriac, Arnold on Typography, Douglis on Visuals, and The Do-It-Yourself Designer.

EMPLOYER DIRECTORIES AND NETWORKING LISTS

10695 ■ The ADWEEK Directory
ADWEEK Magazines
770 Broadway, 7th Fl.
New York, NY 10003-9595
URL: http://www.adweek.com

Annual. $499.00 for individuals; $799.00 for individuals. Covers: Over 23,000 personal listings and it has information on more than 5,900 full-service advertising agencies, public relations firms, media buying services, direct marketing and related organizations. Entries include: Agency name, address, phone, fax/e-mail, URL; names and titles of key personnel; major accounts; Ultimate parent company; headquarters location; major subsidiaries and other operating units; year founded; number of employees; fee income; billings; percentage of billings by medium. Individual listings for each agency branch. Arrangement: Alphabetical. Indexes: Geographical; parent company, subsidiary, branch; ethnic specialties; organization, name changes, agencies opened/closed.

10696 ■ National School Public Relations Association—Directory
National School Public Relations Association
15948 Derwood Rd.
Rockville, MD 20855-2123
Ph: (301)519-0496
Fax: (301)519-0494
URL: http://www.nspra.org

Annual, January. Covers: Approximately 2,000 school system public relations directors, school administrators, principals, and others who are members of the National School Public Relations Association. Entries include: Name, affiliation, address, phone. Arrangement: Geographical.

10697 ■ O'Dwyer's Directory of Public Relations Firms
J.R. O'Dwyer Company Inc.
271 Madison Ave., No. 600
New York, NY 10016
Ph: (212)679-2471
Fax: (212)683-2750
Fr: (866)395-7710
E-mail: john@odwyerpr.com
URL: http://www.odwyerpr.com

Annual, Latest edition 2011. $95.00 for individuals. Covers: Over 1,600 public relations firms; international coverage. Entries include: Firm name, address, phone, principal executives, branch and overseas offices, billings, date founded, and 7,750 clients are cross-indexed. Arrangement: Geographical by country. Indexes: Specialty (beauty and fashions, finance/investor, etc.), geographical, client.

10698 ■ Public Relations Society of America, Chicago Chapter—Membership Directory
Public Relations Society of America, Chicago Chapter
1000 N Rand Rd., Ste. 214
Wauconda, IL 60084
Ph: (847)526-2010
Fax: (847)526-3993
URL: http://prsachicago.com/members.html

Annual, October. Covers: About 550 individuals engaged in public relations and related occupations in Chicago. Entries include: Name, title, affiliation, address, phone, type of membership, year joined, employment history. Arrangement: Alphabetical. Indexes: Firm name.

10699 ■ Public Relations Tactics—Member Services Directory—The Blue Book
Public Relations Society of America
33 Maiden Ln., 11th Fl.
New York, NY 10038-5150

Ph: (212)460-1400
Fax: (212)995-0757
E-mail: 74224.1456@compuserve.com
URL: http://www.prsa.org

Annual, latest edition 2007. Covers: PRSA members—headquaters, staff contacts, and chapter, section, and district information. Entries include: Name, professional affiliation and title, address, phone, membership rank. Arrangement: Alphabetical. Indexes: Geographical, organizational.

HANDBOOKS AND MANUALS

10700 ■ Careers in Communications
The McGraw-Hill Companies
PO Box 182604
Columbus, OH 43272
Fax: (614)759-3749
Fr: 877-883-5524
E-mail: customer.service@mcgraw-hill.com
URL: http://www.mhprofessional.com/
    product.php?isbn=0071454764

Shonan Noronha. Fourth edition, 2004. $15.95 (paper). 192 pages. Examines the fields of journalism, photography, radio, television, film, public relations, and advertising. Gives concrete details on job locations and how to secure a job. Suggests many resources for job hunting.

10701 ■ Careers In Focus: Public Relations
Ferguson Publishing
132 W 31st St., 17th Fl.
New York, NY 10001
Fr: 800-322-8755
E-mail: custserv@factsonfile.com
URL: http://factsonfile.infobasepublishing.com

2007. $32.95. 160 pages. Contains black and white photographs, indexes, resources and interviews. Covers 17 careers in the field of public relations.

10702 ■ FabJob Guide to Become a Public Relations Consultant
FabJob Inc.
4616 - 25th Ave. NE, No. 224
Seattle, WA 98105
Ph: (403)949-4980
Fr: 888-322-5621
URL: http://www.fabjob.com/PublicRelations.asp

Lynne Bliss. $29.97(e-book). 237 pages. Provides information on how to get started and succeed as a public relations consultant, how to get a public relations job, how to start a public relations agency and how to get clients.

10703 ■ Opportunities in Insurance Careers
The McGraw-Hill Companies
PO Box 182604
Columbus, OH 43272
Fax: (614)759-3749
Fr: 877-883-5524
E-mail: customer.service@mcgraw-hill.com
URL: http://www.mhprofessional.com/
    product.php?isbn=0071482075

Robert M. Schrayer. Revised, 2007. $14.95 (paper). 160 pages. A guide to planning for and seeking opportunities in the field. Contains bibliography and illustrations.

10704 ■ Opportunities in Marketing Careers
The McGraw-Hill Companies
PO Box 182604
Columbus, OH 43272
Fax: (614)759-3749
Fr: 877-883-5524
E-mail: customer.service@mcgraw-hill.com
URL: http://www.mhprofessional.com/
    product.php?isbn=0071448985

Margery Steinberg. 2005. $13.95 (paper). 176. Gives guidance on identifying and pursuing job opportunities. Illustrated.

10705 ■ Opportunities in Writing Careers
The McGraw-Hill Companies
PO Box 182604
Columbus, OH 43272
Fax: (614)759-3749
Fr: 877-883-5524
E-mail: customer.service@mcgraw-hill.com
URL: http://www.mhprofessional.com/
    product.php?isbn=0071458727

Elizabeth Foote-Smith. 2006. $13.95 (paper). 160 pages. Discusses opportunities in the print media, broadcasting, advertising or publishing. Business writing, public relations, and technical writing are among the careers covered. Contains bibliography and illustrations.

10706 ■ The Public Relations Handbook
Taylor & Francis Group
711 3rd Ave., 8th Fl.
New York, NY 10017
Ph: (212)216-7800
Fax: (212)563-2269
URL: http://www.taylorandfrancis.com

Alison Theaker. 2011. $44.95. 496 pages. 4th edition. Details the theories and practices of the public relations industry. Covers history and development of public relations, explores its ethical issues and its relationship to politics, and provides advice on training and entry into the profession. Includes examples of promotional strategies and campaigns from businesses and organizations, plus a chapter on corporate social responsibility.

10707 ■ The SAGE Handbook of Public Relations
Sage Publications
2455 Teller Rd.
Thousand Oaks, CA 91320
Fax: 800-583-2665
Fr: 800-818-7243
E-mail: journals@sagepub.com
URL: http://www.sagepub.com

Robert L. Heath. 2010. $150.00 (hardcover). 792 pages. Covers academic research, theory and application, and professional practice of public relations.

EMPLOYMENT AGENCIES AND SEARCH FIRMS

10708 ■ Chaloner Associates
36 Milford St.
Boston, MA 02118
Ph: (617)451-5170
Fax: (617)451-8160
E-mail: info@chaloner.com
URL: http://www.chaloner.com

Executive search firm.

10709 ■ The Esquire Staffing Group Ltd.
1 S Wacker Dr., Ste. 1616
Chicago, IL 60606-4616
Ph: (312)795-4300
URL: http://www.esquirestaffing.com

Employment agency. Fills permanent as well as temporary openings.

10710 ■ Howard-Sloan Professional Search Inc.
261 Madison Ave.
New York, NY 10016
Ph: (212)704-0444
Fr: 800-221-1326
E-mail: info@howardsloan.com
URL: http://www.howardsloan.com

Executive search firm.

ONLINE JOB SOURCES AND SERVICES

10711 ■ New Public Relations Jobs
URL: http://www.newpublicrelationsjobs.com
Description: Provides an online listing of companies with available public relations jobs in all specialties.

10712 ■ PRJobForce.com
URL: http://www.prjobforce.com

Description: Provides resources for public relations professionals including job listings for careers in public relations as well as resume posting.

10713 ■ PublicRelationsSpecialist.com
URL: http://www.publicrelationsspecialist.com

Description: Features job opportunities for public relations specialists.

OTHER SOURCES

10714 ■ ABA Marketing Network (ABAMN)
1120 Connecticut Ave. NW
Washington, DC 20036
Ph: (202)663-5269
Fax: (202)828-5053
Fr: 800-BAN-KERS
E-mail: marketingnetwork@aba.com
URL: http://www.aba.com/MarketingNetwork/default.htm

Description: Marketing and public relations executives for commercial and savings banks, credit unions, and savings and loans associations, and related groups such as advertising agencies and research firms. Provides marketing education, information, and services to the financial services industry. Conducts research; cosponsors summer sessions of fundamentals and advanced courses in marketing at the University of Colorado at Boulder; compiles statistics.

10715 ■ Agricultural Relations Council (ARC)
PO Box 156
New Prague, MN 56071
Ph: (952)758-5811
Fax: (952)758-5813
E-mail: arc@gardnerandgardnercommunications.com
URL: http://www.agrelationscouncil.org

Description: Professional society of agricultural public relations executives employed by private business firms, associations, publications, and government agencies. Operates placement service.

10716 ■ American Marketing Association (AMA)
311 S Wacker Dr., Ste. 5800
Chicago, IL 60606
Ph: (312)542-9000
Fax: (312)542-9001
Fr: 800-262-1150
E-mail: info@ama.org
URL: http://www.marketingpower.com

Description: Serves as a professional society of marketing and market research executives, sales and promotion managers, advertising specialists, academics, and others interested in marketing. Fosters research; sponsors seminars, conferences, and student marketing clubs; provides educational placement service and doctoral consortium.

10717 ■ Association for Women in Communications (AWC)
3337 Duke St.
Alexandria, VA 22314
Ph: (703)370-7436
Fax: (703)342-4311
E-mail: info@womcom.org
URL: http://www.womcom.org

Description: Professional association of journalism and communications.

10718 ■ Council of Public Relations Firms
317 Madison Ave., Ste. 2320
New York, NY 10017
Ph: (212)922-1350
Fax: (212)922-1348
Fr: 877-773-4767
E-mail: kcripps@prfirms.org
URL: http://prfirms.org

Description: Represents the interests of public relations firms. Advances the role of public relations firms in corporate strategy, business performance, and social education. Provides information and sets the standards for the industry.

10719 ■ Entertainment Publicists Professional Society (EPPS)
PO Box 5841
Beverly Hills, CA 90209-5841
Ph: (310)496-4449
Fax: (310)452-9005
Fr: 888-399-3777
E-mail: info@eppsonline.org
URL: http://eppsonline.org

Description: Provides members with a regular forum for networking. Offers regular and special programs that explore current issues, the latest advancements and future directions of the profession. Serves as professional resource for the entertainment industry and academic institutions in matters involving entertainment public relations. Seeks to provide members with the opportunity to exchange information concerning permanent and freelance employment. Encourages the highest professional standards.

10720 ■ Media Alliance (MA)
1904 Franklin St., Ste. 500
Oakland, CA 94612
Ph: (510)832-9000
Fax: (510)238-8557
E-mail: information@media-alliance.org
URL: http://www.media-alliance.org

Description: Writers, photographers, editors, broadcast workers, public relations practitioners, videographers, filmmakers, commercial artists and other media workers and aspiring media workers. Supports free press and independent, alternative journalism that services progressive politics and social justice.

10721 ■ National Black Public Relations Society
14636 Runnymede St.
Van Nuys, CA 91405
Fax: 888-976-0005
Fr: 888-976-0005
URL: http://www.nbprs.org

Description: Serves the interests of black professionals in public relations, media relations, corporate communications, investor relations, government affairs, community relations, and related fields. Addresses the needs of members through programs and partnerships. Offers peer-to-peer support, mentorship, networking, job opportunities, internships, and career advancement.

10722 ■ National School Public Relations Association (NSPRA)
15948 Derwood Rd.
Rockville, MD 20855-2123
Ph: (301)519-0496
Fax: (301)519-0494
E-mail: info@nspra.org
URL: http://www.nspra.org

Description: Represents school system public relations directors, school administrators, and others interested in furthering public understanding of the public schools. Has adopted standards for public relations professionals and programs and an accreditation program.

10723 ■ PROMAXBDA
1522e Cloverfield Blvd.
Santa Monica, CA 90404
Ph: (310)788-7600
Fax: (310)788-7616
E-mail: jbv@promaxbda.org
URL: http://www.promaxbda.org

Description: Advertising, public relations, and promotion managers of cable, radio, and television stations, systems and networks; syndicators. Seeks to: advance the role and increase the effectiveness of promotion and marketing within the industry, related industries, and educational communities. Conducts workshops and weekly fax service for members. Operates employment service. Maintains speakers' bureau, hall of fame, and resource center with print, audio, and visual materials.

10724 ■ Public Relations Society of America (PRSA)
33 Maiden Ln., 11th Fl.
New York, NY 10038-5150
Ph: (212)460-1400
Fax: (212)995-0757
E-mail: william.murray@prsa.org
URL: http://www.prsa.org

Description: Professional society of public relations practitioners in business and industry, counseling firms, government, associations, hospitals, schools, and nonprofit organizations. Conducts professional development programs. Maintains a Professional Resource Center. Offers accreditation program.

SOURCES OF HELP-WANTED ADS

10725 ■ Benchmarking Purchasing
American Purchasing Society
8 E Galena Blvd., Ste. 203
Aurora, IL 60506
Ph: (630)859-0250
Fax: (630)859-0270
URL: http://www.american-purchasing.com
Annual. Professional journal covering issues in purchasing.

10726 ■ Electronic Business
Reed Business Information
360 Park Ave. S
New York, NY 10010-1710
Ph: (646)746-6400
URL: http://www.edn.com/
index.asp?layout=businessCenter
Monthly. Magazine for purchasing managers and buyers of electronic components and materials used in end product manufacture.

10727 ■ NAEP Bulletin
National Association of Educational Procurement
5523 Research Park Dr., Ste. 340
Baltimore, MD 21228
Ph: (443)543-5540
Fax: (443)543-5550
E-mail: mkendig@naepnet.org
URL: http://www.naepnet.org
Description: Monthly, except May and April. Features information on institutional purchasing and news of the Association. Recurring features include a calendar of events, reports of meetings, news of educational opportunities, job listings, book reviews, notices of publications available, and columns titled Professional Perspective, Market Index, and Roamin' With Yeoman.

10728 ■ Professional Purchasing
American Purchasing Society
8 E Galena Blvd., Ste. 203
Aurora, IL 60506
Ph: (630)859-0250
Fax: (630)859-0270
E-mail: propurch@mgci.com
URL: http://www.american-purchasing.com/
default.asp?t=pptext
Description: Monthly. Provides information on policies, procedures, methods, and prices of purchasing. Features price indexes. Recurring features include letters to the editor, news of research, reports of meetings, news of educational opportunities, job listings, book reviews, and notices of publications available.

10729 ■ Purchasing Magazine
Reed Business Information
360 Park Ave. S
New York, NY 10010-1710

Ph: (646)746-6400
E-mail: info.purchasing@reedbusiness.com
URL: http://www.purchasing.com
Monthly. Free. Magazine for buying professionals.

HANDBOOKS AND MANUALS

**10730 ■ Opportunities in Hospital
Administration Careers**
The McGraw-Hill Companies
PO Box 182604
Columbus, OH 43272
Fax: (614)759-3749
Fr: 877-883-5524
E-mail: customer.service@mcgraw-hill.com
URL: http://www.mhprofessional.com/
product.php?isbn=0071467688
I. Donald Snook. 2006. $13.95. 160 pages. Discusses opportunities for administrators in a variety of management settings: hospital, department, clinic, group practice, HMO, mental health, and extended care facilities.

EMPLOYMENT AGENCIES AND SEARCH FIRMS

10731 ■ The Aspire Group
711 Boylston St.
Boston, MA 02116-2616
Fax: (617)500-7284
Fr: 800-487-2967
URL: http://www.bmanet.com/Aspire/index.html
Employment agency.

10732 ■ The Esquire Staffing Group Ltd.
1 S Wacker Dr., Ste. 1616
Chicago, IL 60606-4616
Ph: (312)795-4300
URL: http://www.esquirestaffing.com
Employment agency. Fills permanent as well as temporary openings.

10733 ■ KForce
Fr: 877-4KF-ORCE
URL: http://www.kforce.com
Executive search firm. More than 41 locations throughout the United States and two in the Philippines.

10734 ■ Rocky Mountain Recruiters, Inc.
1776 S Jackson St., Ste. 320
Denver, CO 80210
Ph: (303)296-2000
E-mail: resumes@rmrecruiters.com
URL: http://www.rmrecruiters.com
Accounting, financial, and executive search firm.

10735 ■ Wellington Executive Search
3162 Johnson Ferry Rd., Ste. 260
Marietta, GA 30062
Ph: (770)645-5799
Fax: (678)278-0928
E-mail: jobs@wellingtonsearch.com
URL: http://www.wellingtonsearch.com
Serves as an executive search firm covering sales representative, research and development, food scientists, and purchasing managers.

ONLINE JOB SOURCES AND SERVICES

10736 ■ Purchasing Agent Jobs
URL: http://www.purchasingagentjobs.org
Description: Serves as a resource for purchasing agent jobs and related procurement careers.

10737 ■ PurchasingCrossing.com
URL: http://www.purchasingcrossing.com
Description: Lists purchasing jobs from Fortune 500 and Fortune 1,000 companies.

TRADESHOWS

**10738 ■ International Supply Management
Conference and Educational Exhibit**
International Supply Management
PO Box 22160
Tempe, AZ 85285-2160
Ph: (480)752-6276
Fax: (480)752-7890
Fr: 800-888-6276
URL: http://www.ism.ws/education/
content.cfm?ItemNumber=7175&navItemNumber=5579
Annual. Offers selection of general supply management topics and workshops on new trends and innovations.

OTHER SOURCES

10739 ■ American Purchasing Society (APS)
PO Box 256
Aurora, IL 60506
Ph: (630)859-0250
Fax: (630)859-0270
E-mail: propurch@propurch.com
URL: http://www.american-purchasing.com
Description: Seeks to certify qualified purchasing personnel. Maintains speakers' bureau and placement service. Conducts research programs; compiles statistics including salary surveys. Provides consulting service for purchasing, materials management, and marketing. Conducts seminars and online courses.

10740 ■ Institute for Supply Management (ISM)
PO Box 22160
Tempe, AZ 85285-2160
Ph: (480)752-6276
Fax: (480)752-7890
Fr: 800-888-6276
E-mail: sidney.johnson@delphi.com
URL: http://www.ism.ws

Description: Represents industrial, commercial and utility firms; educational institutions and government agencies. Disseminates information on procurement. Works to develop more efficient supply management methods. Conducts program for certification as a supply manager. Cosponsors executive purchasing management institutes at Michigan State University and Arizona State University. Provides in-company training. Maintains speakers' bureau and reference service.

10741 ■ National Contract Management Association (NCMA)
21740 Beaumeade Cir., Ste. 125
Ashburn, VA 20147
Ph: (571)382-0082
Fax: (703)448-0939
Fr: 800-344-8096
E-mail: couture@ncmahq.org
URL: http://www.ncmahq.org

Description: Professional individuals concerned with administration, procurement, acquisition, negotiation and management of contracts and subcontracts. Works for the education, improvement and professional development of members and nonmembers through national and chapter programs, symposia and educational materials. Offers certification in Contract Management (CPCM, CFCM, and CCCM) designations as well as a credential program. Operates speakers' bureau.

10742 ■ National Institute of Governmental Purchasing (NIGP)
151 Spring St.
Herndon, VA 20170
Ph: (703)736-8900
Fax: (703)736-2818
Fr: 800-FOR-NIGP
E-mail: membershipinfo@nigp.org
URL: http://www.nigp.org

Description: Federal, state, provincial, county, and local government buying agencies; hospital, school, prison, and public utility purchasing agencies in the U.S. and Canada. Also provides services to the International procurement community. Develops standards and specifications for governmental buying; promotes uniform purchasing laws and procedures; conducts specialized education and research programs. Administers certification program for the Universal Public Purchasing Certification Council (UPPCC) for Certified Professional Public Buyer (CPPB) and Certified Public Purchasing Officer (CPPO); offers audit consulting services and cost saving programs and tools for governmental agencies, including product commodity code to online specifications library. Maintains speakers' bureau; compiles statistics, web based products and services.

10743 ■ National Management Association (NMA)
2210 Arbor Blvd.
Dayton, OH 45439
Ph: (937)294-0421
Fax: (937)294-2374
E-mail: nma@nma1.org
URL: http://www.nma1.org

Description: Business and industrial management personnel; membership comes from supervisory level, with the remainder from middle management and above. Seeks to develop and recognize management as a profession and to promote the free enterprise system. Prepares chapter programs on basic management, management policy and practice, communications, human behavior, industrial relations, economics, political education, and liberal education. Maintains speakers' bureau and hall of fame. Maintains educational, charitable, and research programs. Sponsors charitable programs.

10744 ■ Next Level Purchasing
PO Box 1360
Moon Township, PA 15108
Ph: (412)294-1990
Fax: (412)294-1992
E-mail: help@nextlevelpurchasing.com
URL: http://www.nextlevelpurchasing.com

Description: Helps purchasing professionals achieve rewarding careers. Offers purchasing professionals an online program to earn a Senior Professional in Supply Management certification.

ONLINE JOB SOURCES AND SERVICES

10745 ■ JCCWorks.com
URL: http://www.jccworks.com

Description: Works as a resource for Jewish job search. Allows users to browse Jewish community center jobs and careers across the United States and Canada. Offers connections to Jewish job counselors for consultations.

10746 ■ JewishJobs.com
URL: http://www.jewishjobs.com

Description: Serves as a clearinghouse for Jewish communal jobs. Offers links to positions with Jewish organizations and an option for employers to list jobs.

TRADESHOWS

10747 ■ National Association of Jewish Chaplains Conference
National Association of Jewish Chaplains
901 Rte. 10
Whippany, NJ 07981-1156
Ph: (973)929-3168
E-mail: info@najc.org
URL: http://www.najc.org

Annual. Promotes social and educational opportunities for Jewish chaplains.

OTHER SOURCES

10748 ■ Central Conference of American Rabbis (CCAR)
355 Lexington Ave.
New York, NY 10017
Ph: (212)972-3636
Fax: (212)692-0819
E-mail: info@ccarnet.org
URL: http://ccarnet.org

Description: National organization of Reform rabbis. Offers placement service; compiles statistics. Maintains 38 committees.

10749 ■ JCC Association
520 8th Ave.
New York, NY 10018
Ph: (212)532-4949
Fax: (212)481-4174
E-mail: info@jcca.org
URL: http://www.jcca.org

Description: Promotes the Jewish community center movement; aims to provide educational, cultural, social, Jewish identity building and recreational programs; fosters connections between North American Jews and Israel and world Jewry. Jewish military personnel and their dependents in the U.S. Armed Forces and Veterans Administration Hospitals through the JWB Jewish Chaplains Council. Operates research center; compiles statistics; maintains placement services for professional Jewish community center and YM and YWHA workers. Jewish military personnel and their dependents in the U.S. Armed Forces and Veterans Administration Hospitals through the JWB Jewish Chaplains Council. Operates research center; compiles statistics; maintains placement services for professional Jewish community center and YM andYWHA workers

10750 ■ Jewish Education Service of North America (JESNA)
318 W 39th St., 5th Fl.
New York, NY 10018
Ph: (212)284-6950
Fax: (212)284-6951
E-mail: info@jesna.org
URL: http://www.jesna.org

Description: Widely recognized leader in the areas of research and program evaluation, organizational change and innovative program design and dissemination. Operates the Mandell J. Berman Jewish Heritage Center for Research and Evaluation. Supports the Covenant Foundation, a joint venture with the Crown Family, which makes awards and grants for creativity in Jewish education.

10751 ■ Jewish Educators Assembly (JEA)
PO Box 413
Cedarhurst, NY 11516
Ph: (516)569-2537
Fax: (516)295-9039
E-mail: jewisheducators@jewisheducators.org
URL: http://www.jewisheducators.org

Description: Educational and supervisory personnel serving Jewish educational institutions. Seeks to: advance the development of Jewish education in the congregation on all levels in consonance with the philosophy of the Conservative Movement; cooperate with the United Synagogue of America Commission on Jewish Education as the policy-making body of the educational enterprise; join in cooperative effort with other Jewish educational institutions and organizations; establish and maintain professional standards for Jewish educators; serve as a forum for the exchange of ideas; promote the values of Jewish education as a basis for the creative continuity of the Jewish people. Maintains placement service and speaker's bureau.

10752 ■ Jewish Reconstructionist Federation (JRF)
101 Greenwood Ave., Ste. 430
Jenkintown, PA 19046
Ph: (215)885-5601
Fax: (215)885-5603
E-mail: csheingold@jrf.org
URL: http://jrf.org

Description: Federation of synagogues and fellowships committed to the philosophy and program of the Jewish Reconstructionist Movement. Maintains placement service and consulting services. Organize services to affiliates.

10753 ■ National Association of Jewish Chaplains
901 Rte. 10
Whippany, NJ 07981-1156
Ph: (973)929-3168
E-mail: info@najc.org
URL: http://www.najc.org

Description: Comprised of rabbis, cantors, and other Jewish professionals. Strives to enhance the kedusha of Jewish Chaplains in order for them to provide quality Jewish, religious, and spiritual care. Sets certification standards and certifies qualified Jewish chaplains. Acts as an advocate for Jewish chaplains and Jewish chaplaincy.

10754 ■ National Association of Temple Administrators (NATA)
PO Box 936
Ridgefield, WA 98642
Ph: (360)887-0464
Fax: (866)767-3791
Fr: 800-966-NATA
E-mail: nataoffice@natanet.org
URL: http://natanet.org

Description: Full-time administrators of Jewish synagogues affiliated with the Union of American Hebrew Congregations. Conducts educational programs; has established code of standards and ethics. Offers congregational survey service and compiles synagogue research reports and salary reports. Conducts placement service and maintains speakers' bureau.

10755 ■ National Association of Temple Educators (NATE)
633 3rd Ave.
New York, NY 10017-6778
Ph: (212)452-6510
Fax: (212)452-6512
E-mail: sschickler@natenet.org
URL: http://www.natenet.org

Description: Directors of education in Reform Jewish religious schools, principals, heads of departments, supervisors, educational consultants, students, and authors. Purposes are to: assist in the growth and development of Jewish religious education consistent with the aims of Reform Judaism; stimulate communal interest in Jewish religious education; represent and encourage the profession of temple educator. Conducts surveys on personnel practices, confirmation practices, religious school organization and administration, curricular practices, and other aspects of religious education. Sponsors institutes for principals and educational directors; maintains placement service.

10756 ■ National Council of Young Israel (NCYI)
111 John St., Ste. 450
New York, NY 10038

Ph: (212)929-1525
Fax: (212)727-9526
E-mail: ncyi@youngisrael.org
URL: http://www.youngisrael.org

Description: Families of traditional Jewish faith in the U.S., Canada, and Israel. Seeks "to perpetuate traditional Judaism; instill a love for Americanism and the principles of democracy; bring Jewish youth back to the synagogue; educate the youth and adults in the heritage and culture of the Jewish people". Benevolent Association in the New York City area; conducts programs nationwide for adults and youths. Sponsors Institute for Jewish Studies, which provides specialized programs in Jewish education. The Institute maintains the Torah Tape Library of cassette tapes on Jewish philosophy, law, the Talmud, and related topics. Sponsors children's services, charitable program, and competitions. Maintains speakers' bureau; compiles statistics.

10757 ■ Rabbinical Assembly (RA)
3080 Broadway
New York, NY 10027
Ph: (212)280-6000
Fax: (212)749-9166
E-mail: info@rabbinicalassembly.org
URL: http://www.rabbinicalassembly.org

Description: Seeks to be a creative force shaping the ideology, programs and practices of the Conservative movement; committed to building and strengthening the totality of Jewish life. Publishes learned textbooks, prayerbooks, and works of Jewish interest; administers the work of the Committee on Jewish Law and Standards for the Conservative Movement. Serves the professional and personal needs of members through publications, conferences, and benefit programs; coordinates the Joint Placement Commission of the Conservative movement.

10758 ■ Schechter Day School Network
820 2nd Ave.
New York, NY 10017
Ph: (212)533-7800
E-mail: cohen@uscj.org
URL: http://www.ssdsa.org

Description: A division of the United Synagogue of Conservative Judaism Commission on Jewish Education. Jewish elementary day schools and high schools with a total of over 21,500 students. Named for Solomon Schecher (1850-1915), scholar of Talmud and rabbinical literature at Cambridge and founder of the United Synagogue of America and the Jewish Theological Seminary. Provides visitations and consultations regarding education, governance and administration; publication of advisories and position papers, biennial conferences for lay leaders, annual conferences of the principals council, Shibboley Schechter newsletter, listserves for presidents, School heads, Business managers, and development directors. Also provides dissemination of demographics and statistics, chartering and accreditation of schools, seminars and board training for lay leaders, Schechter website, SHAR"R, 7th and 8th grade trips to Israel, placement service, MaToK-TaNaKH curriculum development project for Solomon Schecter Day schools, residency fellowship program to prepare professional leadership (SREL) and a listing of consultants.

10759 ■ Young Israel Council of Rabbis (YICR)
National Council of Young Israel
111 John St., Ste. 450
New York, NY 10038
Ph: (212)929-1525
Fax: (212)727-9526
E-mail: ncyi@youngisrael.org
URL: http://www.youngisrael.org/content/yicr.cfm

Description: Rabbis serving 200 Young Israel congregations in the U.S., Canada, and Israel. Encourages study and observance of Judaism and provides spiritual leadership to the Young Israel Movement. Adjudicates issues relating to the Young Israel Synagogues. Maintains speakers' bureau; conducts research and educational programs; provides placement service. Is concerned with welfare of rabbis.

SOURCES OF HELP-WANTED ADS

10760 ■ AFTRA Magazine
American Federation of Television and Radio Artists
260 Madison Ave.
New York, NY 10016-2401
Ph: (212)532-0800
Fax: (212)532-2242
URL: http://www.aftra.org/

Quarterly. $3.00/year for individuals. Membership magazine covering issues in television and radio broadcasting.

10761 ■ B-Stats
SNL Kagan
40 Ragsdale Dr., Ste. 250
Monterey, CA 93940
Ph: (831)624-1536
Fax: (831)625-3225
Fr: (866)296-3743
E-mail: sales@snl.com
URL: http://www.snl.com/Sectors/Media/Default.aspx

Description: Monthly. Discusses the sale of broadcast stations in the U.S., covering both AM and FM radio and television stations. Provides financial data on station transfers and contains five-year projections of revenues for all broadcast markets. Also available via e-mail and fax.

10762 ■ Broadcasting & Cable
Reed Business Information (New York, New York)
360 Park Ave. S
New York, NY 10010
Ph: (646)746-6400
Fax: (646)746-7431
Fr: 800-446-6551
URL: http://www.reedbusiness.com

$199.00/year for individuals; $249.99/year for Canada; $360.99/year for other countries. News magazine covering The Fifth Estate (radio, TV, cable, and satellite), and the regulatory commissions involved.

10763 ■ Current
Routledge
711 3 Ave., 8 Fl.
New York, NY 10016
Ph: (212)216-7800
Fax: (212)563-2269
Fr: 800-634-7064
URL: http://www.tandf.co.uk/journals/titles/
00113131.asp

$50.00/year for individuals, print only; $141.00/year for institutions, print & online. Journal that reprints articles on education, politics, and other social issues.

10764 ■ Daily Variety
Reed Business Information
360 Park Ave. S
New York, NY 10010-1710
Ph: (646)746-7764

Fax: (646)746-7583
URL: http://www.reedbusiness.com/
index.asp?layout=theListProfile&

Daily. $329.99/year for individuals. Global entertainment newspaper (tabloid).

10765 ■ Editor & Publisher
Editor & Publisher Magazine
17782 Cowan, Ste. A
Irvine, CA 92614
Ph: (949)660-6150
Fax: (949)660-6172
URL: http://www.editorandpublisher.com/

Weekly (Mon.). $65.00/year for individuals, print and online; $125.00/year for two years, print and online; $85.00/year for other countries; $49.00/year for individuals, digital only. Magazine focusing on newspaper journalism, advertising, printing equipment and interactive services.

10766 ■ Feminist Media Studies
Routledge Journals
270 Madison Ave.
New York, NY 10016-0601
Ph: (212)216-7800
Fax: (212)563-2269
URL: http://www.tandf.co.uk/journals/titles/
14680777.asp

Quarterly. $700.00/year for institutions, print + online; $129.00/year for individuals, print only; $630.00/year for institutions, online only. Journal covering media and communication studies.

10767 ■ Insiders Sportsletter
American Sportscasters Association Inc.
225 Broadway, Ste. 2030
New York, NY 10007
Ph: (212)227-8080
Fax: (212)571-0556
E-mail: inquiry@americansportscastersonline.com
URL: http://www.americansportscastersonline.com

Description: Quarterly. Highlights Association programs promoting excellence and recognition in the field of sportscasting. Carries profiles of award winners and interviews with sportscasting professionals. Recurring features include news of research, employment opportunities, and a calendar of events.

10768 ■ NAB RadioWeek
National Association of Broadcasters
1771 N St., NW
Washington, DC 20036
Ph: (202)429-5300
Fr: 800-342-2460
E-mail: nab@nab.org
URL: http://www.nab.org

Description: Weekly. Covers radio broadcasting from legislative, regulatory, political, technical, management, and sales/marketing perspectives. Contains pertinent industry news, promotions of NAB conferences, product announcements, and coverage of

awards competitions. Disseminated via broadcast fax only; not mailed. For NAB members only.

10769 ■ NAB World
National Association of Broadcasters
1771 N St., NW
Washington, DC 20036
Ph: (202)429-5300
Fax: (202)775-2145
Fr: 800-342-2460
E-mail: nab@nab.org
URL: http://www.nab.org

Description: Monthly. Tracks the domestic and international broadcasting industry (radio and television) with emphasis on public policy, and engineering/technology issues. Features pertinent industry news and information on NAB conferences, products, and services.

10770 ■ Public Broadcasting Report
Warren Communications News
2115 Ward Ct., NW
Washington, DC 20037
Ph: (202)872-9202
Fax: (202)318-8350
Fr: 800-771-9202
E-mail: newsroom@warren-news.com
URL: http://www.warren-news.com

Description: Biweekly. Covers funding, programming, and regulations involving public television and radio. Monitors activities at National Public Radio (NPR), the Public Broadcasting System (PBS), the Federal Communications Commission (FCC), the National Telecommunications and Information Administration (NTIA), and the Corporation for Public Broadcasting (CPB).

10771 ■ QST
Amateur Radio Relay League Inc.
225 Main St.
Newington, CT 06111-1400
Ph: (860)594-0200
Fax: (860)594-0259
Fr: 888-277-5289
E-mail: qst@arrl.org
URL: http://www.arrl.org/qst/

Monthly. $34.00/year for individuals. Amateur radio magazine.

10772 ■ Radio Journal
M Street Publications
365 Union St.
Littleton, NH 03561
E-mail: info@insideradio.com
URL: http://www.insideradio.com

Description: Weekly. Reports on radio station regulatory applications, actions, and filings; construction permit activity; format changes; and other U.S. and Canadian radio news of interest to the broadcast industry. Covers all radio markets, large and small.

10773 ■ Radio and Records
Nielsen Business Media
770 Broadway
New York, NY 10003-9595
E-mail: nbb@omeda.com
URL: http://www.radioandrecords.com

Weekly. $24.95/year for individuals, monthly, print &
online; $299.00/year for individuals, print & online;
$19.95/year for individuals, monthly, online. Magazine
covering every format of music radio, regulatory
developments, news radio, talk radio, and satellite
radio.

10774 ■ Small Market Radio Newsletter
Jay Mitchell Associates
4 Ventana
Aliso Viejo, CA 92656-6062
Ph: (949)533-4912
Fax: (949)666-5045
Fr: 800-JAY-RADIO
E-mail: mitchell@jaymitchell.com
URL: http://www.jaymitchell.com/newsletter.htm

Description: Weekly. Provides news and information
for the radio industry and small market owners and
managers. Recurring features include letters to the
editor, interviews, news of research, a calendar of
events, book reviews, and columns titled FCC Actions, Editorials, and Promotions Page.

10775 ■ SMPTE Motion Imaging Journal
Society of Motion Picture and Television Engineers
3 Barker Ave., 5th Fl.
White Plains, NY 10601
Ph: (914)761-1100
Fax: (914)761-3115
URL: http://www.smpte.org

Monthly. $130.00/year for individuals. Peer-reviewed
journal containing articles pertaining to new developments in motion picture and television technology;
standards and recommended practices; general news
of the industry.

10776 ■ TelevisionWeek
Crain Communications Inc. (Detroit, Michigan)
1155 Gratiot Ave.
Detroit, MI 48207-2997
Ph: (313)446-6000
Fax: (313)567-7681
URL: http://www.tvweek.com/

Weekly. $119.00/year for individuals; $171.00/year
for Canada, incl. GST; $309.00/year for other coun-
tries, airmail. Newspaper covering management,
programming, cable and trends in the television and
the media industry.

10777 ■ Weatherwise
Routledge
711 3 Ave., 8 Fl.
New York, NY 10016
Ph: (212)216-7800
Fax: (212)563-2269
Fr: 800-634-7064
URL: http://www.weatherwise.org/

Bimonthly. $48.00/year for individuals, print and on-
line; $162.00/year for institutions, print and online;
$162.00/year for institutions, print only. Popular
weather magazine for students, teachers, and
professionals.

EMPLOYER DIRECTORIES AND NETWORKING LISTS

10778 ■ ADWEEK Marketer's Guide to Media
ADWEEK Magazines
770 Broadway, 7th Fl.
New York, NY 10003-9595
URL: http://www.adweek.com

Annual, April. Covers: Television, radio, cable,
magazines, newspapers, out-of-home, interactive,
Hispanic, and promotion media. Entries include: Current rates, audience demographics, industry trends,

market data for all areas of media. Arrangement:
Classified by type of media.

10779 ■ Bacon's Metro California Media
Cision US Inc.
332 S Michigan Ave., Ste. 900
Chicago, IL 60604
Ph: (312)363-9793
Fax: (312)922-9387
Fr: (866)639-5087
URL: http://us.cision.com/

Annual, Latest edition 2012. $445.00 for individuals.
Covers: Consumer media in the state of California
including newspapers, radio television & cable stations, magazines, and broadcast programs, ethnic
media, news services & syndicates. Entries include:
Name, address, phone, names of editors and creative
staff, with titles or indication of assignments. Arrangement: Geographical, classified by type of outlet.
Indexes: Alphabetical.

10780 ■ Bacon's Radio/TV/Cable Directory, Volume 1
Cision US Inc.
332 S Michigan Ave., Ste. 900
Chicago, IL 60604
Ph: (312)363-9793
Fax: (312)922-9387
Fr: (866)639-5087
URL: http://us.cision.com

Annual, Latest edition 2012. $650.00 for individuals.
Covers: over 13,500 radio and television stations,
including college radio and public television stations,
and cable companies. Entries include: For radio and
television stations—Call letters, address, phone,
names and titles of key personnel, programs, times
broadcast, name of contact, network affiliation,
frequency or channel number, target audience data.
For cable companies—Name, address, phone,
description of activities. Arrangement: Geographical.

10781 ■ BIA's Television Yearbook
BIA Financial Network Inc.
15120 Enterprise Ct., Ste. 100
Chantilly, VA 20151
Ph: (703)818-2425
Fax: (703)803-3299
Fr: 800-331-5086
E-mail: sales@bia.com
URL: http://www.bia.com

Annual, Latest edition 2011. $630.00 for individuals.
Covers: U.S. Television markets and their inclusive
stations, television equipment manufacturers, and
related service providers and trade associations.
Entries include: For stations—Call letters, address;
name and phone of general manager, owner, and
other key personnel; technical attributes, rep firm,
network affiliation, last acquisition date and price and
ratings for total day and prime time. For others—
Company or organization name, address, phone,
description. Arrangement: Classified by market.
Indexes: Numerical by market rank; call letters.

10782 ■ Bowker's News Media Directory
R.R. Bowker L.L.C.
630 Central Ave.
New Providence, NJ 07974
Ph: (908)286-1090
Fr: 888-269-5372
E-mail: wpn@bowker.com
URL: http://www.bowker.com

Annual, Latest edition 2009. $668.00 for individuals.
Covers: In three separate volumes, syndicates and
over 8,500 daily and weekly newspapers; 1,750
newsletters; over 16,800 radio and television stations; 5,500 magazines; 1,000 internal publications.
Entries include: Name of publication or station, address, phone, fax, e-mail and URL, names of executives, editors, writers, etc., as appropriate. Broadcasting and magazine volumes include data on kinds of
material accepted. Technical and mechanical requirements for publications are given. Arrangement:
Magazines are classified by subject; newspapers and
broadcasting stations geographical. Indexes: News-

paper department/editor by interest, metro area,
feature syndicate subject; magazine subject, publication title; television director/personnel by subject,
radio personnel and director by subject.

10783 ■ Broadcasting & Cable Yearbook
R.R. Bowker L.L.C.
630 Central Ave.
New Providence, NJ 07974
Ph: (908)286-1090
Fr: 888-269-5372
URL: http://www.bowker.com

Annual, latest edition 2010. $395.00 for individuals.
Covers: Over 17,000 television and radio stations in
the United States, its territories, and Canada; cable
MSOs and their individual systems; television and
radio networks, broadcast and cable group owners,
station representatives, satellite networks and
services, film companies, advertising agencies,
government agencies, trade associations, schools,
and suppliers of professional and technical services,
including books, serials, and videos; communications
lawyers. Entries include: Company name, address,
phone, fax, names of executives. Station listings
include broadcast power, other operating details. Arrangement: Stations and systems are geographical,
others are alphabetical. Indexes: Alphabetical.

10784 ■ Career Opportunities in Radio
Facts On File Inc.
132 W 31st St., 17th Fl.
New York, NY 10001
Ph: (212)967-8800
Fax: 800-678-3633
Fr: 800-322-8755
URL: http://www.infobasepublishing.com

Published April, 2004. $49.50 for individuals. Covers:
More than 70 jobs, such as on-air personality/disc
jockey, business reporter, sportscaster, advertising
account representative, billing specialist, publicist,
studio engineer, program director, website content
producer, and more.

10785 ■ Careers in Focus—Broadcasting
Facts On File Inc.
132 W 31st St., 17th Fl.
New York, NY 10001
Ph: (212)967-8800
Fax: 800-678-3633
Fr: 800-322-8755
URL: http://factsonfile.infobasepublishing.com

Latest edition 3rd, March 2007. $32.95 for individuals.
Covers: An overview of broadcasting, followed by a
selection of jobs profiled in detail, including the nature
of the job, earnings, prospects for employment, what
kind of training and skills it requires, and sources for
further information.

10786 ■ CPB Public Broadcasting Directory
Corporation for Public Broadcasting
401 9th St. NW
Washington, DC 20004-2129
Ph: (202)879-9600
Fax: (202)879-9699
Fr: 800-272-2190
URL: http://www.cpb.org/stations/isis

Annual. Covers: Public television and radio stations,
national and regional public broadcasting organizations and networks, state government agencies and
commissions, and other related organizations. Entries
include: For radio and television stations—Station
call letters, frequency or channel, address, phone,
licensee name, licensee type, date on air, antenna
height, area covered, names and titles of key
personnel. For organizations—Name, address,
phone, name and title of key personnel. Arrangement: National and regional listings are alphabetical;
state groups and the public radio and television stations are each geographical; other organizations and
agencies are alphabetical. Indexes: Geographical,
personnel, call letter, licensee type (all in separate
indexes for radio and television).

10787 ■ *Discovering Careers for Your Future—Radio & Television*
Facts On File Inc.
132 W 31st St., 17th Fl.
New York, NY 10001
Ph: (212)967-8800
Fax: 800-678-3633
Fr: 800-322-8755
URL: http://factsonfile.infobasepublishing.com

Published 2005. $21.95 for individuals. Covers: Actors, audio recording engineers, disc jockeys, radio and television anchors, reporters, talent agents and scouts, and weather forecasters; links career education to curriculum, helping children investigate the subjects they are interested in, and the careers those subjects might lead to.

10788 ■ *Gebbie Press All-in-One Media Directory*
Gebbie Press Inc.
143 Glford Schoolhouse Rd.
PO Box 1000
New Paltz, NY 12561
Ph: (845)255-7560
Fax: 888-345-2790
URL: http://www.gebbieinc.com/aio.htm

Annual, Latest edition 40th edition, 2011. $175.00 for individuals; $175.00 for individuals; $175.00 for individuals; $175.00 for individuals; $440.00 for individuals; $565.00 for individuals. Covers: 1,453 daily newspapers, 6,202 weekly newspapers, 10,789 radio stations, 1,445 television stations, 268 general-consumer magazines, 430 professional business publications, 3,100 trade magazines, 320 farm publications, list of the Black press and radio, Hispanic press and radio, and a list of news syndicates. Entries include: For periodicals—Name, address, phone, fax, frequency, editor, circulation, readership. For newspapers—Name, address, phone, fax, circulation. For radio and television stations—Call letters, address, phone, format. Arrangement: Classified by type of media.

10789 ■ *International Television and Video Almanac*
Quigley Publishing Company Inc.
64 Wintergreen Ln.
Groton, MA 01450-4129
Ph: (978)448-0272
Fax: (978)448-9325
Fr: 800-231-8239
URL: http://quigleypublishing.com/

Annual, January; latest edition 2011. $235.00 for individuals. Covers: "Who's Who in Motion Pictures and Television and Home Video," television networks, major program producers, major group station owners, cable television companies, distributors, firms serving the television and home video industry, equipment manufacturers, casting agencies, literary agencies, advertising and publicity representatives, television stations, associations, list of feature films produced for television; statistics, industry's year in review, award winners, satellite and wireless cable provider, primetime programming, video producers, distributors, wholesalers. Entries include: Generally, company name, address, phone; manufacturer and service listings may include description of products and services and name of contact; producing, distributing, and station listings include additional detail, and contacts for cable and broadcast networks. Arrangement: Classified by service or activity. Indexes: Full.

10790 ■ *North Carolina News Media Directory*
News Media Directories
PO Box 316
Mount Dora, FL 32757
Ph: (352)589-9020
Fax: (866)586-7020
Fr: 800-749-6399
URL: http://www.newsmediadirectories.net/categorys/28.htm

Annual, Latest edition 2011. $70.00 for individuals;

$145.00 for individuals; $100.00 for individuals. Covers: About 730 newspapers, periodicals, radio and television broadcasting stations, and press services operating in North Carolina. Entries include: Publisher or company name, address, phone, names and titles of key personnel, publication title, call letters, hours of operation, and frequency. Arrangement: Classified by type of media. Indexes: Title, call letters, county index.

10791 ■ *The R & R Directory*
Billboard.biz
PO Box 3595
Northbrook, IL 60065-3595
Ph: (847)559-7531
Fr: 800-658-8372
E-mail: moreinfo@rronline.com
URL: http://www.radioandrecords.com/RRDirectory/Directory_Main.as

Semiannual, Spring and Fall. $75.00. Covers: More than 3,000 radio group owners, equipment manufacturers, jingle producers, TV production houses and spot producers, record companies, representative firms, research companies, consulting firms, media brokers, networks, program suppliers, trade associations, and other organizations involved in the radio and record industry. Entries include: Organization name, address, phone, fax, E-mail, name and title of contacts, branch offices or subsidiary names and locations. Arrangement: Alphabetical; classified by subject. Indexes: Company.

10792 ■ *Radio Advertising Source*
SRDS
1700 Higgins Rd.
Des Plaines, IL 60018-5605
Ph: (847)375-5000
Fax: (847)375-5001
Fr: 800-851-7737
URL: http://www.srds.com

Quarterly, Latest edition 2011. $699.00 for individuals. Covers: Over 10,500 AM and FM stations, networks, syndicators, group owners, and representative firms. Entries include: Call letters, name of owning company, address, phone; names of representatives and station personnel; demonstration detail, station format, signal strength, programming opportunities, special features. Arrangement: Geographical by state, then Arbitron metro and nonmetro area.

10793 ■ *RTNDA Communicator—Directory Issues*
Radio-Television News Directors Association
1025 F St. NW, Ste. 700
Washington, DC 20004
Ph: (202)467-5214
Fax: (202)223-4007
Fr: 800-80R-TNDA
URL: http://www.rtnda.org

Semiannual, January and July. Number of listings: 3,000; membership includes Canada and some foreign countries. Entries include: Member name, address, phone; and name of radio or television station, network, or other news organization with which affiliated. Arrangement: Same information given in alphabetical and geographical arrangements.

10794 ■ *Television & Cable Factbook*
Warren Communications News
2115 Ward Ct. NW
Washington, DC 20037-1209
Ph: (202)872-9200
Fax: (202)318-8350
Fr: 800-771-9202
URL: http://www.warren-news.com/factbook.htm

Annual, Latest edition 2012. $945.00 for individuals; $295.00 for individuals; $195.00 for individuals; $995.00 for individuals. Covers: Commercial and noncommercial television stations and networks, including educational, low-power and instructional TV stations, and translators; United States cable television systems; cable and television group owners; program and service suppliers; and brokerage and financing companies. Entries include: For stations—

Call letters, licensee name and address, studio address and phone; identification of owners, sales and legal representatives and chief station personnel; rates, technical data, map of service area, and Nielsen circulation data. For cable systems—Name, address, basic and pay subscribers, programming and fees, physical plant; names of personnel and ownership. Ownership. Arrangement: Geographical by state, province, city, county, or country. Indexes: Call letters, product/service, name, general subject.

10795 ■ *TV and Cable Source*
SRDS
1700 Higgins Rd.
Des Plaines, IL 60018-5605
Ph: (847)375-5000
Fax: (847)375-5001
Fr: 800-851-7737
URL: http://www.srds.com

Quarterly, Latest edition 2011. $699.00. Covers: All domestic and international commercial television stations and networks; public television stations, cable networks, systems, interconnects, rep firms, and group owners. Includes separate section showing production specifications of stations and systems. Entries include: Call letters, parent company, address, phone, representative, personnel, facilities, special features, programming. Production specifications section shows call letters or system name, address, and preferred specifications for ad copy. Arrangement: Classified by DMA ranking, then by call letters.

10796 ■ *What Can I Do Now—Radio and TV*
Facts On File Inc.
132 W 31st St., 17th Fl.
New York, NY 10001
Ph: (212)967-8800
Fax: 800-678-3633
Fr: 800-322-8755
URL: http://www.infobasepublishing.com

Latest edition 2nd; Published April, 2007. $32.95 for individuals. Covers: Radio producers and disc jockeys, radio and television anchors, reporters and correspondents, and television directors.

HANDBOOKS AND MANUALS

10797 ■ *Career Opportunities in Television and Cable*
Facts On File Inc.
132 W 31st St., 17th Fl.
New York, NY 10001
Fax: 800-678-3633
Fr: 800-322-8755
E-mail: custserv@factsonfile.com
URL: http://factsonfile.infobasepublishing.com

2006. $49.50. Covers job profiles in television and cable industry, followed by the descriptions of the nature of the job, earnings, prospects for employment, what kind of training and skills it requires, and sources of other relevant information.

10798 ■ *Careers in Communications*
The McGraw-Hill Companies
PO Box 182604
Columbus, OH 43272
Fax: (614)759-3749
Fr: 877-883-5524
E-mail: customer.service@mcgraw-hill.com
URL: http://www.mhprofessional.com/product.php?isbn=0071454764

Shonan Noronha. Fourth edition, 2004. $15.95 (paper). 192 pages. Examines the fields of journalism, photography, radio, television, film, public relations, and advertising. Gives concrete details on job locations and how to secure a job. Suggests many resources for job hunting.

10799 ■ *Opportunities in Broadcasting Careers*
The McGraw-Hill Companies
PO Box 182604
Columbus, OH 43272

Fax: (614)759-3749
Fr: 877-883-5524
E-mail: customer.service@mcgraw-hill.com
URL: http://www.mhprofessional.com/
product.php?isbn=0071454578

Elmo I. Ellis. 2004. $13.95. 176 pages. Discusses opportunities and job search techniques in broadcasting, television, and radio. Illustrated.

10800 ■ Opportunities in Writing Careers

The McGraw-Hill Companies
PO Box 182604
Columbus, OH 43272
Fax: (614)759-3749
Fr: 877-883-5524
E-mail: customer.service@mcgraw-hill.com
URL: http://www.mhprofessional.com/
product.php?isbn=0071458727

Elizabeth Foote-Smith. 2006. $13.95 (paper). 160 pages. Discusses opportunities in the print media, broadcasting, advertising or publishing. Business writing, public relations, and technical writing are among the careers covered. Contains bibliography and illustrations.

10801 ■ Starting Your Career in Broadcasting: Working On and Off the Air in Radio and Television

Allworth Press
307 W 36th St., 11th Fl.
New York, NY 10018
Ph: (212)643-6816
Fax: (212)643-6819
URL: http://www.allworth.com

Chris Schneider. 2007. $19.95 (paper). 240 pages. Provides information on how to get into the communications business. Includes chapters on specific on-air and behind-the-scenes jobs, academic programs in broadcasting, what news and program directors seek in job candidates, how an aspiring broadcaster can buy time on the air, weathering the ups and downs of a competitive industry, and how professionals of all kinds can host their own talk shows.

10802 ■ What's Up Dawg: How to Become a Superstar in the Music Business

Hyperion Books
114 Fifth Ave.
New York, NY 10011
Ph: (917)661-2072
Fax: (917)661-6411
Fr: 800-242-7737
URL: http://www.hyperionbooks.com

Randy Jackson and K.C. Baker. 2004. $19.95 (paper). 208 pages.

EMPLOYMENT AGENCIES AND SEARCH FIRMS

10803 ■ Talent Dynamics

600 E Las Colinas Blvd., Ste. 100
Irving, TX 75039
Ph: (214)640-3139
Fax: (214)951-9610
E-mail: connell@talentdynamics.com
URL: http://www.talentdynamics.com

Description: Provides media recruitment and placement services. Features an online talent library, media appearance consultation and TV jobs.

ONLINE JOB SOURCES AND SERVICES

10804 ■ JournalismJobs.com

Ph: (510)653-1521
E-mail: info@journalismjobs.com
URL: http://www.journalismjobs.com

Description: Career-related site for journalists and other media professionals. Seekers can search for jobs, post a resume online, and manage the search

online with the Job Seeker Folder feature. They also can receive free job announcements by e-mail.

10805 ■ Media-Match.com

URL: http://www.media-match.com/usa

Description: Serves as an online database of TV and film professionals' resumes and availabilities. Provides an up-to-date television production jobs board and film production jobs board for new openings in the film and TV production business across the United States.

10806 ■ TVandRadioJobs.com

URL: http://tvandradiojobs.com/cgi-bin/classifieds/
classifieds.cgi

Description: Provides listings of jobs available in the broadcasting industry. Focuses on television and radio employment opportunities.

TRADESHOWS

10807 ■ NAB Show

National Association of Broadcasters
1771 N. St., N.W.
Washington, DC 20036
Ph: (202)429-5300
Fax: (202)429-4199
Fr: 800-342-2460
E-mail: nab@nab.org
URL: http://www.nab.org

Annual. Primary Exhibits: Radio and television broadcasting equipment, supplies, and services; supplies and services for production, post-production, computing, multimedia, telecommunications and corporate communications. Dates and Locations: 2012 Apr 14-19; Las Vegas, NV; Las Vegas Convention Center.

10808 ■ National Federation of Press Women Conference

National Federation of Press Women
PO Box 5556
Arlington, VA 22205
Fax: (703)237-9808
Fr: 800-780-2715
E-mail: presswomen@aol.com
URL: http://www.nfpw.org

Annual. Features speakers as well as other activities, workshops, resources, and networking opportunities.

10809 ■ NATPE Annual Conference

National Association Television Program Executives
NATPE
5757 Wilshire Blvd.
Penthouse 10
Los Angeles, CA 90036-3681
Ph: (310)453-4440
Fax: (310)453-5258
Fr: 800-NATPE-GO
URL: http://www.natpe.com

Annual. Primary Exhibits: Equipment, supplies, and services for media content production, development, distribution, marketing, advertising, licensing and technology.

10810 ■ Public Radio News Directors National Conference

Public Radio News Directors
c/o Christine Paige Diers, Business Mgr.
PO Box 838
Sturgis, SD 57785-0838
Ph: (605)490-3033
E-mail: cpaigediers@gmail.com
URL: http://www.prndi.org

Annual. Features events and activities that aim to strengthen the skills and professional position of news directors and, through them, strengthen public radio's local news and public affairs efforts in ways that are embraced by audiences, station leaders, networks and supporters.

OTHER SOURCES

10811 ■ American Sportscasters Association (ASA)

225 Broadway, Ste. 2030
New York, NY 10007
Ph: (212)227-8080
Fax: (212)571-0556
E-mail: info@americansportscastersonline.com
URL: http://www.americansportscastersonline.com

Description: Radio and television sportscasters. Sponsors seminars, clinics, and symposia for aspiring announcers and sportscasters. Compiles statistics. Operates speakers' bureau, placement service, hall of fame, and biographical archives. Maintains American Sportscaster Hall of Fame Trust. Is currently implementing Hall of Fame Museum, Community Programs.

10812 ■ Association for Women in Communications (AWC)

3337 Duke St.
Alexandria, VA 22314
Ph: (703)370-7436
Fax: (703)342-4311
E-mail: info@womcom.org
URL: http://www.womcom.org

Description: Professional association of journalism and communications.

10813 ■ Association for Women in Sports Media

161 W Sylvania Ave.
Neptune City, NJ 07753
URL: http://www.awsmonline.org

Description: Comprised of women sportswriters, editors, broadcasters and media relations directors and others who are interested in sports media career. Supports and fosters advancement of women involved in sports media. Works to promote and increase diversity in sports media through its internship/scholarship programs.

10814 ■ Broadcast Education Association (BEA)

1771 N St. NW
Washington, DC 20036-2800
Ph: (202)429-3935
Fax: (202)775-2981
E-mail: 20hbirks@nab.org
URL: http://www.beaweb.org

Description: Universities and colleges; faculty and students; promotes improvement of curriculum and teaching methods, broadcasting research, television and radio production, and programming teaching on the college level.

10815 ■ Corporation for Public Broadcasting (CPB)

401 9th St. NW
Washington, DC 20004-2129
Ph: (202)879-9600
Fr: 800-272-2190
URL: http://www.cpb.org

Description: Promotes and finances the growth and development of noncommercial radio and television. Makes grants to local public television and radio stations, program producers, and program distribution networks; studies emerging technologies; works to provide adequate long-range financing from the U.S. government and other sources for public broadcasting. Supports children's services; compiles statistics; sponsors training programs.

10816 ■ Country Radio Broadcasters (CRB)

819 18th Ave. S
Nashville, TN 37203
Ph: (615)327-4487
Fax: (615)329-4492
E-mail: bill@crb.org
URL: http://www.crb.org

Description: Seeks to advance and promote the

study of the science of broadcasting through the mutual exchange of ideas by conducting seminars and workshops, as well as providing scholarships to broadcasting students.

10817 ■ National Association of Black Owned Broadcasters (NABOB)

1201 Connecticut Ave. NW, Ste. 200
Washington, DC 20036
Ph: (202)463-8970
Fax: (202)429-0657
E-mail: nabobinfo@nabob.org
URL: http://www.nabob.org

Description: Black broadcast station owners; black formatted stations not owned or controlled by blacks; organizations having an interest in the black consumer market or black broadcast industry; individuals interested in becoming owners; and communications schools, departments and professional groups and associations. Represents the interests of existing and potential black radio and television stations. Works with the Office of Federal Procurement Policy to determine which government contracting major advertisers and advertising agencies are complying with government initiatives to increase the amount of advertising dollars received by minority-owned firms. Conducts lobbying activities; provides legal representation for the protection of minority ownership policies. Sponsors annual Communications Awards Dinner each March. Conducts workshops; compiles statistics.

10818 ■ National Association of Broadcasters (NAB)

1771 N St. NW
Washington, DC 20036
Ph: (202)429-5300
Fax: (202)429-4199
E-mail: nab@nab.org
URL: http://www.nab.org

Description: Serves as the voice for the nation's radio and television broadcasters. Advances the interests of members in federal government, industry and public affairs; improves the quality and profitability of broadcasting; encourages content and technology innovation; and spotlights the important and unique ways stations serve their communities. Delivers value to its members through advocacy, education and innovation. Relies on the grassroots strength of its television and radio members and state broadcast associations. Helps broadcasters seize opportunities in the digital age. Offers broadcasters a variety of programs to help them grow in their careers, promote diversity in the workplace and strengthen their businesses.

10819 ■ National Association of Farm Broadcasting (NAFB)

PO Box 500
Platte City, MO 64079
Ph: (816)431-4032
Fax: (816)431-4087
E-mail: info@nafb.com
URL: http://www.nafb.com

Description: Radio and television farm directors actively engaged in broadcasting or telecasting farm news and information; associate members are persons with agricultural interests who are affiliated with advertising agencies, government agencies, farm organizations, and commercial firms. Works to improve quantity and quality of farm programming and serve as a clearinghouse for new ideas in farm broadcasting. Provides placement information.

10820 ■ National Association of Television Program Executives

5757 Wilshire Blvd., Penthouse 10
Los Angeles, CA 90036-3681
Ph: (310)453-4440
Fax: (310)453-5258
URL: http://www.natpe.org/natpe

Description: Comprised of television program professionals, exhibitors, buyers and faculty. Focuses on the creation, development and distribution of televised programming in all forms across all mature and emerging media platforms. Provides members with education, networking, professional enhancement and technological guidance through year-round activities and events, and directories.

10821 ■ National Federation of Press Women

PO Box 5556
Arlington, VA 22205
Fax: (703)237-9808
Fr: 800-780-2715
E-mail: presswomen@aol.com
URL: http://www.nfpw.org

Description: Serves as a group of professional women and men pursuing careers across the communications spectrum.

10822 ■ National Religious Broadcasters (NRB)

9510 Technology Dr.
Manassas, VA 20110
Ph: (703)330-7000
Fax: (703)330-7100
E-mail: info@nrb.org
URL: http://www.nrb.org

Description: Christian communicators. Fosters electronic media access for the Gospel; promotes standards of excellence; integrity and accountability; and provides networking and fellowship opportunities for members.

10823 ■ Radio-Television Digital News Association (RTDNA)

529 14th St. NW, Ste. 425
Washington, DC 20045
Ph: (202)659-6510
Fax: (202)223-4007
Fr: 800-807-8632
E-mail: barbarac@rtnda.org
URL: http://rtdna.org

Description: Comprises of heads of news departments for broadcast and cable stations and networks; associate members are journalists engaged in the preparation and presentation of broadcast news and teachers of electronic journalism; other members represent industry services, public relations departments of business firms, public relations firms, and networks. Works to improve standards of electronic journalism; defends rights of journalists to access news; promotes journalism training to meet specific needs of the industry. Operates placement service and speakers' bureau.

10824 ■ Women in Cable Telecommunications (WICT)

14555 Avion Pkwy., Ste. 250
Chantilly, VA 20151
Ph: (703)234-9810
Fax: (703)817-1595
E-mail: mbrennan@wict.org
URL: http://www.wict.org

Description: Empowers and educates women to achieve their professional goals by providing opportunities for leadership, networking and advocacy.

Radiologic Technologists

SOURCES OF HELP-WANTED ADS

10825 ■ *ADVANCE for Imaging and Radiation Therapy Professionals*
Merion Publications Inc.
2900 Horizon Dr.
PO Box 61556
King of Prussia, PA 19406-0956
Ph: (610)278-1400
Fr: 800-355-5627
URL: http://imaging-radiology-oncology-technologist.advanceweb.co

Biweekly. Free to qualified subscribers. Professional medical magazine reaching radiology managers, technologists, and therapists.

10826 ■ *Applied Radiation and Isotopes*
Mosby Inc.
11830 Westline Industrial Dr.
St. Louis, MO 63146-3326
Ph: (314)872-8370
Fax: (314)432-1380
Fr: 800-325-4177
URL: http://www.elsevier.com/wps/find/journaldescription.cws_home

Monthly. $3,616.00/year for institutions, for all countries except Europe, Japan and Iran; $3,230.00/year for institutions, for European countries and Iran; $429,300.00/year for institutions. Journal for radiologists.

10827 ■ *Applied Radiology*
Anderson Publishing Ltd.
180 Glenside Ave.
Scotch Plains, NJ 07076
Ph: (908)301-1995
Fax: (908)301-1997
URL: http://www.appliedradiology.com

Monthly. $115.00/year for individuals; $210.00/year for two years; $215.00/year for other countries. Magazine for radiologists, chief radiologic technologists, radiology department administrators and key managers in HMOs. Presents articles written by radiologic professionals on all aspects of general diagnostic radiology, the diagnostic radiologic subspecialties, radiation therapy and the socioeconomics of imaging.

10828 ■ *ASRT Scanner*
American Society of Radiologic Technologists
15000 Central Ave. SE
Albuquerque, NM 87123-3909
Ph: (505)298-4500
Fax: (505)298-5063
Fr: 800-444-2778
URL: http://www.asrt.org/content/publications/asrtscanner/member

Bimonthly. Magazine offering news about the American Society of Radiologic Technologists and the radiologic technology profession.

10829 ■ *ASTRO News*
American Society for Therapeutic Radiology and Oncology
8280 Willow Oaks Corporate Dr., Ste. 500
Fairfax, VA 22031
Ph: (703)502-1550
Fax: (703)502-7852
Fr: 800-962-7876
URL: http://www.astro.org/publications/astronews/

Quarterly. Included in membership. Professional magazine covering radiology.

10830 ■ *CME Supplement to Radiologic Clinics of North America*
Elsevier Science Inc.
360 Park Ave. S
New York, NY 10010-1710
Ph: (212)989-5800
Fax: (212)633-3990
Fr: 888-437-4636
URL: http://www.elsevier.com/wps/find/journaldescription.cws_home

$283.00/year for individuals; $283.00/year for other countries. Journal covering radiology, nuclear medicine and medical imaging.

10831 ■ *Diagnostic Imaging*
United business Media L.L.C
240 W 35th St.
New York, NY 10001
Ph: (516)562-5000
URL: http://www.diagnosticimaging.com/

Monthly. News and analysis on clinical and economic developments in medical imaging.

10832 ■ *Investigative Radiology*
Lippincott Williams & Wilkins
530 Walnut St.
Philadelphia, PA 19106-3619
Ph: (215)521-8300
Fax: (215)521-8902
Fr: 800-638-3030
URL: http://journals.lww.com/investigativeradiology/pages/default

Monthly. $500.00/year for individuals; $1,343.00/year for institutions; $678.00/year for other countries; $1,704.40/year for institutions, other countries; $253.00/year for U.S., in-training; $279.40/year for other countries, in-training. Journal covering clinical and laboratory investigations in diagnostic imaging.

10833 ■ *Journal of Clinical Ultrasound*
John Wiley & Sons Inc.
111 River St.
Hoboken, NJ 07030-5773
Ph: (201)748-6000
Fax: (201)748-6088
Fr: 800-825-7550
URL: http://onlinelibrary.wiley.com/journal/10.1002/(ISSN)1097-00

$321.00/year for U.S., Canada, and Mexico, print only; $1,905.00/year for institutions, print with online; $375.00/year for other countries, print only; $1,657.00/year for institutions, print only; $1,783.00/year for institutions, Canada and Mexico, print only; $1,846.00/year for institutions, other countries, print only; $2,031.00/year for institutions, Canada and Mexico, print with online; $2,094.00/year for institutions, other countries, print with online. International journal devoted to the clinical applications of ultrasound in medicine. Features include scholarly, peer-reviewed articles on research procedures and techniques encompassing all phases of diagnostic ultrasound.

10834 ■ *Journal of Computer-Assisted Tomography*
Lippincott Williams & Wilkins
351 W Camden St.
Baltimore, MD 21201
Ph: (410)528-4000
Fr: 800-638-3030
URL: http://journals.lww.com/jcat/pages/default.aspx

Bimonthly. $424.00/year for individuals; $1,290.00/year for institutions; $198.00/year for individuals, in-training; $535.00/year for individuals, international; $1,383.00/year for institutions, other countries; $220.00/year for other countries, in-training. Peer-reviewed radiology journal.

10835 ■ *Magnetic Resonance Imaging Clinics*
Mosby Inc.
11830 Westline Industrial Dr.
St. Louis, MO 63146-3326
Ph: (314)872-8370
Fax: (314)432-1380
Fr: 800-325-4177
URL: http://www.mri.theclinics.com

Quarterly. $448.00/year for other countries; $628.00/year for institutions, other countries; $228.00/year for students, other countries; $309.00/year for individuals; $501.00/year for institutions; $158.00/year for students; $628.00/year for institutions, Canada; $228.00/year for students, Canada; $345.00/year for Canada. Journal publishing articles and research on the latest trends in magnetic resonance imagining clinics and patient management.

10836 ■ *Magnetic Resonance in Medicine*
International Society for Magnetic Resonance in Medicine
2030 Addison St., 7th Fl.
Berkeley, CA 94704
Ph: (510)841-1899
Fax: (510)841-2340
URL: http://www.ismrm.org/journals.htm

Monthly. $903.00/year for individuals, online; $903.00/year for Canada and Mexico, online; $903.00/year for other countries, online; $2,714.00/year for institutions, print or online; $3,121.00/year for institutions, Canada and Mexico; $3,373.00/year for institutions, other countries, print & online. Journal covering radiology worldwide.

10837 ■ *Neuroimaging Clinics of North America*

Mosby Inc.
11830 Westline Industrial Dr.
St. Louis, MO 63146-3326
Ph: (314)872-8370
Fax: (314)432-1380
Fr: 800-325-4177
URL: http://www.neuroimaging.theclinics.com

Quarterly. $546.00/year for institutions, international; $461.00/year for individuals, international; $226.00/year for students, international; $436.00/year for institutions, U.S.; $158.00/year for students, U.S.; $363.00/year for individuals, Canada; $226.00/year for students, Canada; $546.00/year for institutions, Canada. Journal publishing articles on newest advances in neuroimaging and patient treatment options.

10838 ■ *Practical Radiation Oncology*

Elsevier
1600 John F. Kennedy Blvd., Ste. 1800
Philadelphia, PA 19103-2822
Ph: (215)239-3900
Fax: (215)238-7883
E-mail: pro@astro.org
URL: http://www.practicalradonc.org/

Peer-reviewed journal featuring information about radiation oncology practice.

10839 ■ *RadioGraphics*

Radiological Society of North America
820 Jorie Blvd.
Oak Brook, IL 60523-2284
Ph: (630)571-2670
Fax: (630)571-7837
Fr: 800-381-6660
E-mail: rarnold@rsna.org
URL: http://radiographics.rsnajnls.org/

Bimonthly. $150.00/year for U.S., Canada, and Mexico, print & online; $120.00/year for U.S., Canada, and Mexico, online only; $300.00/year for institutions, print & online; $240.00/year for institutions, online only; $185.00/year for other countries, print & online; $120.00/year for other countries, online only; $335.00/year for institutions, other countries, print & online; $240.00/year for institutions, other countries, online. Scientific publication for radiologists.

10840 ■ *Radiologic Clinics of North America*

Mountain Association for Community Economic Development
433 Chestnut St.
Berea, KY 40403-1510
Ph: (859)986-2373
Fax: (859)986-1299
URL: http://www.radiologic.theclinics.com

$386.00/year for individuals; $185.00/year for students; $450.00/year for Canada; $266.00/year for students, Canada; $556.00/year for other countries; $266.00/year for students, other countries. Journal publishing articles written by leading experts, along with high-quality reproductions of radiographs, MR images, CT scans and sonograms.

10841 ■ *Radiologic Technology*

American Society of Radiologic Technologists
15000 Central Ave. SE
Albuquerque, NM 87123-3909
Ph: (505)298-4500
Fax: (505)298-5063
Fr: 800-444-2778
E-mail: communications@asrt.org
URL: http://www.asrt.org/content/Publications/
radiologictechnolo

Bimonthly. $60.00/year for individuals; $90.00/year for other countries; $108.00/year for two years; $162.00/year for two years, other countries; $108.00/year for institutions, 2 years. Medical imaging technology. Includes annual index.

10842 ■ *RSNA News*

Radiological Society of North America
820 Jorie Blvd.
Oak Brook, IL 60523-2284
Ph: (630)571-2670
Fax: (630)571-7837
Fr: 800-381-6660
URL: http://www.rsna.org/Publications/index.cfm

Monthly. Magazine providing information about radiology.

10843 ■ *RT Image*

Valley Forge Publishing Group
2570 Boulevard of the Generals, Ste. 220
Norristown, PA 19403
Ph: (610)854-3770
Fax: (610)854-3780
Fr: 800-983-7737
E-mail: info@rt-image.com
URL: http://www.valleyforgepress.com

Weekly. Provides radiology professionals with a variety of timely, accurate, reader-focused articles and resources to promote their careers and provide information about prevailing techniques and technologies.

10844 ■ *Seminars in Roentgenology*

Mosby Inc.
11830 Westline Industrial Dr.
St. Louis, MO 63146-3326
Ph: (314)872-8370
Fax: (314)432-1380
Fr: 800-325-4177
URL: http://www.seminarsinroentgenology.com/

Quarterly. $286.00/year for individuals, U.S.; $144.00/year for students, U.S.; $440.00/year for other countries; $220.00/year for students, other countries; $500.00/year for institutions; $633.00/year for institutions, other countries. Journal covering for the practicing radiologist and for the resident.

EMPLOYER DIRECTORIES AND NETWORKING LISTS

10845 ■ *Crain's List—Chicago's Largest Hospitals*

Crain Communications Inc.
360 N Michigan Ave.
Chicago, IL 60601
Ph: (312)649-5200
URL: http://www.chicagobusiness.com/section/lists

Published November, 2010. $25.00 for individuals; $45.00 for individuals. Covers: 25 hospitals in Chicago area ranked by net patient revenues. Entries include: Name, address, phone number, fax, web address, corporate e-mail, hospital administrator, network affiliation, 2009 net patient revenue, percentage change from 2008, 2009 net profits, percentage change from 2008, inpatient days, available beds, daily occupancy rate, number of hospital employees as of December 31, 2009, fiscal year end, Chairman, President, CEO, Chief Financial Officer, Human Resources Manager, Media Relations/Public Relations Director, and Hospital Administrator.

10846 ■ *Directory of Hospital Personnel*

Grey House Publishing
4919 Rte. 22
PO Box 56
Amenia, NY 12501
Ph: (518)789-8700
Fax: (518)789-0556
Fr: 800-562-2139
URL: http://www.greyhouse.com/hospital_
personnel.htm

Annual, Latest edition 2011. $325.00 for individuals. Covers: 200,000 executives at 6,000 U.S. Hospitals. Entries include: Name of hospital, address, phone, number of beds, type and JCAHO status of hospital, names and titles of key department heads and staff, medical and nursing school affiliations; number of

residents, interns, and nursing students. Arrangement: Geographical. Indexes: Hospital name, personnel, hospital size.

10847 ■ *Directory of Personnel Responsible for Radiological Health Programs*

Conference of Radiation Control Program Directors Inc.
1030 Burlington Ln., Ste. 4B
Frankfort, KY 40601
Ph: (502)227-4543
Fax: (502)227-7862
URL: http://www.crcpd.org

Annual, Latest edition 2010. $55.00 for individuals. Covers: About 350 individuals who conduct radiological health program activities in federal, state, and local government agencies; members of the conferences. Entries include: For directors—Name and title, name of agency address, phone; office hours listed with state heading. For members—name, address, phone, affiliation, department, and title. Arrangement: Directors are by level of agency and geographical. Indexes: Personal name, agency, state.

10848 ■ *Hospital Blue Book*

Billian Publishing Inc. and Trans World Publishing Inc.
2100 River Edge Pky.
Atlanta, GA 30328
Ph: (770)955-5656
Fax: (770)952-0669
Fr: 800-800-5668
E-mail: blu-book@billian.com
URL: http://www.billianshealthdata.com/Products/
bluebook.html

Annual, Latest edition 2010. $575.00 for individuals; $575.00 for individuals. Covers: More than 6,500 hospitals; some listings also appear in a separate southern edition of this publication. Entries include: Name of hospital, accreditation, mailing address, phone, fax, number of beds, type of facility (nonprofit, general, state, etc.); list of administrative personnel and chiefs of medical services, with specific titles. Arrangement: Geographical.

10849 ■ *Medical and Health Information Directory*

Gale
PO Box 6904
Florence, KY 41022-6904
Fr: 800-354-9706
URL: http://www.gale.cengage.com

Annual, Latest edition April 2011. $1190.00 for individuals; $501.00 for individuals. Covers: In volume 1, more than 33,000 medical and health oriented associations, organizations, institutions, and government agencies, including health maintenance organizations (HMOs), preferred provider organizations (PPOs), insurance companies, pharmaceutical companies, research centers, and medical and allied health schools. In Volume 2, over 20,000 medical book publishers; medical periodicals, directories, audiovisual producers and services, medical libraries and information centers, electronic resources, and health-related internet search engines. In Volume 3, more than 40,500 clinics, treatment centers, care programs, and counseling/diagnostic services for 34 subject areas. Entries include: Institution, service, or firm name, address, phone, fax, email and URL; many include names of key personnel and, when pertinent, descriptive annotation. Volume 3 was formerly listed separately as Health Services Directory. Arrangement: Classified by organization activity, service, etc. Indexes: Each volume has a complete alphabetical name and keyword index.

HANDBOOKS AND MANUALS

10850 ■ *Careers in Health Care*

The McGraw-Hill Companies
PO Box 182604
Columbus, OH 43272
Fax: (614)759-3749

Fr: 877-883-5524
E-mail: customer.service@mcgraw-hill.com
URL: http://www.mhprofessional.com/
product.php?isbn=0071466533

Barbara M. Swanson. Fifth edition, 2005. $19.95
(paper). 192 pages. Describes job duties, work settings, salaries, licensing and certification requirements, educational preparation, and future outlook.
Gives ideas on how to secure a job.

10851 ■ Expert Resumes for Health Care Careers

Jist Works
875 Montreal Way
St. Paul, MN 55102
Fr: 800-648-5478
E-mail: educate@emcp.com
URL: http://www.jist.com

Wendy S. Enelow and Louise M. Kursmark. 2010.
$16.95. 288 pages.

10852 ■ Health Careers Today

Elsevier
11830 Westline Industrial Dr.
St. Louis, MO 63146
Ph: (314)453-7010
Fax: (314)453-7095
Fr: 800-545-2522
E-mail: usbkinfo@elsevier.com
URL: http://www.elsevier.com

Gerdin, Judith. Fourth edition. 2007. $74.95. 496
pages. Covers more than 45 health careers. Discusses the roles and responsibilities of various occupations and provides a solid foundation in the skills
needed for all health careers.

10853 ■ Opportunities in Health and Medical Careers

The McGraw-Hill Companies
PO Box 182604
Columbus, OH 43272
Fax: (614)759-3749
Fr: 877-883-5524
E-mail: customer.service@mcgraw-hill.com
URL: http://www.mhprofessional.com/
product.php?isbn=0071437274

I. Donald Snook, Jr. and Leo D'Orazio. 2004. $14.95
(paper). 157 pages. Covers the full range of medical
and health occupations. Illustrated.

10854 ■ Opportunities in Medical Imaging Careers

The McGraw-Hill Companies
PO Box 182604
Columbus, OH 43272
Fax: (614)759-3749
Fr: 877-883-5524
E-mail: customer.service@mcgraw-hill.com
URL: http://www.mhprofessional.com/
product.php?isbn=0071458719

Clifford J. Sherry. 2006. $13.95. 160 pages.

EMPLOYMENT AGENCIES AND SEARCH FIRMS

10855 ■ Access Staffing

360 Lexington Ave., 8th Fl.
New York, NY 10017
Ph: (212)687-5440
Fax: (212)557-2544
URL: http://www.accessstaffingco.com

Serves as a staffing firm covering accounting/
financial, advertising, bilingual Japanese, creative,
event planning, fashion/retail, healthcare/ human
services, human resources, information technology,
insurance, legal, light industrial and office support.

10856 ■ Axis Medical Staffing

100 W Harrison St., Ste. 550
Seattle, WA 98119
Ph: (206)285-6300

Fax: (206)285-6302
Fr: 888-299-AXIS
E-mail: info@axismedicalstaffing.com
URL: http://www.axismedicalstaffing.com

Description: Focuses on recruiting medical professionals and matching their requirements to the needs
of facilities. Provides quality medical staffing for facilities nationwide. Specializes in per diem staffing, lo-
cal/national travel assignments and direct hire full-
time placements for nursing/nursing aides, radiological technologists and business services.

10857 ■ Break the Box Career Group

36 Unity Ave.
Belmont, MA 02478
Ph: (617)489-8706
E-mail: info@btbcareergroup.com
URL: http://www.btbcareergroup.com

Serves as a national recruiting and placement
specializing in healthcare Features pharmacy jobs,
physician jobs and radiology jobs.

10858 ■ Charles Aris, Inc.

300 N Greene St., Ste. 1800
Greensboro, NC 27401
Ph: (336)378-1818
Fax: (336)378-0129
E-mail: info@charlesaris.com
URL: http://www.charlesaris.com

Provides executive search and placement services in
the areas of consumer packaged goods, retail,
strategy/business development, global life sciences,
healthcare, chemicals, textiles/apparel, private equity,
and business services.

10859 ■ CompHealth

PO Box 713100
Salt Lake City, UT 84171-3100
Ph: (801)930-3000
Fax: (801)930-4517
Fr: 800-453-3030
E-mail: info@comphealth.com
URL: http://www.comphealth.com

Provides healthcare staffing and recruiting services
covering certified registered nurse anesthetist, dosimetrist, imaging and radiation therapy, laboratory
technology, medical physicist, nurse practitioner,
nursing, pharmacy, physician, physician assistant,
rehab therapy and respiratory therapy.

10860 ■ Cross Country TravCorps

6551 Park of Commerce Blvd.
Boca Raton, FL 33487-8247
Fax: (561)998-8533
Fr: 800-530-6125
E-mail: sms@cctc.com
URL: http://www.crosscountrytravcorps.com/cctc/

Places traveling nurses in assignments nationwide.

10861 ■ Harper Associates

31000 NW Hwy., Ste. 240
Farmington Hills, MI 48334
Ph: (248)932-1170
Fax: (248)932-1214
E-mail: info@harperjobs.com
URL: http://www.harperjobs.com

Executive search firm and employment agency.

10862 ■ JPM International

26034 Acero
Mission Viejo, CA 92691
Ph: (949)699-4300
Fax: (949)699-4333
Fr: 800-685-7856
E-mail: qtek37@yahoo.com
URL: http://www.jpmintl.com/pages/qss.html

Executive search firm and employment agency.

10863 ■ MedTeam Staffing

160 International Pkwy., Ste. 110
Heathrow, FL 32746
Ph: (407)936-0411
Fax: (407)936-0417

Fr: 888-864-3030
E-mail: info@medteamstaffing.com
URL: http://www.medteamstaffing.com

Description: Specializes in the nationwide recruitment of healthcare professionals. Offers employment
opportunities for radiology, ultrasound, nuclear
medicine and related allied health careers.

10864 ■ Professional Placement Associates, Inc.

287 Bowman Ave.
Purchase, NY 10577-2517
Ph: (914)251-1000
Fax: (914)251-1055
E-mail: careers@ppasearch.com
URL: http://www.ppasearch.com

Executive search firm specializing in the health and
medical field.

10865 ■ Stat Group, LLC

PO Box 1674
Owensboro, KY 42302-1674
Ph: (270)663-8020
Fax: 877-998-9940
Fr: 877-998-9930
E-mail: info@statgroupllc.com
URL: http://www.statgroupllc.com

Description: Serves as a healthcare staffing firm
which provides healthcare facilities with a workforce
pool. Attracts and retains medical professionals to
assist healthcare facilities throughout the United
States.

ONLINE JOB SOURCES AND SERVICES

10866 ■ Employment for Physicians.com

URL: http://www.employmentforphysicians.com

Description: Provides physician employment in various specialties such as cardiology, anesthesiology,
radiology, plastic surgery, family practice and
psychiatry.

10867 ■ Health Care Recruitment Online

E-mail: info@healthcarerecruitment.com
URL: http://healthcarerecruitment.com

Description: Helps seekers find healthcare positions
through on-line postings with national staffing companies and hospital partners. Main files include: Featured Employers, Job Search, Immediate Openings,
Relocating, Career Management, State boards, and
more.

10868 ■ HEALTHeCAREERS Network

Fr: 888-884-8242
E-mail: info@healthecareers.com
URL: http://www.healthecareers.com

Description: Career search site for jobs in all health
care specialties; educational resources; visa and
licensing information for relocation; interesting
articles; relocation tools; links to professional organizations and general resources.

10869 ■ Hospital Jobs OnLine

E-mail: support@hospitaljobsonline.com
URL: http://www.hospitaljobsonline.com

Description: Serves as a niche healthcare job board
designed exclusively for hospitals, healthcare companies, and healthcare job seekers.

10870 ■ Hot Radiology Jobs

E-mail: info@hotradiologyjobs.com
URL: http://www.hotradiologyjobs.com

Description: Provides a database of job listings in
the field of radiology. Features a resume database
for its users.

10871 ■ Monster Healthcare

URL: http://healthcare.monster.com

Description: Delivers nationwide access to healthcare recruiting. Employers can post job listings or

ads. Job seekers can post and code resumes, and search over 150,000 healthcare job listings, healthcare career advice columns, career resources information, and member employer profiles and services.

10872 ■ ProHealthJobs.com
Ph: (484)443-8545
Fax: (484)443-8549
E-mail: info@prohealthjobs.com
URL: http://prohealthjobs.com/jobboard

Description: Career resources site for the medical and health care field. Lists professional opportunities, product information, continuing education and open positions.

10873 ■ radiologictechnologistjobs.us
URL: http://www.radiologictechnologistjobs.us

Description: Serves as a job board for radiologic technologists.

10874 ■ RadiologistCareer.com
URL: http://www.radiologistcareer.com

Description: Job board for radiologists and job listings for those who work in radiology. Includes career resources, equipment, product and services.

10875 ■ RadiologyWorkers.com
URL: http://www.radiologyworkers.com

Description: Provides information about the field of radiology, radiology schools, and radiology jobs across the country.

10876 ■ RadWorking.com
E-mail: service@atsradworking.com
URL: http://www.radworking.com

Description: Employment resource dedicated to the profession of radiology. Site is divided into various job-search sections based on job type or nature of support position.

10877 ■ RTstudents.com
URL: http://www.rtstudents.com

Description: Features medical imaging job listings and career information to help radiology students find jobs upon graduation.

10878 ■ TechniciansNow.com
URL: http://www.techniciansnow.com

Description: Provides an avenue to showcase jobs and products vital to the mechanical and technical trade communities.

10879 ■ United Search Associates: Health Network USA
PO Box 342
Vinita, OK 74301
Ph: (918)323-4165
E-mail: jobs@hnusa.com
URL: http://homepage.mac.com/hnusa

Description: Visitors may explore healthcare positions, submit an electronic resume, or advertise with the site.

10880 ■ XRayJobs.com
URL: http://www.xrayjobs.com

Description: Serves as a niche job board for radiology and x-ray professionals who are returning or first-time job seekers.

TRADESHOWS

10881 ■ American Healthcare Radiology Administrators Annual Meeting and Exposition
American Healthcare Radiology Administrators
490B Boston Post Rd., No. 200
Sudbury, MA 01776
Ph: (978)443-7591
Fax: (978)443-8046

Fr: 800-334-2472
URL: http://www.ahraonline.org

Annual. Offers sessions addressing management issues including finance, human resources, communication and information, operations, assets and other topics relevant to professional development. 2012 August 12-15; Orlando, FL; Gaylord Palms; 2013 July 28-31; Minneapolis, MN; Minneapolis Convention Center.

10882 ■ American Society of Emergency Radiology Annual Scientific Meeting and Postgraduate Course
American Society of Emergency Radiology
4550 Post Oak Pl., Ste. 342
Houston, TX 77027
Ph: (713)965-0566
Fax: (713)960-0488
E-mail: aser@meetingmanagers.com
URL: http://www.aseronline.org

Annual. Features educational sessions covering advances and trends in emergency and trauma radiologic diagnosis and sessions presenting new and original scientific work. Provides an opportunity to meet with international colleagues and discuss new and challenging aspects of emergency and trauma imaging. 2012 September 12-15; New Orleans, LO; New Orleans Marriott.

10883 ■ American Society of Spine Radiology Annual Symposium
2210 Midwest Rd., Ste. 207
Oak Brook, IL 60523-8205
Ph: (630)574-0220
Fax: (630)574-0661
E-mail: kcammarata@asnr.org
URL: http://theassr.org

Annual. Provides a forum for presentation and discussion of new and important developments in spine radiology. Includes didactic lectures, discussions, case-based reviews, and workshops with recognized experts.

10884 ■ Radiological Society of North America Scientific Assembly and Annual Meeting
Radiological Society of North America
820 Jorie Blvd.
Oak Brook, IL 60523-2251
Ph: (630)571-2670
Fax: (630)571-7837
Fr: 800-381-6600
E-mail: exhibits@rsna.org
URL: http://www.rsna.org

Annual. Primary Exhibits: Radiologic equipment, supplies, services, and publications. Dates and Locations: 2012 Nov 25-30; Chicago, IL; McCormick Place; 2013 Dec 01-06; Chicago, IL; McCormick Place; 2014 Nov 30 - Dec 05; Chicago, IL; McCormick Place.

10885 ■ SDMS Annual Conference
Society of Diagnostic Medical Sonographers
2745 Dallas Pkwy. Ste. 350
Plano, TX 75093-8730
Ph: (214)473-8057
Fax: (214)473-8563
Fr: 800-229-9506
URL: http://www.sdms.org

Annual. Primary Exhibits: Exhibits related to the science of diagnostic medical sonography. Dates and Locations: 2012 Sep 20-23; Seattle, WA; Washington State Convention and Trade Center.

OTHER SOURCES

10886 ■ American Association of Medical Dosimetrists
2325 Dulles Corner Blvd., Ste. 500
Herndon, VA 20171
Ph: (703)677-8071

Fax: (703)677-8071
E-mail: aamd@medicaldosimetry.org
URL: http://www.medicaldosimetry.org

Description: Promotes and supports the medical dosimetry profession. Provides opportunities for education, a forum for professional interaction and a representative voice in the healthcare community. Seeks to promote an ideal of professional conduct to which its members should aspire and endorses high standards of patient care.

10887 ■ American Association for Women Radiologists
4550 Post Oak Pl., Ste. 342
Houston, TX 77027
Ph: (713)965-0566
Fax: (713)960-0488
E-mail: admin@aawr.org
URL: http://www.aawr.org

Description: Physicians involved in diagnostic or therapeutic radiology, nuclear medicine, or radiologic physics. Serves as resource organization for women in the practice of radiology and medicine and as a support for women training in radiology. Provides a forum wherein radiologists can consider, discuss, develop and disseminate knowledge and information concerning the fields of radiology and medicine. Sponsors meetings, forums, seminars and educational institutes dealing with the subject of radiology and related topics.

10888 ■ American Institute of Ultrasound in Medicine (AIUM)
14750 Sweitzer Ln., Ste. 100
Laurel, MD 20707-5906
Ph: (301)498-4100
Fax: (301)498-4450
Fr: 800-638-5352
E-mail: admin@aium.org
URL: http://www.aium.org

Description: Comprises of professionals from many medical specialties, as well as basic scientists, engineers, manufacturers, nurses, physicists, radiologic technologists, sonographers and veterinarians involved with diagnostic medical ultrasound. Aims to advance the art and science of ultrasound in medicine through educational, scientific, literary and professional activities.

10889 ■ American Registry of Diagnostic Medical Sonography (ARDMS)
Plaza East One
51 Monroe St.
Rockville, MD 20850-2400
Ph: (301)738-8401
Fax: (301)738-0312
Fr: 800-541-9754
URL: http://www.ardms.org

Description: Administers examinations in the field of diagnostic medical sonography and vascular technology throughout the U.S. and Canada and registers candidates passing those exams in the specialties of their expertise. Maintains central office for administering examination plans and schedules and assisting registered candidates and those interested in becoming registered.

10890 ■ American Registry of Radiologic Technologists (ARRT)
1255 Northland Dr.
St. Paul, MN 55120-1155
Ph: (651)687-0048
URL: http://www.arrt.org

Description: Radiologic technologist certification board that administers examinations, issues certificates of registration to radiographers, nuclear medicine technologists, and radiation therapists, and investigates the qualifications of practicing radiologic technologists. Governed by trustees appointed from American College of Radiology and American Society of Radiologic Technologists.

10891 ■ American Society of Emergency Radiology
4550 Post Oak Pl., Ste. 342
Houston, TX 77027
Ph: (713)965-0566
Fax: (713)960-0488
E-mail: aser@meetingmanagers.com
URL: http://www.aseronline.org

Description: Advances the quality of diagnosis and treatment of acutely ill or injured patients by means of medical imaging. Works to enhance teaching and research in emergency radiology.

10892 ■ American Society for Radiation Oncology
8280 Willow Oaks Corporate Dr., Ste. 500
Fairfax, VA 22031
Ph: (703)502-1550
Fax: (703)502-7852
Fr: 800-962-7876
URL: http://www.astro.org

Description: Comprised of radiation oncologists, radiation oncology nurses, medical physicists, radiation therapists, dosimetrists and biologists. Advances the practice of radiation oncology by promoting excellence in patient care, providing opportunities for educational and professional development, promoting research and disseminating research results. Focuses on fostering collaboration between radiation oncologists and the larger medical community.

10893 ■ American Society of Radiologic Technologists (ASRT)
15000 Central Ave. SE
Albuquerque, NM 87123-3909
Ph: (505)298-4500
Fax: (505)298-5063
Fr: 800-444-2778
E-mail: memberservices@asrt.org
URL: http://www.asrt.org

Description: Serves as professional society of diagnostic radiography, radiation therapy, ultrasound, and nuclear medicine technologists. Advances the science of radiologic technology; establishes and maintains high standards of education; evaluates the quality of patient care; improves the welfare and socioeconomics of radiologic technologists. Operates ASRT Education and Research Foundation, which provides educational materials to radiologic technologists.

10894 ■ Association of Educators in Imaging and Radiologic Science
PO Box 90204
Albuquerque, NM 87199
Ph: (505)823-4740

Fax: (505)823-4740
E-mail: office@aeirs.org
URL: http://www.aeirs.org

Description: Advances the profession of radiological science through research. Encourages the exchange of educational concepts and methodologies of radiological sciences and related specialty areas among members. Provides educational programs and networking activities.

10895 ■ Association for Radiologic and Imaging Nursing
7794 Grow Dr.
Pensacola, FL 32514
Ph: (850)474-7292
Fax: (850)484-8762
Fr: (866)486-2762
E-mail: arin@dancyamc.com
URL: http://www.arinursing.org

Description: Represents nurses who practice in the diagnostic, neuro/cardiovascular, interventional, ultrasonography, computerized tomography, nuclear medicine, magnetic resonance, and radiation oncology. Fosters the professional growth of nurses who advance the standard of care in the imaging environment.

10896 ■ Association of Vascular and Interventional Radiographers
12100 Sunset Hills Rd., Ste. 130
Reston, VA 20190
Ph: (703)234-4055
Fax: (703)435-4390
URL: http://www.avir.org

Description: Advances the interests and concerns of health care professionals working in vascular and interventional radiology. Promotes professionalism and high standards of practice and care among members. Offers continuing education and networking for obtaining information and employment opportunities.

10897 ■ International Society for Clinical Densitometry (ISCD)
306 Industrial Park Rd., Ste. 208
Middletown, CT 06457
Ph: (860)259-1000
Fax: (860)259-1030
E-mail: iscd@iscd.org
URL: http://www.iscd.org

Description: Raises awareness and understanding of the clinical application of bone mass measurement technology. Seeks to adopt an industry and technology neutral approach towards advances in the field. Encourages improvements in patient care through appropriate utilization of densitometry. Fosters continuing professional education and certification for clinicians and technologists.

10898 ■ International Society for Magnetic Resonance in Medicine
2030 Addison St., 7th Fl.
Berkeley, CA 94704
Ph: (510)841-1899
Fax: (510)841-2340
E-mail: info@ismrm.org
URL: http://www.ismrm.org

Description: Consists of clinicians, physicists, engineers, biochemists, and technologists. Promotes communication, research, development, and applications in the field of magnetic resonance. Provides opportunities for continuing education for all members.

10899 ■ Society of Diagnostic Medical Sonography (SDMS)
2745 N Dallas Pkwy., Ste. 350
Plano, TX 75093-8730
Ph: (214)473-8057
Fax: (214)473-8563
Fr: 800-229-9506
E-mail: dhaydon@sdms.org
URL: http://www.sdms.org

Description: Works to enhance the art and science of medicine by advancing medical sonography.

10900 ■ Society for Imaging Informatics in Medicine
19440 Golf Vista Plaza, Ste. 300
Leesburg, VA 20176
Ph: (703)723-0432
Fax: (703)723-0415
E-mail: info@siimweb.org
URL: http://www.siimweb.org

Description: Serves as a professional organization for medical imaging and information technology professionals. Advances research, education and discovery of innovative solutions, new technologies, and applications to improve the delivery of medical imaging services and the quality and safety of patient care.

10901 ■ Society of NeuroInterventional Surgery
3975 Fair Ridge Dr., Ste. 200
Fairfax, VA 22033
Ph: (703)691-2272
Fax: (703)537-0650
URL: http://www.snisonline.org

Description: Represents physicians and scientists interested in interventional and therapeutic neuroradiology. Develops and supports standards of post-graduate training and practice in interventional and therapeutic neuroradiology. Advances the development of interventional and therapeutic neuroradiology through education and scientific research.

Sources of Help-Wanted Ads

10902 ■ *Clayton-Fillmore Report*
Clayton-Fillmore Ltd.
PO Box 480894
Denver, CO 80248
Ph: (303)663-0606
Fax: (303)663-1616

Monthly. $195.00/year for individuals. Periodical covering real estate and business.

10903 ■ *Commercial Property News*
Nielsen Business Media
770 Broadway
New York, NY 10003-9595
URL: http://www.commercialpropertynews.com/cpn/index.jsp

Semimonthly. $199.00/year for individuals. Twice-monthly magazine for senior level executive in the commercial real estate market, including brokers, developers, investors, lenders, property managers, owners, and corporate real estate executives.

10904 ■ *eConnect*
Women's Council of Realtors
430 N Michigan Ave.
Chicago, IL 60611
Ph: (312)329-5967
Fax: (312)329-3290
Fr: 800-245-8512
E-mail: wcr@wcr.org
URL: http://www.wcr.org

Description: Monthly. Carries articles on personal and career growth topics relating to women in real estate. Includes council news.

10905 ■ *Journal of Property Management*
Institute of Real Estate Management
430 N Michigan Ave.
Chicago, IL 60611
Ph: (312)329-6000
Fax: 800-338-4736
Fr: 800-837-0706
E-mail: jpmsub@irem.org
URL: http://www.irem.org/sechome.cfm?sec=JPM

Bimonthly. $72.32/year for Canada; $62.95/year for individuals; $115.50/year for two years; $110.99/year for other countries, airmail; $169.10/year for individuals, 3 years. Magazine serving real estate managers.

10906 ■ *Journal of Real Estate Literature*
American Real Estate Society
Clemson University
314 Sirrine Hall
Clemson, SC 29634-1343
Ph: (864)656-1373
Fax: (864)656-3748
URL: http://cbeweb-1.fullerton.edu/finance/jrel/

Semiannual. Professional journal covering real estate issues.

10907 ■ *Journal of Real Estate Portfolio Management*
American Real Estate Society
Clemson University
314 Sirrine Hall
Clemson, SC 29634-1343
Ph: (864)656-1373
Fax: (864)656-3748
URL: http://realestate.fiu.edu/journals_jrepm.html

Quarterly. Journal for real estate professionals.

10908 ■ *Journal of Real Estate Research*
American Real Estate Society
Clemson University
314 Sirrine Hall
Clemson, SC 29634-1343
Ph: (864)656-1373
Fax: (864)656-3748
URL: http://aux.zicklin.baruch.cuny.edu/jrer

Journal focusing on scholarly real estate research.

10909 ■ *Lives of Real Estate*
REAL Trends Inc.
7501 Village Sq. Dr., Ste. 200
Castle Rock, CO 80108
Ph: (303)741-1000
Fax: (303)741-1070
URL: http://www.loremagazine.com/

Bimonthly. Free to qualified subscribers. Magazine that profiles personnel in the residential real estate industry.

10910 ■ *New England Real Estate Journal*
East Coast Publications
PO Box 55
Accord, MA 02018-0055
Ph: (781)878-4540
Fax: (781)871-1853
Fr: 800-654-4993
E-mail: nerej@rejournal.com
URL: http://www.rejournal.com/ne/homeNE.aspx

Weekly (Fri.). $139.00/year for individuals. Newspaper publishing commercial, industrial, and investment real estate news.

10911 ■ *Property Management Association-Bulletin*
Property Management Association
7508 Wisconsin Ave., 4th Fl.
Bethesda, MD 20814
Ph: (301)657-9200
Fax: (301)907-9326
E-mail: info@pma-dc.org
URL: http://www.pma-dc.org/content/38/pma-bulletin

Description: Monthly. Reports market trends and other information related to property management. Contains information on the Association and tips for members. Recurring features include news of research, a calendar of events, reports of meetings, news of educational opportunities, job listings, book reviews, and notices of publications available.

10912 ■ *Real Estate Issues*
The Counselors of Real Estate
430 N Michigan Ave.
Chicago, IL 60611-4089
Ph: (312)329-8427
Fax: (312)329-8881
E-mail: rei@cre.org
URL: http://www.cre.org/publications/rei.cfm

$48.00/year for individuals; $15.00/year for single issue. Trade publication covering the real estate industry.

Employer Directories and Networking Lists

10913 ■ *CRS Referral Directory*
Council of Residential Specialists
430 N Michigan Ave., Ste. 300
Chicago, IL 60611
Ph: (312)321-4400
Fax: (312)329-8882
Fr: 800-462-8841
URL: http://www.crs.com

Annual, November. Free. Covers: 35,000 Certified Residential Specialists (CRS). Entries include: Member name, firm name, address, phone, fax; designations held, areas of specialization, e-mail; web page address; years of experience, voicemail; 2nd business phone. Arrangement: Geographical. Indexes: Alphabetical.

10914 ■ *Directory of Real Estate Development & Related Education Programs*
Urban Land Institute
1025 Thomas Jefferson St., NW, Ste. 500 W
Washington, DC 20007
Ph: (202)624-7000
Fax: (202)624-7140
Fr: 800-321-5011
URL: http://www.uli.org

Biennial, latest edition 11th, 2008. $19.95 for members; $24.95 for nonmembers. Covers: over 60 real estate development education programs currently being offered at colleges and universities. Entries include: College or university name, address, list of faculty members, curriculum, tuition, length of program, degrees offered, financial aid information, job placement services, international programs, e-mail addresses. Indexes: Faculty, Programs by degree type, Programs by geographical.

10915 ■ *National Association of Real Estate Companies—Membership Directory*
National Association of Real Estate Cos.
216 W Jackson Blvd., Ste. 625
Chicago, IL 60606-6945
Ph: (312)263-1755

Fax: (312)750-1203
E-mail: cindy@narec.org
URL: http://www.narec.org

Quarterly. Covers: about 200 real estate development companies. Entries include: Company name,
address, phone, name of contact.

**10916 ■ Nelson Information's Directory of
Institutional Real Estate**
Nelson Information
c/o Thomson Financial
195 Broadway
New York, NY 10007-3100
Fax: (646)822-3000
Fr: 800-333-6357
URL: http://www.nelsoninformation.com

Annual, August. Covers: 300 real estate investment
managers, 1,700 plan sponsor investors in real
estate, 1,400 real estate service firms and consultants, 1,000 insurance companies with real estate
investments, 2,000 corporations with active real
estate operations and 280 real estate investment
trusts. Arrangement: Separate sections for real estate
investment managers, plan sponsors, corporations,
insurance companies, real estate service providers,
and REITs. Indexes: Geographical, product/service.

10917 ■ U.S. Real Estate Register
Barry Inc.
PO Box 551
Wilmington, MA 01887-0551
Ph: (978)658-0441
Fax: (978)657-8691
E-mail: sales@barryinc.com
URL: http://www.usrealestateregister.com

Annual, latest edition 37th. $95.00 for individuals.
Covers: Real estate departments of large national
companies, industrial economic/development organizations, utilities, real estate brokers, and railroads
involved in commercial and industrial real estate
development. Entries include: Company or organization name, address; many listings include name of
contact. Arrangement: Companies are alphabetical;
others are geographical.

HANDBOOKS AND MANUALS

**10918 ■ The Everything Guide to Being a
Real Estate Agent**
Adams Media Corporation
57 Littlefield St.
Avon, MA 02322
Ph: (508)427-7100
Fax: (508)427-6790
Fr: 800-872-5627
URL: http://www.adamsmedia.com

Shahri Masters. $14.95. 304 pages.

**10919 ■ FabJob Guide to Become a Real
Estate Agent**
FabJob Inc.
4616 - 25th Ave. NE, No. 224
Seattle, WA 98105
Ph: (403)949-4980
Fr: 888-322-5621
URL: http://www.fabjob.com/RealEstateAgent.asp

Pamela Gray. $29.97(e-book). 157 pages. Contains
guide on becoming a real estate agent and maintaining a career in real estate.

**10920 ■ Real Estate Blues: A Guide to Jump
Start Your Real Estate Career**
PublishAmerica, Incorporated
PO Box 151
Frederick, MD 21705
Ph: (301)695-1707
Fax: (301)631-9073
URL: http://www.publishamerica.com

David H. Lawrence. May 2004. $19.95 (paper). 138
pages.

**10921 ■ Real Estate Brokerage: A Guide to
Success**
Cengage Learning
PO Box 6904
Florence, KY 41022
Fax: 800-487-8488
Fr: 800-345-9706
E-mail: esales@cengage.com
URL: http://www.cengage.com

Dan Hamilton. 2007. $55.95. Recruiting and retention
strategies for running a successful real estate brokerage are covered. The book is designed to meet the
requirements of a real estate brokerage course.

EMPLOYMENT AGENCIES AND SEARCH
FIRMS

**10922 ■ 20-20 Foresight Executive Search
Inc.**
150 N Michigan Ave., Ste. 2800
Chicago, IL 60601
Ph: (708)246-2100
E-mail: bcavoto@202-4.com
URL: http://www.2020-4.com

Executive search firm. Affiliate offices in California
and Washington DC.

**10923 ■ American Human Resources
Associates Ltd. (AHRA)**
PO Box 18269
Cleveland, OH 44118-0269
Ph: (440)317-0981
E-mail: ahra@ahrasearch.com
URL: http://www.ahrasearch.com

Executive search firm. Focused on real estate, banking and credit & collection.

10924 ■ Crown Advisors Inc.
100 McKnight Park Dr., Ste. 110
Pittsburgh, PA 15237
Ph: (412)348-1540
E-mail: info@crownsearch.com
URL: http://www.crownsearch.com

Executive search firm.

10925 ■ Insperity, Inc.
19001 Crescent Springs Dr.
Kingwood, TX 77339-3802
Ph: (281)358-8986
Fr: 800-237-3170
E-mail: douglas.sharp@insperity.com
URL: http://www.insperity.com

Description: Serves as a full-service human resources department for small and medium-sized businesses throughout the United States. Provides client
companies with benefits and services such as
employment administration, government compliance,
recruiting and selection, performance management,
benefits management, employer liability management, training and development, and business
services.

10926 ■ Maison Group
7200 Wisconsin Ave., Ste. 402
Bethesda, MD 20814
Ph: (240)395-0480
Fax: (240)395-0481
E-mail: info@themaisongroup.com
URL: http://www.themaisongroup.com

Executive search firm focused exclusively within the
real estate industry. Represents organizations
involved in acquiring, developing, building, managing,
owning, financing, and advising across every major
asset class within the real estate industry.

10927 ■ Real Estate Executive Search, Inc.
225 E Dania Beach Blvd. Ste., 200
Dania Beach, FL 33004
Ph: (954)927-6000

Fax: (954)927-6003
E-mail: reesearch954@aol.com
URL: http://reesearchinc.com

Executive search firm for the real estate and finance
fields.

ONLINE JOB SOURCES AND SERVICES

10928 ■ Locate Real Estate Jobs
URL: http://www.locaterealestatejobs.com

Description: Serves as a job board for real estate
professionals. Focuses on bringing together employers and employment candidates in the real estate
field.

10929 ■ New Real Estate Jobs
URL: http://www.newrealestatejobs.com

Description: Provides an online listing of companies
with available real estate jobs in all specialties.

10930 ■ RealEstateAndLandCrossing.com
URL: http://www.realestateandlandcrossing.com

Description: Provides job listings and other resources related to real estate employment
opportunities.

TRADESHOWS

**10931 ■ American Real Estate Society
Annual Meeting**
American Real Estate Society
5353 Parkside Dr.
Cleveland State Univ.
Coll. of Bus.
Dept. of Finance, UC513
Jupiter, FL 33458
Ph: (561)799-8664
Fax: (561)799-8535
E-mail: dcooper@fau.edu
URL: http://www.aresnet.org

Annual. Primary Exhibits: Exhibits relating to decision-
making within real estate finance, real estate market
analysis, investment, valuation, development, and
other areas related to real estate in the private sector.
Data providers, book publishers, etc. Dates and Locations: 2012 Apr 17-22; St. Petersburg, FL.

**10932 ■ South Dakota Association of
Realtors Convention**
South Dakota Association of Realtors
204 N. Euclid Ave.
Pierre, SD 57501
Ph: (605)224-0554
Fax: (605)224-8975
Fr: 800-227-5877
E-mail: sdar@sdrealtor.org
URL: http://www.sdrealtor.org

Annual. Primary Exhibits: Real estate.

OTHER SOURCES

**10933 ■ American Real Estate and Urban
Economics Association (AREUEA)**
PO Box 9958
Richmond, VA 23228-9958
Fax: 877-273-8323
Fr: (866)273-8321
E-mail: areuea@areuea.org
URL: http://www.areuea.org

Description: University faculty, individuals in real
estate and related areas, and firms and organizations
active in real estate and research. Promotes education and encourages research in real estate, urban
land economics, and allied fields; improves communication in real estate and allied matters among
college and university faculty who are teaching or
conducting research in fields of interest to the association; facilitates the mutual association of

academic and research persons in real estate, urban land economics, and allied fields.

10934 ■ Association of Real Estate Women
1201 Wakarusa Dr., Ste. C3
Lawrence, KS 66049
Ph: (212)599-6181
Fax: (785)832-1551
Fr: 888-329-2739
E-mail: info@arew.org
URL: http://www.arew.org

Description: Provides programs and networking opportunities that can contribute to the career growth of both men and women in all segments and all levels of the real estate industry. Helps members find new employment opportunities.

10935 ■ Counselors of Real Estate (CRE)
430 N Michigan Ave.
Chicago, IL 60611
Ph: (312)329-8427
E-mail: info@cre.org
URL: http://www.cre.org

Description: Professional society of individuals with extensive experience in all phases of real estate who provide a counseling service. Members are entitled to use the Professional Designation CRE (Counselor of Real Estate). Conducts educational programs during three national meetings.

10936 ■ National Apartment Association (NAA)
4300 Wilson Blvd., Ste. 400
Arlington, VA 22203
Ph: (703)518-6141
Fax: (703)248-9440
E-mail: info@naahq.org
URL: http://www.naahq.org

Description: Federation of 155 state and local associations of industry professionals engaged in all aspects of the multifamily housing industry, including owners, builders, investors, developers, managers, and allied service representatives. Provides education and certification for property management executives, on-site property managers, maintenance personnel, property supervisors, and leasing agents. Offers a nationwide legislative network concerned with governmental decisions at the federal, state, and local levels.

10937 ■ National Association of Independent Real Estate Brokers (NAIREB)
7102 Mardyke Ln.
Indianapolis, IN 46226
Ph: (317)549-1709
E-mail: director@nationalrealestatebrokers.org
URL: http://nationalrealestatebrokers.org

Description: Aims to educate independent real estate brokers and real estate agents. Promotes the value of independent real estate brokers and real estate agents nationwide through national promotional campaigns. Works to introduce the general public to independent real estate brokers and real estate agents, their real estate companies and the benefits they offer.

10938 ■ National Association of Real Estate Brokers (NAREB)
5504 Brentwood Stair Rd.
Fort Worth, TX 76112
Ph: (817)446-7715
Fax: (817)446-7744
E-mail: wvincent.wimbish@nareb.com
URL: http://www.nareb.com

Description: Members of the real estate industry. Research, educational and certification programs include: Real Estate Management Brokers Institute; National Society of Real Estate Appraisers; Real Estate Brokerage Institute; United Developers Council. Encourages unity among those who are engaged in real estate. Promotes and maintains high standards of conduct. Protects the public against unethical, improper, or fraudulent practices connected with the real estate business. Conducts research; compiles statistics on productivity, marketing and development. Gives members license to use "Realtist" symbol. Sponsors educational seminars. Maintains Willis E. Carson Library.

10939 ■ National Association of Real Estate Consultants (NAREC)
2758 W River Dr.
Lenore, ID 83541
Ph: (208)746-7963
Fr: 800-445-8543
E-mail: julie@narec.com
URL: http://www.narec.com

Description: Works to assist real estate professionals in reframing their focus as real estate consultants to better meet the needs of today's savvy consumer. Helps promote alternative or fee-for-service real estate business models.

10940 ■ National Association of Realtors (NAR)
430 N Michigan Ave.
Chicago, IL 60611-4087
Fr: 800-874-6500
URL: http://www.realtor.org

Description: Federation of 54 state and territory associations and 1,860 local real estate boards whose members are real estate brokers and agents; terms are registered by the association in the U.S. Patent and Trademark Office and in the states. Promotes education, high professional standards and modern techniques in specialized real estate work such as brokerage, appraisal, property management, land development, industrial real estate, farm brokerage and counseling. Conducts research programs.

10941 ■ Realtors Land Institute (RLI)
430 N Michigan Ave.
Chicago, IL 60611
Ph: (312)329-8446
Fax: (312)329-8633
Fr: 800-441-5263
E-mail: rli@realtors.org
URL: http://www.rliland.com

Description: Real estate brokers and salespersons selling, managing, appraising, or developing all types of land. Maintains educational programs for real estate brokers; promotes competence and accredits members. Sponsors courses for realtors and others seeking professional excellence on Land Brokerage, Agricultural Land Brokerage, Exchanging Properties, Estate Planning, Subdivision Development and Financial Analysis of Land Investment.

10942 ■ Society of Industrial and Office Realtors (SIOR)
1201 New York Ave. NW, Ste. 350
Washington, DC 20005-6126
Ph: (202)449-8200
Fax: (202)216-9325
E-mail: admin@sior.com
URL: http://www.sior.com

Description: Real estate brokers specializing in industrial and office properties; representatives of utilities, financial institutions, corporations, and industrial park developments. Conducts studies on special problems of industrial development, development of sale-lease back techniques, surveys of plants or site locations, and availability. Conducts six educational courses and eight seminars annually. Sponsors SIOR Educational Foundation. Compiles statistics.

10943 ■ Women's Council of Realtors (WCR)
430 N Michigan Ave.
Chicago, IL 60611
Ph: (312)329-8481
Fax: (312)329-3290
Fr: 800-245-8512
E-mail: wcr@wcr.org
URL: http://www.wcr.org

Description: Women and men real estate brokers and salespeople. Provides opportunity for real estate professionals to participate at local, state, and national levels. Makes programs available for personal and career growth. Offers courses in leadership training, referral and relocation business. Members may earn the Leadership Training Graduate (LTG) designation.

Real Estate Appraisers

SOURCES OF HELP-WANTED ADS

10944 ■ Clayton-Fillmore Report
Clayton-Fillmore Ltd.
PO Box 480894
Denver, CO 80248
Ph: (303)663-0606
Fax: (303)663-1616

Monthly. $195.00/year for individuals. Periodical covering real estate and business.

10945 ■ Commercial Property News
Nielsen Business Media
770 Broadway
New York, NY 10003-9595
URL: http://www.commercialpropertynews.com/cpn/index.jsp

Semimonthly. $199.00/year for individuals. Twice-monthly magazine for senior level executive in the commercial real estate market, including brokers, developers, investors, lenders, property managers, owners, and corporate real estate executives.

10946 ■ Journal of Property Management
Institute of Real Estate Management
430 N Michigan Ave.
Chicago, IL 60611
Ph: (312)329-6000
Fax: 800-338-4736
Fr: 800-837-0706
E-mail: jpmsub@irem.org
URL: http://www.irem.org/sechome.cfm?sec=JPM

Bimonthly. $72.32/year for Canada; $62.95/year for individuals; $115.50/year for two years; $110.99/year for other countries, airmail; $169.10/year for individuals, 3 years. Magazine serving real estate managers.

10947 ■ Journal of Real Estate Literature
American Real Estate Society
Clemson University
314 Sirrine Hall
Clemson, SC 29634-1343
Ph: (864)656-1373
Fax: (864)656-3748
URL: http://cbeweb-1.fullerton.edu/finance/jrel/

Semiannual. Professional journal covering real estate issues.

10948 ■ Journal of Real Estate Portfolio Management
American Real Estate Society
Clemson University
314 Sirrine Hall
Clemson, SC 29634-1343
Ph: (864)656-1373
Fax: (864)656-3748
URL: http://realestate.fiu.edu/journals_jrepm.html

Quarterly. Journal for real estate professionals.

10949 ■ Journal of Real Estate Research
American Real Estate Society
Clemson University
314 Sirrine Hall
Clemson, SC 29634-1343
Ph: (864)656-1373
Fax: (864)656-3748
URL: http://aux.zicklin.baruch.cuny.edu/jrer

Journal focusing on scholarly real estate research.

10950 ■ Lives of Real Estate
REAL Trends Inc.
7501 Village Sq. Dr., Ste. 200
Castle Rock, CO 80108
Ph: (303)741-1000
Fax: (303)741-1070
URL: http://www.loremagazine.com/

Bimonthly. Free to qualified subscribers. Magazine that profiles personnel in the residential real estate industry.

10951 ■ New England Real Estate Journal
East Coast Publications
PO Box 55
Accord, MA 02018-0055
Ph: (781)878-4540
Fax: (781)871-1853
Fr: 800-654-4993
E-mail: nerej@rejournal.com
URL: http://www.rejournal.com/ne/homeNE.aspx

Weekly (Fri.). $139.00/year for individuals. Newspaper publishing commercial, industrial, and investment real estate news.

10952 ■ Real Estate Issues
The Counselors of Real Estate
430 N Michigan Ave.
Chicago, IL 60611-4089
Ph: (312)329-8427
Fax: (312)329-8881
E-mail: rei@cre.org
URL: http://www.cre.org/publications/rei.cfm

$48.00/year for individuals; $15.00/year for single issue. Trade publication covering the real estate industry.

EMPLOYER DIRECTORIES AND NETWORKING LISTS

10953 ■ Appraisal Institute—Directory of Designated Members
Appraisal Institute
200 W Madison, Ste. 1500
Chicago, IL 60606
Ph: (312)335-4401
Fax: (312)335-4415
Fr: 888-756-4624
E-mail: directory@appraisalinstitute.org
URL: http://www.appraisalinstitute.org

Covers: Over 25,000 real estate appraisers of all types of real property in the United States and Canada who hold the MAI, SRPA, or SREA general appraisal, and/or SRA or RM residential appraisal membership designations of the Appraisal Institute; includes limited overseas listings. Entries include: Name of individual member, company name, address, phone, fax, and email address. Arrangement: Geographical.

10954 ■ National Association of Independent Fee Appraisers—National Membership Directory
National Association of Independent Fee Appraisers
401 N Michigan Ave., Ste. 2200
Chicago, IL 60611
Ph: (312)321-6830
Fax: (312)673-6652
URL: http://www.naifa.com

Annual, January. Covers: 4,300 independent real estate appraisers. Entries include: Name, address, phone, level of membership. Arrangement: Geographical.

10955 ■ National Association of Real Estate Companies—Membership Directory
National Association of Real Estate Cos.
216 W Jackson Blvd., Ste. 625
Chicago, IL 60606-6945
Ph: (312)263-1755
Fax: (312)750-1203
E-mail: cindy@narec.org
URL: http://www.narec.org

Quarterly. Covers: about 200 real estate development companies. Entries include: Company name, address, phone, name of contact.

10956 ■ U.S. Real Estate Register
Barry Inc.
PO Box 551
Wilmington, MA 01887-0551
Ph: (978)658-0441
Fax: (978)657-8691
E-mail: sales@barryinc.com
URL: http://www.usrealestateregister.com

Annual, latest edition 37th. $95.00 for individuals. Covers: Real estate departments of large national companies, industrial economic/development organizations, utilities, real estate brokers, and railroads involved in commercial and industrial real estate development. Entries include: Company or organization name, address; many listings include name of contact. Arrangement: Companies are alphabetical; others are geographical.

10957 ■ Vault Guide to the Top Real Estate Employers
Vault.com Inc.
150 W 22nd St., 5th Fl.
New York, NY 10011
Ph: (212)366-4212
Fax: (212)366-6117

Fr: 888-562-8285

URL: http://www.vault.com/store/book_
preview.jsp?product_id=38818

Latest edition October, 2005. $19.95 for individuals; $19.95 for members. Covers: Real estate employers. Entries include: Name, address, phone, fax, website, branch office location, and major departments. Also include company overviews, recent company news, information on the hiring process, key competitors, and employment contact.

EMPLOYMENT AGENCIES AND SEARCH FIRMS

10958 ■ Real Estate Executive Search, Inc.
225 E Dania Beach Blvd. Ste., 200
Dania Beach, FL 33004
Ph: (954)927-6000
Fax: (954)927-6003
E-mail: reesearch954@aol.com
URL: http://reesearchinc.com

Executive search firm for the real estate and finance fields.

ONLINE JOB SOURCES AND SERVICES

10959 ■ AbcAppraiserDirectory.com
URL: http://www.abcappraiserdirectory.com

Description: Offers job placement services to current and future real estate appraisers.

10960 ■ New Real Estate Jobs
URL: http://www.newrealestatejobs.com

Description: Provides an online listing of companies with available real estate jobs in all specialties.

10961 ■ RealEstateAndLandCrossing.com
URL: http://www.realestateandlandcrossing.com

Description: Provides job listings and other resources related to real estate employment opportunities.

OTHER SOURCES

10962 ■ American Real Estate and Urban Economics Association (AREUEA)
PO Box 9958
Richmond, VA 23228-9958
Fax: 877-273-8323
Fr: (866)273-8321
E-mail: areuea@areuea.org
URL: http://www.areuea.org

Description: University faculty, individuals in real estate and related areas, and firms and organizations active in real estate and research. Promotes education and encourages research in real estate, urban land economics, and allied fields; improves communication in real estate and allied matters among college and university faculty who are teaching or conducting research in fields of interest to the association; facilitates the mutual association of academic and research persons in real estate, urban land economics, and allied fields.

10963 ■ American Society of Agricultural Appraisers (ASAA)
PO Box 186
Twin Falls, ID 83303-0186
Ph: (208)733-1122
Fax: (208)733-2326
Fr: 800-488-7570
E-mail: ag@amagappraisers.com
URL: http://www.amagappraisers.com

Description: Appraisers of livestock, farm equipment and other agricultural properties, supplies and products. Promotes adherence to high standards of

ethics and practice in the field of agricultural appraising. Sponsors educational programs.

10964 ■ American Society of Farm Managers and Rural Appraisers (ASFMRA)
950 S Cherry St., Ste. 508
Denver, CO 80246-2664
Ph: (303)758-3513
Fax: (303)758-0190
E-mail: info@asfmra.org
URL: http://www.asfmra.org

Description: Professional farm managers, appraisers, lenders, consultants, educators and researchers in farm and ranch management and/or rural appraisal. Bestows registered ARA (Accredited Rural Appraiser), Accredited Agricultural Consultant (ACC), AFM (Accredited Farm Manager) and RPRA (Real Property Review Appraiser) designations. Operates management and appraisal schools, Internet course offerings. Maintains placement service.

10965 ■ Appraisal Institute (AI)
550 W Van Buren St., Ste. 1000
Chicago, IL 60607
Ph: (312)335-4100
Fax: (312)335-4400
Fr: 888-756-4624
E-mail: aiceo@appraisalinstitute.org
URL: http://www.appraisalinstitute.org

Description: General appraisers who hold the MAI designation, and residential members who hold the SRA designation. Enforces Code of Professional Ethics and Standards of Professional Appraisal Practice. Confers one general designation, the MAI, and one residential designation, the SRA. Provides training in valuation of residential and income properties, market analysis, and standards of professional appraisal practice. Sponsors courses in preparation for state certification and licensing; offers continuing education programs for designated members.

10966 ■ Association of Appraiser Regulatory Officials (AARO)
13200 Strickland Rd., Ste. 114-264
Raleigh, NC 27613
Ph: (919)235-4544
Fax: (919)870-5392
E-mail: milneallen@charter.com
URL: http://www.aaro.net

Description: Represents real estate appraiser licensing agencies in the United States and its territories. Seeks to improve the administration and enforcement of real estate appraisal laws. Provides education, research, communication and cooperation among appraiser regulatory officials.

10967 ■ Association of Online Appraiser (AOA)
PO Box 1292
Frederick, MD 21702
Ph: (301)228-2279
Fax: (240)436-6044
E-mail: info@aoaonline.org
URL: http://www.aoaonline.org

Description: Represents personal property appraisers who are either offering traditional appraisal reports or who are involved in offering online written appraisal reports through the use of digital images and internet online reporting. Seeks to empower the professional property appraisal community. Promotes and encourages education, professionalism, and ethical conduct among personal property appraisers.

10968 ■ Association of Real Estate Women
1201 Wakarusa Dr., Ste. C3
Lawrence, KS 66049
Ph: (212)599-6181
Fax: (785)832-1551
Fr: 888-329-2739
E-mail: info@arew.org
URL: http://www.arew.org

Description: Provides programs and networking opportunities that can contribute to the career growth of both men and women in all segments and all levels

of the real estate industry. Helps members find new employment opportunities.

10969 ■ Counselors of Real Estate (CRE)
430 N Michigan Ave.
Chicago, IL 60611
Ph: (312)329-8427
E-mail: info@cre.org
URL: http://www.cre.org

Description: Professional society of individuals with extensive experience in all phases of real estate who provide a counseling service. Members are entitled to use the Professional Designation CRE (Counselor of Real Estate). Conducts educational programs during three national meetings.

10970 ■ International Real Estate Institute (IREI)
PO Box 879
Palm Springs, CA 92263
Ph: (760)327-5284
Fax: (760)327-5631
Fr: 877-743-6799
E-mail: support@assoc-hdqts.org
URL: http://irei-assoc.org

Description: Professionals in 120 countries specializing in the development, finance, investment and valuation of real estate. Conducts educational seminars and regional programs; operates speakers' bureau and placement service. Compiles statistics, consults United Nations on property issues.

10971 ■ National Association of Real Estate Appraisers (NAREA)
PO Box 879
Palm Springs, CA 92263
Ph: (760)327-5284
Fax: (760)327-5631
Fr: 877-815-4172
E-mail: support@assoc-hdqts.org
URL: http://www.narea-assoc.org

Description: Real estate appraisers. Aims to make available the services of the most highly qualified real estate appraisers. Offers certification to members.

10972 ■ National Association of Real Estate Brokers (NAREB)
5504 Brentwood Stair Rd.
Fort Worth, TX 76112
Ph: (817)446-7715
Fax: (817)446-7744
E-mail: wvincent.wimbish@nareb.com
URL: http://www.nareb.com

Description: Members of the real estate industry. Research, educational and certification programs include: Real Estate Management Brokers Institute; National Society of Real Estate Appraisers; Real Estate Brokerage Institute; United Developers Council. Encourages unity among those who are engaged in real estate. Promotes and maintains high standards of conduct. Protects the public against unethical, improper, or fraudulent practices connected with the real estate business. Conducts research; compiles statistics on productivity, marketing and development. Gives members license to use "Realtist" symbol. Sponsors educational seminars. Maintains Willis E. Carson Library.

10973 ■ National Association of Realtors (NAR)
430 N Michigan Ave.
Chicago, IL 60611-4087
Fr: 800-874-6500
URL: http://www.realtor.org

Description: Federation of 54 state and territory associations and 1,860 local real estate boards whose members are real estate brokers and agents; terms are registered by the association in the U.S. Patent and Trademark Office and in the states. Promotes education, high professional standards and modern techniques in specialized real estate work such as brokerage, appraisal, property management, land development, industrial real estate, farm brokerage and counseling. Conducts research programs.

10974 ■ National Association of Review Appraisers and Mortgage Underwriters (NARA/MU)
810 N Farrell Dr.
Palm Springs, CA 92262
Ph: (760)327-5284
Fax: (760)327-5631
E-mail: support@assoc-hdqts.org
URL: http://www.naramu.org

Description: Real estate professionals and mortgage underwriters who aid in determining value of property. Acts as umbrella group for real estate appraisers. Conducts educational seminars; maintains speakers' bureau; operates placement service.

10975 ■ Realtors Land Institute (RLI)
430 N Michigan Ave.
Chicago, IL 60611
Ph: (312)329-8446
Fax: (312)329-8633

Fr: 800-441-5263
E-mail: rli@realtors.org
URL: http://www.rliland.com

Description: Real estate brokers and salespersons selling, managing, appraising, or developing all types of land. Maintains educational programs for real estate brokers; promotes competence and accredits members. Sponsors courses for realtors and others seeking professional excellence on Land Brokerage, Agricultural Land Brokerage, Exchanging Properties, Estate Planning, Subdivision Development and Financial Analysis of Land Investment.

Sources of Help-Wanted Ads

10976 ■ American City and County
Penton Media Inc.
9800 Metcalf Ave.
Overland Park, KS 66212
Ph: (913)341-1300
Fax: (913)967-1898
URL: http://americancityandcounty.com

Monthly. Municipal and county administration magazine.

10977 ■ Camping Magazine
American Camp Association
5000 State Rd. 67 N
Martinsville, IN 46151-7902
Ph: (765)342-8456
Fax: (765)342-2065
E-mail: magazine@aca-camps.org
URL: http://www.acacamps.org/campmag/

Bimonthly. $29.95/year for individuals, U.S. mainland; $56.00/year for two years, U.S. mainland; $48.00/year for individuals, Alaska, Hawaii, Puerto Rico; Canada & Mexico; $92.00/year for two years, Alaska, Hawaii, Puerto Rico; Canada & Mexico; $54.00/year for other countries; $104.00/year for other countries, 2 years. Magazine on organized camp management.

10978 ■ The Municipality
League of Wisconsin Municipalities
122 W Washington Ave., Ste. 300
Madison, WI 53703-2715
Ph: (608)267-2380
Fax: (608)267-0645
Fr: 800-991-5502
URL: http://www.lwm-info.org/

Monthly. Magazine for officials of Wisconsin's local municipal governments.

10979 ■ NRPA Career Center
National Recreation and Park Association, Professional Services Div.
22377 Belmont Ridge Rd.
Ashburn, VA 20148
Ph: (703)858-0784
Fax: (703)858-0794
Fr: 800-626-6772
E-mail: customerservice@nrpa.org
URL: http://www.nrpa.org

Description: Provides listings of employment opportunities in the park, recreation, and leisure services field.

10980 ■ Sailing World
Miller Sports Group L.L.C.
79 Madison Ave., 8th Fl.
New York, NY 10016-7802
Ph: (212)636-2700
E-mail: editor@sailingworld.com
URL: http://www.sailingworld.com/index.jsp

$14.97/year for individuals; $23.97/year for Canada; $36.97/year for other countries. Magazine on performance sailing.

10981 ■ Ski Area Management
Beardsley Publishing Corp.
45 Main St. N
PO Box 644
Woodbury, CT 06798
Ph: (203)263-0888
Fax: (203)266-0452
URL: http://www.saminfo.com

Bimonthly. $59.00/year for individuals; $88.00/year for two years; $110.00/year for individuals, three years; $62.00/year for Canada; $78.00/year for other countries. Trade magazine covering ski area management.

10982 ■ Strategies
American Alliance for Health, Physical Education, Recreation & Dance
1900 Association Dr.
Reston, VA 20191-1598
Ph: (703)476-3400
Fax: (703)476-9527
Fr: 800-213-7193
E-mail: strategies@aahperd.org
URL: http://www.aahperd.org/naspe/publications/
    journals/strategie

Bimonthly. $130.00/year for U.S. and Canada, institutions, schools & libraries; print & online; $50.00/year for U.S. and Canada, add $5 GST; $62.00/year for other countries, schools & libraries, print & online; $130.00/year for institutions, other countries, schools & libraries, online; $142.00/year for institutions, other countries, schools & libraries, print; $162.00/year for institutions, other countries, schools & libraries, print & online. Peer-reviewed journal providing practical, hands-on information to physical educators and coaches.

10983 ■ Tourist Attractions & Parks Magazine
Kane Communications Inc.
10 E Athens Ave., Ste. 208
Ardmore, PA 19003
Ph: (610)645-6940
Fax: (610)645-6943
E-mail: tapmag@kanec.com
URL: http://www.tapmag.com

$49.00/year for individuals; $55.00/year for two years; $55.00/year for other countries; $61.00/year for other countries, 2 years. Magazine on the management of amusement parks, carnivals, arcades, museums, zoos, campgrounds, fun centers, arenas, miniature golf, and water sports.

10984 ■ Western City
League of California Cities
1400 K St., 4th Fl.
Sacramento, CA 95814
Ph: (916)658-8200

Fax: (916)658-8240
Fr: 800-262-1801
URL: http://www.westerncity.com

Monthly. $39.00/year for individuals; $63.00/year for two years; $52.00/year for other countries; $26.50/year for students. Municipal interest magazine.

10985 ■ Workamper News
709 W Searcy St.
Heber Springs, AR 72543-3761
Ph: (501)362-2637
Fax: (501)362-6769
E-mail: info@workamper.com
URL: http://www.workamper.com

Description: Bimonthly. Provides a list of information on seasonal and full-time job openings at campgrounds, forests, public and private resort areas, and motorsports events.

Employer Directories and Networking Lists

10986 ■ Guide to ACA-Accredited Camps
American Camp Association
5000 State Rd. 67 N
Martinsville, IN 46151-7902
Ph: (765)342-8456
Fax: (765)342-2065
URL: http://bookstore.acacamps.org/

Annual, January; Latest edition 2004. Covers: Over 2,400 summer camps. Entries include: Name of camp, address, phone, fax, email addresses, age and sex of children accepted, rates, season, capacity, facilities, programs, activities offered and camp philosophy. Arrangement: Geographical, then by day or resident camp. Indexes: Activity, special clientele, camp name, specific disabilities.

10987 ■ Membership and Peer Network Directory
ESM Association
568 Spring Rd., Ste. D
Elmhurst, IL 60126-3896
Fax: (630)559-0025
URL: http://www.esmassn.org/
    Default.aspx?pageId=160954

Annual, April. Covers: over 4,500 personnel managers, recreation directors, suppliers, and certified administrators in employee recreation, fitness, and services. Entries include: Name, address, phone, fax and e-mail. Arrangement: Alphabetical.

10988 ■ Recreational Sports Directory
National Intramural-Recreational Sports Association
4185 SW Research Way
Corvallis, OR 97333-1067
Ph: (541)766-8211
Fax: (541)766-8284
URL: http://www.nirsa.org

Annual, Latest edition 2011. $45.00 for members; $125.00 for nonmembers. Covers: Recreational sports programs in approximately 2,500 four-year colleges and universities, nearly 700 junior and community colleges, Canadian colleges and universities, and over 350 military installations. Entries include: Institution name and address; institution enrollment; name of president; names, phone numbers, fax numbers, Internet access, and job titles of recreational directors and staff; existing sports clubs; degrees offered in physical education and recreation; whether graduate assistantships or internships are available. A Buyer's Guide is included with supplier addresses and descriptions of products and services. Arrangement: Classified by institution type, then alphabetical. Indexes: Alphabetical, geographical, personal name, recreational sports program.

10989 ■ *White Book of Ski Areas*
Inter-Ski Services Inc.
1502 27th St. NW
PO Box 3775, Georgetown Sta.
Washington, DC 20007
Ph: (202)342-0886
URL: http://www.inter-ski.com

Annual, latest edition 30th. Free. Covers: About 500 lift-equipped ski areas and resorts. Entries include: Name of ski area, location, phone; snow condition phone numbers; ski statistics (elevation, lift capacity, etc.); season and rates; equipment and schooling available; lodging availability and phone, restaurants, apres-ski, and other recreational facilities in vicinity; shops; travel instructions. Special industry edition available with more comprehensive information; $395. Arrangement: Geographical within four regions—West, North Central, South, and Northeast. Indexes: Geographical.

10990 ■ *YMCA Resident Camp Directory*
Camping Programs
101 N Wacker Dr.
Chicago, IL 60606
Ph: (312)977-0031
Fr: 800-872-9622
URL: http://www.ymca.net/find_ymca_camps/

updated weekly. Database covers: Over 235 resident camps and conference and retreat centers operated by local YMCA associations in the United States. Entries include: Association name, camp name, address and phone of winter office, camp location and summer address and phone, name of director, seasons of operation, capacity; whether coed or restricted to boys or girls, or available for family and adult camping; special programs offered. Arrangement: Classified by type of camp (resident, family, conference centers).

HANDBOOKS AND MANUALS

10991 ■ *Careers for Health Nuts and Others Who Like to Stay Fit*
The McGraw-Hill Companies
PO Box 182604
Columbus, OH 43272
Fax: (614)759-3749
Fr: 877-883-5524
E-mail: customer.service@mcgraw-hill.com
URL: http://www.mhprofessional.com

Blythe Camenson. Second edition. $13.95 (paper). 208 pages.

10992 ■ *Careers in Travel, Tourism, and Hospitality*
The McGraw-Hill Companies
PO Box 182604
Columbus, OH 43272
Fax: (614)759-3749
Fr: 877-883-5524
E-mail: customer.service@mcgraw-hill.com
URL: http://www.mhprofessional.com

Marjorie Eberts, Linda Brothers, and Ann Gisler. Second edition, 2005. $15.95 (paper). 224 pages.

10993 ■ *Opportunities in Child Care Careers*
The McGraw-Hill Companies
PO Box 182604
Columbus, OH 43272
Fax: (614)759-3749
Fr: 877-883-5524
E-mail: customer.service@mcgraw-hill.com
URL: http://www.mhprofessional.com/
    product.php?isbn=0071467661

Renee Wittenberg. 2006. $13.95 (paper). 160 pages. Discusses various job opportunities and how to secure a position. Illustrated.

ONLINE JOB SOURCES AND SERVICES

10994 ■ Online Sports Career Center
Fr: 800-856-2638
E-mail: comments@atsonlinesports.com
URL: http://www.onlinesports.com/pages/
    careercenter.html

Description: Resource for sports-related career opportunities, as well as a resume bank for the perusal of potential employers within the sports and recreation industries. Main files include: Job Bank, Resume Bank, Newsletter, Work With Online Sports, Other Internet Resources.

10995 ■ SportsAndRecreationCrossing.com
URL: http://www.sportsandrecreationcrossing.com

Description: Serves as a clearinghouse for individuals looking for employment in the sports and recreation industry.

10996 ■ WaterParkJobs.com
URL: http://www.waterparkjobs.com

Description: Serves as niche board for returning or first-time job seekers looking for work in the water-park industry.

TRADESHOWS

10997 ■ IDEA World Fitness and Personal Trainer Convention
IDEA, Health & Fitness Association
10455 Pacific Center Ct.
San Diego, CA 92121-4339
Ph: (858)535-8979
Fax: (858)535-8234
Fr: 800-999-4332
E-mail: contact@ideafit.com
URL: http://www.ideafit.com

Annual. Primary Exhibits: Aerobic clothing and footwear, exercise products, equipment companies, related services. Dates and Locations: 2012 Jul 05-08; San Diego, CA.

10998 ■ North Carolina Recreation and Park Association Conference
North Carolina Recreation and Park Society
883 Washington St.
Raleigh, NC 27605
Ph: (919)832-5868
Fax: (919)832-3323
E-mail: info@ncrpa.net
URL: http://www.ncrpa.net

Annual. Primary Exhibits: Parks and recreation equipment, supplies, and services.

OTHER SOURCES

10999 ■ American Alliance for Health, Physical Education, Recreation and Dance (AAHPERD)
1900 Association Dr.
Reston, VA 20191-1598
Ph: (703)476-3400
Fax: (703)476-9527

Fr: 800-213-7193
E-mail: membership@aahperd.org
URL: http://www.aahperd.org

Description: Students and educators in physical education, dance, health, athletics, safety education, recreation, and outdoor education. Works to improve its fields of education at all levels through such services as consultation, periodicals and special publications, leadership development, determination of standards, and research. Sponsors placement service.

11000 ■ American Association for Horsemanship Safety
5304 Reeve Rd.
Mazomanie, WI 53560
Ph: (608)767-2593
Fax: (608)767-2590
E-mail: mail@horsemanshipsafety.com
URL: http://horsemanshipsafety.com

Description: Schools of horsemanship; equine programs at colleges and technical schools; riding instructors and students; medical personnel. To educate equestrians and instructors in safe horsemanship practices. Trains instructors in leadership techniques; conducts group and private lessons for children and adults; sponsors seminars and speaking engagements by certified clinicians. Conducts riding instructor clinics for adults. Certifies instructors at 4 levels: assistant riding instructor, horsemanship safety instructor, associate instructor, and clinic instructor. Certified instructors must renew certification every 3 years. Provides on-site consultation. Offers Expert Witness service. Compiles statistics; maintains speakers' bureau and placement service. Operates job placement services.

11001 ■ American Association for Physical Activity and Recreation (AAPAR)
1900 Association Dr.
Reston, VA 20191-1598
Ph: (703)476-3430
Fax: (703)476-9527
Fr: 800-213-7193
E-mail: aapar@aahperd.org
URL: http://www.aahperd.org/aapar

Description: Aims to promote and support education, physical activity, and recreation by developing quality programming and professional training; providing leadership opportunities; disseminating guidelines and standards; enhancing public understanding of the importance of leisure and recreation in maintaining a creative and healthy lifestyle. Goals and objectives are to serve as a forum for professionals, students and organizations to educate and exchange information and ideas on physical activity and recreation services; develop and promote professional standards for education, physical activity and recreation services; increase public awareness, understanding, appreciation, and support for lifelong education, physical activity and recreation services; encourage professional training for all with an interest in education, leisure and recreation services; advance, encourage, conduct and publish scientific knowledge and research in the field of education, physical activity, and recreation services.

11002 ■ American Camp Association (ACA)
5000 State Rd., 67 N
Martinsville, IN 46151-7902
Ph: (765)342-8456
Fax: (765)342-2065
Fr: 800-428-CAMP
E-mail: 2020@acacamps.org
URL: http://www.acacamps.org

Description: Camp owners, directors, program directors, businesses, and students interested in resident and day camp programming for youth and adults. Conducts camp standards. Offers educational programs in areas of administration, staffing, child development, promotion, and programming.

11003 ■ American Council on Exercise (ACE)
4851 Paramount Dr.
San Diego, CA 92123
Ph: (858)576-6500
Fax: (858)576-6564
Fr: 888-825-3636
E-mail: support@acefitness.org
URL: http://www.acefitness.org

Description: Promotes the benefits of physical activity and protects consumers against unsafe and ineffective fitness products and instruction. Sponsors university-based exercise science research and testing that targets fitness products and trends. Sets standards for fitness professionals.

11004 ■ American Sail Training Association (ASTA)
PO Box 1459
Newport, RI 02840
Ph: (401)846-1775
Fax: (401)849-5400
E-mail: asta@tallshipsamerica.org
URL: http://tallships.sailtraining.org

Description: Organizations operating sail training programs; corporations and educational institutions supporting sail training; private citizens with an interest in sailing and sail training. Promotes sail training as an educational and character-building experience for youth of all ages. Seeks to bring together the sail training ships of the world in a spirit of friendship and international goodwill. Sponsors Tall Ships events including sail training rallies. Maintains billet bank/placement service; compiles statistics.

11005 ■ American Senior Fitness Association (SFA)
PO Box 2575
New Smyrna Beach, FL 32170
Ph: (386)423-6634
Fax: 877-365-3048
Fr: 888-689-6791
E-mail: asfa@seniorfitness.net
URL: http://www.seniorfitness.net

Description: Promotes excellence in older adult fitness. Provides comprehensive training, recognized certification, professional resources and member support for fitness professionals who serve older adults. Offers senior fitness specialist courses for colleges and universities.

11006 ■ Employee Services Management Foundation (ESM)
PO Box 10517
Rockville, MD 20849
Ph: (630)559-0020
Fax: (630)559-0025
E-mail: esmahq@esmassn.org
URL: http://www.esmassn.org

Description: Corporations and governmental agencies that sponsor recreation, fitness, and service programs for their employees; associate members are manufacturers and suppliers in the employee recreation market and distributors of consumer products and services. Serves as an information resource network for members nationwide. Implements and maintains a diverse range of employee services; believes that employee services, as practical solutions to work/life issues, are essential to sound business management. Conducts programs that improves relations between employees and management, increases overall productivity, boosts morale, and reduces absenteeism and turnover.

11007 ■ Exercise Safety Association (ESA)
PO Box 547916
Orlando, FL 32854-7916
Ph: (407)246-5090
E-mail: askesa@aol.com
URL: http://www.exercisesafety.com

Description: Fitness instructors, personal trainers, health spas, YMCAs, community recreation departments, and hospital wellness programs. Purposes are: to improve the qualifications of exercise instructors; to train instructors to develop safe exercise programs that will help people avoid injury while exercising; to prepare instructors for national certification. Offers training in aerobics and exercise and on the physiological aspects of exercise. Conducts exercise safety and research programs. Sponsors charitable program; maintains speakers' bureau. Offers instructor placement services.

11008 ■ IDEA Health and Fitness Association
10455 Pacific Center Ct.
San Diego, CA 92121
Ph: (858)535-8979
Fax: (858)535-8234
Fr: 800-999-IDEA
E-mail: contact@ideafit.com
URL: http://www.ideafit.com

Description: Provides continuing education for fitness professionals including; fitness instructors, personal trainers, program directors, and club/studio owners. Offers workshops for continuing education credits.

11009 ■ International Society of Professional Trackers (ISPT)
445 Laguna Rd.
Rohnert Park, CA 94928
Ph: (707)338-4760
E-mail: del903@sbcglobal.net
URL: http://www.ispt.org

Description: Provides a framework wherein all trackers, tracking students, and people interested in tracking worldwide can share and preserve the knowledge of tracking in all its forms and disciplines. Facilitates communication between members worldwide, while remaining a neutral and safe entity for all the different tracking styles, practices, philosophies and skills. Disseminates information on schools and programs to new tracking students.

11010 ■ Jackie Robinson Foundation (JRF)
One Hudson Sq.
75 Varick St., 2nd Fl.
New York, NY 10013-1917
Ph: (212)290-8600
Fax: (212)290-8081
E-mail: general@jackierobinson.org
URL: http://www.jackierobinson.org

Description: Seeks to develop the leadership and achievement potential of minority and urban youth. Founded by the friends and family of Jackie Robinson (1919-72), the first black athlete to play major league baseball. Trains minority and poor youths for sports management careers. Provides counseling, support, and placement services. Awards full college scholarships to promising minority students. Maintains collection of Jackie Robinson memorabilia; has produced a national touring exhibit of archival materials pertaining to Robinson.

11011 ■ Maine Professional Guides Association
55 Morrison Hill Rd.
Wilton, ME 04294
E-mail: info@maineguides.org
URL: http://www.maineguides.org

Members: Registered Maine guides. **Purpose:** Promotes a quality, ethical, and legal outdoor experience for all. **Activities:** Monitors new and proposed legislation that affects the guiding industry. Issues guide licenses. Provides an online searchable database of members.

11012 ■ National Association for Girls and Women in Sport (NAGWS)
1900 Association Dr.
Reston, VA 20191-1598
Ph: (703)476-3452
Fax: (703)476-4566
Fr: 800-213-7193
E-mail: nagws@aahperd.org
URL: http://www.aahperd.org/nagws

Description: Represents teachers, coaches, athletic trainers, officials, athletic administrators, and students. Has 4 main structures: Advocacy Coaching Enhancement; Minority Representation; Professional Development Publications, and Student Representation. Supports and fosters the development of quality sports programs that will enrich the lives of all participants. Holds training sessions for leadership development. Conducts research programs.

11013 ■ National Association of Recreation Resource Planners (NARRP)
PO Box 221
Marienville, PA 16239
Ph: (814)927-8212
Fax: (814)927-6659
E-mail: info@narrp.org
URL: http://www.narrp.org

Description: Individuals working in state and federal recreation and resource agencies and private organizations who are responsible for recreation planning. Seeks to increase the professional expertise of membership and to coordinate positions with respect to federal planning requirements and policy and funding issues.

11014 ■ National Association of Underwater Instructors (NAUI)
PO Box 89789
Tampa, FL 33689-0413
Ph: (813)628-6284
Fax: (813)628-8253
Fr: 800-553-6284
E-mail: nauihq@naui.org
URL: http://www.naui.org

Description: Certified instructors of basic, advanced, and specialized courses in underwater diving. Offers instructor certification programs and training programs. Conducts seminars, workshops, and symposia. Sells diving education books. Sponsors competitions; maintains speakers' bureau and placement service; conducts charitable programs.

11015 ■ National Forest Recreation Association (NFRA)
PO Box 488
Woodlake, CA 93286
Ph: (559)564-2365
Fax: (559)564-2048
E-mail: info@nfra.org
URL: http://www.nfra.org

Description: Owners and operators of resorts, winter sports areas, marinas, campgrounds, stores, river trip outfitters, packer-outfitters, restaurants, and motels located on or adjacent to federal land. Participates in trade and public relations matters that is of interest to members, including legislation and relationships with U.S. agencies; state and local officials in matters of taxation, insurance, finance, health, and building requirements; and employment.

11016 ■ Outdoor Industries Women's Coalition (OIWC)
PO Box 36261
Cincinnati, OH 45236
Ph: (208)860-6370
Fax: 877-686-6492
E-mail: info@oiwc.org
URL: http://www.oiwc.org

Description: Seeks equality of power, influence, and opportunities for women in the outdoor industries. Fosters the professional development of women in the outdoor industries through educational programming, networking, and mentoring. Acts as a vehicle to promote the views and interests of women engaged in or impassioned by the outdoor industry and the snow sports, action sports, and bicycling industries.

11017 ■ Professional Association of Parasail Operators (PAPO)
844 W Mission Bay Dr., Ste. A
San Diego, CA 92109
Ph: (858)488-9100
Fax: (858)488-6500
E-mail: admin@teampapo.org
URL: http://www.teampapo.org

Description: Promotes safety and professionalism in the parasailing industry. Assists in the development, implementation, and management of industry operating standards and guidelines for the parasailing industry. Provides a risk management component designed to effectively manage the inherent risks associated with commercial parasailing, in the interest of public safety and self-preservation.

11018 ■ Resort and Commercial Recreation Association (RCRA)
PO Box 1564
Dubuque, IA 52004
E-mail: lisa.linden@rcra.org
URL: http://www.rcra.org

Description: Professionals, agencies, vendors, educators, and students involved in the resort and commercial recreation field. Seeks to advance the resort and commercial recreation industries; increase the profitability of commercial recreation enterprises; foster communication among members; promote professionalism within the industry; provide opportunities for continuing education. Acts as a vehicle for networking; offers program exchange and job placement services. Holds specialized educational presentations; operates student chapters; encourages and facilitates internships. Provides car rental discount program.

11019 ■ United States Mountain Guides Association (USMGA)
PO Box 267
Intervale, NH 03845
E-mail: domain@seo99.com
URL: http://www.usmga.net

Description: Seeks to raise the standard of American guiding and to improve the quality of the climbing public's guided experience. Supports and encourages programs that promote education within the guiding industry. Offers training courses and guide certification exams in mountaineering.

11020 ■ YMCA International Camp Counselor Program (ICCP)
5 W 63rd St., 2nd Fl.
New York, NY 10023
Ph: (212)727-8800
Fax: (212)724-2344
Fr: 888-477-9622
E-mail: ips@ymcanyc.org
URL: http://www.internationalymca.org/ICCP/ymca_international.htm

Description: Serves as a work-travel program designed to introduce international university students and teachers and social workers aged 19-30 to life in America; the students spend 8 to 9 weeks counseling in children's camps across the country, followed by a period of independent or group travel. Sponsors ICCP-Abroad placement service for American university students aged 18-25 wishing to serve as camp counselors in Africa, Asia, Australia, Hungary, New Zealand, and South America.

SOURCES OF HELP-WANTED ADS

11021 ■ American Therapeutic Recreation Association Newsletter
American Therapeutic Recreation Association
629 N Main St.
Hattiesburg, MS 39401
Ph: (601)450-2872
Fax: (601)582-3354
E-mail: national@atra-online.com
URL: http://www.atra-online.com

Semi-monthly. Covers industry news, occupational advances, and legislative alerts.

EMPLOYER DIRECTORIES AND NETWORKING LISTS

11022 ■ Directory of Hospital Personnel
Grey House Publishing
4919 Rte. 22
PO Box 56
Amenia, NY 12501
Ph: (518)789-8700
Fax: (518)789-0556
Fr: 800-562-2139
URL: http://www.greyhouse.com/hospital_personnel.htm

Annual, Latest edition 2011. $325.00 for individuals. Covers: 200,000 executives at 6,000 U.S. Hospitals. Entries include: Name of hospital, address, phone, number of beds, type and JCAHO status of hospital, names and titles of key department heads and staff, medical and nursing school affiliations; number of residents, interns, and nursing students. Arrangement: Geographical. Indexes: Hospital name, personnel, hospital size.

11023 ■ Hospital Blue Book
Billian Publishing Inc. and Trans World Publishing Inc.
2100 River Edge Pky.
Atlanta, GA 30328
Ph: (770)955-5656
Fax: (770)952-0669
Fr: 800-800-5668
E-mail: blu-book@billian.com
URL: http://www.billianshealthdata.com/Products/bluebook.html

Annual, Latest edition 2010. $575.00 for individuals; $575.00 for individuals. Covers: More than 6,500 hospitals; some listings also appear in a separate southern edition of this publication. Entries include: Name of hospital, accreditation, mailing address, phone, fax, number of beds, type of facility (nonprofit, general, state, etc.); list of administrative personnel and chiefs of medical services, with specific titles. Arrangement: Geographical.

11024 ■ Medical and Health Information Directory
Gale
PO Box 6904
Florence, KY 41022-6904
Fr: 800-354-9706
URL: http://www.gale.cengage.com

Annual, Latest edition April 2011. $1190.00 for individuals; $501.00 for individuals. Covers: In volume 1, more than 33,000 medical and health oriented associations, organizations, institutions, and government agencies, including health maintenance organizations (HMOs), preferred provider organizations (PPOs), insurance companies, pharmaceutical companies, research centers, and medical and allied health schools. In Volume 2, over 20,000 medical book publishers; medical periodicals, directories, audiovisual producers and services, medical libraries and information centers, electronic resources, and health-related internet search engines. In Volume 3, more than 40,500 clinics, treatment centers, care programs, and counseling/diagnostic services for 34 subject areas. Entries include: Institution, service, or firm name, address, phone, fax, email and URL; many include names of key personnel and, when pertinent, descriptive annotation. Volume 3 was formerly listed separately as Health Services Directory. Arrangement: Classified by organization activity, service, etc. Indexes: Each volume has a complete alphabetical name and keyword index.

HANDBOOKS AND MANUALS

11025 ■ Careers in Health Care
The McGraw-Hill Companies
PO Box 182604
Columbus, OH 43272
Fax: (614)759-3749
Fr: 877-883-5524
E-mail: customer.service@mcgraw-hill.com
URL: http://www.mhprofessional.com/product.php?isbn=0071466533

Barbara M. Swanson. Fifth edition, 2005. $19.95 (paper). 192 pages. Describes job duties, work settings, salaries, licensing and certification requirements, educational preparation, and future outlook. Gives ideas on how to secure a job.

11026 ■ Careers in Social and Rehabilitation Services
The McGraw-Hill Companies
PO Box 182604
Columbus, OH 43272
Fax: (614)759-3749
Fr: 877-883-5524
E-mail: customer.service@mcgraw-hill.com
URL: http://www.mhprofessional.com/product.php?isbn=0071641955

Geraldine O. Garner. 2008. $16.95. 192 pages.

11027 ■ Opportunities in Health and Medical Careers
The McGraw-Hill Companies
PO Box 182604
Columbus, OH 43272
Fax: (614)759-3749
Fr: 877-883-5524
E-mail: customer.service@mcgraw-hill.com
URL: http://www.mhprofessional.com/product.php?isbn=0071437274

I. Donald Snook, Jr. and Leo D'Orazio. 2004. $14.95 (paper). 157 pages. Covers the full range of medical and health occupations. Illustrated.

11028 ■ Resumes for Health and Medical Careers
The McGraw-Hill Companies
PO Box 182604
Columbus, OH 43272
Fax: (614)759-3749
Fr: 877-883-5524
E-mail: customer.service@mcgraw-hill.com
URL: http://www.mhprofessional.com/product.php?isbn=0071545352

Third edition, 2008. $12.95 (paper). 144 pages.

EMPLOYMENT AGENCIES AND SEARCH FIRMS

11029 ■ Cross Country TravCorps
6551 Park of Commerce Blvd.
Boca Raton, FL 33487-8247
Fax: (561)998-8533
Fr: 800-530-6125
E-mail: sms@cctc.com
URL: http://www.crosscountrytravcorps.com/cctc/

Places traveling nurses in assignments nationwide.

11030 ■ Harper Associates
31000 NW Hwy., Ste. 240
Farmington Hills, MI 48334
Ph: (248)932-1170
Fax: (248)932-1214
E-mail: info@harperjobs.com
URL: http://www.harperjobs.com

Executive search firm and employment agency.

11031 ■ Professional Placement Associates, Inc.
287 Bowman Ave.
Purchase, NY 10577-2517
Ph: (914)251-1000
Fax: (914)251-1055
E-mail: careers@ppasearch.com
URL: http://www.ppasearch.com

Executive search firm specializing in the health and medical field.

ONLINE JOB SOURCES AND SERVICES

11032 ■ ActivityJobs.com
URL: http://www.activityjobs.com

Description: Provides employment listing for recreation therapists, activity therapists, activity coordinators, creative arts therapists and leisure counselors.

11033 ■ HEALTHeCAREERS Network
Fr: 888-884-8242
E-mail: info@healthecareers.com
URL: http://www.healthecareers.com

Description: Career search site for jobs in all health care specialties; educational resources; visa and licensing information for relocation; interesting articles; relocation tools; links to professional organizations and general resources.

11034 ■ ProHealthJobs.com
Ph: (484)443-8545
Fax: (484)443-8549
E-mail: info@prohealthjobs.com
URL: http://prohealthjobs.com/jobboard

Description: Career resources site for the medical and health care field. Lists professional opportunities, product information, continuing education and open positions.

11035 ■ Recreational Therapist Jobs
URL: http://www.recreationaltherapistjobs.org

Description: Features nationwide job search listings for recreational therapists. Offers professional resume writing services.

11036 ■ RecreationalTherapistJobs.com
URL: http://recreationaltherapistjobs.com

Description: Features job sites, company career pages and associations for recreational therapist jobs.

11037 ■ Therapeutic Recreation Directory
URL: http://www.recreationtherapy.com

Description: Provides resources and interworking opportunities for recreation therapists and activity directors. Includes a job bulletin, internship directory, activity and treatment resources, articles and news, chatroom, bulletin boards, and surveys.

TRADESHOWS

11038 ■ American Therapeutic Recreation Association Annual Conference
American Therapeutic Recreation Association
629 N Main St.
Hattiesburg, MS 39401
Ph: (601)450-2872
Fax: (601)582-3354
E-mail: national@atra-online.com
URL: http://atra-online.com

Annual. Offers educational sessions to address recreational therapy issues and trends in healthcare and community settings. 2012 October 12-15; Phoenix, AZ.

OTHER SOURCES

11039 ■ American Association for Physical Activity and Recreation (AAPAR)
1900 Association Dr.
Reston, VA 20191-1598
Ph: (703)476-3430
Fax: (703)476-9527
Fr: 800-213-7193
E-mail: aapar@aahperd.org
URL: http://www.aahperd.org/aapar

Description: Aims to promote and support education, physical activity, and recreation by developing quality programming and professional training; provid-

ing leadership opportunities; disseminating guidelines and standards; enhancing public understanding of the importance of leisure and recreation in maintaining a creative and healthy lifestyle. Goals and objectives are to serve as a forum for professionals, students and organizations to educate and exchange information and ideas on physical activity and recreation services; develop and promote professional standards for education, physical activity and recreation services; increase public awareness, understanding, appreciation, and support for lifelong education, physical activity and recreation services; encourage professional training for all with an interest in education, leisure and recreation services; advance, encourage, conduct and publish scientific knowledge and research in the field of education, physical activity, and recreation services.

11040 ■ American Health Care Association (AHCA)
1201 L St. NW
Washington, DC 20005
Ph: (202)842-4444
Fax: (202)842-3860
E-mail: hr@ahca.org
URL: http://www.ahcancal.org/Pages/Default.aspx

Description: Federation of state associations of long-term health care facilities. Promotes standards for professionals in long-term health care delivery and quality care for patients and residents in a safe environment. Focuses on issues of availability, quality, affordability, and fair payment. Operates as liaison with governmental agencies, Congress, and professional associations. Compiles statistics.

11041 ■ American Kinesiotherapy Association (AKTA)
118 College Dr., No. 5142
Hattiesburg, MS 39406
Fr: 800-296-2582
E-mail: info@akta.org
URL: http://www.akta.org

Description: Professional society of kinesiotherapists, associate and student members with interest in therapeutic exercise and education. Kinesiotherapy is the application of scientifically-based exercise principles adapted to enhance the strength, endurance and mobility of individuals with functional limitations of those requiring extended physical reconditioning. Seeks to serve the interest of members and represent the profession to the public through the promotion of continuing competency and continuing educational opportunities.

11042 ■ American Therapeutic Recreation Association (ATRA)
629 N Main St.
Hattiesburg, MS 39401
Ph: (601)450-2872
Fax: (601)582-3354
E-mail: national@atra-online.org
URL: http://www.atra-online.com

Description: Therapeutic recreation professionals and students; interested others. Promotes the use of therapeutic recreation in hospitals, mental rehabilitation centers, physical rehabilitation centers, senior citizen treatment centers, and other public health facilities. Conducts discussions on certification, legislative and regulatory concerns that affect the industry. Sponsors seminars and workshops; conducts research.

11043 ■ Association on Higher Education and Disability (AHEAD)
107 Commerce Center Dr., Ste. 204
Huntersville, NC 28078
Ph: (704)947-7779
Fax: (704)948-7779
E-mail: ahead@ahead.org
URL: http://www.ahead.org

Description: Individuals interested in promoting the equal rights and opportunities of disabled postsecondary students, staff, faculty, and graduates. Provides an exchange of communication for those

professionally involved with disabled students; collects, evaluates, and disseminates information; encourages and supports legislation for the benefit of disabled students. Conducts surveys on issues pertinent to college students with disabilities; offers resource referral system and employment exchange for positions in disability student services. Conducts research programs; compiles statistics.

11044 ■ Child Life Council (CLC)
11821 Parklawn Dr., Ste. 310
Rockville, MD 20852-2539
Ph: (301)881-7090
Fax: (301)881-7092
Fr: 800-252-4515
E-mail: clcadmin@childlife.org
URL: http://www.childlife.org

Description: Professional organization representing child life personnel, patient activities specialists, and students in the field. Promotes psychological well-being and optimum development of children, adolescents, and their families in health care settings. Works to minimize the stress and anxiety of illness and hospitalization. Addresses professional issues such as program standards, competencies, and core curriculum. Provides resources and conducts research and educational programs. Offers a Job Bank Service listing employment openings.

11045 ■ National Council for Therapeutic Recreation Certification (NCTRC)
7 Elmwood Dr.
New City, NY 10956
Ph: (845)639-1439
Fax: (845)639-1471
E-mail: nctrc@nctrc.org
URL: http://www.nctrc.org

Description: Objectives are to: establish standards for certification and recertification of individuals who work in the therapeutic recreation field; grant recognition to individuals who voluntarily apply and meet established standards; monitor adherence to standards by certified personnel.

11046 ■ National Rehabilitation Association (NRA)
633 S Washington St.
Alexandria, VA 22314
Ph: (703)836-0850
Fax: (703)836-0848
E-mail: info@nationalrehab.org
URL: http://www.nationalrehab.org

Description: Provides opportunities through knowledge and diversity for professionals in the fields of rehabilitation of people with disabilities.

11047 ■ Special Recreation for disABLED International (SRDI)
701 Oaknoll Dr.
Iowa City, IA 52246-5168
Ph: (319)466-3192
Fax: (319)351-6772
E-mail: john-nesbitt@uiowa.edu
URL: http://www.globalvisionproject.org

Description: Seeks to serve and advocate special and therapeutic play and recreation for infants, children, youth, adults, and seniors throughout the world. Services include advisory and consultation, awards, employment information, professional education, public education, publishing, research, resource information and referral, technical assistance on programs and management methods, and an international library. Does international service work to: collect and disseminate international information on special recreation services for disabled persons, special recreation programs, and personnel training; conduct, provide, and support international exchange of technical, professional, and general information on special recreation for the disabled; cooperate with both governmental and voluntary organizations on national and international levels. Offers career guidance and placement service. Maintains speakers' bureau; compiles statistics.

SOURCES OF HELP-WANTED ADS

11048 ■ *AANA Journal*
AANA Publishing Inc.
222 S Prospect Ave.
Park Ridge, IL 60068-4001
Ph: (847)692-7050
Fax: (847)692-6968
URL: http://www.aana.com/
Resources.aspx?id=5324&linkidentifier=id

Bimonthly. Nursing and anesthesia journal.

11049 ■ *AAOHN Journal*
SLACK Incorporated
6900 Grove Rd.
Thorofare, NJ 08086-9447
Ph: (856)848-1000
Fax: (856)848-6091
E-mail: aaohn@slackinc.com
URL: http://www.slackjournals.com/aaohn

Monthly. $115.00/year for individuals; $230.00/year for individuals, two years; $345.00/year for individuals, three years; $259.00/year for institutions; $518.00/year for institutions, two years; $777.00/year for institutions, three years; $29.00/year for single issue. Official journal of the American Association of Occupational Health Nurses.

11050 ■ *AAOHN News*
American Association of Occupational Health Nurses Inc.
7794 Grow Dr.
Pensacola, FL 32514
Ph: (850)474-6963
Fax: (850)484-8762
Fr: 800-241-8014
E-mail: aaohn@dancyamc.com
URL: http://www.aaohn.org/membership/corporate-partnerships.html

Description: Quarterly. Covers Association events as well as trends and legislation affecting occupational and environmental health nursing. Recurring features include news of research, a calendar of events, reports of meetings, news of educational opportunities, job listings, notices of publications available, resources for career-building, briefs on governmental issues concerning occupational and environment health, and a President's column.

11051 ■ *ADVANCE for Nurse Practitioners*
Merion Publications Inc.
2900 Horizon Dr.
PO Box 61556
King of Prussia, PA 19406-0956
Ph: (610)278-1400
Fr: 800-355-5627
URL: http://nurse-practitioners-and-physician-assistants.advancew

Monthly. Free to qualified subscribers. For practicing nurse practitioner students with senior status.

11052 ■ *Advances in Neonatal Care*
National Association of Neonatal Nurses
4700 W Lake Ave.
Glenview, IL 60025
Ph: (847)375-3660
Fax: (866)927-5321
Fr: 800-451-3795
E-mail: info@nann.org
URL: http://www.nann.org

Bimonthly. $100.99/year for individuals in the U.S.; $236/year for institutions in the U.S.; $169.22/year for international individuals; $319.22/year for international institutions. Contains research and clinical practice articles. Features various job opportunities in the field.

11053 ■ *Advances in Nursing Science (ANS)*
Lippincott Williams & Wilkins
530 Walnut St.
Philadelphia, PA 19106-3619
Ph: (215)521-8300
Fax: (215)521-8902
Fr: 800-638-3030
URL: http://www.lww.com/product/?0161-9268

Quarterly. $114.99/year for individuals; $432.00/year for institutions; $68.49/year for individuals, in-training; $219.73/year for other countries; $561.73/year for institutions, other countries. Academic medical journal focusing on nursing research and education.

11054 ■ *American Family Physician*
American Academy of Family Physicians
11400 Tomahawk Creek Pky.
PO Box 11210
Leawood, KS 66211-2680
Ph: (913)906-6000
Fax: (913)906-6075
Fr: 800-274-2237
E-mail: afpedit@aafp.org
URL: http://www.aafp.org/online/en/home/publications/journals/afp

Semimonthly. $101.00/year for individuals, healthcare professionals; $164.00/year for Canada, healthcare professionals; $227.00/year for other countries, healthcare professionals; $173.00/year for individuals, physicians and other individuals; $240.00/year for Canada, physicians and other individuals; $299.00/year for other countries, physicians and other individuals; $236.00/year for institutions; $299.00/year for institutions, Canada; $362.00/year for institutions, other countries. Peer-reviewed clinical journal for family physicians and others in primary care. Review articles detail the latest diagnostic and therapeutic techniques in the medical field. Department features in each issue include 'Tips from other Journals,' CME credit opportunities and course calendar.

11055 ■ *American Journal of Medicine*
Excerpta Medica Inc.
685 US-202
Bridgewater, NJ 08807
Ph: (908)547-2100

Fax: (908)547-2200
URL: http://www.amjmed.com/

Monthly. $373.00/year for other countries; $145.00/year for U.S. and Canada; $80.00/year for students, other countries; $84.00/year for students. Medical journal.

11056 ■ *American Journal of Nursing*
American Journal of Nursing
c/o Lippincott, Williams & Wilkins
2 Commerce Sq., 2001 Market St.
Philadelphia, PA 19103
Ph: (215)521-8300
Fax: (215)521-8902
URL: http://www.nursingcenter.com

Monthly. $51.00/year for individuals; $425.00/year for institutions; $129.00/year for other countries; $465.00/year for institutions, other countries. Peer-reviewed journal promoting excellence in nursing and health care.

11057 ■ *The American Nurse*
American Nurses Association
8515 Georgia Ave., Ste. 400
Silver Spring, MD 20910
Ph: (301)628-5000
Fax: (301)628-5001
Fr: 800-274-4262
E-mail: adsales@ana.org
URL: http://nursingworld.org/tan/

Monthly. $20.00/year for individuals, practicing nurses; $10.00/year for students. Newspaper (tabloid) for the nursing profession.

11058 ■ *AORN Journal*
Association of periOperative Registered Nurses (AORN)
2170 S Parker Rd., Ste. 400
Denver, CO 80231
Ph: (303)755-6304
Fax: (303)750-3212
Fr: 800-755-2676
E-mail: aornjournal@aorn.org
URL: http://www.aorn.org/AORNJournal

Monthly. $150.00/year for individuals; $213.00/year for individuals, Canada; $213.00/year for other countries; $213.00/year for individuals, Mexico. Peer-reviewed journal publishing perioperative nurses and other health care professionals with practical and theoretical information.

11059 ■ *Cancer Nursing*
Lippincott Williams & Wilkins
530 Walnut St.
Philadelphia, PA 19106-3619
Ph: (215)521-8300
Fax: (215)521-8902
Fr: 800-638-3030
E-mail: editor@gator.net
URL: http://journals.lww.com/cancernursingonline/pages/default.as

Bimonthly. $109.99/year for individuals; $378.00/year

for institutions; $63.99/year for individuals, in-training; $203.22/year for other countries; $518.22/year for institutions, other countries. Medical journal covering problems arising in the care and support of cancer patients.

11060 ■ *Clinical Nurse Specialist*
Lippincott Williams & Wilkins
530 Walnut St.
Philadelphia, PA 19106-3619
Ph: (215)521-8300
Fax: (215)521-8902
Fr: 800-638-3030
E-mail: jasfulto@iupui.edu
URL: http://journals.lww.com/cns-journal/pages/default.aspx

Bimonthly. $104.99/year for individuals; $356.00/year for institutions; $63.99/year for individuals, in-training; $218.22/year for other countries; $535.22/year for institutions, other countries. Nursing journal.

11061 ■ *Critical Care Medicine*
Society of Critical Care Medicine
500 Midway Dr.
Mount Prospect, IL 60056-9969
Ph: (847)827-6869
Fax: (847)827-6886
URL: http://journals.lww.com/ccmjournal/pages/default.aspx

Monthly. $402.00/year for individuals; $711.00/year for institutions; $538.00/year for other countries; $848.00/year for institutions, other countries; $380.00/year for other countries, in-training; $258.00/year for individuals, in-training. Interdisciplinary journal for ICU and CCU specialists.

11062 ■ *Critical Care Nurse*
Critical Care Nurse
101 Columbia
Aliso Viejo, CA 92656
Ph: (949)362-2000
Fax: (949)362-2020
Fr: 800-899-2226
URL: http://ccn.aacnjournals.org

Bimonthly. Included in membership; $265.00/year for institutions, print & online. Nursing journal.

11063 ■ *Dialysis & Transplantation*
John Wiley & Sons Inc.
111 River St.
Hoboken, NJ 07030-5773
Ph: (201)748-6000
Fax: (201)748-6088
Fr: 800-825-7550
URL: http://onlinelibrary.wiley.com/journal/10.1002/(ISSN)1932-69

Monthly. $128.00/year for U.S. and other countries, institution; print only; $65.00/year for institutions, print only; $82.00/year for institutions, print only. Multidisciplinary, peer-reviewed journal on clinical applications in dialysis, transplantation and nephrology for renal-care team.

11064 ■ *Emergency Medical Services*
Cygnus Business Media
1233 Janesville Ave.
Fort Atkinson, WI 53538
Ph: (920)563-6388
Fax: (920)563-1702
Fr: 800-547-7377
URL: http://www.emsworld.com

Monthly. Magazine covering emergency care, rescue and transportation.

11065 ■ *EndoNurse*
Virgo Publishing Inc.
PO Box 40079
Phoenix, AZ 85067-0079
Ph: (480)990-1101
Fax: (480)990-0819
URL: http://endonurse.com/

Bimonthly. $40.00/year for individuals; $60.00/year

for Canada; $70.00/year for other countries. Magazine covering endoscopic nursing.

11066 ■ *Fertility and Sterility*
The American Society for Reproductive Medicine
1209 Montgomery Hwy.
Birmingham, AL 35216-2809
Ph: (205)978-5000
Fax: (205)978-5005
URL: http://www.asrm.org/FertilityAndSterility/

Monthly. Included in membership. Medical journal covering all aspects of reproductive medicine.

11067 ■ *Geriatric Nursing*
Mosby Inc.
10801 Executive Center Dr., Ste. 509
Little Rock, AR 72211
Ph: (501)223-5165
Fax: (501)223-0519
URL: http://journals.elsevierhealth.com/periodicals/ymgn

Bimonthly. $80.00/year for individuals; $141.00/year for individuals, Canada; $141.00/year for individuals, Mexico; $141.00/year for individuals, international. Magazine for nurses in geriatric and gerontologic nursing practice, the primary professional providers of care for the aging. Provides news on issues affecting elders and clinical information on techniques and procedures.

11068 ■ *Health Progress*
Healing Ministry of Catholic Health Care
4455 Woodson Rd.
St. Louis, MO 63134
Ph: (314)427-2500
Fax: (314)427-0029
URL: http://www.chausa.org/pages/publications/health_progress/cur

Bimonthly. $50.00/year for members, CHA; $61.00/year for other countries; $55.00/year for individuals, ministry partners; $10.00/year for nonmembers, single copy; for free, to members, single copy; $3.00/year for nonmembers, special section reprints; for free, to members, special section reprints. Magazine for administrative-level and other managerial personnel in Catholic healthcare and related organizations. Featured are articles on management concepts, legislative and regulatory trends, and theological, sociological, ethical, legal, and technical issues.

11069 ■ *Heart and Lung*
Mosby
1600 John F. Kennedy Blvd., Ste. 1800
Philadelphia, PA 19103-2899
Ph: (215)239-3275
Fax: (215)239-3286
URL: http://www.elsevier.com/wps/find/journaldescription.cws_home

Bimonthly. $103.00/year for individuals; $445.00/year for institutions; $524.00/year for institutions, other countries; $153.00/year for other countries. Journal offering articles prepared by nurse and physician members of the critical care team, recognizing the nurse's role in the care and management of major organ-system conditions in critically ill patients.

11070 ■ *Home Healthcare Nurse*
Lippincott Williams & Wilkins
530 Walnut St.
Philadelphia, PA 19106-3619
Ph: (215)521-8300
Fax: (215)521-8902
Fr: 800-638-3030
URL: http://journals.lww.com/homehealthcarenurseonline/pages/defa

$62.14/year for individuals; $324.00/year for institutions; $156.11/year for other countries; $481.11/year for institutions, other countries; $40.99/year for individuals, in-training. Magazine for the practicing professional nurse working in the home health, community health, and public health areas.

11071 ■ *HomeCare Magazine*
Penton Media
249 W 17th St.
New York, NY 10011-5390
Ph: (212)204-4200
URL: http://homecaremag.com/

Monthly. Free, in US; $135.00/year for Canada; $150.00/year for two years, Canada; $250.00/year for other countries; $250.00/year for two years, other countries. Magazine serving home medical equipment suppliers, including independent and chain centers specializing in home care, pharmacies or chain drug stores with home care products, and joint-ventured hospital home health care businesses. Contains industry news and new product launches and marketing strategies.

11072 ■ *Hospitals & Health Networks*
Health Forum L.L.C.
155 N Wacker Dr., Ste. 400
Chicago, IL 60606
Ph: (312)893-6800
Fax: (312)422-4500
Fr: 800-821-2039
URL: http://www.hhnmag.com

Weekly. Free. Publication covering the health care industry.

11073 ■ *The IHS Primary Care Provider*
Indian Health Service
The Reyes Bldg.
801 Thompson Ave., Ste. 400
Rockville, MD 20852-1627
Ph: (301)443-1011
URL: http://www.ihs.gov/provider

Monthly. Journal for health care professionals, physicians, nurses, pharmacists, dentists, and dietitians.

11074 ■ *Imprint*
National Student Nurses' Association Inc.
45 Main St., Ste. 606
Brooklyn, NY 11201
Ph: (718)210-0705
Fax: (718)797-1186
E-mail: nsna@nsna.org
URL: http://www.nsna.org/Publications.aspx

$18.00/year for individuals; $30.00/year for other countries; $36.00/year for institutions. Magazine for nursing students, focusing on issues and trends in nursing.

11075 ■ *Intensive and Critical Care Nursing*
Mosby Inc.
11830 Westline Industrial Dr.
St. Louis, MO 63146-3326
Ph: (314)872-8370
Fax: (314)432-1380
Fr: 800-325-4177
URL: http://www.elsevier.com/wps/find/journaldescription.cws_home

Bimonthly. $114.00/year for individuals, for all countries except Europe, Japan & Iran; $501.00/year for institutions, for all countries except Europe, Japan & Iran; $124.00/year for individuals, for European countries and Iran; $565.00/year for institutions, for European countries and Iran. Journal for nurses in intensive and critical care nursing.

11076 ■ *International Journal of Nursing Education Scholarship*
Berkeley Electronic Press
2809 Telegraph Ave., Ste. 202
Berkeley, CA 94705-1167
Ph: (510)665-1200
Fax: (510)665-1201
URL: http://www.bepress.com/ijnes

Annual. $525.00/year corporate; $175.00/year academic. Journal that publishes original papers on nursing education issues and research.

11077 ■ *International Journal of Nursing Practice*
John Wiley & Sons Inc.
350 Main St., Commerce Pl.
Malden, MA 02148-5089
Ph: (781)388-8200
Fax: (781)388-8210
URL: http://www.wiley.com/bw/journal.asp?ref=1322-7114

Bimonthly. $146.00/year for individuals, print and online; $1,053.00/year for institutions, print and online; $916.00/year for institutions, print or online; $651.00/year for institutions, other countries, print and online; $566.00/year for institutions, other countries, print or online; $850.00/year for institutions, print and premium online, Australia/New Zealand; $739.00/year for institutions, print or online, Australia/New Zealand. Journal publishing articles about advances the international understanding and development of nursing, both as a profession and as an academic discipline.

11078 ■ *International Journal of Orthopaedic and Trauma Nursing*
Mosby Inc.
11830 Westline Industrial Dr.
St. Louis, MO 63146-3326
Ph: (314)872-8370
Fax: (314)432-1380
Fr: 800-325-4177
URL: http://www.elsevier.com/wps/find/journaldescription.cws_home

Quarterly. $106.00/year for individuals, for all countries except Europe, Japan and Iran; $409.00/year for institutions, for all countries except Europe, Japan and Iran. Journal for orthopaedic nurses.

11079 ■ *International Nursing Review*
John Wiley & Sons Inc.
350 Main St., Commerce Pl.
Malden, MA 02148-5089
Ph: (781)388-8200
Fax: (781)388-8210
URL: http://www.wiley.com/bw/journal.asp?ref=0020-8132

Quarterly. $63.00/year for individuals, UK & non Euro zone; print + online; $71.00/year for U.S. and other countries, members; $223.00/year for institutions, print + online; $202.00/year for institutions, print or online; $118.00/year for individuals, print + online; $431.00/year for institutions, print + online; $374.00/year for institutions, print or online; $95.00/year for individuals, print + online; $295.00/year for institutions, print + online; $256.00/year for institutions, print or online. Journal focusing on current concerns and issues of modern day nursing and health care from an international perspective.

11080 ■ *Journal of Addictions Nursing*
Informa Healthcare
52 Vanderbilt Ave., 7th Fl.
New York, NY 10017-3846
Ph: (212)520-2777
URL: http://informahealthcare.com/journal/jan

$342.00/year for institutions; $556.00/year for institutions; $444.00/year for institutions. Journal for nursing addiction professionals.

11081 ■ *Journal of Clinical Nursing*
John Wiley & Sons Inc.
350 Main St., Commerce Pl.
Malden, MA 02148-5089
Ph: (781)388-8200
Fax: (781)388-8210
E-mail: jcn@oxon.blackwellpublishing.com
URL: http://www.wiley.com/bw/journal.asp?ref=0962-1067

Monthly. $381.00/year for individuals, print and online; $208.00/year for students, print and online; $2,428.00/year for institutions, print and online; $2,111.00/year for institutions, print or online; $312.00/year for individuals, print and online; $167.00/year for students, print and online; $1,315.00/year for institutions, other countries, print

and online; $1,143.00/year for institutions, other countries, print or online. Peer-reviewed scientific journal that seeks to promote the development and exchange of knowledge that is directly relevant to spheres of nursing and midwifery practice.

11082 ■ *The Journal of Continuing Education in Nursing*
SLACK Incorporated
6900 Grove Rd.
Thorofare, NJ 08086-9447
Ph: (856)848-1000
Fax: (856)848-6091
E-mail: jcen@slackinc.com
URL: http://www.slackjournals.com/jcen

Monthly. $124.00/year for individuals; $248.00/year for two years; $29.00/year for single issue; $355.00/year for institutions. Peer-reviewed journal for nurses involved in planning and implementing educational programs for the practitioner and others in patient care.

11083 ■ *Journal of the Dermatology Nurses' Association*
Dermatology Nurses' Association
15000 Commerce Pkwy., Ste. C
Mount Laurel, NJ 08054
Fax: (856)439-0525
Fr: 800-454-4362
E-mail: dna@dnanurse.org
URL: http://www.dnanurse.org

Bimonthly. Features clinical snapshots, patient perspective pieces, a product review section, a legal forum, health policy and advocacy articles, nursing research studies, and rotating topical columns on a variety of dermatology nursing related issues. Contains product and recruitment/placement advertising.

11084 ■ *Journal of Emergency Nursing*
Mosby
1600 John F. Kennedy Blvd., Ste. 1800
Philadelphia, PA 19103-2899
Ph: (215)239-3275
Fax: (215)239-3286
URL: http://www.elsevier.com/wps/find/journaleditorialboard.cws_h

Bimonthly. $96.00/year for individuals; $380.00/year for institutions; $121.00/year for other countries; $408.00/year for institutions, other countries. Journal containing peer-reviewed articles on clinical aspects of emergency care by, and for, emergency nurses. Presents information about professional, political, administrative, and educational aspects of emergency nursing and nursing in general.

11085 ■ *Journal For Nurse Practitioners*
American College of Nurse Practitioners
225 Reinekers Ln., Ste. 525
Alexandria, VA 22314
Ph: (703)740-2529
Fax: (703)740-2533
E-mail: acnp@acnpweb.org
URL: http://www.acnpweb.org

Ten times per year. Provides resources that help nurse practitioners stay current with the clinical and policy concerns affecting their practice. Features continuing education opportunities as well as opinions and commentary on pressing legislative, regulatory, and clinical practice issues. Contains recruitment and classified print advertising.

11086 ■ *Journal of Gerontological Nursing*
SLACK Incorporated
6900 Grove Rd.
Thorofare, NJ 08086-9447
Ph: (856)848-1000
Fax: (856)848-6091
E-mail: jgn@slackinc.com
URL: http://www.slackjournals.com/jgn

Monthly. $95.00/year for individuals; $190.00/year for two years; $315.00/year for institutions; $630.00/year for institutions, two years; $29.00/year for single issue. Gerontological nursing journal.

11087 ■ *Journal of Infusion Nursing*
Infusion Nurses Society
315 Norwood Park S
Norwood, MA 02062
Ph: (781)440-9408
Fax: (781)440-9409
Fr: 800-694-0298
E-mail: ins@ins1.org
URL: http://www.ins1.org

Bimonthly. Features new research, clinical reviews, case studies, and professional development information relevant to the practice of infusion therapy. Also features product, recruitment, and classified advertisements.

11088 ■ *Journal of the National Medical Association*
National Medical Association
8403 Colesville Rd., Ste. 920
Silver Spring, MD 20910
Ph: (202)347-1895
Fax: (202)898-2510
E-mail: aredd@nmanet.org
URL: http://www.nmanet.org/index.php?option=com_content&view=arti

Monthly. $125.00/year for individuals; $275.00/year for institutions; $50.00/year for individuals, intern, resident, fellow, student; $22.00/year for single issue. Journal on specialized clinical research related to the health problems of African-Americans and other minorities. Recognizes significant contributions by black physicians and others involved with minority health issues and health disparities.

11089 ■ *Journal of Nursing Administration (JONA)*
Lippincott Williams & Wilkins
530 Walnut St.
Philadelphia, PA 19106-3619
Ph: (215)521-8300
Fax: (215)521-8902
Fr: 800-638-3030
E-mail: jonaeditor@aol.com
URL: http://journals.lww.com/jonajournal/pages/default.aspx

$126.99/year for individuals; $69.99/year for individuals, in-training; $261.10/year for other countries; $544.00/year for institutions; $74.63/year for individuals, in-training; $690.70/year for institutions, other countries. Journal covering developments and advances in nursing administration and management.

11090 ■ *Journal of Nursing Scholarship*
John Wiley & Sons Inc.
350 Main St., Commerce Pl.
Malden, MA 02148-5089
Ph: (781)388-8200
Fax: (781)388-8210
URL: http://www.wiley.com/bw/journal.asp?ref=1527-6546&site=1

Quarterly. $63.00/year for individuals, print & online; $263.00/year for institutions, print & online; $228.00/year for institutions, print; online; $73.00/year for individuals, print & online; $191.00/year for institutions, other countries, print & online; $243.00/year for institutions, print & online; $49.00/year for individuals, print & online. Peer-reviewed journal covering nursing.

11091 ■ *Journal of Obstetric, Gynecologic and Neonatal Nursing (JOGNN)*
John Wiley & Sons Inc.
350 Main St., Commerce Pl.
Malden, MA 02148-5089
Ph: (781)388-8200
Fax: (781)388-8210
URL: http://www.wiley.com/bw/journal.asp?ref=0884-2175&site=1

Bimonthly. $121.00/year for individuals, print & online; $1,117.00/year for institutions, print & online; $971.00/year for institutions, online only; $102.00/year for individuals, print & online; $788.00/year for institutions, print & online; $685.00/year for institutions, online only; $68.00/year for individuals, print &

online; $621.00/year for institutions, print & online; $540.00/year for institutions, online only. Journal covering trends, policies, and research. Official publication of the Association of Women's Health, Obstetric, and Neonatal Nurses (AWHONN).

11092 ■ Journal of Pediatric Health Care
Mosby
1600 John F. Kennedy Blvd., Ste. 1800
Philadelphia, PA 19103-2899
Ph: (215)239-3275
Fax: (215)239-3286
URL: http://www.elsevier.com/wps/find/
   journaldescription.cws_home

Bimonthly. $141.00/year for other countries; $347.00/year for institutions, other countries; $302.00/year for institutions; $100.00/year for individuals. Official publication of the National Association of Pediatric Nurse Practitioners. Provides current information on pediatric clinical topics as well as research studies, health policy, and legislative issues applicable to pediatric clinical practice.

11093 ■ Journal of Pediatric Nursing
Elsevier
3251 Riverport Ln.
Maryland Heights, MO 63043
Ph: (314)447-8878
Fax: (314)447-8077
Fr: 877-839-7126
E-mail: journalcustomerservice-usa@elsevier.com
URL: http://www.elsevier.com

Bimonthly. $417/year for institutions; $254/year for individuals. Features original, peer-reviewed research that is based on the philosophy that pediatric nursing incorporates a family-centered approach. Strives to provide divergent points of view to encourage discussion and facilitate promotion of child and family health. Topics include pharmacology, nutrition, pain management, diabetes, endocrinology, asthma, special needs, etc. Contains product, recruitment, and classified advertising.

11094 ■ Journal of PeriAnesthesia Nursing
Mosby Inc.
11830 Westline Industrial Dr.
St. Louis, MO 63146-3326
Ph: (314)872-8370
Fax: (314)432-1380
Fr: 800-325-4177
URL: http://www.elsevier.com/wps/find/
   journaldescription.cws_home

Bimonthly. $454.00/year for institutions; $134.00/year for individuals; $328.00/year for institutions; $298.00/year for individuals. Peer-reviewed journal publishing research for a primary audience that includes nurses in perianesthesia settings, including ambulatory surgery, preadmission testing, postanesthesia (Phases I, II, and III) care, and pain management. Journal providing forum for sharing professional knowledge and experience relating to management, ethics, legislation, research, and other aspects of perianesthesia nursing.

11095 ■ Journal of Psychosocial Nursing and Mental Health Services
SLACK Incorporated
6900 Grove Rd.
Thorofare, NJ 08086-9447
Ph: (856)848-1000
Fax: (856)848-6091
E-mail: jpn@slackinc.com
URL: http://www.slackjournals.com/jpn

Monthly. $95.00/year for individuals; $190.00/year for individuals, two years; $315.00/year for institutions; $630.00/year for institutions, two years; $29.00/year for single issue. Peer-reviewed journal presenting original, peer-reviewed articles on psychiatric/mental health nursing.

11096 ■ Journal of Radiology Nursing
Mosby Inc.
11830 Westline Industrial Dr.
St. Louis, MO 63146-3326

Ph: (314)872-8370
Fax: (314)432-1380
Fr: 800-325-4177
URL: http://www.radiologynursing.org

Quarterly. $80.00/year for individuals, U.S.; $152.00/year for institutions, U.S.; $121.00/year for individuals, International; $202.00/year for institutions, International. Journal publishing articles about patient care in the diagnostic and therapeutic imaging environments.

11097 ■ Journal for Specialists in Pediatric Nursing
John Wiley & Sons Inc.
350 Main St., Commerce Pl.
Malden, MA 02148-5089
Ph: (781)388-8200
Fax: (781)388-8210
URL: http://www.wiley.com/bw/journal.asp?ref=1539-
   0136&site=1

Quarterly. $88.00/year for individuals, U.S. print and online; $221.00/year for institutions, U.S. print and online; $192.00/year for institutions, U.S. print or online; $92.00/year for individuals, print and online; $155.00/year for institutions, print and online; $134.00/year for institutions, print or online. Peer-reviewed journal focusing on nurses who specialize in the care of children and families.

11098 ■ LPN2009
Lippincott Williams & Wilkins
530 Walnut St.
Philadelphia, PA 19106-3619
Ph: (215)521-8300
Fax: (215)521-8902
Fr: 800-638-3030
URL: http://www.lww.com/product/?1553-0582

Bimonthly. $149.96/year for institutions; $29.96/year for individuals; $22.75/year for individuals, in-training; $75.96/year for other countries; $214.96/year for institutions, other countries. Peer-reviewed journal that focuses on bedside care skills for practical nurses.

11099 ■ McKnight's Long-Term Care News
McKnight's Long-Term Care News
1 Northfield Plz., Ste. 521
Northfield, IL 60093-1216
Ph: (847)784-8706
Fax: (847)784-9346
Fr: 800-558-1703
URL: http://www.mcknightsonline.com/home

$60.00/year for individuals; $108.00/year for two years; $75.00/year for Canada; $135.00/year for Canada, two years; $75.00/year for other countries; $135.00/year for other countries, two years. Professional magazine.

11100 ■ MCN, The American Journal of Maternal/Child Nursing
Lippincott Williams & Wilkins
530 Walnut St.
Philadelphia, PA 19106-3619
Ph: (215)521-8300
Fax: (215)521-8902
Fr: 800-638-3030
URL: http://journals.lww.com/mcnjournal/pages/
   default.aspx

Bimonthly. $63.99/year for individuals; $300.00/year for institutions; $149.22/year for other countries; $421.22/year for institutions, other countries; $42.43/year for individuals, in-training. Peer-reviewed journal focusing on maternal/child nursing and health.

11101 ■ Military Medicine
AMSUS - The Society of the Federal Health Agencies
9320 Old Georgetown Rd.
Bethesda, MD 20814
Ph: (301)897-8800
Fax: (301)503-5446
Fr: 800-761-9320
URL: http://www.amsus.org/index.php/journal

Monthly. $170.00/year for individuals, print and online; $225.00/year for other countries. Journal for professional personnel affiliated with the Federal medical services.

11102 ■ Modern Healthcare
Crain Communications Inc.
360 N Michigan Ave.
Chicago, IL 60601
Ph: (312)649-5200
E-mail: subs@crain.com
URL: http://www.modernhealthcare.com

Weekly. $164.00/year for individuals; $255.00/year for Canada; $218.00/year for other countries. Weekly business news magazine for healthcare management.

11103 ■ NANN Central
National Association of Neonatal Nurses
4700 W Lake Ave.
Glenview, IL 60025-1485
Ph: (847)375-3660
Fax: (866)927-5321
Fr: 800-451-3795
E-mail: info@nann.org
URL: http://www.nann.org

Three times a year. Features association news, announcements, and meeting information along with the latest information, educational, and employment opportunities and products related to the care of neonatal patients.

11104 ■ Neonatal Network
The Academy of Neonatal Nursing
1425 N McDowell Blvd., Ste. 105
Petaluma, CA 94954
Ph: (707)795-2168
Fax: (707)569-0786
E-mail: editorial@neonatalnetwork.com
URL: http://www.academyonline.org

Bimonthly. Contains the latest information on neonatal nursing practice. Features articles on current developments in neonatal care.

11105 ■ Nephrology Nursing Journal
American Nephrology Nurses' Association
East Holly Ave.
PO Box 56
Pitman, NJ 08071-0056
Ph: (856)256-2320
Fax: (856)589-7463
Fr: 888-600-2662
URL: http://www.annanurse.org/cgi-bin/WebObjects/
   ANNANurse.woa/wa

Bimonthly. $42.00/year for individuals; $69.00/year for institutions; $15.00/year for single issue; $72.00/year for other countries; $99.00/year for institutions, other countries; $20.00/year for single issue, other countries. Nursing journal.

11106 ■ The New England Journal of Medicine
Massachusetts Medical Society
Waltham Woods Corporate Ctr.
860 Winter St.
Waltham, MA 02451-1413
Ph: (781)893-3800
Fax: (781)893-8009
URL: http://content.nejm.org/

Weekly. $139.00/year for individuals, online only; $169.00/year for individuals, print & online. Journal for the medical profession.

11107 ■ Newborn and Infant Nursing Reviews
Elsevier Inc.
1600 John F. Kennedy Blvd., Ste. 1800
Philadelphia, PA 19103
Ph: (215)239-3900
Fax: (215)238-7883
URL: http://www.elsevier.com

Quarterly. $275/year for institution; $99/year individual. Provides a comprehensive overview of newborn, infant, and neonatal nursing and all its practice settings. Contains product print advertising, recruitment, and classified print advertising.

11108 ■ *Nurse Education in Practice*
Mosby Inc.
11830 Westline Industrial Dr.
St. Louis, MO 63146-3326
Ph: (314)872-8370
Fax: (314)432-1380
Fr: 800-325-4177
URL: http://www.elsevier.com/wps/find/journaldescription.cws_home

Bimonthly. $105.00/year for individuals, for all countries except Europe, Japan & Iran; $399.00/year for institutions, for all countries except Europe, Japan & Iran. Journal enabling lecturers and practitioners to both share and disseminate evidence that demonstrates the actual practice of education as it is experienced in the realities of their respective work environments.

11109 ■ *Nurse Leader*
Mosby Inc.
11830 Westline Industrial Dr.
St. Louis, MO 63146-3326
Ph: (314)872-8370
Fax: (314)432-1380
Fr: 800-325-4177
URL: http://www.nurseleader.com

$73.00/year for individuals; $185.00/year for institutions; $297.00/year for institutions, other countries; $122.00/year for other countries. Journal publishing articles on the vision, skills, and tools needed by nurses currently aspiring to leadership positions.

11110 ■ *The Nurse Practitioner*
Lippincott Williams & Wilkins
530 Walnut St.
Philadelphia, PA 19106-3619
Ph: (215)521-8300
Fax: (215)521-8902
Fr: 800-638-3030
E-mail: npedit@wolterskluwer.com
URL: http://journals.lww.com/tnpj/pages/default.aspx

Monthly. $86.76/year for individuals; $401.76/year for institutions; $52.72/year for U.S., in-training; $176.49/year for other countries, individual; $620.49/year for institutions. Magazine presenting clinical information to nurses in advanced primary care practice. Also covers legal, business, economic, ethical, research, and pharmaceutical issues.

11111 ■ *Nursing Clinics of North America*
Mosby Inc.
11830 Westline Industrial Dr.
St. Louis, MO 63146-3326
Ph: (314)872-8370
Fax: (314)432-1380
Fr: 800-325-4177
URL: http://www.elsevier.com/wps/find/journaldescription.cws_home

Quarterly. $135.00/year for individuals; $343.00/year for institutions; $74.00/year for students; $197.00/year for Canada; $419.00/year for institutions, Canada; $121.00/year for students, Canada. Journal publishing articles by experts in the field provide current, practical information geared to the active nurse.

11112 ■ *Nursing Economics*
Jannetti Publications Inc.
East Holly Ave., Box 56
Pitman, NJ 08071-0056
Ph: (856)256-2300
E-mail: nejrnl@ajj.com
URL: http://www.nursingeconomics.net/cgi-bin/WebObjects/NECJourna

Bimonthly. $72.00/year for individuals; $120.00/year for two years; $89.00/year for institutions; $150.00/year for institutions, 2 years; $120.00/year for institutions, other countries; $180.00/year for other countries, 2 years; $210.00/year for institutions, other countries, 2 years. Business magazine for nursing administrators.

11113 ■ *Nursing Education Perspectives*
National League for Nursing
61 Broadway, 33rd Fl.
New York, NY 10006-2701
Ph: (212)363-5555
Fax: (212)812-0393
Fr: 800-669-1656
URL: http://www.nln.org/nlnjournal/index.htm

Bimonthly. $40.00/year for individuals; $90.00/year for nonmembers; $110.00/year for Canada, nonmembers; $120.00/year for other countries, nonmember; $152.00/year for institutions; $172.00/year for libraries; $182.00/year for other countries, libraries. Professional journal for nurses. Includes articles on health policy, social and economic issues affecting health care, and nursing education and practice.

11114 ■ *Nursing Management*
Lippincott Williams & Wilkins
530 Walnut St.
Philadelphia, PA 19106-3621
Ph: (215)521-8300
Fax: (215)521-8902
URL: http://journals.lww.com/nursingmanagement/pages/default.aspx

Monthly. $76.76/year for individuals; $371.76/year for institutions; $168.49/year for other countries; $518.49/year for institutions, other countries. Magazine focusing on nursing management.

11115 ■ *Nursing Outlook*
Mosby Inc.
10801 Executive Center Dr., Ste. 509
Little Rock, AR 72211
Ph: (501)223-5165
Fax: (501)223-0519
URL: http://journals.elsevierhealth.com/periodicals/ymno

Bimonthly. $133.00/year for Canada; $84.00/year for individuals; $133.00/year for individuals, Mexico; $133.00/year for other countries. Official journal of the American Academy of Nursing, reporting on trends and issues in nursing.

11116 ■ *Ob.Gyn. News*
International Medical News Group
60 Columbia Rd., Bldg. B
Morristown, NJ 07960
Ph: (973)290-8200
Fax: (973)290-8250
E-mail: obnews@elsevier.com
URL: http://www.obgynnews.com/

Semimonthly. $109.00/year for individuals; $173.00/year for other countries. Obstetrics and gynecology tabloid distributed to obstetricians and gynecologists.

11117 ■ *Oncology*
S. Karger Publishers Inc.
26 W Avon Rd.
PO Box 529
Unionville, CT 06085-1162
Ph: (860)675-7834
Fax: (203)675-7302
Fr: 800-828-5479
URL: http://content.karger.com/ProdukteDB/produkte.asp?Aktion=Jou

$2,972.00/year for institutions, print or online; $2,202.00/year for institutions, in Germany; print or online; $2,778.00/year for institutions, print or online; $3,270.00/year for institutions, combined print and online; $2,422.00/year for institutions, in Germany; combined print and online; $3,056.00/year for institutions, combined print and online. Peer-reviewed medical journal presenting experimental and clinical findings on cancer.

11118 ■ *Pediatric Nursing*
Jannetti Publications Inc.
East Holly Ave., Box 56
Pitman, NJ 08071-0056
Ph: (856)256-2300
URL: http://www.pediatricnursing.net

Bimonthly. $47.00/year for individuals; $80.00/year for two years; $72.00/year for institutions; $125.00/year for institutions, 2 years; $77.00/year for other countries; $140.00/year for other countries, 2 years; $102.00/year for institutions, other countries; $185.00/year for institutions, other countries, 2 years; $15.00/year for single issue, current issue; $15.00/year for single issue, back future issue. Professional nursing magazine.

11119 ■ *Provider*
American Health Care Association
1201 L St. NW
Washington, DC 20005
Ph: (202)842-4444
Fax: (202)842-3860
E-mail: sales@ahca.org
URL: http://www.providermagazine.com

Monthly. $48.00/year for U.S.; $61.00/year for Canada and Mexico; $85.00/year for other countries; free to qualified subscribers. Provider Magazine.

11120 ■ *Rehabilitation Nursing*
Rehabilitation Nursing
4700 W Lake Ave.
Glenview, IL 60025
Ph: (847)375-4710
Fax: (847)375-6481
Fr: 800-229-7530
E-mail: info@rehabnurse.org
URL: http://www.awebsource.com/clients/arn/ws_resource/public_index.p

Bimonthly. $120.00/year for individuals, regular; $150.00/year for individuals, premium; $195.00/year for other countries, regular; $240.00/year for other countries, premium; $175.00/year for institutions, regular (USA); $220.00/year for institutions, premium (USA); $195.00/year for institutions, regular (international); $240.00/year for institutions, premium (international). Magazine focusing on rehabilitation nursing involving clinical practice, research, education, and administration.

11121 ■ *Research in Nursing & Health*
John Wiley & Sons Inc.
111 River St.
Hoboken, NJ 07030-5773
Ph: (201)748-6000
Fax: (201)748-6088
Fr: 800-825-7550
URL: http://onlinelibrary.wiley.com/journal/10.1002/(ISSN)1098-24

Bimonthly. $164.00/year for U.S., Canada, and Mexico, print only; $206.00/year for other countries, print only; $1,483.00/year for institutions, print only; $1,567.00/year for institutions, Canada and Mexico, print only; $1,609.00/year for institutions, other countries, print only. Peer-reviewed journal publishing wide range of research and theory that will inform the practice of nursing and other health disciplines.

11122 ■ *RN*
Advanstar Communications Inc.
641 Lexington Ave., 8th Fl.
New York, NY 10022
Ph: (212)951-6600
Fax: (212)951-6793
Fr: 800-346-0085
E-mail: rnmagazine@advanstar.com
URL: http://rn.modernmedicine.com/

Monthly. $24.97/year for individuals; $50.00/year for Canada. Clinical journal for registered nurses.

11123 ■ *Seminars in Oncology Nursing*
Mosby Inc.
11830 Westline Industrial Dr.
St. Louis, MO 63146-3326
Ph: (314)872-8370
Fax: (314)432-1380
Fr: 800-325-4177
URL: http://www.nursingoncology.com

Quarterly. $105.00/year for individuals; $298.00/year for institutions; $212.00/year for individuals, International; $402.00/year for institutions, other countries.

Journal publishing material to disseminate knowledge in the complex field of cancer nursing.

11124 ■ Supporting Innovations in Gerontological Nursing
National Gerontological Nursing Association
3493 Lansdowne Dr., Ste. 2
Lexington, KY 40517
Ph: (859)977-7453
Fax: (859)271-0607
Fr: 800-723-0560
E-mail: info@ngna.org
URL: http://www.ngna.org

Bimonthly. Provides updates on NGNA's activities as well as other information of interest to gerontological nurses. Features job opportunities in the field.

11125 ■ Teaching and Learning in Nursing
Elsevier Science Inc.
360 Park Ave. S
New York, NY 10010-1710
Ph: (212)989-5800
Fax: (212)633-3990
Fr: 888-437-4636
URL: http://www.elsevier.com/wps/find/journaldescription.cws_home

Quarterly. $232.00/year for institutions, other countries; $134.00/year for other countries; $160.00/year for institutions; $91.00/year for individuals. Journal devoted to associate degree nursing education and practice.

11126 ■ World Journal of AIDS
Scientific Research Publishing
PO Box 54821
Irvine, CA 92619-4821
E-mail: wja@scirp.org
URL: http://www.scirp.org/journal/wja/

Quarterly. $156.00/year for individuals. Peer-reviewed journal publishing articles on research data and education in all aspects of HIV and AIDS.

11127 ■ World Journal of Vaccines
Scientific Research Publishing
PO Box 54821
Irvine, CA 92619-4821
E-mail: wjv@scirp.org
URL: http://www.scirp.org/journal/wjv/

Quarterly. $156.00/year for individuals. Peer-reviewed journal publishing articles on the latest advancements in vaccine.

11128 ■ Worldviews on Evidence-Based Nursing
John Wiley & Sons Inc.
350 Main St., Commerce Pl.
Malden, MA 02148-5089
Ph: (781)388-8200
Fax: (781)388-8210
URL: http://www.wiley.com/bw/journal.asp?ref=1545-102X

Quarterly. $149.00/year for individuals, print and online; $142.00/year for individuals, online only; $450.00/year for institutions, print and online; $391.00/year for institutions, print or online; $161.00/year for individuals, print and online; $154.00/year for individuals, online only. Peer-reviewed journal that offers research, policy and practice, education and management for nursing.

EMPLOYER DIRECTORIES AND NETWORKING LISTS

11129 ■ American Group Psychotherapy Association—Membership Directory
American Group Psychotherapy Association Inc.
25 E 21st St., 6th Fl.
New York, NY 10010
Ph: (212)477-2677
Fax: (212)979-6627

Fr: 877-668-2472
URL: http://www.agpa.org

Covers: 4,500 physicians, psychologists, clinical social workers, psychiatric nurses, and other mental health professionals interested in treatment of emotional problems by group methods. Entries include: Name, office or home address, highest degree held, office or home phone number. Arrangement: Alphabetical. Indexes: Geographical.

11130 ■ Careers in Focus—Nursing
Facts On File Inc.
132 W 31st St., 17th Fl.
New York, NY 10001
Ph: (212)967-8800
Fax: 800-678-3633
Fr: 800-322-8755
URL: http://www.infobasepublishing.com

Latest edition 4th, Published May, 2011. $32.95 for individuals. Covers: An overview of nursing, followed by a selection of jobs profiled in detail, including the nature of the job, earnings, prospects for employment, what kind of training and skills it requires, and sources for further information.

11131 ■ Crain's List—Chicago's Largest Hospitals
Crain Communications Inc.
360 N Michigan Ave.
Chicago, IL 60601
Ph: (312)649-5200
URL: http://www.chicagobusiness.com/section/lists

Published November, 2010. $25.00 for individuals; $45.00 for individuals. Covers: 25 hospitals in Chicago area ranked by net patient revenues. Entries include: Name, address, phone number, fax, web address, corporate e-mail, hospital administrator, network affiliation, 2009 net patient revenue, percentage change from 2008, 2009 net profits, percentage change from 2008, inpatient days, available beds, daily occupancy rate, number of hospital employees as of December 31, 2009, fiscal year end, Chairman, President, CEO, Chief Financial Officer, Human Resources Manager, Media Relations/Public Relations Director, and Hospital Administrator.

11132 ■ Directory of Child Life Programs
Child Life Council Inc.
11821 Parklawn Dr., Ste. 310
Rockville, MD 20852-2539
Ph: (301)881-7090
Fax: (301)881-7092
URL: http://www.childlife.org

Biennial, latest edition 14th, 2006. Covers: Over 400 child life programs. Entries include: Facility name, address, phone, name of child life department and director, reporting structure, staff statistics, educational requirements for employment, and internship or educational opportunities. Arrangement: Geographical. Indexes: Speciality areas, internship sessions, program size, fellowships.

11133 ■ Directory of Hospital Personnel
Grey House Publishing
4919 Rte. 22
PO Box 56
Amenia, NY 12501
Ph: (518)789-8700
Fax: (518)789-0556
Fr: 800-562-2139
URL: http://www.greyhouse.com/hospital_personnel.htm

Annual, Latest edition 2011. $325.00 for individuals. Covers: 200,000 executives at 6,000 U.S. Hospitals. Entries include: Name of hospital, address, phone, number of beds, type and JCAHO status of hospital, names and titles of key department heads and staff, medical and nursing school affiliations; number of residents, interns, and nursing students. Arrangement: Geographical. Indexes: Hospital name, personnel, hospital size.

11134 ■ Hospital Blue Book
Billian Publishing Inc. and Trans World Publishing Inc.
2100 River Edge Pky.
Atlanta, GA 30328
Ph: (770)955-5656
Fax: (770)952-0669
Fr: 800-800-5668
E-mail: blu-book@billian.com
URL: http://www.billianshealthdata.com/Products/bluebook.html

Annual, Latest edition 2010. $575.00 for individuals; $575.00 for individuals. Covers: More than 6,500 hospitals; some listings also appear in a separate southern edition of this publication. Entries include: Name of hospital, accreditation, mailing address, phone, fax, number of beds, type of facility (nonprofit, general, state, etc.); list of administrative personnel and chiefs of medical services, with specific titles. Arrangement: Geographical.

11135 ■ How to Survive and Maybe Even Love Nursing School!
F.A. Davis Co.
1915 Arch St.
Philadelphia, PA 19103
Ph: (215)568-2270
Fax: (215)568-5065
Fr: 800-523-4049
URL: http://www.fadavis.com

Latest edition 3rd. $28.95 for individuals. Publication includes: List of resources for nursing students such as Web sites and organizations. Principal content of publication is information about succeeding in nursing school.

11136 ■ Medical and Health Information Directory
Gale
PO Box 6904
Florence, KY 41022-6904
Fr: 800-354-9706
URL: http://www.gale.cengage.com

Annual, Latest edition April 2011. $1190.00 for individuals; $501.00 for individuals. Covers: In volume 1, more than 33,000 medical and health oriented associations, organizations, institutions, and government agencies, including health maintenance organizations (HMOs), preferred provider organizations (PPOs), insurance companies, pharmaceutical companies, research centers, and medical and allied health schools. In Volume 2, over 20,000 medical book publishers; medical periodicals, directories, audiovisual producers and services, medical libraries and information centers, electronic resources, and health-related internet search engines. In Volume 3, more than 40,500 clinics, treatment centers, care programs, and counseling/diagnostic services for 34 subject areas. Entries include: Institution, service, or firm name, address, phone, fax, email and URL; many include names of key personnel and, when pertinent, descriptive annotation. Volume 3 was formerly listed separately as Health Services Directory. Arrangement: Classified by organization activity, service, etc. Indexes: Each volume has a complete alphabetical name and keyword index.

11137 ■ Peterson's Guide to Nursing Programs
Peterson's
Princeton Pike Corporate Ctr.
2000 Lenox Dr.
PO Box 67005
Lawrenceville, NJ 08648
Ph: (609)896-1800
Fax: (609)896-4531
Fr: 800-338-3282
URL: http://www.petersons.com/

Annual, Latest edition 2009. $18.48 for individuals. Covers: Over 700 institutions offering approximately 3,600 accredited nursing programs in the U.S. and Canada. Entries include: Academic information, extracurricular issues, costs, financial aid.

11138 ■ Saunders Student Nurse Planners
W.B. Saunders Company
c/o Elsevier
30 Corporate Dr., 4th Fl.
Burlington, MA 01803
Ph: (781)313-4700
Fax: (781)313-4880
URL: http://www.elsevier.com

Latest edition 7th. $19.95 for individuals. Covers: nursing orientation. Publication includes: telephone and address directory.

11139 ■ What Can I Do Now—Nursing
Facts On File Inc.
132 W 31st St., 17th Fl.
New York, NY 10001
Ph: (212)967-8800
Fax: 800-678-3633
Fr: 800-322-8755
URL: http://www.infobasepublishing.com

Latest edition 2nd; Published April, 2007. $29.95 for individuals. Covers: Licensed practical nurses, nurse anesthetists, nurse assistants, nurse midwives, nurse practitioners, registered nurses, and surgical nurses.

Handbooks and Manuals

11140 ■ 101 Careers in Nursing
Springer-Verlag New York, Inc.
11 W 42nd St., 15th Fl.
New York, NY 10036
Ph: (212)431-4370
Fax: (212)941-7842
Fr: 877-687-7476
URL: http://www.springerpub.com/product/
    9780826102713

Jeanne M. Novotny, Doris T. Lippman, Nicole K. Sanders, Joyce J. Fitzpatrick. June 2006. $18.00 (paper). Illustrated. 240 pages.

11141 ■ Career Opportunities in Health Care (Career Opportunities)
Facts On File Inc.
132 W 31st St., 17th Fl.
New York, NY 10001-2006
Fax: 800-678-3633
Fr: 800-322-8755
E-mail: custserv@factsonfile.com
URL: http://www.infobasepublishing.com

Shelly Field. 2007. Third Edition. $49.50. 304 pages. Part of the Career Opportunities Series.

11142 ■ Careers in Health Care
The McGraw-Hill Companies
PO Box 182604
Columbus, OH 43272
Fax: (614)759-3749
Fr: 877-883-5524
E-mail: customer.service@mcgraw-hill.com
URL: http://www.mhprofessional.com/
    product.php?isbn=0071466533

Barbara M. Swanson. Fifth edition, 2005. $19.95 (paper). 192 pages. Describes job duties, work settings, salaries, licensing and certification requirements, educational preparation, and future outlook. Gives ideas on how to secure a job.

11143 ■ Careers in Medicine
The McGraw-Hill Companies
PO Box 182604
Columbus, OH 43272
Fax: (614)759-3749
Fr: 877-883-5524
E-mail: customer.service@mcgraw-hill.com
URL: http://www.mhprofessional.com/
    product.php?isbn=0071458743

Terence J. Sacks. Third edition, 2006. $15.95 (paper). 192 pages. Examines the many paths open to M.D.s, D.O.s, and M.D./Ph.D.s, including clinical private or group practice, hospitals, public health organizations, the armed forces, emergency rooms, research institutions, medical schools, pharmaceutical companies

and private industry, and research/advocacy groups like the World Health Organization. A special chapter on osteopathy and chiropractic explores this branch of medicine.

11144 ■ Clinical Nurse Specialist Toolkit
Springer Publishing Company
11 W 42nd St., 15th Fl.
New York, NY 10036
Ph: (212)431-4370
Fax: (212)941-7842
Fr: 877-687-7476
URL: http://www.springerpub.com

Melanie Duffy, Susan Dresser and Janet Fulton. 2009. $40.00. 192 pages (spiral bound). Contains advice and guidelines on getting a job as a clinical nurse specialist.

11145 ■ Developing Your Career in Nursing
Sage Publications, Inc.
2455 Teller Rd.
Thousand Oaks, CA 91320-2218
Fax: 800-583-2665
Fr: 800-818-7243
E-mail: info@sagepub.com
URL: http://www.sagepub.com/books/Book226518

Robert Newell, editor. $37.95. 184 pages.

11146 ■ The Everything New Nurse Book
Adams Media
4700 E Galbraith Rd.
Cincinnati, OH 45236
Fr: (855)278-0402
URL: http://www.adamsmediastore.com

Kathy Quan. 2011. $16.95 (paper). 304 pages. Serves as a guide to novice nurses. Concentrates on issues new nurses face such as dealing with patients, balancing a hectic schedule and managing multiple responsibilities.

11147 ■ Expert Resumes for Health Care Careers
Jist Works
875 Montreal Way
St. Paul, MN 55102
Fr: 800-648-5478
E-mail: educate@emcp.com
URL: http://www.jist.com

Wendy S. Enelow and Louise M. Kursmark. 2010. $16.95. 288 pages.

11148 ■ Exploring Health Careers
Delmar Cengage Learning
5 Maxwell Dr.
Clifton Park, NY 12065
Fr: 800-648-7450
URL: http://www.delmarlearning.com/about/
    contact.aspx

Maureen McCutcheon, Mary Phillips. 2006. $98.95. Provides an overview of the many career opportunities available within the health care field. Covers career descriptions, including educational requirements, salary information, skills and procedures performed within the various careers and more.

11149 ■ Fast Facts for the Travel Nurse
Springer Publishing Company
11 W 42nd St., 15th Fl.
New York, NY 10036
Ph: (212)431-4370
Fax: (212)941-7842
Fr: 877-687-7476
URL: http://www.springerpub.com

Michele Angell Landrum. 2009. $25.00 (paper). 240 pages. Provides a broad base of information intended to guide professional nurses in pursuing a travel nursing career. Includes tips on how to enter the field of travel nursing, negotiate assignment contracts, increase pay, improve benefits and enhance travel assignments.

11150 ■ Health Careers Today
Elsevier
11830 Westline Industrial Dr.
St. Louis, MO 63146
Ph: (314)453-7010
Fax: (314)453-7095
Fr: 800-545-2522
E-mail: usbkinfo@elsevier.com
URL: http://www.elsevier.com

Gerdin, Judith. Fourth edition. 2007. $74.95. 496 pages. Covers more than 45 health careers. Discusses the roles and responsibilities of various occupations and provides a solid foundation in the skills needed for all health careers.

11151 ■ How to Run Your Own Nurse Practitioner Business: A Guide for Success
Springer Publishing Company
11 W 42nd St., 15th Fl.
New York, NY 10036
Ph: (212)431-4370
Fax: (212)941-7842
Fr: 877-687-7476
E-mail: cs@springerpub.com
URL: http://www.springerpub.com

Sheila Grossman and Martha Burke O'Brien. 2010. $60.00. 328 pages. Serves as authoritative reference for nurse practitioners (NPs), masters and doctoral level students, and administrators interested in developing and managing high-quality, cost-effective and patient-accessible healthcare in NP settings. Provides templates of policies, procedures and documents. Discusses all aspects of running a clinic such as: staff evaluation; job descriptions; managing patient records; business plans; and sample budgets.

11152 ■ Introduction to the Health Professions
Jones & Bartlett Learning, LLC
PO Box 417289
Boston, MA 02241-7289
Ph: (978)443-5000
Fax: (978)443-8000
Fr: 800-832-0034
E-mail: info@jblearning.com
URL: http://www.jblearning.com

Peggy S. Stanfield, Y. H. Hui and Nanna Cross. 2012. $93.95. 502 pages. Sixth edition. Provides current coverage of all major health professions. Outlines health-related careers, a review of the U.S. healthcare delivery system, managed care, and impact of new technology on healthcare services.

11153 ■ LPN-to-RN Bridge: Transitions to Advance Your Career
Jones & Bartlett Learning
5 Wall St.
Burlington, MA 01803
Ph: (978)443-5000
Fax: (978)443-8000
Fr: 800-832-0034
E-mail: info@jblearning.com
URL: http://www.jblearning.com

Allison J. Terry. 2012. $46.95. 300 pages. Serves as a resource for students who have previously acquired training as a licensed practical nurse and are currently pursuing a degree as a registered nurse. Includes preparation for licensure examination.

11154 ■ The Medical Services Professional Career Guidebook
CRC Press
6000 Broken Sound Pkwy. NW, Ste. 300
Boca Raton, FL 33487
Fax: 800-374-3401
Fr: 800-272-7737
URL: http://www.crcpress.com

Donna K. Goestenkors and Georgia Day. 2011. 140 pages. Details a series of building blocks to help MSPs fulfill job requirements and successfully navigate career progression, including sample job descriptions, sample performance profile, glossary, and reference materials.

11155 ■ Mosby's Tour Guide to Nursing School: A Student's Road Survival Guide
Mosby
11830 Westline Industrial Dr.
St. Louis, MO 63146
Ph: (314)872-8370
Fax: (314)432-1280
Fr: 800-325-4177
URL: http://www.elsevier.com

Melodie Chenevert. Sixth edition, 2011. $29.95 (paper). 240 pages.

11156 ■ The Nursing Experience: Trends, Challenges & Transitions
The McGraw-Hill Companies
PO Box 182604
Columbus, OH 43272
Fax: (614)759-3749
Fr: 877-883-5524
E-mail: customer.service@mcgraw-hill.com
URL: http://www.mhprofessional.com

Lucille A. Joel and L.Y. Kelly. Fifth edition, 2006. $44.95 (paper). 792 pages.

11157 ■ The Nursing Profession: Development, Challenges, and Opportunities
Jossey-Bass
c/o John Wiley & Sons, Inc.
111 River St.
Hoboken, NJ 07030-5774
Ph: (201)748-6000
Fax: (201)748-6088
URL: http://www.josseybass.com

Diane J. Mason, Stephen L. Isaacs and David C. Colby. 2011. $75.00 (paper). 432 pages. Gives health practitioners, researchers and students a better understanding of the nursing field and the vital issues nursing professionals encounter.

11158 ■ Nursing Today: Transition and Trends
W. B. Saunders Co.
6277 Sea Harbor Dr.
Orlando, FL 32887
Ph: (407)345-2000
Fr: 800-545-2522
URL: http://www.elsevier.com

JoAnn Zerwekh and Jo C. Claborn, editors. Sixth edition, 2009. $52.95 (paper). 640 pages.

11159 ■ Nursing: Transition to Professional Practice
Oxford University Press
198 Madison Ave.
New York, NY 10016
Ph: (212)726-6000
Fr: 800-445-9714
E-mail: custserv.us@oup.com
URL: http://www.oup.com/us

Rob Burton and Gramham Ormrod. 2011. $42.95 (paper). 384 pages. Provides information on the principles of professional practice and skills of the qualified nurse. Aims to develop an understanding of the underlying issues central to being a staff nurse. Features a section on job hunting that will prepare readers to get the first job that they want. Includes interactive online exercises.

11160 ■ Opportunities in Health and Medical Careers
The McGraw-Hill Companies
PO Box 182604
Columbus, OH 43272
Fax: (614)759-3749
Fr: 877-883-5524
E-mail: customer.service@mcgraw-hill.com
URL: http://www.mhprofessional.com/
   product.php?isbn=0071437274

I. Donald Snook, Jr. and Leo D'Orazio. 2004. $14.95 (paper). 157 pages. Covers the full range of medical and health occupations. Illustrated.

11161 ■ Opportunities in Physician Assistant Careers
The McGraw-Hill Companies
PO Box 182604
Columbus, OH 43272
Fax: (614)759-3749
Fr: 877-883-5524
E-mail: customer.service@mcgraw-hill.com
URL: http://www.mhprofessional.com/
   product.php?isbn=0071400613

Terence J. Sacks. $15.95. 160 pages.

11162 ■ Pathways to a Nursing Education Career
Springer Publishing Company
11 W 42nd St., 15th Fl.
New York, NY 10036
Ph: (212)431-4370
Fax: (212)941-7842
Fr: 877-687-7476
URL: http://www.springerpub.com

Judith A. Halstead and Betsy Frank. 2010. $45.00 (paper). 210 pages. Provides a guide to aid novice educators and faculty-in-training in making a smooth transition from nursing practice to the world of academia.

11163 ■ Plunkett's Health Care Industry Almanac 2012
Plunkett Research, Ltd.
PO Drawer 541737
Houston, TX 77254-1737
Ph: (713)932-0000
Fax: (713)932-7080
E-mail: customersupport@plunkettresearch.com
URL: http://www.plunkettresearch.com

Jack W. Plunkett. 2011. $299.99. 717 pages. Features in-depth profiles of leading companies, associations and professional societies in the healthcare field. Covers major issues and trends, market forecasts and industry statistics.

11164 ■ Resumes for Health and Medical Careers
The McGraw-Hill Companies
PO Box 182604
Columbus, OH 43272
Fax: (614)759-3749
Fr: 877-883-5524
E-mail: customer.service@mcgraw-hill.com
URL: http://www.mhprofessional.com/
   product.php?isbn=0071545352

Third edition, 2008. $12.95 (paper). 144 pages.

11165 ■ Resumes for Nursing Careers
The McGraw-Hill Companies
PO Box 182604
Columbus, OH 43272
Fax: (614)759-3749
Fr: 877-883-5524
E-mail: customer.service@mcgraw-hill.com
URL: http://www.mhprofessional.com/
   product.php?isbn=0071509860

2007. $11.95 (paper). 144 pages.

11166 ■ Top 100 Health-Care Careers, Third Edition: Your Complete Guidebook to Training and Jobs in Allied Health, Nursing, Medicine, and More
JIST Publishing
875 Montreal Way
St. Paul, MN 55102
Fax: 800-547-8329
Fr: 800-648-5478
E-mail: info@jist.com
URL: http://www.jist.com/shop/
   product.php?productid=2990&cat=0&page=2

Dr. Saul Wischnitzer and Edith Wischnitzer. 2011. $25.95. 464 pages. Offers a self-assessment for choosing the right career in the field, as well as guidance on common admissions tests, information on financial aid, and job search tips.

11167 ■ Your Career in Nursing: Get the Most Out of Your Nursing Career Today and Tomorrow
Kaplan Publishing
1 Liberty Plaza, 24th Fl.
New York, NY 10006
Ph: (212)618-2405
Fax: (212)618-2499
Fr: 800-527-4836
URL: http://www.kaplanpublishing.com

Annette Vallano. Fifth edition. $17.00. Illustrated. 384 Pages. Vocational guide.

11168 ■ Your First Year As a Nurse
Three Rivers Press
c/o Random House, Inc.
1745 Broadway
New York, NY 10019
Ph: (212)782-9000
URL: http://www.randomhouse.com

Donna Cardillo. 2010. Second Edition. $20.00. 304 pages. Guides the readers as beginners to the professional nursing field. Provides career advice and opportunities related to nursing.

EMPLOYMENT AGENCIES AND SEARCH FIRMS

11169 ■ Access Staffing
360 Lexington Ave., 8th Fl.
New York, NY 10017
Ph: (212)687-5440
Fax: (212)557-2544
URL: http://www.accessstaffingco.com

Serves as a staffing firm covering accounting/ financial, advertising, bilingual Japanese, creative, event planning, fashion/retail, healthcare/ human services, human resources, information technology, insurance, legal, light industrial and office support.

11170 ■ Actuary Resources
115 N Castle Heights Ave., Ste. 202
Lebanon, TN 37087-2768
Ph: (615)360-5171
Fax: (615)360-5173
E-mail: info@actuaryresources.org
URL: http://www.actuaryresources.org

Provides staffing services to several different types of industries. Offers a free screening service to clients.

11171 ■ Advanced Care Providers
PO Box 972
Minocqua, WI 54548
Ph: (715)661-0030
Fax: (323)375-3290
URL: http://www.acpstaff.com

Specializes in the placement of physician assistants and nurse practitioners. Matches qualified providers with healthcare facilities in need of temporary or permanent staffing.

11172 ■ Axis Medical Staffing
100 W Harrison St., Ste. 550
Seattle, WA 98119
Ph: (206)285-6300
Fax: (206)285-6302
Fr: 888-299-AXIS
E-mail: hr@axismedicalstaffing.com
URL: http://www.axismedicalstaffing.com

Description: Focuses on recruiting medical professionals and matching their requirements to the needs of facilities. Provides quality medical staffing for facilities nationwide. Specializes in per diem staffing, local/national travel assignments and direct hire full-time placements for nursing/nursing aides, radiological technologists and business services.

11173 ■ B. E. Smith
9777 Ridge Dr.
Lenexa, KS 66219

Fr: 800-467-9117
URL: http://www.besmith.com

Serves as an executive search to healthcare organizations across the nation. Offers permanent and interim placements.

11174 ■ Beck-Field and Associates
9330 Corporate Dr., Ste. 103
Selma, TX 78154
Ph: (210)651-4337
Fax: (210)651-4338
Fr: 800-304-3095
URL: http://www.beck-field.com

Recruitment firm specializing in the permanent placement of registered nurses, physicians, and other healthcare related staff.

11175 ■ CompHealth
PO Box 713100
Salt Lake City, UT 84171-3100
Ph: (801)930-3000
Fax: (801)930-4517
Fr: 800-453-3030
E-mail: info@comphealth.com
URL: http://www.comphealth.com

Provides healthcare staffing and recruiting services covering certified registered nurse anesthetist, dosimetrist, imaging and radiation therapy, laboratory technology, medical physicist, nurse practitioner, nursing, pharmacy, physician, physician assistant, rehab therapy and respiratory therapy.

11176 ■ CoreMedical Group
2 Keewaydin Dr.
Salem, NH 03079
Ph: (603)893-4515
Fax: (603)893-8442
Fr: 800-995-2673
E-mail: info@coremedicalgroup.com
URL: http://www.coremedicalgroup.com

Provides career resources and staffing solutions for nursing jobs, travel nurses and permanent nursing assignments.

11177 ■ Cross Country TravCorps
6551 Park of Commerce Blvd.
Boca Raton, FL 33487-8247
Fax: (561)998-8533
Fr: 800-530-6125
E-mail: sms@cctc.com
URL: http://www.crosscountrytravcorps.com/cctc/

Places traveling nurses in assignments nationwide.

11178 ■ Diversified Staffing Group, Inc.
85 Newbury St.
Boston, MA 02116
Ph: (617)259-1001
Fax: (617)259-1009
Fr: 877-229-1118
E-mail: info@dsgworld.com
URL: http://www.dsgworld.com/main.htm

Description: Serves as an executive search firm for nursing professionals.

11179 ■ Foundation Medical Staffing
416 W 15th St., Bldg. 700
Edmond, OK 73013
Fax: 800-774-9252
Fr: (866)349-4688
URL: http://www.foundationmedicalstaffing.com

Provides job opportunities for registered nurse specializing in dialysis services.

11180 ■ Harper Associates
31000 NW Hwy., Ste. 240
Farmington Hills, MI 48334
Ph: (248)932-1170
Fax: (248)932-1214
E-mail: info@harperjobs.com
URL: http://www.harperjobs.com

Executive search firm and employment agency.

11181 ■ Harris Brand Recruiting
4 Avis Dr., Ste. 1
Latham, NY 12110
Ph: (518)782-5250
Fr: 800-288-1730
E-mail: info@harrisbrand.com
URL: http://www.harrisbrand.com

Offers resource for physician jobs and practice opportunities for primary care and specialty doctors, physician assistants, nurse practitioners and certified nurse midwives.

11182 ■ Keystone Healthcare Management
6075 Poplar Ave., Ste. 727
Memphis, TN 38119
Ph: (901)795-3600
Fax: (901)795-6060
Fr: (866)291-8600
E-mail: scross@keystonehealthcare.com
URL: http://www.keystonehealthcare.com

Specializes in the organization and management of emergency physician groups, offering support services in emergency department management, emergency medicine and physician placement.

11183 ■ NurseChoice
12400 High Bluff Dr.
San Diego, CA 92130
Fax: (866)493-3969
Fr: (866)557-6050
E-mail: info@nursechoice.com
URL: http://www.nursechoice.com

Serves as a travel nurse recruitment agency. Offers quick-start, short-term travel nurse jobs and flexible travel nurse hours to a select group of travel nurses.

11184 ■ NursesPro.com
1616 S Voss, Ste. 350
Houston, TX 77057
Ph: (713)979-2601
Fax: (713)979-2602
Fr: 888-668-7735
URL: http://www.nursespro.com

Nurse staffing agency. Provides for the needs of healthcare delivery organizations through contract travel nursing.

11185 ■ Nursing Technomics
814 Sunset Hollow Rd.
West Chester, PA 19380-1848
Ph: (610)436-4551
Fax: (610)436-0255

Administrative nursing consultants offer expertise in the design and implementation of customized software applications for departments of nursing, organizational design and implementation and executive nurse search. Also specializes in department staffing, scheduling and nurse recruitment. Serves private industries as well as government agencies.

11186 ■ Preferred Healthcare Staffing
9089 Clairemont Mesa Blvd., No. 200
San Diego, CA 92123
Fr: 800-787-6787
E-mail: staffing@preferredregistry.com
URL: http://preferredregistry.com

Description: Specializes in placing registered nurses on travel nursing assignments.

11187 ■ Professional Placement Associates, Inc.
287 Bowman Ave.
Purchase, NY 10577-2517
Ph: (914)251-1000
Fax: (914)251-1055
E-mail: careers@ppasearch.com
URL: http://www.ppasearch.com

Executive search firm specializing in the health and medical field.

11188 ■ RN Network
2000 NW Corporate Blvd., Ste. 150
Boca Raton, FL 33431

Fax: 800-359-8480
Fr: (866)285-5137
URL: http://www.rnnetwork.com

Comprised of recruiters dedicated to the travel nursing industry.

11189 ■ Skilled Nursing Inc. Staffing and Search
955 Horsham Rd., Ste. 205
Horsham, PA 19044
Ph: (267)532-1620
Fr: 800-284-4764
E-mail: inquiry@snistaffing.com
URL: http://www.snistaffing.com

Description: Works to broker registered nurses and nurse practitioners to a variety of health care clients to meet temporary fluctuations in staffing needs and other extended assignments such as clinical research trials.

11190 ■ Stat Group, LLC
PO Box 1674
Owensboro, KY 42302-1674
Ph: (270)663-8020
Fax: 877-998-9940
Fr: 877-998-9930
E-mail: info@statgroupllc.com
URL: http://www.statgroupllc.com

Description: Serves as a healthcare staffing firm which provides healthcare facilities with a workforce pool. Attracts and retains medical professionals to assist healthcare facilities throughout the United States.

11191 ■ Team Placement Service, Inc.
1414 Prince St., Ste. 202
Alexandria, VA 22314
Ph: (703)820-8618
Fax: (703)820-3368
Fr: 800-495-6767
E-mail: 4jobs@teamplace.com
URL: http://www.teamplace.com

Full-service personnel consultants provide placement for healthcare staff, physician and dentist, private practice, and hospitals. Conduct interviews, tests, and reference checks to select the top 20% of applicants. Survey applicants' skill levels, provide backup information on each candidate, select compatible candidates for consideration, and insure the hiring process minimizes potential legal liability. Industries served: healthcare and government agencies providing medical, dental, biotech, laboratory, hospitals, and physician search.

11192 ■ Whitaker Medical
1200 Enclave Pkwy., Ste. 200
Houston, TX 77077
Ph: (281)870-1000
Fax: (866)513-0183
Fr: 800-444-5628
URL: http://www.whitakermedical.com

Exists as a healthcare recruitment firm that provides staffing solutions for healthcare professionals and facilities across the nation.

ONLINE JOB SOURCES AND SERVICES

11193 ■ BestNurseJobs.com
URL: http://www.bestnursejobs.com

Description: Features nursing jobs across the United States. Provides nursing job listings that allow individuals to apply directly to hospitals, medical centers, and private practices or browse through nursing jobs listed by travel and permanent nurse recruitment companies.

11194 ■ CareerVitals.com
URL: http://www.careervitals.com

Description: Serves as a job board for healthcare professionals in different specializations.

11195 ■ EmployMED: Healthcare Job Listings
E-mail: customerservice@evalumed.com
URL: http://www.evalumed.com/EmployMed.aspx

Description: Lists practice opportunities throughout North America for all medical specialties. Contains job listings directory. Posting option is available for those who wish to advertise jobs. Fee: $25 per month per posting for minimum of two months.

11196 ■ GasWork.com: The Largest Internet Anesthesia Employment Resource
E-mail: support@gaswork.com
URL: http://www.gaswork.com

Description: The largest anesthesia employment resource. Lists positions for anesthesiologists, CRNA's, and more. Visitors may post or search jobs.

11197 ■ GreatPharmaJobs.com
URL: http://greatpharmajobs.com

Description: Offers job vacancies in healthcare industry.

11198 ■ Health Care Job Store
395 South End Ave., Ste. 15-D
New York, NY 10280
Ph: (561)630-5201
E-mail: jobs@healthcarejobstore.com
URL: http://www.healthcarejobstore.com

Description: Job sites include every job title in the healthcare industry, every healthcare industry and every geographic location in the U.S.

11199 ■ Health Care Recruitment Online
E-mail: info@healthcarerecruitment.com
URL: http://healthcarerecruitment.com

Description: Helps seekers find healthcare positions through on-line postings with national staffing companies and hospital partners. Main files include: Featured Employers, Job Search, Immediate Openings, Relocating, Career Management, State boards, and more.

11200 ■ HealthcareCrossing.com
URL: http://www.healthcarecrossing.com

Description: Provides a collection of health care jobs, hospitals and medical jobs, nursing jobs and healthcare employment. Includes a variety of employers in the health care business.

11201 ■ HealthCareerWeb.com
URL: http://www.healthcareerweb.com

Description: Advertises jobs for healthcare professionals. Main files include: Jobs, Employers, Resumes, Jobwire. Relocation tools and career guidance resources available.

11202 ■ HEALTHeCAREERS Network
Fr: 888-884-8242
E-mail: info@healthecareers.com
URL: http://www.healthecareers.com

Description: Career search site for jobs in all health care specialties; educational resources; visa and licensing information for relocation; interesting articles; relocation tools; links to professional organizations and general resources.

11203 ■ HireNursing.com
URL: http://www.hirenursing.com

Description: Provides job opportunities for professional nurses. Features career tools, educational resources, networking, and industry news.

11204 ■ Hospital Jobs OnLine
E-mail: support@hospitaljobsonline.com
URL: http://www.hospitaljobsonline.com

Description: Serves as a niche healthcare job board designed exclusively for hospitals, healthcare companies, and healthcare job seekers.

11205 ■ JobsInLTC.com
URL: http://www.jobsinltc.com

Description: Serves as a job board for long-term care jobs for nursing home administrators, assisted living staff, directors of nursing, MDS coordinators, and other related fields.

11206 ■ Lippincott's NursingCenter.com
URL: http://www.nursingcenter.com

Description: Helps spread clinical information to nurses in rural areas who would otherwise not have access to the latest journals and technology. Provides access to job openings as well as upcoming clinical expos and job fairs.

11207 ■ Locate Nurse Jobs
URL: http://www.locatenursejobs.com

Description: Serves as an online job search and employee recruiting resource. Provides opportunities for nurses in a wide range of health care settings from hospitals to home health care.

11208 ■ MedExplorer.com
E-mail: medmaster@medexplorer.com
URL: http://www.medexplorer.com

Description: Employment postings make up one module of this general medical site. Other sections contain: Newsletter, Classifieds, and Discussion Forum.

11209 ■ Medzilla.com
URL: http://www.medzilla.com

Description: General medical website which matches employers and job hunters to their ideal employees and jobs through search capabilities. Main files include: Post Jobs, Search Resumes, Post Resumes, Search Jobs, Head Hunters, Articles, Salary Survey.

11210 ■ Monster Healthcare
URL: http://healthcare.monster.com

Description: Delivers nationwide access to healthcare recruiting. Employers can post job listings or ads. Job seekers can post and code resumes, and search over 150,000 healthcare job listings, healthcare career advice columns, career resources information, and member employer profiles and services.

11211 ■ nurse-recruiter.com
URL: http://www.nurse-recruiter.com

Description: Serves as a resource of jobs for the nursing and allied health fields.

11212 ■ NurseJobsLink.com
URL: http://www.nursejobslink.com

Description: Provides job opportunities for nursing professionals.

11213 ■ NurseJungle.com
URL: http://www.nursejungle.com

Description: Serves as career center for nurses, providing resume posting, job search and career development resources. Provides job postings for employers in the nursing community.

11214 ■ NursePath.com
URL: http://www.nursepath.com

Description: Serves as a clearinghouse for those seeking nursing positions. Contains job postings by specialty in critical care, education, emergency, gerontology, and psychiatry.

11215 ■ Nurses123.com
URL: http://www.nurses123.com

Description: Offers nursing job information through its listing of job opportunities nationwide. Helps nurses search for work, research healthcare organizations and access career-related resources.

11216 ■ Nurses.info
URL: http://www.nurses.info

Description: Provides healthcare information for the professional development of nurses and health professionals. Provides links to a range of educational and vocational information, conferences, journals and other nursing related resources.

11217 ■ NursesRX.com
12400 High Bluff Dr.
Huntersville, NC 28078
Fax: 877-744-9052
Fr: 800-733-9354
E-mail: info@nursesrx.com
URL: http://www.nursesrx.com

Description: Job board site for travel nursing. In addition to traditional travel nursing, Nurses RX provides staffing possibilities from temporary-to-permanent, traditional permanent placement, staffing/recruitment outsourcing, new graduate internship programs, and a full Canadian Placement Division.

11218 ■ NurseZone.com
URL: http://www.nursezone.com

Description: Aims to provide nurses with professional and personal development information and opportunities. Provides student nurses, new graduates, and experienced nurses with the resources needed to succeed in the profession.

11219 ■ Nursing Job Source
URL: http://www.nursingjobsource.com

Description: Provides career services and maintains a job board for nurses, nursing professionals, and others in the nursing industry.

11220 ■ Nursing-Jobs.us
URL: http://www.nursing-jobs.us

Description: Features permanent, per diem, or travel nursing jobs. Partners with hospitals, travel nurse companies and recruitment agencies to assist job seekers in the nursing industry.

11221 ■ NursingCrossing.com
URL: http://www.nursingcrossing.com

Description: Provides job listings and other resources related to nursing employment opportunities.

11222 ■ United Search Associates: Health Network USA
PO Box 342
Vinita, OK 74301
Ph: (918)323-4165
E-mail: jobs@hnusa.com
URL: http://homepage.mac.com/hnusa

Description: Visitors may explore healthcare positions, submit an electronic resume, or advertise with the site.

TRADESHOWS

11223 ■ Academy of Medical-Surgical Nurses Annual Convention
Academy of Medical-Surgical Nurses
East Holly Ave.
Box 56
Pitman, NJ 08071
Fr: (866)877-2676
E-mail: amsn@ajj.com
URL: http://www.amsn.org

Annual. Includes exhibits of various products, technologies, and publications specific to medical-surgical nursing care and services. 2012 October 4-7; Salt Lake City, UT; Salt Palace Convention Center.

11224 ■ ACNP National Clinical Conference
American College of Nurse Practitioners
225 Reinekers Ln., Ste. 525
Alexandria, VA 22314
Ph: (703)740-2529

Fax: (703)740-2533
E-mail: acnp@acnpweb.org
URL: http://www.acnpweb.org

Annual. Contains exhibits of pharmaceutical and medical products as well as health care services. 2013 October 2-6; Las Vegas, NV. Provides networking opportunities for all professionals working in the field.

11225 ■ American Academy of Ambulatory Care Nursing Annual Conference
American Academy of Ambulatory Care Nursing
East Holly Ave., Box 56
Pitman, NJ 08071-0056
Fr: 800-262-6877
E-mail: aaacn@ajj.com
URL: http://www.aaacn.org

Annual. Includes speakers presenting the latest information on topics pertinent and timely to ambulatory care nursing. 2013 April 23-25; Las Vegas, NV; Las Vegas Hilton.

11226 ■ American Association of Nurse Anesthetists Annual Meeting
American Association of Nurse Anesthetists
222 S Prospect Ave.
Park Ridge, IL 60068-4001
Ph: (847)692-7050
Fax: (847)692-6968
E-mail: info@aana.com
URL: http://www.aana.com

Annual. Includes exhibits of new innovations in clinical care, technology, products, and services in the anesthesiology field. 2012 August 4-8; San Francisco, CA; Moscone West Convention Center.

11227 ■ American Nephrology Nurses Association Symposium
Anthony J. Jannetti, Inc.
E Holly Ave.
PO Box 56
Pitman, NJ 08071-0056
Ph: (856)256-2300
Fax: (856)589-7463
E-mail: contact@ajj.com
URL: http://www.ajj.com

Annual. Primary Exhibits: Equipment, supplies, pharmaceuticals, and services related to the field of nephrology. Dates and Locations: 2012 Apr 29 - May 02; Orlando, FL; Walt Disney World Dolphin.

11228 ■ American Organization of Nurse Executives Annual Meeting and Exposition
Dallas Hyatt Regency
300 Reunion Blvd.
Dallas, TX 75207
Ph: (214)651-1234
Fax: (214)742-8126
URL: http://www.dallasregency.hyatt.com

Annual. Primary Exhibits: Patient-care equipment and supplies; computer hardware and software related to the administration of hospital nursing services; communications systems; intensive care units; medical supplies and equipment; recruiting and staffing services; and related equipment, supplies, and services. Dates and Locations: 2012 Mar 21-24; Boston, MA.

11229 ■ Annual RNS Conference
Rheumatology Nurses Society
1810-J York Rd. No. 178
Lutherville, MD 21093
Fax: (410)384-4222
Fr: 800-380-7081
E-mail: brent.carver@rns-network.org
URL: http://www.rns-network.org

Annual. Provides workshops, exhibits, peer networking and didactic sessions. Includes exhibits of products and services for rheumatology nurses. 2012 August 2-4; Tampla, FL; Grand Hyatt Tampa Bay.

11230 ■ APHON Annual Conference and Exhibit
Association of Pediatric Hematology/Oncology Nurses
4700 W Lake Ave.
Glenview, IL 60025
Ph: (847)375-4724
Fax: (847)375-6478
E-mail: info@aphon.org
URL: http://www.aphon.org

Annual. Includes exhibits of pharmaceutical products, medical equipment, blood services, educational materials, training programs, publications, support services, therapeutic products, and recruitment services. 2012 October 4-6; Pittsburgh, PA; David L. Lawrence Convention Center.

11231 ■ Association of Perioperative Registered Nurses Annual Congress
Association of Perioperative Registered Nurses
AORN
2170 S. Parker Rd., Ste. 400
Denver, CO 80231-5711
Ph: (303)755-6304
Fax: (303)750-3212
Fr: 800-755-2676
E-mail: custserv@aorn.org
URL: http://www.aorn.org

Annual. Primary Exhibits: Surgical equipment, supplies, and services; recruiting firms, computer software, endoscopes, online buying services.

11232 ■ Association of Rehabilitation Nurses Annual Educational Conference
Association of Rehabilitation Nurses
4700 W Lake Ave.
Glenview, IL 60025-1485
Ph: (847)375-4710
Fax: (847)375-6481
Fr: 800-229-7530
E-mail: info@rehabnurse.org
URL: http://www.rehabnurse.org

Annual. Gives rehabilitation professionals the opportunity to present their work within an atmosphere of support by peers and national rehabilitation leaders.

11233 ■ Conference of the National Association of Pediatric Nurse Associates and Practitioners
National Association of Pediatric Nurse Associates and Practitioners
20 Brace Rd., Ste. 200
Cherry Hill, NJ 08034-2634
Ph: (856)857-9700
Fax: (856)857-1600
Fr: 877-662-7627
E-mail: info@napnap.org
URL: http://www.napnap.org

Annual. Primary Exhibits: Equipment, supplies, and services for pediatric, school, and family nurse practitioners. Dates and Locations: 2012 Mar 28-31; San Antonio, TX.

11234 ■ DNA Annual Convention
Dermatology Nurses' Association
15000 Commerce Pkwy., Ste. C
Mount Laurel, NJ 08054
Fax: (856)439-0525
Fr: 800-454-4362
E-mail: dna@dnanurse.org
URL: http://www.dnanurse.org

Annual. Includes exhibits of new technologies, products and services, supplies, and equipment in the field of dermatology nursing. 2013 April 4-7; New Orleans, LA; Sheraton New Orleans Hotel.

11235 ■ Emergency Nurses Association Annual Meeting
Emergency Nurses Association
915 Lee St.
Des Plaines, IL 60016-6569

Fr: 800-900-9659
URL: http://www.ena.org

Annual. Primary Exhibits: Exhibits relating to emergency room care.

11236 ■ INS Annual Meeting and Industrial Exhibition
Infusion Nurses Society
315 Norwood Park S
Norwood, MA 02062
Ph: (781)440-9408
Fax: (781)440-9409
Fr: 800-694-0298
E-mail: ins@ins1.org
URL: http://www.ins1.org

Annual. Includes exhibits of homecare and infusion services, dialysis products, infusion medications and solutions, injection products, pharmacy services, specimen management products, medical devices, and other services used in infusion therapy.

11237 ■ International Nurses Society on Addictions Annual Educational Conference
International Nurses Society on Addictions
PO Box 14846
Lenexa, KS 66285
Fax: (913)895-4652
Fr: 877-646-8672
E-mail: intnsa@intnsa.org
URL: http://intnsa.org/home/index.asp

Annual. Features discussions of issues, practices and innovations related to the treatment and prevention of substance addictions.

11238 ■ International Society of Psychiatric-Mental Health Nurses Annual Conference
International Society of Psychiatric - Mental Health Nurses
2424 American Ln.
Madison, WI 53704-3102
Ph: (608)443-2463
Fax: (608)443-2474
Fr: (866)330-7227
E-mail: info@ispn-psych.org
URL: http://www.ispn-psych.org

Annual. Primary Exhibits: Psychiatric nursing equipment, supplies, and services.

11239 ■ NADONA's Conference
National Association Directors of Nursing Administration
Reed Hartman Tower
11353 Reed Hartman Hwy., Ste. 210
Cincinnati, OH 45241
Ph: (513)791-3679
Fax: (513)791-3699
Fr: 800-222-0539
URL: http://www.nadona.org

Annual. Discusses new topics in the field and features exhibits of new technology, products, and services. 2012 July 21-25; Nashville, TN; Gaylord Opryland Resort.

11240 ■ NANN Annual Educational Conference
National Association of Neonatal Nurses
4700 W Lake Ave.
Glenview, IL 60025-1485
Ph: (847)375-3660
Fax: (866)927-5321
Fr: 800-451-3795
E-mail: info@nann.org
URL: http://www.nann.org

Annual. Includes exhibits of the latest products and services. Provides opportunities for neonatal nurses to network and interact with each other. 2012 October 17-20; Palm Springs, CA; Palm Springs Convention Center and Renaissance Hotel.

11241 ■ National Advanced Practice Neonatal Nurses Conference
The Academy of Neonatal Nursing
1425 N McDowell Blvd., Ste. 105
Petaluma, CA 94954
Ph: (707)568-2168
Fax: (707)569-0786
URL: http://www.academyonline.org

Annual. Includes exhibits to promote advancement of the organization's service opportunities, strategic educational developments, and product innovations relevant in today's neonatal and mother-baby specialty health care markets.

11242 ■ National Association of Orthopedic Nurses Annual Congress
Smith, Bucklin and Associates, Inc. (Chicago, Illinois)
401 N Michigan Ave.
Chicago, IL 60611-4267
Ph: (312)321-6610
Fax: (312)673-6670
Fr: 800-289-NAON
E-mail: info@smithbucklin.com
URL: http://www.smithbucklin.com

Annual. Primary Exhibits: Pharmaceuticals, medical equipment, medical instruments, and publications.

11243 ■ National Student Nurses' Association Convention
National Student Nurse Association
45 Main St., Ste. 606
Brooklyn, NY 11201
Ph: (718)210-0705
Fax: (718)797-1186
E-mail: nsna@nsna.org
URL: http://www.nsna.org

Annual. Primary Exhibits: Equipment, supplies, and services for the student nurse. Dates and Locations: 2012 Apr 11-15; Pittsburgh, PA; David L. Lawrence Convention Center.

11244 ■ Oncology Nursing Society Meeting
Oncology Nursing Society
125 Enterprise Dr.
Pittsburgh, PA 15275-1214
Ph: (412)859-6100
Fax: (412)859-6162
Fr: 877-369-5497
E-mail: customer.service@ons.org
URL: http://www.ons.org

Annual. Primary Exhibits: Oncology nursing equipment, supplies, and services.

11245 ■ Society of Urologic Nurses and Associates Annual Conference
Society of Urologic Nurses Associates
East Holly Ave., Box 56
Pitman, NJ 08071-0056
Fr: 888-827-7862
E-mail: suna@ajj.com
URL: http://www.suna.org

Annual. Provides urologic professionals with an opportunity to share research studies and findings with colleagues via brief oral or poster presentations. 2012 November 2-5; Washington, DC; Marriott Wardman Park; 2013 October 11-14; Chicago, IL; Hyatt Regency Chicago; 2014 October 31-November 3; Lake Buena Vista, FL; Disney's Contemporary Resort.

OTHER SOURCES

11246 ■ Academy of Medical-Surgical Nurses
East Holly Ave.
Box 56
Pitman, NJ 08071
Ph: (856)256-2422
Fax: (856)589-7463
Fr: (866)877-2676
E-mail: amsn@ajj.com
URL: http://www.amsn.org

Description: Represents registered, licensed practical, licensed vocational nurses, clinical nurse specialists, nurse practitioners, educators, researchers, administrators, and students. Promotes standards of nursing practice and facilitates the implementation of practice guidelines. Provides education programs for members, fosters scholarly activities and disseminates new ideas for all areas of adult health/medical-surgical nursing.

11247 ■ Air & Surface Transport Nurses Association
7995 E Prentice Ave., Ste. 100
Greenwood Village, CO 80111
Fax: (303)770-1614
Fr: 800-897-6362
URL: http://www.astna.org

Description: Exists as an organization of professional nurses who practice transport nursing. Works to advance the practice of transport nursing and enhance the quality of patient care. Serves as an information resource on transport nursing and air medical care delivery systems.

11248 ■ American Academy of Ambulatory Care Nursing
PO Box 56
Pitman, NJ 08071-0056
Fr: 800-262-6877
E-mail: aaacn@ajj.com
URL: http://www.aaacn.org

Description: Comprised of nurses and other professionals interested in ambulatory care and telehealth nursing. Serves as a voice for ambulatory care nurses across the continuum of health care delivery. Provides education to ambulatory care professionals through conference, audio-conferences, and newsletter.

11249 ■ American Assembly for Men in Nursing (AAMN)
PO Box 130220
Birmingham, AL 35213
Ph: (205)956-0146
Fax: (205)956-0149
E-mail: aamn@aamn.org
URL: http://aamn.org

Description: Registered nurses. Works to: help eliminate prejudice in nursing; interest men in the nursing profession; provide opportunities for the discussion of common problems; encourage education and promote further professional growth; advise and assist in areas of professional inequity; help develop sensitivities to various social needs; promote the principles and practices of positive health care. Acts as a clearinghouse for information on men in nursing. Conducts educational programs. Promotes education and research about men's health issues.

11250 ■ American Association for Long Term Care Nursing
PO Box 62956
Cincinnati, OH 45262-0956
Fax: (513)791-1477
Fr: 888-458-2687
E-mail: charlotte@ltcnursing.org
URL: http://ltcnursing.org

Description: Represents the interests of long-term care nurses and other professionals who wish to achieve excellence in the specialty of long-tem care nursing. Provides educational resources that bridge current practices with managerial and clinical activities.

11251 ■ American Association of Managed Care Nurses
4435 Waterfront Dr., Ste. 101
Glen Allen, VA 23060
Ph: (804)747-9698
Fax: (804)747-5316
E-mail: phulcher@aamcn.org
URL: http://www.aamcn.org

Description: Comprised of managed health care professionals, including registered nurses, licensed practical nurses, and nurse practitioners. Seeks to enhance the abilities of members to meet the future needs of the managed health care profession through education. Establishes standards for managed care nursing practice and formulates public policies regarding managed health care delivery.

11252 ■ American Association of Nurse Anesthetists
222 S Prospect Ave.
Park Ridge, IL 60068
Ph: (847)692-7050
Fax: (847)692-6968
E-mail: info@aana.com
URL: http://www.aana.com

Description: Represents Certified Registered Nurse Anesthetists (CRNAS) and student nurse anesthetists nationwide. Seeks to advance patient safety and excellence in anesthesia. Promulgates education and practice standards and guidelines and consults with both private and governmental entities regarding nurse anesthetists and practice.

11253 ■ American Association of Nurse Attorneys (TAANA)
PO Box 14218
Lenexa, KS 66285-4218
Fax: (913)895-4652
Fr: 877-538-2262
E-mail: taana_executive_office@goamp.com
URL: http://www.taana.org

Description: Nurse attorneys, nurses in law school, and attorneys in nursing school. Aims to inform the public on matters of nursing, health care and law. Facilitates communication and information sharing between professional groups; establishes an employment network; assists new and potential nurse attorneys; develops the profession; promotes the image of nurse attorneys as experts and consultants in nursing and law. Maintains educational foundation.

11254 ■ American Association of Occupational Health Nurses (AAOHN)
7794 Grow Dr.
Pensacola, FL 32514
Ph: (850)474-6963
Fax: (850)484-8762
Fr: 800-241-8014
E-mail: aaohn@aaohn.org
URL: http://www.aaohn.org

Description: Represents registered professional nurses employed by business and industrial firms; nurse educators, nurse editors, nurse writers, and others interested in occupational health nursing. Promotes and sets standards for the profession. Provides and approves continuing education; maintains governmental affairs program; offers placement service.

11255 ■ American College of Nurse-Midwives (ACNM)
8403 Colesville Rd., Ste. 1550
Silver Spring, MD 20910
Ph: (240)485-1800
Fax: (240)485-1818
E-mail: memb@acnm.org
URL: http://www.midwife.org

Description: Seeks to develop and support the profession of certified nurse-midwives in order to promote the health and well-being of women and infants within their families and communities. Represents licensed health care practitioner educated in the two disciplines of nursing and midwifery. Provides gynecological services and care of mothers and babies throughout the maternity cycle. Cooperates with allied groups to enable nurse-midwives to concentrate their efforts in the improvement of services for mothers and newborn babies. Studies and evaluates activities of nurse-midwives in order to establish qualifications. Conducts research and continuing education workshops. Compiles statistics. Maintains speakers' bureau and archives; offers placement service.

11256 ■ American College of Nurse Practitioners

1501 Wilson Blvd., Ste. 509
Arlington, VA 22209
Ph: (703)740-2529
Fax: (703)740-2533
E-mail: acnp@acnpweb.org
URL: http://www.acnpweb.org

Description: Represents individual nurse practitioners as well as national and state nurse practitioner organizations. Aims to ensure a solid policy and regulatory foundation that enables nurse practitioners to continue providing accessible healthcare to the nation.

11257 ■ American Health Care Association (AHCA)

1201 L St. NW
Washington, DC 20005
Ph: (202)842-4444
Fax: (202)842-3860
E-mail: hr@ahca.org
URL: http://www.ahcancal.org/Pages/Default.aspx

Description: Federation of state associations of long-term health care facilities. Promotes standards for professionals in long-term health care delivery and quality care for patients and residents in a safe environment. Focuses on issues of availability, quality, affordability, and fair payment. Operates as liaison with governmental agencies, Congress, and professional associations. Compiles statistics.

11258 ■ American Holistic Nurses Association

323 N San Francisco St., Ste. 201
Flagstaff, AZ 86001
Ph: (928)526-2196
Fax: (928)526-2752
Fr: 800-278-2462
E-mail: info@ahna.org
URL: http://www.ahna.org

Description: Comprised of nurses and other holistic healthcare professionals. Advances the profession of holistic nursing by providing continuing education, helping to improve the health care workplace through the incorporation of the concepts of holistic nursing, and educating professionals and the public about holistic nursing and integrative health care. Promotes research and scholarship in the field of holistic nursing.

11259 ■ American Hospital Association (AHA)

155 N Wacker Dr.
Chicago, IL 60606
Ph: (312)422-3000
Fax: (312)422-4796
E-mail: rich@aha.org
URL: http://www.aha.org

Description: Represents health care provider organizations. Seeks to advance the health of individuals and communities. Leads, represents, and serves health care provider organizations that are accountable to the community and committed to health improvement.

11260 ■ American Nurses Association (ANA)

8515 Georgia Ave., Ste. 400
Silver Spring, MD 20910
Ph: (301)628-5000
Fax: (301)628-5001
Fr: 800-274-4262
E-mail: memberinfo@ana.org
URL: http://www.nursingworld.org

Description: Serves as membership association representing registered nurses. Advances the nursing profession by fostering high standards of nursing practice, promoting the rights of nurses in the workplace, projecting a positive and realistic view of nursing, and by lobbying the Congress and regulatory agencies on health care issues affecting nurses and the public.

11261 ■ American Organization of Nurse Executives (AONE)

325 Seventh St. NW
Liberty Pl.
Washington, DC 20004
Ph: (202)626-2240
Fax: (202)638-5499
E-mail: aone@aha.org
URL: http://www.aone.org

Description: Provides leadership, professional development, advocacy, and research to advance nursing practice and patient care, promote nursing leadership and excellence, and shape healthcare public policy. Supports and enhances the management, leadership, educational, and professional development of nursing leaders. Offers placement service through Career Development and Referral Center.

11262 ■ American Psychiatric Nurses Association

1555 Wilson Blvd., Ste. 530
Arlington, VA 22209
Ph: (703)243-2443
Fax: (703)243-3390
Fr: (866)243-2443
E-mail: ncroce@apna.org
URL: http://www.apna.org

Description: Represents psychiatric nurses who are at all levels of education from basic to doctoral and work in a variety of settings including inpatient, outpatient, research, education, administration, clinical, private practice, military, and forensic.

11263 ■ American Public Health Association (APHA)

800 I St. NW
Washington, DC 20001
Ph: (202)777-2742
Fax: (202)777-2534
E-mail: comments@apha.org
URL: http://www.apha.org

Description: Professional organization of physicians, nurses, educators, academicians, environmentalists, epidemiologists, new professionals, social workers, health administrators, optometrists, podiatrists, pharmacists, dentists, nutritionists, health planners, other community and mental health specialists, and interested consumers. Seeks to protect and promote personal, mental, and environmental health. Services include: promulgation of standards; establishment of uniform practices and procedures; development of the etiology of communicable diseases; research in public health; exploration of medical care programs and their relationships to public health. Sponsors job placement service.

11264 ■ American School Health Association (ASHA)

4340 East West Hwy., Ste. 403
Bethesda, MD 20814
Ph: (301)652-8072
Fax: (301)652-8077
Fr: 800-445-2742
E-mail: info@ashaweb.org
URL: http://www.ashaweb.org

Description: School physicians, school nurses, counselors, nutritionists, psychologists, social workers, administrators, school health coordinators, health educators, and physical educators working in schools, professional preparation programs, public health, and community-based organizations. Promotes coordinated school health programs that include health education, health services, a healthful school environment, physical education, nutrition services, and psycho-social health services offered in schools collaboratively with families and other members of the community. Offers professional reference materials and professional development opportunities. Conducts pilot programs that inform materials development, provides technical assistance to school professionals, advocates for school health.

11265 ■ American Society of Extra-Corporeal Technology (AmSECT)

2209 Dickens Rd.
Richmond, VA 23230-2005
Ph: (804)565-6363
Fax: (804)282-0090
E-mail: stewart@amsect.org
URL: http://www.amsect.org

Description: Perfusionists, technologists, doctors, nurses, and others actively employed and using the applied skills relating to the practice of extracorporeal technology (involving heart-lung machines); student members. Disseminates information necessary to the proper practice of the technology. Conducts programs in continuing education and professional-public liaison and hands-on workshops. Maintains placement service.

11266 ■ Association of Black Nursing Faculty (ABNF)

PO Box 580
Lisle, IL 60532
Ph: (630)969-0221
Fax: (630)969-3895
E-mail: drsallie@gmail.com
URL: http://www.abnf.net

Description: Black nursing faculty teaching in nursing programs accredited by the National League for Nursing. Works to promote health-related issues and educational concerns of interest to the black community and ABNF. Serves as a forum for communication and the exchange of information among members; develops strategies for expressing concerns to other individuals, institutions, and communities. Assists members in professional development; develops and sponsors continuing education activities; fosters networking and guidance in employment and recruitment activities. Promotes health-related issues of legislation, government programs, and community activities. Supports black consumer advocacy issues. Encourages research. Maintains speakers' bureau and hall of fame.

11267 ■ Association of Nurses in AIDS Care

3538 Ridgewood Rd.
Akron, OH 44333
Ph: (330)670-0101
Fax: (330)670-0109
Fr: 800-260-6780
E-mail: anac@anacnet.org
URL: http://www.nursesinaidscare.org

Description: Comprised of nurses, healthcare professionals, and others who are committed to HIV/AIDS nursing. Advances the development of nurses involved in the delivery of health care to persons infected or affected by the human immune deficiency virus (HIV). Promotes social awareness concerning issues related to HIV/AIDS.

11268 ■ Association of Operating Room Nurses

2170 S Parker Rd., Ste. 400
Denver, CO 80231
Ph: (303)755-6304
Fax: (303)750-3212
Fr: 800-755-2676
E-mail: custsvc@aorn.org
URL: http://www.aorn.org

Description: Represents registered professional nurses, individuals pursuing education leading to eligibility to sit for the registered nurse licensing exam, and registered professional nurses who are retired from the health care industry. Aims to promote safety and optimal outcomes for patients undergoing operative and other invasive procedures by providing practice support and professional development opportunities to perioperative nurses. Advocates for excellence in perioperative practice and healthcare.

11269 ■ Association of Pediatric Hematology/Oncology Nurses

4700 W Lake Ave.
Glenview, IL 60025-1485
Ph: (847)375-4724

Fax: (847)375-6478
E-mail: info@aphon.org
URL: http://www.aphon.org

Description: Represents pediatric hematology/oncology nurses and other pediatric hematology/oncology healthcare professionals. Promotes optimal nursing care for children, adolescents, and young adults with cancer and blood disorders and their families. Provides leadership and expertise to pediatric hematology/oncology nurses.

11270 ■ Association for Radiologic and Imaging Nursing
7794 Grow Dr.
Pensacola, FL 32514
Ph: (850)474-7292
Fax: (850)484-8762
Fr: (866)486-2762
E-mail: arin@dancyamc.com
URL: http://www.arinursing.org

Description: Represents nurses who practice in the diagnostic, neuro/cardiovascular, interventional, ultrasonography, computerized tomography, nuclear medicine, magnetic resonance, and radiation oncology. Fosters the professional growth of nurses who advance the standard of care in the imaging environment.

11271 ■ Association of Rehabilitation Nurses
4700 W Lake Ave.
Glenview, IL 60025-1485
Ph: (847)375-4710
Fax: (847)375-6481
Fr: 800-229-7530
E-mail: info@rehabnurse.org
URL: http://www.rehabnurse.org

Description: Comprised of registered nurses and other individuals concerned with or actively engaged in the practice of rehabilitation nursing. Promotes and advances professional rehabilitation nursing practice through education, advocacy, collaboration, and research. Works to enhance the quality of life of those affected by disability and chronic illness.

11272 ■ Association of Staff Physician Recruiters (ASPR)
1000 Westgate Dr., Ste. 252
St. Paul, MN 55114
Ph: (651)290-7475
Fax: (651)290-2266
Fr: 800-830-2777
E-mail: admin@aspr.org
URL: http://www.aspr.org

Description: Recruits physicians and other healthcare providers to staff hospitals, clinics and managed care organizations where the members are employed. Sponsors educational programs and meetings on various recruitment issues.

11273 ■ Association of Women's Health, Obstetric and Neonatal Nurses
2000 L St. NW, Ste. 740
Washington, DC 20036
Ph: (202)261-2400
Fax: (202)728-0575
Fr: 800-673-8499
E-mail: customerservice@awhonn.org
URL: http://www.awhonn.org

Description: Seeks to improve and promote the health of women and newborns and to strengthen the nursing profession through the delivery of superior advocacy, research, education, and other professional and clinical resources to nurses and other health care professionals.

11274 ■ Community Oncology Alliance (COA)
1101 Pennsylvania Ave. NW, Ste. 700
Washington, DC 20004
Ph: (202)756-2258
E-mail: tokon@coacancer.org
URL: http://www.communityoncology.org

Description: Seeks to protect and foster the community oncology delivery system in the United States through public policy, advocacy and education. Enhances the effectiveness and efficiency of cancer care in the community by increasing awareness of community cancer care delivery systems.

11275 ■ Council of International Neonatal Nurses
94 Lyall Ter.
Boston, MA 02132
Ph: (405)684-1476
E-mail: info@coinnurses.org
URL: http://www.coinnurses.org

Description: Represents nurses who specialize in the care of newborn infants and their families. Promotes high standards in neonatal nursing practice and care. Creates guidelines for neonatal nursing issues.

11276 ■ Dermatology Nurses' Association
15000 Commerce Pkwy., Ste. C
Mount Laurel, NJ 08054
Fax: (856)439-0525
Fr: 800-454-4362
E-mail: dna@dnanurse.org
URL: http://www.dnanurse.org

Description: Represents registered nurses, nurse practitioners, licensed practical nurses or licensed vocational nurses, medical assistants, and other associate members. Focuses on providing quality care through sharing of knowledge and expertise. Promotes excellence in dermatologic care.

11277 ■ Infusion Nurses Society
315 Norwood Park S
Norwood, MA 02062
Ph: (781)440-9408
Fax: (781)440-9409
Fr: 800-694-0298
E-mail: ins@ins1.org
URL: http://www.ins1.org

Description: Represents infusion nurses, home infusion therapists, health-system pharmacists, and all other healthcare professionals involved in or interested in the specialty practice or application of infusion therapy. Aims to advance the delivery of quality therapy to patients, enhance the specialty through standards of practice and professional ethics, and promote research and education in the infusion nursing field. Offers educational meetings, professional development opportunities, publications, printed and multimedia resources, and access to a national network of infusion experts.

11278 ■ International Nurses Society on Addictions
PO Box 14846
Lenexa, KS 66285
Fax: (913)895-4652
Fr: 877-646-8672
E-mail: intnsa@intnsa.org
URL: http://intnsa.org

Description: Represents nurses committed to the prevention, intervention, treatment, and management of addictive disorders including alcohol and other drug dependencies, nicotine dependencies, eating disorders, dual and multiple diagnosis, and process addictions such as gambling. Advances excellence in addictions nursing practice through advocacy, collaboration, education, research and policy development. Promotes quality-nursing care for persons addicted to alcohol and other drugs, and their families.

11279 ■ International Palestinian Cardiac Relief Organization (IPCRO)
PO Box 1926
Kent, OH 44240
Ph: (330)678-2645
Fax: (330)678-2661
E-mail: pcrf1@pcrf.net
URL: http://www.pcrf.net/?page_id=529

Description: Seeks to provide medical and humanitarian assistance to people in the Middle East. Sends volunteer teams of doctors and nurses to provide expert surgical treatment for sick children as well as training for local staff. Helps local institutions in the Middle East get the resources to further their medical services for poor and needy patients throughout the region.

11280 ■ National Alliance of Wound Care
5464 N Port Washington Rd., No. 134
Glendale, WI 53217
Fax: 800-352-8339
Fr: 877-922-6292
E-mail: information@nawccb.org
URL: http://www.nawccb.org

Description: Represents the interests of wound care certified professionals. Provides resources and support to advance professional recognition of members.

11281 ■ National Association Directors of Nursing Administration
Reed Hartman Tower
11353 Reed Hartman Hwy., Ste. 210
Cincinnati, OH 45241
Ph: (513)791-3679
Fax: (513)791-3699
Fr: 800-222-0539
URL: http://www.nadona.org

Description: Represents the interests of nurses and administrators in long term care. Promotes ethical principles and practices within the long term care continuum. Advocates for the benefit of directors of nursing, assistant directors of nursing, and registered nurses in long term care. Supports and promotes quality of care for individuals who are receiving long-term care.

11282 ■ National Association of Neonatal Nurses
4700 W Lake Ave.
Glenview, IL 60025
Ph: (847)375-3660
Fax: (866)927-5321
Fr: 800-451-3795
E-mail: info@nann.org
URL: http://www.nann.org

Description: Represents registered neonatal nurse practitioners and registered nurses who support neonatal nursing. Aims to address the educational and practice needs within the evolving specialty of neonatal nursing. Provides educational programs, research and translation, advocacy, and membership engagement.

11283 ■ National Association of Pediatric Nurse Practitioners (NAPNAP)
20 Brace Rd., Ste. 200
Cherry Hill, NJ 08034-2634
Ph: (856)857-9700
Fax: (856)857-1600
Fr: 877-662-7627
E-mail: info@napnap.org
URL: http://www.napnap.org

Description: Pediatric, school, and family nurse practitioners and interested persons. Seeks to improve the quality of infant, child, and adolescent health care by making health care services accessible and providing a forum for continuing education of members. Facilitates and supports legislation designed to promote the role of pediatric nurse practitioners; promotes salary ranges commensurate with practitioners' responsibilities; facilitates exchange of information between prospective employers and job seekers in the field. Supports research programs; compiles statistics.

11284 ■ National Black Nurses Association
8630 Fenton St., Ste. 330
Silver Spring, MD 20910
Ph: (301)589-3200
Fax: (301)589-3223
E-mail: contact@nbna.org
URL: http://www.nbna.org

Description: Consists of registered nurses, licensed vocational/practical nurses, nursing students, and retired nurses. Facilitates the professional development and career advancement of nurses. Serves as a forum for collective action by African American nurses to investigate, define, and determine the health care needs of African Americans.

11285 ■ National Gerontological Nursing Association
3493 Landowne Dr., Ste. 2
Lexington, KY 40517
Ph: (859)977-7453
Fax: (859)271--060
Fr: 800-723-0560
E-mail: info@ngna.org
URL: http://www.ngna.org

Description: Dedicated to the clinical care of older adults across diverse care settings. Represents the interests of clinicians, educators, and researchers with vastly different educational preparation, clinical roles, and interests in practice issues.

11286 ■ National League for Nursing (NLN)
61 Broadway, 33rd Fl.
New York, NY 10006
Ph: (212)363-5555
Fax: (212)812-0391
Fr: 800-669-1656
E-mail: generalinfo@nln.org
URL: http://www.nln.org

Description: Champions the pursuit of quality nursing education. A professional association of nursing faculty, education agencies, health care agencies, allied/public agencies, and public members whose mission is to advance quality nursing education that prepares the nursing workforce to meet the needs of diverse populations in an ever-changing health care environment. Serves as the primary source of information about every type of nursing education program, from the LVN and LPN to the EdD and PhD. There are 20 affiliated constituent leagues that provide a local forum for members. The National League for Nursing Accrediting Commission is an independent corporate affiliate of the NLN, responsible for providing accreditation services to all levels of nursing education.

11287 ■ National Rural Health Association (NRHA)
Administrative Office
521 E 63rd St.
Kansas City, MO 64110-3329

Ph: (816)756-3140
Fax: (816)756-3144
E-mail: mail@nrharural.org
URL: http://www.ruralhealthweb.org

Description: Administrators, physicians, nurses, physician assistants, health planners, academicians, and others interested or involved in rural health care. Creates a better understanding of health care problems unique to rural areas; utilizes a collective approach in finding positive solutions; articulates and represents the health care needs of rural America; supplies current information to rural health care providers; serves as a liaison between rural health care programs throughout the country. Offers continuing education credits for medical, dental, nursing, and management courses.

11288 ■ National Student Nurses' Association (NSNA)
45 Main St., Ste. 606
Brooklyn, NY 11201
Ph: (718)210-0705
Fax: (718)797-1186
E-mail: nsna@nsna.org
URL: http://www.nsna.org

Description: Students enrolled in state-approved schools for the preparation of registered nurses. Seeks to aid in the development of the individual nursing student and to urge students of nursing, as future leaders and health professionals, to be aware of and to contribute to improving the health care of all people. Encourages programs and activities in state groups concerning nursing, health, and the community. Provides assistance for state board review, as well as materials for preparation for state RN licensing examination. Cooperates with nursing organizations in recruitment of nurses and in professional, community, and civic programs. Sponsors Foundation of the National Student Nurses' Association in memory of Frances Tompkins.

11289 ■ Nurses' House
2113 Western Ave., Ste. 2
Guilderland, NY 12084-9559
Ph: (518)456-7858
Fax: (518)452-3760
E-mail: mail@nurseshouse.org
URL: http://www.nurseshouse.org

Description: Registered nurses and interested individuals united to assist registered nurses in financial and other crises. Provides short-term

financial aid for shelter, food, and utilities until nurses obtain entitlements or jobs. Offers counseling and referrals. Encourages homebound or retired nurses through a volunteer corps.

11290 ■ Society of Pediatric Nurses
7044 S 13th St.
Oak Creek, WI 53154
Ph: (850)494-9467
Fax: (850)484-8762
Fr: 800-723-2902
E-mail: spn@dancyamc.com
URL: http://www.pedsnurses.org

Description: Comprised of nurses involved in the care of children and families, including staff nurses, school and outpatient nurses, clinical nurse specialists, practitioners, administrators, educators and researchers. Offers its members the opportunity to interact with colleagues of similar interests, and to share ideas, research and expertise.

11291 ■ Society of Urologic Nurses and Associates
PO Box 56
Pitman, NJ 08071-0056
Fax: (856)589-7463
Fr: 888-827-7862
E-mail: suna@ajj.com
URL: http://www.suna.org

Description: Comprised of nurses and other health care providers working in the field of urology. Promotes excellence in urological education and establishes standards of care for urology patients. Conducts educational programs, holds examinations, bestows professional certification, and facilitates communication among members.

11292 ■ Visiting Nurse Associations of America (VNAA)
900 19th St. NW, Ste. 200
Washington, DC 20006
Ph: (202)384-1420
Fax: (202)384-1444
Fr: 888-866-8773
E-mail: vnaa@vnaa.org
URL: http://www.vnaa.org

Description: Home health care agencies. Develops competitive strength among community-based nonprofit visiting nurse organizations; works to strengthen business resources and economic programs through contracting, marketing, governmental affairs and publications.

Reporters and Correspondents

Sources of Help-Wanted Ads

11293 ▪ AeroSpaceNews.com
AeroSpaceNews.com
PO Box 1748
Ojai, CA 93024-1748
Ph: (805)985-2320
URL: http://www.aerospacenews.com/content/view/
41/33/

Monthly. $19.95/year for individuals, private. Journal reporting on the insights, impressions and images of tomorrow's technological wonders in the field of aerospace.

11294 ▪ Broadcasting & Cable
Reed Business Information (New York, New York)
360 Park Ave. S
New York, NY 10010
Ph: (646)746-6400
Fax: (646)746-7431
Fr: 800-446-6551
URL: http://www.reedbusiness.com

$199.00/year for individuals; $249.99/year for Canada; $360.99/year for other countries. News magazine covering The Fifth Estate (radio, TV, cable, and satellite), and the regulatory commissions involved.

11295 ▪ Columbia Journalism Review
Columbia Journalism Review
2950 Broadway, Journalism Bldg.
Columbia University
New York, NY 10027
Ph: (212)854-1881
Fax: (212)854-8367
URL: http://www.cjr.org/

Bimonthly. $19.95/year for individuals; $27.95/year for other countries. Magazine focusing on journalism.

11296 ▪ Current
Routledge
711 3 Ave., 8 Fl.
New York, NY 10016
Ph: (212)216-7800
Fax: (212)563-2269
Fr: 800-634-7064
URL: http://www.tandf.co.uk/journals/titles/
00113131.asp

$50.00/year for individuals, print only; $141.00/year for institutions, print & online. Journal that reprints articles on education, politics, and other social issues.

11297 ▪ Editor & Publisher
Editor & Publisher Magazine
17782 Cowan, Ste. A
Irvine, CA 92614
Ph: (949)660-6150
Fax: (949)660-6172
URL: http://www.editorandpublisher.com/

Weekly (Mon.). $65.00/year for individuals, print and online; $125.00/year for two years, print and online; $85.00/year for other countries; $49.00/year for individuals, digital only. Magazine focusing on newspaper journalism, advertising, printing equipment and interactive services.

11298 ▪ Global Media Journal
Global Media Journal
Purdue University Calumet
Dept. of Communication & Creative Arts
2200 169th St.
Hammond, IN 46323-2094
Ph: (219)989-2880
Fax: (219)989-2008
URL: http://lass.calumet.purdue.edu/cca/gmj/gmj_
about_us.htm

Semiannual. Free, e-mail. Electronic journal that seeks to address the interests of media and journalism scholars, researchers, teachers, students, and institutions engaged in international activities, particularly communication.

11299 ▪ In These Times
Institute for Public Affairs Inc.
2040 N Milwaukee Ave.
Chicago, IL 60647
Ph: (773)772-0100
Fax: (773)772-4180
E-mail: itt@inthesetimes.com
URL: http://www.inthesetimes.com

Biweekly. $19.95/year for individuals; $34.95/year for two years; $34.95/year for Canada; $40.95/year for other countries. National political newsmagazine.

11300 ▪ Journalism Practice
Routledge Journals
270 Madison Ave.
New York, NY 10016-0601
Ph: (212)216-7800
Fax: (212)563-2269
URL: http://www.tandf.co.uk/journals/titles/
17512786.asp

$706.00/year for institutions, print + online; $635.00/year for institutions, online only; $159.00/year for individuals, print only. Journal focusing on professional practice of journalism.

11301 ▪ Metro Magazine
Bobit Business Media
3520 Challenger St.
Torrance, CA 90503
Ph: (310)533-2400
E-mail: info@metro-magazine.com
URL: http://www.metro-magazine.com

Free. Magazine on public transportation.

11302 ▪ The New Republic
The New Republic L.L.C.
1331 H St. NW, Ste. 700
Washington, DC 20005
Ph: (202)508-4444
Fax: (202)628-9380

Fr: 800-827-1289
E-mail: tnrcustserv@cdsfulfillment.com
URL: http://www.tnr.com

Weekly. $44.97/year for individuals, print; $29.97/year for individuals, digital. Journal featuring current events comments and reviews.

11303 ▪ Publishers Weekly
Publishers Weekly
71 W 23 St., No. 1608
New York, NY 10010
Ph: (212)377-5500
URL: http://www.publishersweekly.com

Weekly. $249.99/year for individuals; $299.99/year for Canada; $399.99/year for other countries, air delivery. Magazine for publishers.

11304 ▪ TelevisionWeek
Crain Communications Inc. (Detroit, Michigan)
1155 Gratiot Ave.
Detroit, MI 48207-2997
Ph: (313)446-6000
Fax: (313)567-7681
URL: http://www.tvweek.com/

Weekly. $119.00/year for individuals; $171.00/year for Canada, incl. GST; $309.00/year for other countries, airmail. Newspaper covering management, programming, cable and trends in the television and the media industry.

11305 ▪ Writer's Digest
F+W Media Inc.
4700 E Galbraith Rd.
Cincinnati, OH 45236
Ph: (513)531-2690
Fax: (513)531-0798
Fr: 800-289-0963
E-mail: writersdigest@fwmedia.com
URL: http://www.writersdigest.com

$19.96/year for individuals; $29.96/year for Canada, including GST/HST; $31.96/year for other countries, surface delivery. Professional magazine for writers.

Employer Directories and Networking Lists

11306 ▪ ANR National Directory of Community Newspapers
American Newspaper Representatives Inc.
2075 W Big Beaver Rd., Ste. 310
Troy, MI 48084
Ph: (248)643-9910
Fax: (248)643-9914
Fr: 800-550-7557
URL: http://gotoanr.com/directory/

Weekly (Mon.), Latest edition 2010. $125.00 for individuals; $75.00 for individuals. Number of listings: 9,000. Entries include: Name of weekly newspaper, address, county, type of area, circulation, day published, name of publisher, and information on advertising rates and production specifications. Arrangement: Geographical.

11307 ■ Broadcasting & Cable Yearbook

R.R. Bowker L.L.C.
630 Central Ave.
New Providence, NJ 07974
Ph: (908)286-1090
Fr: 888-269-5372
URL: http://www.bowker.com

Annual, latest edition 2010. $395.00 for individuals. Covers: Over 17,000 television and radio stations in the United States, its territories, and Canada; cable MSOs and their individual systems; television and radio networks, broadcast and cable group owners, station representatives, satellite networks and services, film companies, advertising agencies, government agencies, trade associations, schools, and suppliers of professional and technical services, including books, serials, and videos; communications lawyers. Entries include: Company name, address, phone, fax, names of executives. Station listings include broadcast power, other operating details. Arrangement: Stations and systems are geographical, others are alphabetical. Indexes: Alphabetical.

11308 ■ CPB Public Broadcasting Directory

Corporation for Public Broadcasting
401 9th St. NW
Washington, DC 20004-2129
Ph: (202)879-9600
Fax: (202)879-9699
Fr: 800-272-2190
URL: http://www.cpb.org/stations/isis

Annual. Covers: Public television and radio stations, national and regional public broadcasting organizations and networks, state government agencies and commissions, and other related organizations. Entries include: For radio and television stations—Station call letters, frequency or channel, address, phone, licensee name, licensee type, date on air, antenna height, area covered, names and titles of key personnel. For organizations—Name, address, phone, name and title of key personnel. Arrangement: National and regional listings are alphabetical; state groups and the public radio and television stations are each geographical; other organizations and agencies are alphabetical. Indexes: Geographical, personnel, call letter, licensee type (all in separate indexes for radio and television).

11309 ■ Directory of Small Press—Magazine Editors and Publishers

Dustbooks
PO Box 100
Paradise, CA 95967
Ph: (530)877-6110
Fax: (530)877-0222
Fr: 800-477-6110
URL: http://www.dustbooks.com/de.htm

Annual, Latest edition 42nd; 2011-2012. $49.95 for individuals; $21.00 for individuals. Covers: About 7,500 publishers and editors. Entries include: Individual name, title of press or magazine, address and phone number. Arrangement: Alphabetical.

11310 ■ Editor & Publisher International Year Book

Editor & Publisher Magazine
17782 Cowan, Ste. A
Irvine, CA 92614
Ph: (949)660-6150
Fax: (949)660-6172
URL: http://www.editorandpublisher.com

Annual, Latest edition 2009. $150.00 for individuals; $135.00 for individuals; $75.00 for individuals; $239.00 for individuals; $180.00 for individuals. Covers: Daily and Sunday newspapers in the United States and Canada; weekly newspapers; foreign daily newspapers; special service newspapers; newspaper syndicates; news services; journalism schools; foreign language and Black newspapers in the United States; news, picture, and press services; feature

and news syndicates; comic and magazine services; advertising clubs; trade associations; clipping bureaus; house organs; journalism awards; also lists manufacturers of equipment and supplies. Entries include: For daily papers—Publication name, address, phone, fax, e-mail, web site URL, names of executives and departmental editors (business, financial, book, food, etc.), circulation and advertising data, production information including format of paper and equipment used. Similar but less detailed information for other publications. Arrangement: Publications and schools are geographical; most other lists are alphabetical.

11311 ■ Editorial Freelancers Association—Membership Directory

Editorial Freelancers Association Inc.
71 W 23rd St., 4th Fl.
New York, NY 10010-4181
Ph: (212)929-5400
URL: http://www.the-efa.org

Annual, spring. Covers: 1,100 member editorial freelancers. Entries include: Personal name, address, phone, services provided, specialties. Arrangement: Alphabetical. Indexes: Product/service, special interest, geographical, computer skills.

11312 ■ International Directory of Little Magazines and Small Presses

Dustbooks
PO Box 100
Paradise, CA 95967
Ph: (530)877-6110
Fax: (530)877-0222
Fr: 800-477-6110
URL: http://www.dustbooks.com/d.htm

Annual, Latest edition 47th; 2011-2012. $65.00 for individuals; $49.95 for individuals; $30.00 for individuals. Covers: Over 4,000 small, independent magazines, presses, and papers. Entries include: Name, address, size, circulation, frequency, price, type of material used, number of issues or books published annually, and other pertinent data. Arrangement: Alphabetical. Indexes: Subject, regional.

11313 ■ International Television and Video Almanac

Quigley Publishing Company Inc.
64 Wintergreen Ln.
Groton, MA 01450-4129
Ph: (978)448-0272
Fax: (978)448-9325
Fr: 800-231-8239
URL: http://quigleypublishing.com/

Annual, January; latest edition 2011. $235.00 for individuals. Covers: "Who's Who in Motion Pictures and Television and Home Video," television networks, major program producers, major group station owners, cable television companies, distributors, firms serving the television and home video industry, equipment manufacturers, casting agencies, literary agencies, advertising and publicity representatives, television stations, associations, list of feature films produced for television; statistics, industry's year in review, award winners, satellite and wireless cable provider, primetime programming, video producers, distributors, wholesalers. Entries include: Generally, company name, address, phone; manufacturer and service listings may include description of products and services and name of contact; producing, distributing, and station listings include additional detail, and contacts for cable and broadcast networks. Arrangement: Classified by service or activity. Indexes: Full.

11314 ■ National Directory of Magazines

Oxbridge Communications Inc.
186 5th Ave.
New York, NY 10010-5202
Ph: (212)741-0231
Fax: (212)633-2938
Fr: 800-955-0231
URL: http://www.oxbridge.com

latest edition 2011. $995.00 for individuals; $1,195.00

for individuals; $1,995.00 for individuals. Covers: Over 20,000 magazines; coverage includes Canada. Entries include: Title, publisher name, address, phone, fax number, names and titles of contact and key personnel, financial data, editorial and advertising information, circulation. Arrangement: Classified by subject. Indexes: Title, geographical, publisher.

11315 ■ RTNDA Communicator—Directory Issues

Radio-Television News Directors Association
1025 F St. NW, Ste. 700
Washington, DC 20004
Ph: (202)467-5214
Fax: (202)223-4007
Fr: 800-80R-TNDA
URL: http://www.rtnda.org

Semiannual, January and July. Number of listings: 3,000; membership includes Canada and some foreign countries. Entries include: Member name, address, phone; and name of radio or television station, network, or other news organization with which affiliated. Arrangement: Same information given in alphabetical and geographical arrangements.

11316 ■ SRDS International Media Guides

SRDS
1700 Higgins Rd.
Des Plaines, IL 60018-5605
Ph: (847)375-5000
Fax: (847)375-5001
Fr: 800-851-7737
URL: http://www.srds.com

Annual. $455.00 for individuals. Covers: approximately 19,000 newspapers and color newspaper magazines/supplements from 200 countries, including the United States. Entries include: Publication name; publisher name, address, phone, fax, e-mail, URL, names of editor, advertising manager, and representatives in the United States and worldwide; advertising rates in U.S. dollars and/or local currency, circulation, mechanical data, ad closing, readership description, etc. Arrangement: Geographical.

11317 ■ Ulrich's Periodicals Directory

R.R. Bowker L.L.C.
630 Central Ave.
New Providence, NJ 07974
Ph: (908)286-1090
Fr: 888-269-5372
E-mail: ulrichs@bowker.com
URL: http://www.bowker.com

Annual, Latest edition 2010. $1,260.00 for individuals. Covers: Nearly 200,000 current periodicals and newspapers published worldwide. Entries include: In main list—Publication title; Dewey Decimal Classification number, Library of Congress Classification Number (where applicable), CODEN designation (for sci-tech serials), British Library Document Supply Centre shelfmark number, country code, ISSN; subtitle, language(s) of text, year first published, frequency, subscription prices, sponsoring organization, publishing company name, address, phone, fax, e-mail and website addresses, editor and publisher names; regular features (reviews, advertising, abstracts, bibliographies, trade literature, etc.), indexes, circulation, format, brief description of content; availability of microforms and reprints; whether refereed; CD-ROM availability with vendor name; online availability with service name; services that index or abstract the periodical, with years covered; advertising rates and contact; right and permissions contact name and phone; availability through document deliver Arrangement: Main listing is classified by subject; U.S. general daily and weekly newspapers are listed in a separate volume; lists of cessations, online services, and CD-ROM vendors are alphabetical. Indexes: Cessations, subjects, title (including variant, former, and ceased titles), ISSN, periodicals available on CD-ROM, online periodical title, refereed serial, and international organization publication title.

HANDBOOKS AND MANUALS

11318 ■ *Career Opportunities in Journalism*
Ferguson Publishing Company
132 W 31st St., 17th Fl.
New York, NY 10001
Fax: 800-678-3633
Fr: 800-322-8755
E-mail: custserv@factsonfile.com
URL: http://ferguson.infobasepublishing.com/
Bookdetail.aspx?ISBN=0816064199&eBooks=0

Jennifer Bobrow Burns. 2007. $49.50 (hardcover). 336 pages. Covers journalism careers in a variety of contexts, from newspapers and broadcasting to education and new media. Contains appendixes of related educational programs, professional associations and publications, companies, and internship and scholarship resources.

11319 ■ *Careers in Communications*
The McGraw-Hill Companies
PO Box 182604
Columbus, OH 43272
Fax: (614)759-3749
Fr: 877-883-5524
E-mail: customer.service@mcgraw-hill.com
URL: http://www.mhprofessional.com/
product.php?isbn=0071454764

Shonan Noronha. Fourth edition, 2004. $15.95 (paper). 192 pages. Examines the fields of journalism, photography, radio, television, film, public relations, and advertising. Gives concrete details on job locations and how to secure a job. Suggests many resources for job hunting.

11320 ■ *Careers in Journalism*
The McGraw-Hill Companies
PO Box 182604
Columbus, OH 43272
Fax: (614)759-3749
Fr: 877-883-5524
E-mail: customer.service@mcgraw-hill.com
URL: http://www.mhprofessional.com/
product.php?isbn=0071466371

Jan Goldberg. Third edition, 2005. $15.95 (paper). 192 pages.

11321 ■ *Careers for Mystery Buffs and Other Snoops and Sleuths*
The McGraw-Hill Companies
PO Box 182604
Columbus, OH 43272
Fax: (614)759-3749
Fr: 877-883-5524
E-mail: customer.service@mcgraw-hill.com
URL: http://www.mhprofessional.com

Blythe Camenson. Second edition. $14.95 (hardback). 160 pages.

11322 ■ *Great Jobs for English Majors*
The McGraw-Hill Companies
PO Box 182604
Columbus, OH 43272
Fax: (614)759-3749
Fr: 877-883-5524
E-mail: customer.service@mcgraw-hill.com
URL: http://www.mhprofessional.com

Julie DeGalan and Stephen Lambert. Third edition, 2006. $15.95 (paper). 192 pages.

11323 ■ *Great Jobs for Liberal Arts Majors*
The McGraw-Hill Companies
PO Box 182604
Columbus, OH 43272
Fax: (614)759-3749
Fr: 877-883-5524
E-mail: customer.service@mcgraw-hill.com
URL: http://www.mhprofessional.com/
product.php?isbn=0071482148

Blythe Camenson. Second edition, 2007. $16.95 (paper). 192 pages.

11324 ■ *Opportunities in Writing Careers*
The McGraw-Hill Companies
PO Box 182604
Columbus, OH 43272
Fax: (614)759-3749
Fr: 877-883-5524
E-mail: customer.service@mcgraw-hill.com
URL: http://www.mhprofessional.com/
product.php?isbn=0071458727

Elizabeth Foote-Smith. 2006. $13.95 (paper). 160 pages. Discusses opportunities in the print media, broadcasting, advertising or publishing. Business writing, public relations, and technical writing are among the careers covered. Contains bibliography and illustrations.

ONLINE JOB SOURCES AND SERVICES

11325 ■ JournalismJobs.com
Ph: (510)653-1521
E-mail: info@journalismjobs.com
URL: http://www.journalismjobs.com

Description: Career-related site for journalists and other media professionals. Seekers can search for jobs, post a resume online, and manage the search online with the Job Seeker Folder feature. They also can receive free job announcements by e-mail.

11326 ■ JournalismNow.com
URL: http://www.journalismnow.com

Description: Assists journalism job candidates in securing employment. Lists job opportunities with newspapers, online media, TV, radio, and magazines. Includes articles that relate to the field of journalism and current events.

OTHER SOURCES

11327 ■ American Sportscasters Association (ASA)
225 Broadway, Ste. 2030
New York, NY 10007
Ph: (212)227-8080
Fax: (212)571-0556
E-mail: info@americansportscastersonline.com
URL: http://www.americansportscastersonline.com

Description: Radio and television sportscasters. Sponsors seminars, clinics, and symposia for aspiring announcers and sportscasters. Compiles statistics. Operates speakers' bureau, placement service, hall of fame, and biographical archives. Maintains American Sportscaster Hall of Fame Trust. Is currently implementing Hall of Fame Museum, Community Programs.

11328 ■ Asian American Journalists Association (AAJA)
5 Third St., Ste. 1108
San Francisco, CA 94103
Ph: (415)346-2051
Fax: (415)346-6343
E-mail: national@aaja.org
URL: http://www.aaja.org

Description: Serves Asian Americans and Pacific Islanders by encouraging young people to consider journalism as a career, developing managers in the media industry, and promoting fair and accurate news coverage. Serves as an alliance partner in UNITY Journalists of Color, along with the Native American Journalists Association, National Association of Hispanic Journalists, and National Association of Black Journalists.

11329 ■ Association for Women in Communications (AWC)
3337 Duke St.
Alexandria, VA 22314
Ph: (703)370-7436

Fax: (703)342-4311
E-mail: info@womcom.org
URL: http://www.womcom.org

Description: Professional association of journalism and communications.

11330 ■ Association for Women in Sports Media
161 W Sylvania Ave.
Neptune City, NJ 07753
URL: http://www.awsmonline.org

Description: Comprised of women sportswriters, editors, broadcasters and media relations directors and others who are interested in sports media career. Supports and fosters advancement of women involved in sports media. Works to promote and increase diversity in sports media through its internship/scholarship programs.

11331 ■ Broadcast Education Association (BEA)
1771 N St. NW
Washington, DC 20036-2800
Ph: (202)429-3935
Fax: (202)775-2981
E-mail: 20hbirks@nab.org
URL: http://www.beaweb.org

Description: Universities and colleges; faculty and students; promotes improvement of curriculum and teaching methods, broadcasting research, television and radio production, and programming teaching on the college level.

11332 ■ Dow Jones Newspaper Fund (DJNF)
PO Box 300
Princeton, NJ 08543-0300
Ph: (609)452-2820
Fax: (609)520-5804
E-mail: djnf@dowjones.com
URL: http://www.newsfund.org

Description: Established by Dow Jones and Company, publisher of *The Wall Street Journal*, to encourage careers in journalism. Operates newspaper's editing, and Sports Copy Editing Internship Programs for all junior, senior, and graduate level college students interested in journalism. Also offers Business Reporting Intern Program for minority college sophomores and juniors to complete summer internships on daily newspapers as business reporters. Students receive monetary scholarships to return to school in the fall. Offers information on careers in journalism.

11333 ■ Editorial Freelancers Association (EFA)
71 W 23rd St., 4th Fl.
New York, NY 10010
Ph: (212)929-5400
Fax: (212)929-5439
Fr: (866)929-5439
E-mail: office@the-efa.org
URL: http://www.the-efa.org

Description: Represents persons who work full or part-time as freelance writers or editorial freelancers. Promotes professionalism and facilitates the exchange of information and support. Conducts professional training seminars; and offers job listings.

11334 ■ Education Writers Association (EWA)
2122 P St. NW, Ste. 201
Washington, DC 20037
Ph: (202)452-9830
Fax: (202)452-9837
E-mail: ewa@ewa.org
URL: http://www.ewa.org

Description: Education writers and reporters of daily and weekly newspapers, national magazines of general circulation, and radio and television stations; associate members are school and college public relations personnel and others with a serious interest in education writing. Improves the quality of education reporting and interpretation; encourages the development of education coverage by the press; to help attract top-notch writers and reporters to the education field. Sponsors regional and special workshops. Provides job referral/bank services.

11335 ■ Investigative Reporters and Editors
Missouri School of Journalism
141 Neff Annex
Columbia, MO 65211
Ph: (573)882-2042
Fax: (573)882-5431
E-mail: info@ire.org
URL: http://www.ire.org

Description: Fosters excellence in investigative journalism. Provides training, resources and a community of support to investigative journalists.

11336 ■ National Arab American Journalists Association (NAAJA)
PO Box 2127
Orland Park, IL 60462
Fax: (708)575-9078
E-mail: rayhanania@comcast.net
URL: http://www.naaja-us.com

Description: Represents the interests of professional journalists of Arab American heritage working in the mainstream American news media and Arab American media. Creates and promotes opportunities for the professional development and growth of Arab American journalists. Facilitates communication and cooperation among members.

11337 ■ National Association of Broadcasters (NAB)
1771 N St. NW
Washington, DC 20036
Ph: (202)429-5300
Fax: (202)429-4199
E-mail: nab@nab.org
URL: http://www.nab.org

Description: Serves as the voice for the nation's radio and television broadcasters. Advances the interests of members in federal government, industry and public affairs; improves the quality and profitability of broadcasting; encourages content and technology innovation; and spotlights the important and unique ways stations serve their communities. Delivers value to its members through advocacy, education and innovation. Relies on the grassroots strength of its television and radio members and state broadcast associations. Helps broadcasters seize opportunities in the digital age. Offers broadcasters a variety of programs to help them grow in their careers, promote diversity in the workplace and strengthen their businesses.

11338 ■ National Association of Hispanic Journalists (NAHJ)
1050 Connecticut Ave. NW, 10th Fl.
Washington, DC 20036-5334
Ph: (202)662-7145
Fax: (202)662-7144
E-mail: nahj@nahj.org
URL: http://www.nahj.org

Description: Aims to organize and support Hispanics involved in news gathering and dissemination. Encourages journalism and communications study and practice by Hispanics. Seeks recognition for Hispanic members of the profession regarding their skills and achievements. Promotes fair and accurate media treatment of Hispanics; opposes job discrimination and demeaning stereotypes. Works to increase educational and career opportunities and development for Hispanics in the field. Seeks to foster greater awareness of members' cultural identity, interests, and concerns. Provides a united voice for Hispanic journalists with the aim of achieving national visibility. Offers placement services to Hispanic students. Activities include: a census of Hispanic media professionals nationwide; writing contest for Hispanic students. Offers scholarships, seminars, and training workshops.

11339 ■ National Journalism Center (NJC)
529 14th St. NW, Ste. 937
Washington, DC 20045
Ph: (202)628-1490
Fax: (202)628-1491
Fr: 800-872-1776
URL: http://www.yaf.org/
  NationalJournalismCenter.aspx

Description: Advances awareness and understanding of America's traditional values and free enterprise system through the publication and distribution of studies on major issues of public policy. Conducts educational programs for youth and trains college students in journalistic skills. Sponsors internship program that features research projects, writing assignments, and weekly seminars with professional journalists. Operates a job bank to match potential candidates with media-related jobs.

11340 ■ National Religious Broadcasters (NRB)
9510 Technology Dr.
Manassas, VA 20110
Ph: (703)330-7000
Fax: (703)330-7100
E-mail: info@nrb.org
URL: http://www.nrb.org

Description: Christian communicators. Fosters

electronic media access for the Gospel; promotes standards of excellence; integrity and accountability; and provides networking and fellowship opportunities for members.

11341 ■ Radio-Television Digital News Association (RTDNA)
529 14th St. NW, Ste. 425
Washington, DC 20045
Ph: (202)659-6510
Fax: (202)223-4007
Fr: 800-807-8632
E-mail: barbarac@rtnda.org
URL: http://rtdna.org

Description: Comprises of heads of news departments for broadcast and cable stations and networks; associate members are journalists engaged in the preparation and presentation of broadcast news and teachers of electronic journalism; other members represent industry services, public relations departments of business firms, public relations firms, and networks. Works to improve standards of electronic journalism; defends rights of journalists to access news; promotes journalism training to meet specific needs of the industry. Operates placement service and speakers' bureau.

11342 ■ Society of Professional Journalists (SPJ)
Eugene S. Pulliam National Journalism Center
3909 N Meridian St.
Indianapolis, IN 46208
Ph: (317)927-8000
Fax: (317)920-4789
E-mail: hlimor@wcpo.com
URL: http://www.spj.org

Description: Professional society - journalism. Promotes a free and unfettered press; high professional standards and ethical behavior; journalism as a career. Conducts lobbying activities; maintains legal defense fund. Sponsors Pulliam/Kilgore Freedom of Information Internships in Washington, DC, and Indianapolis, IN. Holds forums on the free press.

11343 ■ Women in Cable Telecommunications (WICT)
14555 Avion Pkwy., Ste. 250
Chantilly, VA 20151
Ph: (703)234-9810
Fax: (703)817-1595
E-mail: mbrennan@wict.org
URL: http://www.wict.org

Description: Empowers and educates women to achieve their professional goals by providing opportunities for leadership, networking and advocacy.

Respiratory Therapists

SOURCES OF HELP-WANTED ADS

11344 ■ AARC Times
Daedalus Enterprises Inc.
11030 Ables Ln.
PO Box 29686
Dallas, TX 75229
Ph: (972)243-2272
Fax: (972)484-2720
URL: http://www.aarc.org/resources/

Monthly. $85.00/year for individuals. Professional magazine for respiratory therapists and other cardiopulmonary specialists.

11345 ■ ADVANCE for Respiratory Care Practitioners
Merion Publications Inc.
2900 Horizon Dr.
PO Box 61556
King of Prussia, PA 19406-0956
Ph: (610)278-1400
Fr: 800-355-5627
URL: http://www.advanceweb.com/publications.asp?pub=RC

Biweekly. Free to qualified subscribers. Magazine for RRT's, CRTT's, and cardiopulmonary technologists across the country.

11346 ■ Annals of Medicine
Informa Healthcare
52 Vanderbilt Ave., 7th Fl.
New York, NY 10017-3846
Ph: (212)520-2777
URL: http://informahealthcare.com/ann

$595.00/year for institutions; $980.00/year for institutions; $780.00/year for institutions. Journal covering health science and medical education.

11347 ■ Clinical Medicine & Research
Marshfield Clinic
1000 N Oak Ave.
Marshfield, WI 54449
Ph: (715)387-5511
Fax: (715)389-3808
Fr: 800-782-8581
E-mail: clinmedres@mcrf.mfldclin.edu
URL: http://www.clinmedres.org/

Quarterly. Free within the U.S. Peer-reviewed journal that publishes scientific medical research that is relevant to a broad audience of medical researchers and healthcare professionals.

11348 ■ CME Supplement to Emergency Medicine Clinics of North America
Elsevier Science Inc.
360 Park Ave. S
New York, NY 10010-1710
Ph: (212)989-5800
Fax: (212)633-3990
Fr: 888-437-4636
URL: http://www.elsevier.com/wps/find/journaldescription.cws_home

$209.00/year for individuals. Journal covering emergency medicine clinics.

11349 ■ Discovery Medicine
Discovery Medicine
10 Gerard Ave., Ste. 201
Timonium, MD 21093
Ph: (410)773-9938
Fax: 888-833-0526
URL: http://www.discoverymedicine.com

Bimonthly. $599.00/year for institutions, digital edition; $99.95/year for individuals, digital edition. On-line journal that publishes articles on diseases, biology, new diagnostics, and treatments for medical professionals.

11350 ■ Education & Treatment of Children
West Virginia University Press
139 Stansbury Hall
PO Box 6295
Morgantown, WV 26506
Ph: (304)293-8400
Fax: (304)293-6585
URL: http://www.educationandtreatmentofchildren.net

Quarterly. $85.00/year for institutions; $45.00/year for individuals; $100.00/year for institutions, elsewhere; $60.00/year for individuals, elsewhere. Periodical featuring information concerning the development of services for children and youth. Includes reports written for educators and other child care and mental health providers focused on teaching, training, and treatment effectiveness.

11351 ■ Global Change, Peace & Security
Routledge
711 3 Ave., 8 Fl.
New York, NY 10016
Ph: (212)216-7800
Fax: (212)563-2269
Fr: 800-634-7064
URL: http://www.tandfonline.com/toc/cpar20/current

$160.00/year for individuals, print; $602.00/year for individuals, online only; $669.00/year for individuals, print & online. Journal promoting physical therapy and integration.

11352 ■ Heart and Lung
Mosby
1600 John F. Kennedy Blvd., Ste. 1800
Philadelphia, PA 19103-2899
Ph: (215)239-3275
Fax: (215)239-3286
URL: http://www.elsevier.com/wps/find/journaldescription.cws_home

Bimonthly. $103.00/year for individuals; $445.00/year for institutions; $524.00/year for institutions, other countries; $153.00/year for other countries. Journal offering articles prepared by nurse and physician members of the critical care team, recognizing the nurse's role in the care and management of major organ-system conditions in critically ill patients.

11353 ■ Hospitals & Health Networks
Health Forum L.L.C.
155 N Wacker Dr., Ste. 400
Chicago, IL 60606
Ph: (312)893-6800
Fax: (312)422-4500
Fr: 800-821-2039
URL: http://www.hhnmag.com

Weekly. Free. Publication covering the health care industry.

11354 ■ The IHS Primary Care Provider
Indian Health Service
The Reyes Bldg.
801 Thompson Ave., Ste. 400
Rockville, MD 20852-1627
Ph: (301)443-1011
URL: http://www.ihs.gov/provider

Monthly. Journal for health care professionals, physicians, nurses, pharmacists, dentists, and dietitians.

11355 ■ Injury
Mosby Inc.
11830 Westline Industrial Dr.
St. Louis, MO 63146-3326
Ph: (314)872-8370
Fax: (314)432-1380
Fr: 800-325-4177
URL: http://www.elsevier.com/wps/find/journaldescription.cws_home

Monthly. $200.00/year for individuals, European countries and Iran; $224.00/year for individuals, all countries except Europe, Japan and Iran; $26,500.00/year for individuals; $1,381.00/year for institutions, European countries and Iran; $1,543.00/year for institutions, all Countries except Europe, Japan and Iran; $183,200.00/year for institutions. Journal publishing articles and research related to the treatment of injuries such as trauma systems and management; surgical procedures; epidemiological studies; surgery (of all tissues); resuscitation; biomechanics; rehabilitation; anaesthesia; radiology and wound management.

11356 ■ Journal of the American Society of Podiatric Medical Assistants
American Society of Podiatric Medical Assistants
1616 N 78th Ct.
Elmwood Park, IL 60707
Fr: 888-882-7762
URL: http://www.aspma.org

Quarterly. Included in membership. Professional journal covering issues in podiatry.

11357 ■ Journal of Cardiopulmonary Rehabilitation (JCR)
Lippincott Williams & Wilkins
530 Walnut St.
Philadelphia, PA 19106-3619

Ph: (215)521-8300
Fax: (215)521-8902
Fr: 800-638-3030
E-mail: jcr@sba.com
URL: http://journals.lww.com/jcrjournal/pages/
default.aspx

$134.00/year for individuals; $410.00/year for institutions; $262.00/year for other countries; $558.00/year for institutions, other countries; $65.49/year for individuals, in-training. Medical journal.

11358 ■ Journal of Health and Life Sciences Law
American Health Lawyers Association
1620 Eye St. NW, 6th Fl.
Washington, DC 20006-4010
Ph: (202)833-1100
Fax: (202)833-1105
URL: http://www.healthlawyers.org

Quarterly. $149.00/year for individuals. Professional journal covering healthcare issues and cases and their impact on the health care arena.

11359 ■ Journal of Hospital Medicine
John Wiley & Sons Inc.
111 River St.
Hoboken, NJ 07030-5773
Ph: (201)748-6000
Fax: (201)748-6088
Fr: 800-825-7550
URL: http://onlinelibrary.wiley.com/journal/10.1002/
(ISSN)1553-56

$827.00/year for U.S., Canada, and Mexico, print only; $827.00/year for institutions, other countries, print only. Journal on hospital medicine.

11360 ■ USA Body Psychotherapy Journal
United States Association for Body Psychotherapy
8639 B 16th St., Ste. 119
Silver Spring, MD 20910
Ph: (202)466-1619
E-mail: admin@usabp.org
URL: http://www.usabp.org/
displaycommon.cfm?an=4

Semiannual. Academic journal that seeks to support, promote and stimulate the exchange of ideas, scholarship and research within the field of body psychotherapy as well as an interdisciplinary exchange with related fields of clinical practice and inquiry.

11361 ■ Year Book of Critical Care Medicine
Elsevier Science Inc.
360 Park Ave. S
New York, NY 10010-1710
Ph: (212)989-5800
Fax: (212)633-3990
Fr: 888-437-4636
URL: http://www.elsevier.com/wps/find/
journaldescription.cws_home

Annual. $271.00/year for institutions, other countries; $197.00/year for other countries; $103.00/year for students, other countries; $250.00/year for institutions; $167.00/year for individuals; $81.00/year for students. Journal focused on treatment of severe sepsis and septic shock, echocardiography in the evaluation of hemo-dynamically unstable patients & mechanical ventilation of acute respiratory distress syndrome.

EMPLOYER DIRECTORIES AND NETWORKING LISTS

11362 ■ Crain's List—Chicago's Largest Hospitals
Crain Communications Inc.
360 N Michigan Ave.
Chicago, IL 60601
Ph: (312)649-5200
URL: http://www.chicagobusiness.com/section/lists

Published November, 2010. $25.00 for individuals;

$45.00 for individuals. Covers: 25 hospitals in Chicago area ranked by net patient revenues. Entries include: Name, address, phone number, fax, web address, corporate e-mail, hospital administrator, network affiliation, 2009 net patient revenue, percentage change from 2008, 2009 net profits, percentage change from 2008, inpatient days, available beds, daily occupancy rate, number of hospital employees as of December 31, 2009, fiscal year end, Chairman, President, CEO, Chief Financial Officer, Human Resources Manager, Media Relations/Public Relations Director, and Hospital Administrator.

11363 ■ Directory of Hospital Personnel
Grey House Publishing
4919 Rte. 22
PO Box 56
Amenia, NY 12501
Ph: (518)789-8700
Fax: (518)789-0556
Fr: 800-562-2139
URL: http://www.greyhouse.com/hospital_
personnel.htm

Annual, Latest edition 2011. $325.00 for individuals. Covers: 200,000 executives at 6,000 U.S. Hospitals. Entries include: Name of hospital, address, phone, number of beds, type and JCAHO status of hospital, names and titles of key department heads and staff, medical and nursing school affiliations; number of residents, interns, and nursing students. Arrangement: Geographical. Indexes: Hospital name, personnel, hospital size.

11364 ■ Hospital Blue Book
Billian Publishing Inc. and Trans World Publishing Inc.
2100 River Edge Pky.
Atlanta, GA 30328
Ph: (770)955-5656
Fax: (770)952-0669
Fr: 800-800-5668
E-mail: blu-book@billian.com
URL: http://www.billianshealthdata.com/Products/
bluebook.html

Annual, Latest edition 2010. $575.00 for individuals; $575.00 for individuals. Covers: More than 6,500 hospitals; some listings also appear in a separate southern edition of this publication. Entries include: Name of hospital, accreditation, mailing address, phone, fax, number of beds, type of facility (nonprofit, general, state, etc.); list of administrative personnel and chiefs of medical services, with specific titles. Arrangement: Geographical.

11365 ■ Medical and Health Information Directory
Gale
PO Box 6904
Florence, KY 41022-6904
Fr: 800-354-9706
URL: http://www.gale.cengage.com

Annual, Latest edition April 2011. $1190.00 for individuals; $501.00 for individuals. Covers: In volume 1, more than 33,000 medical and health oriented associations, organizations, institutions, and government agencies, including health maintenance organizations (HMOs), preferred provider organizations (PPOs), insurance companies, pharmaceutical companies, research centers, and medical and allied health schools. In Volume 2, over 20,000 medical book publishers; medical periodicals, directories, audiovisual producers and services, medical libraries and information centers, electronic resources, and health-related internet search engines. In Volume 3, more than 40,500 clinics, treatment centers, care programs, and counseling/diagnostic services for 34 subject areas. Entries include: Institution, service, or firm name, address, phone, fax, email and URL; many include names of key personnel and, when pertinent, descriptive annotation. Volume 3 was formerly listed separately as Health Services Directory. Arrangement: Classified by organization activity, service, etc. Indexes: Each volume has a complete alphabetical name and keyword index.

HANDBOOKS AND MANUALS

11366 ■ Careers in Health Care
The McGraw-Hill Companies
PO Box 182604
Columbus, OH 43272
Fax: (614)759-3749
Fr: 877-883-5524
E-mail: customer.service@mcgraw-hill.com
URL: http://www.mhprofessional.com/
product.php?isbn=0071466533

Barbara M. Swanson. Fifth edition, 2005. $19.95 (paper). 192 pages. Describes job duties, work settings, salaries, licensing and certification requirements, educational preparation, and future outlook. Gives ideas on how to secure a job.

11367 ■ Expert Resumes for Health Care Careers
Jist Works
875 Montreal Way
St. Paul, MN 55102
Fr: 800-648-5478
E-mail: educate@emcp.com
URL: http://www.jist.com

Wendy S. Enelow and Louise M. Kursmark. 2010. $16.95. 288 pages.

11368 ■ Health Careers Today
Elsevier
11830 Westline Industrial Dr.
St. Louis, MO 63146
Ph: (314)453-7010
Fax: (314)453-7095
Fr: 800-545-2522
E-mail: usbkinfo@elsevier.com
URL: http://www.elsevier.com

Gerdin, Judith. Fourth edition. 2007. $74.95. 496 pages. Covers more than 45 health careers. Discusses the roles and responsibilities of various occupations and provides a solid foundation in the skills needed for all health careers.

11369 ■ Opportunities in Health and Medical Careers
The McGraw-Hill Companies
PO Box 182604
Columbus, OH 43272
Fax: (614)759-3749
Fr: 877-883-5524
E-mail: customer.service@mcgraw-hill.com
URL: http://www.mhprofessional.com/
product.php?isbn=0071437274

I. Donald Snook, Jr. and Leo D'Orazio. 2004. $14.95 (paper). 157 pages. Covers the full range of medical and health occupations. Illustrated.

11370 ■ Resumes for Health and Medical Careers
The McGraw-Hill Companies
PO Box 182604
Columbus, OH 43272
Fax: (614)759-3749
Fr: 877-883-5524
E-mail: customer.service@mcgraw-hill.com
URL: http://www.mhprofessional.com/
product.php?isbn=0071545352

Third edition, 2008. $12.95 (paper). 144 pages.

EMPLOYMENT AGENCIES AND SEARCH FIRMS

11371 ■ CompHealth
PO Box 713100
Salt Lake City, UT 84171-3100
Ph: (801)930-3000
Fax: (801)930-4517

Fr: 800-453-3030
E-mail: info@comphealth.com
URL: http://www.comphealth.com

Provides healthcare staffing and recruiting services covering certified registered nurse anesthetist, dosimetrist, imaging and radiation therapy, laboratory technology, medical physicist, nurse practitioner, nursing, pharmacy, physician, physician assistant, rehab therapy and respiratory therapy.

11372 ■ Cross Country TravCorps
6551 Park of Commerce Blvd.
Boca Raton, FL 33487-8247
Fax: (561)998-8533
Fr: 800-530-6125
E-mail: sms@cctc.com
URL: http://www.crosscountrytravcorps.com/cctc/

Places traveling nurses in assignments nationwide.

11373 ■ JPM International
26034 Acero
Mission Viejo, CA 92691
Ph: (949)699-4300
Fax: (949)699-4333
Fr: 800-685-7856
E-mail: qtek37@yahoo.com
URL: http://www.jpmintl.com/pages/qss.html

Executive search firm and employment agency.

11374 ■ MedPro Healthcare Staffing
1580 Sawgrass Corporate Pkwy., Ste. 100
Sunrise, FL 33323
Ph: (954)739-4247
Fax: 800-370-0755
Fr: 800-886-8108
E-mail: medprogeneralinquiries@medprostaffing.com
URL: http://www.medprostaffing.com

Provides temporary and contract staffing services to healthcare facilities.

11375 ■ Professional Placement Associates, Inc.
287 Bowman Ave.
Purchase, NY 10577-2517
Ph: (914)251-1000
Fax: (914)251-1055
E-mail: careers@ppasearch.com
URL: http://www.ppasearch.com

Executive search firm specializing in the health and medical field.

ONLINE JOB SOURCES AND SERVICES

11376 ■ HEALTHeCAREERS Network
Fr: 888-884-8242
E-mail: info@healthecareers.com
URL: http://www.healthecareers.com

Description: Career search site for jobs in all health care specialties; educational resources; visa and licensing information for relocation; interesting articles; relocation tools; links to professional organizations and general resources.

11377 ■ Hospital Jobs OnLine
E-mail: support@hospitaljobsonline.com
URL: http://www.hospitaljobsonline.com

Description: Serves as a niche healthcare job board designed exclusively for hospitals, healthcare companies, and healthcare job seekers.

11378 ■ ProHealthJobs.com
Ph: (484)443-8545
Fax: (484)443-8549
E-mail: info@prohealthjobs.com
URL: http://prohealthjobs.com/jobboard

Description: Career resources site for the medical and health care field. Lists professional opportunities, product information, continuing education and open positions.

11379 ■ RehabJobs Online
E-mail: support@atsrehabjobs.com
URL: http://www.rehabjobsonline.com

Description: Resource center for the professional therapist. Main files include: Therapists Only, Therapy Forums, Nationwide Job Search (database), Therapy Job Outlook, Therapy Job Search Utilities, Therapy Links, Information for Employers and Recruiters.

11380 ■ TherapyJobBoard.com
URL: http://www.therapyjobboard.com

Description: Serves as an employment resource for job seekers and employers in the physical therapy, occupational therapy, speech therapy and respiratory therapy professions.

TRADESHOWS

11381 ■ AARC International Respiratory Congress
American Association for Respiratory Care
9425 N MacArthur Blvd., Ste. 100
Irving, TX 75063
Ph: (972)243-2272
Fax: (972)484-2720
E-mail: info@aarc.org
URL: http://www.aarc.org

Annual. Brings together respiratory care practitioners, managers, educators, students, manufacturers, service providers, and more. Offers the latest products and services in respiratory care. Provides opportunities for professional networking. 2012 November 10-13; New Orleans, LA; 2012 November 16-19; Anaheim, CA.

OTHER SOURCES

11382 ■ American Association for Respiratory Care (AARC)
9425 N MacArthur Blvd., Ste. 100
Irving, TX 75063-4706
Ph: (972)243-2272
Fax: (972)484-2720
E-mail: info@aarc.org
URL: http://www.aarc.org

Description: Allied health society of respiratory therapists and other respiratory caregivers employed by hospitals, skilled nursing facilities, home care companies, group practices, educational institutions, and municipal organizations. Encourages, develops, and provides educational programs for persons interested in the profession of respiratory care; and advances the science of respiratory care.

11383 ■ American Public Health Association (APHA)
800 I St. NW
Washington, DC 20001
Ph: (202)777-2742
Fax: (202)777-2534
E-mail: comments@apha.org
URL: http://www.apha.org

Description: Professional organization of physicians, nurses, educators, academicians, environmentalists, epidemiologists, new professionals, social workers, health administrators, optometrists, podiatrists, pharmacists, dentists, nutritionists, health planners, other community and mental health specialists, and interested consumers. Seeks to protect and promote personal, mental, and environmental health. Services include: promulgation of standards; establishment of uniform practices and procedures; development of the etiology of communicable diseases; research in public health; exploration of medical care programs and their relationships to public health. Sponsors job placement service.

11384 ■ Committee on Accreditation for Respiratory Care (COARC)
1248 Harwood Rd.
Bedford, TX 76021-4244
Ph: (817)283-2835
Fax: (817)354-8519
E-mail: tom@coarc.com
URL: http://www.coarc.com

Description: Physicians, respiratory therapists, and a public representative. Purposes are to develop standards and requirements for accredited educational programs of respiratory therapy for recommendation to the American Medical Association; to conduct evaluations of educational programs that have applied for accreditation of the AMA and to make recommendations to the AMA's Committee on Allied Health Education and Accreditation; to maintain a working liaison with other organizations interested in respiratory therapy education and evaluation.

11385 ■ National Board for Respiratory Care (NBRC)
18000 W 105th St.
Olathe, KS 66061-7543
Ph: (913)895-4900
Fax: (913)895-4650
Fr: 888-341-4811
E-mail: nbrc-info@nbrc.org
URL: http://www.nbrc.org

Description: Offers credentialing examinations for respiratory therapists, respiratory therapy technicians, pulmonary technologists, and perinatal/pediatric respiratory care specialists.

SOURCES OF HELP-WANTED ADS

11386 ▪ Airport Press
P.A.T.I. Inc.
PO Box 300879, JFK Sta.
Jamaica, NY 11430-0879
Ph: (718)244-6788
Fax: (718)995-3432
Fr: 800-982-5832
E-mail: airprtpres@aol.com
URL: http://www.airportpress.us

Monthly. $48.00/year for individuals; $96.00/year for other countries. Newspaper for the airport industry.

11387 ▪ Beverage World
Beverage World
200 E Randolph St., 7th Fl.
Chicago, IL 60601
Ph: (646)708-7300
Fax: (646)708-7399
Fr: (866)890-8541
URL: http://www.beverageworld.com

Monthly. $99.00/year for individuals. Trade magazine for corporate, marketing, distribution, production, and purchasing top and middle management in the multi-product beverage industry.

11388 ▪ Chef
Talcott Communication Corp.
233 N Michigan Ave., Ste. 1780
Chicago, IL 60601
Ph: (312)849-2220
Fax: (312)849-2174
E-mail: chef@talcott.com
URL: http://www.chefmagazine.com

$32.00/year for individuals; $47.00/year for two years; $64.00/year for individuals, 3 years; $43.00/year for Canada; $96.00/year for other countries. Food information for chefs.

11389 ▪ Food Management
Penton Media Inc.
249 W 17th St.
New York, NY 10011
Ph: (212)204-4200
URL: http://food-management.com/

Monthly. Magazine for foodservice professionals in the onsite 'noncommercial' market.

11390 ▪ FoodService Director
Ideal Media L.L.C.
200 E Randolph St., 70th Fl.
Chicago, IL 60601
Ph: (312)456-2822
Fax: (312)240-0742
URL: http://www.fsdmag.com

Monthly. $79.00/year for individuals; $99.00/year for Canada; $235.00/year for out of country. Tabloid

newspaper of the noncommercial foodservice market.

11391 ▪ Foodservice East
The Newbury Street Group Inc.
93 Massachusetts Ave., Ste. 306
Boston, MA 02115
Ph: (617)267-2224
Fax: (617)267-5554
URL: http://www.foodserviceeast.com/

Bimonthly. $30.00/year for individuals. Compact Tabloid covering trends and analysis of the foodservice industry in the Northeast. A business-to-business publication featuring news, analysis and trends for the Northeast food service professional.

11392 ▪ Hotel F & B Executive
Hotel Forums L.L.C.
613 Kane St.
West Dundee, IL 60118
Ph: (847)551-9956
URL: http://www.hotelfandb.com

Bimonthly. $49.00/year for individuals; $15.00/year for students; $59.00/year for institutions. Magazine that addresses the needs of the hospitality F&B markets, which include hotels, resorts, cruise lines and conference, and convention & meeting centers.

11393 ▪ Hotel & Motel Management
Questex Media Group
275 Grove St., 2-130
Newton, MA 02466
Ph: (617)219-8300
Fax: (617)219-8310
Fr: 888-552-4346
URL: http://www.hospitalityworldnetwork.com/hotel-management

$58.85/year for individuals; $81.40/year for Canada and Mexico; $143.00/year for other countries; $75.00/year for individuals, additional airmail shipping; free to qualified subscribers. Magazine (tabloid) covering the global lodging industry.

11394 ▪ HOTELS
Marketing & Technology Group
1415 N Dayton St.
Chicago, IL 60622
Ph: (312)274-2200
Fax: (312)266-3363
URL: http://www.hotelsmag.com/

Monthly. Free. Magazine covering management and operations as well as foodservice and design in the hospitality industry.

11395 ▪ Midwest Food Network
Pinnacle Publishing Group
8205-F Estates Pky.
Plain City, OH 43064
Ph: (614)873-1644
Fax: (614)873-1650
URL: http://www.midwestfoodnetwork.com/

Bimonthly. $24.00/year for free to qualified subscribers; $24.00/year for individuals, others. Food service trade magazine featuring new products and suppliers

and other industry news including food news, restaurant association updates, news of chefs, restaurant concepts, earnings, and openings and closings.

11396 ▪ Nightclub & Bar Magazine
Questex Media
275 Grove St., Ste. 2-130
Newton, MA 02466
Ph: (617)219-8300
Fax: (617)219-8310
Fr: 888-552-4346
URL: http://www.nightclub.com

Free to qualified subscribers; $30.00/year for individuals; $45.00/year for Canada and Mexico; $85.00/year for other countries. Trade magazine covering management, lighting, sound, food, beverage, promotions, current trends, and other bar industry news.

11397 ▪ Restaurant Business
VNU Business Publications
770 Broadway
New York, NY 10003
Ph: (646)654-5000
URL: http://www.foodservicetoday.com

Monthly. $119.00/year for individuals; $212.00/year for Canada; $468.00/year for other countries, rest of the world. Trade magazine for restaurants and commercial food service.

11398 ▪ Restaurant Hospitality
Penton Media Inc.
249 W 17th St.
New York, NY 10011
Ph: (212)204-4200
URL: http://restaurant-hospitality.com

Monthly. Free. Dedicated to the success of full service restaurants and edited for chefs and other commercial foodservice professionals. Includes new food and equipment products and trends, menu and recipe ideas, industry news, new technology, food safety, emerging new concepts, consumer attitudes and trends, labor and training, and profiles of successful operations.

11399 ▪ Restaurant Startup & Growth
Specialized Publications Company
5215 Nw Crooked Rd.
Parkville, MO 64152
Ph: (816)741-3120
Fax: (816)741-6458
E-mail: rsg@spc-mag.com
URL: http://www.restaurantowner.com/mag/

Monthly. Magazine about starting and operating a restaurant business.

11400 ▪ Southeast Food Service News
Southeast Publishing Company Inc.
5672 Peachtree Pky., Ste. E
Norcross, GA 30092
Ph: (770)499-9800
Fax: (770)499-9802
URL: http://www.sfsn.com

Monthly. $36.00/year for individuals; $5.00/year for single issue; $59.00/year for individuals, directory issue. Magazine (tabloid) serving the food industry.

11401 ■ Special Events
Penton Media
249 W 17th St.
New York, NY 10011-5390
Ph: (212)204-4200
URL: http://specialevents.com

Monthly. $59.00/year, for free to qualified subscribers; $110.00/year for Canada; $106.00/year for other countries; $200.00/year for Canada, two years; $200.00/year for other countries, two years. Magazine for special event professionals.

11402 ■ Sunbelt Foodservice
Shelby Publishing Company Inc.
517 Green St. NW
Gainesville, GA 30501
Ph: (770)534-8380
Fax: (678)343-2197
URL: http://www.shelbypublishing.com/
    index.php?option=com_content

Monthly. $36.00/year for individuals; $60.00/year for two years. Trade newspaper (tabloid) covering the food industry geared toward restaurant operators.

EMPLOYER DIRECTORIES AND NETWORKING LISTS

11403 ■ Directory of Chain Restaurant Operators
Chain Store Guide
3922 Coconut Palm Dr.
Tampa, FL 33619
Ph: (813)627-6800
Fax: (813)627-6888
Fr: 800-927-9292
URL: http://www.chainstoreguide.com

Annual, Latest edition 2010. $425.00 for individuals; $495.00 for individuals; $1,175.00 for individuals; $695.00 for individuals; $1,475.00 for individuals. Covers: 7,100 chain restaurant and chain hotel operators, nontraditional foodservice operators and food service management operators who operate 2 or more food service locations. Entries include: 32,500 chain restaurant buyers, chefs, executives—company name, address, phone and fax numbers; 15,000 personal e-mail and web addresses; type of business; listing type; total annual sales; food service sales; system wide sales; percent of sales of alcohol; percent of sales from Internet; alcohol types served; total units; company owned units; units franchised to and from; trade names; co-branded names and numbers; food service management location types; trading areas; foreign trading areas; units by primary menu types and type of foodservice; self distributing and catering services indicators; franchise affiliations names and locations; primary distributors names and locations; parent and subsidiary company names and locations; regional; divisional; and branch office locations; distribution centers locations; year founded; public company indicator; key personnel with titles. For chain hotel operators—includes number of restaurants in hotels. For food service management operators—includes number of food service management accounts and total number of locations served. Arrangement: Geographical. Indexes: Alphabetical, type of food service, menu type, franchisee, food service management, state, exclusions.

11404 ■ Directory of Hospital Personnel
Grey House Publishing
4919 Rte. 22
PO Box 56
Amenia, NY 12501
Ph: (518)789-8700
Fax: (518)789-0556
Fr: 800-562-2139
URL: http://www.greyhouse.com/hospital_
    personnel.htm

Annual, Latest edition 2011. $325.00 for individuals. Covers: 200,000 executives at 6,000 U.S. Hospitals. Entries include: Name of hospital, address, phone, number of beds, type and JCAHO status of hospital, names and titles of key department heads and staff, medical and nursing school affiliations; number of residents, interns, and nursing students. Arrangement: Geographical. Indexes: Hospital name, personnel, hospital size.

HANDBOOKS AND MANUALS

11405 ■ Becoming a Culinary Arts Professionals
LearningExpress, LLC
2 Rector St., 26th Fl.
New York, NY 10006
Fr: 800-295-9556
E-mail: customerservice@learningexpressllc.com
URL: http://www.learningexpressllc.com

LearningExpress Editors. 2010. $16.95 (paper). 208 pages. Details how to navigate the hundreds of paths to a culinary career available in the United States. Provides many culinary career options and addresses how to develop new skills or refine current skills and how to understand the certification process.

11406 ■ Career Opportunities in the Food and Beverage Industry
Facts on File, Inc.
132 W 31st St., 17th Fl.
New York, NY 10001-2006
Ph: (212)967-8800
Fax: 800-678-3633
Fr: 800-322-8755
E-mail: custserv@factsonfile.com
URL: http://www.infobasepublishing.com

Barbara Sims-Bell. 2010. $18.95 (paper). 223 pages. Provides the job seeker with information about locating and landing 80 skilled and unskilled jobs in the industry. Includes detailed job descriptions for many specific positions and lists trade associations, recruiting organizations, and major agencies. Contains index and bibliography.

11407 ■ Careers for Health Nuts and Others Who Like to Stay Fit
The McGraw-Hill Companies
PO Box 182604
Columbus, OH 43272
Fax: (614)759-3749
Fr: 877-883-5524
E-mail: customer.service@mcgraw-hill.com
URL: http://www.mhprofessional.com

Blythe Camenson. Second edition. $13.95 (paper). 208 pages.

11408 ■ Careers in Travel, Tourism, and Hospitality
The McGraw-Hill Companies
PO Box 182604
Columbus, OH 43272
Fax: (614)759-3749
Fr: 877-883-5524
E-mail: customer.service@mcgraw-hill.com
URL: http://www.mhprofessional.com

Marjorie Eberts, Linda Brothers, and Ann Gisler. Second edition, 2005. $15.95 (paper). 224 pages.

11409 ■ Opportunities in Hospital Administration Careers
The McGraw-Hill Companies
PO Box 182604
Columbus, OH 43272
Fax: (614)759-3749
Fr: 877-883-5524
E-mail: customer.service@mcgraw-hill.com
URL: http://www.mhprofessional.com/
    product.php?isbn=0071467688

I. Donald Snook. 2006. $13.95. 160 pages. Discusses opportunities for administrators in a variety of management settings: hospital, department, clinic, group practice, HMO, mental health, and extended care facilities.

11410 ■ Opportunities in Restaurant Careers
The McGraw-Hill Companies
PO Box 182604
Columbus, OH 43272
Fax: (614)759-3749
Fr: 877-883-5524
E-mail: customer.service@mcgraw-hill.com
URL: http://www.mhprofessional.com/
    product.php?isbn=0071442480

Carol Caprione Chmelynski. 2004. $13.95 (paper). 160 pages. Covers opportunities in the food service industry and details salaries, benefits, training opportunities, and professional associations. Special emphasis is put on becoming a successful restaurant manager by working up through the ranks. Illustrated.

11411 ■ The Professional Caterer's Handbook: How to Open and Operate a Financially Successful Catering Business
Atlantic Publishing Company
1210 SW 23rd Pl.
Ocala, FL 34474-7014
Fax: (352)622-1875
Fr: 800-814-1132
E-mail: sales@atlantic-pub.com
URL: http://www.atlantic-pub.com

Douglas Robert Brown and Lora Arduser. 2005. $79.95. Comprehensive guide for planning, starting, and operating a catering business; includes companion CD-ROM. Covers marketing, management, budgeting, home-based catering, ways for restaurants to add catering services to existing businesses, forms, Web sites, and more.

11412 ■ Remarkable Service: A Guide to Winning and Keeping Customers for Servers, Managers, and Restaurant Owners
John Wiley & Sons, Inc.
111 River St.
Hoboken, NJ 07030
Ph: (201)748-6000
Fax: (201)748-6088
E-mail: info@wiley.com
URL: http://www.wiley.com

The Culinary Institute of America. 2009. $29.95 (paperback). 304 pages. Addresses the service needs of dining establishments, from casual and outdoor dining, to upscale restaurants and catering operations. Covers topics from training and hiring staff, service preparation, money handling, service challenges, plus tips on solving it. Includes up-to-date information on serving customers in the contemporary restaurant industry.

EMPLOYMENT AGENCIES AND SEARCH FIRMS

11413 ■ The Alfus Group Inc.
353 Lexington Ave.
New York, NY 10016
Ph: (212)599-1000
Fax: (212)599-1523
E-mail: mail@thealfusgroup.com
URL: http://www.thealfusgroup.com

Executive search firm. Specializes in the hospitality industry.

11414 ■ Anderson & Associates
112 S Tryon St., Ste. 700
Charlotte, NC 28284
Ph: (704)347-0090
Fax: (704)347-0064
E-mail: info@andersonexecsearch.com
URL: http://www.andersonexecsearch.com

Executive search firm. Branch in Cumming, Georgia.

11415 ■ Atlantic Personnel Search
9624 Old Marlboro Pike
Upper Marlboro, MD 20772-3670
Ph: (301)599-2108
Fax: (301)599-2109
Fr: 888-757-7055
E-mail: contact@atlanticpersonnel.com
URL: http://www.atlanticpersonnel.com
Description: Serves as an executive search and placement firm specializing in recruiting professionals of all levels for the hospitality, restaurant, and food service industries.

11416 ■ Boutique Search Firm
1173 Rodeo Dr.
Los Angeles, CA 90035
Ph: (310)552-2221
Fax: (310)552-2224
URL: http://www.boutiquesearchfirm.com
Serves as a recruiting firm specializing in hospitality management. Offers jobs in luxury hotels and resorts worldwide.

11417 ■ Bristol Associates, Inc.
5757 W Century Blvd., Ste. 855
Los Angeles, CA 90045
Ph: (310)670-0525
Fax: (310)670-4075
E-mail: bfarber@bristolassoc.com
URL: http://www.bristolassoc.com
Description: Executive search firm specializing in direct marketing, hospitality and food industries. Applicants can post their resumes online for recruiters' viewing and search current job databank. Also contains job tools and resources.

11418 ■ CraigSearch
1130 E Arapaho Rd., Ste. 180
Richardson, TX 75081
Ph: (972)644-3264
E-mail: search@craigsearch.com
URL: http://www.craigsearch.com
Executive search firm.

11419 ■ dd factor
2615 190th St., Ste. 221
Redondo Beach, CA 90278
Ph: (310)376-0870
Fax: (310)376-1840
URL: http://ddfactor.com
Operates as a hospitality search firm that specializes in chefs, sous chefs, and kitchen managers.

11420 ■ Derba & Derba
7 Whispering Pines Dr.
Andover, MA 01810
Ph: (978)470-8270
Fax: (978)470-4592
E-mail: rderba@derbaandderba.com
URL: http://derbaandderba.com
Executive search firm focused on the hospitality industry.

11421 ■ Food Management Search
235 State St., Ste. 326
Springfield, MA 01103
Ph: (413)732-2666
Fax: (413)732-6466
E-mail: recruiters@foodmanagementsearch.com
URL: http://foodmanagementsearch.com/index.cfm
Specializes in contingency recruiting projects exclusively in the food manufacturing and food service industries. Provides positions covering food production/manufacturing, supply chain, food service, sales and marketing.

11422 ■ Gecko Hospitality
718 Ogden Ave., Ste. 202
Downers Grove, IL 60515
Ph: (630)390-1000
Fax: (630)598-0753
URL: http://www.geckohospitality.com

Serves as a hospitality recruiter specializing in placing candidates in hospitality jobs as well as securing qualified hospitality professionals for its clients. Provides a database of hospitality jobs, restaurant jobs, hotel jobs, and casino jobs.

11423 ■ Global Hospitality
3579 E Foothill Blvd., Ste. 229
Pasadena, CA 91107
Ph: (626)836-1222
Fax: (626)836-1223
E-mail: mail@globalhospitality.com
URL: http://www.globalhospitality.com
Executive search firm that specializes in identifying, evaluating, and placing leadership and management talent in the hospitality industry.

11424 ■ Hospitality International
236 5th Ave., Ste. 907
New York, NY 10001
Ph: (212)696-1661
Fax: (212)696-1669
E-mail: jar@hospitalityinternational.com
URL: http://www.hospitalityinternational.com
Executive search firm. Branch office in New York, NY.

11425 ■ Hospitality Marketing & Recruiting
PO Box 970023
Boca Raton, FL 33497
Ph: (561)289-1873
Fax: (561)852-6447
E-mail: rstevens@hospitalityjobsbyhmr.com
URL: http://www.hospitalityjobsbyhmr.com
Description: Provides executive search and placement services of management level hospitality personnel for hotels, country clubs, cruise ships, attractions and restaurants.

11426 ■ Hospitality Pro Search
12134 Attlee Dr.
Houston, TX 77077
Ph: (281)584-0601
Fax: (832)230-5504
E-mail: gary@hprosearch.com
URL: http://www.hprosearch.com
Serves as an executive search firm for the hospitality industry. Specializes in worldwide management placements for restaurants, hotels and resorts, entertainment venues, and private clubs.

11427 ■ HospitalityStaff.com
3195 Tamiami Trail, Ste. 204
Port Charlotte, FL 33952
Ph: (941)743-8540
Fax: (941)743-9684
Fr: 800-987-1555
URL: http://www.hospitalitystaff.com
Serves as a placement agency, specializing in the supply of temporary and permanent staff to the hospitality industry.

11428 ■ J.D. Hersey and Associates
8 E Poplar Ave.
Columbus, OH 43215
Ph: (614)228-4022
Fax: (614)228-4085
URL: http://www.jdhersey.com
Executive search firm for permanent and contingency placements.

11429 ■ LW Foote Company
PO Box 52762
Bellevue, WA 98004
Ph: (425)451-1660
E-mail: email@lwfoote.com
URL: http://www.lwfoote.com
Executive search firm.

11430 ■ National Restaurant Search
700 E Diehl Rd., Ste. 130
Naperville, IL 60563
Ph: (630)482-2900

Fax: (630)482-2922
E-mail: admin@restaurantheadhunter.com
URL: http://www.restaurantheadhunter.com
Executive search firm specializing in the restaurant/hospitality industry at the executive level on a national and international basis.

11431 ■ Tierney Restaurant Services
433 W 68th Terr.
Kansas City, MO 64113
Ph: (816)361-1463
Fax: (816)333-3180
URL: http://www.tdcareers.com
Executive and unit level search firm serving the hospitality industry. Specializes in the placement of the finest restaurant management professionals with the top national, regional and local hospitality groups across the United States.

ONLINE JOB SOURCES AND SERVICES

11432 ■ BestfoodJobs.com
URL: http://www.bestfoodjobs.com
Description: Provides information on employment opportunities for the restaurant and food service industry.

11433 ■ FoodIndustryJobs.com
E-mail: jobboards@hrsmart.com
URL: http://www.foodindustryjobs.com
Description: Job databank and resume submission service for food industry workers.

11434 ■ Foodservice.com
URL: http://www.foodservice.com
Description: Serves as an online community of foodservice professionals. Provides services such as a virtual foodshow, employment center, market reports, daily industry news and editorials, discussion forums, culinary school connections, and the weekly foodservice.com express e-Newsletter.

11435 ■ FoodServicesCrossing.com
URL: http://www.foodservicescrossing.com
Description: Features job listings for the food services industry.

11436 ■ HCareers.com
E-mail: hospitalitydivision@hcareers.com
URL: http://www.hcareers.com
Description: Connects employers and candidates within the hospitality industry. Enables candidates to search for jobs within a specific industry or location.

11437 ■ Hospitality Jobs Online
URL: http://www.hospitalityonline.com
Description: Enables hospitality industry job seekers to find career information, information about employers and tips and techniques to help them succeed. Provides daily updates of hotel jobs, resort jobs, restaurant jobs and club jobs nationwide.

11438 ■ Hospitality Recruiters
10706 Cortland Ridge Ln.
Cypress, TX 77433
Fax: 877-684-3106
Fr: 877-735-1133
E-mail: career@hospitalityrecruiters.com
URL: http://www.hospitalityrecruiters.com
Description: Specializes in the placement of managers within the restaurant and hotel industries.

11439 ■ HotelJobs.com
URL: http://www.hoteljobs.com
Description: Provides job postings and resume database for hotel, casino and cruise ship professionals and recruiters.

11440 ■ New Restaurant and Food Jobs
URL: http://www.newrestaurantandfoodjobs.com

Description: Provides an online listing of companies with available restaurant and food jobs in all specialties.

11441 ■ RestaurantManager.net
URL: http://www.restaurantmanager.net

Description: Exists as a job site for professional restaurant managers.

11442 ■ RestaurantOperator.com
E-mail: customerservice@restaurantoperator.com
URL: http://www.restaurantoperator.com

Description: Exists as a virtual community created for the benefit of restaurant operators and employees. Offers a variety of services that encompass all facets of the restaurant business. Provides services on product information, distributor and supplier information, professional services, associations and trade show listings, publications, restaurants for sale, business opportunities, and an employment center.

TRADESHOWS

11443 ■ ACF National Convention and Trade Show
American Culinary Federation
180 Ctr. Place Way
St. Augustine, FL 32095
Ph: (904)824-4468
Fax: (904)825-4758
Fr: 800-624-9458
E-mail: acf@acfchefs.net
URL: http://www.acfchefs.org

Annual. Includes exhibits featuring apparel, equipment, cookware, books and media, seasonings, packaged goods, and similar merchandise. Provides networking opportunities for attendees. 2012 July 14-17; Sunny Orlando, FL.

11444 ■ Annual Hotel, Motel, and Restaurant Supply Show of the Southeast
Leisure Time Unlimited, Inc.
708 Main St.
PO Box 332
Myrtle Beach, SC 29577
Ph: (843)448-9483
Fax: (843)626-1513
Fr: 800-261-5591
E-mail: ltushows@sc.rr.com
URL: http://www.leisuretimeunlimited.com/

Annual. Primary Exhibits: Carpeting, furniture, coffee makers, produce companies, wine and beer and food companies, and services to motels, hotels, and restaurants. Dates and Locations: 2012 Jan 24-26; Myrtle Beach, SC; Myrtle Beach Convention Center.

11445 ■ Denver Food and Kitchen Expo
Professional Chefs Association
1207 Hawkeye Ct.
Fort Collins, CO 80525
Ph: (970)223-4004
Fax: 877-392-1443
URL: http://www.professionalchef.com

Annual. Features all things related to food, kitchens, and cooking.

11446 ■ International Restaurant & Foodservice Show of New York
Reed Exhibitions North American Headquarters
383 Main Ave.
Norwalk, CT 06851
Ph: (203)840-4800
Fax: (203)840-5805
E-mail: inquiry@reedexpo.com
URL: http://www.reedexpo.com

Annual. Primary Exhibits: Equipment, supplies, and services for the food products, foodservice, restaurant, and institutional food service industries. Dates

and Locations: 2012 Mar 04-06; New York, NY; Jacob K. Javits Center.

11447 ■ Jobbernaut Career Fairs
Jobbernaut, Inc.
PO Box 2267
Lynnwood, WA 98036
Ph: (425)397-7114
Fax: (425)397-7505
URL: http://jobbernautcareerfairs.com

Brings together over 1500 companies to recruit and hire applicants from the following industries: sales, management, restaurant and retail; technical, engineering, computers; administrative, general office, and customer service; and banking and financial. 2012 October 3; Seattle, WA.

11448 ■ Louisiana Foodservice Expo
Louisiana Restaurant Association
2700 N. Arnoult Rd.
Metairie, LA 70002
Ph: (504)454-2277
Fax: (504)454-2299
Fr: 800-256-4572
E-mail: tomw@lra.org
URL: http://www.lra.org/

Annual. Primary Exhibits: Food service equipment, supplies, and services, food products, furniture, tableware. Dates and Locations: 2012 Aug 11-13; New Orleans, LA; New Orleans Morial Convention Center.

11449 ■ Midsouthwest Foodservice Convention and Exposition
Oklahoma Restaurant Association
3800 N. Portland Ave.
Oklahoma City, OK 73112
Ph: (405)942-8181
Fax: (405)942-0541
Fr: 800-375-8181
URL: http://www.okrestaurants.com

Annual. Primary Exhibits: Providers of foodservice and hospitality products, services and equipment.

11450 ■ School Nutrition Association Conference
School Nutrition Association
120 Waterfront St., Ste. 300
National Harbor, MD 20745
Ph: (301)686-3100
Fax: (301)686-3115
E-mail: servicecenter@schoolnutrition.org
URL: http://www.schoolnutrition.org

Annual. Primary Exhibits: Food service supplies and equipment, including educational services and computers. Dates and Locations: 2012 Jul 15-18; Denver, CO; 2013 Jul 13-17; Kansas City, MO; 2014 Jul 12-16; Boston, MA; 2015 Jul 11-15; Salt Lake City, UT; 2016 Jul 10-13; San Antonio, TX; 2017 Jul 09-12; Atlanta, GA; 2018 Jul 08-11; Las Vegas, NV; 2019 Jul 14-17; St. Louis, MO.

OTHER SOURCES

11451 ■ Association of Correctional Food Service Affiliates (ACFSA)
210 N Glenoaks Blvd., Ste. C
Burbank, CA 91502
Ph: (818)843-6608
Fax: (818)843-7423
E-mail: jonnichols@acfsa.org
URL: http://www.acfsa.org

Description: Food service professionals from federal, state and county correctional institutions and vendors that serve them. Works to advance skills and professionalism through education, information and networking.

11452 ■ Association for Healthcare Foodservice
455 S 4th St., Ste. 650
Louisville, KY 40202

Fax: (502)589-3602
Fr: 888-528-9552
E-mail: info@healthcarefoodservice.org
URL: http://www.healthcarefoodservice.org

Description: Represents professionals and suppliers in the self-operated healthcare foodservice industry. Advances healthcare foodservice professionals by ensuring that food and nutrition is a core competency. Provides education, advocacy, and management tools to support members.

11453 ■ Association for International Practical Training (AIPT)
10400 Little Patuxent Pkwy., Ste. 250
Columbia, MD 21044-3519
Ph: (410)997-2200
Fax: (410)992-3924
E-mail: aipt@aipt.org
URL: http://www.aipt.org

Description: Providers worldwide of on-the-job training programs for students and professionals seeking international career development and life-changing experiences. Arranges workplace exchanges in hundreds of professional fields, bringing employers and trainees together from around the world. Client list ranges from small farming communities to Fortune 500 companies.

11454 ■ Club Managers Association of America (CMAA)
1733 King St.
Alexandria, VA 22314
Ph: (703)739-9500
Fax: (703)739-0124
E-mail: cmaa@cmaa.org
URL: http://www.cmaa.org

Description: Professional managers and assistant managers of private golf, yacht, athletic, city, country, luncheon, university, and military clubs. Encourages education and advancement of members and promotes efficient and successful club operations. Provides reprints of articles on club management. Supports courses in club management. Compiles statistics; maintains management referral service.

11455 ■ International Council on Hotel, Restaurant, and Institutional Education (CHRIE)
2810 N Parham Rd., Ste. 230
Richmond, VA 23294
Ph: (804)346-4800
Fax: (804)346-5009
E-mail: kmccarty@chrie.org
URL: http://www.chrie.org

Description: Schools and colleges offering specialized education and training in hospitals, recreation, tourism and hotel, restaurant, and institutional administration; individuals, executives, and students. Provides networking opportunities and professional development.

11456 ■ Les Amis d'Escoffier Society of New York
787 Ridgewood Rd.
Millburn, NJ 07041
Ph: (212)414-5820
Fax: (973)379-3117
URL: http://www.escoffier-society.com

Description: An educational organization of professionals in the food and wine industries. Maintains museum, speakers' bureau, hall of fame, and placement service. Sponsors charitable programs.

11457 ■ National Management Association (NMA)
2210 Arbor Blvd.
Dayton, OH 45439
Ph: (937)294-0421
Fax: (937)294-2374
E-mail: nma@nma1.org
URL: http://www.nma1.org

Description: Business and industrial management personnel; membership comes from supervisory level, with the remainder from middle management and above. Seeks to develop and recognize management as a profession and to promote the free enterprise system. Prepares chapter programs on basic management, management policy and practice, communications, human behavior, industrial relations, economics, political education, and liberal education. Maintains speakers' bureau and hall of fame. Maintains educational, charitable, and research programs. Sponsors charitable programs.

11458 ■ National Restaurant Association (NRA)
1200 17th St. NW
Washington, DC 20036
Ph: (202)331-5900
Fax: (202)331-2429
Fr: 800-424-5156
URL: http://www.restaurant.org

Description: Represents restaurants, cafeterias, clubs, contract foodservice management, drive-ins, caterers, institutional food services and other members of the foodservice industry; also represents establishments belonging to non-affiliated state and local restaurant associations in governmental affairs. Supports foodservice education and research in several educational institutions. Is affiliated with the Educational Foundation of the National Restaurant Association to provide training and education for operators, food and equipment manufacturers, distributors and educators. Has 300,000 member locations.

11459 ■ National Restaurant Association Educational Foundation (NRAEF)
175 W Jackson Blvd., Ste. 1500
Chicago, IL 60604-2702
Ph: (312)715-1010
Fr: 800-765-2122
E-mail: info@restaurant.org
URL: http://www.nraef.org

Description: Serves as an educational foundation supported by the National Restaurant Association and all segments of the foodservice industry including restaurateurs, foodservice companies, food and equipment manufacturers, distributors and trade associations. Advances the professional standards of the industry through education and research. Offers video training programs, management courses and careers information. Conducts research and maintains hall of fame.

11460 ■ Professional Chefs Association
1207 Hawkeye Ct.
Fort Collins, CO 80525
Ph: (970)223-4004
Fax: 877-392-1443
E-mail: support@professionalchef.com
URL: http://www.professionalchef.com

Description: Represents the interests of chefs and those associated with the food service industry. Promotes culinary excellence through the exchange of knowledge among chefs. Offers online education courses and certification programs.

11461 ■ Research Chefs Association
1100 Johnson Ferry Rd., Ste. 300
Atlanta, GA 30342
Ph: (404)252-3663
Fax: (404)252-0774
E-mail: rca@kellencompany.com
URL: http://www.culinology.com

Description: Represents the interests of chefs, food scientists, and other industry professionals in the food research and development industry. Offers resources of culinary and technical information for professionals in the field.

11462 ■ Society for Foodservice Management (SFM)
15000 Commerce Pkwy., Ste. C
Mount Laurel, NJ 08054
Ph: (856)380-6829
Fax: (856)439-0525
E-mail: sfm@ahint.com
URL: http://www.sfm-online.org

Description: Operates or maintains food service and vending facilities in businesses and industrial plants, or supply food products, equipment, or other essential industry services. Serves the needs and interests of onsite employee food service executives and management. Provides an opportunity for the exchange of experiences and opinions through study, discussion, and publications; develops greater efficiency and more economical methods of providing high-quality food and service at a reasonable cost; assists members in solving specific operating and management problems; keeps pace with the rapidly changing conditions of the employee food service segment of the industry. Develops and encourages the practice of high standards and professional conduct among management and executive personnel; provides job placement and management personnel recruiting service; sends representative to the U.S. Air Force Hennessey Award Team, which selects the Air Force base having the most superior food service.

SOURCES OF HELP-WANTED ADS

11463 ■ Chain Store Age
Lebhar-Friedman, Inc.
425 Park Ave.
New York, NY 10022
Ph: (212)756-5000
URL: http://www.chainstoreage.com

Monthly. Magazine for management of retail chain headquarters. Reports on marketing, merchandising, strategic planning, physical supports, and shopping center developments, retail technology credit and communications.

11464 ■ The College Store
The College Store
500 E Lorain St.
Oberlin, OH 44074
Fax: (440)775-4769
Fr: 800-622-7498
E-mail: thecollegestore@nacs.org
URL: http://www.nacs.org/publications/thecollegestoremagazine.asp

Bimonthly. $66.00/year for members; $78.00/year for nonmembers. Books and college supplies magazine.

11465 ■ Counterman
Babcox
3550 Embassy Pky.
Akron, OH 44333
Ph: (330)670-1234
URL: http://www.babcox.com/site/our-brands/counterman

Monthly. Free. Magazine devoted to improving the effectiveness of professional automotive parts counter-sales personnel.

11466 ■ CRN
United business Media L.L.C
240 W 35th St.
New York, NY 10001
Ph: (516)562-5000
URL: http://www.crn.com

Weekly. Newspaper for value added resellers, retailers, and distributors in the computer market.

11467 ■ Customer Service Advantage
Progressive Business Publications
370 Technology Dr.
Malvern, PA 19355
Fax: (610)647-8089
Fr: 800-220-5000
E-mail: customer_service@pbp.com
URL: http://www.pbp.com/CSA.asp

Description: Semimonthly. $253/year. Presents practical methods for quantifying customer service benefits and motivating employees day in and day out. Recurring features include interviews, news of research, a calendar of events, news of educational opportunities, and a column titled Sharpen Your Judgment.

11468 ■ DNR
Fairchild Publications Inc.
750 Third Ave., 8th Fl.
New York, NY 10017
Ph: (212)630-4600
Fax: (212)630-4015
URL: http://www.dnrnews.com/

Daily (morn.). $129.00/year for individuals; $99.00/year for individuals, online; $169.00/year for individuals, online + print; $895.00/year for individuals, on-line archive. Daily newspaper reporting on men's and boys' clothing, retailing, and textiles.

11469 ■ Gifts & Decorative Accessories
Sandow Media Corp.
3731 NW 8th Ave.
Boca Raton, FL 33431
Ph: (561)750-0151
Fax: (561)750-0152
URL: http://www.giftsanddec.com/

Monthly. $36.00/year for individuals; $39.00/year for Canada; $135.00/year for other countries. International magazine for retailers of gifts, greeting cards, decorative accessories, and stationery-related merchandise.

11470 ■ Home Channel News
Lebhar-Friedman, Inc.
425 Park Ave.
New York, NY 10022
Ph: (212)756-5000
URL: http://www.homechannelnews.com

$189.00/year for individuals. Business tabloid serving home center/building material retailers.

11471 ■ Master Salesmanship
Clement Communications Inc.
3 Creek Parkway
PO Box 2208
Upper Chichester, PA 19061
Fax: 800-459-1933
Fr: 800-253-6368
E-mail: editor@clement.com
URL: http://www.clement.com

Description: Biweekly. $149.50 per copy. Designed to help sales managers motivate, train, and inform their salespeople. Offers pointers on improving old sales skills and developing new ones. Recurring features include a motivation column, Q&A, and Selling Slants.

11472 ■ Modern Grocer
GC Publishing Company Inc.
744 Main St., Rte. 6A
PO Box 2010
Dennis, MA 02638
Ph: (508)385-7700
Fax: (508)385-0089
URL: http://www.gccomm.net/moderngrocer/index.asp

Monthly. $50.00/year for individuals. Magazine for food retailers, wholesalers, distributors, brokers, manufacturers, and packers in the metro New York and New Jersey marketing area.

11473 ■ Money Making Opportunities
Success Publishing International
11071 Ventura Blvd.
Studio City, CA 91604
Ph: (818)980-9166
Fax: (818)980-7829
URL: http://www.moneymakingopps.com/

Free. Magazine Source for small business opportunity seekers.

11474 ■ Music Inc.
Maher Publications Inc.
102 N Haven Rd.
Elmhurst, IL 60126
Ph: (630)941-2030
Fr: 800-554-7470
E-mail: editor@musicincmag.com
URL: http://www.musicincmag.com/magazine.html

$17.00/year for individuals. Magazine serving retailers of music and sound products.

11475 ■ National Jeweler
Nielsen Business Media
770 Broadway
New York, NY 10003-9595
URL: http://www.nationaljewelernetwork.com/njn/index.jsp

Semimonthly. $10.00/year for single issue, cover; $89.00/year for U.S.; $104.00/year for Canada; $330.00/year for other countries, airmail only. Jewelry industry magazine.

11476 ■ PMA Magazine
PMA
3000 Picture Pl.
Jackson, MI 49201
Ph: (517)788-8100
Fax: (517)788-8371
Fr: 800-762-9287
URL: http://www.pmai.org/content.aspx?id=8110

Monthly. $50.00/year for individuals; $55.00/year for Canada; $70.00/year for out of country; $5.00/year for single issue; $90.00/year for two years; $100.00/year for two years, Canada; $130.00/year for two years, other countries. Trade magazine for photo/video dealers and photo finishers.

11477 ■ Retailing Today
Lebhar-Friedman, Inc.
425 Park Ave.
New York, NY 10022
Ph: (212)756-5000
URL: http://www.retailingtoday.com/

Semimonthly. $119.00/year for individuals; $228.00/year for two years. Retailing business industry news and information.

11478 ■ Sales & Marketing Management
Nielsen Business Media
770 Broadway
New York, NY 10003-9595
URL: http://www.salesandmarketing.com

Bimonthly. $48.00/year for individuals, print + online; $67.00/year for Canada, print + online; $146.00/year for other countries, print + online. Business magazine.

11479 ■ The Selling Advantage
Progressive Business Publications
370 Technology Dr.
Malvern, PA 19355
Fax: (610)647-8089
Fr: 800-220-5000
E-mail: customer_service@pbp.com
URL: http://www.pbp.com/SA.asp

Description: Semimonthly. $94.56/year. Explores new strategies and proven techniques to improve sales performance. Recurring features include book reviews and a column titled Tale of the Sale.

11480 ■ Sporting Goods Dealer
Bill Communications Inc.
1115 Northmeadow Pkwy.
Roswell, GA 30076
Ph: (770)569-1540
Fax: (770)569-5105
Fr: 800-241-9034
URL: http://www.sgdealer.com/sportinggoodsdealer/index.jsp

Bimonthly. Magazine which offers expert reporting on trends affecting team dealers and retailers who service schools, colleges, pro and local teams.

11481 ■ Tire Business
Crain Communications Inc.
77 Franklin St., Ste. 809
Boston, MA 02110-1510
Ph: (617)292-3385
URL: http://www.tirebusiness.com

Semimonthly. $79.00/year for individuals; $148.00/year for two years; $107.00/year for individuals, Canada; $194.00/year for two years, Canada; $119.00/year for other countries; $208.00/year for two years, all other countries; $99.00/year for individuals, web only. Newspaper (tabloid) serving independent tire dealers, retreaders, tire wholesalers and others allied to the tire industry.

11482 ■ Tire Review
Babcox
3550 Embassy Pky.
Akron, OH 44333
Ph: (330)670-1234
URL: http://www.tirereview.com/

Monthly. Free to qualified subscribers. Magazine containing news and business information about the tire, custom wheel, automotive service, and retreading industries.

11483 ■ Visual Merchandising and Store Design
ST Media Group International Inc.
11262 Cornell Park Dr.
Cincinnati, OH 45242
Ph: (513)421-2050
Fax: (513)421-5144
Fr: 800-421-1321
URL: http://www.stmediagroup.com/index.php3?d=pubs&p=vm

Monthly. $42.00/year for individuals, U.S.; $66.00/year for individuals, 2 years, U.S.; $62.00/year for individuals, Canada (surface); $100.00/year for individuals, 2 years, Canada (surface); $65.00/year for individuals, Mexico/Foreign (surface); $105.00/year for individuals, 2 years, Mexico/Foreign (surface); $100.00/year for individuals, Mexico, 1st

Class; $175.00/year for individuals, 2 years, Mexico 1st Class; $115.00/year for individuals, Central/South America; $205.00/year for individuals, 2 years, Central/South America. The leading magazine of the retail design industry covering the latest trends in retail design, store planning, and merchandise presentation.

11484 ■ Watch & Jewelry Review
Golden Bell Press
2403 Champa St.
Denver, CO 80205
Ph: (303)296-1600
Fax: (303)295-2159
URL: http://www.goldenbellpress.com/Pages/front.html

$19.50/year for individuals; $35.00/year for two years; $60.00/year for other countries; $115.00/year for two years, other countries. Magazine on watches and clocks.

11485 ■ What's Working in Sales Management
Progressive Business Publications
370 Technology Dr.
Malvern, PA 19355
Fax: (610)647-8089
Fr: 800-220-5000
E-mail: customer_service@pbp.com
URL: http://www.pbp.com/WSM.asp

Description: Semimonthly. $264/year. Acts as a time-saving resource for busy sales managers. Recurring features include interviews, news of research, a calendar of events, and news of educational opportunities.

EMPLOYER DIRECTORIES AND NETWORKING LISTS

11486 ■ Careers in Focus—Retail
Facts On File Inc.
132 W 31st St., 17th Fl.
New York, NY 10001
Ph: (212)967-8800
Fax: 800-678-3633
Fr: 800-322-8755
URL: http://www.infobasepublishing.com

Latest edition 3rd; Published April, 2007. $32.95 for individuals. Covers: An overview of retail, followed by a selection of jobs profiled in detail, including the nature of the job, earnings, prospects for employment, what kind of training and skills it requires, and sources for further information.

11487 ■ Directory of Department Stores
Chain Store Guide
3922 Coconut Palm Dr.
Tampa, FL 33619
Ph: (813)627-6800
Fax: (813)627-6888
Fr: 800-927-9292
URL: http://www.chainstoreguide.com

Annual, Latest edition 2011. $395.00 for individuals; $445.00 for individuals; $1,075.00 for individuals; $1,375.00 for individuals. Covers: 6,000 department store companies, 1,600 shoe store companies, jewelry store companies, 95 optical store companies, and 70 leather and luggage store companies in the United States and Canada, with annual sales of $160 billion. Entries include: Company name; physical and mailing addresses; phone and fax numbers, company e-mail and web addresses; listing type; total sales; industry sales; total selling square footage; store prototype sizes; total units; units by trade name; trading areas; projected openings and remodeling; self-distributing indicator; distribution center locations; resident buyers' name and location; leased departments area, name, and location; mail order catalog indicator; Internet order processing indicator; private label softlines, hardlines, and credit card indicators; furniture styles and price lines; average number of checkouts; year founded; public company indicator;

parent company name and location; subsidiaries' names and locations; regional and divisional office locations; key personnel with titles; store locations, with address, phone number, and manager name (department stores only); 3,000 personnel email addresses. Arrangement: Geographical. Indexes: Alphabetical, product lines, exclusions.

11488 ■ Directory of Drug Store & HBC Chains
Chain Store Guide
3922 Coconut Palm Dr.
Tampa, FL 33619
Ph: (813)627-6800
Fax: (813)627-6888
Fr: 800-927-9292
URL: http://www.chainstoreguide.com/

Annual, latest edition 2010. $395.00 for individuals; $445.00 for individuals; $1,375.00 for individuals; $1,075.00 for individuals. Covers: More than 1,200 drug store chains operation two or more units, including mass merchants and grocers with pharmacies; 215 wholesale drug companies in the United States and Canada. Entries include: For retailers—company name; phone and fax numbers; physical and mailing addresses; company e-mail and web addresses; listing type; number of stores; product lines; percentage of sales by product line; total sales; prescription drug sales; percentage of prescriptions filled with generic drugs; number of prescriptions filled daily; percentage of prescriptions filled with private third party, cash, and Medicaid; number of stores by type; mail order pharmacy indicator; managed care division indicator; projected openings and remodeling; store prototype sizes; total selling square footage; trading area; franchise group headquarters' name and location; distribution center and primary wholesaler names and locations; number of specialty departments; packaged liquor indicators; private label indicators; computerized pharmacy indicator; average number of checkouts; year founded; public company indicator; parent company name and location; regional and divisional office locations; headquarters personnel with titles. For wholesalers—company name, address, phone, and fax; e-mail and web addresses; listing type; product lines; percentage of sales by product line; total sales; percentage of sales by customer type; total stores served; number of member and non-member stores served; trading area; group store trading names; wholesaler type; distribution center locations; private label indicator; year founded; public company indicator; headquarters personnel with titles. Arrangement: Separate geographical sections for retailers and wholesalers. Indexes: Alphabetical, exclusions.

11489 ■ STORES—Top 100 Retailers Issue
National Retail Federation
325 7th St. NW, Ste. 1100
Washington, DC 20004
Ph: (202)783-7971
Fax: (202)737-2849
Fr: 800-673-4692
URL: http://www.stores.org

Annual, Latest edition 2011. $75.00. Publication includes: 100 U.S. retail companies having largest estimated sales during preceding year.

HANDBOOKS AND MANUALS

11490 ■ Great Jobs for Business Majors
The McGraw-Hill Companies
PO Box 182604
Columbus, OH 43272
Fax: (614)759-3749
Fr: 877-883-5524
E-mail: customer.service@mcgraw-hill.com
URL: http://www.mhprofessional.com/product.php?isbn=0071544836

Stephen Lambert. Third edition, 2008. $16.95 (paper). 240 pages.

EMPLOYMENT AGENCIES AND SEARCH FIRMS

11491 ■ Allen Associates
3805 Edwards Rd., Ste. 550
Cincinnati, OH 45209
Ph: (513)563-3040
E-mail: feedback@allensearch.com
URL: http://www.allensearch.com
Executive senior-level search firm.

11492 ■ APA Search Inc.
1 Byram Brook Pl., Ste. 104
Armonk, NY 10504
Ph: (914)273-6000
Fax: (914)273-8025
E-mail: info@apasearch.com
URL: http://www.apasearch.com
Employment agency specializing in the automotive, retail, and hardware industries.

11493 ■ Bender Executive Search
45 N Station Plaza, Ste. 315
Great Neck, NY 11021
Ph: (516)773-4300
Fax: (516)482-5355
E-mail: benderexec@aol.com
URL: http://www.benderexecutivesearch.com
Executive search firm.

11494 ■ Charles Aris, Inc.
300 N Greene St., Ste. 1800
Greensboro, NC 27401
Ph: (336)378-1818
Fax: (336)378-0129
E-mail: info@charlesaris.com
URL: http://www.charlesaris.com
Provides executive search and placement services in the areas of consumer packaged goods, retail, strategy/business development, global life sciences, healthcare, chemicals, textiles/apparel, private equity, and business services.

11495 ■ Fairfaxx Corp.
338 Commerce Dr.
Fairfield, CT 06825-0252
Ph: (203)337-3900
Fax: (203)337-3910
E-mail: jjt@fairfaxx.com
Offers specialization in apparel and retail industry positions.

11496 ■ Gene Kaufman Associates Ltd.
450 7th Ave., Ste. 913
New York, NY 10123-0101
Ph: (212)643-0625
Fax: (212)643-8598
Personnel consultant specializing in recruiting on all levels for the apparel industry in the areas of design, sales, merchandising, production, operations and administration.

11497 ■ Generator Group
17933 NW Evergreen Pkwy., Ste. 240
Beaverton, OR 97006
Ph: (503)224-4811
URL: http://www.generatorgroup.net
Works as a talent management services firm that delivers executive search and talent management consulting to organizations in consumer products and retail, technology, and public transportation.

11498 ■ J.D. Hersey and Associates
8 E Poplar Ave.
Columbus, OH 43215
Ph: (614)228-4022
Fax: (614)228-4085
URL: http://www.jdhersey.com
Executive search firm for permanent and contingency placements.

11499 ■ Joel H. Wilensky Associates, Inc.
PO Box 155
Sudbury, MA 01776-0155
Ph: (978)443-5176
Fax: (978)443-3009
E-mail: jhwassoc@joelhwilensky.com
URL: http://www.joelhwilensky.com
Executive search firm.

11500 ■ National Register - USA
550 Polaris Pkwy., Ste. 530
Westerville, OH 43082
Ph: (614)890-1200
Fax: (614)890-1259
E-mail: sales@nrcols.com
URL: http://www.nrcols.com
Employment agency. Offices in Akron and Toledo, OH.

11501 ■ National Sales & Marketing Consultants Inc.
5650 Greenwood Plz. Blvd., Ste. 206
Englewood, CO 80111-2309
Ph: (303)771-4201
Fax: (303)740-8640
E-mail: nasmarc@aol.com
Locates, hires, and trains sales representatives, and coordinates on-going activities of manufacturer's representatives for clients in health-care, government, health and beauty aids, sporting goods, consumer products, hardware, and stationery/office supply industries. Assists clients in developing pricing, packaging, advertising, general sales, and promotional policies. Acts as national sales manager for multiple clients.

11502 ■ Plummer and Associates
PO Box 607
New Canaan, CT 06840
Fr: 800-603-9981
E-mail: info@plummersearch.com
URL: http://www.plummersearch.com
Executive search firm that is focused on the retail industry. Offers extra services such as video conferencing, travel services, reference checking, and psychological testing.

11503 ■ Retail Recruiters
2189 Silas Deane Hwy.
Rocky Hill, CT 06067
Ph: (860)721-9550
Fax: (860)257-8813
E-mail: careers@retailrecruitersusa.com
URL: http://www.retailrecruitersusa.com
Employment agency. Affiliate offices in many locations across the country.

11504 ■ SalesPositions.com
Heather Croft
Ste. 250
Egg Harbor Township, NY 08234
Ph: (609)407-4774
Fax: (609)939-0488
E-mail: sales@salespositions.com
URL: http://www.salespositions.com
Employment agency.

ONLINE JOB SOURCES AND SERVICES

11505 ■ New Sales and Marketing Jobs
URL: http://www.newsalesandmarketingjobs.com
Description: Provides an online listing of companies with available sales and marketing jobs in all specialties.

11506 ■ RetailSalesManager.net
URL: http://www.retailsalesmanager.net
Description: Provides career opportunities and professional networking community for aspiring retail sales managers. Offers a database of jobs and resumes for both candidates and employers.

11507 ■ Spherion
2050 Spectrum Blvd.
Fort Lauderdale, FL 33309
Ph: (954)308-7600
Fr: 800-774-3746
E-mail: help@spherion.com
URL: http://www.spherion.com
Description: Recruitment firm specializing in accounting and finance, sales and marketing, interim executives, technology, engineering, retail and human resources.

OTHER SOURCES

11508 ■ Automotive Aftermarket Industry Association (AAIA)
7101 Wisconsin Ave., Ste. 1300
Bethesda, MD 20814-3415
Ph: (301)654-6664
Fax: (301)654-3299
E-mail: aaia@aftermarket.org
URL: http://www.aftermarket.org
Description: Automotive parts and accessories retailers, distributors, manufacturers, and manufacturers' representatives. Conducts research and compiles statistics. Conducts seminars and provides specialized education program.

11509 ■ CBA
PO Box 62000
Colorado Springs, CO 80962-2000
Ph: (719)265-9895
Fax: (719)272-3510
Fr: 800-252-1950
E-mail: info@cbaonline.org
URL: http://www.cbaonline.org
Description: Serves as trade association for retail stores selling Christian books, Bibles, gifts, and Sunday school and church supplies. Compiles statistics; conducts specialized education programs.

11510 ■ Computing Technology Industry Association (CompTIA)
3500 Lacey Rd., Ste. 100
Downers Grove, IL 60515
Ph: (630)678-8300
Fax: (630)678-8384
E-mail: membership@comptia.org
URL: http://www.comptia.org
Description: Trade association of more than 19,000 companies and professional IT members in the rapidly converging computing and communications market. Has members in more than 89 countries and provides a unified voice for the industry in the areas of e-commerce standards, vendor-neutral certification, service metrics, public policy and workforce development. Serves as information clearinghouse and resource for the industry; sponsors educational programs.

11511 ■ National Association of College Stores (NACS)
500 E Lorain St.
Oberlin, OH 44074
Fax: (440)775-4769
Fr: 800-622-7498
E-mail: webteam@nacs.org
URL: http://www.nacs.org
Description: Institutional, private, leased, and cooperative college stores selling books, supplies, and other merchandise to college students, faculty, and staff; associate members include publishers and suppliers. Seeks to effectively serve higher education by providing educational research, advocacy and other to college stores and their suppliers. Maintains NACSCORP, Inc., a wholly owned subsidiary corporation, which distributes trade and mass market books and educational software. Sponsors seminars. Conducts manager certification, specialized education, and research programs. Maintains College Stores Research and Educational Foundation which

provides grants for educational programs and conducts research.

11512 ■ National Retail Federation (NRF)
325 7th St. NW, Ste. 1100
Washington, DC 20004
Ph: (202)783-7971
Fax: (202)737-2849
Fr: 800-673-4692
E-mail: shaym@nrf.com
URL: http://www.nrf.com

Description: Represents state retail associations, several dozen national retail associations, as well as large and small corporate members representing the breadth and diversity of the retail industry's establishment and employees. Conducts informational and educational conferences related to all phases of retailing including financial planning and cash management, taxation, economic forecasting, expense planning, shortage control, credit, electronic data processing, telecommunications, merchandise management, buying, traffic, security, supply, materials handling, store planning and construction, personnel administration, recruitment and training, and advertising and display.

11513 ■ Retail Industry Leaders Association
1700 N Moore St., Ste. 2250
Arlington, VA 22209
Ph: (703)841-2300
Fax: (703)841-1184
URL: http://www.rila.org

Description: Represents retailers, product manufacturers, and associate companies. Promotes consumer choice and economic freedom through public policy and industry operational excellence. Focuses on five core areas: supply chain, asset protection, finance, human resources, and enterprise issues. Provides educational and networking events that provide forums for sharing ideas and expertise among peers and industry experts.

SOURCES OF HELP-WANTED ADS

11514 ■ *Assembly Magazine*
BNP Media
2401 W Big Beaver Rd., Ste. 700
Troy, MI 48084
E-mail: asm@halldata.com
URL: http://www.assemblymag.com

Serves the information needs of manufacturing professionals responsible for engineering and managing product assembly operations. Helps make assembly-related decisions and develop solutions to assembly problems.

11515 ■ *Robotica*
Cambridge University Press
32 Avenue of the Americas
New York, NY 10013-2473
Ph: (212)924-3900
Fax: (212)691-3239
E-mail: ad_sales@cambridge.org
URL: http://journals.cambridge.org/action/
 displayJournal?jid=ROB

Bimonthly. $700.00/year for institutions, online & print; $615.00/year for institutions, online; $175.00/year for individuals, online & print; $1,250.00/year for institutions, online & print; $1,100.00/year for institutions, online; $300.00/year for individuals, online & print; $45.00/year for individuals, article. Peer-reviewed journal on robotics studies.

11516 ■ *Robotics Trends*
Robotics Trends Publishing
111 Speen St., Ste. 200
Framingham, MA 01701
Ph: (508)663-1500
Fax: (508)464-0234
E-mail: rerb@ehpub.com
URL: http://www.roboticstrends.com

Description: Monthly. Focuses on business and technology trends for people who build, buy, invest in and seek to understand the personal, service, mobile and military robotics market.

11517 ■ *Robotics World*
Briefings Media Group
2807 N Parham Rd., Ste. 200
Richmond, VA 23294
Ph: (570)567-1982
Fr: 800-791-8699
URL: http://www.roboticsworld.com

$72.00/year; free in U.S.; $99.00/year for Canada and Mexico; $112.00/year for other countries; $162.00/year for Canada and Mexico, 2 years; $162.00/year for other countries, 2 years. Professional magazine covering flexible automation and intelligent machines.

11518 ■ *Servo Magazine*
T & L Publications
PO Box 15277
North Hollywood, CA 91615-5277
Ph: (818)487-4545
Fax: (818)487-4550
Fr: 877-525-2539
E-mail: editor@servomagazine.com
URL: http://www.servomagazine.com

Monthly. Contains feature articles, interviews, tutorials, DIY projects, hacks, part sources and more. Keeps members abreast of advances in the robotics field. Features a section for beginner robotics who wish to start a career in the robotics field, or who are just starting robotics as a hobby.

PLACEMENT AND JOB REFERRAL SERVICES

11519 ■ Argus & Associates
28064 Center Oaks Ct.
Wixom, MI 48393
Ph: (248)344-8700
Fax: (248)344-9433
E-mail: argusinfo@argus-associates.com
URL: http://www.argus-associates.com

Description: Offers robotics, engineering and staffing services. Serves a broad range of industries including aerospace, automotive, transportation, consumer goods and computers.

EMPLOYER DIRECTORIES AND NETWORKING LISTS

11520 ■ *Robotics Industry Directory*
Robotics Industries Association
900 Victors Way, Ste. 140
Ann Arbor, MI 48108
Ph: (734)994-6088
Fax: (734)994-3338
URL: http://www.robotics.org

Annual. Includes more than 200 leading suppliers, integrators, consultants and researchers serving the robotics industry. Highlights each company's profile and place in the industry. Features a 'Product Showcase Finder' section and one-of-a-kind User's Guide to Robot Systems Integrators.

HANDBOOKS AND MANUALS

11521 ■ *Careers in Robotics*
Rosen Publishing Group
29 E 21st St.
New York, NY 10010
Fr: 800-237-9932
URL: http://www.rosenpublishing.com

2007. $27.95. 64 pages. Focuses on the automotive industry and discusses the possible paths to follow in starting a career in robotics.

EMPLOYMENT AGENCIES AND SEARCH FIRMS

11522 ■ AutomationTechies.com
PO Box 44759
Eden Prairie, MN 55344
Ph: (952)563-5440
Fax: (952)563-5449
Fr: 877-300-6792
URL: http://www.automationtechies.com

Recruitment and staffing firm for automation professionals. Specializes in placing automation professionals in both contract and direct-hire positions.

ONLINE JOB SOURCES AND SERVICES

11523 ■ Automation.com
URL: http://www.automation.com

Description: Offers complimentary press releases, articles, and publication services for industrial automation and process control professionals.

11524 ■ Get Robotics Jobs
URL: http://www.getroboticsjobs.com/about.php

Description: Serves as a community for robotics job seekers. Provides an easy-to-use resume template to make the job application process easy and convenient.

11525 ■ Learn About Robots
URL: http://www.learnaboutrobots.com

Description: Specifically designed for individuals intending to learn about robots and robotics engineering. Provides information to assist people in learning about robots. Covers a varied scope about robotics from robot vision, motion control, research and forward kinematics.

11526 ■ Motion Control Online
URL: http://www.motioncontrolonline.org

Description: Features available positions by location, specialty and other criteria. Serves automation companies involved in robotics, machine vision, motion control and related technologies.

11527 ■ Robot Report
URL: http://www.therobotreport.com

Description: Online site that tracks the business of robotics. Maintains a comprehensive worldwide database of public and private companies that are participants in the robotics industry. Gathers and reports industry news, tracks the business of robotics and develops proprietary methods to compare and report industry stock performance to the NASDAQ Composite Index. Also features startup companies.

11528 ■ TechRepublic
URL: http://www.techrepublic.com
Description: Online community for IT professionals. Provides a forum where IT professionals can interact, exchange advise and discuss IT topics of interest. Lists employment opportunities by date of posting, job title, company and location.

TRADESHOWS

11529 ■ Automate
Automation Technologies Council
900 Victors Way, Ste. 140
Ann Arbor, MI 48108
Ph: (734)994-6088
Fax: (734)994-3338
URL: http://www.robots-vision-show.info

Annual. Addresses the issues that affect the application of robots, machine vision and motion control. Showcases the latest products and services in the robot industry and offers exhibits and products that attendees can operate on their own with no formal training.

11530 ■ Automation Technology Expo - East
UBM Canon
11444 W Olympic Blvd.
Los Angeles, CA 90064-1549
Ph: (310)445-4200
Fax: (310)445-4299
E-mail: atxinfo@ubm.com
URL: http://www.canontradeshows.com/expo/atxe11

Annual. Resource event for the automation technology field. Features suppliers that offer experience in every market segment. Provides networking opportunities for industry professionals.

11531 ■ International Manufacturing Technology Show
AMT - Association For Manufacturing Technology
7901 Westpark Dr.
McLean, VA 22102
Fax: (703)893-1151
Fr: 800-524-0475
E-mail: amt@amtonline.org
URL: http://www.imts.com

Biannual. For manufacturing industry professionals and equipment producers around the world. Brings together experts from the industry to give attendees useful and up to date technical information. Features live robot combat action. 2012 September 10-15; Chicago, IL; McCormick Place.

11532 ■ NDIA Ground Robotics Capabilities Conference and Exhibition
National Defense Industrial Association
2111 Wilson Blvd., Ste. 400
Arlington, VA 22201
Ph: (703)522-1820
E-mail: tfletcher@ndia.org
URL: http://www.ndia.org

Annual. Brings together warfighters and homeland security users, technology developers (government, industry and academia) and acquisition professionals to address increased responsiveness to user needs. Provides a forum for the exchange of information, ideas and methodologies to provide U.S. forces with unmanned ground technologies.

11533 ■ RoboBusiness Conference and Exposition
EH Publishing, Inc.
111 Speen St., Ste. 200
Framingham, MA 01701-2000
Ph: (508)663-1500
Fax: (508)663-1599
URL: http://www.robobusiness.com

Annual. For business or technical professionals who wish to develop, understand or invest in the next generation of robotics, automation and intelligent systems products and technology.

11534 ■ Robotics: Science and Systems Conference
University of Washington
PO Box 352350
Seattle, WA 98195-2350
Ph: (206)543-1695
Fax: (206)543-2969
URL: http://robotics.washington.edu/rss2009

Annual. Brings together researchers working on algorithmic or mathematical foundations of robotics, robotics applications and analysis of robotic systems.

OTHER SOURCES

11535 ■ Acoustical Society of America
2 Huntington Quadrangle, Ste. 1NO1
Melville, NY 11747-4502
Ph: (516)576-2360
Fax: (516)576-2377
E-mail: asa@aip.org
URL: http://acousticalsociety.org

Description: Represents members from various fields related to sound including physics, electrical, mechanical and aeronautical engineering, oceanography, biology, physiology, psychology, architecture, speech, noise and noise control, and music. Aims to increase and diffuse the knowledge of acoustics and its practical applications. Organizes meetings, provides reprints of out-of-print classic texts in acoustics, and translation books.

11536 ■ Automated Imaging Association
900 Victors Way, Ste. 140
Ann Arbor, MI 48108
Ph: (734)994-6088
Fax: (734)994-3338
E-mail: dwhalls@robotics.org
URL: http://www.machinevisiononline.org

Description: Manufacturers of machine vision components and systems, users, system integrators, universities and non-profit research groups and financial firms that track the machine vision industry. Promotes the use and understanding of image capture and analysis technology.

11537 ■ Automation Association
7300 Hudson Blvd. N, Ste. 285
Oakdale, MN 55128
Ph: (651)264-9841
E-mail: al.hammel@automationassociation.com
URL: http://www.automationassociation.com

Description: Represents over 200 engineers, scientists and machine builders focused on developing proprietary products, processes and technology solutions for manufacturing. Provides office space and support staff for qualified individuals while on assignment.

11538 ■ Automation Tooling Systems
PO Box 12650
Rock Hill, SC 29731
Ph: (803)324-9300
Fax: (803)324-9360
E-mail: info@atsautomation.com
URL: http://www.atsautomation.com/profile/
worldwide/pro_atscarolina.asp

Description: Specializes in assembly and material handling solutions: automotive, semiconductor, medical, consumer and packaging. Provides innovative, custom designed, built and installed manufacturing solutions to companies.

11539 ■ IEEE Robotics and Automation Society
445 Hoes Ln.
Piscataway, NJ 08855-4141
Ph: (732)981-0060

Fax: (732)981-0225
Fr: 800-701-IEEE
URL: http://www.ieee-ras.org

Description: Engineers and scientists in the robotics and automation engineering and allied fields. Strives for the advancement of the theory and practice of robotics and automation engineering as well as other allied arts and sciences. Provides aid in promoting close cooperation and exchange of technical information among professionals. Conducts meetings for the presentation of papers and their discussion.

11540 ■ International Society of Automation
67 Alexander Dr.
Research Triangle Park, NC 27709
Ph: (919)549-8411
Fax: (919)549-8288
E-mail: info@isa.org
URL: http://www.isa.org

Description: Automation professionals. Helps members and other professionals solve difficult technical problems, while enhancing their leadership and personal career capabilities. Develops standards and certifies industry professionals. Maintains a career library that provides information about educational institutions, certification programs and jobs in automation.

11541 ■ Laboratory Robotics Interest Group
1730 W Cir. Dr.
Martinsville, NJ 08836-2147
Ph: (732)672-4452
E-mail: andy.zaayenga@lab-robotic.org
URL: http://www.lab-robotics.org

Description: Serves as an interest group focused on laboratory automation. Consists of scientists and engineers. Provides physical and virtual meeting places for scientists, engineers and academics interested in furthering their careers in the field of laboratory automation.

11542 ■ National Robotics Engineering Center
10 40th St.
Pittsburgh, PA 15201
Ph: (412)681-6900
Fax: (412)681-6961
URL: http://www.rec.ri.cmu.edu

Description: Develops and commercializes robotics technology. Strives to develop, mature and apply innovative robotics technology to solve real world problems.

11543 ■ Robotic Industries Association
900 Victors Way, Ste. 140
Ann Arbor, MI 48108
Ph: (734)994-6088
Fax: (734)994-3338
URL: http://www.robotics.org

Description: Member companies include robot manufacturers, users, system integrators, component suppliers, research groups, and consulting firms. Promotes the advancement of the robotic industry. Provides information to help engineers, managers, and executives apply and justify robotics and flexible automation. Sponsors the biennial International Robots and Vision Show, develops the ANSI/RIA national robot safety standard, and collects and reports robotics industry statistics.

11544 ■ Robotics Institute
5000 Forbes Ave.
Pittsburgh, PA 15213-3890
Ph: (412)268-3818
Fax: (412)268-6436
E-mail: robotics@ri.cmu.edu
URL: http://www.ri.cmu.edu

Description: Represents faculty, adjunct faculty, students, postdoctoral fellows, alumni and others. Seeks to combine the practical and the theoretical by diversifying its efforts and approaches to robotics science while retaining its original goal of realizing the potential of the robotics field. Conducts basic and applied research in robotics technologies relevant to industrial and societal tasks.

11545 ■ Society for Laboratory Automation and Screening
100 Illinois St., Ste. 242
St. Charles, IL 60174
Ph: (630)256-7527

Fax: (630)741-7527
Fr: 877-990-7527
E-mail: slas@slas.org
URL: http://www.slas.org

Description: Advances science and education related to laboratory automation by encouraging the study, advancing the science and improving the practice of laboratory automation. Serves academic, commercial and government researchers, scientists and engineers from around the world who conduct research and develop new technologies to increase productivity, elevate experimental data quality, reduce lab process cycle times or enable experimentation that otherwise would be impossible. Partners with other related associations to share and exchange short courses and other education programs.

SOURCES OF HELP-WANTED ADS

11546 ■ Asphalt Roofing Manufacturers Association Newsletter
Asphalt Roofing Manufacturers Association
750 National Press Bldg.
529 14th St., NW
Washington, DC 20045
Ph: (202)207-0917
Fax: (202)223-9741
URL: http://www.asphaltroofing.org/

Description: Semi-annual. Reports news and information of interest to professionals in the asphalt roofing industry. Highlights Association activities and discusses developments in the industry, including occupational safety and health measures, changes in industry codes and standards, environmental issues, and legislative and regulatory actions.

11547 ■ Builder
Hanley-Wood L.L.C.
1 Thomas Cir. NW, Ste. 600
Washington, DC 20005-5803
Ph: (202)452-0800
Fax: (202)785-1974
E-mail: builder@omeda.com
URL: http://www.hanleywood.com/default.aspx?page=magazines

$29.95/year for U.S. and Canada; $54.95/year for U.S. and Canada, 2 years; $192.00/year for other countries. Magazine covering housing and construction industry.

11548 ■ Constructor
Associated General Contractors of America
2300 Wilson Blvd., Ste. 400
Arlington, VA 22201
Ph: (703)548-3118
Fax: (703)548-3119
Fr: 800-242-1767
URL: http://constructor.agc.org/

Bimonthly. $95.00/year for individuals. Management magazine for the Construction Industry.

11549 ■ Professional Builder
SGC Horizon LLC
3030 W Salt Creek Ln., Ste. 201
Arlington Heights, IL 60005
Ph: (847)391-1000
Fax: (847)390-0408
URL: http://www.housingzone.com/pb/pubhome/

Monthly. Free. The integrated engineering magazine of the building construction industry.

11550 ■ Professional Roofing
National Roofing Contractors Association
10255 W Higgins Rd., Ste. 600
Rosemont, IL 60018-5607
Ph: (847)299-9070
Fax: (847)299-1183
Fr: 800-323-9545
URL: http://www.professionalroofing.net/
Monthly. Free. Roofing industry magazine.

11551 ■ Residential Design & Build
Cygnus Business Media Inc.
3 Huntington Quadrangle, Ste. 301 N
Melville, NY 11747
Ph: (631)845-2700
Fax: (631)845-7109
Fr: 800-308-6397
URL: http://www.rdbmagazine.com

Magazine providing advice and insight on the design/build project delivery method, as well as information on the latest design trends, new products and home building professionals.

EMPLOYER DIRECTORIES AND NETWORKING LISTS

11552 ■ ABC Today—Associated Builders and Contractors National Membership Directory Issue
Associated Builders and Contractors Inc.
4250 N Fairfax Dr., 9th Fl.
Arlington, VA 22203-1607
Ph: (703)812-2000
Fax: (703)812-8235
URL: http://www.abc.org

Annual, December. $150.00. Publication includes: List of approximately 19,000 member construction contractors and suppliers.

11553 ■ ENR—Top 400 Construction Contractors Issue
McGraw-Hill Inc.
PO Box 182604
Columbus, OH 43218
Ph: (614)430-4000
Fax: (614)759-3749
Fr: 877-833-5524
URL: http://enr.construction.com/toplists/Contractors/001-100.asp

Annual, Latest edition 2011. $35.00 for individuals. Publication includes: List of 400 United States contractors receiving largest dollar volumes of contracts in preceding calendar year. Separate lists of 50 largest design/construct management firms; 50 largest program and construction managers; 25 building contractors; 25 heavy contractors.

11554 ■ National Roofing Contractors Association—Membership Directory
National Roofing Contractors Association
10255 W Higgins Rd., Ste. 600
Rosemont, IL 60018-5607
Ph: (847)299-9070
Fax: (847)299-1183
Fr: 800-323-9545
URL: http://www.nrca.net

Annual, July. Covers: 5,000 contractors applying all types of commercial and residential roofing; 600 associate member manufacturers, suppliers, and distributors; 300 foreign members; and 100 institutions and related industries. Entries include: Company name, address, phone, and names of voting representatives. Arrangement: Alphabetical. Indexes: Geographical, voting representative, Alphabetical, member product guide.

ONLINE JOB SOURCES AND SERVICES

11555 ■ Get Roofing Jobs
URL: http://www.getroofingjobs.com

Description: Serves as a resource for roofing job seekers and employers. Offers free roofer job postings and career opportunities.

11556 ■ Locate Roofing Jobs
URL: http://www.locateroofingjobs.com

Description: Serves as a job board dedicated exclusively to roofing jobs. Offers updated job listings for candidates and job posting for employers.

11557 ■ RooferJobs.org
URL: http://rooferjobs.org

Description: Features job sites, company career pages and associations for roofer jobs.

TRADESHOWS

11558 ■ Midwest Roofing Contractors Association National Conference
Midwest Roofing Contractors Association
4700 W. Lake Ave.
Glenview, IL 60025
Fax: (847)375-6473
Fr: 800-497-6722
E-mail: mrca@mrca.org
URL: http://www.mrca.org

Annual. Primary Exhibits: Roofing products, materials, and related industries and services.

OTHER SOURCES

11559 ■ Associated Builders and Contractors (ABC)
4250 N Fairfax Dr., 9th Fl.
Arlington, VA 22203-1607
Ph: (703)812-2000
Fax: (703)812-8201
E-mail: gotquestions@abc.org
URL: http://www.abc.org

Description: Construction contractors, subcontractors, suppliers and associates. Aims to foster and perpetuate the principles of rewarding construction workers and management on the basis of merit. Sponsors management education programs and craft training; also sponsors apprenticeship and skill training programs. Disseminates technological and labor relations information.

11560 ■ Associated General Contractors of America (AGC)

2300 Wilson Blvd., Ste. 400
Arlington, VA 22201
Ph: (703)548-3118
Fax: (703)548-3119
Fr: 800-242-1767
E-mail: info@agc.org
URL: http://www.agc.org

Description: General construction contractors; subcontractors; industry suppliers; service firms. Provides market services through its divisions. Conducts special conferences and seminars designed specifically for construction firms. Compiles statistics on job accidents reported by member firms. Maintains 65 committees, including joint cooperative committees with other associations and liaison committees with federal agencies.

11561 ■ Associated Specialty Contractors (ASC)

3 Bethesda Metro Ctr., Ste. 1100
Bethesda, MD 20814
E-mail: dgw@necanet.org
URL: http://www.assoc-spec-con.org

Description: Works to promote efficient management and productivity. Coordinates the work of specialized branches of the industry in management information, research, public information, government relations and construction relations. Serves as a liaison among specialty trade associations in the areas of public relations, government relations, and with other organizations. Seeks to avoid unnecessary duplication of effort and expense or conflicting programs among affiliates. Identifies areas of interest and problems shared by members, and develops positions and approaches on such problems.

11562 ■ National Association of Home Builders (NAHB)

1201 15th St. NW
Washington, DC 20005
Ph: (202)266-8200
Fax: (202)266-8400
Fr: 800-368-5242
E-mail: jhoward@nahb.com
URL: http://www.nahb.org

Description: Single and multifamily home builders, commercial builders, and others associated with the building industry. Lobbies on behalf of the housing industry and conducts public affairs activities to increase public understanding of housing and the economy. Collects and disseminates data on current developments in home building and home builders' plans through its Economics Department and nationwide Metropolitan Housing Forecast. Maintains NAHB Research Center, which functions as the research arm of the home building industry. Sponsors seminars and workshops on construction, mortgage credit, labor relations, cost reduction, land use, remodeling, and business management. Compiles statistics; offers charitable program, spokesman training, and placement service; maintains speakers' bureau, and Hall of Fame. Subsidiaries include the National Council of the Housing Industry. Maintains over 50 committees in many areas of construction; operates National Commercial Builders Council, National Council of the Multifamily Housing Industry, National Remodelers Council, and National Sales and Marketing Council.

11563 ■ National Association of Women in Construction (NAWIC)

327 S Adams St.
Fort Worth, TX 76104
Ph: (817)877-5551
Fax: (817)877-0324
Fr: 800-552-3506
E-mail: nawic@nawic.org
URL: http://www.nawic.org

Description: Seeks to enhance the success of women in the construction industry.

11564 ■ National Roofing Contractors Association

10255 W Higgins Rd., Ste. 600
Rosemont, IL 60018-5607
Ph: (847)299-9070
Fax: (847)299-1183
URL: http://www.nrca.net

Description: Members have the opportunity to have their resume and business listed free of charge. NRCA provides a complimentary hyperlink to a member's Web site if an address is provided.

SOURCES OF HELP-WANTED ADS

11565 ■ Academy of Management Journal
Academy of Management
235 Elm Rd.
PO Box 3020
Briarcliff Manor, NY 10510-8020
Ph: (914)923-2607
Fax: (914)923-2615
URL: http://journals.aomonline.org/amj/

Bimonthly. Professional journal covering management.

11566 ■ Academy of Management Learning & Education
Academy of Management
235 Elm Rd.
PO Box 3020
Briarcliff Manor, NY 10510-8020
Ph: (914)923-2607
Fax: (914)923-2615
URL: http://journals.aomonline.org/amle

Quarterly. $85.00/year for individuals, print; $130.00/year for individuals, print & online; $125.00/year for libraries, print; $170.00/year for libraries, print and online; $105.00/year for other countries, print; $150.00/year for other countries, print & online; $195.00/year for other countries, print, corporate library; $235.00/year for other countries, print & online, corporate library. Journal covering management issues for professionals.

11567 ■ Business Performance Management
Penton Media Inc.
249 W 17th St.
New York, NY 10011
Ph: (212)204-4200
URL: http://www.bpmmag.net/

Free to qualified subscribers. Magazine for business managers. Covers organizing, automating, and analyzing of business methodologies and processes.

11568 ■ Customer Service Advantage
Progressive Business Publications
370 Technology Dr.
Malvern, PA 19355
Fax: (610)647-8089
Fr: 800-220-5000
E-mail: customer_service@pbp.com
URL: http://www.pbp.com/CSA.asp

Description: Semimonthly. $253/year. Presents practical methods for quantifying customer service benefits and motivating employees day in and day out. Recurring features include interviews, news of research, a calendar of events, news of educational opportunities, and a column titled Sharpen Your Judgment.

11569 ■ CXO
IDG Communications Inc.
3 Speen St.
Framingham, MA 01701
Ph: (508)875-5000
URL: http://www.idg.com/www/IDGProducts.nsf/0/022796185EED5984852

Monthly. Magazine providing technology information for chief officers and managers.

11570 ■ D & O Advisor
American Lawyer Media L.P.
120 Broadway, 5th Fl.
New York, NY 10271
Ph: (212)457-9400
Fax: (646)417-7705
Fr: 800-603-6571
URL: http://www.alm.com

Quarterly. Magazine that offers advice and perspective on corporate oversight responsibilities for directors and officers.

11571 ■ E Journal of Organizational Learning and Leadership
WeLEAD Inc.
PO Box 202
Litchfield, OH 44253
Fr: 877-778-5494
URL: http://www.leadingtoday.org/weleadinlearning/

Semiannual. Free. Online academic journal about organizational leadership.

11572 ■ Event Management
Cognizant Communications Corp.
3 Hartsdale Rd.
Elmsford, NY 10523-3701
Ph: (914)592-7720
Fax: (914)592-8981
URL: http://www.cognizantcommunication.com/journal-titles/event-

Quarterly. $445.00/year for institutions, online only; $525.00/year for institutions, online & hard copy; $52.00/year for individuals, professional; $50.00/year for members, online & hard copy; $65.00/year for single issue. Peer-reviewed journal covering research and analytic needs of a rapidly growing profession focused on events.

11573 ■ Executive Legal Adviser
Incisive Media
120 Broadway, 5th Fl.
New York, NY 10271
Ph: (212)457-9400
Fax: (646)417-7705
URL: http://www.executivelegaladviser.com

Bimonthly. Free to qualified subscribers. Magazine that offers legal advice for corporate executives.

11574 ■ Fleet Maintenance
Cygnus Business Media Inc.
3 Huntington Quadrangle, Ste. 301 N
Melville, NY 11747

Ph: (631)845-2700
Fax: (631)845-7109
Fr: 800-308-6397
URL: http://www.fleetmag.com

Business tabloid magazine offering a chapterized curriculum of technical, regulatory and managerial information designed to help maintenance managers, directors and supervisors better perform their jobs and reduce their overall cost-per-mile.

11575 ■ Forrester
Forrester Research Inc.
400 Technology Sq.
Cambridge, MA 02139
Ph: (617)613-5730
Fr: (866)367-7378
URL: http://www.forrester.com/mag

Free. Journal that aims to provide ideas and advice that is relevant to today's CEOs.

11576 ■ International Journal of Business Research
International Academy of Business and Economics
PO Box 2536
Ceres, CA 95307
Ph: (702)560-0653
Fax: (702)508-9166
URL: http://www.iabe.eu/domains/iabeX/journal.aspx?journalid=12

Peer-reviewed journal publishing theoretical, conceptual, and applied research on topics related to research, practice and teaching in all areas of business, management, and marketing.

11577 ■ Journal of Academic Leadership
Academic Leadership
600 Park St.
Rarick Hall 219
Hays, KS 67601-4099
Ph: (785)628-4547
URL: http://www.academicleadership.org/

Journal focusing on the leadership issues in the academic world.

11578 ■ Journal of Business and Psychology
Springer-Verlag New York Inc.
233 Spring St.
New York, NY 10013-1578
Ph: (212)460-1500
Fax: (212)460-1575
Fr: 800-777-4643
URL: http://www.springer.com/psychology/community+%26+environment

$904.00/year for institutions, print or online; $1,085.00/year for institutions, print & enchanced access. Journal covering all aspects of psychology that apply to the business segment. Includes topics such as personnel selection and training, organizational assessment and development, risk management and loss control, marketing and consumer behavior research.

11579 ■ *Journal of International Business Strategy*
International Academy of Business and Economics
PO Box 2536
Ceres, CA 95307
Ph: (702)560-0653
Fax: (702)508-9166
URL: http://www.iabe.eu/domains/iabeX/
   journal.aspx?journalid=7

Peer-reviewed journal publishing theoretical, conceptual, and applied research on topics related to strategy in international business.

11580 ■ *Management Research*
M.E. Sharpe Inc.
80 Business Pk. Dr.
Armonk, NY 10504
Ph: (914)273-1800
Fax: (914)273-2106
Fr: 800-541-6563
URL: http://www.mesharpe.com/mall/
   results1.asp?ACR=JMR

$75.00/year for individuals; $399.00/year for institutions; $87.00/year for other countries; $441.00/year for institutions, other countries. International journal dedicated to advancing the understanding of management in private and public sector organizations through empirical investigation and theoretical analysis. Attempts to promote an international dialogue between researchers, improve the understanding of the nature of management in different settings, and achieve a reasonable transfer of research results to management practice in several contexts. Receptive to research across a broad range of management topics such as human resource management, organizational behavior, organizational theory, and strategic management. While not regional in nature, articles dealing with Iberoamerican issues are particularly welcomed.

11581 ■ *Master Salesmanship*
Clement Communications Inc.
3 Creek Parkway
PO Box 2208
Upper Chichester, PA 19061
Fax: 800-459-1933
Fr: 800-253-6368
E-mail: editor@clement.com
URL: http://www.clement.com

Description: Biweekly. $149.50 per copy. Designed to help sales managers motivate, train, and inform their salespeople. Offers pointers on improving old sales skills and developing new ones. Recurring features include a motivation column, Q&A, and Selling Slants.

11582 ■ *Organization Management Journal*
Eastern Academy of Management
c/o Vicki Fairbanks Taylor, VP
John I. Grove College of Business
45 Keefer Way
Mechanicsburg, PA 17011
Ph: (518)762-4651
Fax: (518)736-1716
E-mail: omj@palgrave.com
URL: http://www1.wnec.edu/omj

Free to qualified subscribers. Refereed, online journal focusing on organization management issues.

11583 ■ *Public Performance and Management Review*
M.E. Sharpe Inc.
80 Business Pk. Dr.
Armonk, NY 10504
Ph: (914)273-1800
Fax: (914)273-2106
Fr: 800-541-6563
URL: http://www.mesharpe.com/mall/
   results1.asp?ACR=pmr

Quarterly. $95.00/year for individuals; $528.00/year for institutions; $111.00/year for other countries; $560.00/year for institutions, other countries. Journal addressing a broad range of factors influencing the performance of public and nonprofit organizations

and agencies. Aims to facilitate the development of innovative techniques and encourage a wider application of those already established; stimulate research and critical thinking about the relationship between public and private management theories; present integrated analyses of theories, concepts, strategies and techniques dealing with productivity, measurement and related questions of performance improvement; and provide a forum for practitioner-academic exchange. Continuing themes include managing for productivity, measuring and evaluating performance, improving budget strategies, managing human resources, building partnerships, and applying new technologies.

11584 ■ *The Selling Advantage*
Progressive Business Publications
370 Technology Dr.
Malvern, PA 19355
Fax: (610)647-8089
Fr: 800-220-5000
E-mail: customer_service@pbp.com
URL: http://www.pbp.com/SA.asp

Description: Semimonthly. $94.56/year. Explores new strategies and proven techniques to improve sales performance. Recurring features include book reviews and a column titled Tale of the Sale.

11585 ■ *Supply Chain Management Review*
Reed Business Information
360 Park Ave. S
New York, NY 10010-1710
Ph: (646)746-6400
URL: http://www.scmr.com

$199.00/year for individuals; $199.00/year for Canada; $337.00/year for other countries. Publication covering business and management.

11586 ■ *What's Working in Sales Management*
Progressive Business Publications
370 Technology Dr.
Malvern, PA 19355
Fax: (610)647-8089
Fr: 800-220-5000
E-mail: customer_service@pbp.com
URL: http://www.pbp.com/WSM.asp

Description: Semimonthly. $264/year. Acts as a time-saving resource for busy sales managers. Recurring features include interviews, news of research, a calendar of events, and news of educational opportunities.

HANDBOOKS AND MANUALS

11587 ■ *Career Opportunities in the Retail and Wholesale Industry*
Facts On File Inc.
132 W 31st St., 17th Fl.
New York, NY 10001-2006
Ph: (212)967-8800
Fax: 800-678-3633
Fr: 800-322-8755
E-mail: custserv@factsonfile.com
URL: http://www.infobasepublishing.com

Field, Shelly. Second edition, 2009. $49.50. 352 pages.

11588 ■ *Sales and Marketing Resumes for $100,000 Careers*
JIST Publishing
875 Montreal Way
St. Paul, MN 55102
Fr: 800-648-5478
E-mail: info@jist.com
URL: http://www.jist.com

Louise M. Kursmark. 2009. $19.95 (softcover). 352 pages. Provides advice on writing and polishing resumes and cover letters, managing the job search, and using strategies to land a $100,000 job.

11589 ■ *Successful Local Broadcast Sales*
AMACOM Publishing
c/o American Management Association
1601 Broadway
New York, NY 10019-7434
Ph: (212)586-8100
Fax: (518)891-0368
Fr: 800-714-6395
E-mail: pubs_cust_serv@amanet.org
URL: http://www.amacombooks.org

Paul Weyland. 2007. $17.95 (paper) 240 pages. Includes a guide that gives media professionals tips on how to boost sales and woo clients. Gives readers the tools that they need to get appointments, write proposals and presentations, sell against other media like newspapers and the internet, overcome rate resistance, close sales without alienating their clients, create genius creative without being a creative genius, calculate return on investment (ROI) for the client's advertising dollar, land long-term contracts with local businesses, and negotiate effectively.

EMPLOYMENT AGENCIES AND SEARCH FIRMS

11590 ■ Abacus Employment
1800 Roswell Rd., Ste. 3020
Marietta, GA 30062
Ph: (770)509-2490
Fax: (770)620-3801
E-mail: info@abacusjobs.com
URL: http://www.abacusjobs.com

Description: Serves as employment agency specializing in the placement of sales, sales management, hardware and software sales and marketing professionals.

11591 ■ APA Search Inc.
1 Byram Brook Pl., Ste. 104
Armonk, NY 10504
Ph: (914)273-6000
Fax: (914)273-8025
E-mail: info@apasearch.com
URL: http://www.apasearch.com

Employment agency specializing in the automotive, retail, and hardware industries.

11592 ■ Apple and Associates
PO Box 996
Chapin, SC 29036
Ph: (803)932-2000
E-mail: info@appleassoc.com
URL: http://www.appleassoc.com

Provides staffing services to medical device, plastics, pharmaceutical and performance materials industries.

11593 ■ Baldwin Gilman, LLC
4760 Red Bank Expy., Ste. 216
Cincinnati, OH 45227
Ph: (513)272-2400
Fax: (513)527-5929
Fr: 800-745-2373
E-mail: tgilman@baldwingilman.com
URL: http://www.baldwingilman.com

Executive search firm.

11594 ■ Barcus Associates
PO Box 1059
Van Alstyne, TX 75495
Ph: (903)482-1362
E-mail: moreinfo@barcusassociates.com
URL: http://www.barcusassociates.com

Executive search firm.

11595 ■ Barrett & Co. Inc.
59 Stiles Rd., Ste. 105
Salem, NH 03079
Ph: (603)890-1111
URL: http://www.barrettcompany.com

Executive search firm.

11596 ■ Bishop Partners
28 W 44th St., Ste. 2100A
New York, NY 10036
Ph: (212)986-3419
Fax: (212)575-1050
E-mail: info@bishoppartners.com
URL: http://www.bishoppartners.com

A retainer based executive search firm specializing in media and communications. This includes cable, broadcasting, publishing, Internet and interactive media, entertainment. Consulting closely with clients, finds the right person to fill a specific need or solve a specific business issue in functional areas which include CEO and COO, sales, marketing, finance, human resources, programming and production, and ecommerce.

11597 ■ Bosch & Associates LLC
PO Box 1030
Greens Farms, CT 06838
Ph: (203)255-8700
Fax: (203)259-4959
E-mail: human.resources@boschllc.com
URL: http://www.boschllc.com

Executive search firm.

11598 ■ Brownstone Sales & Marketing Group Inc.
6 W 18th St., 8th Fl.
New York, NY 10011
Ph: (212)219-4022
E-mail: jr@b-stone.com
URL: http://www.b-stone.com

Executive search firm.

11599 ■ Bryant Bureau Sales Recruiters
2435 Kimberly Rd., Ste. 110 N
Bettendorf, IA 52722-3505
Ph: (563)355-4411
Fax: (563)355-3635
E-mail: bbureau@netexpress.net
URL: http://www.bbureau.com

Executive search firm.

11600 ■ C. Anderson Associates
420 Summit Ave.
St. Paul, MN 55102-2624
Ph: (651)695-8555
Fax: (480)287-8144
E-mail: info@candersonassociates.com
URL: http://candersonassociates.com

Executive search and recruiter services firm that specializes exclusively in the placement of top sales, sales management and business development professionals.

11601 ■ CAA Search
5469 Sunbird Dr.
Loves Park, IL 61111
Ph: (815)654-8535
Fax: (815)654-0469
E-mail: info@caasearch.com
URL: http://www.caasearch.com

Executive search firm.

11602 ■ Career Advocates International
1539 Ave. A
Katy, TX 77493
Ph: (281)395-9848
Fax: (281)574-3949
URL: http://www.careeradvocates.org

Provides permanent placement and temporary staffing for executive and staff level positions. Specializes in multiple niches including: sales and marketing, accounting and financial services, banking, communications, human resources, chemicals, oil and gas, medical and dental, legal, information technology, energy, technology, engineering, manufacturing, construction, and light industrial.

11603 ■ Career Forum Inc.
PO Box 746439
Arvada, CO 80006

Ph: (303)279-9200
Fax: (303)279-9296
E-mail: stangrebe@careerforum.com
URL: http://www.careerforum.com

Executive search firm.

11604 ■ A la Carte International Inc.
1609 Bohnhoff Dr.
Virginia Beach, VA 23454
Ph: (757)425-6111
Fax: (757)481-2071
Fr: 800-446-3037
E-mail: mjr@wedofood.com
URL: http://www.wedofood.com

Executive search firm.

11605 ■ Carter/MacKay
140 E Ridgewood Ave., Ste. 415
Paramus, NJ 07652
Ph: (201)940-7353
E-mail: info.nj@cartermackay.com
URL: http://www.cartermackay.com

Executive search firm.

11606 ■ Centennial, Inc.
8044 Montgomery Rd., Ste. 260
Cincinnati, OH 45236
Ph: (513)366-3760
Fax: (513)366-3761
E-mail: info@centennialinc.com
URL: http://www.centennialinc.com

Serves as an executive search firm specializing in the areas of executive and general management, accounting and finance, human resources, information technology, manufacturing, engineering, marketing and advertising, not-for-profit, sales and business development, and supply chain and logistics. Performs executive coaching as well as career coaching for clients.

11607 ■ Century Associates Inc.
1420 Walnut St., Ste. 1402
Philadelphia, PA 19102
Ph: (215)732-4311
Fax: (215)735-1804
E-mail: dallen@centuryassociates.com
URL: http://www.centuryassociates.com

Executive search firm.

11608 ■ Clinton, Charles, Wise & Co.
PO Box 161965
Altamonte Springs, FL 32714
Ph: (407)682-6790
Fax: (407)682-1697
E-mail: ccwc@cfl.rr.com
URL: http://www.recruitersofccwc.com

Executive search firm.

11609 ■ Comprehensive Search Corp.
201 W Padonia Rd., Ste. 204
Lutherville Timonium, MD 21093-2126
Ph: (410)252-8911
Fax: (410)252-7289
Fr: 800-535-8466

Provides recruitment services for sales, management, marketing and technical positions. Industries served: business, environmental, and engineering industries.

11610 ■ Corporate Dynamix
6619 N Scottsdale Rd.
Scottsdale, AZ 85250
Ph: (480)607-0040
Fax: (480)607-0054
E-mail: david@cdynamix.com
URL: http://www.cdynamix.com

Executive search firm.

11611 ■ Dan Bolen & Associates LLC
9741 N 90th Pl., Ste. 200
Scottsdale, AZ 85258-5045
Ph: (480)767-9000

Fax: (480)767-0100
E-mail: danbolen@mindspring.com
URL: http://www.danbolenassoc.com

Executive search firm.

11612 ■ Don Allan Associates Inc.
PO Box 12988
La Jolla, CA 92039-2988
Fax: (858)777-3490
Fr: 800-291-6900
E-mail: myresume@globalstaffing.com
URL: http://www.globalstaffing.com

Executive search firm.

11613 ■ The Donnelly Group Sales Recruiters Inc.
12536 Glenlea Dr.
St. Louis, MO 63043
Ph: (314)469-6400
Fax: (561)258-3187
E-mail: ddonnelly@primary.net
URL: http://www.donnellysearch.com

Executive search firm.

11614 ■ Dorothy W. Farnath & Associates Inc.
26 Breckenridge Dr.
Shamong, NJ 08088
Ph: (856)810-2200
Fax: (856)810-2140
E-mail: info@farnath.com
URL: http://www.farnath.com

Executive search firm.

11615 ■ DSML Executive Search
120 N La Salle St., Ste. 2600
Chicago, IL 60602
Ph: (312)268-6166
E-mail: contact@dsmlexecutivesearch.com
URL: http://www.dsmlexecutivesearch.com

Provides recruiting services for European companies doing business in the United States. Specializes in the recruitment of qualified personnel for sales, marketing and operational management positions.

11616 ■ DuVall & Associates
4203 Costa Salada
San Clemente, CA 92673
Ph: (949)488-8790
Fax: (949)488-8793
E-mail: karen@ducall.com
URL: http://www.duvall.com

Executive search firm specializing in management team placement.

11617 ■ Edge Recruiting Solutions, Inc.
4852 S 133rd St., Ste. 101-W
Omaha, NE 68137
Ph: (402)896-3343
Fax: (402)408-6911
URL: http://edgerecruiters.com

Specializes in recruiting sales and sales management professionals for the pharmaceutical, medical and B2B related industries.

11618 ■ Execusearch
PO Box 3990
Plant City, FL 33564
Ph: (813)659-9665
Fax: (813)759-6303
Fr: 800-896-5912
E-mail: donna@execusearchusa.com
URL: http://www.execusearch.net

Executive search firm.

11619 ■ Fast Switch Ltd.
4900 Blazer Pkwy.
Dublin, OH 43017
Ph: (614)336-1122

Fax: (614)336-3695
E-mail: webresumes@fastswitch.com
URL: http://www.fastswitch.com
Executive search firm.

11620 ■ Food Management Search
235 State St., Ste. 326
Springfield, MA 01103
Ph: (413)732-2666
Fax: (413)732-6466
E-mail: recruiters@foodmanagementsearch.com
URL: http://foodmanagementsearch.com/index.cfm

Specializes in contingency recruiting projects exclusively in the food manufacturing and food service industries. Provides positions covering food production/manufacturing, supply chain, food service, sales and marketing.

11621 ■ Georgia Sales Development Inc.
3625 Brookside Pkwy., Ste. 165
Alpharetta, GA 30022
Ph: (770)475-3835
E-mail: lissa@sandler.com
URL: http://www.georgiasales.sandler.com
Executive search firm.

11622 ■ Gowdy Consultants
12059 Starcrest Dr.
San Antonio, TX 78247
Ph: (210)499-4444
Fax: (210)499-4676
E-mail: gowdycts@texas.net
URL: http://gowdyconsultants-jobs.com
Executive search firm.

11623 ■ Hager Executive Search
1483 Sutter St., Ste. 1003
San Francisco, CA 94109
Ph: (415)441-2234
E-mail: connect@hagerexecutivesearch.com
URL: http://www.hagerexecutivesearch.com

Specializes in executive and C level talent searches in marketing/branding, business development, sales and digital media across varied business sectors.

11624 ■ Hilleren & Associates
3800 American Blvd. W, Ste. 880
Minneapolis, MN 55431
Ph: (952)956-9090
Fax: (952)956-9009
E-mail: heather@hilleren.com
URL: http://www.hilleren.com

Provides executive search services in sales, marketing and management in the healthcare and pharmaceutical manufacturing industry.

11625 ■ J H Dugan & Company
225 Crossroads Blvd., Ste. 415
Carmel, CA 93923
Fax: 888-530-5610
Fr: 800-254-3396
E-mail: plastic-recruiter@jhdugan.com
URL: http://www.jhdugan.com
Executive search firm.

11626 ■ JS Robertson Retained Search
75 E Santa Clara St., Ste. 1388
San Jose, CA 95113
Ph: (408)292-9292
Fax: (408)292-4555
E-mail: info@jsrobertson.com
URL: http://www.jsrobertson.com
Executive search firm.

11627 ■ Kensington International Inc.
1515 W 22nd St., Ste. 500
Oak Brook, IL 60523
Ph: (630)571-0123
Fax: (630)571-3139
E-mail: info@kionline.com
URL: http://www.kionline.com
Executive search firm.

11628 ■ Marcom Choices Staffing
PO Box 620632
Woodside, CA 94062-0632
Ph: (650)851-9055
E-mail: marketingjobs@marcomchoices.com
URL: http://www.marcomchoices.com

Description: Executive search firm which specializes and excels in placing product marketing, sales and corporate communications professionals.

11629 ■ Medical Recruiters Inc.
7733 Forsyth Blvd., Ste. 670
St. Louis, MO 63105
Ph: (314)222-4200
Fax: (314)222-4211
E-mail: resumes@medrecinc.com
URL: http://medicalrecruitersincorporated.com
Executive search firm.

11630 ■ MH Executive Search Group
30617 US Hwy. 19 N, Ste. 502
Palm Harbor, FL 34684
Ph: (727)786-8877
E-mail: packagingjobs@yahoo.com
URL: http://www.mhgroup.com
Executive search firm.

11631 ■ Mid-American Placement Service Inc.
1941 S 42nd St., Ste. 520
Omaha, NE 68105-2945
Ph: (402)341-3338
Fax: (402)341-6266
E-mail: info@nejobs.net
URL: http://www.nejobs.net
Executive search firm.

11632 ■ MJS Executive Search
2 Overhill Rd., Ste. 400
Scarsdale, NY 10583
Ph: (914)631-1774
Fax: (914)631-0435
E-mail: info@mjsearch.com
URL: http://www.mjsearch.com

Serves as a retained executive recruiting firm specializing in placing professionals in consumer goods, entertainment, media, social media, sports, marketing services and other industries.

11633 ■ MRI Management Recruiters of Atlanta West
4260 Bankhead Hwy., Ste. A
Lithia Springs, GA 30122-1752
Ph: (770)948-5560
Fax: (770)948-5762
E-mail: steve@mraw.net
URL: http://www.mrinetwork.com
Executive search firm.

11634 ■ MRI Network Sales Consultants of Southampton
928 Jaymor Rd., Ste. A-200
Southampton, PA 18966
Ph: (215)364-7559
Fax: (215)364-7579
E-mail: customerservice@mriscs.com
URL: http://www.mriscs.com
Executive search firm.

11635 ■ MRI Network The Lawler Group
1333 W Towne Square Rd.
Mequon, WI 53092
Ph: (262)241-1600
Fax: (262)241-1640
E-mail: tim@lawlergroup.com
URL: http://www.lawlergroup.com
Executive search firm.

11636 ■ MRI Sales Consultants of Morris County, NJ
364 Parsippany Rd.
Parsippany, NJ 07054-5109

Ph: (973)887-3838
Fax: (973)887-2304
E-mail: scmorris@marketing-sales.com
URL: http://www.marketing-sales.com
Executive search firm.

11637 ■ MRI Sales Consultants of Providence-Warwick
2348 Post Rd., Ste. 101
Airport Professional Park
Warwick, RI 02886-2271
Ph: (401)737-3200
Fax: (401)737-4322
E-mail: bestsalestalent@mrisales.net
URL: http://www.mrisales.net
Executive search firm.

11638 ■ MRI Sales Consultants of Syracuse
4383 Brickyard Falls Rd.
Manlius, NY 13104
Ph: (315)692-4801
Fax: (315)692-4802
E-mail: dwelker@welkerrecruiting.com
URL: http://www.mrinetwork.com
Executive search firm.

11639 ■ MRI Search Consultants Intracoastal, Inc.
3000 NE 30th Pl., Ste. 308
Fort Lauderdale, FL 33306
Ph: (954)772-5100
Fax: (954)772-0777
E-mail: resume@mri-sc-usa.com
URL: http://www.mri-sc-usa.com
Executive search firm.

11640 ■ MRINetwork Management Recruiters of Mercer
1717 Arch St., 36th Fl.
Philadelphia, PA 19103
Fax: (215)751-1757
Fr: (866)836-9890
URL: http://www.mrinetwork.com
Executive search firm.

11641 ■ National Sales & Marketing Consultants Inc.
5650 Greenwood Plz. Blvd., Ste. 206
Englewood, CO 80111-2309
Ph: (303)771-4201
Fax: (303)740-8640
E-mail: nasmarc@aol.com

Locates, hires, and trains sales representatives, and coordinates on-going activities of manufacturer's representatives for clients in health-care, government, health and beauty aids, sporting goods, consumer products, hardware, and stationery/office supply industries. Assists clients in developing pricing, packaging, advertising, general sales, and promotional policies. Acts as national sales manager for multiple clients.

11642 ■ Navin Group
200 Cordwainer Dr., Ste. 100
Norwell, MA 02061
Ph: (781)871-6770
Fax: (781)878-8703
Fr: 888-837-1300
E-mail: search@navingroup.com
URL: http://www.navingroup.com
Executive search firm.

11643 ■ Next Step Group, Inc
940 W 141st Way
Westminster, CO 80023
Ph: (303)635-0101
Fr: 800-867-0713
E-mail: glenn@4nextstep.com
URL: http://www.4nextstep.com
Executive search firm.

11644 ■ Oliver & Rozner Associates
598 Madison Ave., Ste. 11
New York, NY 10022
Ph: (212)688-1850

Performs executive search for top tiers of management including presidents, general management, advertising account management, division management, group executive and vice presidential line positions in such areas as marketing, research, operations, sales, finance, human resources and others; hard-to-find specialists including specific marketing/advertising executives, research and development expertise, computer/data processing knowledge, scientific, physicians-product efficacy and occupational medicine and engineering. Industries served include pharmaceutical, health care, hospital, advertising, consumer products and packaged goods, house wares, direct selling, cosmetics/toiletries, industrial products, high technology products, forest products, engineering, construction, environment/resource recovery, graphic arts, chemical and government agencies.

11645 ■ Opus Productivity
1421 N Wanda, Ste. 110
Orange, CA 92867
Ph: (714)289-3925
Fr: 800-982-1260
E-mail: info@opusproductivity.com
URL: http://www.opusproductivity.com

Executive search firm.

11646 ■ Page Consulting LLC
688 Cypress Point Dr.
Egg Harbor City, NJ 08215
Ph: (609)965-3300
Fax: (609)965-3339
E-mail: abrown@turntothepage.com
URL: http://www.turntothepage.com

Executive search firm.

11647 ■ Pat Licata & Associates
1149 Executive Cir., Ste. C-1
Cary, NC 27511
E-mail: resumes@patlicata.com
URL: http://www.patlicata.com

Executive search firm for the pharmaceutical and medical industries.

11648 ■ Professional Recruiters Inc.
705 1st St., NE
Little Falls, MN 56345
Ph: (320)616-5849
Fr: 800-594-8414
E-mail: info@professionalrecruiters.com
URL: http://www.professionalrecruiters.com/index2.htm

Executive search firm.

11649 ■ Recruiting Partners
3494 Camino Tassajara Rd., No. 404
Danville, CA 94506
Ph: (925)964-0249
E-mail: info@recruitingpartners.com
URL: http://www.recruitingpartners.com

Description: Serves as an executive and technical recruiting firm that specializes in accounting, legal, information technology, engineering, executive management and technical writing.

11650 ■ Sales Talent
8015 SE 28th St., Ste. 314
Mercer Island, WA 98040
Ph: (425)739-9979
Fax: (425)605-0726
URL: http://www.salestalentinc.com

Sales recruiting firm that specializes in the placement of sales professionals and sales management.

11651 ■ Sanford Rose Associates-Norcross
9810-B Medlock Bridge Rd., Ste. 201
Johns Creek, GA 30097
Ph: (770)232-9900

Fax: (770)232-1933
E-mail: norcrossresume@sanfordrose.com
URL: http://www.sanfordrose.com/norcross

Executive search firm.

11652 ■ Search Group
6102 Seven Lakes W
Seven Lakes, NC 27376
Ph: (910)687-0064
Fax: (910)687-0067
E-mail: results@theesearchgroup.com
URL: http://search-one.com

Partners with clients in need of executive, managerial, IT, engineering, and sales positions supporting materials handling, logistics, and supply chain management.

11653 ■ Search North America Inc.
PO Box 3577
Sunriver, OR 97707-0577
Ph: (503)222-6461
Fax: (503)227-2804
E-mail: mylinda@searchna.com
URL: http://www.searchna.com

An executive search and recruiting firm whose focus is placing engineers, operations and maintenance managers, sales and marketing management, financial and general management executives (both domestic and international). Industries served: forest products, pulp and paper, waste to energy, environmental services, consulting and equipment suppliers for above related industries.

11654 ■ SHS of Cherry Hill
207 Barclay Pavilion W
Cherry Hill, NJ 08034
Ph: (856)216-9030
Fax: (856)216-7784
E-mail: shs@shsofcherryhill.com
URL: http://www.shsofcherryhill.com

Personnel recruiters operating in the disciplines of accounting, sales, insurance, engineering, and administration. Industries served: insurance, distribution, manufacturing, and service.

11655 ■ Sports Group International
7317 Spyglass Way, Ste. 400
Raleigh, NC 27615
Ph: (919)855-0226
Fax: (919)855-0793
E-mail: sgisearch@aol.com
URL: http://www.sgisearch.com

Serves as an executive search firm for the sporting goods and recreational products industries. Specializes in the recruitment of senior and middle level managers who excel in sales, marketing, product design and development, and general management.

11656 ■ SR & Associates
5001 Birch St.
Newport Beach, CA 92660
Ph: (949)756-3271
Fax: (949)756-6565
E-mail: sraross@srassociatesinc.com
URL: http://www.srassociatesinc.com

Executive search firm.

11657 ■ Strategic Associates Inc.
PO Box 203278
Austin, TX 78720-3278
Ph: (512)218-8222
Fax: (512)218-8102
E-mail: sai@strategicassociates.com
URL: http://www.strategicassociates.com

Executive search firm.

11658 ■ Treeline, Inc.
599 North Ave., Ste. 6
Wakefield, MA 01880
Ph: (781)876-8100

Fax: (781)224-9797
E-mail: employment@treeline-inc.com
URL: http://www.treeline-inc.com/treeline_inc/index.html

Specializes in the recruitment of professionals for sales, sales management and sales executive positions.

11659 ■ Wellington Executive Search
3162 Johnson Ferry Rd., Ste. 260
Marietta, GA 30062
Ph: (770)645-5799
Fax: (678)278-0928
E-mail: jobs@wellingtonsearch.com
URL: http://www.wellingtonsearch.com

Serves as an executive search firm covering sales representative, research and development, food scientists, and purchasing managers.

11660 ■ Whitney Group
555 Fifth Ave., 6th Fl.
New York, NY 10017
Ph: (212)508-3500
Fax: (212)508-3540
URL: http://www.whitneypartners.net

Executive search firm.

11661 ■ William Halderson Associates Inc.
PO Box 20056
St. Simons Island, GA 31522
Ph: (912)638-8430
URL: http://www.haldersonsearch.com

Executive search firm.

ONLINE JOB SOURCES AND SERVICES

11662 ■ 6Figurejobs.com
E-mail: info@6figurejobs.com
URL: http://www.6figurejobs.com

Description: Provides executives and experienced professionals with access to some of the most exclusive executive jobs, executive recruiters and career management tools available. Includes tools for both posting and viewing jobs, resume refinement, company research and more.

11663 ■ AccountManager.com
E-mail: info@careermarketplace.com
URL: http://www.accountmanager.com

Description: Features account manager jobs and products to the account management community.

11664 ■ AgentsandSalesManagers.com
URL: http://www.agentsandsalesmanagers.com

Description: Online job search for agents and sales managers. Includes job, resume posting and more.

11665 ■ Heidrick & Struggles Management Search
233 S Wacker Dr.
Willis Tower, Ste. 4200
Chicago, IL 60606-6303
Ph: (312)496-1200
URL: http://www.heidrick.com/pages/default.aspx

Description: Executive search firm that will distribute registered resumes to recruiters with suitable positions available.

11666 ■ Justmeans - CSR JOBS
URL: http://www.justmeans.com

Description: Serves as online resource that provides available career opportunities for the sustainable business industry.

11667 ■ MediaBistro.com
URL: http://www.mediabistro.com

Description: Serves as a career resource for anyone who creates or works with content, or who is a non-creative professional working in a content/creative industry (including editors, writers, producers, graphic designers, book publishers, and others in industries including magazines, television, film, radio, newspapers, book publishing, online media, advertising, PR, and design). Provides opportunities to meet, share resources, become informed of job opportunities and interesting projects and news, improve career skills, and showcase one's work.

11668 ■ New Sales and Marketing Jobs
URL: http://www.newsalesandmarketingjobs.com

Description: Provides an online listing of companies with available sales and marketing jobs in all specialties.

11669 ■ Omni Search, Inc.
E-mail: omni@omnisearch.biz
URL: http://www.omnisearch.biz/opps.htm

Description: Job search engine for those in the sales and marketing positions in the pharmaceutical, medical and consumer industries.

11670 ■ Sales Classifieds
URL: http://www.salesclassifieds.com

Description: Serves as career site for sales professionals. Provides resources such as job search agents, resume creation and postings.

11671 ■ SalesHeads.com
URL: http://www.salesheads.com

Description: Offers job listings and resources for the sales industry. Features sales positions for sales professionals.

11672 ■ SalesManagementCentral.com
URL: http://www.salesmanagementcentral.com

Description: Provides resources for sales managers. Offers sales management jobs and products.

11673 ■ SellingCareers.com
URL: http://www.sellingcareers.com

Provides job opportunities for sales professionals.

11674 ■ SellingCrossing.com
URL: http://www.sellingcrossing.com

Description: Provides collection of sales jobs, including sales manager, sales director, sales consultant, and media sales positions. Also features industry-specific articles relating to job searches and developments in the professional field.

11675 ■ Spherion
2050 Spectrum Blvd.
Fort Lauderdale, FL 33309
Ph: (954)308-7600
Fr: 800-774-3746
E-mail: help@spherion.com
URL: http://www.spherion.com

Description: Recruitment firm specializing in accounting and finance, sales and marketing, interim executives, technology, engineering, retail and human resources.

TRADESHOWS

11676 ■ ERA D2C Convention
Electronic Retailing Association
2000 N. 14th St., Ste. 300
Arlington, VA 22201
Ph: (703)841-1751
Fax: (703)841-8290
Fr: 800-987-6462
E-mail: info@retailing.org
URL: http://www.retailing.org

Annual. Primary Exhibits: Equipment, supplies, and services for the growth, development, and acceptance of electronic retailing worldwide. Dates and Locations: 2012 Sep 11-13; Las Vegas, NV; Wynn Las Vegas.

11677 ■ Jobbernaut Career Fairs
Jobbernaut, Inc.
PO Box 2267
Lynnwood, WA 98036
Ph: (425)397-7114
Fax: (425)397-7505
URL: http://jobbernautcareerfairs.com

Brings together over 1500 companies to recruit and hire applicants from the following industries: sales, management, restaurant and retail; technical, engineering, computers; administrative, general office, and customer service; and banking and financial. 2012 October 3; Seattle, WA.

OTHER SOURCES

11678 ■ American Management Association (AMA)
1601 Broadway
New York, NY 10019-7420
Ph: (212)586-8100
Fax: (212)903-8168
Fr: 877-566-9441
E-mail: customerservice@amanet.org
URL: http://www.amanet.org

Description: Provides educational forums worldwide where members and their colleagues learn superior, practical business skills and explore best practices of world-class organizations through interaction with each other and expert faculty practitioners. **Purpose:** Maintains a publishing program providing tools individuals use to extend learning beyond the classroom in a process of life-long professional growth and development through education.

11679 ■ American Society of Association Executives (ASAE)
1575 I St. NW
Washington, DC 20005
Ph: (202)371-0940
Fax: (202)371-8315

Fr: 888-950-2723
E-mail: asaeservice@asaecenter.org
URL: http://www.asaecenter.org

Description: Professional society of paid executives of international, national, state, and local trade, professional, and philanthropic associations. Seeks to educate association executives on effective management, including: the proper objectives, functions, and activities of associations; the basic principles of association management; the legal aspects of association activity; policies relating to association management; efficient methods, procedures, and techniques of association management; the responsibilities and professional standards of association executives. Maintains information resource center. Conducts resume, guidance, and consultation services; compiles statistics in the form of reports, surveys, and studies; carries out research and education. Maintains ASAE Services Corporation to provide special services and ASAE Foundation to do future-oriented research and make grant awards. Offers executive search services and insurance programs. Provides CEO center for chief staff executives. Conducts Certified Association Executive (CAE) program.

11680 ■ National Association of Sales Professionals
555 Friendly St.
Pontiac, MI 48341-2650
Fax: (248)254-6757
Fr: (866)365-1520
URL: http://www.nasp.com

Description: Professional salespersons. Serves the training, educational and developmental needs of men and women in sales to earn designation as a Certified Professional Sales Person.

11681 ■ National Management Association (NMA)
2210 Arbor Blvd.
Dayton, OH 45439
Ph: (937)294-0421
Fax: (937)294-2374
E-mail: nma@nma1.org
URL: http://www.nma1.org

Description: Business and industrial management personnel; membership comes from supervisory level, with the remainder from middle management and above. Seeks to develop and recognize management as a profession and to promote the free enterprise system. Prepares chapter programs on basic management, management policy and practice, communications, human behavior, industrial relations, economics, political education, and liberal education. Maintains speakers' bureau and hall of fame. Maintains educational, charitable, and research programs. Sponsors charitable programs.

Sources of Help-Wanted Ads

11682 ■ American Biotechnology Laboratory
American Laboratory/Labcompare
30 Controls Dr.
Shelton, CT 06484-0870
Ph: (203)926-9300
Fax: (203)926-9310
URL: http://
www.americanbiotechnologylaboratory.com

Biotechnology magazine.

11683 ■ Annual Review of Microbiology
Annual Reviews Inc.
4139 El Camino Way
Palo Alto, CA 94306
Ph: (650)493-4400
Fax: (650)424-0910
Fr: 800-523-8635
URL: http://www.annualreviews.org/journal/micro

Annual. $86.00/year for individuals, print & online; $263.00/year for institutions, print & online; $219.00/year for institutions, online; $219.00/year for institutions, print. Periodical covering microbiology and the biological sciences.

11684 ■ AWIS Magazine
Association for Women in Science
1321 Duke St., Ste. 210
Alexandria, VA 22314
Ph: (703)894-4490
Fax: (703)894-4489
Fr: (866)657-2947
URL: http://www.awis.org/
displaycommon.cfm?an=1&subarticlenbr=2

Quarterly. Included in membership. Professional magazine covering the status of women in science.

11685 ■ Chemical Equipment
Reed Business Information (New York, New York)
360 Park Ave. S
New York, NY 10010
Ph: (646)746-6400
Fax: (646)746-7431
Fr: 800-446-6551
URL: http://www.reedbusinessinteractive.com

Free for qualified professionals; $72.90/year for individuals, cover price. Tabloid on the chemical process industry.

11686 ■ Engineering in Life Sciences
John Wiley & Sons Inc.
111 River St.
Hoboken, NJ 07030-5773
Ph: (201)748-6000
Fax: (201)748-6088
Fr: 800-825-7550
URL: http://onlinelibrary.wiley.com/journal/10.1002/
(ISSN)1618-28

Bimonthly. $989.00/year for institutions, European,

online only; $1,512.00/year for institutions, online only, Switzerland and Liechtenstein; $1,299.00/year for institutions, other countries, online only; $663.00/year for institutions, European, online only; $1,299.00/year for institutions, online only; $1,299.00/year for institutions, Canada and Mexico, online only. Journal focusing on the field of biotechnology and related topics including microbiology, genetics, biochemistry, and chemistry.

11687 ■ Harvard Science Review
Harvard University Press
79 Garden St.
Cambridge, MA 02138
Ph: (401)531-2800
Fax: (401)531-2801
Fr: 800-405-1619
E-mail: hsr@hcs.harvard.edu
URL: http://www.hcs.harvard.edu/~hsr/

Semiannual. A science journal.

11688 ■ InterJournal
New England Complex Systems Institute
283 Main St., Ste. 319
Cambridge, MA 02142
Ph: (617)547-4100
Fax: (617)661-7711
URL: http://www.interjournal.org/

Journal covering the fields of science and engineering.

11689 ■ The Internet Journal of Forensic Science
Internet Scientific Publications L.L.C.
23 Rippling Creek Dr.
Sugar Land, TX 77479
Ph: (832)443-1193
URL: http://www.ispub.com/ostia/
index.php?xmlFilePath=journals/ij

Free, online. Electronic journal for medical professionals focusing on the field of forensic science.

11690 ■ Invertebrate Biology
John Wiley & Sons Inc.
350 Main St., Commerce Pl.
Malden, MA 02148-5089
Ph: (781)388-8200
Fax: (781)388-8210
URL: http://www.amicros.org/

Quarterly. $268.00/year for institutions, online or print; $309.00/year for institutions, print & online; $163.00/year for institutions, print or online; $188.00/year for institutions, print & online. Scientific journal covering the biology of invertebrate animals and research in the fields of cell and molecular biology, ecology, physiology, systematics, genetics, biogeography and behavior.

11691 ■ Journal of Women and Minorities in Science and Engineering
Begell House Inc.
50 Cross Hwy.
Redding, CT 06896

Ph: (203)938-1300
Fax: (203)938-1304
URL: http://www.begellhouse.com/journals/
00551c876cc2f027

$248.00/year for institutions. Peer-reviewed journal featuring innovative ideas and programs for classroom teachers, scientific studies, and formulation of concepts related to the education, recruitment, and retention of under-represented groups in science and engineering.

11692 ■ Nature Biotechnology
Nature Publishing Group
75 Varick St., 9th Fl.
New York, NY 10013-1917
Ph: (212)726-9200
Fax: (212)696-9006
Fr: 888-331-6288
E-mail: biotech@natureny.com
URL: http://www.nature.com/nbt/index.html

Monthly. $250.00/year for individuals, print + online; $425.00/year for two years, print + online. Scientific research journal.

11693 ■ Nature International Weekly Journal of Science
Nature Publishing Group
75 Varick St., 9th Fl.
New York, NY 10013-1917
Ph: (212)726-9200
Fax: (212)696-9006
Fr: 888-331-6288
E-mail: nature@natureny.com
URL: http://www.nature.com/nature/index.html

Weekly. $199.00/year for individuals, print and online; $338.00/year for two years, print and online. Magazine covering science and technology, including the fields of biology, biochemistry, genetics, medicine, earth sciences, physics, pharmacology, and behavioral sciences.

11694 ■ Popular Science
Time4 Media Inc.
1271 Avenue of the Americas
New York, NY 10020-1300
Ph: (212)522-1212
URL: http://www.popsci.com/popsci

Monthly. $14.00/year for individuals; $24.00/year for two years; $26.00/year for Canada; $45.00/year for other countries, USA. General interest science magazine.

11695 ■ Psychology Journal
Psychological Publishing
PO Box 176
Natchitoches, LA 71458
E-mail: psychjournal@aol.com
URL: http://www.psychologicalpublishing.com/

Quarterly. $90.00/year for individuals; $175.00/year for institutions. Journal dedicated to all areas of the science and practice of counseling and clinical psychology.

11696 ■ *Science*
American Association for the Advancement of Science
1200 New York Ave., NW
Washington, DC 20005
Ph: (202)326-6550
URL: http://www.scienceonline.org

Weekly (Fri.). $146.00/year for members, professional, print & online; $119.00/year for individuals, NPA postdoctoral, print & online; $99.00/year for individuals, postdoctoral/resident, print & online; $75.00/year for students, print & online; $146.00/year for individuals, k-12 teacher, print & online; $310.00/year for individuals, patron, print & online; $115.00/year for individuals, emeritus, print & online; $211.05/year for Canada, professional members, print & online; $161.00/year for Canada, postdoctoral/resident, print & online; $136.50/year for students, Canada, print & online. Magazine devoted to science, scientific research, and public policy.

11697 ■ *The Scientist*
The Scientist Inc.
121 W 27th St., Ste. 604
New York, NY 10001
Ph: (212)461-4470
Fax: (347)626-2385
URL: http://www.the-scientist.com

Monthly. $39.95/year for individuals, print only; $49.95/year for individuals, print & online; $64.95/year for other countries, print only; $74.95/year for other countries, print & online. News journal (tabloid) for life scientists featuring news, opinions, research, and professional section.

11698 ■ *The Southeastern Naturalist*
Humboldt Field Research Institute
59 Eagle Hill Rd.
PO Box 9
Steuben, ME 04680-0009
Ph: (207)546-2821
Fax: (207)546-3042
E-mail: office@eaglehill.us
URL: http://www.eaglehill.us/programs/journals/sena/southeastern-

Quarterly. $50.00/year for individuals; $40.00/year for students; $150.00/year for institutions, organization; $70.00/year for Canada; $90.00/year for other countries; $60.00/year for students, In Canada; $80.00/year for students, other countries; $170.00/year for institutions, in Canada; $190.00/year for institutions, other countries. Peer-reviewed interdisciplinary scientific journal covering field ecology, biology, behavior, biogeography, taxonomy, anatomy, physiology, geology and related fields in the southeastern United States.

11699 ■ *Wetlands*
Society of Wetland Scientists
1313 Dolley Madison Blvd., Ste. 402
Mc Lean, VA 22101
Ph: (703)790-1745
Fax: (703)790-2672
URL: http://www.sws.org/wetlands/index.mgi

Quarterly. $100.00/year for individuals; $35.00/year for students; $500.00/year for institutions; $200.00/year for libraries; $65.00/year for members, paper & electronic, from developing country. Scholarly journal covering all aspects of wetlands biology, ecology, hydrology, water chemistry, soil and sediment characteristics, management, and laws and regulations.

HANDBOOKS AND MANUALS

11700 ■ *Jobs in Environmental Cleanup and Emergency Hazmat Response*
Rosen Publishing Group
29 E 21st St.
New York, NY 10010
Fax: 888-436-4643
Fr: 800-237-9932
URL: http://www.rosenpublishing.com

Daniel E. Harmon. 2010. $31.95 (library bound). 80 pages. Features jobs in environmental cleanup and emergency hazmat response. Explores numerous career paths for different environmental jobs that require special training or four-year and/or postgraduate degrees. Includes job profiles for professionals such as environmental engineers, geologists, microbiologists, science technicians, conservationists, foresters, park rangers, soil scientists, air control technicians, toxicologists, dredge operators, ecologists, hazardous waste managers, and zoologists.

11701 ■ *Opportunities in Biological Science Careers*
The McGraw-Hill Companies
PO Box 182604
Columbus, OH 43272
Fax: (614)759-3749
Fr: 877-883-5524
E-mail: customer.service@mcgraw-hill.com
URL: http://www.mhprofessional.com/product.php?isbn=007143187X

Charles A. Winter. 2004. $13.95 (paper). 160 pages. Identifies employers and outlines opportunities in plant and animal biology, biological specialties, biomedical sciences, applied biology, and other areas. Illustrated.

EMPLOYMENT AGENCIES AND SEARCH FIRMS

11702 ■ Banner Personnel Service
300 W Adams St., Ste. 810
Chicago, IL 60606
Ph: (312)580-2500
Fax: (312)580-2515
URL: http://www.bannerpersonnel.com

Employment agency. Executive search firm. Branch offices in Downers Grove, Libertyville and Naperville, IL.

ONLINE JOB SOURCES AND SERVICES

11703 ■ TechniciansNow.com
URL: http://www.techniciansnow.com

Description: Provides an avenue to showcase jobs and products vital to the mechanical and technical trade communities.

TRADESHOWS

11704 ■ American Association for the Advancement of Science Annual Meeting & Science Innovation Exposition
American Association for the Advancement of Science AAAS
1200 New York Ave. N.W.
Washington, DC 20005
Ph: (202)326-6400
URL: http://www.aaas.org/

Annual. Primary Exhibits: Scientific supplies and services, including books and journals, educational and informational services, government agencies, and scientific associations. Dates and Locations: 2012 Feb 16-20; Vancouver, BC, Canada ; 2013 Feb 14-18; Boston, MA; 2014 Feb 13-17; Chicago, IL; 2015 Feb 12-16; San Jose, CA.

OTHER SOURCES

11705 ■ American Chemical Society (ACS)
1155 16th St. NW
Washington, DC 20036
Ph: (202)872-4600

Fr: 800-227-5558
E-mail: help@acs.org
URL: http://portal.acs.org/portal/acs/corg/content

Description: Scientific and educational society of chemists and chemical engineers. Conducts: studies and surveys; special programs for disadvantaged persons; legislation monitoring, analysis, and reporting; courses for graduate chemists and chemical engineers; radio and television programming. Offers career guidance counseling; administers the Petroleum Research Fund and other grants and fellowship programs. Operates Employment Clearing Houses. Compiles statistics. Maintains speakers' bureau and 33 divisions.

11706 ■ American Institute of Biological Sciences (AIBS)
1313 Dolley Madison Blvd.
McLean, VA 22101
Ph: (703)790-1745
Fax: (703)790-2672
E-mail: adm@aibs.org
URL: http://www.aibs.org

Description: Professional member organization and federation of biological associations, laboratories, and museums whose members have an interest in the life sciences. Promotes unity and effectiveness of effort among persons engaged in biological research, education, and application of biological sciences, including agriculture, environment, and medicine. Seeks to further the relationships of biological sciences to other sciences and industries. Conducts roundtable series; provides names of prominent biologists who are willing to serve as speakers and curriculum consultants; provides advisory committees and other services to the Department of Energy, Environmental Protection Agency, National Science Foundation, Department of Defense, and National Aeronautics and Space Administration. Maintains educational consultant panel.

11707 ■ American Society of Agronomy (ASA)
5585 Guilford Rd.
Madison, WI 53711
Ph: (608)273-8080
Fax: (608)273-2021
E-mail: headquarters@agronomy.org
URL: http://www.agronomy.org

Description: Professional society of agronomists, plant breeders, physiologists, soil scientists, chemists, educators, technicians, and others concerned with crop production and soil management, and conditions affecting them. Sponsors fellowship program and student essay and speech contests. Provides placement service.

11708 ■ American Society for Histocompatibility and Immunogenetics (ASHI)
15000 Commerce Pkwy., Ste. C
Mount Laurel, NJ 08054-2212
Ph: (856)638-0428
Fax: (856)439-0525
E-mail: info@ashi-hla.org
URL: http://www.ashi-hla.org

Description: Scientists, physicians, and technologists involved in research and clinical activities related to histocompatibility testing (a state of mutual tolerance that allows some tissues to be grafted effectively to others). Conducts proficiency testing and educational programs. Maintains liaison with regulatory agencies; offers placement services and laboratory accreditation. Has co-sponsored development of histocompatibility specialist and laboratory certification program.

11709 ■ Association for International Practical Training (AIPT)
10400 Little Patuxent Pkwy., Ste. 250
Columbia, MD 21044-3519
Ph: (410)997-2200

Fax: (410)992-3924
E-mail: aipt@aipt.org
URL: http://www.aipt.org

Description: Providers worldwide of on-the-job training programs for students and professionals seeking international career development and life-changing experiences. Arranges workplace exchanges in hundreds of professional fields, bringing employers and trainees together from around the world. Client list ranges from small farming communities to Fortune 500 companies.

11710 ■ RTI International
PO Box 12194
Research Triangle Park, NC 27709
Ph: (919)485-2666
E-mail: listen@rti.org
URL: http://www.rti.org

Description: Seeks individuals who understand the connection between focused research and social results furthering a career in science and study.

11711 ■ Society for Range Management (SRM)
10030 W 27th Ave.
Wheat Ridge, CO 80215-6601

Ph: (303)986-3309
Fax: (303)986-3892
E-mail: info@rangelands.org
URL: http://www.rangelands.org

Description: Professional international society of scientists, technicians, ranchers, administrators, teachers, and students interested in the study, use, and management of rangeland resources for livestock, wildlife, watershed, and recreation.

SOURCES OF HELP-WANTED ADS

11712 ■ About Campus
John Wiley & Sons Inc.
111 River St.
Hoboken, NJ 07030-5773
Ph: (201)748-6000
Fax: (201)748-6088
Fr: 800-825-7550
URL: http://onlinelibrary.wiley.com/journal/10.1002/
    (ISSN)1536-06

Bimonthly. $207.00/year for institutions, print only;
$267.00/year for institutions, Canada and Mexico,
print only; $318.00/year for institutions, other coun-
tries, print only; $60.00/year for U.S., Canada, and
Mexico, print only; $96.00/year for other countries,
print only. Journal focused on the critical issues faced
by both student affairs and academic affairs staff as
they work on helping students learn.

11713 ■ American Academic
American Federation of Teachers
555 New Jersey Ave. NW
Washington, DC 20001
Ph: (202)879-4400
URL: http://www.aft.org/pubs-reports/american_
    academic/index.htm

Higher education policy journal.

11714 ■ The American Biology Teacher
National Association of Biology Teachers
1313 Dolley Madison Blvd., Ste. 402
McLean, VA 22101
Ph: (703)264-9696
Fax: (703)264-7778
Fr: 800-406-0775
URL: http://www.nabt.org/websites/institution/
    index.php?p=26

$9.00/year for members; $24.00/year for nonmembers; $24.00/year for institutions. Peer-reviewed
journal featuring articles on biology, science, and
education for elementary, high school and college
level biology teachers. Includes audio-visual, book,
computer, and research reviews.

11715 ■ Annals of Medicine
Informa Healthcare
52 Vanderbilt Ave., 7th Fl.
New York, NY 10017-3846
Ph: (212)520-2777
URL: http://informahealthcare.com/ann

$595.00/year for institutions; $980.00/year for institutions; $780.00/year for institutions. Journal covering
health science and medical education.

**11716 ■ Assessment & Evaluation in Higher
    Education**
Routledge Journals
270 Madison Ave.
New York, NY 10016-0601
Ph: (212)216-7800
Fax: (212)563-2269
URL: http://www.tandf.co.uk/journals/titles/
    02602938.asp

Bimonthly. $1,316.00/year for institutions, online only;
$2,547.00/year for institutions, print + online;
$1,462.00/year for individuals, print + online;
$2,292.00/year for institutions, online only; $578.00/
year for individuals, print only; $314.00/year for
individuals, print only. Peer-reviewed journal focusing
on publishing papers and reports on all aspects of
assessment and evaluation within higher education.

11717 ■ Better
The Johns Hopkins University Press
2715 N Charles St.
Baltimore, MD 21218-4319
Ph: (410)516-6900
Fax: (410)516-6968
URL: http://www.press.jhu.edu/journals/better_
    evidence_based_educ

$29.50/year for individuals, print and electronic;
$80.00/year for institutions, print and electronic.
Magazine for educators and policy makers interested
in evidence-based education reform.

**11718 ■ Brookings Papers on Education
    Policy**
Brookings Institution Press
1775 Massachusetts Ave. NW
Washington, DC 20036
Ph: (202)797-6000
URL: http://www.brookings.edu/press/Journals/2007/
    brookingspapers

$36.00/year for individuals. Journal dealing with all
aspects of American education.

11719 ■ The Council Chronicle
National Council of Teachers of English
1111 W Kenyon Rd.
Urbana, IL 61801-1096
Ph: (217)328-3870
Fax: (217)328-9645
Fr: 877-369-6283
E-mail: chronicle@ncte.org
URL: http://www.ncte.org/magazine

Quarterly. Magazine for teachers of English or
language arts at all levels who are members of the
National Council of Teachers of English.

11720 ■ Creative Education
Scientific Research Publishing
PO Box 54821
Irvine, CA 92619-4821
E-mail: ce@scirp.org
URL: http://www.scirp.org/journal/ce/

$195.00/year for individuals. Peer-reviewed journal
publishing articles on the latest advancements in
creative education.

11721 ■ Education & Treatment of Children
West Virginia University Press
139 Stansbury Hall
PO Box 6295
Morgantown, WV 26506
Ph: (304)293-8400
Fax: (304)293-6585
URL: http://www.educationandtreatmentofchildren.net

Quarterly. $85.00/year for institutions; $45.00/year for
individuals; $100.00/year for institutions, elsewhere;
$60.00/year for individuals, elsewhere. Periodical
featuring information concerning the development of
services for children and youth. Includes reports written for educators and other child care and mental
health providers focused on teaching, training, and
treatment effectiveness.

11722 ■ Education Week
Editorial Projects in Education Inc.
6935 Arlington Rd., Ste. 100
Bethesda, MD 20814-5287
Ph: (301)280-3100
Fax: (301)280-3200
Fr: 800-346-1834
E-mail: ew@epe.org
URL: http://www.edweek.org/ew

$90.00/year for individuals, print plus online. Profes-
sional newspaper for elementary and secondary
school educators.

**11723 ■ Educational Research and
    Evaluation**
Routledge Journals
270 Madison Ave.
New York, NY 10016-0601
Ph: (212)216-7800
Fax: (212)563-2269
URL: http://www.tandf.co.uk/journals/titles/
    13803611.asp

Bimonthly. $428.00/year for institutions, print + on-
line; $385.00/year for institutions, online only;
$165.00/year for individuals, print only; $731.00/year
for institutions, print + online; $658.00/year for institu-
tions, online only; $275.00/year for individuals, print
only. Peer-reviewed journal on theory and practice.

11724 ■ Educational Researcher
American Educational Research Association
1430 K St. NW, Ste. 1200
Washington, DC 20005
Ph: (202)238-3200
Fax: (202)238-3250
URL: http://www.aera.net/publications/?id=317

Monthly. $48.00/year for individuals, plus foreign mail-
ing charges; $150.00/year for institutions, plus foreign
mailing charges. Educational research journal.

11725 ■ Environmental Education Research
Routledge Journals
270 Madison Ave.
New York, NY 10016-0601
Ph: (212)216-7800

Fax: (212)563-2269
URL: http://www.tandf.co.uk/journals/titles/
13504622.asp

Bimonthly. $1,373.00/year for institutions, print + online; $1,236.00/year for institutions, online only; $364.00/year for individuals, print only. Journal covering all aspects of environmental education.

11726 ■ Essays in Education
University of South Carolina
471 University Pky.
Aiken, SC 29801
Ph: (803)648-6851
URL: http://www.usca.edu/essays/

Monthly. Journal covering issues that impact and influence education.

11727 ■ Hematology
American Society of Hematology
2021 L St. NW, Ste. 900
Washington, DC 20036
Ph: (202)776-0544
Fax: (202)776-0545
URL: http://asheducationbook.hematologylibrary.org

Annual. $75.00/year for members; $125.00/year for nonmembers. Journal providing continuing medical education for physicians.

11728 ■ Interdisciplinary Journal of Teaching and Learning
Southern University at Baton Rouge
PO Box 9942
Baton Rouge, LA 70813
Ph: (225)711-4500
Fax: (225)771-4400
URL: http://www.subr.edu/CollegeofEducation/
COE%20ONLINE%20Journa

Online academic journal that publishes research and scholarly articles in the field of education and learning.

11729 ■ The International Electronic Journal of Health Education
American Alliance for Health, Physical Education, Recreation & Dance
1900 Association Dr.
Reston, VA 20191-1598
Ph: (703)476-3400
Fax: (703)476-9527
Fr: 800-213-7193
URL: http://www.aahperd.org/aahe/publications/iejhe/

Annual. Free, health education professionals and students. Journal promoting health through education and other systematic strategies.

11730 ■ International Journal of Critical Pedagogy
University of North Carolina at Greensboro
1400 Spring Garden St.
Greensboro, NC 27412
Ph: (336)334-5000
URL: http://libjournal.uncg.edu/ojs/index.php/ijcp/
index

Peer-reviewed journal publishing innovative understandings and applications of critical pedagogy.

11731 ■ International Journal of Early Years Education
Routledge Journals
270 Madison Ave.
New York, NY 10016-0601
Ph: (212)216-7800
Fax: (212)563-2269
URL: http://www.tandf.co.uk/journals/titles/
09669760.asp

$705.00/year for institutions, online only; $783.00/year for institutions, print + online; $271.00/year for individuals, print only. Journal focusing on education world-wide.

11732 ■ International Journal of Inclusive Education
Routledge Journals
270 Madison Ave.
New York, NY 10016-0601
Ph: (212)216-7800
Fax: (212)563-2269
URL: http://www.tandf.co.uk/journals/titles/
13603116.asp

$589.00/year for individuals, print only; $1,135.00/year for institutions, online only; $1,261.00/year for individuals, print + online; $355.00/year for individuals, print only; $694.00/year for institutions, online only; $771.00/year for institutions, print + online. Journal providing information on the nature of schools, universities and technical colleges for the educators and educational policy-makers.

11733 ■ International Journal of Leadership in Education
Routledge
711 3 Ave., 8 Fl.
New York, NY 10016
Ph: (212)216-7800
Fax: (212)563-2269
Fr: 800-634-7064
E-mail: ijle@txstate.edu
URL: http://www.tandf.co.uk/journals/tf/
13603124.html

Quarterly. $240.00/year for individuals, print only; $612.00/year for institutions, online only; $680.00/year for institutions, print and online; $408.00/year for institutions, print and online; $367.00/year for institutions, online only; $142.00/year for individuals, print only. Journal dealing with leadership in education.

11734 ■ International Journal of Progressive Education
International Journal of Progressive Education
c/o Alex Jean-Charles, PhD, Asst. Mng. Ed.
320 Fitzelle Hall, Ravine Pky.
Oneonta, NY 13820
URL: http://www.inased.org/ijpe.htm

$35.00/year for members; $45.00/year for individuals; $140.00/year for institutions, library; $35.00/year for students; $25.00/year for single issue; $50.00/year for students, other countries. Peer-reviewed online journal that aims to create an open and continuing dialogue about current educational issues and future conceptions of educational theory.

11735 ■ International Journal of Whole Schooling
Whole Schooling Press
Wayne State University
217 Education
Detroit, MI 48202
URL: http://www.wholeschooling.net/Journal_of_
Whole_Schooling/IJW

Free. International, refereed academic journal dedicated to exploring ways to improve learning and schooling for all children.

11736 ■ Journal of Academic Leadership
Academic Leadership
600 Park St.
Rarick Hall 219
Hays, KS 67601-4099
Ph: (785)628-4547
URL: http://www.academicleadership.org/

Journal focusing on the leadership issues in the academic world.

11737 ■ Journal of Cases in Educational Leadership
Sage Publications Inc.
2455 Teller Rd.
Thousand Oaks, CA 91320-2218
Ph: (805)499-9774
Fax: (805)583-2665
Fr: 800-818-7243
URL: http://jel.sagepub.com

Quarterly. $411.00/year for institutions, e-access;

$94.00/year for individuals, e-access. Journal covering cases appropriate for use in programs that prepare educational leaders.

11738 ■ Journal of Curriculum and Supervision
Association for Supervision and Curriculum Development
1703 N Beauregard St.
Alexandria, VA 22311-1714
Ph: (703)578-9600
Fax: (703)575-5400
Fr: 800-933-2723
URL: http://www.ascd.org/publications/jcs/fall2002/
On_Community.a

Scholarly journal focusing on curriculum and supervision.

11739 ■ Journal of Direct Instruction
Association for Direct Instruction
PO Box 10252
Eugene, OR 97440
Ph: (541)485-1293
Fax: (541)868-1397
Fr: 800-995-2464
URL: http://www.adihome.org/
index.php?option=com_content&view=art

Quarterly. Included in membership. Journal covering education.

11740 ■ Journal of Language, Identity, and Education
Routledge Journals
270 Madison Ave.
New York, NY 10016-0601
Ph: (212)216-7800
Fax: (212)563-2269
URL: http://www.tandf.co.uk/journals/titles/
15348458.asp

$316.00/year for institutions, print + online; $284.00/year for institutions, online; $43.00/year for individuals, print + online; $527.00/year for institutions, print + online; $474.00/year for institutions, online; $71.00/year for individuals, print + online; $421.00/year for institutions, print + online; $379.00/year for institutions, online; $57.00/year for individuals, print + online. Scholarly, interdisciplinary journal covering issues in language, identity and education worldwide for academics, educators and policy specialists in a variety of disciplines, and others.

11741 ■ Journal of Latinos and Education
Routledge Journals
270 Madison Ave.
New York, NY 10016-0601
Ph: (212)216-7800
Fax: (212)563-2269
URL: http://www.tandf.co.uk/journals/titles/
15348431.asp

Quarterly. $286.00/year for institutions, print + online; $257.00/year for institutions, online; $38.00/year for individuals, print + online; $480.00/year for institutions, print + online; $432.00/year for institutions, online; $63.00/year for individuals, print + online; $331.00/year for institutions, print + online; $343.00/year for institutions, online; $51.00/year for individuals, print + online. Scholarly, multidisciplinary journal covering educational issues that impact Latinos for researchers, teaching professionals, academics, scholars, institutions, and others.

11742 ■ Journal of Learning Disabilities
Sage Publications Inc.
2455 Teller Rd.
Thousand Oaks, CA 91320-2218
Ph: (805)499-9774
Fax: (805)583-2665
Fr: 800-818-7243
URL: http://www.sagepub.com/
journalsProdDesc.nav?ct_p=boardsII

Bimonthly. $77.00/year for individuals, print & e-access; $260.00/year for institutions, print & e-access; $255.00/year for institutions, print only;

$234.00/year for institutions, e-access. Special education journal.

11743 ■ *Journal of STEM Education*
Auburn University
9088 Haley Ctr.
Auburn, AL 36849
Ph: (334)844-9088
Fax: (334)844-9027
URL: http://ojs.jstem.org/index.php?journal=JSTEM

Semiannual. Journal for educators in Science, Technology, Engineering, and Mathematics (STEM) education.

11744 ■ *Leadership and Policy in Schools*
Routledge Journals
270 Madison Ave.
New York, NY 10016-0601
Ph: (212)216-7800
Fax: (212)563-2269
URL: http://www.tandf.co.uk/journals/titles/15700763.asp

Quarterly. $567.00/year for institutions, print and online; $260.00/year for individuals, print only; $510.00/year for institutions, online only. Journal providing information about leadership and policy in primary and secondary education.

11745 ■ *Music Educators Journal*
MENC: The National Association for Music Education
1806 Robert Fulton Dr.
Reston, VA 20191
Ph: (703)860-4000
Fax: (703)860-1531
Fr: 800-336-3768
URL: http://www.menc.org/resources/view/menc-journals

$165.00/year for institutions, print & E-access; $149.00/year for institutions, E-access; $162.00/year for institutions, print only. Journal covering all levels of music education. Published on alternate months with Teaching Music.

11746 ■ *NJEA Review*
New Jersey Education Association
180 W State St.
PO Box 1211
Trenton, NJ 08607-1211
Ph: (609)599-4561
Fax: (609)392-6321
E-mail: njeareview@njea.org
URL: http://www.njea.org/page.aspx?z=1094&pz=8

Monthly. $250.00/year for nonmembers. Educational journal for public school employees.

11747 ■ *Oxford Review of Education*
Routledge Journals
270 Madison Ave.
New York, NY 10016-0601
Ph: (212)216-7800
Fax: (212)563-2269
URL: http://www.tandf.co.uk/journals/titles/03054985.asp

$709.00/year for institutions, print + online; $1,224.00/year for institutions, print + online; $249.00/year for individuals, print only; $454.00/year for individuals, print only. Journal covering advance study of education.

11748 ■ *The Physics Teacher*
American Association of Physics Teachers
1 Physics Ellipse
College Park, MD 20740-3845
Ph: (301)209-3311
Fax: (301)209-0845
URL: http://tpt.aapt.org

; $434.00/year for nonmembers, domestic; $469.00/year for nonmembers, international. Scientific education magazine.

11749 ■ *School and Community*
Missouri State Teachers Association
407 S Sixth St.
PO Box 458
Columbia, MO 65205
Ph: (573)442-3127
Fax: (573)443-5079
Fr: 800-392-0532
URL: http://www.msta.org/resources/publications/snc/

Quarterly. Education magazine.

11750 ■ *School Effectiveness and School Improvement*
Routledge
711 3 Ave., 8 Fl.
New York, NY 10016
Ph: (212)216-7800
Fax: (212)563-2269
Fr: 800-634-7064
URL: http://www.tandf.co.uk/journals/titles/09243453.asp

Quarterly. $387.00/year for institutions, print and online; $348.00/year for institutions, online only; $186.00/year for individuals, print only; $660.00/year for institutions, print and online; $594.00/year for institutions, online only; $312.00/year for individuals, print only. Journal focusing on educational progress of all students.

11751 ■ *The Science Teacher*
National Science Teachers Association
1840 Wilson Blvd.
Arlington, VA 22201-3000
Ph: (703)243-7100
Fax: (703)243-7177
URL: http://www.nsta.org/highschool/

Peer-reviewed journal for secondary science teachers.

11752 ■ *Strategies*
American Alliance for Health, Physical Education, Recreation & Dance
1900 Association Dr.
Reston, VA 20191-1598
Ph: (703)476-3400
Fax: (703)476-9527
Fr: 800-213-7193
E-mail: strategies@aahperd.org
URL: http://www.aahperd.org/naspe/publications/journals/strategie

Bimonthly. $130.00/year for U.S. and Canada, institutions, schools & libraries; print & online; $50.00/year for U.S. and Canada, add $5 GST; $62.00/year for other countries, schools & libraries, print & online; $130.00/year for institutions, other countries, schools & libraries, online; $142.00/year for institutions, other countries, schools & libraries, print; $162.00/year for institutions, other countries, schools & libraries, print & online. Peer-reviewed journal providing practical, hands-on information to physical educators and coaches.

11753 ■ *Teacher Magazine*
Editorial Projects in Education Inc.
6935 Arlington Rd., Ste. 100
Bethesda, MD 20814-5287
Ph: (301)280-3100
Fax: (301)280-3200
Fr: 800-346-1834
URL: http://www.teachermagazine.org/tm/index.html

$90.00/year for individuals. Professional magazine for elementary and secondary school teachers.

11754 ■ *Teaching Exceptional Children*
Council for Exceptional Children
2900 Crystal Dr., Ste. 1000
Arlington, VA 22202
Ph: (703)620-3660
Fax: (703)264-9494
Fr: 888-232-7733
URL: http://www.cec.sped.org/Content/NavigationMenu/Publications2

$90.00/year for individuals, print; $152.00/year for

two years, print; $101.00/year for Canada, print; $169.00/year for two years, Canada; $197.00/year for institutions, print; $332.00/year for two years, print; $208.00/year for institutions, Canada, print; $236.00/year for institutions, other countries, print; $399.00/year for two years, institutional (print); $225.00/year for institutions, Canada, print and online. Peer-reviewed journal exploring practical methods for teaching students who have exceptionalities and those who are gifted and talented.

11755 ■ *Teaching and Learning in Nursing*
Elsevier Science Inc.
360 Park Ave. S
New York, NY 10010-1710
Ph: (212)989-5800
Fax: (212)633-3990
Fr: 888-437-4636
URL: http://www.elsevier.com/wps/find/journaldescription.cws_home

Quarterly. $232.00/year for institutions, other countries; $134.00/year for other countries; $160.00/year for institutions; $91.00/year for individuals. Journal devoted to associate degree nursing education and practice.

11756 ■ *Tech Directions*
Prakken Publications Inc.
832 Phoenix Dr.
Ann Arbor, MI 48108
Ph: (734)975-2800
Fax: (734)975-2787
Fr: 800-530-9673
E-mail: tdedit@techdirections.com
URL: http://www.techdirections.com

Monthly. $30.00/year for individuals, U.S.; $47.00/year for institutions; $50.00/year for other countries; $100.00/year for individuals, domestic. Magazine covering issues, programs, and projects in industrial education, technology education, trade and industry, and vocational-technical career education. Articles are geared for teacher and administrator use and reference from elementary school through postsecondary levels.

11757 ■ *Technology and Engineering Teacher*
International Technology Education Association
1914 Association Dr., Ste. 201
Reston, VA 20191-1539
Ph: (703)860-2100
Fax: (703)860-0353
URL: http://www.iteaconnect.org/Publications/ttt.htm

$35.00/year for individuals, professional U.S., 2 years; $70.00/year for individuals, professional U.S.; $30.00/year for students, undergrad student- first time member; $35.00/year for students, full-time grad/renewing undergrad student; $55.00/year for students, bridge - one-time student to professional; $410.00/year for institutions, group membership, 2 years; $210.00/year for institutions, group membership; $690.00/year for individuals, group membership, 2 years; $350.00/year for individuals, group membership; $270.00/year for individuals, group membership, 2 years. Magazine on technology education.

11758 ■ *Theory and Research in Education*
Sage Publications Inc.
2455 Teller Rd.
Thousand Oaks, CA 91320-2218
Ph: (805)499-9774
Fax: (805)583-2665
Fr: 800-818-7243
URL: http://www.sagepub.com/journalsProdDesc.nav?prodId=Journal20

$546.00/year for institutions, print and e-access; $491.00/year for institutions, e-access; $535.00/year for institutions, print; $85.00/year for individuals, print; $196.00/year for single issue, institutional; $37.00/year for single issue, individual. Interdisciplinary journal covering normative and theoretical issues concerning education including multi-faceted philosophical analysis of moral, social, political and epistemological problems and issues arising from educational practice.

EMPLOYER DIRECTORIES AND NETWORKING LISTS

11759 ■ Boarding Schools Directory
The Association of Boarding Schools
9 SW Pack Sq., Ste. 201
Asheville, NC 28801-3526
Ph: (828)258-5354
Fax: (828)258-6428
URL: http://www.schools.com

Annual, Latest edition 2007-2008. for U.S. and Canada. Covers: Boarding schools that are members of the Association of Boarding Schools. Entries include: School name, address, phone, e-mail and url's, grades for which boarding students are accepted, enrollment, brief description. Arrangement: Classified by type of school. Indexes: Geographical; program; Alphabetical.

11760 ■ Career Ideas for Teens in Education and Training
Facts On File Inc.
132 W 31st St., 17th Fl.
New York, NY 10001
Ph: (212)967-8800
Fax: 800-678-3633
Fr: 800-322-8755
URL: http://factsonfile.infobasepublishing.com

Published 2005. $40.00 for individuals. Covers: A multitude of career possibilities based on a teenager's specific interests and skills and links his/her talents to a wide variety of actual professions.

11761 ■ Careers in Focus—Education
Facts On File Inc.
132 W 31st St., 17th Fl.
New York, NY 10001
Ph: (212)967-8800
Fax: 800-678-3633
Fr: 800-322-8755
URL: http://www.infobasepublishing.com

Latest edition 3rd; Published February, 2009. $32.95 for individuals. Covers: An overview of education, followed by a selection of jobs profiled in detail, including the nature of the job, earnings, prospects for employment, what kind of training and skills it requires, and sources for further information.

11762 ■ Christian Schools International—Directory
Christian Schools International
3350 E Paris Ave. SE
Grand Rapids, MI 49512-2907
Ph: (616)957-1070
Fax: (616)957-5022
Fr: 800-635-8288
URL: http://www.store.csionline.org/index.php?main_
page=index&cPath=

Annual, Latest edition 2007-2008. $15.00 for members. Covers: Nearly 450 Reformed Christian elementary and secondary schools; related associations; societies without schools. Entries include: For schools—School name, address, phone; name, title, and address of officers; names of faculty members. Arrangement: Geographical.

11763 ■ Directory of Public School Systems in the U.S.
American Association for Employment in Education
3040 Riverside Dr., Ste. 117
Columbus, OH 43221
Ph: (614)485-1111
Fax: (360)244-7802
E-mail: office@aaee.org
URL: http://www.aaee.org/

Annual, Winter; latest edition 2004-2005 edition. $55.00 for members; $80.00 for nonmembers. Covers: About 14,000 public school systems in the United

States and their administrative personnel. Entries include: System name, address, phone, website address, name and title of personnel administrator, levels taught and approx. Student population. Arrangement: Geographical by state.

11764 ■ Educators Resource Directory
Grey House Publishing
4919 Rte. 22
PO Box 56
Amenia, NY 12501
Ph: (518)789-8700
Fax: (518)789-0556
Fr: 800-562-2139
E-mail: books@greyhouse.com
URL: http://www.greyhouse.com/education.htm

Annual, latest edition 2011-2012. $145.00 for individuals. Covers: Publishing opportunities, state by state information on enrollment, funding and grant resources, associations and conferences, teaching jobs abroad all geared toward elementary and secondary school professionals. Also covers online databases, textbook publishers, school suppliers, plus state and federal agencies. Entries include: Contact name, address, phone, fax, description, publications. A unique compilation of over 6,500 educational resources and over 130 tables and charts of education statistics and rankings. Arrangement: By subject categories. Indexes: Entry, geographical, publisher, web sites.

11765 ■ Ganley's Catholic Schools in America—Elementary/Secondary/College & University
Fisher Publishing Co.
PO Box 5729
Sun City West, AZ 85376
Ph: (623)328-8326
URL: http://www.ganleyscatholicschools.com

Annual, summer; Latest edition 38th, 2010. $67.00 for individuals. Covers: over 8,400 Catholic K-12 Schools. Arrangement: Geographical by state, then alphabetical by Diocese name.

11766 ■ Handbook of Private Schools
Porter Sargent Publishers Inc.
11 Beacon St., Ste. 1400
Boston, MA 02108-3099
Ph: (617)523-1670
Fax: (617)523-1021
Fr: 800-342-7470
URL: http://www.portersargent.com

Annual, latest edition 92nd, 2011-2012. $99.00 for individuals. Covers: More than 1,700 elementary and secondary boarding and day schools in the United States. Entries include: School name, address, phone, fax, E-mail, URL, type of school (boarding or day), sex and age range, names and titles of administrators, grades offered, academic orientation, curriculum, new admissions yearly, tests required for admission, enrollment and faculty, graduate record, number of alumni, tuition and scholarship figures, summer session, plant evaluation and endowment, date of establishment, calendar, association membership, description of school's offerings and history, test score averages, uniform requirements, geographical, and demographic date. Arrangement: Geographical. Indexes: Alphabetical by school name, cross indexed by state, region, grade range, sexes accepted, school features and enrollment.

11767 ■ Independent Schools Association of the Southwest—Membership List
Independent Schools Association of the Southwest
Energy Sq., 505 N Big Spring St., Ste. 406
Midland, TX 79701
Ph: (432)684-9550
Fax: (432)684-9401
Fr: 800-688-5007
URL: http://www.isasw.org

Annual, August. Covers: Over 84 schools located in Arizona, Kansas, Louisiana, Mexico, New Mexico, Oklahoma, and Texas enrolling over 38,000 students. Entries include: School name, address, phone, chief

administrative officer, structure, and enrollment. Arrangement: Geographical. Indexes: Alphabetical.

11768 ■ MDR's School Directories
Market Data Retrieval
6 Armstrong Rd., Ste. 301
Shelton, CT 06484-4722
Ph: (203)926-4800
Fax: (203)926-1826
Fr: 800-333-8802
URL: http://www.schooldata.com/mdrdir.asp

Annual, Latest edition 2008-2009. Covers: Over 90,000 public, 8,000 Catholic, and 15,000 other private schools (grades K-12) in the United States; over 15,000 school district offices, 76,000 school librarians; and 27,000 media specialists, 33,000 technology coordinators. Includes names of over 165,000 school district administrators and staff members in county and state education administration. Entries include: District name and address; telephone and fax number; number of schools; number of teachers in the district; district enrollment; special Ed students; limited-English proficient students; minority percentage by race, college bound students; expenditures per student for instructional materials; poverty level; title 1 dollars; site-based management; district open/close dates; construction indicator; technologies and quantities; district-level administrators, *new superintendents shaded*; school name and address—new public shaded; telephone and fax number; principal new principal shaded; librarian, media specialist and technology coordinator; grade span; special programs and school type; student enrollment; technologies and quantities (instructional computer brand noting predominant brand); Multi-Media Computers; Internet connection or access; Tech Sophistication Index. Arrangement: Geographical. Indexes: District County; District Personnel; Principal; New Public Schools and Key Personnel; District and School Telephone; District URLs.

11769 ■ National Directory for Employment in Education
American Association for Employment in Education
3040 Riverside Dr., Ste. 117
Columbus, OH 43221
Ph: (614)485-1111
Fax: (360)244-7802
URL: http://www.aaee.org/

Annual, winter; latest edition 2008-2009. $20.00 for nonmembers; $10.00 for members. Covers: about 600 placement offices maintained by teacher-training institutions and 300 school district personnel officers and/or superintendents responsible for hiring professional staff. Entries include: Institution name, address, phone, contact name, email address, and website. Arrangement: Geographical. Indexes: Personal name, subject-field of teacher training, institutions which provide vacancy bulletins and placement services to non-enrolled students.

11770 ■ Patterson's American Education
Educational Directories Inc.
1025 W Wise Rd., Ste. 101
PO Box 68097
Schaumburg, IL 60168-0097
Ph: (847)891-1250
Fax: (847)891-0945
Fr: 800-357-6183
URL: http://www.ediusa.com

Annual, Latest edition 2012, vol. 108. $97.00 for individuals. Covers: Over 11,000 school districts in the United States; more than 34,000 public, private, and Catholic high schools, middle schools, and junior high schools; Approximately 300 parochial superintendents; 400 state department of education personnel. Entries include: For school districts and schools—District and superintendent Name, address, phone, fax, grade ranges, enrollment, school names, addresses, phone numbers, grade ranges, enrollment, names of principals. For postsecondary schools—School name, address, phone number, URL, e-mail, names of administrator or director of admissions. For private and Catholic high schools—

name, address, phone, fax, enrollment, grades offered, name of principal. Postsecondary institutions are covered in 'Patterson's Schools Classified'. Arrangement: Geographical by state, then alphabetical by city.

11771 ■ Private Independent Schools
Bunting and Lyon Inc.
615 Broad Swamp Rd.
Cheshire, CT 06410
Ph: (203)668-1897
Fax: (203)269-8908
URL: http://www.buntingandlyon.com

Annual, Latest edition 2010. $115.00 for individuals. Covers: 1,200 English-speaking elementary and secondary private schools and summer programs in North America and abroad. Entries include: School name, address, phone, fax, e-mail, website, enrollment, tuition and other fees, financial aid information, administrator's name and educational background, director of admission, regional accreditation, description of programs, curriculum, activities, learning differences grid. Arrangement: Geographical. Indexes: School name; geographical. Summer programs, general classification grid, learning differences reference grid.

11772 ■ Requirements for Certification of Teachers, Counselors, Librarians, Administrators for Elementary and Secondary Schools
University of Chicago Press
Journals Division
1427 E 60th St.
Chicago, IL 60637-2954
Ph: (773)702-7636
Fax: (773)702-9756
URL: http://www.press.uchicago.edu

Annual, Latest edition 74th. $53.00. Publication includes: List of state and local departments of education. Entries include: Office name, address, phone. Principal content of publication is summaries of each state's teaching and administrative certification requirements. Arrangement: Geographical.

HANDBOOKS AND MANUALS

11773 ■ Best Careers for Teachers: Making the Most of Your Teaching Degree
LearningExpress, LLC
2 Rector St., 26th Fl.
New York, NY 10006
Fr: 800-295-9556
E-mail: customerservice@learningexpressllc.com
URL: http://www.learningexpressllc.com

LearningExpress Editors. 2010. $16.95 (paper). 208 pages. Serves as a guide for current, former and aspiring teachers towards ways to leverage their teaching education and experiences and find and establish a more rewarding career.

11774 ■ Careers in Horticulture and Botany
The McGraw-Hill Companies
PO Box 182604
Columbus, OH 43272
Fax: (614)759-3749
Fr: 877-883-5524
E-mail: customer.service@mcgraw-hill.com
URL: http://www.mhprofessional.com/
   product.php?isbn=0071467734

Jerry Garner. 2006. 16.95 (paper). 192 pages. Includes bibliographical references.

11775 ■ Careers in Journalism
The McGraw-Hill Companies
PO Box 182604
Columbus, OH 43272
Fax: (614)759-3749
Fr: 877-883-5524
E-mail: customer.service@mcgraw-hill.com
URL: http://www.mhprofessional.com/
   product.php?isbn=0071466371

Jan Goldberg. Third edition, 2005. $15.95 (paper). 192 pages.

11776 ■ Ferguson Career Coach: Managing Your Career in Education
Facts On File
132 W 31st St., 17th Fl.
New York, NY 10001
Fax: 800-678-3633
Fr: 800-322-8755
E-mail: custserv@factsonfile.com
URL: http://factsonfile.infobasepublishing.com

Shelly Field. 2008. $39.95 (hardcover). 272 pages. Contains tips on achieving career success in the field of education. Provides students with advice on making contacts, interviewing, and career strategies.

11777 ■ Get That Teaching Job!
Continuum International Publishing Group
80 Maiden Ln., Ste. 704
New York, NY 10038
Ph: (212)953-5858
Fax: (212)953-5944
E-mail: info@continuum-books.com
URL: http://www.continuumbooks.com

Paul K. Ainsworth. 2012. $27.95 (paperback). 184 pages. Serves as job search guide for primary and secondary school teachers. Features role-specific advice on developing an application letter and preparing for the interview. Includes list of interview questions and curriculum vitae templates.

11778 ■ Great Jobs for English Majors
The McGraw-Hill Companies
PO Box 182604
Columbus, OH 43272
Fax: (614)759-3749
Fr: 877-883-5524
E-mail: customer.service@mcgraw-hill.com
URL: http://www.mhprofessional.com

Julie DeGalan and Stephen Lambert. Third edition, 2006. $15.95 (paper). 192 pages.

11779 ■ Great Jobs for History Majors
The McGraw-Hill Companies
PO Box 182604
Columbus, OH 43272
Fax: (614)759-3749
Fr: 877-883-5524
E-mail: customer.service@mcgraw-hill.com
URL: http://www.mhprofessional.com

Julie DeGalan and Stephen Lambert. 2007. $16.95 (paper). 192 pages.

11780 ■ Great Jobs for Liberal Arts Majors
The McGraw-Hill Companies
PO Box 182604
Columbus, OH 43272
Fax: (614)759-3749
Fr: 877-883-5524
E-mail: customer.service@mcgraw-hill.com
URL: http://www.mhprofessional.com/
   product.php?isbn=0071482148

Blythe Camenson. Second edition, 2007. $16.95 (paper). 192 pages.

11781 ■ Great Jobs for Music Majors
The McGraw-Hill Companies
PO Box 182604
Columbus, OH 43272
Fax: (614)759-3749
Fr: 877-883-5524
E-mail: customer.service@mcgraw-hill.com
URL: http://www.mhprofessional.com/
   product.php?isbn=0071454616

Jan Goldberg. Second edition, 2004. $15.95 (paper). 180 pages.

11782 ■ Great Jobs for Theater Majors
The McGraw-Hill Companies
PO Box 182604
Columbus, OH 43272
Fax: (614)759-3749

Fr: 877-883-5524
E-mail: customer.service@mcgraw-hill.com
URL: http://www.mhprofessional.com/
   product.php?isbn=007143853X

Jan Goldberg and Julie DeGalan. 2005. $15.95 (paper). 192 pages.

11783 ■ The Inside Secrets of Finding a Teaching Job
Jist Works
875 Montreal Way
St. Paul, MN 55102
Fr: 800-648-5478
E-mail: info@jist.com
URL: http://www.jist.com

Jack Warner and Clyde Bryan. Third edition, 2006. $12.95. 208 pages. Tips from educators on finding an entry-level teaching position.

11784 ■ Inside Secrets of Finding a Teaching Job, Third Edition: The Most Effective Search Methods for Both New and Experienced Educators
JIST Publishing
875 Montreal Way
St. Paul, MN 55102
Fax: 800-547-8329
Fr: 800-648-5478
E-mail: info@jist.com
URL: http://www.jist.com/shop/
   product.php?productid=3423

Jack Warner and Clyde Bryan. 2006. $6.47. 208 pages. Covers researching job opportunities; preparing resumes, cover letters, mission statements, teacher portfolios, and demonstration videos; preparing for interviews; and finding the inside track.

11785 ■ Opportunities in Overseas Careers
The McGraw-Hill Companies
PO Box 182604
Columbus, OH 43272
Fax: (614)759-3749
Fr: 877-883-5524
E-mail: customer.service@mcgraw-hill.com
URL: http://www.mhprofessional.com/
   product.php?isbn=0071454470

Blythe Camenson. 2004. $13.95 (paper). 173 pages.

11786 ■ Opportunities in Teaching Careers
The McGraw-Hill Companies
PO Box 182604
Columbus, OH 43272
Fax: (614)759-3749
Fr: 877-883-5524
E-mail: customer.service@mcgraw-hill.com
URL: http://www.mhprofessional.com/
   product.php?isbn=0071438173

Janet Fine. 2005. $13.95 (paper). 160 pages. Discusses licensing and accreditation programs, sources of placement information, job-seeking correspondence, selection procedures, and paths to advancement. Also covers professional associations, non-traditional teaching opportunities, and jobs abroad.

ONLINE JOB SOURCES AND SERVICES

11787 ■ ABCTeachingJobs.com
URL: http://www.abcteachingjobs.com

Description: Serves as a source of teacher job postings and recruitment. Offers jobs for K-12 teachers and administrators.

11788 ■ Academic Employment Network
URL: http://www.academploy.com

Description: Online position announcement service. Lists available positions in colleges, primary and secondary educational institutions for faculty, staff, and administrative professionals. Fee: Free searching and browsing features.

11789 ■ MyTeachingJobSearch.com
URL: http://www.myteachingjobsearch.com

Description: Provides teaching and teacher jobs at public and private schools and school districts across the United States.

11790 ■ School-Jobs.net
URL: http://www.school-jobs.net/jobs

Description: Matches teachers, administrators, support staff, and other school employees to related jobs across the country. Features jobs by salary, location, and area of expertise.

11791 ■ SchoolSpring.com
E-mail: contact@schoolspring.com
URL: http://www.schoolspring.com

Description: Serves as an employment source for educators. Offers teaching jobs and other education job listings including complete archiving of all necessary documents and certifications, as well as access to all education jobs in a specific area.

11792 ■ WantToTeach.com
URL: http://www.wanttoteach.com

Description: Serves as an education website to search for administrative, instructional and support openings throughout the United States. Features job openings and job fairs and allows access to various education resources.

TRADESHOWS

11793 ■ American Council on the Teaching of Foreign Languages Convention
American Council on the Teaching of Foreign Languages
1001 N. Fairfax St., Ste. 200
Alexandria, VA 22314
Ph: (703)894-2900
Fax: (703)894-2905
E-mail: headquarters@actfl.org
URL: http://www.actfl.org

Annual. Primary Exhibits: Textbooks, tapes, and supplementary material in foreign languages. Dates and Locations: 2012 Nov 16-18; Philadelphia, PA; Pennsylvania Convention Center and Philadelphia Marriott Hot; 2013 Nov 15-17; Orlando, FL; Orange County Convention Center and Rosen Centre Hotel ; 2014 Nov 21-23; San Antonio, TX; Henry B. Gonzalez Convention Center and Grand Hyatt San Anto.

11794 ■ Association for Childhood Education International Annual International Conference & Exhibition
Association for Childhood Education International
17904 Georgia Ave., Ste. 215
Olney, MD 20832
Ph: (301)570-2111
Fax: (301)570-2212
Fr: 800-423-3563
E-mail: headquarters@acei.org
URL: http://www.acei.org

Annual. Primary Exhibits: Commercial and educational exhibits of interest to teachers, teacher educators, college students, daycare personnel and other care givers.

11795 ■ National Art Education Association National Convention
National Art Education Association
1806 Robert Fulton Dr., Ste. 300
Reston, VA 20191
Ph: (703)860-8000
Fax: (703)860-2960
Fr: 800-299-8321
E-mail: info@arteducators.org
URL: http://www.naea-reston.org

Annual. Primary Exhibits: Art materials; art-related books and magazines; art career education information; arts and crafts supplies. Dates and Locations:

2012 Mar 01-04; New York, NY; 2013 Mar 07-10; Fort Worth, TX.

11796 ■ National Association for Bilingual Education Conference
National Association for Bilingual Education
8701 Georgia Ave., Ste. 611
Silver Spring, MD 20910
Ph: (240)450-3700
Fax: (240)450-3799
E-mail: nabe@nabe.org
URL: http://www.nabe.org

Annual. Features speakers, sessions, product exhibits, and job fair.

11797 ■ National Association for Developmental Education Conference
National Association for Developmental Education
PMB 412
500 N Estrella Pkwy.
Goodyear, AZ 85338
Fax: (623)792-5747
Fr: 877-233-9455
E-mail: office@nade.net
URL: http://www.nade.net

Annual. Offers an opportunity for personal and professional growth. Includes job fair. 2013 February 27-March 2; Denver, CO; Sheraton Denver Hotel. 2014 March 5-8; Dallas, TX; Hilton Anatole.

11798 ■ National Association for the Education of Young Children Annual Conference
National Association for the Education of Young Children
1313 L St. NW, Ste. 500
Washington, DC 20005
Ph: (202)232-8777
Fax: (202)328-1846
Fr: 800-424-2460
URL: http://www.naeyc.org

Annual. Primary Exhibits: Educational materials and equipment designed for children ages birth through eight years old. Dates and Locations: 2012 Nov 07-10; Atlanta, GA.

11799 ■ National Council for Geographic Education Conference
National Council for Geographic Education
206-A Martin Hall
Jacksonvill State University
Jacksonville, AL 36265-1602
Ph: (256)782-5293
Fax: (256)782-5336
E-mail: ncge@jsucc.jsu.edu
URL: http://www.ncge.org

Annual. Primary Exhibits: Geographic teaching aids and materials.

11800 ■ National Council for the Social Studies Conference
National Council for the Social Studies
8555 16th St., Ste. 500
Silver Spring, MD 20910
Ph: (301)588-1800
Fax: (301)588-2049
E-mail: ncss@ncss.org
URL: http://www.ncss.org

Annual. Primary Exhibits: Educational materials, software, publications, and textbooks.

11801 ■ National Middle School Association Annual Conference & Exhibit
National Middle School Association
4151 Executive Pkwy., Ste. 300
Westerville, OH 43081
Ph: (614)895-4730
Fax: (614)895-4750
Fr: 800-528-6672
E-mail: info@amle.org
URL: http://www.nmsa.org

Annual. Primary Exhibits: Educational materials and services relating to middle level school (ages 10-15).

OTHER SOURCES

11802 ■ American Alliance for Health, Physical Education, Recreation and Dance (AAHPERD)
1900 Association Dr.
Reston, VA 20191-1598
Ph: (703)476-3400
Fax: (703)476-9527
Fr: 800-213-7193
E-mail: membership@aahperd.org
URL: http://www.aahperd.org

Description: Students and educators in physical education, dance, health, athletics, safety education, recreation, and outdoor education. Works to improve its fields of education at all levels through such services as consultation, periodicals and special publications, leadership development, determination of standards, and research. Sponsors placement service.

11803 ■ American Association of Christian Schools (AACS)
602 Belvoir Ave.
East Ridge, TN 37412
Ph: (423)629-4280
Fax: (423)622-7461
E-mail: info@aacs.org
URL: http://www.aacs.org

Description: Maintains teacher/administrator certification program and placement service. Participates in school accreditation program. Sponsors National Academic Tournament. Maintains American Christian Honor Society. Compiles statistics; maintains speakers' bureau and placement service.

11804 ■ American Association for Health Education (AAHE)
1900 Association Dr.
Reston, VA 20191-1599
Ph: (703)476-3400
Fax: (703)476-9527
Fr: 800-213-7193
E-mail: aahe@aahperd.org
URL: http://www.aahperd.org/aahe

Description: Professionals who have responsibility for health education in schools, colleges, communities, hospitals and clinics, and industries. Aims to advance the health education through program activities and federal legislation; encourage close working relationships between all health education and health service organizations; achieve good health and well-being for all Americans automatically, without conscious thought and endeavor. Member of the American Alliance for Health, Physical Education, Recreation and Dance.

11805 ■ American Association of Teachers of French (AATF)
Southern Illinois University
Mail Code 4510
Carbondale, IL 62901
Ph: (618)453-5731
Fax: (618)453-5733
E-mail: aatf@frenchteachers.org
URL: http://www.frenchteachers.org

Description: Teachers of French in public and private elementary and secondary schools, colleges and universities. Sponsors National French Week each November to take French out of the classroom and into the schools and community. Conducts National French Contest in elementary and secondary schools and awards prizes at all levels. Maintains Materials Center with promotional and pedagogical materials; National French Honor Society (high school), Placement Bureau, summer scholarships.

11806 ■ American Association of Teachers of German (AATG)
112 Haddontowne Ct., No. 104
Cherry Hill, NJ 08034-3668
Ph: (856)795-5553

Fax: (856)795-9398
E-mail: headquarters@aatg.org
URL: http://www.aatg.org

Description: Represents teachers of German at all levels; individuals interested in German language and culture. Offers in-service teacher-training workshops, materials, student honor society, national German examination and stipends/scholarships.

11807 ■ American Association of Teachers of Spanish and Portuguese (AATSP)
900 Ladd Rd.
Walled Lake, MI 48390
Ph: (248)960-2180
Fax: (248)960-9570
E-mail: aatspoffice@aatsp.org
URL: http://www.aatsp.org

Description: Teachers of Spanish and Portuguese languages and literatures and others interested in Hispanic culture. Operates placement bureau and maintains pen pal registry. Sponsors honor society, Sociedad Honoraria Hispanica and National Spanish Examinations for secondary school students.

11808 ■ American Classical League (ACL)
Miami University
422 Wells Mills Dr.
Oxford, OH 45056-1694
Ph: (513)529-7741
Fax: (513)529-7742
E-mail: info@aclclassics.org
URL: http://www.aclclassics.org

Description: Teachers of classical languages in high schools and colleges. Works to promote the teaching of Latin and other classical languages. Presents scholarship. Maintains placement service, teaching materials, and resource center at Miami University in Oxford, OH to sell teaching aids to Latin and Greek teachers.

11809 ■ American Federation of Teachers (AFT)
555 New Jersey Ave. NW
Washington, DC 20001
Ph: (202)879-4400
E-mail: online@aft.org
URL: http://www.aft.org

Description: Affiliated with the AFL-CIO. Works with teachers and other educational employees at the state and local level in organizing, collective bargaining, research, educational issues, and public relations. Conducts research in areas such as educational reform, teacher certification, and national assessments and standards. Represents members' concerns through legislative action; offers technical assistance. Serves professionals with concerns similar to those of teachers, including state employees, healthcare workers, and paraprofessionals.

11810 ■ American Mathematical Society (AMS)
201 Charles St.
Providence, RI 02904-2213
Ph: (401)455-4000
Fax: (401)331-3842
Fr: 800-321-4AMS
E-mail: ams@ams.org
URL: http://www.ams.org

Description: Professional society of mathematicians and educators. Promotes the interests of mathematical scholarship and research. Holds institutes, seminars, short courses, and symposia to further mathematical research; awards prizes. Offers placement services; compiles statistics.

11811 ■ American Orff-Schulwerk Association (AOSA)
PO Box 391089
Cleveland, OH 44139-8089
Ph: (440)543-5366
Fax: (440)543-2687
E-mail: info@aosa.org
URL: http://www.aosa.org

Description: Music and movement educators, music therapists, and church choir directors united to promote and encourage the philosophy of Carl Orff's (1895-1982, German composer) Schulwerk (Music for Children) in America. Distributes information on the activities and growth of Orff Schulwerk in America. Conducts research; offers information on teacher training. Operates clearinghouse.

11812 ■ Association of Christian Schools International (ACSI)
PO Box 65130
Colorado Springs, CO 80962-5130
Fax: (719)531-0631
Fr: 800-367-0798
E-mail: acsi_email@acsi.org
URL: http://www.acsi.org

Description: Seeks to enable Christian educators and schools worldwide to effectively prepare students for life.

11813 ■ Association for Direct Instruction (ADI)
PO Box 10252
Eugene, OR 97440
Ph: (541)485-1293
Fax: (541)868-1397
Fr: 800-995-2464
E-mail: brywick@adihome.org
URL: http://www.adihome.org

Description: Public school regular and special education teachers and university instructors. Encourages, promotes, and engages in research aimed at improving educational methods. Promotes dissemination of developmental information and skills that facilitate the education of adults and children. Administers a preschool for developmentally delayed children. Offers educational training workshops for instructors. Maintains speaker's bureau and placement service.

11814 ■ Council for Supervision and Leadership (ITEEA-CSL)
International Technology and Engineering Educators Association
Maryland Dept. of Education
200 W Baltimore St.
Baltimore, MD 21201
Ph: (410)767-0177
Fax: (410)333-2099
E-mail: lrhine@msde.state.md.us
URL: http://itea-cs.org

Description: Technology education supervisors from the U.S. Office of Education; local school department chairpersons; state departments of education, local school districts, territories, provinces, and foreign countries. Improves instruction and supervision of programs in technology education. Conducts research; compiles statistics. Sponsors competitions. Maintains speakers' bureau.

11815 ■ Friends Council on Education (FCE)
1507 Cherry St.
Philadelphia, PA 19102
Ph: (215)241-7245
Fax: (215)241-7299
E-mail: info@friendscouncil.org
URL: http://www.friendscouncil.org

Description: Representatives appointed by Friends Yearly Meetings; heads of Quaker secondary and elementary schools and colleges; members-at-large. Acts as a clearinghouse for information on Quaker schools and colleges. Holds meetings and conferences on education and provides in-service training for teachers, administrators and trustees in Friends schools.

11816 ■ Geography Education National Implementation Project
Texas A & M University
College Station, TX 77843-3147
Ph: (979)845-1579

Fax: (979)862-4487
E-mail: s-bednarz@tamu.edu
URL: http://genip.tamu.edu

Description: Consortium of geographic associations committed to improving the status and quality of geography education.

11817 ■ Green Parent Association
2601 Westhall Ln.
Maitland, FL 32751
Ph: (407)493-1372
E-mail: joy@greenparentassociation.org
URL: http://www.greenparentassociation.org

Description: Strives to empower families, teachers and businesses to live greener lifestyles through education and awareness. Seeks to share information about clean, healthy living that benefits families and the communities in which they live. Aims to inspire parents to continue to improve their children's lives through the food that they eat and the world in which they live.

11818 ■ International Association of Baptist Colleges and Universities (IABCU)
8120 Sawyer Brown Rd., Ste. 108
Nashville, TN 37221-1410
Ph: (615)673-1896
Fax: (615)662-1396
E-mail: marrington@baptistschools.org
URL: http://www.baptistschools.org

Description: Southern Baptist senior colleges, universities, junior colleges, academies, and Bible schools. Promotes Christian education through literature, faculty workshops, student recruitment, teacher placement, trustee orientation, statistical information, and other assistance to members.

11819 ■ The International Educator (TIE)
PO Box 513
Cummaquid, MA 02637
Ph: (508)790-1990
Fax: (508)790-1922
Fr: 877-375-6668
E-mail: tie@tieonline.com
URL: http://www.tieonline.com

Description: Facilitates the placement of teachers and administrators in American, British, and international schools. Seeks to create a network that provides for professional development opportunities and improved financial security of members. Offers advice and information on international school news, recent educational developments, job placement, and investment, consumer, and professional development opportunities. Makes available insurance and travel benefits. Operates International Schools Internship Program.

11820 ■ International Reading Association (IRA)
PO Box 8139
Newark, DE 19714-8139
Ph: (302)731-1600
Fax: (302)731-1057
Fr: 800-336-7323
E-mail: pubinfo@reading.org
URL: http://www.reading.org

Description: Represents teachers, reading specialists, consultants, administrators, supervisors, researchers, psychologists, librarians, and parents interested in promoting literacy. Seeks to improve the quality of reading instruction and promote literacy worldwide. Disseminates information pertaining to research on reading, including information on adult literacy, early childhood and literacy development, international education, literature for children and adolescents, and teacher education and professional development. Maintains over 40 special interest groups and over 70 committees.

11821 ■ Jewish Education Service of North America (JESNA)
318 W 39th St., 5th Fl.
New York, NY 10018
Ph: (212)284-6950

Fax: (212)284-6951
E-mail: info@jesna.org
URL: http://www.jesna.org

Description: Widely recognized leader in the areas of research and program evaluation, organizational change and innovative program design and dissemination. Operates the Mandell J. Berman Jewish Heritage Center for Research and Evaluation. Supports the Covenant Foundation, a joint venture with the Crown Family, which makes awards and grants for creativity in Jewish education.

11822 ■ Jewish Educators Assembly (JEA)
PO Box 413
Cedarhurst, NY 11516
Ph: (516)569-2537
Fax: (516)295-9039
E-mail: jewisheducators@jewisheducators.org
URL: http://www.jewisheducators.org

Description: Educational and supervisory personnel serving Jewish educational institutions. Seeks to: advance the development of Jewish education in the congregation on all levels in consonance with the philosophy of the Conservative Movement; cooperate with the United Synagogue of America Commission on Jewish Education as the policy-making body of the educational enterprise; join in cooperative effort with other Jewish educational institutions and organizations; establish and maintain professional standards for Jewish educators; serve as a forum for the exchange of ideas; promote the values of Jewish education as a basis for the creative continuity of the Jewish people. Maintains placement service and speaker's bureau.

11823 ■ NAFSA: Association of International Educators (NAFSA)
1307 New York Ave. NW, 8th Fl.
Washington, DC 20005-4701
Ph: (202)737-3699
Fax: (202)737-3657
E-mail: inbox@nafsa.org
URL: http://www.nafsa.org

Description: Individuals, organizations, and institutions dealing with international educational exchange, including foreign student advisers, overseas educational advisers, credentials and admissions officers, administrators and teachers of English as a second language, community support personnel, study-abroad administrators, and embassy cultural or educational personnel. Promotes self-regulation standards and responsibilities in international educational exchange; offers professional development opportunities primarily through publications, workshops, grants, and regional and national conferences. Advocates for increased awareness and support of international education and exchange on campuses, in government, and in communities. Offers services including: a job registry for employers and professionals involved with international education; a consultant referral service. Sponsors joint liaison activities with a variety of other educational and government organizations to conduct a census of foreign student enrollment in the U.S.; conducts workshops about specific subjects and countries.

11824 ■ National Alliance of Black School Educators (NABSE)
310 Pennsylvania Ave. SE
Washington, DC 20003
Ph: (202)608-6310
Fax: (202)608-6319
Fr: 800-221-2654
E-mail: info@nabse.org
URL: http://www.nabse.org

Description: Black educators from all levels; others indirectly involved in the education of black youth. Promotes awareness, professional expertise, and commitment among black educators. Goals are to: eliminate and rectify the results of racism in education; work with state, local, and national leaders to raise the academic achievement level of all black students; increase members' involvement in legislative activities; facilitate the introduction of a curriculum

that more completely embraces black America; improve the ability of black educators to promote problem resolution; create a meaningful and effective network of strength, talent, and professional support. Sponsors workshops, commission meetings, and special projects. Encourages research, especially as it relates to blacks, and the presentation of papers during national conferences. Plans to establish a National Black Educators Data Bank and offer placement service.

11825 ■ National Art Education Association (NAEA)
1806 Robert Fulton Dr., Ste. 300
Reston, VA 20191
Ph: (703)860-8000
Fax: (703)860-2960
Fr: 800-299-8321
E-mail: info@arteducators.org
URL: http://www.arteducators.org

Description: Teachers of art at elementary, middle, secondary, and college levels; colleges, libraries, museums, and other educational institutions. Studies problems of teaching art; encourages research and experimentation. Serves as a clearinghouse for information on art education programs, materials, and methods of instruction. Sponsors special institutes. Cooperates with other national organizations for the furtherance of creative art experiences for youth.

11826 ■ National Association for Bilingual Education
8701 Georgia Ave., Ste. 611
Silver Spring, MD 20910
Ph: (240)450-3700
Fax: (240)450-3799
E-mail: nabe@nabe.org
URL: http://www.nabe.org

Description: Comprised of bilingual and English language learner (ELL) teachers, parents, paraprofessionals, administrators, professors, advocates, researchers, and policy makers. Promotes English proficiency and respect for cultural and linguistic diversity. Creates and supports policies, programs, research, pedagogy, and professional development to achieve bilingualism and biliteracy.

11827 ■ National Association of Blind Teachers (NABT)
2200 Wilson Blvd., Ste. 650
Arlington, VA 22201
Ph: (202)467-5081
Fax: (703)465-5085
Fr: 800-424-8666
E-mail: info@acb.org
URL: http://www.acb.org

Description: Public school teachers, teachers of the visually impaired, college and university professors, and teachers in residential schools for the blind. Promotes employment and professional goals of blind persons entering the teaching profession or those established in their respective teaching fields. Serves as a vehicle for the dissemination of information and the exchange of ideas addressing special problems of members.

11828 ■ National Association of Catholic School Teachers (NACST)
1700 Sansom St., Ste. 903
Philadelphia, PA 19103
Fr: 800-99N-ACST
E-mail: nacst.nacst@verizon.net
URL: http://www.nacst.com

Description: Catholic school teachers. Aims to unify, advise, and assist Catholic school teachers in matters of collective bargaining. Promotes the welfare and rights of Catholic schools and teachers; determines needs of Catholic schools and teachers. Monitors legislation, trends, and statistics concerning Catholic education; promotes legislation favorable to nonpublic schools and Catholic school teachers; offers legal advice and addresses issues such as unemployment compensation; assists teachers in

organizing and negotiating contracts. Maintains speakers' bureau.

11829 ■ National Association for Developmental Education
PMB 412
500 N Estrella Pkwy.
Goodyear, AZ 85338
Fax: (623)792-5747
Fr: 877-233-9455
E-mail: office@nade.net
URL: http://www.nade.net

Description: Seeks to improve the theory and practice of developmental education. Enhances the professional capabilities of development educators. Facilitates communication among developmental education professionals.

11830 ■ National Association of Episcopal Schools (NAES)
815 2nd Ave., Ste. 819
New York, NY 10017-4594
Ph: (212)716-6134
Fax: (212)286-9366
Fr: 800-334-7626
E-mail: info@episcopalschools.org
URL: http://www.episcopalschools.org

Description: Represents Episcopal day and boarding schools and preschools. Promotes the educational ministry of the Episcopal Church. Provides publications, consultation services and conference focusing on Episcopal identity of schools, worship, religious education, spirituality, leadership development and governance for heads/directors, administrators, chaplains and teachers of religion, trustees, rectors and other church and school leaders.

11831 ■ National Association of Independent Schools (NAIS)
1620 L St. NW, Ste. 1100
Washington, DC 20036-5695
Ph: (202)973-9700
Fax: (202)973-9790
Fr: 800-793-6701
E-mail: bassett@nais.org
URL: http://www.nais.org

Description: Independent elementary and secondary school members; regional associations of independent schools and related associations. Provides curricular and administrative research and services. Conducts educational programs; compiles statistics.

11832 ■ National Association for Research in Science Teaching (NARST)
12100 Sunset Hills Rd., Ste. 130
Reston, VA 20190-3221
Ph: (703)234-4138
Fax: (703)435-4390
E-mail: info@narst.org
URL: http://www.narst.org

Description: Science teachers, supervisors, and science educators specializing in research and teacher education. Promotes and coordinates science education research and interprets and reports the results.

11833 ■ National Association for Sport and Physical Education (NASPE)
1900 Association Dr.
Reston, VA 20191-1598
Ph: (703)476-3410
Fax: (703)476-8316
Fr: 800-213-7193
E-mail: naspe@aahperd.org
URL: http://www.naspeinfo.org

Description: Men and women professionally involved with physical activity and sports. Seeks to improve the total sport and physical activity experience in America. Conducts research and education programs in such areas as sport psychology, curriculum development, kinesiology, history, philosophy, sport sociology, and the biological and behavioral basis of human activity. Develops and distributes public information materials which explain the value of physical education programs. Supports councils involved in organizing and supporting elementary, secondary, and college physical education and sport programs; administers the National Council of Athletic Training in conjunction with the National Association for Girls and Women in Sport; serves the professional interests of coaches, trainers, and officials. Maintains hall of fame, placement service, and media resource center for public information and professional preparation. Member benefits include group insurance and discounts.

11834 ■ National Communication Association (NCA)

1765 N St. NW
Washington, DC 20036
Ph: (202)464-4622
Fax: (202)464-4600
E-mail: nkidd@natcom.org
URL: http://www.natcom.org

Description: Elementary, secondary, college, and university teachers, speech clinicians, media specialists, communication consultants, students, theater directors, and other interested persons; libraries and other institutions. Works to promote study, criticism, research, teaching, and application of the artistic, humanistic, and scientific principles of communication, particularly speech communication. Sponsors the publication of scholarly volumes in speech. Conducts international debate tours in the U.S. and abroad. Maintains placement service.

11835 ■ National Community Education Association (NCEA)

3929 Old Lee Hwy., No. 91-A
Fairfax, VA 22030-2401
Ph: (703)359-8973
Fax: (703)359-0972
E-mail: ncea@ncea.com
URL: http://www.ncea.com

Description: Community school directors, principals, superintendents, professors, teachers, students, and laypeople. Promotes and establishes community schools as an integral part of the educational plan of every community. Emphasizes community and parent involvement in the schools, lifelong learning, and enrichment of K-12 and adult education. Serves as a clearinghouse for the exchange of ideas and information, and the sharing of efforts. Offers leadership training.

11836 ■ National Council for Accreditation of Teacher Education (NCATE)

2010 Massachusetts Ave. NW, Ste. 500
Washington, DC 20036
Ph: (202)466-7496
Fax: (202)296-6620
E-mail: ncate@ncate.org
URL: http://www.ncate.org

Description: Representatives from constituent colleges and universities, state departments of education, school boards, teacher, and other professional groups. Voluntary accrediting body devoted exclusively to: evaluation and accreditation of institutions for preparation of elementary and secondary school teachers; preparation of school service personnel, including school principals, supervisors, superintendents, school psychologists, instructional technologists, and other specialists for school-oriented positions.

11837 ■ National Council for Geographic Education (NCGE)

1145 17th St. NW, Rm. 7620
Washington, DC 20036
Ph: (202)857-7695
Fax: (202)618-6249
E-mail: ncge@ncge.org
URL: http://www.ncge.org

Description: Teachers of geography and social studies in elementary and secondary schools, colleges and universities; geographers in governmental agencies and private businesses. Encourages the training of teachers in geographic concepts, practices, teaching methods and techniques; works to develop effective geographic educational programs in schools and colleges and with adult groups; stimulates the production and use of accurate and understandable geographic teaching aids and materials.

11838 ■ National Council of Teachers of Mathematics (NCTM)

1906 Association Dr.
Reston, VA 20191-1502
Ph: (703)620-9840
Fax: (703)476-2970
Fr: 800-235-7566
E-mail: nctm@nctm.org
URL: http://www.nctm.org

Description: Aims to improve teaching and learning of mathematics.

11839 ■ Organization of American Historians (OAH)

112 N Bryan Ave.
Bloomington, IN 47408-4141
Ph: (812)855-7311
Fax: (812)855-0696
E-mail: questions@oah.org
URL: http://www.oah.org

Description: Professional historians, including college faculty members, secondary school teachers, graduate students, and other individuals in related fields; institutional subscribers are college, university, high school and public libraries, and historical agencies. Promotes historical research and study. Sponsors 12 prize programs for historical writing; maintains speakers' bureau. Conducts educational programs.

11840 ■ *Overseas Employment Opportunities for Educators: Department of Defense Dependents Schools*

DIANE Publishing Co.
PO Box 617
Darby, PA 19023-0617
Fr: 800-782-3833
URL: http://www.dianepublishing.net

Barry Leonard, editor. $20.00. 52 pages. An introduction to teachings positions in the Dept. of Defense Dependents Schools (DoDDS), a worldwide school system, operated by the DoD in 14 countries.

11841 ■ U.S.-China Education Foundation (USCEF)

4140 Oceanside Blvd., Ste. 159, No. 112
Oceanside, CA 92056-6005
E-mail: info@sage-usa.net
URL: http://www.sage-usa.net

Description: Aims to promote the learning of the Chinese languages (including Mandarin, Cantonese, and minority languages such as Mongolian) by Americans, and the learning of English by Chinese. Conducts short-term travel-study program to prepare Americans and Chinese for stays of four, six, or eight months or one to four years in China or the U.S., respectively. Operates teacher placement service and speakers' bureau. A project of The Society for the Development of Global Education (S.A.G.E. Inc.).

Sources of Help-Wanted Ads

11842 ■ *ACJS Today*
Academy of Criminal Justice Sciences (ACJS)
PO Box 960
Greenbelt, MD 20768-0960
Ph: (301)446-6300
Fax: (301)446-2819
Fr: 800-757-2257
E-mail: info@acjs.org
URL: http://www.acjs.org/

Description: Four issues/year. Circulation is 2,000. Contains criminal justice information.

11843 ■ *EHS Today*
Penton Media Inc.
249 W 17th St.
New York, NY 10011
Ph: (212)204-4200
URL: http://ehstoday.com/

Monthly. Free to qualified subscribers. Monthly publication for safety professionals featuring information to meet OSHA and EPA compliance requirements, improve management of safety, industrial hygiene and environmental programs and find products and services to protect employees and property.

11844 ■ *Journal of Information Security*
Scientific Research Publishing
PO Box 54821
Irvine, CA 92619-4821
E-mail: jis@scirp.org
URL: http://www.scirp.org/journal/jis/

Quarterly. $156.00/year for individuals. Peer-reviewed journal publishing articles on different areas of information security.

11845 ■ *National Locksmith*
National Publishing Company Inc.
1533 Burgundy Pkwy.
Streamwood, IL 60107
Ph: (630)837-2044
Fax: (630)837-1210
E-mail: info@thenationallocksmith.com
URL: http://www.thenationallocksmith.com/

Magazine focusing on physical security and locksmithing.

11846 ■ *Police & Security News*
Days Communications
1208 Juniper St.
Quakertown, PA 18951-1520
Ph: (215)538-1240
Fax: (215)538-1208
E-mail: advertising@policeandsecuritynews.com
URL: http://policeandsecuritynews.com

Bimonthly. $18.00/year for by mail; $75.00/year for other countries, mail. Tabloid for the law enforcement and private security industries. Includes articles on training, new products, and new technology.

11847 ■ *Security*
BNP Media
2401 W Big Beaver Rd., Ste. 700
Troy, MI 48084
Ph: (248)362-3700
Fax: (248)362-5103
Fr: 800-952-6643
E-mail: security@bnpmedia.com
URL: http://www.securitymagazine.com

Monthly. Free. Magazine presenting news and technology for loss prevention and asset protection.

11848 ■ *Security Sales & Integration*
Bobit Business Media
3520 Challenger St.
Torrance, CA 90503
Ph: (310)533-2400
E-mail: secsales@bobit.com
URL: http://www.securitysales.com

Monthly. Free. Magazine covering the security industry.

Employer Directories and Networking Lists

11849 ■ *Associated Locksmiths of America—Membership Directory*
Associated Locksmiths of America
3500 Easy St.
Dallas, TX 75247
Ph: (214)819-9733
Fr: 800-532-2562
URL: http://www.aloa.org/

Annual, March. Publication includes: Roster of about 9,500 members of the association.

11850 ■ *International Security Management Association—Membership Directory*
International Security Management Association
9004 113th St.
PO Box 623
Blue Grass, IA 52726
Ph: (563)381-4008
Fax: (563)381-4283
Fr: 800-368-1894
URL: http://isma.com/

Covers: Member senior security officers of multinational firms and chief executive officers of security consultation services.

Handbooks and Manuals

11851 ■ *Careers for Legal Eagles and Other Law-and-Order Types*
The McGraw-Hill Companies
PO Box 182604
Columbus, OH 43272
Fax: (614)759-3749

Fr: 877-883-5524
E-mail: customer.service@mcgraw-hill.com
URL: http://www.mhprofessional.com/
   product.php?isbn=0071466207

Blythe Camenson. Second edition, 2005. $13.95 (paper). 176 pages.

Employment Agencies and Search Firms

11852 ■ Conselium
14850 Montfort Dr., Ste. 106
Dallas, TX 75254
Ph: (972)934-8444
E-mail: maurice@conselium.com
URL: http://www.conselium.com

Executive search firm with a core expertise in corporate compliance, audit and information technology security.

11853 ■ Robert A. Borissoff, Security Consultant
Nor-Cal Bldg., 2016 Oakdale Ave.
San Francisco, CA 94124
Ph: (415)221-0600
Fax: (415)668-7174
E-mail: rborissoff@aol.com

Safety and security specialist in the development, design, and installation of personnel security programs, guard services, surveillance services, and personnel testing. Industries served: legal, security and government agencies worldwide.

Online Job Sources and Services

11854 ■ PhysicalSecurityCrossing.com
URL: http://www.physicalsecuritycrossing.com

Description: Offers a comprehensive collection of researched job openings in the physical security field. Lists security jobs from Fortune 500 and Fortune 1,000 companies.

11855 ■ Security Jobs Network
URL: http://www.securityjobs.net

Description: Lists job postings for security, loss prevention, and law enforcement related executive positions.

Tradeshows

11856 ■ ACFE Fraud Conference & Exhibition
Association of Certified Fraud Examiners
716 West Ave.
Austin, TX 78701
Ph: (512)478-9000

Fax: (512)478-9297
Fr: 800-245-3321
E-mail: info@acfe.com
URL: http://www.fraudconference.com

Annual. Features the latest development in detecting and preventing fraud in organizations.

11857 ■ RSA Conference
RSA
174 Middlesex Tpke.
Bedford, MA 01730
Fr: (866)397-5093
E-mail: rsaconferencehelp@rsaconference.com
URL: http://www.rsaconference.com

Annual. Brings together IT professionals, developers, policy makers, industry leaders and academics to share information and exchange ideas on technology trends and best practices in identity theft, hacking, cyber-terrorism, biometrics, network forensics, perimeter defense, secure web services, encryption and related topics.

OTHER SOURCES

11858 ■ ASIS International
1625 Prince St.
Alexandria, VA 22314-2818
Ph: (703)519-6200
Fax: (703)519-6299
E-mail: asis@asisonline.org
URL: http://www.asisonline.org

Description: Security professionals responsible for loss prevention, asset protection and security for businesses, government, or public organizations and institutions. Serves as a group for security professionals dedicated to increasing the effectiveness and productivity of people involved in the industry. Advocates the role and value of the security management profession to business, the media, government entities, and the public. Sponsors educational programs on security principles and current security issues. Administers professional certification programs (CPP, PCI, PSP). Offers networking opportunities to professionals and provides an online service for employment and resumes, publishes books, directories, and other resources.

11859 ■ ASIS International
1625 Prince St.
Alexandria, VA 22314-2818
Ph: (703)519-6200
Fax: (703)519-6299
E-mail: asis@asisonline.org
URL: http://www.asisonline.org

Description: Security professionals responsible for loss prevention, asset protection and security for businesses, government, or public organizations and institutions. Sponsors educational programs on security principles (basic through advanced levels) and current security issues. Administers professional certification programs (CPP, PCI, PSP). Offers networking opportunities to professionals; provides an online service for employment and resumes, publishes books, directories, and other resources.

11860 ■ Associated Locksmiths of America (ALOA)
3500 Easy St.
Dallas, TX 75247
Ph: (214)819-9733
Fax: (214)819-9736
Fr: 800-532-2562
URL: http://www.aloa.org

Description: Retail locksmiths; associate members are manufacturers and distributors of locks, keys, safes, and burglar alarms. Aims to educate and provide current information to individuals in the physical security industry. Maintains information and referral services for members; offers insurance and bonding programs. Holds annual five-day technical training classes and 3-day technical exhibit. Maintains museum.

11861 ■ Association of Threat Assessment Professionals (ATAP)
1215 K St., No. 2290
Sacramento, CA 95814
Ph: (916)231-2146
Fax: (916)231-2141
E-mail: ecardwell@atapworldwide.org
URL: http://www.atapworldwide.org

Description: Advances knowledge on how to protect the victims of stalking, harassment and threat situations. Shares and facilitates experiences and techniques of professionals in the field of threat assessment and management. Provides networking opportunities and enhances the professional growth of threat and violence risk assessment professionals.

11862 ■ Federal Criminal Investigators Association (FCIA)
PO Box 23400
Washington, DC 20026
Ph: (630)969-8537
Fr: 800-403-3374
E-mail: fcianat@aol.com
URL: http://www.fedcia.org

Description: Serves as professional fraternal organization dedicated to the advancement of federal law enforcement officers and the citizens they serve. Aims to ensure law enforcement professionals have the tools and support network to meet the challenges of future criminal investigations while becoming more community oriented. Intends to pursue mission by promoting professionalism, enhancing the image of federal officers, fostering cooperation among all law enforcement professionals, providing a fraternal environment for the advancement of the membership and community. Helps charitable programs and organizations.

11863 ■ Information Systems Security Association
9220 SW Barbur Blvd., No. 119-333
Portland, OR 97219
Ph: (206)388-4584
Fax: (206)299-3366
Fr: (866)349-5818
URL: http://www.issa.org

Description: Computer security practitioners, electronic data processing auditors, contingency planners, consultants, and individuals in related fields. Aims to increase knowledge about information security. Sponsors educational programs, research, discussion, and dissemination of information. Provides criteria for specific levels of expertise within the field of information security and protection.

11864 ■ International Association of Campus Law Enforcement Administrators (IACLEA)
342 N Main St.
West Hartford, CT 06117-2507
Ph: (860)586-7517
Fax: (860)586-7550
E-mail: info@iaclea.org
URL: http://www.iaclea.org

Description: Advances public safety for educational institutions by providing educational resources, advocacy, and professional development. Promotes professional ideals and standards in the administration of campus security/public safety/law enforcement. Works to make campus security/public safety/law enforcement an integral part of the educational community.

11865 ■ International Association for Healthcare Security and Safety (IAHSS)
PO Box 5038
Glendale Heights, IL 60139
Ph: (630)529-3913
Fax: (630)529-4139
Fr: 888-353-0990
E-mail: info@iahss.org
URL: http://www.iahss.org

Description: Administrative and supervisory personnel in the field of hospital security and safety. Develops, promotes, and coordinates better security/

safety programs in medical care facilities. Offers placement services; conducts specialized education programs.

11866 ■ International Association of Professional Security Consultants (IAPSC)
575 Market St., Ste. 2125
San Francisco, CA 94105
Ph: (415)536-0288
Fax: (415)764-4915
E-mail: iapsc@iapsc.org
URL: http://www.iapsc.org

Description: Security management, technical, training and forensic consultants. Promotes understanding and cooperation among members and industries or individuals requiring such services. Seeks to enhance members' knowledge through seminars, training programs and educational materials. Works to foster public awareness of the security consulting industry; serves as a clearinghouse for consultants' requirements. Maintains code of conduct, ethics and professional standards. Offers consultant referral service; operates speakers' bureau.

11867 ■ International Association of Property Crime Investigators (IAPCI)
10685-B Hazelhurst Dr., No. 1503
Houston, TX 77043
Ph: (206)426-1689
Fax: (206)426-1689
E-mail: info@iapci.org
URL: http://www.iapci.org

Description: Aims to enhance the effectiveness of property crime investigations through education and training. Promotes international professional standards for property crime investigators. Fosters collaboration and information sharing between law enforcement, insurance and loss prevention communities. Provides a forum for property crime investigators to share information, strategy and techniques.

11868 ■ International Association of Security and Investigative Regulators (IASIR)
PO Box 93
Waterloo, IA 50704
Fax: (319)232-1488
Fr: 888-354-2747
E-mail: contact@iasir.org
URL: http://www.iasir.org

Description: Seeks to enhance members' abilities to regulate and assist in promoting professionalism in the security, investigative, alarm and related industries. Assists states in developing and enforcing laws and regulations. Encourages reciprocity between states. Provides training and education opportunities for state regulators.

11869 ■ International Security Management Association (ISMA)
PO Box 623
Buffalo, IA 52728
Ph: (563)381-4008
Fax: (563)381-4283
E-mail: isma3@aol.com
URL: http://www.isma.com

Description: Senior security executives of multinational business firms and chief executive officers of full service security services companies. Aims to assist senior security executives in coordinating and exchanging information about security management and to establish high business and professional standards.

11870 ■ National Association of Legal Investigators (NALI)
235 N Pine St.
Lansing, MI 48933
Ph: (517)702-9835
Fax: (517)372-1501
Fr: (866)520-6254
E-mail: pjaeb@heartlandinfo.com
URL: http://www.nalionline.org

Description: Legal investigators, both independent and law firm staff, who specialize in investigation of personal injury matters for the plaintiff and criminal defense. Promotes professionalization of the legal investigator, accomplished by seminars and a professional certification program. Provides nationwide network of contact among members. Compiles statistics.

11871 ■ Nine Lives Associates (NLA)

Executive Protection Institute
16 Penn Pl., Ste. 1570
New York, NY 10001
Ph: (212)268-4555
Fax: (212)563-4783
Fr: 800-947-5827
E-mail: info@personalprotection.com
URL: http://www.personalprotection.com/nla.cfm

Description: Law enforcement, correctional, military, and security professionals who have been granted Personal Protection Specialist Certification through completion of the protective services program offered by the Executive Protection Institute; conducts research; EPI programs emphasize personal survival skills and techniques for the protection of others. Provides professional recognition for qualified individuals engaged in executive protection assignments. Maintains placement service. Operates speakers' bureau; compiles statistics.

11872 ■ Society of Professional Investigators (SPI)

233 Broadway, Ste. 2201
New York, NY 10279
Ph: (646)584-9081
URL: http://spionline.info

Description: Persons with at least 5 years' investigative experience for an official federal, state, or local government agency or for a quasi-official agency formed for law enforcement or related activities. Seeks to advance knowledge of the science and technology of professional investigation, law enforcement, and police science; maintains high standards and ethics; promotes efficiency of investigators in the services they perform.

Sources of Help-Wanted Ads

11873 ■ *BtoB Magazine*
Crain Communications Inc.
360 N Michigan Ave.
Chicago, IL 60601
Ph: (312)649-5200
URL: http://www.btobonline.com

Monthly. $59.00/year for individuals; $69.00/year for Canada; $89.00/year for other countries. Trade magazine on business-to-business marketing news, strategy, and tactics.

11874 ■ *CRM Buyer*
NewsFactor Network
23679 Calabasas Rd.
Calabasas, CA 91302
Ph: (818)713-2500
Fax: (818)713-2502
URL: http://www.crmbuyer.com/

Monthly. Magazine covering customer relationship management solutions.

11875 ■ *Money Making Opportunities*
Success Publishing International
11071 Ventura Blvd.
Studio City, CA 91604
Ph: (818)980-9166
Fax: (818)980-7829
URL: http://www.moneymakingopps.com/

Free. Magazine Source for small business opportunity seekers.

11876 ■ *Sales & Marketing Management*
Nielsen Business Media
770 Broadway
New York, NY 10003-9595
URL: http://www.salesandmarketing.com

Bimonthly. $48.00/year for individuals, print + online; $67.00/year for Canada, print + online; $146.00/year for other countries, print + online. Business magazine.

11877 ■ *Service Revenue*
Center for Services Marketing Inc.
300 Hess Ave., Bldg. II
Golden, CO 80401
Ph: (720)746-1900
Fax: (720)746-0599
URL: http://www.csmhub.com/

Bimonthly. $149.00/year for members. Newsletter giving information on marketing and sales knowledge for the service industry.

Employment Agencies and Search Firms

11878 ■ Bender Executive Search
45 N Station Plaza, Ste. 315
Great Neck, NY 11021
Ph: (516)773-4300
Fax: (516)482-5355
E-mail: benderexec@aol.com
URL: http://www.benderexecutivesearch.com

Executive search firm.

11879 ■ National Register - USA
550 Polaris Pkwy., Ste. 530
Westerville, OH 43082
Ph: (614)890-1200
Fax: (614)890-1259
E-mail: sales@nrcols.com
URL: http://www.nrcols.com

Employment agency. Offices in Akron and Toledo, OH.

11880 ■ Sales Executives Inc.
33900 W 8 Mile Rd., Ste. 171
Farmington Hills, MI 48335
Ph: (248)615-0100
E-mail: dale@salesexecutives.com
URL: http://www.salesexecutives.com

Employment agency. Executive search firm.

11881 ■ SalesPositions.com
Heather Croft
Ste. 250
Egg Harbor Township, NY 08234
Ph: (609)407-4774
Fax: (609)939-0488
E-mail: sales@salespositions.com
URL: http://www.salespositions.com

Employment agency.

Online Job Sources and Services

11882 ■ New Sales and Marketing Jobs
URL: http://www.newsalesandmarketingjobs.com
Description: Provides an online listing of companies with available sales and marketing jobs in all specialties.

Sources of Help-Wanted Ads

11883 ■ American City and County
Penton Media Inc.
9800 Metcalf Ave.
Overland Park, KS 66212
Ph: (913)341-1300
Fax: (913)967-1898
URL: http://americancityandcounty.com

Monthly. Municipal and county administration magazine.

11884 ■ Catalyst
North American Association of Christians in Social Work
PO Box 121
Botsford, CT 06404-0121
Fr: 888-426-4712
E-mail: info@nacsw.org
URL: http://www.nacsw.org

Quarterly. Seeks to inform and educate the membership on topics related to the mission and programs of the association. Strives to be an open forum for members to express their perspectives on a wide range of issues of interest to Christians in social work.

11885 ■ Child and Adolescent Social Work Journal
Springer-Verlag New York Inc.
233 Spring St.
New York, NY 10013-1578
Ph: (212)460-1500
Fax: (212)460-1575
Fr: 800-777-4643
URL: http://www.springer.com/psychology/personality+%26+social+ps

$925.00/year for institutions, print or online; $1,110.00/year for institutions, print & enchanced access. Journal dealing with issues in clinical social work practice with children, adolescents, and their families.

11886 ■ Children & Schools
National Association of Social Workers
750 1st St. NE, Ste. 700
Washington, DC 20002-4241
Ph: (202)408-8600
URL: http://www.naswpress.org/publications/journals/cs.html

Quarterly. $59.00/year for members; $95.00/year for nonmembers; $40.00/year for students; $135.00/year for institutions. Journal.

11887 ■ Children & Society
John Wiley & Sons Inc.
111 River St.
Hoboken, NJ 07030-5773
Ph: (201)748-6000
Fax: (201)748-6088

Fr: 800-825-7550
URL: http://onlinelibrary.wiley.com/journal/10.1111/(ISSN)1099-08

Bimonthly. $211.00/year for individuals, print & online; $171.00/year for individuals, print & online; $114.00/year for individuals, print & online; $126.00/year for other countries, print & online, rest of World; $756.00/year for institutions, print & online; $374.00/year for institutions, print & online; $475.00/year for institutions, print & online; $807.00/year for institutions, other countries, print & online. Journal focusing on children and services for children.

11888 ■ EAP Digest
Performance Resource Press Inc.
1270 Rankin Dr., Ste. F
Troy, MI 48083-2843
Ph: (248)588-7733
Fax: (248)588-6633
Fr: 800-453-7733
URL: http://store.prponline.net/index.php/ea-providers/eaprovider

Quarterly. $36.00/year for individuals; $60.00/year for two years; $72.00/year for individuals, 3years. Magazine covering planning, development, and administration of employee assistance programs.

11889 ■ Intellectual and Developmental Disabilities
American Association on Intellectual and Developmental Disabilities
501 3rd St. NW, Ste. 200
Washington, DC 20001-2730
Ph: (202)387-1968
Fax: (202)387-2193
Fr: 800-424-3688
URL: http://www.aaiddjournals.org/

Bimonthly. $348.00/year for institutions, tier 1, print + online; $398.00/year for institutions, other countries, tier 1, print + online; $308.00/year for institutions, tier 1, online only. Magazine featuring articles on mental retardation for professionals and parents.

11890 ■ Journal of Family Social Work
Routledge Journals
270 Madison Ave.
New York, NY 10016-0601
Ph: (212)216-7800
Fax: (212)563-2269
URL: http://www.tandf.co.uk/journals/WFSW

$133.00/year for individuals, online only; $141.00/year for individuals, print + online; $341.00/year for institutions, online only; $379.00/year for institutions, print + online. Journal serves as a forum for family practitioners, scholars, and educators in the field of social work.

11891 ■ The Lutheran
Augsburg Fortress, Publishers
PO Box 1209
Minneapolis, MN 55440
Ph: (612)330-3300

Fax: (612)330-3455
E-mail: lutheran@thelutheran.org
URL: http://www.thelutheran.org

Monthly. $17.95/year for individuals; $30.95/year for two years; $40.95/year for individuals, three years. Magazine of the Evangelical Lutheran Church in America.

11892 ■ Modern Healthcare
Crain Communications Inc.
360 N Michigan Ave.
Chicago, IL 60601
Ph: (312)649-5200
E-mail: subs@crain.com
URL: http://www.modernhealthcare.com

Weekly. $164.00/year for individuals; $255.00/year for Canada; $218.00/year for other countries. Weekly business news magazine for healthcare management.

11893 ■ NASW News
National Association of Social Workers
750 1st St. NE, Ste. 700
Washington, DC 20002-4241
Ph: (202)408-8600
Fax: (202)336-8312
Fr: 800-742-4089
E-mail: naswnews@naswdc.org
URL: http://www.socialworkers.org

Description: Monthly except August and December. $17/year for students; $33/year for nonmembers, libraries, and institutions. Recurring features include letters to the editor, job listings, notices of publications available, and columns titled From the President, From the Director, and Social Work in the Public Eye.

11894 ■ The New Social Worker
White Hat Communications
2001 N Front St., Blvd. 2, Ste. 325
PO Box 5390
Harrisburg, PA 17110-0390
Ph: (717)238-3787
Fax: (717)238-2090
URL: http://www.socialworker.com

Quarterly. $15.00/year for individuals. Publication offering career guidance for social work students.

11895 ■ The NonProfit Times
NPT Publishing Group Inc.
201 Littleton Rd., 2nd Fl.
Morris Plains, NJ 07950
Ph: (973)401-0202
Fax: (973)401-0404
E-mail: ednchief@nptimes.com
URL: http://www.nptimes.com/

$49.95/year for individuals, print; $19.95/year for individuals, digital only; $59.95/year for individuals, digital & print. Trade journal serving nonprofit organizations.

11896 ■ The Pennsylvania Social Worker
National Association of Social Workers-Pennsylvania Chapter
425 N 21st. St., Ste. 401
Camp Hill, PA 17011
Ph: (717)232-4125
Fax: (717)232-4140
Fr: 800-272-6279
E-mail: exec@nasw-pa.org
URL: http://www.nasw-pa.org
Description: Bimonthly. Provides information on state, local, and national Association activities. Tracks legislative actions. Recurring features include interviews, a calendar of events, news of educational opportunities, job listings, book reviews, and columns titled President's Report and Division Report.

11897 ■ Practice
Routledge Journals
270 Madison Ave.
New York, NY 10016-0601
Ph: (212)216-7800
Fax: (212)563-2269
URL: http://www.tandf.co.uk/journals/titles/
    09503153.asp
$253.00/year for institutions, print + online; $228.00/year for institutions, online only; $83.00/year for individuals, print only; $409.00/year for institutions, print + online; $368.00/year for institutions, online only; $135.00/year for individuals, print only. Journal for a strong base in social work practice.

11898 ■ Social Work
National Association of Social Workers
750 1st St. NE, Ste. 700
Washington, DC 20002-4241
Ph: (202)408-8600
URL: http://www.naswpress.org/publications/journals/
    sw.html
Quarterly. $40.00/year for students; $95.00/year for nonmembers; $138.00/year for institutions; for Included in membership. Journal for social workers.

11899 ■ Teaching Exceptional Children
Council for Exceptional Children
2900 Crystal Dr., Ste. 1000
Arlington, VA 22202
Ph: (703)620-3660
Fax: (703)264-9494
Fr: 888-232-7733
URL: http://www.cec.sped.org/Content/
    NavigationMenu/Publications2
$90.00/year for individuals, print; $152.00/year for two years, print; $101.00/year for Canada, print; $169.00/year for two years, Canada; $197.00/year for institutions, print; $332.00/year for two years, print; $208.00/year for institutions, Canada, print; $236.00/year for institutions, other countries, print; $399.00/year for two years, institutional (print); $225.00/year for institutions, Canada, print and online. Peer-reviewed journal exploring practical methods for teaching students who have exceptionalities and those who are gifted and talented.

EMPLOYER DIRECTORIES AND NETWORKING LISTS

11900 ■ American Group Psychotherapy Association—Membership Directory
American Group Psychotherapy Association Inc.
25 E 21st St., 6th Fl.
New York, NY 10010
Ph: (212)477-2677
Fax: (212)979-6627
Fr: 877-668-2472
URL: http://www.agpa.org
Covers: 4,500 physicians, psychologists, clinical social workers, psychiatric nurses, and other mental health professionals interested in treatment of emotional problems by group methods. Entries include: Name, office or home address, highest

degree held, office or home phone number. Arrangement: Alphabetical. Indexes: Geographical.

11901 ■ Christian Association for Psychological Studies International—Membership Directory
Christian Association for Psychological Studies
PO Box 365
Batavia, IL 60510-0365
Ph: (630)639-9478
Fax: (630)454-3799
URL: http://www.caps.net
Annual, June. $12.00 for Canada; $12.00 for other countries. Covers: 2,300 Christians involved in psychology, psychiatry, counseling, sociology, social work, ministry, and nursing. Entries include: Name, office address and phone number, highest degree held, area of occupational specialization, and career data. Arrangement: Geographical. Indexes: Alphabetical.

11902 ■ Directory of Catholic Charities USA Directories
Catholic Charities USA
66 Canal Center Pl., Ste. 600
Alexandria, VA 22314-1583
Ph: (703)549-1390
Fax: (703)549-1656
URL: http://www.catholiccharitiesusa.org
Annual. $25.00 for individuals. Covers: Nearly 1,200 Catholic community and social service agencies. Listings include diocesan agencies, state Catholic conferences. Entries include: Organization name, address, name and title of director, phone, fax. Arrangement: Geographical by state, then classified by diocese.

11903 ■ Directory of Child Life Programs
Child Life Council Inc.
11821 Parklawn Dr., Ste. 310
Rockville, MD 20852-2539
Ph: (301)881-7090
Fax: (301)881-7092
URL: http://www.childlife.org
Biennial, latest edition 14th, 2006. Covers: Over 400 child life programs. Entries include: Facility name, address, phone, name of child life department and director, reporting structure, staff statistics, educational requirements for employment, and internship or educational opportunities. Arrangement: Geographical. Indexes: Speciality areas, internship sessions, program size, fellowships.

11904 ■ Public Human Services Directory
American Public Human Services Association
1133 19th St., NW, Ste. 400
Washington, DC 20036-3631
Ph: (202)682-0100
Fax: (202)289-6555
URL: http://www.aphsa.org
Annual, Latest edition 2009. $225.00 for individuals; $200.00 for members; $350.00 for institutions. Covers: Federal, state, territorial, county, and major municipal public human service agencies. Entries include: Agency name, address, phone, fax, e-mail address, web site address, names of key personnel, program area. Arrangement: Geographical.

HANDBOOKS AND MANUALS

11905 ■ 101 Careers in Social Work
Springer Publishing Company
11 W 42nd St., 15th Fl.
New York, NY 10036
Ph: (212)431-4370
Fax: (212)941-7842
Fr: 877-687-7476
E-mail: cs@springerpub.com
URL: http://www.springerpub.com
Jessica Ritter. 2008. $25.00 (softcover). 400 pages. Serves both as a catalog of social work job descriptions as well as a guide to career planning. Discusses

the interdisciplinary nature of social work and includes options such as forensic social work, entrepreneurship, working in political systems, international careers, community planning, and more. Features a catalog of social work careers, career development tools, guidance on educational requirements, licensure and continuing education, and a chapter dedicated to job-hunting tips and career planning advice.

11906 ■ Careers for Good Samaritans and Other Humanitarian Types
The McGraw-Hill Companies
PO Box 182604
Columbus, OH 43272
Fax: (614)759-3749
Fr: 877-883-5524
E-mail: customer.service@mcgraw-hill.com
URL: http://www.mhprofessional.com
Marjorie Eberts and Margaret Gisler. Third edition, 2006. $16.95 (paper). 160 pages. Contains hundreds of ideas for turning good work into paid work. Inventories opportunities in service organizations like the Red Cross, Goodwill, and the Salvation Army; religious groups, VISTA, the Peace Corps, and UNICEF; and agencies at all levels of the government. Part of Careers for You series.

11907 ■ Careers in Health Care
The McGraw-Hill Companies
PO Box 182604
Columbus, OH 43272
Fax: (614)759-3749
Fr: 877-883-5524
E-mail: customer.service@mcgraw-hill.com
URL: http://www.mhprofessional.com/
    product.php?isbn=0071466533
Barbara M. Swanson. Fifth edition, 2005. $19.95 (paper). 192 pages. Describes job duties, work settings, salaries, licensing and certification requirements, educational preparation, and future outlook. Gives ideas on how to secure a job.

11908 ■ Careers in Social and Rehabilitation Services
The McGraw-Hill Companies
PO Box 182604
Columbus, OH 43272
Fax: (614)759-3749
Fr: 877-883-5524
E-mail: customer.service@mcgraw-hill.com
URL: http://www.mhprofessional.com/
    product.php?isbn=0071641955
Geraldine O. Garner. 2008. $16.95. 192 pages.

11909 ■ Great Jobs for Liberal Arts Majors
The McGraw-Hill Companies
PO Box 182604
Columbus, OH 43272
Fax: (614)759-3749
Fr: 877-883-5524
E-mail: customer.service@mcgraw-hill.com
URL: http://www.mhprofessional.com/
    product.php?isbn=0071482148
Blythe Camenson. Second edition, 2007. $16.95 (paper). 192 pages.

11910 ■ Great Jobs for Sociology Majors
The McGraw-Hill Companies
PO Box 182604
Columbus, OH 43272
Fax: (614)759-3749
Fr: 877-883-5524
E-mail: customer.service@mcgraw-hill.com
URL: http://www.mhprofessional.com/
    product.php?isbn=0071642056
Stephen Lambert. Second edition, 2008. $16.95 (paper). 192 pages.

11911 ■ Opportunities in Child Care Careers
The McGraw-Hill Companies
PO Box 182604
Columbus, OH 43272

Fax: (614)759-3749
Fr: 877-883-5524
E-mail: customer.service@mcgraw-hill.com
URL: http://www.mhprofessional.com/
   product.php?isbn=0071467661

Renee Wittenberg. 2006. $13.95 (paper). 160 pages. Discusses various job opportunities and how to secure a position. Illustrated.

11912 ■ Opportunities in Health and Medical Careers
The McGraw-Hill Companies
PO Box 182604
Columbus, OH 43272
Fax: (614)759-3749
Fr: 877-883-5524
E-mail: customer.service@mcgraw-hill.com
URL: http://www.mhprofessional.com/
   product.php?isbn=0071437274

I. Donald Snook, Jr. and Leo D'Orazio. 2004. $14.95 (paper). 157 pages. Covers the full range of medical and health occupations. Illustrated.

11913 ■ Professional Development in Social Work: Complex Issues in Practice
Routledge
711 3rd Ave., 8th Fl.
New York, NY 10017
Ph: (212)216-7800
Fax: (212)563-2269
URL: http://www.taylorandfrancis.com

Janet Seden, Sarah Matthews, Mick McCormick and Alun Morgan. 2010. $39.95 (paper). 226 pages. Helps social workers build on their initial studies to develop professionally in the field. Discusses the contexts of social work practice such as law, policies and theories, as well as the skills needed to be developed in order to deal with the field's complexity.

11914 ■ Resumes for Social Service Careers
The McGraw-Hill Companies
PO Box 182604
Columbus, OH 43272
Fax: (614)759-3749
Fr: 877-883-5524
E-mail: customer.service@mcgraw-hill.com
URL: http://www.mhprofessional.com/
   product.php?isbn=0071467815

2006. $11.95 (paper). 144 pages.

11915 ■ The SAGE Handbook of Social Work
Sage Publications
2455 Teller Rd.
Thousand Oaks, CA 91320
Fax: 800-583-2665
Fr: 800-818-7243
E-mail: journals@sagepub.com
URL: http://www.sagepub.com

Mel Gray, James Midgley and Stephen Webb. 2012. $150.00 (hardcover). 592 pages. Provides authoritative guide to the theory, method and values of social work. Investigates the policy dimensions, practice, perspectives, values and ethics, and context of social work.

11916 ■ Social Work Career Development: A Handbook for Job Hunting and Career Planning
National Association of Social Workers
750 1st St., NE, Ste. 700
Washington, DC 20002-4241
Ph: (202)408-8600
Fax: (202)336-8312
Fr: 800-227-3590
URL: http://www.naswpress.org

Carol Nesslein Doelling, editor. Second edition. $50.99 (paper). 251 pages.

11917 ■ Social Work: The Basics
Routledge
711 3rd Ave., 8th Fl.
New York, NY 10017
Ph: (212)216-7800

Fax: (212)563-2269
URL: http://www.routledge.com

Mark Doel. 2012. $19.95 (paper). 240 pages. Aims to dispel myths surrounding social work, address media debates and present a balanced view of what social work is and what social workers do. Provides a helpful introduction for students considering a career in social work, those beginning social work courses and professionals engaged in multi-agency approaches with social workers who have little direct experience.

11918 ■ The Social Worker as Manager: A Practical Guide to Success
Pearson
1 Lake St.
Upper Saddle River, NJ 07458
Fr: 800-922-0579
URL: http://www.pearsonhighered.com

Robert Weinbach and Lynne Taylor. 2010. $103.00 (paper). 368 pages. Aims to help social workers perform management tasks at any level and in the public, private and non-profit sectors. Includes case examples and questions. Covers topics on diversity, management ethics and evidence-based practice.

11919 ■ The Survival Guide for Newly Qualified Child and Family Social Workers: Hitting the Ground Running
Jessica Kingsley Publishers
400 Market St., Ste. 400
Philadelphia, PA 19106
Ph: (215)922-1161
Fax: (215)922-1474
Fr: (866)416-1078
E-mail: orders@jkp.com
URL: http://www.jkp.com

Helen Donnellan and Gordon Jack. 2009. $34.95 (paper). 224 pages. Serves as a guide for all students, post-qualification and returning practitioners specializing in the fields of child and family social work in sustaining their commitment to their chosen profession and working successfully within it. Includes a checklist of key points as a ready reference for practitioners preparing to face the daily challenges of their new professional status.

11920 ■ The Survival Guide for Newly Qualified Social Workers in Adult and Mental Health Services: Hitting the Ground Running
Jessica Kingsley Publishers
400 Market St., Ste. 400
Philadelphia, PA 19106
Ph: (215)922-1161
Fax: (215)922-1474
Fr: (866)416-1078
E-mail: orders@jkp.com
URL: http://www.jkp.com

Diane Galpin, Jenny Bigmore and Jo Parker. 2011. $34.95 (paper). 192 pages. Explores the practicalities of starting work in a new organization and the professional demands particular to adult and mental health services. Includes a range of strategies for keeping up with the demands of social work while staying motivated and developing support networks.

ONLINE JOB SOURCES AND SERVICES

11921 ■ Delta T Group
E-mail: cfassl@deltatg.com
URL: http://www.delta-tgroup.com

Description: Specialized contract temporary staffing source for healthcare professionals in the fields of social service, psychiatry, mental health, and substance abuse. Organizations may request services and staffing; job seekers may view services provided, submit a resume, or peruse jobs available.

11922 ■ RehabWorld.com
URL: http://www.rehabworld.com

Description: Site for rehabilitation professionals to

learn about the profession and locate jobs. Includes user groups, salary surveys, and chat capabilities. Main files include: Physical Therapy, Occupational Therapy, Speech Therapy, Mental Health, Employer World, Student World, International World, Forum.

11923 ■ Social Work Job Search
E-mail: support@socialworkjobsearch.com
URL: http://www.socialworkjobsearch.com/
   socialworkjobsearch.cgi

Description: Provides a database of jobs for social workers, counselors, mental health providers, social services professionals, school social workers and counselors, therapists, case managers, and all other helping professionals.

11924 ■ Social Work and Social Services Jobs Online
George Warren Brown School of Social Work
Washington University
Campus Box 1196
1 Brookings Dr.
St. Louis, MO 63130-4899
Ph: (314)935-6600
Fax: (314)935-4859
Fr: 800-321-2426
URL: http://gwbweb.wustl.edu/CareerDevelopment/
   JobsOnline/Pages/Overview.aspx

Description: Specialized database of social work and social services jobs gives a large list of openings sorted by location (both within and outside the United States). Employers may submit job openings. Site also contains career resources and links to related internet job sites.

11925 ■ SocialService.com
E-mail: info@socialservice.com
URL: http://www.socialservice.com

Description: Offers social service or social work jobs, whether in mental health, substance abuse, children and youth, medical social work, criminal justice, domestic violence, counseling, community organizing an outreach, EAP, mentoring homelessness or a variety of other human service areas.

11926 ■ SocialServiceNetwork.com
URL: http://socialservicenetwork.com

Description: Provides a database of social work positions. Includes various listings of social work jobs, social services jobs, human services jobs, mental health jobs, counseling jobs, and more.

11927 ■ SocialWorkJobBank.com
URL: http://www.socialworkjobbank.com

Description: Serves as an online job board and career center devoted to helping match professional social workers with employers. Allows finding and posting of jobs in all areas of professional social work.

TRADESHOWS

11928 ■ North American Association of Christians in Social Work Convention
PO Box 121
Botsford, CT 06404-0121
Fr: 888-426-4712
E-mail: info@nacsw.org
URL: http://www.nacsw.org

Annual. Features workshops and poster presentations in six tracks focused on practice, policy and administration, community development, social work education, faith of the social worker, and rural social work.

OTHER SOURCES

11929 ■ Alliance for Children and Families
11700 W Lake Park Dr.
Milwaukee, WI 53224-3099

Ph: (414)359-1040
Fax: (414)359-1074
E-mail: severson@alliance1.org
URL: http://www.alliance1.org

Description: Membership organization of local agencies in thousands of communities providing family counseling, family life education, residential treatment, and family advocacy services, and other programs to help families with parent-child, marital, mental health, and other problems. Assists member agencies in developing capacity and maintaining high performance. Compiles statistics; conducts research. Maintains extensive files of unpublished materials from member agencies.

11930 ■ American Association of Psychiatric Technicians (AAPT)
1220 S St., Ste. 100
Sacramento, CA 95811-7138
Fax: (916)329-9145
Fr: 800-391-7589
E-mail: aapt@psychtechs.net
URL: http://www.psychtechs.org

Description: Administers the Nationally Certified Psychiatric Technician examination to non-licensed direct-care workers in the fields of mental illness, developmental disabilities and substance abuse.

11931 ■ American Mental Health Alliance (AMHA)
PO Box 4075
Portland, OR 97208-4075
Ph: (503)227-2027
Fr: 888-826-3682
E-mail: memberinfo@americanmentalhealth.com
URL: http://www.americanmentalhealth.com

Description: Represents mental health professionals licensed or certified for independent practice. Creates a professional community that provides therapy of the highest quality and ethical standards. Supports and markets competent, ethical mental health services that preserve privacy and confidentiality. Supports education, supervision, and research opportunities for members. Opposes legislation and regulations that invade patent privacy and confidentiality.

11932 ■ American Public Health Association (APHA)
800 I St. NW
Washington, DC 20001
Ph: (202)777-2742
Fax: (202)777-2534
E-mail: comments@apha.org
URL: http://www.apha.org

Description: Professional organization of physicians, nurses, educators, academicians, environmentalists, epidemiologists, new professionals, social workers, health administrators, optometrists, podiatrists, pharmacists, dentists, nutritionists, health planners, other community and mental health specialists, and interested consumers. Seeks to protect and promote personal, mental, and environmental health. Services include: promulgation of standards; establishment of uniform practices and procedures; development of the etiology of communicable diseases; research in public health; exploration of medical care programs and their relationships to public health. Sponsors job placement service.

11933 ■ Association on Higher Education and Disability (AHEAD)
107 Commerce Center Dr., Ste. 204
Huntersville, NC 28078
Ph: (704)947-7779
Fax: (704)948-7779
E-mail: ahead@ahead.org
URL: http://www.ahead.org

Description: Individuals interested in promoting the equal rights and opportunities of disabled postsecondary students, staff, faculty, and graduates. Provides an exchange of communication for those professionally involved with disabled students; collects, evaluates, and disseminates information; encourages and supports legislation for the benefit of disabled students. Conducts surveys on issues pertinent to college students with disabilities; offers resource referral system and employment exchange for positions in disability student services. Conducts research programs; compiles statistics.

11934 ■ Association for Humanistic Counseling
PO Box 791006
Baltimore, MD 21279-1006
Ph: (703)823-9800
Fax: 800-473-2329
Fr: 800-347-6647
E-mail: cmalchiodi@insightbb.com
URL: http://www.c-ahead.org

Description: A division of the American Counseling Association. Teachers, educational administrators, community agency workers, counselors, school social workers, and psychologists; others interested in the area of human development. Aims to assist individuals in improving their quality of life. Provides forum for the exchange of information about humanistically-oriented administrative and instructional practices. Supports humanistic practices and research on instructional and organizational methods for facilitating humanistic education; encourages cooperation among related professional groups.

11935 ■ Child Welfare League of America (CWLA)
1726 M St. NW, Ste. 500
Washington, DC 20036-4522
Ph: (202)688-4200
Fax: (202)833-1689
E-mail: register@cwla.org
URL: http://www.cwla.org

Description: Works to improve care and services for abused, dependent, or neglected children, youth, and their families. Provides training and consultation; conducts research; maintains information service and develops standards for child welfare practice.

11936 ■ Council on Social Work Education
1701 Duke St., Ste. 200
Alexandria, VA 22314
Ph: (703)683-8080
Fax: (703)683-8099
E-mail: info@cswe.org
URL: http://www.cswe.org

Description: Aims to promote and strengthen the quality of social work education through preparation of competent social work professionals. Provides national leadership and a forum for collective action. Maintains policy and program standards, promotes research and faculty development, and advocates for social work education.

11937 ■ Employee Assistance Society of North America (EASNA)
2001 Jefferson Davis Hwy., Ste. 1004
Arlington, VA 22202-3617
Ph: (703)416-0060
Fax: (703)416-0014
E-mail: bmclean@easna.org
URL: http://www.easna.org

Description: Individuals in the field of employee assistance, including psychiatrists, psychologists, and managers. Facilitates communication among members; provides resource information; serves as a network for employee assistance programs nationwide. Conducts research.

11938 ■ International Association of Counselors and Therapists (IACT)
8852 SR 3001
Laceyville, PA 18623
Ph: (570)869-1021
Fax: (570)869-1249
Fr: 800-553-6886
E-mail: info@iact.org
URL: http://www.iact.org

Description: Mental health professionals, medical professionals, social workers, clergy, educators, hypnotherapists, counselors, and individuals interested in the helping professions. Promotes enhanced professional image and prestige for complementary therapy. Provides a forum for exchange of information and ideas among practitioners of traditional and nontraditional therapies and methodologies; fosters unity among "grassroots" practitioners and those with advanced academic credentials. Facilitates the development of new therapy programs. Conducts educational, research, and charitable programs. Awards credits for continuing education. Maintains speakers' bureau and library; operates referral and placement services; compiles statistics. Assists in the development of local chapters.

11939 ■ National Association of Puerto Rican Hispanic Social Workers
PO Box 651
Brentwood, NY 11717
Ph: (631)864-1536
Fax: (631)864-1536
URL: http://www.naprhsw.org

Description: Comprised of social workers and other human service professionals. Commits to the enhancement and general welfare of Puerto Rican and other Hispanic families. Strengthens, develops and improves the resources and services to meet the needs of Puerto Rican/Hispanic families.

11940 ■ National Association of Social Workers (NASW)
750 1st St. NE, Ste. 700
Washington, DC 20002-4241
Ph: (202)408-8600
Fax: (202)336-8313
Fr: 800-742-4089
E-mail: membership@naswdc.org
URL: http://www.naswdc.org

Description: Regular members are persons who hold a minimum of a baccalaureate degree in social work. Associate members are persons engaged in social work who have a baccalaureate degree in another field. Student members are persons enrolled in accredited (by the Council on Social Work Education) graduate or undergraduate social work programs. Works to create professional standards for social work practice; advocate sound public social policies through political and legislative action; provide a wide range of membership services, including continuing education opportunities and an extensive professional program. Operates National Center for Social Policy and Practice. Conducts research; compiles statistics.

11941 ■ National Council of Certified Dementia Practitioners (NCCDP)
103 Valley View Trail
Sparta, NJ 07871
Fax: (973)860-2244
Fr: 877-729-5191
E-mail: nationalccdp@aol.com
URL: http://www.nccdp.org

Description: Represents professionals with varying work and personal experiences in the field of dementia care. Seeks to develop and encourage standards of excellence in the profession and delivery of dementia care. Promotes and enhances the knowledge, skills and practice of all persons who provide care and services to dementia clients.

11942 ■ National Organization for Human Services (NOHS)
5341 Old Hwy. 5, Ste. 206, No. 214
Woodstock, GA 30188
Ph: (770)924-8899
Fax: (678)494-5076
E-mail: admin@nationalhumanservices.org
URL: http://www.nationalhumanservices.org

Description: Human service professionals, faculty, and students. Fosters excellence in teaching, research and curriculum planning in the human service area. Encourages and supports the development of local, state, and national human services organizations. Aids faculty and professional members in their career development. Provides a medium for cooperation and communication among members. Maintains registry of qualified consultants in human service education. Conducts professional development workshop. Operates speakers' bureau.

11943 ■ National Staff Development and Training Association (NSDTA)
PO Box 112
Merced, CA 95341-0112
Ph: (209)385-3000
Fax: (209)354-2501
E-mail: apagan@hsa.co.merced.ca.us
URL: http://nsdta.aphsa.org

Description: Social welfare workers engaged in staff development and training. Attempts to: support people in the field; influence welfare policy-making on the national level; form a network of contacts for members. Provides technical assistance. Maintains speakers' bureau; offers placement services.

11944 ■ North American Association of Christians in Social Work (NACSW)
PO Box 121
Botsford, CT 06404-0121
Fr: 888-426-4712
E-mail: info@nacsw.org
URL: http://www.nacsw.org

Description: Professional social workers and related professionals, students, interested individuals. Supports the integration of Christian faith and professional social work practice in the lives of its members, the profession and the church, promoting love and justice in social service and social reform. Provides opportunities for Christian fellowship, education and service opportunities; articulates informed Christian voice on social welfare practice and policy to the social work profession; provides professional understanding and help for the social ministry of the church; and promotes social welfare services and policies in society that bring about greater justice and meet basic human needs.

SOURCES OF HELP-WANTED ADS

11945 ■ American Studies Association Newsletter
American Studies Association
1120 19th St. NW, Ste. 301
Washington, DC 20036
Ph: (202)467-4783
Fax: (202)467-4786
E-mail: asastaff@theasa.net
URL: http://www.theasa.net/

Description: Quarterly. Has a circulation of approximately 6,000. Promotes the interdisciplinary study of American culture. Presents news of research, publications, and conferences. Also includes information on grants, employment opportunities, and Association activities.

11946 ■ Child and Adolescent Social Work Journal
Springer-Verlag New York Inc.
233 Spring St.
New York, NY 10013-1578
Ph: (212)460-1500
Fax: (212)460-1575
Fr: 800-777-4643
URL: http://www.springer.com/psychology/personality+%26+social+ps

$925.00/year for institutions, print or online; $1,110.00/year for institutions, print & enchanced access. Journal dealing with issues in clinical social work practice with children, adolescents, and their families.

11947 ■ Children & Society
John Wiley & Sons Inc.
111 River St.
Hoboken, NJ 07030-5773
Ph: (201)748-6000
Fax: (201)748-6088
Fr: 800-825-7550
URL: http://onlinelibrary.wiley.com/journal/10.1111/(ISSN)1099-08

Bimonthly. $211.00/year for individuals, print & online; $171.00/year for individuals, print & online; $114.00/year for individuals, print & online; $126.00/year for other countries, print & online, rest of World; $756.00/year for institutions, print & online; $374.00/year for institutions, print & online; $475.00/year for institutions, print & online; $807.00/year for institutions, other countries, print & online. Journal focusing on children and services for children.

11948 ■ The Gerontologist
Gerontological Society of America
1220 L St. NW, Ste. 901
Washington, DC 20005
Ph: (202)842-1275
Fax: (202)842-1150
E-mail: tg@gmu.edu
URL: http://gerontologist.oxfordjournals.org

Bimonthly. $270.00/year for institutions, print only; $406.00/year for institutions, print only; $40.00/year for institutions, print only; $294.00/year for institutions, print & online; $443.00/year for institutions, print & online; $443.00/year for institutions, print & online. Multidisciplinary peer-reviewed journal presenting new concepts, clinical ideas, and applied research in gerontology. Includes book and audiovisual reviews.

11949 ■ Innovations
National Council on the Aging
1901 L St. NW 4th Fl.
Washington, DC 20036
Ph: (202)479-1200
Fax: (202)479-0735
Fr: 800-373-4906
E-mail: scott.parkin@ncoa.org
URL: http://www.ncoa.org/news-ncoa-publications/publications/inno

Quarterly. Free to members; $225.00/year for nonmembers, for organizations; $50.00/year for nonmembers. Magazine exploring significant developments in the field of aging.

EMPLOYER DIRECTORIES AND NETWORKING LISTS

11950 ■ Christian Association for Psychological Studies International—Membership Directory
Christian Association for Psychological Studies
PO Box 365
Batavia, IL 60510-0365
Ph: (630)639-9478
Fax: (630)454-3799
URL: http://www.caps.net

Annual, June. $12.00 for Canada; $12.00 for other countries. Covers: 2,300 Christians involved in psychology, psychiatry, counseling, sociology, social work, ministry, and nursing. Entries include: Name, office address and phone number, highest degree held, area of occupational specialization, and career data. Arrangement: Geographical. Indexes: Alphabetical.

HANDBOOKS AND MANUALS

11951 ■ Careers in Health Care
The McGraw-Hill Companies
PO Box 182604
Columbus, OH 43272
Fax: (614)759-3749
Fr: 877-883-5524
E-mail: customer.service@mcgraw-hill.com
URL: http://www.mhprofessional.com/product.php?isbn=0071466533

Barbara M. Swanson. Fifth edition, 2005. $19.95 (paper). 192 pages. Describes job duties, work settings, salaries, licensing and certification requirements, educational preparation, and future outlook. Gives ideas on how to secure a job.

11952 ■ Careers for Mystery Buffs and Other Snoops and Sleuths
The McGraw-Hill Companies
PO Box 182604
Columbus, OH 43272
Fax: (614)759-3749
Fr: 877-883-5524
E-mail: customer.service@mcgraw-hill.com
URL: http://www.mhprofessional.com

Blythe Camenson. Second edition. $14.95 (hardback). 160 pages.

11953 ■ Careers in Sociology
Pearson Allyn & Bacon
1 Lake St.
Upper Saddle River, NJ 07458
Ph: (201)236-7000
Fr: 800-922-0579
URL: http://www.pearsonhighered.com/educator

W. Richard Stephens. Third edition, 2004. $14.20 (paper). 192 pages.

11954 ■ Great Jobs for Sociology Majors
The McGraw-Hill Companies
PO Box 182604
Columbus, OH 43272
Fax: (614)759-3749
Fr: 877-883-5524
E-mail: customer.service@mcgraw-hill.com
URL: http://www.mhprofessional.com/product.php?isbn=0071642056

Stephen Lambert. Second edition, 2008. $16.95 (paper). 192 pages.

11955 ■ Opportunities in Social Science Careers
The McGraw-Hill Companies
PO Box 182604
Columbus, OH 43272
Fax: (614)759-3749
Fr: 877-883-5524
E-mail: customer.service@mcgraw-hill.com
URL: http://www.mcgraw-hill.com

Rosanne J. Marek. 2004. $13.95. 160 Pages. VGM Opportunities Series.

TRADESHOWS

11956 ■ American Association for State and Local History Annual Meeting
American Association for State and Local History
1717 Church St.
Nashville, TN 37203-2991
Ph: (615)320-3203

Fax: (615)327-9013
E-mail: membership@aaslh.org
URL: http://www.aaslh.org

Annual. Primary Exhibits: Products and services directed toward the museum and history field, including: publications, fund-raising devices, software, exhibit design, historic preservation, historic research and technical information.

11957 ■ American Sociological Association Annual Meeting
American Sociological Association
1430 K St. N.W., Ste. 600
Washington, DC 20005-4701
Ph: (202)383-9005
Fax: (202)638-0882
E-mail: executive.office@asanet.org
URL: http://www.asanet.org

Annual. Primary Exhibits: Scholarly book publishers, statistical software supplies, government agencies, and information/data centers. Dates and Locations: 2012 Aug 17-20; Denver, CO; Colorado Convention Center and Hyatt Regency.

11958 ■ Association of Black Sociologists Conference
Association of Black Sociologists
3473 S Martin Luther King Dr., Box 495
Chicago, IL 60616-4108
Ph: (312)342-7618
URL: http://www.associationofblacksociologists.org

Annual. Provides members with professional networking opportunities and scholarly forums to discuss their research. 2012 August 16-18; Denver, CO.

11959 ■ Association for the Sociology of Religion Annual Meeting
Association for the Sociology of Religion
618 SW 2nd Ave.
Galva, IL 61434-1912
Ph: (309)932-2727
Fax: (309)932-2282
URL: http://www.sociologyofreligion.com

Annual. Provides avenue for presentations of papers and discussions on a broad range of issues in the sociological study of religion. 2012 August 17-18; Denver, CO.

11960 ■ Eastern Sociological Society Annual Meeting
Exhibit Promotions Plus, Inc.
11620 Vixens Path
Ellicott City, MD 21042-1539
Ph: (410)997-0763
Fax: (410)997-0764
E-mail: exhibit@epponline.com
URL: http://www.epponline.com

Annual. Primary Exhibits: Publishers with titles in fields of sociology, anthropology, and psychology. Dates and Locations: 2012 Feb 23-26; New York, NY; Millennium Broadway Hotel.

11961 ■ Society for the Study of Social Problems Annual Meeting
901 McClung Tower
University of Tennessee
Knoxville, TN 37996-0490
Ph: (865)689-1531
Fax: (865)689-1534
E-mail: mkoontz3@utk.edu
URL: http://www.sssp1.org

Annual. Features discussions on societal and/or sociological issues such as race, ethnicity, and more. 2012 August 16-18; Denver, CO; Grand Hyatt Denver Hotel; 2013 August 9-11; New York, NY; Westin New York at Times Square; 2014 August 15-17; San Francisco, CA; San Francisco Marriot Marquis.

OTHER SOURCES

11962 ■ American Academy of Political and Social Science (AAPSS)
Annenberg Policy Center
202 S 36th St.
Philadelphia, PA 19104-3806

Ph: (215)746-6500
Fax: (215)573-2667
E-mail: ewood@asc.upenn.edu
URL: http://www.aapss.org

Description: Professionals and laymen concerned with the political and social sciences and related fields. Promotes the progress of political and social science through publications and meetings. The academy does not take sides in controversial issues, but seeks to gather and present reliable information to assist the public in forming an intelligent and accurate judgment.

11963 ■ American Society of Criminology (ASC)
1314 Kinnear Rd., Ste. 212
Columbus, OH 43212-1156
Ph: (614)292-9207
Fax: (614)292-6767
E-mail: asc@asc41.com
URL: http://www.asc41.com

Description: Represents professional and academic criminologists, students of criminology in accredited universities, psychiatrists, psychologists, and sociologists. Develops criminology as a science and academic discipline. Aids in the construction of criminological curricula in accredited universities. Upgrades the practitioner in criminological fields (police, prisons, probation, parole, delinquency workers). Conducts research programs and sponsors three student paper competitions. Provides placement service at annual convention.

11964 ■ American Sociological Association (ASA)
1430 K St. NW, Ste. 600
Washington, DC 20005
Ph: (202)383-9005
Fax: (202)638-0882
E-mail: executive.office@asanet.org
URL: http://www.asanet.org

Description: Sociologists, social scientists, and others interested in research, teaching, and application of sociology; graduate and undergraduate sociology students. Compiles statistics. Operates the ASA Teaching Resources Center, which develops a variety of materials useful in teaching sociology. Sponsors Minority Fellowship and Professional Development Programs and Teaching Project. Maintains 44 sections including: Aging; Criminology; Medical; Population.

11965 ■ Association for Applied and Clinical Sociology (AACS)
Eastern Michigan University
Dept. of Sociology, Anthropology, and Criminology Office
926 E. Forest Ave.
Ypsilanti, MI 48197
Ph: (734)845-1206
E-mail: sac_aacs@emich.edu
URL: http://www.aacsnet.org/wp

Description: Promotes the application of sociology to individual and social change and advances theory, research, and methods to this end; develops opportunities for the employment and use of clinically trained sociologists; provides a common ground for sociological practitioners, allied professionals, and interested scholars and students. Promotes training and educational opportunities to further sociological practice. Sponsors sessions and programs in clinical and applied sociology at national and regional meetings of other sociological associations. Has conducted a survey on skills, licenses, education, and experience of members. Conducts national certification program.

11966 ■ Association of Black Sociologists
3473 S Martin Luther King Dr., Box 495
Chicago, IL 60616-4108
Ph: (312)342-7618
URL: http://www.blacksociologists.org

Description: Represents sociologists and social scientists. Enhances the academic opportunities of

black sociologists and fosters recognition of their scholarly works.

11967 ■ Association for the Sociology of Religion
618 SW 2nd Ave.
Galva, IL 61434-1912
Ph: (309)932-2727
Fax: (309)932-2282
URL: http://www.sociologyofreligion.com

Description: Aims to stimulate concerted study and research in the sociology of religion. Serves as a medium of communication among sociologists and as a means through which the results of sociological research on religion may be communicated to appropriate organizations and to the general public. Promotes the highest professional and scientific standards for research and publication in the sociology of religion.

11968 ■ Institute for the Study of Man (ISM)
1133 13th St. NW, Ste. C-2
Washington, DC 20005
Ph: (202)371-2700
Fax: (202)371-1523
E-mail: iejournal@aol.com
URL: http://www.jies.org

Description: Aims to publish books and journals in areas related to anthropology, historical linguistics, and the human sciences.

11969 ■ International Visual Sociology Association (IVSA)
126 Redfield Ave.
Fayetteville, NY 13066
E-mail: margolis@asu.edu
URL: http://www.visualsociology.org

Description: Promotes the study, production and use of visual images, data and materials in teaching, research and applied activities. Fosters the development and use of still photographs, film, video and electronically transmitted images in sociology and other social sciences. Encourages free speech, self-expression and academic freedom in the field of visual sociology.

11970 ■ National Association for Professional Gerontologists (NAPG)
PO Box 1209
Los Altos, CA 94023
Ph: (650)947-9132
E-mail: office@napgerontologists.org
URL: http://www.napgerontologists.org

Description: Promotes career advancement in the field of gerontology. Offers credentialing for gerontology professionals. Conducts networking activities for members.

11971 ■ Population Association of America (PAA)
8630 Fenton St., Ste. 722
Silver Spring, MD 20910-3812
Ph: (301)565-6710
Fax: (301)565-7850
E-mail: membersvc@popassoc.org
URL: http://www.popassoc.org

Description: Professional society of individuals interested in demography and its scientific aspects.

11972 ■ Rural Sociological Society (RSS)
Brigham Young University
2019 JFSB
Provo, UT 84602
Ph: (801)422-7386
Fax: (801)422-0625
E-mail: rural_sociology@byu.edu
URL: http://www.ruralsociology.org

Description: Educators and others employed in the field of rural sociology. Promotes the development of rural sociology through research, teaching, and extension work.

11973 ■ Society for the Study of Social Problems
901 McClung Tower
University of Tennessee
Knoxville, TN 37996-0490
Ph: (865)689-1531
Fax: (865)689-1534
E-mail: sssp@utk.edu
URL: http://www.sssp1.org

Description: Members are often social scientists working in colleges and universities, in non-profit organizations and in other applied and policy settings. Aims to advance research on and serious examination of problems of social life and to solve these problems and develop an informed social policy. Promotes research and dialogue through meetings, publications, awards to community groups, committee participation, consultation, and the generation of new ideas.

11974 ■ Sociologists for Women in Society (SWS)
10 Chaffee Rd.
Kingston, RI 02881
Ph: (401)874-9510
Fax: (401)874-2588
E-mail: swseo@socwomen.org
URL: http://www.socwomen.org

Description: Members are mainly national and international professional social scientists, sociologists and students of sociology, though membership is open to anyone interested in the purposes of the organization. Maximizes the effectiveness of and professional opportunities for women in sociology. Explores the contributions which sociology can, does, and should make to the investigation of an improvement in the status of women in society. Acts as watchdog of the American Sociological Association to ensure that it does not ignore the special needs of women in the profession; has organized a job market service to bring potential jobs and applicants together; established a discrimination committee offering advice and organizational support for women who pursue cases charging sex discrimination; hasaided women to establish social, professional, and intellectual contacts with each other. Supports minority scholarships, breast cancer research and academic mentoring activities

SOURCES OF HELP-WANTED ADS

11975 ■ ACM Transactions on Internet Technology
Association for Computing Machinery
PO Box 30777
New York, NY 10087
Ph: (212)626-0500
Fax: (212)944-1318
Fr: 800-342-6626
URL: http://toit.acm.org

Quarterly. $190.00/year for nonmembers, print only; $152.00/year for nonmembers, online only; $228.00/year for nonmembers, online and print. Publication of the Association for Computing Machinery. Brings together many computing disciplines including computer software engineering, computer programming languages, middleware, database management, security, knowledge discovery and data mining, networking and distributed systems, communications, performance and scalability, and more. Covers the results and roles of the individual disciplines and the relationships among them.

11976 ■ AVIOS Journal
Applied Voice Input/Output Society
PO Box 20817
San Jose, CA 95160
Ph: (408)323-1783
Fax: (408)323-1782
URL: http://www.avios.com/

Annual. Journal covering issues in computer science.

11977 ■ C++ Scientific Programming
John Wiley & Sons Inc.
111 River St.
Hoboken, NJ 07030-5773
Ph: (201)748-6000
Fax: (201)748-6088
Fr: 800-825-7550
URL: http://as.wiley.com/WileyCDA/WileyTitle/productCd-0471412104

Quarterly. $88.95/year for individuals. Journal containing information on the practical experience of software engineering and scientific computing.

11978 ■ Computers and Composition
Elsevier Science Inc.
360 Park Ave. S
New York, NY 10010-1710
Ph: (212)989-5800
Fax: (212)633-3990
Fr: 888-437-4636
URL: http://www.elsevier.com/wps/find/journaldescription.cws_home

$454.00/year for institutions, all countries except Europe, Japan and Iran; $405.00/year for institutions, European countries and Iran; $53,500.00/year for institutions, Japan; $82.00/year for individuals, all countries except Europe, Japan and Iran; $62.00/year for individuals, European countries and Iran;

$8,900.00/year for individuals, Japan. Journal covering computers in writing classes, programs, and research.

11979 ■ Computers Programs/PC World
IDG Communications Inc.
3 Speen St.
Framingham, MA 01701
Ph: (508)875-5000
URL: http://www.idg.com

Magazine devoted to IT specialists, covering practical questions of computing including purchase and usage of the computer technology, software, computer components and peripherals.

11980 ■ Computerworld
101 Communications
9121 Oakdale Ave., Ste. 101
Chatsworth, CA 91311
Ph: (818)814-5200
Fax: (818)734-1522
URL: http://www.computerworld.com

Weekly. $129.00/year for individuals; $129.00/year for Canada; $295.00/year for other countries; $250.00/year for individuals, Mexico/Central/South America; $29.00/year for individuals, digital edition. Newspaper for information systems executives.

11981 ■ Computerworld/Correio Informatico
IDG Communications Inc.
3 Speen St.
Framingham, MA 01701
Ph: (508)875-5000
URL: http://www.idg.com/www/IDGProducts.nsf/0/B1E40F5ABD0169AB852

Weekly. Magazine providing news on latest developments in computer industry.

11982 ■ Computerworld Top 100
IDG Communications Inc.
3 Speen St.
Framingham, MA 01701
Ph: (508)875-5000
URL: http://www.idg.com/www/IDGProducts.nsf/0/E7EDD4EC98463F2C852

Annual. Magazine for analyzing trends and events of information technology business.

11983 ■ Computing SA
IDG Communications Inc.
3 Speen St.
Framingham, MA 01701
Ph: (508)875-5000
URL: http://www.idg.com/www/IDGProducts.nsf/0/12C44C74D05A07DF852

Monthly. Newspaper focusing computer hardware, software, networking, telecommunications, channel management and online computing.

11984 ■ CXO
IDG Communications Inc.
3 Speen St.
Framingham, MA 01701
Ph: (508)875-5000
URL: http://www.idg.com/www/IDGProducts.nsf/0/022796185EED5984852

Monthly. Magazine providing technology information for chief officers and managers.

11985 ■ Eclipse Review
BZ Media L.L.C.
7 High St., Ste. 407
Huntington, NY 11743
Ph: (631)421-4158
Fax: (631)421-4130
URL: http://www.eclipsesource.com/contact.htm

Magazine for IT professionals.

11986 ■ Electronic Markets
Springer-Verlag New York Inc.
233 Spring St.
New York, NY 10013-1578
Ph: (212)460-1500
Fax: (212)460-1575
Fr: 800-777-4643
URL: http://www.springer.com/business/business+information+system

$618.00/year for institutions, print or online; $742.00/year for institutions, print & enchanced access. Journal covering all system concepts of electronic commerce.

11987 ■ Engineering
Scientific Research Publishing
PO Box 54821
Irvine, CA 92619-4821
E-mail: eng@scirp.org
URL: http://www.scirp.org/journal/eng/

Monthly. $708.00/year for individuals. Peer-reviewed journal publishing articles on the latest advancements in engineering.

11988 ■ Foundations and Trends in Networking
Now Publishers
PO Box 1024
Hanover, MA 02339-1001
Ph: (781)871-0245
URL: http://www.nowpublishers.com/product.aspx?product=NET

$390.00/year for individuals, online only; $450.00/year for individuals, print and online; $390.00/year for other countries, online only; $450.00/year for other countries, print and online. Academic journal publishing new research in computer networking.

11989 ■ Government Computer News
PostNewsweek Tech Media
10 G St. NE, Ste. 500
Washington, DC 20002-4228
Ph: (202)772-2500

Fax: (202)772-2511
Fr: (866)447-6864
URL: http://gcn.com/

Semimonthly. Magazine for professionals interested in government IT.

11990 ■ Graduating Engineer & Computer Careers
Career Recruitment Media
2 LAN Dr., Ste. 100
Westford, MA 01886
Ph: (978)692-5092
Fax: (978)692-4174
URL: http://www.graduatingengineer.com

Quarterly. $16.95/year for individuals. Magazine focusing on employment, education, and career development for entry-level engineers and computer scientists.

11991 ■ High Technology Careers Magazine
HTC
4701 Patrick Henry Dr., No. 1901
Santa Clara, CA 95054
Fax: (408)567-0242
URL: http://www.hightechcareers.com

Bimonthly. $29.00/year; $35.00/year for Canada; $85.00/year for out of country. Magazine (tabloid) containing employment opportunity information for the engineering and technical community.

11992 ■ IEEE Computer Graphics and Applications
IEEE Computer Society
10662 Los Vaqueros Cir.
PO Box 3014
Los Alamitos, CA 90720-1314
Ph: (714)821-8380
Fax: (714)821-4010
Fr: 800-272-6657
E-mail: cga-ma@computer.org
URL: http://www.computer.org/portal/web/cga

Bimonthly. $1,020.00/year for individuals, online; $1,065.00/year for individuals, print; $1,330.00/year for individuals, print and online. Magazine addressing the interests and needs of professional designers and users of computer graphics hardware, software, and systems.

11993 ■ IEEE Security & Privacy Magazine
IEEE Computer Society
10662 Los Vaqueros Cir.
PO Box 3014
Los Alamitos, CA 90720-1314
Ph: (714)821-8380
Fax: (714)821-4010
Fr: 800-272-6657
URL: http://www.computer.org/portal/site/security/

Bimonthly. $735.00/year for individuals, online; $770.00/year for individuals, print; $965.00/year for individuals, print and online. Journal that aims to explore role and importance of networked infrastructure and developing lasting security solutions.

11994 ■ IEEE Software
IEEE Computer Society
10662 Los Vaqueros Cir.
PO Box 3014
Los Alamitos, CA 90720-1314
Ph: (714)821-8380
Fax: (714)821-4010
Fr: 800-272-6657
E-mail: software@computer.org
URL: http://www.computer.org/portal/web/software/home

Bimonthly. $990.00/year for individuals, online; $1,040.00/year for individuals, print; $1,300.00/year for individuals, print and online. Magazine covering the computer software industry for the community of leading software practitioners.

11995 ■ Information Security
TechTarget
117 Kendrick St., Ste. 800
Needham, MA 02494
Ph: (781)657-1000
Fax: (781)657-1100
Fr: 888-274-4111
URL: http://searchsecurity.techtarget.com/

Monthly. Free to qualified subscribers. Magazine covering information security topics.

11996 ■ International Journal of Computer Games Technology
Hindawi Publishing Corp.
410 Park Ave., 15th Fl.
287 PMB
New York, NY 10022-4407
Fax: (215)893-4392
E-mail: ijcgt@hindawi.com
URL: http://www.hindawi.com/journals/ijcgt/

$195.00/year for individuals. Journal covering research and development aspects of games technology.

11997 ■ International Journal for Multiscale Computational Engineering
Begell House Inc.
50 Cross Hwy.
Redding, CT 06896
Ph: (203)938-1300
Fax: (203)938-1304
URL: http://www.begellhouse.com/journals/61fd1b191cf7e96f

$1,245.00/year for institutions. Journal featuring the advancement of multiscale computational science and engineering.

11998 ■ International Journal of Software Engineering and Knowledge Engineering
World Scientific Publishing
27 Warren St., Ste. 401-402
Hackensack, NJ 07601
Ph: (201)487-9655
Fax: (201)487-9656
Fr: 800-227-7562
URL: http://www.worldscinet.com/ijseke/ijseke.shtml

Bimonthly. $1,011.00/year for institutions, electronic + print; $813.00/year for institutions, electronic + print; $917.00/year for institutions, electronic only; $780.00/year for individuals, electronic only. Journal focusing on the interplay between software engineering and knowledge engineering.

11999 ■ IT Solutions Guide
SYS-CON Media
577 Chestnut Ridge Rd.
Woodcliff Lake, NJ 07677
Ph: (201)802-3000
Fax: (201)782-9601
URL: http://itsolutions.sys-con.com/

Quarterly. Magazine for IT professionals.

12000 ■ Journal of Active and Passive Electronic Devices
Old City Publishing
628 N 2nd St.
Philadelphia, PA 19123-3002
Ph: (215)925-4390
Fax: (215)925-4371
URL: http://www.oldcitypublishing.com/JAPED/JAPED.html

Quarterly. $766.00/year for institutions, print and online; $157.00/year for individuals, print only; $635.00/year for institutions, print and online; $148.00/year for individuals, print only; $76,372.00/year for institutions, print and online; $19,859.00/year for individuals, print only. International journal devoted to the science and technology of all types of electronic components.

12001 ■ Journal of Computer Science
Science Publications
Vails Gate Heights Dr.
PO Box 879
Vails Gate, NY 12584-0879
URL: http://thescipub.com/jcs.toc

Scholarly journal covering many areas of computer science, including: concurrent, parallel and distributed processing; artificial intelligence; image and voice processing; quality software and metrics; computer-aided education; wireless communication; real time processing; evaluative computation; and data bases and information recovery and neural networks.

12002 ■ Journal of Computer Systems, Networks, and Communications
Hindawi Publishing Corp.
410 Park Ave., 15th Fl.
287 PMB
New York, NY 10022-4407
Fax: (215)893-4392
E-mail: jcsnc@hindawi.com
URL: http://www.hindawi.com/journals/jcsnc/

$195.00/year for individuals, print & online. Journal covering important areas of information technology.

12003 ■ Journal of Software Engineering and Applications
Scientific Research Publishing
PO Box 54821
Irvine, CA 92619-4821
URL: http://www.scirp.org/journal/jsea/

Peer-reviewed journal covering software engineering and applications.

12004 ■ Journal of Software Maintenance and Evolution
John Wiley & Sons Inc.
111 River St.
Hoboken, NJ 07030-5773
Ph: (201)748-6000
Fax: (201)748-6088
Fr: 800-825-7550
URL: http://onlinelibrary.wiley.com/journal/10.1002/(ISSN)1096-90

$2,741.00/year for institutions, print; $2,741.00/year for institutions, other countries, print; $1,399.00/year for institutions, print; $1,769.00/year for institutions, print; $2,741.00/year for institutions, Canada and Mexico, print. Journal devoted to maintaining the viability of software through swift software evolution cycles.

12005 ■ Journal of Statistical Software
American Statistical Association
732 N Washington St.
Alexandria, VA 22314-1943
Ph: (703)684-1221
Fax: (703)684-2037
Fr: 888-231-3473
URL: http://www.jstatsoft.org/

Peer-reviewed journal publishing articles, book reviews, code snippets, and software reviews on the subject of statistical software and algorithms.

12006 ■ Journal of Women and Minorities in Science and Engineering
Begell House Inc.
50 Cross Hwy.
Redding, CT 06896
Ph: (203)938-1300
Fax: (203)938-1304
URL: http://www.begellhouse.com/journals/00551c876cc2f027

$248.00/year for institutions. Peer-reviewed journal featuring innovative ideas and programs for classroom teachers, scientific studies, and formulation of concepts related to the education, recruitment, and retention of under-represented groups in science and engineering.

12007 ■ *Monitor*
Capital PC User Group
19209 Mt. Airey Rd.
Brookeville, MD 20833
Ph: (301)560-6442
Fax: (301)760-3303
E-mail: editor@cpcug.org
URL: http://monitor.cpcug.org/index.html

Quarterly. Magazine covering computer hardware and software reviews, special interest user group news, advertisers and author/subject index, and calendar of events.

12008 ■ *PC WORLD*
101 Communications
9121 Oakdale Ave., Ste. 101
Chatsworth, CA 91311
Ph: (818)814-5200
Fax: (818)734-1522
E-mail: pcwletters@pcworld.com
URL: http://www.pcworld.com

Quarterly. $19.97/year for individuals; $29.97/year for two years. Technology or business magazine meeting the informational needs of tech-savvy managers, both at work and at home.

12009 ■ *Queue*
Association for Computing Machinery
PO Box 30777
New York, NY 10087
Ph: (212)626-0500
Fax: (212)944-1318
Fr: 800-342-6626
E-mail: queue@acm.org
URL: http://queue.acm.org/

Monthly. Free, U.S./Canadian residents and all members. Online magazine aimed at the computer professional. Magazine editorial does not provide solutions for the "here-and-now", but instead helps decision-makers plan future projects by examining the challenges and problems they are most likely to face.

12010 ■ *Revenue*
Montgomery Media International
55 New Montgomery St., Ste. 617
San Francisco, CA 94105
Ph: (415)371-8800
URL: http://www.revenuetoday.com/

Free to qualified subscribers. Magazine covering internet marketing strategies.

12011 ■ *Software*
John Wiley & Sons Inc.
111 River St.
Hoboken, NJ 07030-5773
Ph: (201)748-6000
Fax: (201)748-6088
Fr: 800-825-7550
URL: http://onlinelibrary.wiley.com/journal/10.1002/
(ISSN)1097-02

$4,705.00/year for institutions, print; $4,705.00/year for institutions, other countries, print; $3,036.00/year for institutions, other countries, print; $2,401.00/year for institutions, print; $4,705.00/year for institutions, Canada and Mexico, print. Journal for those who design, implement, or maintain computer software.

12012 ■ *Software Process*
John Wiley & Sons Inc.
111 River St.
Hoboken, NJ 07030-5773
Ph: (201)748-6000
Fax: (201)748-6088
Fr: 800-825-7550
URL: http://onlinelibrary.wiley.com/journal/10.1002/
(ISSN)1099-16

$209.00/year for individuals, print; $363.00/year for other countries, print; $727.00/year for institutions, other countries, print; $469.00/year for institutions, other countries, print; $370.00/year for institutions, print. Journal for those involved in the software

development process. Features experience reports, research papers, and critical discussion.

12013 ■ *SWE, Magazine of the Society of Women Engineers*
Society of Women Engineers
120 S La Salle St., Ste. 1515
Chicago, IL 60603
Ph: (312)596-5223
Fr: 877-793-4636
URL: http://societyofwomenengineers.swe.org/
index.php

Quarterly. $30.00/year for nonmembers. Magazine for engineering students and for women and men working in the engineering and technology fields. Covers career guidance, continuing development and topical issues.

12014 ■ *Ubiquity*
Association for Computing Machinery
PO Box 30777
New York, NY 10087
Ph: (212)626-0500
Fax: (212)944-1318
Fr: 800-342-6626
URL: http://ubiquity.acm.org

Weekly. Free. Web-based magazine of the Association for Computing Machinery dedicated to fostering critical analysis and in-depth commentary, including book reviews, on issues relating to the nature, constitution, structure, science, engineering, cognition, technology, practices and paradigms of the IT profession.

12015 ■ *WITI FastTrack*
United business Media L.L.C
240 W 35th St.
New York, NY 10001
Ph: (516)562-5000
URL: http://www.witi.com/corporate/fasttrack.php

Semiannual. Semiannual publication featuring in-depth content on the issues facing today's women professionals in technology.

12016 ■ *Woman Engineer*
Equal Opportunity Publications, Inc.
445 Broadhollow Rd., Ste. 425
Melville, NY 11747
Ph: (631)421-9421
Fax: (631)421-1352
E-mail: info@eop.com
URL: http://www.eop.com

Annual. Magazine that is offered at no charge to qualified female engineering, computer-science, and information-technology students and professionals seeking to find employment and advancement in their careers.

EMPLOYER DIRECTORIES AND NETWORKING LISTS

12017 ■ *American Men and Women of Science*
Gale
PO Box 6904
Florence, KY 41022-6904
Fr: 800-354-9706
URL: http://www.gale.cengage.com

Biennial, even years; New edition expected 29th, June 2011. $1,368.00 for individuals. Covers: Over 135,000 U.S. and Canadian scientists active in the physical, biological, mathematical, computer science, and engineering fields; includes references to previous edition for deceased scientists and nonrespondents. Entries include: Name, address, education, personal and career data, memberships, honors and awards, research interest. Arrangement: Alphabetical. Indexes: Discipline (in separate volume).

12018 ■ *Career Opportunities in Computers and Cyberspace*
Facts On File Inc.
132 W 31st St., 17th Fl.
New York, NY 10001
Ph: (212)967-8800
Fax: 800-678-3633
Fr: 800-322-8755
URL: http://www.infobasepublishing.com

Published March, 2004. Covers: Nearly 200 professions, clustering them by skill, objectives, and work conditions. Entries include: Education, salaries, employment prospects.

12019 ■ *Computer Directory*
Computer Directories Inc.
23815 Nichols Sawmill Rd.
Hockley, TX 77447
Ph: (281)259-5959
Fax: (281)259-5959
Fr: 800-234-4353
URL: http://www.compdirinc.com

Annual, fall. Covers: Approximately 130,000 computer installations; 19 separate volumes for Alaska/Hawaii, Connecticut/New Jersey, Dallas/Ft. Worth, Eastern Seaboard, Far Midwest, Houston, Illinois, Midatlantic, Midcentral, Mideast, Minnesota/Wisconsin, North Central, New England, New York Metro, Northwest, Ohio, Pennsylvania/West Virginia, Southeast, and Southwest Texas. Entries include: Company name, address, phone, fax, email, name and title of contact, hardware used, software application, operating system, programming language, computer graphics, networking system. Arrangement: Geographical. Indexes: Alphabetical, industry, hardware.

12020 ■ *Directory of Contract Staffing Firms*
C.E. Publications Inc.
PO Box 3006
Bothell, WA 98041-3006
Ph: (425)806-5200
Fax: (425)806-5585
URL: http://www.cjhunter.com/dcsf/overview.html

Annual. Covers: Nearly 1,300 contract firms actively engaged in the employment of engineering, IT/IS, and technical personnel for 'temporary' contract assignments throughout the world. Entries include: Company name, address, phone, name of contact, email, web address. Arrangement: Alphabetical. Indexes: Geographical.

12021 ■ *Discovering Careers for Your Future—Computers*
Facts On File Inc.
132 W 31st St., 17th Fl.
New York, NY 10001
Ph: (212)967-8800
Fax: 800-678-3633
Fr: 800-322-8755
URL: http://factsonfile.infobasepublishing.com

Latest edition 2nd, 2008. $21.95 for individuals. Covers: Computer operators, programmers, database specialists, and software engineers; links career education to curriculum, helping children investigate the subjects they are interested in, and the careers those subjects might lead to.

12022 ■ *GIS Markets and Opportunities*
Daratech Inc.
255 Bent St.
PO Box 380410
Cambridge, MA 02141-2001
Ph: (617)354-2339
Fax: (617)354-7822
E-mail: info@daratech.com
URL: http://www.daratech.com

; $6,997.00 for individuals. Covers: over 310 geographic information system software vendors and products. Entries include: Company name, address, phone, names and titles of key personnel, number of employees, geographical area served, financial data, subsidiary and branch names and locations, description of software. Arrangement: Alphabetical. Indexes: Alphabetical by name and product.

12023 ■ Indiana Society of Professional Engineers—Directory

Indiana Society of Professional Engineers
PO Box 20806
Indianapolis, IN 46220
Ph: (317)255-2267
Fax: (317)255-2530
URL: http://www.indspe.org

Annual, fall. Covers: Member registered engineers, land surveyors, engineering students, and engineers in training. Entries include: Member name, address, phone, type of membership, business information, specialty. Arrangement: Alpha by chapter area.

12024 ■ Information Sources

Software & Information Industry Association
1090 Vermont Ave. NW, 6th Fl.
Washington, DC 20005-4095
Ph: (202)289-7442
Fax: (202)289-7097
Fr: 800-388-7478
URL: http://www.siia.net

Continuous. Covers: More than 800 companies involved in the creation, distribution, and use of information products, services, and technology. Entries are prepared by companies described. Entries include: Company name, address, phone, names of executives, international partners, regional offices, trade and brand names, and description of products and services. Arrangement: Alphabetical. Indexes: Product, personal name, trade name, geographical, corporate parents, international and niche markets.

12025 ■ The Software Encyclopedia

R.R. Bowker L.L.C.
630 Central Ave.
New Providence, NJ 07974
Ph: (908)286-1090
Fr: 888-269-5372
URL: http://www.bowker.com/catalog/000103.htm

Annual, latest edition May, 2008. $460.00 for individuals. Contains listings of over 44,600 software programs from 4,646 publishers and distributors. Arrangement: Two alphabetical sections for software, one by title, the other by system/application; also, one alphabetical section for publishers. Indexes: Title, system/application.

HANDBOOKS AND MANUALS

12026 ■ Careers for Computer Buffs and Other Technological Types

The McGraw-Hill Companies
PO Box 182604
Columbus, OH 43272
Fax: (614)759-3749
Fr: 877-883-5524
E-mail: customer.service@mcgraw-hill.com
URL: http://www.mhprofessional.com/
   product.php?isbn=0071458778

Marjorie Eberts and Margaret Gisler. Third edition, 2006. $13.95 (paper). 160 pages. Suggested jobs in a wide range of settings, from the office to the outdoors.

12027 ■ Expert Resumes for Computer and Web Jobs

Jist Publishing
875 Montreal Way
St. Paul, MN 55102
Fr: 800-648-5478
E-mail: info@jist.com
URL: http://www.jist.com

Wendy Enelow and Louise Kursmark. Third edition, 2011. $17.95 (paper). 304 pages.

12028 ■ Expert Resumes for Engineers

JIST Publishing
875 Montreal Way
St. Paul, MN 55102
Fr: 800-648-5478
E-mail: educate@emcp.com
URL: http://www.jist.com

Louise M. Kursmark and Wendy S. Enelow. 2009. $16.95 (softcover). 272 pages. Features a collection of written resume samples for all types of engineers including civil, mechanical, industrial, electrical, electronics, computer, and more. Contains tips and strategies for writing engineering resumes and finding the best jobs.

12029 ■ Ferguson Career Coach: Managing Your Career in the Computer Industry

Facts On File
132 W 31st St., 17th Fl.
New York, NY 10001
Fax: 800-678-3633
Fr: 800-322-8755
E-mail: custserv@factsonfile.com
URL: http://factsonfile.infobasepublishing.com

Shelly Field. 2008. $39.95 (hardcover). 280 pages. Provides tips for students who dream of pursuing a career as a software engineer or a web designer. Contains advice from professionals, career strategies, insider secrets, and more.

12030 ■ Resumes for Scientific and Technical Careers

The McGraw-Hill Companies
PO Box 182604
Columbus, OH 43272
Fax: (614)759-3749
Fr: 877-883-5524
E-mail: customer.service@mcgraw-hill.com
URL: http://www.mhprofessional.com/
   product.php?isbn=0071482199

Third edition, 2007. $12.95 (paper). 144 pages. Provides resume advice for individuals interested in working in scientific and technical careers. Includes sample resumes and cover letters.

EMPLOYMENT AGENCIES AND SEARCH FIRMS

12031 ■ Amtec Human Capital

2749 Saturn St.
Brea, CA 92821
Ph: (714)993-1900
Fax: (714)993-2419
E-mail: info@amtechc.com
URL: http://www.amtechc.com

Employment agency.

12032 ■ Career Development Services

150 State St.
Rochester, NY 14614
Ph: (585)244-0765
Fr: 800-736-6710
E-mail: info@careerdev.org
URL: http://www.careerdev.org

Employment agency.

12033 ■ Carol Maden Group

2019 Cunningham Dr., Ste. 218
Hampton, VA 23666-3316
Ph: (757)827-9010
Fax: (757)827-9081
E-mail: cmaden@hroads.net

Personnel consultants offering placement service in computer technology and engineering; servicing manufacturing and private industries nationwide. Temporary placement servicing clerical and light industrial.

12034 ■ Computer Management

7982 Honeygo Blvd., No. 23
Baltimore, MD 21236
Ph: (410)679-7000
E-mail: info@technicaljobs.com
URL: http://www.technicaljobs.com

Search firm focusing on filling jobs for database administration, network administration, web development, and software.

12035 ■ The Datafinders Group, Inc.

PO Box 1624
Fort Lee, NJ 07024
Ph: (201)845-7700
Fax: (201)969-1065
E-mail: info@datafinders.net
URL: http://www.datafinders.net

Executive search firm.

12036 ■ ENTEGEE

70 Blanchard Rd., Ste. 102
Burlington, MA 01803
Fr: 800-368-3433
E-mail: corporate@entegee.com
URL: http://www.entegee.com

Specializes in recruiting experienced professionals in the engineering and technical industries. Features a searchable database of employment opportunities in the engineering and technical fields.

12037 ■ Generator Group

17933 NW Evergreen Pkwy., Ste. 240
Beaverton, OR 97006
Ph: (503)224-4811
URL: http://www.generatorgroup.net

Works as a talent management services firm that delivers executive search and talent management consulting to organizations in consumer products and retail, technology, and public transportation.

12038 ■ Global Employment Solutions

10375 Park Meadows Dr., Ste. 375
Littleton, CO 80124
Ph: (303)216-9500
Fax: (303)216-9533
URL: http://www.gesnetwork.com

Employment agency.

12039 ■ Houser Martin Morris

110th Ave. NE, 110 Atrium Pl., Ste. 580
Bellevue, WA 98004
Ph: (425)453-2700
Fax: (425)453-8726
E-mail: info@houser.com
URL: http://www.houser.com

Focus is in the areas of retained executive search, professional and technical recruiting. Areas of specialization include software engineering, sales and marketing, information technology, legal, human resources, accounting and finance, manufacturing, factory automation, and engineering.

12040 ■ Integrisource

1689 Mahan Center Blvd., Ste. B
Tallahassee, FL 32308
Ph: (850)575-5454
Fax: (850)575-0984
Fr: 877-575-5454
E-mail: recruiting@integrisource.net
URL: http://www.integrisource.net

Provides information technology staffing services to public and private organizations.

12041 ■ JD Strategies

444 Castro St., Ste. 318
Mountain View, CA 94041
Ph: (650)941-2900
Fax: (650)941-2933
E-mail: jobs@jdstrategies.net
URL: http://www.jdstrategies.net

Specializes in providing workforce solutions for the technical and functional staffing needs of technology companies. Focuses on all areas of engineering product development, testing, and quality assurance.

12042 ■ JES Search Firm Inc.

1021 Stovall Blvd., Ste. 600
Atlanta, GA 30319
Ph: (404)812-0622

Fax: (404)812-1910
E-mail: admin@jessearch.com
URL: http://www.jessearch.com

Contract and permanent information technology search firm specializing in placing software developers as well as other information systems professionals.

12043 ■ JobMonkey, Inc.
PO Box 3956
Seattle, WA 98124
Fr: 800-230-1095
E-mail: adminstaff2@jobmonkey.com
URL: http://www.jobmonkey.com/videogamejobs/
video_game_developer_jobs.html

Recruitment firm specializing in jobs in the technology fields, particularly video game designers.

12044 ■ JPM International
26034 Acero
Mission Viejo, CA 92691
Ph: (949)699-4300
Fax: (949)699-4333
Fr: 800-685-7856
E-mail: qtek37@yahoo.com
URL: http://www.jpmintl.com/pages/qss.html

Executive search firm and employment agency.

12045 ■ Louis Rudzinsky Associates Inc.
394 Lowell St., Ste. 17
PO Box 640
Lexington, MA 02420-2551
Ph: (781)862-6727
Fax: (781)862-6868
E-mail: lra@lra.com
URL: http://www.lra.com

Provides recruitment, placement, and executive search to industry (software, electronics, optics) covering positions in general management, manufacturing, engineering, and marketing. Personnel consulting activities include counsel to small and startup companies. Industries served: electronics, aerospace, optical, laser, computer, software, imaging, electro-optics, biotechnology, advanced materials, and solid-state/semiconductor.

12046 ■ Recruiting Partners
3494 Camino Tassajara Rd., No. 404
Danville, CA 94506
Ph: (925)964-0249
E-mail: info@recruitingpartners.com
URL: http://www.recruitingpartners.com

Description: Serves as an executive and technical recruiting firm that specializes in accounting, legal, information technology, engineering, executive management and technical writing.

12047 ■ Resources Objectives Inc.
581 Boylston St., Ste. 604
Boston, MA 02116-3677
Ph: (617)523-7788
Fax: (617)523-7939

Offers executive outplacement and executive search services particularly in the high technology areas software or hardware engineering, marketing or sales; quality engineering; manufacturing or engineering support, and communications.

12048 ■ Technical Talent Locators Ltd.
5570 Sterrett Pl., Ste. 208
Columbia, MD 21044
Ph: (410)740-0091
E-mail: steve@ttlgroup.com
URL: http://www.ttlgroup.com

Permanent employment agency working within the following fields: software and database engineering; computer, communication, and telecommunication system engineering; and other computer-related disciplines.

12049 ■ Wallach Associates Inc.
7811 Montrose Rd., Ste. 505
Potomac, MD 20854

Ph: (301)340-0300
Fax: (301)340-8008
Fr: 800-296-2084
URL: http://www.wallach.org

Specialists in recruitment of professional personnel, primarily in information technology and electronic systems and engineering, energy research and development, management consulting, operations research, computers, defense systems, and programmers. Specializes in Internet and software engineer for intelligence community.

ONLINE JOB SOURCES AND SERVICES

12050 ■ Benchfolks.com
URL: http://www.benchfolks.com

Description: Provides a one-stop shop for IT professionals, companies/clients and vendors/suppliers by catering to their employment needs. Caters to individual needs like professional standing in terms of qualification, level of expertise, experience gained and requirement of the industry.

12051 ■ ComputerWork.com
Fr: 800-691-8413
URL: http://www.computerwork.com

Description: Job search and resume submission service for professionals in information technology.

12052 ■ Computerworld Careers
URL: http://www.computerworld.com/careertopics/
careers

Description: Offers career opportunities for IT (information technology) professionals. Job seekers may search the jobs database, register at the site, and read about job surveys and employment trends. Employers may post jobs.

12053 ■ Computing Research Association Job Announcements
1828 L St. NW, Ste. 800
Washington, DC 20036-4632
Ph: (202)234-2111
Fax: (202)667-1066
E-mail: info@cra.org
URL: http://www.cra.org/ads

Description: Contains dated links to national college and university computer technology positions.

12054 ■ Dice.com
URL: http://www.dice.com

Description: Job search database for computer consultants and high-tech professionals, listing thousands of high tech permanent contract and consulting jobs for programmers, software engineers, systems administrators, web developers, and hardware engineers. Also free career advice e-mail newsletter and job posting e-alerts.

12055 ■ EnergyCentralJobs.com
E-mail: service@energycentral.com
URL: http://www.energycentraljobs.com

Description: Serves as an on-line job resource for candidates and power companies worldwide. Maintains a job search database dedicated to the power, nuclear, oil and gas career fields.

12056 ■ Engineering Classifieds
URL: http://www.engineeringclassifieds.com

Description: Serves as a career site for engineering professionals. Provides services including job search agents, resume creation and posting.

12057 ■ EngineerJobs.com
URL: http://www.engineerjobs.com

Description: Provides job opportunities for engineering professionals in the following disciplines: aerospace, agricultural, biomedical, chemical, civil, electrical, environmental, industrial, manufacturing, marine, materials, mechanical, mining, nuclear, petroleum,

process, project, quality, sales, software, solar, systems, and structural.

12058 ■ Engineer.net
URL: http://www.engineer.net

Description: Provides engineering employment tools such as job search, job posting, and engineering resumes.

12059 ■ Guru.com
5001 Baum Blvd., Ste. 760
Pittsburgh, PA 15213
Fax: (412)687-4466
Fr: 888-687-1316
URL: http://www.guru.com

Description: Job board specializing in contract jobs for creative and information technology professionals. Also provides online incorporation and educational opportunities for independent contractors along with articles and advice.

12060 ■ InformationTechnologyCrossing.com
URL: http://www.informationtechnologycrossing.com

Description: Provides information on IT jobs.

12061 ■ ItJobs.com
E-mail: comments@itjobsllc.com
URL: http://www.itjobs.com

Description: Provides information technology employment opportunities for the following categories: internet/intranet/extranet, network systems, open systems, client/server, software engineering and development, software QA and testing, ERP applications and management consulting, and legacy systems.

12062 ■ Jobs for Programmers
E-mail: support@jfpresources.com
URL: http://www.prgjobs.com

Description: Job board site for computer programmers that allows them to browse through thousands of programming jobs, even search for special jobs with sign-on bonuses, relocation funding, and 4-day work weeks. Resume posting is free.

12063 ■ NetworkEngineer.com
URL: http://www.networkengineer.com

Description: Provides lists of job and career opportunities for network engineers.

12064 ■ ProgrammingCareers.com
URL: http://www.programmingcareers.com

Description: Provides programming jobs to computer software developers and programmers. Functions mainly as an advertiser, and is not involved in the hiring process. Connects job seekers in related professions with employers and employment recruiters.

12065 ■ Software Engineer Jobs
URL: http://www.jobssoftwareengineer.com

Description: Provides a listing of job and career opportunities for software engineering professionals.

12066 ■ SoftwareEngineer.com
URL: http://www.softwareengineer.com

Description: Provides lists of job and career opportunities for software engineering professionals.

12067 ■ Tech-Engine.com
URL: http://techengine.com

Description: Features employment listings concerning the IT and engineering fields. Features employers and recruiters information, resume posting and career resources.

12068 ■ TechCareers
URL: http://www.techcareers.com

Description: Features career-related resources, news, and job postings for information technology and engineering professionals.

12069 ■ ThinkEnergyGroup.com
E-mail: resumes@thinkjobs.com
URL: http://www.thinkenergygroup.com

Description: Serves as a job board for professionals looking for positions in engineering, power plant, energy, and technical fields. Contains advice and tips on interviews, job searching, resume writing, hiring, and management. Provides choices of work location, pay rates in the field of expertise and contract, temp-to-hire, and direct hiring options.

12070 ■ ZDNet Tech Jobs
URL: http://www.zdnet.com

Description: Site houses a listing of national employment opportunities for professionals in high tech fields. Also contains resume building tips and relocation resources.

TRADESHOWS

12071 ■ Information Architecture Summit
American Society for Information Science and Technology
1320 Fenwick Ln., Ste. 510
Silver Spring, MD 20910
Ph: (301)495-0900
Fax: (301)495-0810
E-mail: asis@asis.org
URL: http://www.asis.org

Annual. Features presentations from research and industry leaders, and opportunities for personal interaction among information architects and other user experience professionals.

OTHER SOURCES

12072 ■ American Association of Engineering Societies (AAES)
1801 Alexander Bell Dr.
Reston, VA 20191
Ph: (202)296-2237
Fax: (202)296-1151
Fr: 888-400-2237
E-mail: dbateson@aaes.org
URL: http://www.aaes.org

Description: Coordinates the efforts of the member societies in the provision of reliable and objective information to the general public concerning issues which affect the engineering profession and the field of engineering as a whole; collects, analyzes, documents, and disseminates data which will inform the general public of the relationship between engineering and the national welfare; provides a forum for the engineering societies to exchange and discuss their views on matters of common interest; and represents the U.S. engineering community abroad through representation in WFEO and UPADI.

12073 ■ American Indian Science and Engineering Society (AISES)
PO Box 9828
Albuquerque, NM 87119-9828
Ph: (505)765-1052
Fax: (505)765-5608
E-mail: info@aises.org
URL: http://www.aises.org

Description: Represents American Indian and non-Indian students and professionals in science, technology, and engineering fields; corporations representing energy, mining, aerospace, electronic, and computer fields. Seeks to motivate and encourage students to pursue undergraduate and graduate studies in science, engineering, and technology. Sponsors science fairs in grade schools, teacher training workshops, summer math/science sessions for 8th-12th graders, professional chapters, and student chapters in colleges. Offers scholarships. Adult members serve as role models, advisers, and mentors for students. Operates placement service.

12074 ■ Association of Software Professionals
PO Box 1522
Martinsville, IN 46151
Ph: (765)349-4740
Fax: (815)301-3756
URL: http://www.asp-shareware.org

Description: Represents independent software developers and vendors. Dedicated to the advancement of shareware also known as try-before-you-buy software as an alternative to conventional retail software. Works to improve the business and make it easier for computer users to find quality software at reasonable prices.

12075 ■ Association for Women in Computing (AWC)
PO Box 2768
Oakland, CA 94602
E-mail: info@awc-hq.org
URL: http://www.awc-hq.org

Description: Individuals interested in promoting the education, professional development, and advancement of women in computing.

12076 ■ Engineering Society of Detroit (ESD)
20700 Civic Center Dr., Ste. 450
Southfield, MI 48076
Ph: (248)353-0735
Fax: (248)353-0736
E-mail: esd@esd.org
URL: http://ww2.esd.org/home.htm

Description: Engineers from all disciplines; scientists and technologists. Conducts technical programs and engineering refresher courses; sponsors conferences and expositions. Maintains speakers' bureau; offers placement services; although based in Detroit, MI, society membership is international.

12077 ■ Entertainment Software Association
575 7th St. NW, Ste. 300
Washington, DC 20004
E-mail: esa@theesa.com
URL: http://www.theesa.com

Dedicated to serving the needs of video game designers and developers through business and consumer research, government relations, an anti-piracy program, and a number of other resources provided to members.

12078 ■ International Association of Software Architects
c/o Paul Preiss, CEO
11044 Research Blvd., Ste. B-400
Austin, TX 78759
Ph: (512)637-4272
Fax: (512)382-5327
Fr: (866)399-4272
E-mail: contactus@iasahome.org
URL: http://www.iasaglobal.org

Description: Seeks to improve the quality of the IT architecture industry by developing and delivering standards and education programs and developing accreditation programs and services that optimize the development of the architecture profession. Works for the advancement and sharing of issues related to software architecture in the enterprise, product, education and government sectors.

12079 ■ National Action Council for Minorities in Engineering (NACME)
440 Hamilton Ave., Ste. 302
White Plains, NY 10601-1813
Ph: (914)539-4010
Fax: (914)539-4032
E-mail: info@nacme.org
URL: http://www.nacme.org

Description: Leads the national effort to increase access to careers in engineering and other science-based disciplines. Conducts research and public policy analysis, develops and operates national demonstration programs at precollege and university levels, and disseminates information through publications, conferences and electronic media. Serves as a privately funded source of scholarships for minority students in engineering.

12080 ■ National Society of Professional Engineers (NSPE)
1420 King St.
Alexandria, VA 22314-2794
Ph: (703)684-2800
Fax: (703)836-4875
Fr: 888-285-6773
E-mail: memserv@nspe.org
URL: http://www.nspe.org

Description: Represents professional engineers and engineers-in-training in all fields registered in accordance with the laws of states or territories of the U.S. or provinces of Canada; qualified graduate engineers, student members, and registered land surveyors. Is concerned with social, professional, ethical, and economic considerations of engineering as a profession; encompasses programs in public relations, employment practices, ethical considerations, education, and career guidance. Monitors legislative and regulatory actions of interest to the engineering profession.

12081 ■ Society of Hispanic Professional Engineers (SHPE)
13181 Crossroads Pkwy. N, Ste. 450
City of Industry, CA 91746-3496
Ph: (323)725-3970
Fax: (323)725-0316
E-mail: shpenational@shpe.org
URL: http://oneshpe.shpe.org/wps/portal/national

Description: Represents engineers, student engineers, and scientists. Aims to increase the number of Hispanic engineers by providing motivation and support to students. Sponsors competitions and educational programs. Maintains placement service and speakers' bureau; compiles statistics.

12082 ■ Society of Women Engineers (SWE)
203 N La Salle St., Ste. 1675
Chicago, IL 60601
Ph: (312)596-5223
Fax: (312)596-5252
Fr: 877-SWE-INFO
E-mail: hq@swe.org
URL: http://societyofwomenengineers.swe.org

Description: Educational and service organization representing both students and professional women in engineering and technical fields.

12083 ■ Special Interest Group on Accessible Computing (SIGACCESS)
2 Penn Plz., Ste. 701
New York, NY 10121-0701
Ph: (212)626-0500
Fax: (212)944-1318
Fr: 800-342-6626
E-mail: chair_sigaccess@acm.org
URL: http://www.sigaccess.org

Description: Promotes the professional interests of computing personnel with physical disabilities and the application of computing and information technology in solving relevant disability problems. Works to educate the public to support careers for the disabled.

SOURCES OF HELP-WANTED ADS

12084 ■ About Campus
John Wiley & Sons Inc.
111 River St.
Hoboken, NJ 07030-5773
Ph: (201)748-6000
Fax: (201)748-6088
Fr: 800-825-7550
URL: http://onlinelibrary.wiley.com/journal/10.1002/
(ISSN)1536-06
Bimonthly. $207.00/year for institutions, print only;
$267.00/year for institutions, Canada and Mexico,
print only; $318.00/year for institutions, other coun-
tries, print only; $60.00/year for U.S., Canada, and
Mexico, print only; $96.00/year for other countries,
print only. Journal focused on the critical issues faced
by both student affairs and academic affairs staff as
they work on helping students learn.

12085 ■ American Academic
American Federation of Teachers
555 New Jersey Ave. NW
Washington, DC 20001
Ph: (202)879-4400
URL: http://www.aft.org/pubs-reports/american_
academic/index.htm
Higher education policy journal.

12086 ■ Annals of Medicine
Informa Healthcare
52 Vanderbilt Ave., 7th Fl.
New York, NY 10017-3846
Ph: (212)520-2777
URL: http://informahealthcare.com/ann
$595.00/year for institutions; $980.00/year for institutions; $780.00/year for institutions. Journal covering
health science and medical education.

**12087 ■ Assessment & Evaluation in Higher
Education**
Routledge Journals
270 Madison Ave.
New York, NY 10016-0601
Ph: (212)216-7800
Fax: (212)563-2269
URL: http://www.tandf.co.uk/journals/titles/
02602938.asp
Bimonthly. $1,316.00/year for institutions, online only;
$2,547.00/year for institutions, print + online;
$1,462.00/year for individuals, print + online;
$2,292.00/year for institutions, online only; $578.00/
year for individuals, print only; $314.00/year for
individuals, print only. Peer-reviewed journal focusing
on publishing papers and reports on all aspects of
assessment and evaluation within higher education.

12088 ■ Better
The Johns Hopkins University Press
2715 N Charles St.
Baltimore, MD 21218-4319

Ph: (410)516-6900
Fax: (410)516-6968
URL: http://www.press.jhu.edu/journals/better_
evidence_based_educ
$29.50/year for individuals, print and electronic;
$80.00/year for institutions, print and electronic.
Magazine for educators and policy makers interested
in evidence-based education reform.

12089 ■ Better
The Johns Hopkins University Press
2715 N Charles St.
Baltimore, MD 21218-4319
Ph: (410)516-6900
Fax: (410)516-6968
URL: http://www.press.jhu.edu/journals/better_
evidence_based_educ
$29.50/year for individuals, print and electronic;
$80.00/year for institutions, print and electronic.
Magazine for educators and policy makers interested
in evidence-based education reform.

**12090 ■ Brookings Papers on Education
Policy**
Brookings Institution Press
1775 Massachusetts Ave. NW
Washington, DC 20036
Ph: (202)797-6000
URL: http://www.brookings.edu/press/Journals/2007/
brookingspapers
$36.00/year for individuals. Journal dealing with all
aspects of American education.

12091 ■ Creative Education
Scientific Research Publishing
PO Box 54821
Irvine, CA 92619-4821
E-mail: ce@scirp.org
URL: http://www.scirp.org/journal/ce/
$195.00/year for individuals. Peer-reviewed journal
publishing articles on the latest advancements in
creative education.

12092 ■ Creative Education
Scientific Research Publishing
PO Box 54821
Irvine, CA 92619-4821
E-mail: ce@scirp.org
URL: http://www.scirp.org/journal/ce/
$195.00/year for individuals. Peer-reviewed journal
publishing articles on the latest advancements in
creative education.

**12093 ■ Education and Training in
Developmental Disabilities**
Council for Exceptional Children
2900 Crystal Dr., Ste. 1000
Arlington, VA 22202
Ph: (703)620-3660
Fax: (703)264-9494

Fr: 888-232-7733
E-mail: etdd@asu.edu
URL: http://www.dddcec.org/publications.htm
Quarterly. $40.00/year for individuals; $25.00/year for
single issue; $175.00/year for institutions; $179.50/
year for institutions, other countries. Journal covering
theory and research in education of individuals with
mental retardation and/or developmental disabilities.

12094 ■ Education & Treatment of Children
West Virginia University Press
139 Stansbury Hall
PO Box 6295
Morgantown, WV 26506
Ph: (304)293-8400
Fax: (304)293-6585
URL: http://www.educationandtreatmentofchildren.net
Quarterly. $85.00/year for institutions; $45.00/year for
individuals; $100.00/year for institutions, elsewhere;
$60.00/year for individuals, elsewhere. Periodical
featuring information concerning the development of
services for children and youth. Includes reports written for educators and other child care and mental
health providers focused on teaching, training, and
treatment effectiveness.

**12095 ■ Educational Research and
Evaluation**
Routledge Journals
270 Madison Ave.
New York, NY 10016-0601
Ph: (212)216-7800
Fax: (212)563-2269
URL: http://www.tandf.co.uk/journals/titles/
13803611.asp
Bimonthly. $428.00/year for institutions, print + on-
line; $385.00/year for institutions, online only;
$165.00/year for institutions, print only; $731.00/year
for institutions, print + online; $658.00/year for institu-
tions, online only; $275.00/year for individuals, print
only. Peer-reviewed journal on theory and practice.

12096 ■ Environmental Education Research
Routledge Journals
270 Madison Ave.
New York, NY 10016-0601
Ph: (212)216-7800
Fax: (212)563-2269
URL: http://www.tandf.co.uk/journals/titles/
13504622.asp
Bimonthly. $1,373.00/year for institutions, print + on-
line; $1,236.00/year for institutions, online only;
$364.00/year for individuals, print only. Journal cover-
ing all aspects of environmental education.

12097 ■ Essays in Education
University of South Carolina
471 University Pky.
Aiken, SC 29801
Ph: (803)648-6851
URL: http://www.usca.edu/essays/

Monthly. Journal covering issues that impact and influence education.

12098 ■ Hematology
American Society of Hematology
2021 L St. NW, Ste. 900
Washington, DC 20036
Ph: (202)776-0544
Fax: (202)776-0545
URL: http://asheducationbook.hematologylibrary.org

Annual. $75.00/year for members; $125.00/year for nonmembers. Journal providing continuing medical education for physicians.

12099 ■ Interdisciplinary Journal of Teaching and Learning
Southern University at Baton Rouge
PO Box 9942
Baton Rouge, LA 70813
Ph: (225)711-4500
Fax: (225)771-4400
URL: http://www.subr.edu/CollegeofEducation/ COE%20ONLINE%20Journa

Online academic journal that publishes research and scholarly articles in the field of education and learning.

12100 ■ The International Electronic Journal of Health Education
American Alliance for Health, Physical Education, Recreation & Dance
1900 Association Dr.
Reston, VA 20191-1598
Ph: (703)476-3400
Fax: (703)476-9527
Fr: 800-213-7193
URL: http://www.aahperd.org/aahe/publications/iejhe/

Annual. Free, health education professionals and students. Journal promoting health through education and other systematic strategies.

12101 ■ International Journal of Critical Pedagogy
University of North Carolina at Greensboro
1400 Spring Garden St.
Greensboro, NC 27412
Ph: (336)334-5000
URL: http://libjournal.uncg.edu/ojs/index.php/ijcp/ index

Peer-reviewed journal publishing innovative understandings and applications of critical pedagogy.

12102 ■ International Journal of Early Years Education
Routledge Journals
270 Madison Ave.
New York, NY 10016-0601
Ph: (212)216-7800
Fax: (212)563-2269
URL: http://www.tandf.co.uk/journals/titles/ 09669760.asp

$705.00/year for institutions, online only; $783.00/ year for institutions, print + online; $271.00/year for individuals, print only. Journal focusing on education world-wide.

12103 ■ International Journal of Inclusive Education
Routledge Journals
270 Madison Ave.
New York, NY 10016-0601
Ph: (212)216-7800
Fax: (212)563-2269
URL: http://www.tandf.co.uk/journals/titles/ 13603116.asp

$589.00/year for individuals, print only; $1,135.00/ year for institutions, online only; $1,261.00/year for individuals, print + online; $355.00/year for individuals, print only; $694.00/year for institutions, online only; $771.00/year for institutions, print + online. Journal providing information on the nature of schools, universities and technical colleges for the educators and educational policy-makers.

12104 ■ International Journal of Leadership in Education
Routledge
711 3 Ave., 8 Fl.
New York, NY 10016
Ph: (212)216-7800
Fax: (212)563-2269
Fr: 800-634-7064
E-mail: ijle@txstate.edu
URL: http://www.tandf.co.uk/journals/tf/ 13603124.html

Quarterly. $240.00/year for individuals, print only; $612.00/year for institutions, online only; $680.00/ year for institutions, print and online; $408.00/year for institutions, print and online; $367.00/year for institutions, online only; $142.00/year for individuals, print only. Journal dealing with leadership in education.

12105 ■ International Journal of Progressive Education
International Journal of Progressive Education
c/o Alex Jean-Charles, PhD, Asst. Mng. Ed.
320 Fitzelle Hall, Ravine Pky.
Oneonta, NY 13820
URL: http://www.inased.org/ijpe.htm

$35.00/year for members; $45.00/year for individuals; $140.00/year for institutions, library; $35.00/year for students; $25.00/year for single issue; $50.00/year for students, other countries. Peer-reviewed online journal that aims to create an open and continuing dialogue about current educational issues and future conceptions of educational theory.

12106 ■ International Journal of Whole Schooling
Whole Schooling Press
Wayne State University
217 Education
Detroit, MI 48202
URL: http://www.wholeschooling.net/Journal_of_ Whole_Schooling/IJW

Free. International, refereed academic journal dedicated to exploring ways to improve learning and schooling for all children.

12107 ■ Journal of Academic Leadership
Academic Leadership
600 Park St.
Rarick Hall 219
Hays, KS 67601-4099
Ph: (785)628-4547
URL: http://www.academicleadership.org/

Journal focusing on the leadership issues in the academic world.

12108 ■ Journal of Cases in Educational Leadership
Sage Publications Inc.
2455 Teller Rd.
Thousand Oaks, CA 91320-2218
Ph: (805)499-9774
Fax: (805)583-2665
Fr: 800-818-7243
URL: http://jel.sagepub.com

Quarterly. $411.00/year for institutions, e-access; $94.00/year for individuals, e-access. Journal covering cases appropriate for use in programs that prepare educational leaders.

12109 ■ Journal of Curriculum and Supervision
Association for Supervision and Curriculum Development
1703 N Beauregard St.
Alexandria, VA 22311-1714
Ph: (703)578-9600
Fax: (703)575-5400
Fr: 800-933-2723
URL: http://www.ascd.org/publications/jcs/fall2002/ On_Community.a

Scholarly journal focusing on curriculum and supervision.

12110 ■ Journal of Direct Instruction
Association for Direct Instruction
PO Box 10252
Eugene, OR 97440
Ph: (541)485-1293
Fax: (541)868-1397
Fr: 800-995-2464
URL: http://www.adihome.org/ index.php?option=com_content&view=art

Quarterly. Included in membership. Journal covering education.

12111 ■ Journal of Language, Identity, and Education
Routledge Journals
270 Madison Ave.
New York, NY 10016-0601
Ph: (212)216-7800
Fax: (212)563-2269
URL: http://www.tandf.co.uk/journals/titles/ 15348458.asp

$316.00/year for institutions, print + online; $284.00/ year for institutions, online; $43.00/year for individuals, print + online; $527.00/year for institutions, print + online; $474.00/year for institutions, online; $71.00/ year for individuals, print + online; $421.00/year for institutions, print + online; $379.00/year for institutions, online; $57.00/year for individuals, print + online. Scholarly, interdisciplinary journal covering issues in language, identity and education worldwide for academics, educators and policy specialists in a variety of disciplines, and others.

12112 ■ Journal of Latinos and Education
Routledge Journals
270 Madison Ave.
New York, NY 10016-0601
Ph: (212)216-7800
Fax: (212)563-2269
URL: http://www.tandf.co.uk/journals/titles/ 15348431.asp

Quarterly. $286.00/year for institutions, print + online; $257.00/year for institutions, online; $38.00/year for individuals, print + online; $480.00/year for institutions, print + online; $432.00/year for institutions, online; $63.00/year for individuals, print + online; $331.00/year for institutions, print + online; $343.00/ year for institutions, online; $51.00/year for individuals, print + online. Scholarly, multidisciplinary journal covering educational issues that impact Latinos for researchers, teaching professionals, academics, scholars, institutions, and others.

12113 ■ The Journal of Special Education
Sage Publications Inc.
2455 Teller Rd.
Thousand Oaks, CA 91320-2218
Ph: (805)499-9774
Fax: (805)583-2665
Fr: 800-818-7243
URL: http://www.sagepub.com/ journalsProdEditBoards.nav?prodId=Jou

Quarterly. $61.00/year for individuals, print & e-access; $194.00/year for institutions, print & e-access; $175.00/year for institutions, e-access; $190.00/year for institutions, print only; $52.00/year for institutions, single print; $20.00/year for single issue. Journal presents research findings in the field of special education.

12114 ■ Journal of Special Education Leadership
Council of Administrators of Special Education
Osigian Office Centre
101 Katelyn Cir., Ste. E
Warner Robins, GA 31088
Ph: (478)333-6892
Fax: (478)333-2453
URL: http://csef.air.org/publications/related/jsel/ jsel.html

Semiannual. Included in membership; $41.00/year for nonmembers; $60.00/year for nonmembers, institutions. Journal covering programs and developments affecting the special education field.

12115 ■ *Journal of STEM Education*
Auburn University
9088 Haley Ctr.
Auburn, AL 36849
Ph: (334)844-9088
Fax: (334)844-9027
URL: http://ojs.jstem.org/index.php?journal=JSTEM
Semiannual. Journal for educators in Science, Technology, Engineering, and Mathematics (STEM) education.

12116 ■ *Leadership and Policy in Schools*
Routledge Journals
270 Madison Ave.
New York, NY 10016-0601
Ph: (212)216-7800
Fax: (212)563-2269
URL: http://www.tandf.co.uk/journals/titles/
15700763.asp
Quarterly. $567.00/year for institutions, print and online; $260.00/year for individuals, print only; $510.00/year for institutions, online only. Journal providing information about leadership and policy in primary and secondary education.

12117 ■ *Oxford Review of Education*
Routledge Journals
270 Madison Ave.
New York, NY 10016-0601
Ph: (212)216-7800
Fax: (212)563-2269
URL: http://www.tandf.co.uk/journals/titles/
03054985.asp
$709.00/year for institutions, print + online; $1,224.00/year for institutions, print + online; $249.00/year for individuals, print only; $454.00/year for individuals, print only. Journal covering advance study of education.

12118 ■ *Remedial and Special Education (RASE)*
Sage Publications Inc.
2455 Teller Rd.
Thousand Oaks, CA 91320-2218
Ph: (805)499-9774
Fax: (805)583-2665
Fr: 800-818-7243
URL: http://www.sagepub.com/
journalsProdEditBoards.nav?prodId=Jou
Bimonthly. $71.00/year for individuals, print & e-access; $221.00/year for institutions, print only; $203.00/year for institutions, e-access; $225.00/year for institutions, print & e-access; $15.00/year for single issue, print; $41.00/year for institutions, single print. Journal interprets research and makes recommendations for practice in the fields of remedial and special education.

12119 ■ *School Effectiveness and School Improvement*
Routledge
711 3 Ave., 8 Fl.
New York, NY 10016
Ph: (212)216-7800
Fax: (212)563-2269
Fr: 800-634-7064
URL: http://www.tandf.co.uk/journals/titles/
09243453.asp
Quarterly. $387.00/year for institutions, print and online; $348.00/year for institutions, online only; $186.00/year for individuals, print only; $660.00/year for institutions, print and online; $594.00/year for institutions, online only; $312.00/year for individuals, print only. Journal focusing on educational progress of all students.

12120 ■ *Teacher Education and Special Education*
Allen Press Inc.
810 E 10th St.
PO Box 368
Lawrence, KS 66044-0368
Ph: (785)843-1234

Fax: (785)843-1226
URL: http://tes.sagepub.com/
Quarterly. $50.00/year for individuals; $167.00/year for libraries, other institutions; $172.00/year for institutions, other countries, libraries. Journal covering personnel preparation in special education.

12121 ■ *Teaching and Learning in Nursing*
Elsevier Science Inc.
360 Park Ave. S
New York, NY 10010-1710
Ph: (212)989-5800
Fax: (212)633-3990
Fr: 888-437-4636
URL: http://www.elsevier.com/wps/find/
journaldescription.cws_home
Quarterly. $232.00/year for institutions, other countries; $134.00/year for other countries; $160.00/year for institutions; $91.00/year for individuals. Journal devoted to associate degree nursing education and practice.

12122 ■ *Theory and Research in Education*
Sage Publications Inc.
2455 Teller Rd.
Thousand Oaks, CA 91320-2218
Ph: (805)499-9774
Fax: (805)583-2665
Fr: 800-818-7243
URL: http://www.sagepub.com/
journalsProdDesc.nav?prodId=Journal20
$546.00/year for institutions, print and e-access; $491.00/year for institutions, e-access; $535.00/year for institutions, print; $85.00/year for individuals, print; $196.00/year for single issue, institutional; $37.00/year for single issue, individual. Interdisciplinary journal covering normative and theoretical issues concerning education including multi-faceted philosophical analysis of moral, social, political and epistemological problems and issues arising from educational practice.

EMPLOYER DIRECTORIES AND NETWORKING LISTS

12123 ■ *Career Ideas for Teens in Education and Training*
Facts On File Inc.
132 W 31st St., 17th Fl.
New York, NY 10001
Ph: (212)967-8800
Fax: 800-678-3633
Fr: 800-322-8755
URL: http://factsonfile.infobasepublishing.com
Published 2005. $40.00 for individuals. Covers: A multitude of career possibilities based on a teenager's specific interests and skills and links his/her talents to a wide variety of actual professions.

HANDBOOKS AND MANUALS

12124 ■ *The Exceptional Teacher's Handbook: The First-Year Special Education Teacher's Guide for Success*
Corwin Press, Incorporated
2455 Teller Rd.
Thousand Oaks, CA 91320-2218
Ph: (805)499-9734
Fax: 800-499-5323
Fr: 800-417-2466
URL: http://www.corwinpress.com/
booksProdDesc.nav?prodId=Book233107&
Carla F. Shelton and Alice B. Pollingue. Third edition, 2009. $38.95 (paper). 240 pages.

12125 ■ *Great Jobs for Liberal Arts Majors*
The McGraw-Hill Companies
PO Box 182604
Columbus, OH 43272

Fax: (614)759-3749
Fr: 877-883-5524
E-mail: customer.service@mcgraw-hill.com
URL: http://www.mhprofessional.com/
product.php?isbn=0071482148
Blythe Camenson. Second edition, 2007. $16.95 (paper). 192 pages.

12126 ■ *The Inside Secrets of Finding a Teaching Job*
Jist Works
875 Montreal Way
St. Paul, MN 55102
Fr: 800-648-5478
E-mail: info@jist.com
URL: http://www.jist.com
Jack Warner and Clyde Bryan. Third edition, 2006. $12.95. 208 pages. Tips from educators on finding an entry-level teaching position.

12127 ■ *Opportunities in Teaching Careers*
The McGraw-Hill Companies
PO Box 182604
Columbus, OH 43272
Fax: (614)759-3749
Fr: 877-883-5524
E-mail: customer.service@mcgraw-hill.com
URL: http://www.mhprofessional.com/
product.php?isbn=0071438173
Janet Fine. 2005. $13.95 (paper). 160 pages. Discusses licensing and accreditation programs, sources of placement information, job-seeking correspondence, selection procedures, and paths to advancement. Also covers professional associations, non-traditional teaching opportunities, and jobs abroad.

ONLINE JOB SOURCES AND SERVICES

12128 ■ *SchoolSpring.com*
E-mail: contact@schoolspring.com
URL: http://www.schoolspring.com
Description: Serves as an employment source for educators. Offers teaching jobs and other education job listings including complete archiving of all necessary documents and certifications, as well as access to all education jobs in a specific area.

12129 ■ *Special Education Teacher Jobs*
URL: http://www.specialeducationteacherjobs.org
Description: Features employment opportunities for special education teachers.

12130 ■ *Spedex.com*
E-mail: spedex.com@gmail.com
URL: http://www.spedex.com
Description: Provides resources for educators, professionals, parents, consumers, students and other individuals interested in special education. Offers links, online documents, listings of professionals, job listings, school and university listings and more.

TRADESHOWS

12131 ■ *Learning Disabilities Association of America International Conference*
Learning Disabilities Association of America
4156 Library Rd.
Pittsburgh, PA 15234-1349
Ph: (412)341-1515
Fax: (412)344-0224
E-mail: info@ldaamerica.org
URL: http://www.ldanatl.org
Annual. Primary Exhibits: Schools, universities, publishers and summer camps. Dates and Locations: 2012 Feb 22-25; Chicago, IL; 2013 Feb 13-16; San Antonio, TX; 2014 Feb 19-22; Anaheim, CA; 2015 Feb 25-28; Chicago, IL.

OTHER SOURCES

12132 ■ American Council on Rural Special Education (ACRES)
West Virginia University
PO Box 6122
Morgantown, WV 26506
Ph: (304)293-4384
Fax: (304)293-6834
Fr: 888-866-3822
E-mail: cathy.keramidas@mail.wvu.edu
URL: http://www.acres-sped.org

Description: Represents rural special educators and administrators, parents of students with disabilities, and university and state department personnel. Works to enhance direct services to rural individuals and agencies serving exceptional students and to increase educational opportunities for rural students with special needs; works to develop models for serving at-risk rural students, and a system for forecasting futures for rural special education and to plan creative service delivery alternatives. Provides professional development opportunities; disseminates information on the current needs of rural special education. Conducts task forces on specific rural problems and professional training.

12133 ■ American Federation of Teachers (AFT)
555 New Jersey Ave. NW
Washington, DC 20001
Ph: (202)879-4400
E-mail: online@aft.org
URL: http://www.aft.org

Description: Affiliated with the AFL-CIO. Works with teachers and other educational employees at the state and local level in organizing, collective bargaining, research, educational issues, and public relations. Conducts research in areas such as educational reform, teacher certification, and national assessments and standards. Represents members' concerns through legislative action; offers technical assistance. Serves professionals with concerns similar to those of teachers, including state employees, healthcare workers, and paraprofessionals.

12134 ■ AVKO Educational Research Foundation (AVKOEFR)
3084 W Willard Rd.
Birch Run, MI 48415-9404
Ph: (810)686-9283
Fax: (810)686-1101

Fr: (866)285-6612
E-mail: donmccabe@aol.com
URL: http://www.avko.org

Description: Teachers and individuals interested in helping others learn to read and spell and in developing reading training materials for individuals with dyslexia or other learning disabilities using a method involving audio, visual, kinesthetic, and oral (AVKO) techniques. Offers advice on the techniques of tutoring, classroom teaching, diagnosis, and remediation. Conducts research into the causes of reading, spelling, and writing disabilities. Publishes and disseminates information on research. Provides a reading and spelling center where children and adults with educational deficiencies can receive diagnostic attention and remediation. Sponsors adult community education courses to train adults in tutoring their spouses or children in reading and spelling skills. Maintains speakers' bureau; compiles statistics.

12135 ■ Council of American Instructors of the Deaf (CAID)
PO Box 377
Bedford, TX 76095-0377
Ph: (817)354-8414
Fax: (585)533-1552
E-mail: caid@swbell.net
URL: http://www.caid.org

Description: Professional organization of teachers, administrators, and professionals in allied fields related to education of the deaf and hard-of-hearing. Provides opportunities for a free interchange of views concerning methods and means of educating the deaf and hard-of-hearing. Promotes such education by the publication of reports, essays, and other information. Develops more effective methods of teaching deaf and hard-of-hearing children.

12136 ■ Council for Exceptional Children (CEC)
2900 Crystal Dr., Ste. 1000
Arlington, VA 22202-3557
Ph: (703)620-3660
Fax: (703)264-9494
Fr: (866)509-0218
E-mail: service@cec.sped.org
URL: http://www.cec.sped.org

Description: Administrators, teachers, parents, and others who work with and on behalf of children with disabilities and/or gifts. Seeks to improve the educational success for individuals with exceptionalities - children, youth, and young adults with disabilities and/or gifts. Advocates for appropriate government policies; provides information to the media. Operates

the ERIC Clearinghouse on Disabilities and Gifted Education, and the National Clearinghouse for Professions in Special Education. Develops programs to help teachers, administrators, and related services professionals improve their practice.

12137 ■ Council for Learning Disabilities (CLD)
11184 Antioch Rd.
Box 405
Overland Park, KS 66210
Ph: (913)491-1011
Fax: (913)491-1012
E-mail: cldinfo@ie-events.com
URL: http://www.cldinternational.org

Description: Professionals interested in the study of learning disabilities. Works to promote the education and general welfare of individuals having specific learning disabilities by: improving teacher preparation programs and local special education programs, and resolving important research issues. Sponsors educational sessions.

12138 ■ Inter-American Conductive Education Association (IACEA)
PO Box 3169
Toms River, NJ 08756-3169
Ph: (732)797-2566
Fax: (732)797-2599
Fr: 800-824-2232
E-mail: info@iacea.org
URL: http://www.iacea.org

Description: Promotes and disseminates the principles of conductive education using the services of parents, conductors, therapists, teachers, and other related health care professionals. Qualifies trained conductors as new professionals to obtain health care, Medicare, Medicaid, and private health insurance reimbursement. Trains and certifies conductive education practitioners working in the United States and Canada.

12139 ■ National Association of Special Education Teachers (NASET)
1250 Connecticut Ave. NW, Ste. 200
Washington, DC 20036
Fr: 800-754-4421
E-mail: contactus@naset.org
URL: http://www.naset.org

Description: Provides support and assistance to professionals who teach children with special needs. Fosters exceptional teaching for exceptional children. Seeks to promote standards of excellence and innovation in special education research, practice, and policy.

Sources of Help-Wanted Ads

12140 ■ *ADVANCE for Speech-Language Pathologists & Audiologists*
Merion Publications Inc.
2900 Horizon Dr.
PO Box 61556
King of Prussia, PA 19406-0956
Ph: (610)278-1400
Fr: 800-355-5627
URL: http://speech-language-pathology-audiology.advanceweb.com/

Weekly. Free to qualified subscribers. Professional medical magazine for qualified speech-language pathologist and audiologists.

12141 ■ *American Annals of the Deaf*
Conference of Educational Administrators Serving the Deaf
Gallaudet University Press
Denison House
Washington, DC 20002
Ph: (202)651-5488
Fax: (202)651-5489
URL: http://gupress.gallaudet.edu/annals/

Quarterly. $55.00/year for individuals; $95.00/year for institutions; $50.00/year for members. Journal focusing on education of the deaf.

12142 ■ *American Journal of Speech Language Pathology*
American Speech-Language-Hearing Association
2200 Research Blvd.
Rockville, MD 20850-3289
Ph: (301)296-5700
Fax: (301)296-8580
Fr: 800-638-8255
URL: http://ajslp.asha.org/

Quarterly. Free, online access to members; $69.00/year for nonmembers, online only; $170.00/year for nonmembers, institutions; online only. Professional journal covering issues in speech, language, and hearing.

12143 ■ *Audiology Today*
American Academy of Audiology
11730 Plz. America Dr., Ste. 300
Reston, VA 20190
Fax: (703)790-8631
Fr: 800-AAA-2336
URL: http://www.audiology.org/resources/audiologytoday/Pages/defa

Monthly. $56.00/year for individuals, online or print; $61.00/year for individuals, online and print; $105.00/year for other countries, online or print; $115.00/year for other countries, online and print; $115.00/year for institutions, print only; $138.00/year for institutions, other countries, print only. Professional magazine covering audiology.

12144 ■ *Topics in Language Disorders (TLD)*
Lippincott Williams & Wilkins
16522 Hunters Green Pky.
Hagerstown, MD 21740
Ph: (301)233-2300
Fax: (301)233-2398
Fr: 800-638-3030
URL: http://www.lww.com/webapp/wcs/stores/servlet/product__11851_

Quarterly. $104.99/year for individuals; $346.00/year for institutions; $197.73/year for other countries; $536.73/year for institutions, other countries; $74.49/year for individuals, in training. Journal intending to clarify the application of theory to practice in the treatment, rehabilitation, and education of individuals with language disorders.

12145 ■ *The Volta Review*
Alexander Graham Bell Association for the Deaf and Hard of Hearing
3417 Volta Pl. NW
Washington, DC 20007
Ph: (202)337-5220
Fax: (202)337-8314
E-mail: mfelzien@agbell.org
URL: http://nc.agbell.org/netcommunity/page.aspx?pid=348

Quarterly. $10.00/year for single issue. Scholarly journal relating to the field of deafness.

Employer Directories and Networking Lists

12146 ■ *Directory of Hospital Personnel*
Grey House Publishing
4919 Rte. 22
PO Box 56
Amenia, NY 12501
Ph: (518)789-8700
Fax: (518)789-0556
Fr: 800-562-2139
URL: http://www.greyhouse.com/hospital_personnel.htm

Annual, Latest edition 2011. $325.00 for individuals. Covers: 200,000 executives at 6,000 U.S. Hospitals. Entries include: Name of hospital, address, phone, number of beds, type and JCAHO status of hospital, names and titles of key department heads and staff, medical and nursing school affiliations; number of residents, interns, and nursing students. Arrangement: Geographical. Indexes: Hospital name, personnel, hospital size.

12147 ■ *Hospital Blue Book*
Billian Publishing Inc. and Trans World Publishing Inc.
2100 River Edge Pky.
Atlanta, GA 30328
Ph: (770)955-5656
Fax: (770)952-0669
Fr: 800-800-5668
E-mail: blu-book@billian.com
URL: http://www.billianshealthdata.com/Products/bluebook.html

Annual, Latest edition 2010. $575.00 for individuals; $575.00 for individuals. Covers: More than 6,500 hospitals; some listings also appear in a separate southern edition of this publication. Entries include: Name of hospital, accreditation, mailing address, phone, fax, number of beds, type of facility (nonprofit, general, state, etc.); list of administrative personnel and chiefs of medical services, with specific titles. Arrangement: Geographical.

12148 ■ *Medical and Health Information Directory*
Gale
PO Box 6904
Florence, KY 41022-6904
Fr: 800-354-9706
URL: http://www.gale.cengage.com

Annual, Latest edition April 2011. $1190.00 for individuals; $501.00 for individuals. Covers: In volume 1, more than 33,000 medical and health oriented associations, organizations, institutions, and government agencies, including health maintenance organizations (HMOs), preferred provider organizations (PPOs), insurance companies, pharmaceutical companies, research centers, and medical and allied health schools. In Volume 2, over 20,000 medical book publishers; medical periodicals, directories, audiovisual producers and services, medical libraries and information centers, electronic resources, and health-related internet search engines. In Volume 3, more than 40,500 clinics, treatment centers, care programs, and counseling/diagnostic services for 34 subject areas. Entries include: Institution, service, or firm name, address, phone, fax, email and URL; many include names of key personnel and, when pertinent, descriptive annotation. Volume 3 was formerly listed separately as Health Services Directory. Arrangement: Classified by organization activity, service, etc. Indexes: Each volume has a complete alphabetical name and keyword index.

Handbooks and Manuals

12149 ■ *Careers in Health Care*
The McGraw-Hill Companies
PO Box 182604
Columbus, OH 43272
Fax: (614)759-3749
Fr: 877-883-5524
E-mail: customer.service@mcgraw-hill.com
URL: http://www.mhprofessional.com/product.php?isbn=0071466533

Barbara M. Swanson. Fifth edition, 2005. $19.95 (paper). 192 pages. Describes job duties, work settings, salaries, licensing and certification requirements, educational preparation, and future outlook. Gives ideas on how to secure a job.

12150 ■ Careers in Social and Rehabilitation Services
The McGraw-Hill Companies
PO Box 182604
Columbus, OH 43272
Fax: (614)759-3749
Fr: 877-883-5524
E-mail: customer.service@mcgraw-hill.com
URL: http://www.mhprofessional.com/product.php?isbn=0071641955

Geraldine O. Garner. 2008. $16.95. 192 pages.

12151 ■ Making a Difference for America's Children: Speech Language Pathologists in Public Schools
Thinking Publications
PO Box 678370
Dallas, TX 75267
Ph: (512)451-3246
Fax: (512)451-8542
Fr: 800-397-7633
URL: http://www.proedinc.com/customer/thinking-publications.html

Barbara J. Moore-Brown and Judy K. Montgomery. 2008. $75.00. 541 pages.

12152 ■ Opportunities in Health and Medical Careers
The McGraw-Hill Companies
PO Box 182604
Columbus, OH 43272
Fax: (614)759-3749
Fr: 877-883-5524
E-mail: customer.service@mcgraw-hill.com
URL: http://www.mhprofessional.com/product.php?isbn=0071437274

I. Donald Snook, Jr. and Leo D'Orazio. 2004. $14.95 (paper). 157 pages. Covers the full range of medical and health occupations. Illustrated.

12153 ■ Opportunities in Speech Language Pathology
McGraw-Hill
PO Box 182604
Columbus, OH 43272
Ph: (609)426-5793
Fax: (609)308-4480
Fr: 800-262-4729
E-mail: customer.service@mcgraw-hill.com
URL: http://www.mhprofessional.com/product.php?isbn=0071467718

Patricia Larkins Hicks. 2006. $13.95. 160 pages. Provides a complete overview of the job possibilities in speech language pathology. Includes salary figures, experience and training required for Speech Language Pathology.

12154 ■ Professional Issues in Speech-Language Pathology and Audiology
Cengage Learning
PO Box 6904
Florence, KY 41022
Fax: 800-487-8488
Fr: 800-354-9706
URL: http://www.cengage.com

Rosemary Lubinski and Melanie W. Hudson. 2012. $103.95 (paperback). 672 pages. 4th edition. Explores relevant and critical issues related to professional practice in the field. Provides up-to-date view of the profession and prepares applicants to earn their American Speech-Language Hearing Association (ASHA) Certificate of Clinical Competence. Includes topics on employment issues and discussions on professional pathways and organizations.

12155 ■ Resumes for Health and Medical Careers
The McGraw-Hill Companies
PO Box 182604
Columbus, OH 43272
Fax: (614)759-3749

Fr: 877-883-5524
E-mail: customer.service@mcgraw-hill.com
URL: http://www.mhprofessional.com/product.php?isbn=0071545352

Third edition, 2008. $12.95 (paper). 144 pages.

EMPLOYMENT AGENCIES AND SEARCH FIRMS

12156 ■ Access Staffing
360 Lexington Ave., 8th Fl.
New York, NY 10017
Ph: (212)687-5440
Fax: (212)557-2544
URL: http://www.accessstaffingco.com

Serves as a staffing firm covering accounting/financial, advertising, bilingual Japanese, creative, event planning, fashion/retail, healthcare/ human services, human resources, information technology, insurance, legal, light industrial and office support.

12157 ■ Advanced Medical Personnel Services
5535 S Williamson Blvd., Ste. 774
Port Orange, FL 32128
Ph: (386)756-4395
Fr: 800-330-7711
URL: http://www.advanced-medical.net

Specializes in the placement of physical therapists, physical therapy assistants, occupational therapists, certified occupational therapy assistants and speech-language pathologists in assignments across the United States.

12158 ■ Cobb Pediatric Therapy Services
3104 Creekside Village Dr., Ste. 404
Kennesaw, GA 30144
Ph: (770)218-6274
Fax: (770)218-8568
Fr: 888-288-1048
E-mail: info@cobbpediatric.com
URL: http://www.cobbpediatric.com

Description: Staffing company that works primarily with school systems to match them with qualified speech language pathologists, occupational therapists, and physical therapists.

12159 ■ CompHealth
PO Box 713100
Salt Lake City, UT 84171-3100
Ph: (801)930-3000
Fax: (801)930-4517
Fr: 800-453-3030
E-mail: info@comphealth.com
URL: http://www.comphealth.com

Provides healthcare staffing and recruiting services covering certified registered nurse anesthetist, dosimetrist, imaging and radiation therapy, laboratory technology, medical physicist, nurse practitioner, nursing, pharmacy, physician, physician assistant, rehab therapy and respiratory therapy.

12160 ■ Foundation Rehab Staffing
416 W 15th St., Bldg. 600
Edmond, OK 73013
Fax: 800-774-9252
Fr: (866)337-6113
URL: http://www.foundationrehabstaffing.com

Provides staffing services; specializes in rehabilitation therapy.

12161 ■ Jackson Therapy Partners
11315 Corporate Blvd., Ste. 100
Orlando, FL 32817
Fr: 800-774-7785
URL: http://www.jacksontherapy.com

Serves as a therapy recruiting firm. Features therapy jobs available across the United States including permanent and travel opportunities.

12162 ■ TheraKare
8596 E 101st St., Ste. H
Tulsa, OK 74146
Ph: (918)251-5982
Fax: (918)251-6047
Fr: 800-258-1036
E-mail: info@therakare.com
URL: http://www.therakare.com

Description: Specializes in providing temporary and permanent placement options for rehabilitation therapy professionals, including physical therapists, occupational therapists and speech language pathologists.

ONLINE JOB SOURCES AND SERVICES

12163 ■ AudiologistJobs.org
URL: http://audiologistjobs.org

Description: Provides a searchable database of audiologist jobs in the United States.

12164 ■ Audiology Online
URL: http://www.audiologyonline.com

Description: Exists as an online resource in the field of hearing healthcare. Strives to be the primary information resource for the benefit of the patients, the profession and the audiology industry.

12165 ■ CareerVitals.com
URL: http://www.careervitals.com

Description: Serves as a job board for healthcare professionals in different specializations.

12166 ■ Get Audiology Jobs
URL: http://www.getaudiologyjobs.com

Description: Serves as a one-step resource for finding and filling audiology positions. Allows employers to post job openings free of charge while also allowing job seekers to search through audiology job listings.

12167 ■ HEALTHeCAREERS Network
Fr: 888-884-8242
E-mail: info@healthecareers.com
URL: http://www.healthecareers.com

Description: Career search site for jobs in all health care specialties; educational resources; visa and licensing information for relocation; interesting articles; relocation tools; links to professional organizations and general resources.

12168 ■ JobsInLTC.com
URL: http://www.jobsinltc.com

Description: Serves as a job board for long-term care jobs for nursing home administrators, assisted living staff, directors of nursing, MDS coordinators, and other related fields.

12169 ■ JobsSLP.com
E-mail: customerservice@jobsslp.com
URL: http://www.jobsslp.com

Description: Serves as job board dedicated specifically to the speech and audiology profession.

12170 ■ PATHcareer.com
URL: http://www.pathcareer.com

Description: Exists as a job board designed to meet the career needs of pathologists.

12171 ■ ProHealthJobs.com
Ph: (484)443-8545
Fax: (484)443-8549
E-mail: info@prohealthjobs.com
URL: http://prohealthjobs.com/jobboard

Description: Career resources site for the medical and health care field. Lists professional opportunities, product information, continuing education and open positions.

12172 ■ RehabCareer.com
URL: http://www.rehabcareer.com
Description: Serves as a job site for physical, occupational and speech therapy.

12173 ■ RehabJobs Online
E-mail: support@atsrehabjobs.com
URL: http://www.rehabjobsonline.com
Description: Resource center for the professional therapist. Main files include: Therapists Only, Therapy Forums, Nationwide Job Search (database), Therapy Job Outlook, Therapy Job Search Utilities, Therapy Links, Information for Employers and Recruiters.

12174 ■ RehabWorld.com
URL: http://www.rehabworld.com
Description: Site for rehabilitation professionals to learn about the profession and locate jobs. Includes user groups, salary surveys, and chat capabilities. Main files include: Physical Therapy, Occupational Therapy, Speech Therapy, Mental Health, Employer World, Student World, International World, Forum.

12175 ■ SLPJob.com
URL: http://www.slpjob.com
Description: Focuses on speech language pathologist-pathology speech therapy jobs.

12176 ■ Speech Language Pathologist Jobs
URL: http://www.speechlanguagepathologistjobs.org
Description: Serves as a job board for speech language pathologist jobs and career opportunities.

12177 ■ Speech Language Pathology Jobs
URL: http://www.speechlanguagepathologyjobs.org
Description: Job board that focuses on speech language pathology employment opportunities and candidate recruiting.

12178 ■ Speech-LanguagePathologist.org
URL: http://www.speech-languagepathologist.org
Description: Serves as a community organization and website portal dedicated to the sharing of resources and information about the field of speech-language pathology. Offers resources for clinicians, students, caregivers, educators, and all who are interested in the study and practice of speech-language pathology.

12179 ■ SpeechPathology.com
URL: http://www.speechpathology.com
Description: Provides speech-language pathologists and other interested professionals with opportunities for continuing education, professional news and information, and career opportunities throughout the world.

12180 ■ TherapistsCentral.com
URL: http://www.therapistscentral.com
Description: Provides lists of job and career opportunities to physical therapists, speech therapists and occupational therapists.

12181 ■ TherapyJobBoard.com
URL: http://www.therapyjobboard.com
Description: Serves as an employment resource for job seekers and employers in the physical therapy, occupational therapy, speech therapy and respiratory therapy professions.

12182 ■ TherapyJobs.com
URL: http://www.therapyjobs.com
Description: Serves as an online career center bringing therapy employers and candidates together.

Tradeshows

12183 ■ American Speech-Language-Hearing Association Annual Convention
American Speech-Language-Hearing Association
2200 Research Blvd.
Rockville, MD 20850-3289
Ph: (301)296-5700
Fax: (301)296-8580
Fr: 800-498-2071
E-mail: actioncenter@asha.org
URL: http://www.asha.org
Annual. Primary Exhibits: Scientific equipment, publications, and testing materials. Dates and Locations: 2012 Nov 15-17; Atlanta, GA; 2013 Nov 14-16; Chicago, IL; 2014 Nov 20-22; Orlando, FL.

12184 ■ Educational Audiology Association Summer Conference
Educational Audiology Association
3030 W 81st Ave.
Westminster, CO 80031
Fr: 800-460-7EAA
E-mail: admin@edaud.org
URL: http://www.edaud.org
Annual. Features sessions, speakers, CEU opportunities, and networking. Includes sessions on Cochlear Implants, Baha, Direct Ear Level and Broadcast Amplification Systems, Auditory Processing Disorders and much more.

12185 ■ National Hearing Conservation Association Conference
3030 W 81st Ave.
Westminster, CO 80031
Ph: (303)224-9022
Fax: (303)458-0002
E-mail: nhcaoffice@hearingconservation.org
URL: http://hearingconservation.org
Annual. Provides an opportunity to learn about the latest research and tools for hearing conservation. Offers a variety of topics presented by experts in the field. 2013 February 21-23; St. Petersburg, FL; Hilton St. Petersburg Bayfront.

12186 ■ North Carolina Speech, Hearing, and Language Association Convention
North Carolina Speech, Hearing, and Language Association
PO Box 28359
Raleigh, NC 27611-8359
Ph: (919)833-3984
Fax: (919)832-0445
E-mail: info@ncshla.org
URL: http://www.ncshla.org
Annual. Primary Exhibits: Equipment, supplies, and services for speech and language pathology and/or audiology. Dates and Locations: 2012 Mar 28-31; Concord, NC; Embassy Suites.

12187 ■ Summer Institute of the Academy of Rehabilitative Audiology
Academy of Rehabilitative Audiology
PO Box 2323
Albany, NY 12220-0323
Fax: (866)547-3073
E-mail: ara@audrehab.org
URL: http://www.audrehab.org
Annual. Primary Exhibits: Exhibits relating to audiology, language, speech pathology, and the education of the deaf.

Other Sources

12188 ■ American Auditory Society (AAS)
19 Mantua Rd.
Mount Royal, NJ 08061
Ph: (856)423-3118
Fax: (856)423-3420
Fr: 800-638-6423
E-mail: aas@talley.com
URL: http://www.amauditorysoc.org
Description: Audiologists, otolaryngologists, scientists, hearing aid industry professionals, and educators of hearing impaired people; individuals involved in industries serving hearing impaired people, including the amplification systems industry. Works to increase knowledge and understanding of: the ear, hearing, and balance; disorders of the ear, hearing, and balance; prevention of these disorders; habilitation and rehabilitation of individuals with hearing and balance dysfunction.

12189 ■ American Health Care Association (AHCA)
1201 L St. NW
Washington, DC 20005
Ph: (202)842-4444
Fax: (202)842-3860
E-mail: hr@ahca.org
URL: http://www.ahcancal.org/Pages/Default.aspx
Description: Federation of state associations of long-term health care facilities. Promotes standards for professionals in long-term health care delivery and quality care for patients and residents in a safe environment. Focuses on issues of availability, quality, affordability, and fair payment. Operates as liaison with governmental agencies, Congress, and professional associations. Compiles statistics.

12190 ■ American Hearing Aid Associates
225 Wilmington W Chester Pike
Chadds Ford, PA 19317
Fax: (610)455-3018
Fr: 800-984-3272
URL: http://www.ahaanet.com
Description: Serves as a group of professional audiologists, hearing aid dispensers, otolaryngologists, hospitals, and universities. Aims to raise the quality of hearing health care throughout America through evaluation and upgrade of the educational standards and technical expertise of hearing aid associates. Creates awareness of hearing loss throughout the country.

12191 ■ Association on Higher Education and Disability (AHEAD)
107 Commerce Center Dr., Ste. 204
Huntersville, NC 28078
Ph: (704)947-7779
Fax: (704)948-7779
E-mail: ahead@ahead.org
URL: http://www.ahead.org
Description: Individuals interested in promoting the equal rights and opportunities of disabled postsecondary students, staff, faculty, and graduates. Provides an exchange of communication for those professionally involved with disabled students; collects, evaluates, and disseminates information; encourages and supports legislation for the benefit of disabled students. Conducts surveys on issues pertinent to college students with disabilities; offers resource referral system and employment exchange for positions in disability student services. Conducts research programs; compiles statistics.

12192 ■ Educational Audiology Association
3030 W 81st Ave.
Westminster, CO 80031
Fr: 800-460-7322
E-mail: admin@edaud.org
URL: http://www.edaud.org
Description: Audiologists and others with an interest in the field. Promotes advancement in the field of audiology and its educational applications. Conducts educational programs.

12193 ■ International Association of Orofacial Myology (IAOM)
2000 NE 42nd Ave., PMB 295
Portland, OR 97213-1305
Ph: (503)280-0614
Fax: (503)345-6858
E-mail: iaomec@msn.com
URL: http://www.iaom.com
Description: Supports the development of research in the area of orofacial myofunctional therapy. Develops communication with the insurance companies. Provides certification and continuing education to professionals and individuals in field of orofacial myology.

12194 ■ Modern Language Association of America (MLA)
26 Broadway, 3rd Fl.
New York, NY 10004-1789
Ph: (646)576-5000
Fax: (646)458-0030
E-mail: execdirector@mla.org
URL: http://www.mla.org

Description: Provides opportunities for the members to share their scholarly findings and teaching experiences with colleagues and to discuss trends in the academy. Works to strengthen the study and teaching of language and literature.

12195 ■ National Black Association for Speech-Language and Hearing
700 McKnight Park Dr., Ste. 708
Pittsburgh, PA 15237
Ph: (412)366-1177
Fax: (412)366-8804
E-mail: nbaslh@nbaslh.org
URL: http://www.nbaslh.org

Description: Serves the needs of black professionals, students, and individuals with communication disorders. Promotes an increase in the number of certified black speech-language hearing professionals. Supports the advancement of research and development of the identification, diagnosis, and treatment of the communicatively handicapped.

12196 ■ National Communication Association (NCA)
1765 N St. NW
Washington, DC 20036
Ph: (202)464-4622
Fax: (202)464-4600
E-mail: nkidd@natcom.org
URL: http://www.natcom.org

Description: Elementary, secondary, college, and university teachers, speech clinicians, media specialists, communication consultants, students, theater directors, and other interested persons; libraries and other institutions. Works to promote study, criticism, research, teaching, and application of the artistic, humanistic, and scientific principles of communication, particularly speech communication. Sponsors the publication of scholarly volumes in speech. Conducts international debate tours in the U.S. and abroad. Maintains placement service.

12197 ■ National Rehabilitation Association (NRA)
633 S Washington St.
Alexandria, VA 22314
Ph: (703)836-0850
Fax: (703)836-0848
E-mail: info@nationalrehab.org
URL: http://www.nationalrehab.org

Description: Provides opportunities through knowledge and diversity for professionals in the fields of rehabilitation of people with disabilities.

12198 ■ Neuro-Developmental Treatment Association (NDTA)
1540 S Coast Hwy., Ste. 203
Laguna Beach, CA 92651
Fax: (949)376-3456
Fr: 800-869-9295
E-mail: info@ndta.org
URL: http://www.ndta.org

Description: Physical and occupational therapists, speech pathologists, special educators, physicians, parents, and others interested in neurodevelopmental treatment. (NDT is a form of therapy for individuals who suffer from central nervous system disorders resulting in abnormal movement. Treatment attempts to initiate or refine normal stages and processes in the development of movement.) Informs members of new developments in the field and with ideas that will eventually improve fundamental independence. Locates articles related to NDT.

Sources of Help-Wanted Ads

12199 ■ *The American Journal of Sports Medicine*
The American Orthopaedic Society for Sports Medicine
6300 N River Rd., Ste. 500
Rosemont, IL 60018
Ph: (847)292-4900
Fax: (847)292-4905
URL: http://ajs.sagepub.com/

$521.00/year for institutions, print & e-access; $117.00/year for individuals, print & e-access; $47.00/year for institutions, single print issue; $13.00/year for single issue, print. Medical journal.

12200 ■ *NAIA News*
National Association of Intercollegiate Athletics
1200 Grand Blvd.
Kansas City, MO 64106
Ph: (816)595-8000
Fax: (816)595-8200
E-mail: naianews@naia.org
URL: http://naia.cstv.com

Description: Daily. Provides news and information on the Association, which strives to "develop intercollegiate athletic programs as an integral part of the total educational program of the college rather than as a separate commercial or promotional adjunct." Aims toward uniformity and equity in policies and practices. Recurring features include news of members and events, notices of awards, and job listings.

12201 ■ *Sailing World*
Miller Sports Group L.L.C.
79 Madison Ave., 8th Fl.
New York, NY 10016-7802
Ph: (212)636-2700
E-mail: editor@sailingworld.com
URL: http://www.sailingworld.com/index.jsp

$14.97/year for individuals; $23.97/year for Canada; $36.97/year for other countries. Magazine on performance sailing.

Employer Directories and Networking Lists

12202 ■ *Blue Book of College Athletics for Senior, Junior & Community Colleges*
Athletic Publishing Company Inc.
2540 E 5th St., Ste. A
PO Box 931
Montgomery, AL 36107-3152
Ph: (334)263-4436
Fax: (334)263-4437
URL: http://www.athleticpubco.com/html/blue_book_info.html

Annual, latest edition 79th, 2011-2012. $54.95 for individuals; $46.00 for individuals. Covers: Over 2,400 colleges and universities that have athletic programs, conferences, and related associations; coverage includes the U.S.; Canada and Puerto Rico. Entries include: For colleges and universities—Name, address, phone, name and title of governing officials, athletic department phone number, enrollment, school colors, team nickname, band nickname and size, band director's name, stadium name and size, other athletic facilities, conference membership; names and phone numbers of athletic directors, coaches, assistants, and trainers; previous year's team records. For conferences and associations—Name, Headquarters address; names and titles of key personnel; name, address, phone commissioner; membership conference/associations championships for previous year. Arrangement: Classified by type of college, conference, or association, then alphabetical. Indexes: Senior colleges and universities in the U.S.; colleges of Canada, and Puerto Rico; senior conferences and associations, senior related associations and organizations; junior and community colleges; junior and community college conferences and associations.

12203 ■ *Careers in Focus—Sports*
Facts On File Inc.
132 W 31st St., 17th Fl.
New York, NY 10001
Ph: (212)967-8800
Fax: 800-678-3633
Fr: 800-322-8755
URL: http://www.infobasepublishing.com

Latest edition 4th; Published July, 2008. $32.95 for individuals. Covers: An overview of sports, followed by a selection of jobs profiled in detail, including the nature of the job, earnings, prospects for employment, what kind of training and skills it requires, and sources for further information.

12204 ■ *Discovering Careers for Your Future—Sports*
Facts On File Inc.
132 W 31st St., 17th Fl.
New York, NY 10001
Ph: (212)967-8800
Fax: 800-678-3633
Fr: 800-322-8755
URL: http://factsonfile.infobasepublishing.com

Latest edition 2nd, 2005. $21.95 for individuals. Covers: Athletic trainers, fitness experts, lifeguards, sports broadcasters and announcers, sports physicians, sports scouts, and yoga and Pilates instructors; links career education to curriculum, helping children investigate the subjects they are interested in, and the careers those subjects might lead to.

12205 ■ *National Directory of College Athletics*
Collegiate Directories Inc.
PO Box 450640
Cleveland, OH 44145
Ph: (440)835-1172

Fax: (440)835-8835
Fr: 800-426-2232
URL: http://www.collegiatedirectories.com/shopping/index.asp

Annual, Latest edition 2010-2012. $49.95 for individuals; $29.95. Covers: Men's athletic departments of 2,100 senior and junior colleges in the United States and Canada. Entries include: School name, address, enrollment, colors, team nicknames, stadium and/or gym capacity; names of president, men's athletic director, athletic administrative staff, physical education director and coaches for each sport; athletic department phones, faxes, etc.; association affiliations. Arrangement: Alphabetical. Indexes: Schools by program and division; Alphabetical by advertisers and products.

12206 ■ *National Directory of High School Coaches*
Athletic Publishing Company Inc.
2540 E 5th St., Ste. A
PO Box 931
Montgomery, AL 36107-3152
Ph: (334)263-4436
Fax: (334)263-4437
URL: http://www.athleticpubco.com

Annual, latest edition 45th, 2008-2009. $72.95 for individuals; $62.00 for individuals. Covers: More than 240,000 high school coaches at over 20,000 high schools. Entries include: School name, address, phone, names of coaches, codes for sports coached, and ETS numbers. Arrangement: Geographical. Indexes: Advertiser, key to symbols, index of high schools by name, city and state.

12207 ■ *Recreational Sports Directory*
National Intramural-Recreational Sports Association
4185 SW Research Way
Corvallis, OR 97333-1067
Ph: (541)766-8211
Fax: (541)766-8284
URL: http://www.nirsa.org

Annual, Latest edition 2011. $45.00 for members; $125.00 for nonmembers. Covers: Recreational sports programs in approximately 2,500 four-year colleges and universities, nearly 700 junior and community colleges, Canadian colleges and universities, and over 350 military installations. Entries include: Institution name and address; institution enrollment; name of president; names, phone numbers, fax numbers, Internet access, and job titles of recreational directors and staff; existing sports clubs; degrees offered in physical education and recreation; whether graduate assistantships or internships are available. A Buyer's Guide is included with supplier addresses and descriptions of products and services. Arrangement: Classified by institution type, then alphabetical. Indexes: Alphabetical, geographical, personal name, recreational sports program.

12208 ■ *What Can I Do Now—Sports*
Facts On File Inc.
132 W 31st St., 17th Fl.
New York, NY 10001

Ph: (212)967-8800
Fax: 800-678-3633
Fr: 800-322-8755
URL: http://www.infobasepublishing.com

Latest edition 2nd; Published April, 2007. $32.95 for individuals. Covers: Professional athletes, sports broadcasters, coaches and trainers, sports physicians and surgeons, sports statisticians, umpires and referees.

12209 ■ White Book of Ski Areas
Inter-Ski Services Inc.
1502 27th St. NW
PO Box 3775, Georgetown Sta.
Washington, DC 20007
Ph: (202)342-0886
URL: http://www.inter-ski.com

Annual, latest edition 30th. Free. Covers: About 500 lift-equipped ski areas and resorts. Entries include: Name of ski area, location, phone; snow condition phone numbers; ski statistics (elevation, lift capacity, etc.); season and rates; equipment and schooling available; lodging availability and phone, restaurants, apres-ski, and other recreational facilities in vicinity; shops; travel instructions. Special industry edition available with more comprehensive information; $ 395. Arrangement: Geographical within four regions—West, North Central, South, and Northeast. Indexes: Geographical.

Handbooks and Manuals

12210 ■ Advances in Functional Training
On Target Publications
PO Box 1335
Aptos, CA 95001
Ph: (831)466-9182
Fax: (831)466-9183
URL: http://ontargetpublications.net

Dave Draper. 2010. $34.95 (paper). 315 pages. Presents modern and effective training strategies for coaches, personal trainers, and athletes. Discusses injury prevention, treatment, rehabilitation and training after injury.

12211 ■ Career Opportunities in the Sports Industry
Ferguson Publishing
132 W 31st St., 17th Fl.
New York, NY 10001
Fax: 800-678-3633
Fr: 800-322-8755
E-mail: custserv@factsonfile.com
URL: http://www.infobasepublishing.com

Shelly Field. 2010. $49.50 (hardcover). 400 pages. Contains profiles of various job types in the sports industry. Includes information on current duties, requirements and salary ranges.

12212 ■ Co-Active Coaching: Changing Business, Transforming Lives
Nicholas Brealey Publishing
20 Park Plz., Ste. 1115A
Boston, MA 02116
Ph: (617)523-3801
Fax: (617)523-3708
E-mail: info@nicholasbrealey.com
URL: http://nicholasbrealey.com

Henry Kimsey-House, Karen Kimsey-House and Phillip Sandahl. 2011. $39.95 (paperback). 3rd edition. Serves as resource in professional coaching. Provides tools and techniques for career success as professional coach. Contains online Coaches' Toolkit, new coaching demonstrations and updated exercises, questionaires, checklists and reproducible forms.

12213 ■ Coaching: A Problem Solving Approach
American Press
60 State St., No. 700
Boston, MA 02109

Ph: (617)247-0022
E-mail: americanpress@flash.net
URL: http://www.americanpresspublishers.com

William F. Stier, Jr. 2009. $43.95 (paperback). 440 pages. 2nd edition. Helps undergraduate students deal with preparation of athletic coaches. Includes problem solving strategies, tactics and techniques within a sport setting.

12214 ■ Coaching for Performance: Growing Human Potential and Purpose: The Principles and Practice of Coaching Leadership
Nicholas Brealey Publishing
20 Park Plz., Ste. 1115A
Boston, MA 02116
Ph: (617)523-3801
Fax: (617)523-3708
E-mail: info@nicholasbrealey.com
URL: http://nicholasbrealey.com

John Whitmore. 2009. $24.95 (paperback). 244 pages. 4th edition. Explains the principles of coaching and illustrates the examples of high performance from business and sport.

12215 ■ The Comprehensive Guide to Careers in Sports
Jones and Bartlett Learning
5 Wall St.
Burlington, MA 01803
Ph: (978)443-5000
Fax: (978)443-8000
Fr: 800-832-0034
E-mail: info@jbpub.com
URL: http://www.jblearning.com

Glenn M. Wong. 2009. $98.95 (paper). 526 pages. Provides an overview of what students should consider and expect from the varied career options in sports. Features case studies and stories, organizational charts, industry segments, career progressions, and job descriptions.

12216 ■ Core Assessment and Training
Human Kinetics
PO Box 5076
Champaign, IL 61825-5076
Fax: (217)351-1549
Fr: 800-747-4457
E-mail: info@hkusa.com
URL: http://www.humankinetics.com

2010. $42.00 (DVD and paper). 160 pages. Serves as reference for coaches, athletic and personal trainers, and physical therapists. Covers all aspects of core training, from basic to advanced core exercises, stretches, and pylometrics. Includes photos, illustrations and instructions for more than 120 exercises. Accompanying DVD features demonstrations of proper exercise techniques and protocols for review. Helps professionals in the field assess clients' needs and design customized training programs.

12217 ■ Emergencies in Sports Medicine
Oxford University Press (USA)
198 Madison Ave.
New York, NY 10016
Ph: (212)726-6000
Fax: (919)677-1303
Fr: 800-445-9714
E-mail: custserv.us@oup.com
URL: http://www.oup.com/us/

Julian Redhead and Jonathan Gordon. 2012. $47.95 (flexicover). 288 pages. Covers every type of sporting emergency from head injuries to altitude sickness, and all aspects of sports medicine, including event planning and communication, to common sports-related emergency situations.

12218 ■ Exploring Coaching: A Step-by-Step Guide to a Fulfilling and Rewarding Career
LearnMore Publishing
885 Arapahoe Ave.
Boulder, CO 80302

Ph: (720)890-9300
E-mail: info@learnmore.com
URL: http://www.exploringcoaching.com
Will Craig. PDF format. April 2004. $9.95. 132 pages.

12219 ■ How to Build an Instructional Coaching Program for Maximum Capacity
Corwin Press
2455 Teller Rd.
Thousand Oaks, CA 91320
Ph: (805)499-9734
Fax: (805)499-5323
Fr: 800-233-9936
E-mail: order@corwin.com
URL: http://www.corwin.com

Nina Jones Morel, Carla Staton Cushman. 2012. $36.95 (paper). 208 pages. Serves as a resource for school and district leaders to develop and sustain an effective coaching program. Provides a practical framework for starting and sustaining a viable instructional coaching program.

12220 ■ Innovative Communication in College Athletics
Human Kinetics
PO Box 5076
Champaign, IL 61825-5076
Fax: (217)351-1549
Fr: 800-747-4457
E-mail: info@hkusa.com
URL: http://www.humankinetics.com

International Journal of Sport Communication. 2012. $25.00 (paper). Covers various sport communication topics that bring a unique perspective to innovative communication issues prevalent in college athletics.

12221 ■ Leading with the Heart: Coach K's Successful Strategies for Basketball, Business and Life
Hachette Book Group
237 Park Ave.
New York, NY 10017
URL: http://www.hachettebookgroup.com

Mike Krzyzewski, Donald T. Phillips. 2010. $9.99 (paper). 336 pages.

12222 ■ NSCA's Essentials of Personal Training
Human Kinetics
PO Box 5076
Champaign, IL 61825-5076
Fax: (217)351-1549
Fr: 800-747-4457
E-mail: info@hkusa.com
URL: http://www.humankinetics.com

National Strength and Conditioning Association. 2012. $295.00. Serves as a tool for personal trainers, health and fitness instructors, and other fitness professionals in taking the NSCA-CPT exam.

12223 ■ Professional Sports Organizations
Ferguson
c/o Infobase Publishing
132 W 31st St., 17th Fl.
New York, NY 10001
Fax: (600)678-3633
Fr: 800-322-8755
E-mail: custserv@factsonfile.com
URL: http://www.infobasepublishing.com

Christian Dahl Schultz. 2012. $34.95 (hardcover). Provides job seekers with different career opportunities in sports. Explains how the industry works and how applicants can plan for career success. Includes a breakdown of key jobs within professional sports organizations, and facts and tips for communications and networking.

12224 ■ Real-Resumes for Sports Industry Jobs
PREP Publishing
1110 1/2 Hay St., Ste. C
Fayetteville, NC 28305
Ph: (910)483-6611

Fax: (910)483-2439
E-mail: preppub@aol.com
URL: http://www.prep-pub.com/Bookstore/sports.htm

Anne McKinney (Editor). April 2004. $16.95 (paper). Illustrated. 192 pages. Real-Resumes Series.

12225 ■ *Successful Sports Officiating*
Human Kinetics
PO Box 5076
Champaign, IL 61825-5076
Fax: (217)351-1549
Fr: 800-747-4457
E-mail: info@hkusa.com
URL: http://www.humankinetics.com

American Sport Education Program. 2011. $24.95 (paper). 208 pages. Serves as a guide for aspiring and inexperienced sports officials. Covers chapters on the current state of officiating, officiating as a career, and mental training. Includes topics on developing an officiating philosophy and the psychology of officiating.

Employment Agencies and Search Firms

12226 ■ SportSearch
2990 E Northern Ave., Ste. B101
Phoenix, AZ 85028-4838
Ph: (602)485-5555
Fax: (602)485-3435
E-mail: info@sportsearch.net
URL: http://sportsearchonline.com

Specializes in retained executive search, customized recruiting and sports career development focused on sports, recreation and live-event industries.

Online Job Sources and Services

12227 ■ American Medical Athletic Association
4405 East-West Hwy., Ste. 405
Bethesda, MD 20814
Ph: (301)913-9517
Fax: (301)913-9520
Fr: 800-776-2732
E-mail: amaa@americanrunning.org
URL: http://www.amaasportsmed.org

Description: Provides information on training, diet, injury prevention, and sports medicine to physicians and other healthcare professionals as leaders in active and healthy lifestyles. Hosts a sports medicine professional referral service made up of doctors, nutritionists, and other sports-oriented professionals.

12228 ■ Athletic Jobs
URL: http://www.athleticjobs.org

Description: Serves as niche job board that provides listings on athletic jobs.

12229 ■ CoachGrader.com
URL: http://www.coachgrader.com

Description: Helps job seekers find career opportunities in the industry of coaching. Provides a listing of college sports jobs.

12230 ■ coachingjobs.com
URL: http://coachingjobs.com

Description: Focuses on helping job seekers find career opportunities in the industry of coaching.

12231 ■ Coachjobs.us
URL: http://www.coachjobs.us

Description: Serves as a job board that focuses on coach employment opportunities and candidate recruiting.

12232 ■ HoopCoach.org
URL: http://www.hoopcoach.org

Serves as a source for NBA, NCAA, NAIA, and high school basketball coaching jobs. Features salary information and networking opportunities with other coaches.

12233 ■ iHireSportsandRecreation.com
URL: http://www.ihiresportsandrecreation.com

Description: Features sports and recreation jobs from job postings, internet job boards, newspapers and classified ads.

12234 ■ JobsInSports.com
URL: http://www.jobsinsports.com

Description: Provides an online database of sports jobs and internships. Features a resume bank for sports industry employers.

12235 ■ Online Sports Career Center
Fr: 800-856-2638
E-mail: comments@atsonlinesports.com
URL: http://www.onlinesports.com/pages/careercenter.html

Description: Resource for sports-related career opportunities, as well as a resume bank for the perusal of potential employers within the sports and recreation industries. Main files include: Job Bank, Resume Bank, Newsletter, Work With Online Sports, Other Internet Resources.

12236 ■ Sports Coach Jobs
URL: http://www.sportscoachjobs.org

Description: Serves as a niche job board specializing in sports coach employment opportunities and candidate recruiting.

12237 ■ SportsAndRecreationCrossing.com
URL: http://www.sportsandrecreationcrossing.com

Description: Serves as a clearinghouse for individuals looking for employment in the sports and recreation industry.

12238 ■ SportsCareerFinder.com
E-mail: admin@sportscareerfinder.com
URL: http://www.sportscareerfinder.com

Description: Serves as a source of sports job and sports careers. Includes job listings, industry information, and company lists.

12239 ■ Volleyball Coaching Jobs
URL: http://www.volleyballcoachingjobs.com

Description: Serves as a job board for volleyball coaching employment positions.

12240 ■ WorkInSports.com
URL: http://www.workinsports.com

Description: Provides listing of current sports jobs and internships.

Tradeshows

12241 ■ American Volleyball Coaches Association Convention
American Volleyball Coaches Association
2365 Harrodsburg Rd., Ste. A325
Lexington, KY 40504
Ph: (859)226-4315
Fax: (859)226-4338
Fr: (866)544-2822
E-mail: members@avca.org
URL: http://www.avca.org

Annual. Presents seminars on topics relevant to handling a volleyball team such as volleyball playing trends, preventing volleyball injuries, improving and facilitating better team communication, leadership and teamwork, organizational considerations, transition skills, defensive strategies and footwork, and more.

Other Sources

12242 ■ American Hockey Coaches Association (AHCA)
7 Concord St.
Gloucester, MA 01930
Ph: (781)245-4177
Fax: (781)245-2492
E-mail: jbertagna@hockeyeastonline.com
URL: http://www.ahcahockey.com

Description: Represents university, college, and secondary school ice hockey coaches. Conducts coaches' clinics throughout the U.S.

12243 ■ American Sail Training Association (ASTA)
PO Box 1459
Newport, RI 02840
Ph: (401)846-1775
Fax: (401)849-5400
E-mail: asta@tallshipsamerica.org
URL: http://tallships.sailtraining.org

Description: Organizations operating sail training programs; corporations and educational institutions supporting sail training; private citizens with an interest in sailing and sail training. Promotes sail training as an educational and character-building experience for youth of all ages. Seeks to bring together the sail training ships of the world in a spirit of friendship and international goodwill. Sponsors Tall Ships events including sail training rallies. Maintains billet bank/placement service; compiles statistics.

12244 ■ American Swimming Coaches Association (ASCA)
5101 NW 21st Ave., Ste. 200
Fort Lauderdale, FL 33309
Ph: (954)563-4930
Fax: (954)563-9813
Fr: 800-356-2722
E-mail: asca@swimmingcoach.org
URL: http://www.swimmingcoach.org

Description: Swimming coaches united for informational and educational purposes. Operates Swim America, a learn-to-swim program. Maintains placement service; conducts research programs; compiles statistics.

12245 ■ Association of Minor League Umpires (AMLU)
80 8th Ave., Ste. 205
New York, NY 10011
E-mail: shaun@amlu.org
URL: http://www.amlu.org

Description: Represents minor league baseball umpires. Aims to protect the fundamental rights and privacy concerns of minor league umpires. Supports members' bargaining power with professional baseball.

12246 ■ Athletic Equipment Managers Association (AEMA)
460 Hunt Hill Rd.
Freeville, NY 13068
Ph: (607)539-6300
Fax: (607)539-6340
E-mail: aema@frontiernet.net
URL: http://www.equipmentmanagers.org

Description: Athletic equipment managers and others who handle sports equipment for junior high and high schools, colleges, recreation centers, and professional sports; individuals involved in athletic management and coaching or the handling or purchasing of athletic, physical education, or recreational equipment. Aims to improve the profession of equipment management and promote a better working relationship among those interested in problems of management. Works collectively to facilitate equipment improvement for greater safety among participants in all sports. Conducts workshops and clinics. Maintains job placement service.

12247 ■ Black Coaches and Administrators (BCA)

Pan American Plaza
201 S Capitol Ave., Ste. 495
Indianapolis, IN 46225
Ph: (317)829-5600
Fax: (317)829-5601
Fr: 877-789-1222
E-mail: fkeith@bcasports.org
URL: http://bcasports.cstv.com

Description: Promotes equitable employment of ethnic minorities in all sports professions; the education, development and scholarship of members and ethnic minority student athletes. Promotes the creation of a positive environment in which issues such as stereotyping, lack of significant media coverage, and discrimination can be exposed, discussed, and resolved. Provides member services. Petitions the NCAA legislative bodies to design, enact, and enforce diligent guidelines and policies to improve professional mobility for minorities.

12248 ■ College Swimming Coaches Association of America (CSCAA)

1640 Maple Ave., No. 803
Evanston, IL 60201
Ph: (847)833-3478
E-mail: r-groseth@northwestern.edu
URL: http://www.cscaa.org

Description: College and university swimming and diving coaches organized to promote college swimming. Disseminates information; maintains placement service and hall of fame.

12249 ■ Exercise Safety Association (ESA)

PO Box 547916
Orlando, FL 32854-7916
Ph: (407)246-5090
E-mail: askesa@aol.com
URL: http://www.exercisesafety.com

Description: Fitness instructors, personal trainers, health spas, YMCAs, community recreation departments, and hospital wellness programs. Purposes are: to improve the qualifications of exercise instructors; to train instructors to develop safe exercise programs that will help people avoid injury while exercising; to prepare instructors for national certification. Offers training in aerobics and exercise and on the physiological aspects of exercise. Conducts exercise safety and research programs. Sponsors charitable program; maintains speakers' bureau. Offers instructor placement services.

12250 ■ IDEA Health and Fitness Association

10455 Pacific Center Ct.
San Diego, CA 92121
Ph: (858)535-8979
Fax: (858)535-8234
Fr: 800-999-IDEA
E-mail: contact@ideafit.com
URL: http://www.ideafit.com

Description: Provides continuing education for fitness professionals including; fitness instructors, personal trainers, program directors, and club/studio owners. Offers workshops for continuing education credits.

12251 ■ Jackie Robinson Foundation (JRF)

One Hudson Sq.
75 Varick St., 2nd Fl.
New York, NY 10013-1917
Ph: (212)290-8600
Fax: (212)290-8081
E-mail: general@jackierobinson.org
URL: http://www.jackierobinson.org

Description: Seeks to develop the leadership and achievement potential of minority and urban youth. Founded by the friends and family of Jackie Robinson (1919-72), the first black athlete to play major league baseball. Trains minority and poor youths for sports management careers. Provides counseling, support, and placement services. Awards full college scholarships to promising minority students. Main-

tains collection of Jackie Robinson memorabilia; has produced a national touring exhibit of archival materials pertaining to Robinson.

12252 ■ National Association for Girls and Women in Sport (NAGWS)

1900 Association Dr.
Reston, VA 20191-1598
Ph: (703)476-3452
Fax: (703)476-4566
Fr: 800-213-7193
E-mail: nagws@aahperd.org
URL: http://www.aahperd.org/nagws

Description: Represents teachers, coaches, athletic trainers, officials, athletic administrators, and students. Has 4 main structures: Advocacy Coaching Enhancement; Minority Representation; Professional Development Publications, and Student Representation. Supports and fosters the development of quality sports programs that will enrich the lives of all participants. Holds training sessions for leadership development. Conducts research programs.

12253 ■ National Association for Sport and Physical Education (NASPE)

1900 Association Dr.
Reston, VA 20191-1598
Ph: (703)476-3410
Fax: (703)476-8316
Fr: 800-213-7193
E-mail: naspe@aahperd.org
URL: http://www.naspeinfo.org

Description: Men and women professionally involved with physical activity and sports. Seeks to improve the total sport and physical activity experience in America. Conducts research and education programs in such areas as sport psychology, curriculum development, kinesiology, history, philosophy, sport sociology, and the biological and behavioral basis of human activity. Develops and distributes public information materials which explain the value of physical education programs. Supports councils involved in organizing and supporting elementary, secondary, and college physical education and sport programs; administers the National Council of Athletic Training in conjunction with the National Association for Girls and Women in Sport; serves the professional interests of coaches, trainers, and officials. Maintains hall of fame, placement service, and media resource center for public information and professional preparation. Member benefits include group insurance and discounts.

12254 ■ National Association of Sports Officials (NASO)

2017 Lathrop Ave.
Racine, WI 53405
Ph: (262)632-5448
Fax: (262)632-5460
Fr: 800-733-6100
E-mail: cservice@naso.org
URL: http://www.naso.org

Description: Active sports officials, umpires, companies, and individuals interested in sports. Develops programs to assist in the education of sports officials; engages in programs to instruct fans, coaches, players, and the media on the role of sports officials. Conducts clinics and camps; sponsors public service ads.

12255 ■ National Association of Underwater Instructors (NAUI)

PO Box 89789
Tampa, FL 33689-0413
Ph: (813)628-6284
Fax: (813)628-8253
Fr: 800-553-6284
E-mail: nauihq@naui.org
URL: http://www.naui.org

Description: Certified instructors of basic, advanced, and specialized courses in underwater diving. Offers instructor certification programs and training programs. Conducts seminars, workshops, and

symposia. Sells diving education books. Sponsors competitions; maintains speakers' bureau and placement service; conducts charitable programs.

12256 ■ National Athletic Trainers' Association (NATA)

2952 Stemmons Fwy., No. 200
Dallas, TX 75247-6196
Ph: (214)637-6282
Fax: (214)637-2206
Fr: 800-879-6282
E-mail: marjea@nata.org
URL: http://www.nata.org

Description: Athletic trainers from universities, colleges, and junior colleges; professional football, baseball, basketball, and ice hockey; high schools, preparatory schools, military establishments, sports medicine clinics, and business/industrial health programs. Maintains hall of fame and placement service. Conducts research programs; compiles statistics.

12257 ■ National Christian College Athletic Association (NCCAA)

302 W Washington St.
Greenville, SC 29601-1919
Ph: (864)250-1199
Fax: (864)250-1141
E-mail: info@thenccaa.org
URL: http://www.thenccaa.org

Description: Christian colleges. Provides national competition for the Christian college movement in baseball, basketball (men's and women's), cross-country (men's and women's), football, golf, soccer (men's and women's), tennis (men's and women's), men's volleyball, women's volleyball, track and field (men's and women's), and softball. Maintains placement service; compiles statistics.

12258 ■ National High School Athletic Coaches Association (NHSACA)

PO Box 5921
Rochester, MN 55903
E-mail: jg.nhsaca@charter.net
URL: http://www.hscoaches.org

Description: High school coaches and athletic directors; athletic directors for school systems; executive secretaries of state high school coaches; state high school coaches associations. Aims to give greater national prestige and professional status to high school coaching and focuses on promoting cooperation among coaches, school administrators, the press, game officials, and the public. Promotes drug and alcohol abuse prevention through National Training Seminars in Drug Prevention in conjunction with the Drug Enforcement Administration, Washington, DC. Conducts Sports medicine/Medical Aspects of Sports seminars in conjunction with national sports and medical groups, and National College Credit Program for coaches and athletic directors.

12259 ■ National Strength and Conditioning Association (NSCA)

1885 Bob Johnson Dr.
Colorado Springs, CO 80906
Ph: (719)632-6722
Fax: (719)632-6367
Fr: 800-815-6826
E-mail: nsca@nsca-lift.org
URL: http://www.nsca-lift.org

Description: Represents professionals in the sports science, athletic, and fitness industries. Promotes the total conditioning of athletes to a level of optimum performance, with the belief that a better conditioned athlete not only performs better but is less prone to injury. Gathers and disseminates information on strength and conditioning techniques and benefits. Conducts national, regional, state, and local clinics and workshops. Operates professional certification program.

12260 ■ NFHS Coaches Association (NFCA)

PO Box 690
Indianapolis, IN 46206

Ph: (317)972-6900
Fax: (317)822-5700
E-mail: tflannery@nfhs.org
URL: http://www.nfhs.org/coach.aspx

Description: High school, middle school and youth athletic coaches. Promotes professional growth and image of interscholastic sports coaches; provides a forum for coaches to make suggestions on rules and procedures in high school sports in the U.S. Cooperates with state high school athletic associations and uses extensive committee structure to ensure grass roots involvement and input from the local, state, and national levels. Maintains hall of fame.

12261 ■ Professional Association of Diving Instructors (PADI)
30151 Tomas St.
Rancho Santa Margarita, CA 92688-2125
Ph: (949)858-7234
Fax: (949)267-1267
Fr: 800-729-7234
URL: http://www.padi.com

Description: Educates and certifies underwater scuba instructors. Sanctions instructor training courses nationwide and in 175 foreign countries. Provides training course criteria, training aids, and national requirements for all aspects of diving instruction. Instructor training courses are held at geographically central locations. Sponsors PADI Travel Network and a retail dive store program. Offers courses in diving specialties; conducts educational programs. Offers placement service; compiles statistics.

12262 ■ Professional Coaches, Mentors and Advisors (PCMA)
PO Box 265
Palos Verdes Estates, CA 90274-0265
Fr: 800-768-6017
E-mail: admin@pcmacoaches.com
URL: http://www.pcmacoaches.com

Description: Represents individuals dedicated to serving business and organizational coaches and mentors. Offers an environment that challenges, inspires, and educates its members. Develops the coaching and mentoring profession and creates successful practices.

12263 ■ Professional Football Chiropractic (PFC)
PO Box 842
Sumner, WA 98390
Ph: (253)948-6039
Fax: (253)435-1053
E-mail: footballchiros@gmail.com
URL: http://www.profootballchiros.com

Description: Provides chiropractic health care to professional football athletes. Enhances the perception of chiropractic in sports and with the general public through education and communication. Initiates an understanding of chiropractic for athletes, coaches, administrative and healthcare staff.

12264 ■ Professional Golfers' Association of America (PGA)
100 Ave. of the Champions
Palm Beach Gardens, FL 33418

Ph: (561)624-8400
URL: http://www.pga.com

Description: Recruits and trains men and women to manage a variety of golf businesses, including golf clubs, courses, and tournaments. Sponsors PGA Championship, PGA Seniors' Championship, Ryder Cup Matches, PGA Grand Slam of Golf, Club Professional Championship, PGA Foundation, and Senior Club Professional Championship; PGA Junior Championship; PGA Assistants Championship. Conducts Professional Golf Management; certifies college programs in golf management at 14 universities. Sponsors winter tournament program for club professionals including tournaments held in south Florida. Offers complementary employment services for PGA members and employers, owns and operates PGA Golf Club and PGA Learning Center.

12265 ■ Professional Skaters Association (PSA)
3006 Allegro Park SW
Rochester, MN 55902
Ph: (507)281-5122
Fax: (507)281-5491
E-mail: office@skatepsa.com
URL: http://skatepsa.com

Description: Professional ice skaters engaged in the teaching, coaching and performing of ice skating. Strives to form a cohesive body of all professional ice skaters for the benefit of the profession, to protect the interests of members' pupils, to advance all aspects of both ice figure skating and recreational skating, and to promote high ethical and professional standards in the field. Grades teachers on the basis of on-ice proficiency and oral examination. Operates placement service.

12266 ■ Professional Tennis Registry (PTR)
PO Box 4739
Hilton Head Island, SC 29938
Ph: (843)785-7244
Fax: (843)686-2033
Fr: 800-421-6289
E-mail: ptr@ptrtennis.org
URL: http://www.ptrtennis.org

Description: Tests, certifies, and registers international tennis teaching professionals. Certification requires successful completion of a written and on-court examinations. Sponsors workshops, tennis clinics, and charitable program. Holds competitions; compiles statistics; maintains placement service.

12267 ■ United States Association of Independent Gymnastic Clubs (USAIGC)
450 N End Ave., Ste. 20F
New York, NY 10282
Ph: (212)227-9792
Fax: (212)227-9793
Fr: 800-480-0201
E-mail: usaigcpsny2@aol.com
URL: http://www.usaigc.com

Description: Gymnastic clubs and independent gymnastic club businesses offering professional class instruction and coaching; manufacturers of gymnastic equipment, apparel, and supplies. Aims to provide services, programs, and business advice to help

gymnastic businesses to grow and prosper; locate organizations and individuals that will provide needed services for members' clientele; further coaching knowledge; advance the U.S. in gymnastic competitions throughout the world. Offers certification for coaches and developmental-training programs for gymnasts to prepare for international competitions. Provides placement service; conducts research programs. Maintains Medical Advisory Board and hall of fame.

12268 ■ United States Judo (USJ)
1 Olympic Plz., Ste. 505
Colorado Springs, CO 80909
Ph: (719)866-4730
Fax: (719)866-4733
E-mail: jose.h.rodriguez@usajudo.us
URL: http://www.usjudo.org

Description: Judo groups and athletes, referees, judges, and interested individuals. Serves as national governing body for amateur judo in the United States. Promotes the sport of judo and trains athletes for competition. Develops eligibility and safety standards; conducts training courses for referees, coaches, and athletes. Sanctions and sponsors national amateur judo competitions. Maintains placement service; compiles statistics.

12269 ■ U.S. Lacrosse
113 W University Pkwy.
Baltimore, MD 21210
Ph: (410)235-6882
Fax: (410)366-6735
E-mail: info@uslacrosse.org
URL: http://www.uslacrosse.org

Description: Serves as the national governing body of men's and women's lacrosse. Runs the Lacrosse Museum and National Hall of Fame.

12270 ■ United States Professional Diving Coaches Association (USPDCA)
PO Box 268
Milford, OH 45150
E-mail: curtis.wilson@cox.net
URL: http://www.uspdca.org

Description: Conducts educational programs; offers placement services.

12271 ■ United States Professional Tennis Association (USPTA)
3535 Briarpark Dr., Ste. 1
Houston, TX 77042
Ph: (713)978-7782
Fax: (713)978-7780
Fr: 800-USPTA-4U
E-mail: uspta@uspta.org
URL: http://www.uspta.com

Description: Professional tennis instructors, tennis-teaching professionals and college coaches. Seeks to improve tennis instruction in the United States; maintains placement bureau and library. Offers specialized education; sponsors competitions; administrates an adult tennis league and a nationwide program to introduce children ages 3-10 to tennis. Sponsors annual "Tennis Across America" program each spring.

SOURCES OF HELP-WANTED ADS

12272 ■ ISEM Newsletter
Institute for the Study of Earth and Man
N.L. Heroy Hall
PO Box 0274
Dallas, TX 75275-0274
Ph: (214)768-2425
E-mail: isem@mail.smu.edu
URL: http://www.smu.edu/isem

Description: Semiannual. Reports on research in the anthropological, geological, and statistical sciences. Includes notices of research funds, grants, and contracts awarded. Provides biographical sketches of new faculty members in the anthropological, geological, and statistical sciences departments at Southern Methodist University. Recurring features include news of research and news of members.

12273 ■ Journal of Financial and Quantitative Analysis
Journal of Financial & Quantitative Analysis
University of Washington
Foster School of Business
115 Lewis Hall
PO Box 353200
Seattle, WA 98195-3200
Ph: (206)543-4598
Fax: (206)616-1894
E-mail: jfqa@u.washington.edu
URL: http://www.jfqa.org/

Quarterly. $85.00/year for individuals, print & online; $65.00/year for individuals, online only; $367.00/year for institutions, online only; $450.00/year for institutions, print & online. Journal on research in finance.

12274 ■ Journal of Mathematics and Statistics
Science Publications
Vails Gate Heights Dr.
PO Box 879
Vails Gate, NY 12584-0879
URL: http://thescipub.com/jms.toc

Quarterly. Peer-reviewed scholarly journal covering all areas of mathematics and statistics.

12275 ■ Journal of Statistical Software
American Statistical Association
732 N Washington St.
Alexandria, VA 22314-1943
Ph: (703)684-1221
Fax: (703)684-2037
Fr: 888-231-3473
URL: http://www.jstatsoft.org/

Peer-reviewed journal publishing articles, book reviews, code snippets, and software reviews on the subject of statistical software and algorithms.

12276 ■ Statistics
Taylor & Francis Group Journals
325 Chestnut St., Ste. 800
Philadelphia, PA 19106-2608
Ph: (215)625-8900
Fax: (215)625-2940
Fr: 800-354-1420
URL: http://www.tandf.co.uk/journals/titles/02331888.asp

Bimonthly. $1,681.00/year for institutions, print and online; $2,224.00/year for institutions, print and online; $1,513.00/year for institutions, online only; $2,002.00/year for institutions, online only; $304.00/year for individuals, print only; $373.00/year for individuals, print only. Journal describing all aspects of statistical data analysis.

EMPLOYER DIRECTORIES AND NETWORKING LISTS

12277 ■ American Men and Women of Science
Gale
PO Box 6904
Florence, KY 41022-6904
Fr: 800-354-9706
URL: http://www.gale.cengage.com

Biennial, even years; New edition expected 29th, June 2011. $1,368.00 for individuals. Covers: Over 135,000 U.S. and Canadian scientists active in the physical, biological, mathematical, computer science, and engineering fields; includes references to previous edition for deceased scientists and nonrespondents. Entries include: Name, address, education, personal and career data, memberships, honors and awards, research interest. Arrangement: Alphabetical. Indexes: Discipline (in separate volume).

HANDBOOKS AND MANUALS

12278 ■ Applied Survey Methods: A Statistical Perspective
John Wiley & Sons, Inc.
111 River St.
Hoboken, NJ 07030-5774
Ph: (201)748-6000
Fax: (201)748-6088
E-mail: info@wiley.com
URL: http://www.wiley.com

Jelke Bethlehem. 2009. $121.00 (hardcover). 375 pages. Provides comprehensive guide to the use of statistical methods for obtaining reliable and practical survey research.

12279 ■ A Career in Statistics: Beyond the Numbers
John Wiley & Sons, Inc.
111 River St.
Hoboken, NJ 07030-5774

Ph: (201)748-6000
Fax: (201)748-6088
URL: http://www.wiley.com

Gerald J. Hahn and Necip Doganaksoy. 2011. $69.95 (paper). 360 pages. Emphasizes essential concepts and practices in a statistician's career. Provides hands-on guidance for career success.

12280 ■ Opportunities in Social Science Careers
The McGraw-Hill Companies
PO Box 182604
Columbus, OH 43272
Fax: (614)759-3749
Fr: 877-883-5524
E-mail: customer.service@mcgraw-hill.com
URL: http://www.mcgraw-hill.com

Rosanne J. Marek. 2004. $13.95. 160 Pages. VGM Opportunities Series.

EMPLOYMENT AGENCIES AND SEARCH FIRMS

12281 ■ Analytic Recruiting, Inc.
144 E 44th St., 3rd Fl.
New York, NY 10017
Ph: (212)545-8511
E-mail: email@analyticrecruiting.com
URL: http://www.analyticrecruiting.com

Executive search firm.

12282 ■ Biomedical Search Consultants
275 Wyman St., Ste. 110
Waltham, MA 02451
Ph: (781)890-8824
Fax: (781)998-1266
E-mail: kprovost@biomedicalsearch.com
URL: http://www.biomedicalsearchconsultants.com

Employment agency.

12283 ■ Placemart Personnel Service
80 Haines St.
Lanoka Harbor, NJ 08734
Ph: (609)242-4346
Fax: (609)242-4347
Fr: 800-394-7522
E-mail: info@placemart.com
URL: http://www.placemart.com

Executive search firm focusing on the field of clinical research.

TRADESHOWS

12284 ■ Joint Statistical Meetings
American Statistical Association
732 N. Washington St.
Alexandria, VA 22314-1943
Ph: (703)684-1221

Fax: (703)684-2037
Fr: 888-231-3473
E-mail: asainfo@amstat.org
URL: http://www.amstat.org
Annual. Primary Exhibits: Publications, software, federal agencies, recruiters, consulting firms. Dates and Locations: 2012 Jul 28 - Aug 02; San Diego, CA; San Diego Convention Center; 2013 Aug 03-08; Montreal, QC, Canada; Palais de Congres de Montreal; 2014 Aug 02-07; Boston, MA; Boston Convention and Exhibition Center; 2015 Aug 08-13; Washington, WA; Washington State Convention & Trade Center.

OTHER SOURCES

12285 ■ American Statistical Association (ASA)
732 N Washington St.
Alexandria, VA 22314-1943
Ph: (703)684-1221
Fax: (703)684-2037
Fr: 888-231-3473
E-mail: asainfo@amstat.org
URL: http://www.amstat.org

Description: Professional society of persons interested in the theory, methodology, and application of statistics to all fields of human endeavor.

12286 ■ Caucus for Women in Statistics (CWS)
7732 Rydal Terr.
Rockville, MD 20855-2057
Ph: (301)827-0170
Fax: (301)827-6661
E-mail: anna.nevius@fda.hhs.gov
URL: http://caucusforwomeninstatistics.com

Description: Individuals, primarily statisticians, united to improve employment and professional opportunities for women in statistics. Conducts technical sessions concerning statistical studies related to women. Maintains biographical archives.

12287 ■ Institute of Mathematical Statistics (IMS)
PO Box 22718
Beachwood, OH 44122
Ph: (216)295-2340
Fax: (216)295-5661

Fr: 877-557-4674
E-mail: ims@imstat.org
URL: http://www.imstat.org

Description: Professional society of mathematicians and others interested in mathematical statistics and probability theory. Seeks to further research in mathematical statistics and probability.

12288 ■ International Society of Parametric Analysts (ISPA)
527 Maple Ave. E, Ste. 301
Vienna, VA 22180
Ph: (703)938-5090
Fax: (703)938-5091
Fr: 877-734-2726
E-mail: ispa@sceaonline.net
URL: http://www.ispa-cost.org

Description: Engineers, designers, statisticians, estimators, and managers in industry, the military, and government who develop and use computerized, parametric cost-estimating models. Conducts educational activities to promote usage of parametric modeling techniques for purposes of cost estimating, risk analysis, and technology forecasting. Sponsors placement service.

EMPLOYER DIRECTORIES AND NETWORKING LISTS

12289 ■ Law and Legal Information Directory
Gale
PO Box 6904
Florence, KY 41022-6904
Fr: 800-354-9706
URL: http://www.gale.cengage.com
Annual, Latest edition 24th; April, 2012. $716.00 for individuals. Covers: More than 21,000 national and international organizations, bar associations, federal and highest state courts, federal regulatory agencies, law schools, firms and organizations offering continuing legal education, paralegal education, sources of scholarships and grants, awards and prizes, special libraries, information systems and services, research centers, publishers of legal periodicals, books, and audiovisual materials, lawyer referral services, legal aid offices, public defender offices, legislature manuals and registers, small claims courts, corporation departments of state, state law enforcement agencies, state agencies, including disciplinary agencies, and state bar requirements. Entries include: All entries include institution or firm name, address, phone; many include names and titles of key personnel and, when pertinent, descriptive annotations. Contents based in part on information selected from several other Gale directories. Arrangement: Classified by type of organization, activity, service, etc. Indexes: Individual sections have special indexes as required.

EMPLOYMENT AGENCIES AND SEARCH FIRMS

12290 ■ Allied Court Reporters
115 Phenix Ave.
Cranston, RI 02920
Ph: (401)946-5500
Fax: (401)946-9228
Fr: 888-44D-EPOS
E-mail: jeff@alliedcourtreporters.com
URL: http://www.alliedcourtreporters.com
Provides services related to court reporting, video conferencing, legal services and litigation support. Provides assistance in professional development and employment.

12291 ■ Attorney Resources, Inc.
750 N St. Paul, Ste. 540
Dallas, TX 75201
Ph: (214)922-8050
E-mail: tlb@attorneyresource.com
URL: http://www.attorneyresource.com
Employment agency. Offices in Austin, Dallas, Fort Worth, Houston and Tulsa, OK. Provides staffing assistance on regular or temporary basis.

12292 ■ Beverly Hills Bar Association Personnel Service
300 S Beverly Dr., Ste. 201
Beverly Hills, CA 90212-4805
Ph: (310)601-2422
Fax: (310)601-2423
URL: http://www.bhba.org
Employment agency.

12293 ■ Hallmark Services
603 Stewart St., Ste. 1021
Seattle, WA 98101
Ph: (206)587-5360
Fax: (206)587-5319
E-mail: hallmark@hallmarkservices.com
URL: http://www.hallmarkservices.com
Employment agency. Fills openings for permanent employment.

12294 ■ Legal Placement Services, Inc.
6737 W Washington St., Ste. 2390
West Allis, WI 53214
Ph: (414)276-6689
Fax: (414)276-1418
E-mail: info@ps-companies.com
URL: http://www.ps-companies.com/legal-placement-services
Employment agency. Periodically fills temporary placements, as well.

12295 ■ Pathfinders, Inc.
229 Peachtree St. NE
International Tower, Ste. 1500
Atlanta, GA 30303
Ph: (404)688-5940
URL: http://www.pathfindersinc.com
Permanent employment agency focusing on the secretarial field.

ONLINE JOB SOURCES AND SERVICES

12296 ■ Court Reporters Board of California
E-mail: jennifer.haupert@dca.ca.gov
URL: http://www.courtreportersboard.ca.gov
Description: Provides users of the Judicial System protection by disseminating information and through regulating and testing of the qualifications, performance, and ethical conduct of CSRs and entities regulated by the Board.

12297 ■ CourtReporterNet.com
URL: http://www.courtreporternet.com
Description: Provides directory of court reporting firms worldwide.

12298 ■ CourtReporters.com
URL: http://www.courtreporters.com
Description: Offers news and information to court reporters such as job opportunities and opportunities for continuing education.

12299 ■ Get Court Reporter Jobs
URL: http://www.getcourtreporterjobs.com
Description: Focuses on providing resources for job seeking court reporters. Features job postings and employment opportunities.

12300 ■ JournalismJobs.com
Ph: (510)653-1521
E-mail: info@journalismjobs.com
URL: http://www.journalismjobs.com
Description: Career-related site for journalists and other media professionals. Seekers can search for jobs, post a resume online, and manage the search online with the Job Seeker Folder feature. They also can receive free job announcements by e-mail.

12301 ■ Law.com: Court Reporter Directory
URL: http://www.almexperts.com/litigation/Court%20Reporters/LitExpert/1125822
Description: An online directory for those seeking services of court reporters.

TRADESHOWS

12302 ■ National Court Reporters Association Annual Convention and Exposition
National Court Reporters Association
8224 Old Courthouse Rd.
Vienna, VA 22182
Ph: (703)556-6272
Fax: (703)556-6291
Fr: 800-556-6272
E-mail: msic@ncrahq.org
URL: http://www.ncraonline.org
Annual. Features seminars, specialized education programs, exhibits, and social and networking events. 2012 August 2-5; Downtown Philadelphia, PA; Philadelphia Marriot.

OTHER SOURCES

12303 ■ California Court Reporters Association
65 Enterprise
Aliso Viejo, CA 92656
Ph: (949)715-4682
Fax: (949)715-6931
E-mail: info@cal-ccra.org
URL: http://www.cal-ccra.org
Description: Mission is to advance the profession of verbatim shorthand reporting by promoting professional reporting excellence through education, research, and the use of state-of-the-art technology; establishing and maintaining professional standards

of practice; and advocating before legislative and regulatory bodies on issues which impact the judicial system and others served by the court reporting profession of California.

12304 ■ National Court Reporters

500 S Ervay St., No. 120A
Dallas, TX 75201-6319
Fax: (866)819-2317
Fr: 800-541-4837
E-mail: nationalreport@aol.com
URL: http://www.nationalcourtreporters.com

Description: Provides comprehensive court reporting services throughout the United States, Canada and all countries overseas.

12305 ■ National Verbatim Reporters Association

629 N Main St.
Hattiesburg, MS 39401
Ph: (601)582-4345
Fax: (601)582-3354
E-mail: nvra@nvra.org
URL: http://www.nvra.org

Description: Serves as a professional organization dedicated to the practice of voice writing. Supports members with official testing and certification, marketing, news and information, legislative advocacy, and professional development services.

12306 ■ United States Court Reporters Association

8430 Gross Point Rd., Ste. 115
Skokie, IL 60077-2036

Ph: (847)471-9500
Fax: (847)470-9505
E-mail: info.uscra@gmail.com
URL: http://www.uscra.org

Description: Represents the federal court reporting profession. Promotes and maintains high standards of verbatim reporting, services, professional ethics, and fidelity to the ideals of the judicial system. Encourages continuing education and utilization of state-of-the-art technologies.

Stockbrokers and Securities Analysts

Sources of Help-Wanted Ads

12307 ■ Registered Rep.
Primedia Business
3585 Engineering Dr., Ste. 100
Norcross, GA 30092
Ph: (678)421-3000
Fr: 800-216-1423
URL: http://registeredrep.com/

Monthly. Magazine providing comprehensive coverage of securities industry trends directly affecting the job performance and productivity of retail stockbrokers.

Employer Directories and Networking Lists

12308 ■ Career Opportunities in Banking, Finance, and Insurance
Facts On File Inc.
132 W 31st St., 17th Fl.
New York, NY 10001
Ph: (212)967-8800
Fax: 800-678-3633
Fr: 800-322-8755
URL: http://factsonfile.infobasepublishing.com

Latest edition 2nd; Published February, 2007. $49.50 for individuals. Publication includes: Lists of colleges with programs supporting banking, finance, and industry; professional associations; professional certifications; regulatory agencies; and Internet resources for career planning. Principal content of publication is job descriptions for professions in the banking, finance, and insurance industries. Indexes: Alphabetical.

12309 ■ Securities Industry Yearbook
Securities Industry and Financial Markets Association
120 Broadway, 35th Fl.
New York, NY 10271-0080
Ph: (212)313-1200
Fax: (212)313-1301
URL: http://archives2.sifma.org/publications/html/securities_indu

Annual, August; latest edition 2007-08. $150.00 for nonmembers; $250.00 for U.S. Covers: over 600 member securities firms, with about 480 of them covered in detail. Entries include: For firms covered in detail—Company name, name of parent company, address, phone, capital position and rank, number of offices and type, number of employees, area of specialization, names and titles of key personnel, number of registered representatives, departments with name of department head, dollar volume of underwriting and syndication by type, other financial data. For other firms—Company name, address, name of delegated liaison to the association. Arrangement: Alphabetical. Indexes: National firms ranked by

capital with capital and rank for prior year, number of offices and rank, number of employees and rank, and number of registered representatives and rank. Same data given in separate ranked list for regional firms.

12310 ■ Standard & Poor's Security Dealers of North America
Standard & Poor's
55 Water St.
New York, NY 10041-0004
Ph: (212)438-2000
Fr: 800-852-1641
URL: http://www2.standardandpoors.com

Semiannual, March and September; supplements available every 6 weeks. Covers: over 10,000 security dealers; includes over 300 offices outside North America. Entries include: Company name, address, phone, main and branch offices, departments, names and titles of principal personnel, exchange memberships, teletype, wire systems, clearing facilities, employer identification number, and date established. Arrangement: Geographical.

Handbooks and Manuals

12311 ■ Careers for Financial Mavens and Other Money Movers
The McGraw-Hill Companies
PO Box 182604
Columbus, OH 43272
Fax: (614)759-3749
Fr: 877-883-5524
E-mail: customer.service@mcgraw-hill.com
URL: http://www.mhprofessional.com/
    product.php?cat=106&isbn=0071454551

Marjorie Eberts and Margaret Gisler. Second edition, 2004. $19.95 (paper). 153 pages.

12312 ■ Opportunities in Financial Careers
The McGraw-Hill Companies
PO Box 182604
Columbus, OH 43272
Fax: (614)759-3749
Fr: 877-883-5524
E-mail: customer.service@mcgraw-hill.com
URL: http://www.mhprofessional.com/
    product.php?isbn=0071442502

Michael Sumichrast and Martin A. Sumichrast. 2004. $13.95 (paper). 160 pages. A guide to planning for and seeking opportunities in this challenging field.

12313 ■ Vault Career Guide to Sales and Trading
Vault.com
75 Varick St., 8th Fl.
New York, NY 10013
Ph: (212)366-4212
Fax: (212)366-6117
URL: http://www.vault.com/wps/portal/usa

Gabriel Kim. December 2007. $29.95 (paper). 160 pages. Series of the Vault Career Library.

Employment Agencies and Search Firms

12314 ■ Ashton Lane Group
51 John F. Kennedy Pkwy., 1st Fl. W
Short Hills, NJ 07078
Ph: (212)372-9795
Fax: (973)218-2661
E-mail: info@ashtonlanegroup.com
URL: http://www.ashtonlanegroup.com

Specializes in the recruitment of professionals in banking, insurance and alternative investment industries.

12315 ■ Essex Consulting Group Inc.
PO Box 550
Essex, MA 01929
Ph: (978)337-6633
E-mail: brad@essexsearch.com
URL: http://www.essexsearch.com

Executive search firm.

12316 ■ ExecuGroup Inc.
142 S Main St.
PO Box 5040
Grenada, MS 38901
Ph: (662)226-9025
Fax: (662)226-9090
E-mail: tray@execugroup.com
URL: http://www.execugroup.com

Executive search firm. Second location in Bethlehem, PA.

12317 ■ Mark Elzweig Co. Ltd.
183 Madison Ave., Ste.1704
New York, NY 10016
Ph: (212)685-7070
Fax: (212)685-7761
E-mail: elzweig@elzweig.com
URL: http://www.elzweig.com

Executive search firm.

12318 ■ Straight and Company
1002 Brown Thrasher Pt.
St. Mary's, GA 31558
Ph: (912)882-3480
E-mail: gary.straight@straightco.com
URL: http://www.straightco.com

Financial services executive search firm.

Online Job Sources and Services

12319 ■ BrokerHunter.com
URL: http://www.brokerhunter.com
Description: Serves as an Internet-based recruiting

solution in the rapidly changing financial services industry. Provides job listings serving the securities, insurance and banking sectors.

12320 ■ Financial Job Network
PO Box 55431
Sherman Oaks, CA 91403
Ph: (818)905-5272
E-mail: info@fjn.com
URL: http://www.fjn.com

Description: Contains information on international and national employment opportunities for those in the financial job market. Job listings may be submitted, as well as resumes. Main files include: Testimonials, Calendar, Corporate Listings, FJN Clients, more. Free to candidates.

12321 ■ GlocapSearch.com
156 W 56th St., 4th Fl.
New York, NY 10019
Ph: (212)333-6400
URL: http://www.glocap.com

Description: Recruitment firm for the private equity, venture capital and hedge fund marketplaces. After registering with website, seekers will be notified weekly of positions available that may interest them. Through returned e-mail, the firm will forward resumes and schedule preliminary interviews with prospective employers.

OTHER SOURCES

12322 ■ CFA Institute
560 Ray C. Hunt Dr.
Charlottesville, VA 22903-2981
Ph: (434)951-5499
Fax: (434)951-5262
Fr: 800-247-8132
E-mail: info@cfainstitute.org
URL: http://www.cfainstitute.org

Description: Security and financial analyst association whose members are practicing investment analysts. Includes private, voluntary self-regulation program in which members are enrolled. Internationally renowned for its rigorous Chartered Financial Analyst curriculum and examination program, which has more than 86,000 candidates from 143 countries enrolled for exams. In addition, it is internationally recognized for its investment performance standards, which investment firms use to document and report investment results, as well as for its Code of Ethics and Standards of Professional Conduct.

12323 ■ Financial Women's Association of New York (FWA)
215 Park Ave. S, Ste. 1712
New York, NY 10003
Ph: (212)533-2141
Fax: (212)982-3008
E-mail: fwaoffice@fwa.org
URL: http://www.fwa.org

Description: Persons of professional status in the field of finance in the New York metropolitan area. Works to promote and maintain high professional standards in the financial and business communities; provide an opportunity for members to enhance one another's professional contacts; achieve recognition of the contribution of women to the financial and business communities; encourage other women to seek professional positions within the financial and business communities. Activities include educational trips to foreign countries; college internship program including foreign student exchange; high school mentorship program; Washington and international briefings; placement service for members. Maintains speakers' bureau.

12324 ■ National Association of Securities Professionals
727 NW 15th St., Ste. 750
Washington, DC 20005

Ph: (202)371-5535
Fax: (202)371-5536
URL: http://www.nasphq.org

Description: Serves as a resource for minorities and women within the securities and investments industry. Provides opportunities to share information about the securities markets. Facilitates educational seminars and networking opportunities.

12325 ■ New York Society of Security Analysts (NYSSA)
1540 Broadway, Ste. 1010
New York, NY 10036-2714
Ph: (212)541-4530
Fax: (212)541-4677
E-mail: webaccess@nyssa.org
URL: http://www.nyssa.org

Description: Security analysts and portfolio managers employed primarily in New York by brokerage houses, banks, insurance companies, mutual funds and other financial institutions. Conducts educational forums on topics relating to the securities markets. Maintains placement service.

12326 ■ Securities Industry and Financial Markets Association (SIFMA)
120 Broadway, 35th Fl.
New York, NY 10271-0080
Ph: (212)313-1200
Fax: (212)313-1301
E-mail: inquiry@sifma.org
URL: http://www.sifma.org

Description: Represents more than 650 member firms of all sizes, in all financial markets in the U.S. and around the world. Enhances the public's trust and confidence in the markets, delivering an efficient, enhanced member network of access and forward-looking services, as well as premiere educational resources for the professionals in the industry and the investors whom they serve. Maintains offices in New York City and Washington, DC.

SOURCES OF HELP-WANTED ADS

12327 ■ American Journal of Emergency Medicine
Mosby Inc.
11830 Westline Industrial Dr.
St. Louis, MO 63146-3326
Ph: (314)872-8370
Fax: (314)432-1380
Fr: 800-325-4177
URL: http://www.elsevier.com/wps/find/journaldescription.cws_home

$340.00/year for individuals; $529.00/year for institutions; $159.00/year for students; $523.00/year for other countries; $711.00/year for institutions, other countries; $261.00/year for students, other countries. Journal reporting on emergency medicine.

12328 ■ American Journal of Surgery
Excerpta Medica Inc.
685 US-202
Bridgewater, NJ 08807
Ph: (908)547-2100
Fax: (908)547-2200
URL: http://americanjournalofsurgery.com/

Monthly. $247.00/year for individuals; $99.00/year for students; $247.00/year for Canada; $481.00/year for other countries; $105.00/year for students, other countries. Surgical journal.

12329 ■ Anesthesiology
Lippincott Williams & Wilkins
530 Walnut St.
Philadelphia, PA 19106-3619
Ph: (215)521-8300
Fax: (215)521-8902
Fr: 800-638-3030
URL: http://journals.lww.com/anesthesiology/pages/default.aspx

Monthly. $655.00/year for individuals; $1,086.00/year for institutions; $725.00/year for other countries; $1,281.00/year for institutions, other countries; $256.00/year for individuals, in-training; $306.60/year for other countries, in-training. Medical journal publishing original manuscripts and brief abstracts from current literature on anesthesiology.

12330 ■ Annals of Medicine
Informa Healthcare
52 Vanderbilt Ave., 7th Fl.
New York, NY 10017-3846
Ph: (212)520-2777
URL: http://informahealthcare.com/ann

$595.00/year for institutions; $980.00/year for institutions; $780.00/year for institutions. Journal covering health science and medical education.

12331 ■ Annals of Surgery
Lippincott Williams & Wilkins
530 Walnut St.
Philadelphia, PA 19106-3619

Ph: (215)521-8300
Fax: (215)521-8902
Fr: 800-638-3030
URL: http://journals.lww.com/annalsofsurgery/pages/default.aspx

Monthly. $326.00/year for individuals; $929.00/year for institutions; $133.00/year for individuals, in-training; $539.50/year for individuals, international; $1,244.50/year for institutions, other countries; $160.50/year for other countries, in-training. Medical journal publishing original manuscripts promoting the advancement of surgical knowledge and practice.

12332 ■ Archives of Surgery
American Medical Association
515 N State St.
Chicago, IL 60654
Fr: 800-621-8335
E-mail: archsurg@jama-archives.org
URL: http://archsurg.ama-assn.org/

Monthly. $125.00/year for members, print and online; $485.00/year for institutions, print and online. Peer-reviewed educational/clinical journal for general surgeons and surgical specialists.

12333 ■ Clinical Medicine & Research
Marshfield Clinic
1000 N Oak Ave.
Marshfield, WI 54449
Ph: (715)387-5511
Fax: (715)389-3808
Fr: 800-782-8581
E-mail: clinmedres@mcrf.mfldclin.edu
URL: http://www.clinmedres.org/

Quarterly. Free within the U.S. Peer-reviewed journal that publishes scientific medical research that is relevant to a broad audience of medical researchers and healthcare professionals.

12334 ■ Clinical Nuclear Medicine
Lippincott Williams & Wilkins
530 Walnut St.
Philadelphia, PA 19106-3619
Ph: (215)521-8300
Fax: (215)521-8902
Fr: 800-638-3030
E-mail: cnm.mlk@verizon.net
URL: http://journals.lww.com/nuclearmed/pages/default.aspx

Monthly. $410.00/year for individuals; $844.00/year for institutions; $576.00/year for other countries; $1,051.00/year for institutions, other countries; $234.10/year for other countries, in-training; $211.00/year for individuals, in-training. Journal publishing original manuscripts about scanning, imaging, and related subjects.

12335 ■ CME Supplement to Emergency Medicine Clinics of North America
Elsevier Science Inc.
360 Park Ave. S
New York, NY 10010-1710

Ph: (212)989-5800
Fax: (212)633-3990
Fr: 888-437-4636
URL: http://www.elsevier.com/wps/find/journaldescription.cws_home

$209.00/year for individuals. Journal covering emergency medicine clinics.

12336 ■ Discovery Medicine
Discovery Medicine
10 Gerard Ave., Ste. 201
Timonium, MD 21093
Ph: (410)773-9938
Fax: 888-833-0526
URL: http://www.discoverymedicine.com

Bimonthly. $599.00/year for institutions, digital edition; $99.95/year for individuals, digital edition. Online journal that publishes articles on diseases, biology, new diagnostics, and treatments for medical professionals.

12337 ■ Education & Treatment of Children
West Virginia University Press
139 Stansbury Hall
PO Box 6295
Morgantown, WV 26506
Ph: (304)293-8400
Fax: (304)293-6585
URL: http://www.educationandtreatmentofchildren.net

Quarterly. $85.00/year for institutions; $45.00/year for individuals; $100.00/year for institutions, elsewhere; $60.00/year for individuals, elsewhere. Periodical featuring information concerning the development of services for children and youth. Includes reports written for educators and other child care and mental health providers focused on teaching, training, and treatment effectiveness.

12338 ■ Global Change, Peace & Security
Routledge
711 3 Ave., 8 Fl.
New York, NY 10016
Ph: (212)216-7800
Fax: (212)563-2269
Fr: 800-634-7064
URL: http://www.tandfonline.com/toc/cpar20/current

$160.00/year for individuals, print; $602.00/year for individuals, online only; $669.00/year for individuals, print & online. Journal promoting physical therapy and integration.

12339 ■ Hospitals & Health Networks
Health Forum L.L.C.
155 N Wacker Dr., Ste. 400
Chicago, IL 60606
Ph: (312)893-6800
Fax: (312)422-4500
Fr: 800-821-2039
URL: http://www.hhnmag.com

Weekly. Free. Publication covering the health care industry.

12340 ■ The IHS Primary Care Provider
Indian Health Service
The Reyes Bldg.
801 Thompson Ave., Ste. 400
Rockville, MD 20852-1627
Ph: (301)443-1011
URL: http://www.ihs.gov/provider

Monthly. Journal for health care professionals, physicians, nurses, pharmacists, dentists, and dietitians.

12341 ■ Injury
Mosby Inc.
11830 Westline Industrial Dr.
St. Louis, MO 63146-3326
Ph: (314)872-8370
Fax: (314)432-1380
Fr: 800-325-4177
URL: http://www.elsevier.com/wps/find/
journaldescription.cws_home

Monthly. $200.00/year for individuals, European countries and Iran; $224.00/year for individuals, all countries except Europe, Japan and Iran; $26,500.00/year for individuals; $1,381.00/year for institutions, European countries and Iran; $1,543.00/year for institutions, all Countries except Europe, Japan and Iran; $183,200.00/year for institutions. Journal publishing articles and research related to the treatment of injuries such as trauma systems and management; surgical procedures; epidemiological studies; surgery (of all tissues); resuscitation; biomechanics; rehabilitation; anaesthesia; radiology and wound management.

12342 ■ Journal of the American Society of Podiatric Medical Assistants
American Society of Podiatric Medical Assistants
1616 N 78th Ct.
Elmwood Park, IL 60707
Fr: 888-882-7762
URL: http://www.aspma.org

Quarterly. Included in membership. Professional journal covering issues in podiatry.

12343 ■ The Journal of Arthroplasty
Elsevier
1600 John F. Kennedy Blvd., Ste. 1800
Philadelphia, PA 19103-2822
Ph: (215)239-3900
Fax: (215)238-7883
E-mail: elspcs@elsevier.com
URL: http://www.us.elsevierhealth.com/
product.jsp?isbn=08835403

$494.00/year for individuals; $802.00/year for institutions; $217.00/year for students. Peer-reviewed medical journal for orthopaedic surgeons. Covering clinical and basic science research on arthroplasty including surgical techniques, prosthetic design, biomechanics, biomaterials, and metallurgy.

12344 ■ Journal of Health and Life Sciences Law
American Health Lawyers Association
1620 Eye St. NW, 6th Fl.
Washington, DC 20006-4010
Ph: (202)833-1100
Fax: (202)833-1105
URL: http://www.healthlawyers.org

Quarterly. $149.00/year for individuals. Professional journal covering healthcare issues and cases and their impact on the health care arena.

12345 ■ Journal of Hospital Medicine
John Wiley & Sons Inc.
111 River St.
Hoboken, NJ 07030-5773
Ph: (201)748-6000
Fax: (201)748-6088
Fr: 800-825-7550
URL: http://onlinelibrary.wiley.com/journal/10.1002/
(ISSN)1553-56

$827.00/year for U.S., Canada, and Mexico, print only; $827.00/year for institutions, other countries, print only. Journal on hospital medicine.

12346 ■ Same-Day Surgery
American Health Consultants Inc.
3525 Piedmont Rd. NE, Bldg. 6-400
Atlanta, GA 30305
Ph: (404)262-5476
Fax: (404)262-5560
Fr: 800-688-2421
E-mail: editorial_questions@ahcmedia.com
URL: http://www.ahcmedia.com/public

Description: Monthly. $499. Focuses on the management, structure, and legal and medical aspects of ambulatory surgery. Carries expert opinions and recommendations on policies and procedures.

12347 ■ Surgical Rounds
Ascend Integrated Media
7015 College Blvd., Ste. 600
Overland Park, KS 66211
Ph: (913)469-1110
Fax: (913)469-0806
URL: http://www.hcplive.com/publications/surgical-rounds

Monthly. Free to qualified subscribers. Peer-reviewed journal featuring clinical articles of interest to office-based and hospital-based surgeons, including residents, full-time staff, and surgical faculty.

12348 ■ Surgical Science
Scientific Research Publishing
PO Box 54821
Irvine, CA 92619-4821
E-mail: ss@scirp.org
URL: http://www.scirp.org/journal/ss/

$390.00/year for individuals. Peer-reviewed journal publishing articles on the latest developments in surgery.

12349 ■ USA Body Psychotherapy Journal
United States Association for Body Psychotherapy
8639 B 16th St., Ste. 119
Silver Spring, MD 20910
Ph: (202)466-1619
E-mail: admin@usabp.org
URL: http://www.usabp.org/
displaycommon.cfm?an=4

Semiannual. Academic journal that seeks to support, promote and stimulate the exchange of ideas, scholarship and research within the field of body psychotherapy as well as an interdisciplinary exchange with related fields of clinical practice and inquiry.

12350 ■ Year Book of Critical Care Medicine
Elsevier Science Inc.
360 Park Ave. S
New York, NY 10010-1710
Ph: (212)989-5800
Fax: (212)633-3990
Fr: 888-437-4636
URL: http://www.elsevier.com/wps/find/
journaldescription.cws_home

Annual. $271.00/year for institutions, other countries; $197.00/year for other countries; $103.00/year for students, other countries; $250.00/year for institutions; $167.00/year for individuals; $81.00/year for students. Journal focused on treatment of severe sepsis and septic shock, echocardiography in the evaluation of hemo-dynamically unstable patients & mechanical ventilation of acute respiratory distress syndrome.

EMPLOYER DIRECTORIES AND NETWORKING LISTS

12351 ■ Crain's List—Chicago's Largest Hospitals
Crain Communications Inc.
360 N Michigan Ave.
Chicago, IL 60601
Ph: (312)649-5200
URL: http://www.chicagobusiness.com/section/lists

Published November, 2010. $25.00 for individuals; $45.00 for individuals. Covers: 25 hospitals in Chicago area ranked by net patient revenues. Entries include: Name, address, phone number, fax, web address, corporate e-mail, hospital administrator, network affiliation, 2009 net patient revenue, percentage change from 2008, 2009 net profits, percentage change from 2008, inpatient days, available beds, daily occupancy rate, number of hospital employees as of December 31, 2009, fiscal year end, Chairman, President, CEO, Chief Financial Officer, Human Resources Manager, Media Relations/Public Relations Director, and Hospital Administrator.

12352 ■ Directory of Hospital Personnel
Grey House Publishing
4919 Rte. 22
PO Box 56
Amenia, NY 12501
Ph: (518)789-8700
Fax: (518)789-0556
Fr: 800-562-2139
URL: http://www.greyhouse.com/hospital_
personnel.htm

Annual, Latest edition 2011. $325.00 for individuals. Covers: 200,000 executives at 6,000 U.S. Hospitals. Entries include: Name of hospital, address, phone, number of beds, type and JCAHO status of hospital, names and titles of key department heads and staff, medical and nursing school affiliations; number of residents, interns, and nursing students. Arrangement: Geographical. Indexes: Hospital name, personnel, hospital size.

12353 ■ Hospital Blue Book
Billian Publishing Inc. and Trans World Publishing Inc.
2100 River Edge Pky.
Atlanta, GA 30328
Ph: (770)955-5656
Fax: (770)952-0669
Fr: 800-800-5668
E-mail: blu-book@billian.com
URL: http://www.billianshealthdata.com/Products/
bluebook.html

Annual, Latest edition 2010. $575.00 for individuals; $575.00 for individuals. Covers: More than 6,500 hospitals; some listings also appear in a separate southern edition of this publication. Entries include: Name of hospital, accreditation, mailing address, phone, fax, number of beds, type of facility (nonprofit, general, state, etc.); list of administrative personnel and chiefs of medical services, with specific titles. Arrangement: Geographical.

12354 ■ Medical and Health Information Directory
Gale
PO Box 6904
Florence, KY 41022-6904
Fr: 800-354-9706
URL: http://www.gale.cengage.com

Annual, Latest edition April 2011. $1190.00 for individuals; $501.00 for individuals. Covers: In volume 1, more than 33,000 medical and health oriented associations, organizations, institutions, and government agencies, including health maintenance organizations (HMOs), preferred provider organizations (PPOs), insurance companies, pharmaceutical companies, research centers, and medical and allied health schools. In Volume 2, over 20,000 medical book publishers; medical periodicals, directories, audiovisual producers and services, medical libraries and information centers, electronic resources, and health-related internet search engines. In Volume 3, more than 40,500 clinics, treatment centers, care programs, and counseling/diagnostic services for 34 subject areas. Entries include: Institution, service, or firm name, address, phone, fax, email and URL; many include names of key personnel and, when pertinent, descriptive annotation. Volume 3 was formerly listed separately as Health Services Directory. Arrangement: Classified by organization activity, service, etc. Indexes: Each volume has a complete alphabetical name and keyword index.

HANDBOOKS AND MANUALS

12355 ■ Careers in Health Care
The McGraw-Hill Companies
PO Box 182604
Columbus, OH 43272
Fax: (614)759-3749
Fr: 877-883-5524
E-mail: customer.service@mcgraw-hill.com
URL: http://www.mhprofessional.com/
   product.php?isbn=0071466533

Barbara M. Swanson. Fifth edition, 2005. $19.95
(paper). 192 pages. Describes job duties, work settings, salaries, licensing and certification requirements, educational preparation, and future outlook.
Gives ideas on how to secure a job.

**12356 ■ Expert Resumes for Health Care
   Careers**
Jist Works
875 Montreal Way
St. Paul, MN 55102
Fr: 800-648-5478
E-mail: educate@emcp.com
URL: http://www.jist.com

Wendy S. Enelow and Louise M. Kursmark. 2010.
$16.95. 288 pages.

12357 ■ Health Careers Today
Elsevier
11830 Westline Industrial Dr.
St. Louis, MO 63146
Ph: (314)453-7010
Fax: (314)453-7095
Fr: 800-545-2522
E-mail: usbkinfo@elsevier.com
URL: http://www.elsevier.com

Gerdin, Judith. Fourth edition. 2007. $74.95. 496
pages. Covers more than 45 health careers. Discusses the roles and responsibilities of various occupations and provides a solid foundation in the skills
needed for all health careers.

**12358 ■ Opportunities in Health and Medical
   Careers**
The McGraw-Hill Companies
PO Box 182604
Columbus, OH 43272
Fax: (614)759-3749

Fr: 877-883-5524
E-mail: customer.service@mcgraw-hill.com
URL: http://www.mhprofessional.com/
   product.php?isbn=0071437274

I. Donald Snook, Jr. and Leo D'Orazio. 2004. $14.95
(paper). 157 pages. Covers the full range of medical
and health occupations. Illustrated.

**12359 ■ Resumes for Health and Medical
   Careers**
The McGraw-Hill Companies
PO Box 182604
Columbus, OH 43272
Fax: (614)759-3749
Fr: 877-883-5524
E-mail: customer.service@mcgraw-hill.com
URL: http://www.mhprofessional.com/
   product.php?isbn=0071545352

Third edition, 2008. $12.95 (paper). 144 pages.

ONLINE JOB SOURCES AND SERVICES

12360 ■ HEALTHeCAREERS Network
Fr: 888-884-8242
E-mail: info@healthecareers.com
URL: http://www.healthecareers.com

Description: Career search site for jobs in all health
care specialties; educational resources; visa and
licensing information for relocation; interesting
articles; relocation tools; links to professional organizations and general resources.

12361 ■ Hospital Jobs OnLine
E-mail: support@hospitaljobsonline.com
URL: http://www.hospitaljobsonline.com

Description: Serves as a niche healthcare job board
designed exclusively for hospitals, healthcare companies, and healthcare job seekers.

12362 ■ ProHealthJobs.com
Ph: (484)443-8545
Fax: (484)443-8549
E-mail: info@prohealthjobs.com
URL: http://prohealthjobs.com/jobboard

Description: Career resources site for the medical
and health care field. Lists professional opportunities,
product information, continuing education and open
positions.

TRADESHOWS

12363 ■ AST Conference
Association of Surgical Technologists
6 W Dry Creek Cir., Ste. 200
Littleton, CO 80120
Ph: (303)694-9130
Fax: (303)694-9169
Fr: 800-637-7433
URL: http://www.ast.org
Annual. Includes targeted workshops for educators,
surgical assistants, students and practitioners seek-
ing intensive, hands-on training, as well as education
sessions that cover a range of specialty areas. 2013
May 21-25; New Orleans, LA; Hilton New Orleans;
2014 May 26-30; Denver, CO; Hyatt Regency Denver.

OTHER SOURCES

**12364 ■ American Academy of Facial Plastic
   and Reconstructive Surgery**
310 S Henry St.
Alexandria, VA 22314
Ph: (703)299-9291
Fax: (703)299-8898
E-mail: info@aafprs.org
URL: http://www.aafprs.org
Description: Represents facial plastic and reconstructive surgeons throughout the world. Promotes
quality facial plastic surgery through education, dissemination of professional information, and the
establishment of professional standards. Serves as
the public's information source on facial plastic
surgery.

**12365 ■ Association of Surgical
   Technologists (AST)**
6 W Dry Creek Cir., Ste. 200
Littleton, CO 80120-8031
Ph: (303)694-9130
Fax: (303)694-9169
Fr: 800-637-7433
E-mail: bteutsch@ast.org
URL: http://www.ast.org
Description: Individuals who have received specific
education and training to deliver surgical patient care
in the operating room. Membership categories are
available for both certified and student surgical
technologists. Emphasis is placed on encouraging
members to participate actively in a continuing education program. Aims are: to study, discuss, and
exchange knowledge, experience, and ideas in the
field of surgical technology; to promote a high
standard of surgical technology performance in the
community for quality patient care; to stimulate interest in continuing education. Local groups sponsor
workshops and institutes. Conducts research.

Handbooks and Manuals

12366 ■ *Applied Survey Data Analysis*
CRC Press
c/o Taylor & Francis Group, LLC
6000 Broken Sound Pkwy., NW
Boca Raton, FL 33487
URL: http://www.crcpress.com

Steven G. Heeringa, Brady T. West and Patricia A. Berglund. 2010. $79.95 (hardback). 487 pages. Provides an intermediate-level statistical overview of the analysis of complex sample survey data.

12367 ■ *Applied Survey Methods: A Statistical Perspective*
John Wiley & Sons, Inc.
111 River St.
Hoboken, NJ 07030-5774
Ph: (201)748-6000
Fax: (201)748-6088
E-mail: info@wiley.com
URL: http://www.wiley.com

Jelke Bethlehem. 2009. $121.00 (hardcover). 375 pages. Provides comprehensive guide to the use of statistical methods for obtaining reliable and practical survey research.

12368 ■ *The Art and Craft of User Research Interviewing*
Rosenfeld Media, LLC
457 Third St., No. 4R
Brooklyn, NY 11215
Ph: (718)568-9756
Fax: (734)661-1655
URL: http://www.rosenfeldmedia.com

Steve Portigal. 2012. Contains guidelines in developing one's skills in research interviewing.

12369 ■ *Cases in Online Interview Research*
SAGE Publications, Inc.
2455 Teller Rd.
Thousand Oaks, CA 91320
Ph: (805)499-0721
Fax: 800-583-2665
Fr: 800-818-7243
E-mail: info@sagepub.com
URL: http://www.sagepub.com

Janet Salmons. 2011. $35.00 (paper). 400 pages. Presents ten cases of research conducted using online interviews, with data collected through text-based, videoconferencing, multichannel meeting, and immersive 3-D environments.

12370 ■ *Collecting Qualitative Data: A Field Manual for Applied Research*
SAGE Publications, Inc.
2455 Teller Rd.
Thousand Oaks, CA 91320
Ph: (805)499-0721
Fax: 800-583-2665
Fr: 800-818-7243
E-mail: info@sagepub.com
URL: http://www.sagepub.com

Greg Guest, Emily E. Namey, and Marilyn L. Mitchell. 2012. $30.00. 256 pages (paperback). 256 pages. Provides beginning, as well as more experienced researchers with a step-by-step guide to collecting and managing qualitative data. Focuses on the three frequently applied forms of qualitative methods: participant observation, in-depth interviews, and focus groups. Includes checklists and tips in using each technique, as well as real-life examples and cases.

12371 ■ *Complex Surveys: A Guide to Analysis Using R*
John Wiley & Sons, Inc.
111 River St.
Hoboken, NJ 07030-5774
Ph: (201)748-6000
Fax: (201)748-6088
E-mail: info@wiley.com
URL: http://www.wiley.com

Thomas Lumley. 2010. $73.50 (paperback). 296 pages. Serves as a guide for applied statisticians and practitioners in the social and health sciences who use statistics in everyday work.

12372 ■ *Conducting Online Surveys*
SAGE Publications
2455 Teller Rd.
Thousand Oaks, CA 91320
Fax: 800-583-2665
Fr: 800-818-7243
URL: http://www.sagepub.com

Valerie M. Sue and Lois A. Ritter. 2011. 264 pages. Serves as a guide to conducting survey research using digital modalities. Includes end-of-chapter exercises.

12373 ■ *Designing and Conducting Your First Interview Project*
Jossey-Bass
989 Market St.
San Francisco, CA 94103-1741
Fax: 888-481-2665
Fr: 888-378-2537
E-mail: jbsubs@jbp.com
URL: http://www.josseybass.com

Bruce K. Friesen. 2010. $40.00 (paperback). 256 pages. Helps develop the skills to conduct an interview. Shows how to organize, analyze and interpret the collected data.

12374 ■ *The Handbook of Online and Social Media Research: Tools and Techniques for Market Researchers*
John Wiley & Sons, Inc.
111 River St.
Hoboken, NJ 07030-5774
Ph: (201)748-6000

Fr: 800-818-7243
E-mail: info@sagepub.com
URL: http://www.sagepub.com

Fax: (201)748-6088
E-mail: info@wiley.com
URL: http://www.wiley.com

Ray Poynter. 2010. $65.00 (hardcover). 464 pages. Serves as reference for today's market researcher. Discusses new techniques in market research via online research communities, blog mining, social networks, mobile research, and predictive markets.

12375 ■ *Handbook of Web Surveys*
John Wiley & Sons, Inc.
111 River St.
Hoboken, NJ 07030-5774
Ph: (201)748-6000
Fax: (201)748-6088
E-mail: info@wiley.com
URL: http://www.wiley.com

Jelke Bethlehem and Silvia Biffignandi. 2011. $149.95 (hardcover). 480 pages. Offers techniques and approaches in creating and conducting web surveys. Discusses the pros and cons of the web survey, as well as common challenges encountered in the data collection process. Includes topics on sampling designs and estimation procedures; weighting techniques; usage of propensity scores; and web panels.

12376 ■ *Interpreting Interviews*
SAGE Publications, Inc.
2455 Teller Rd.
Thousand Oaks, CA 91320
Ph: (805)499-0721
Fax: 800-583-2665
Fr: 800-818-7243
E-mail: info@sagepub.com
URL: http://www.sagepub.com

Mats Alvesson. 2010. $47.00 (paperback); $108.00 (hardcover). 176 pages. Offers interview practitioners and researchers a theoretical framework for conducting and interpreting interviews.

12377 ■ *Interviewing Experts*
Palgrave Macmillan
175 Fifth Ave.
New York, NY 10010
Fax: 800-672-2054
Fr: 888-330-8477
E-mail: customerservice@mpsvirginia.com
URL: http://us.macmillan.com

Alexander Bogner, Beate Littig and Wolfgang Menz. 2009. $100.00 (hardcover). 256 pages. Presents an overview of the theory and practice of expert interviews as standard method of qualitative research.

12378 ■ *Learning in the Field: An Introduction to Quality Research*
SAGE Publications
2455 Teller Rd.
Thousand Oaks, CA 91320
Fax: 800-583-2665
Fr: 800-818-7243
URL: http://www.sagepub.com

Gretchen B. Rossman and Sharon F. Rallis. 2012.

$65.00 (paperback). 392 pages. 3rd edition. Helps the new researcher into the field by explaining the core concepts through theory, research and applied examples.

12379 ■ Marketing Research Tools and Techniques
Oxford University Press
198 Madison Ave.
New York, NY 10016
Ph: (212)726-6000
URL: http://www.oup.com/us/

Nigel Bradley. 2010. $79.95 (paperback). 560 pages. 2nd edition. Provides insight into marketing research. Covers basic tools of marketing research, and evaluates techniques applicable to a specific research. Includes sample questionnaires and case studies in accompanying online resource centre.

12380 ■ Online Interviewing
SAGE Publications, Inc.
2455 Teller Rd.
Thousand Oaks, CA 91320
Ph: (805)499-0721
Fax: 800-583-2665
Fr: 800-818-7243
E-mail: info@sagepub.com
URL: http://www.sagepub.com

Nalita James and Hugh Busher. 2009. $51.00 (paper); $125.00 (hardcover). 176 pages. Provides practical introduction to the challenges and opportunities in designing and conducting online interviews in qualitative research.

12381 ■ Qualitative Research in Education: A User's Guide
SAGE Publications
2455 Teller Rd.
Thousand Oaks, CA 91320
Fax: 800-583-2665
Fr: 800-818-7243
URL: http://www.sagepub.com

Marilyn Lichtman. 2012. $50.00 (paperback). 368 pages. 3rd edition. Covers every stage of the qualitative research process. Contains real-world examples, plus a chapter on the use of social media for data collection, analysis, retrieval and collaboration.

12382 ■ README FIRST for a User's Guide to Qualitative Methods
SAGE Publications
2455 Teller Rd.
Thousand Oaks, CA 91320
Fax: 800-583-2665
Fr: 800-818-7243
URL: http://www.sagepub.com

Lyn Richards and Janice M. Morse. 2012. $55.00 (paperback). 320 pages. 3rd edition. Provides basic information on qualitative inquiry. Offers advice for using qualitative software tools in research planning.

12383 ■ Reflective Interviewing: A Guide to Theory and Practice
SAGE Publications
2455 Teller Rd.
Thousand Oaks, CA 91320
Fax: 800-583-2665
Fr: 800-818-7243
URL: http://www.sagepub.com

Kathryn Roulston. 2010. $49.00 (paperback); $112.00 (hardcover). 216 pages. Provides a theoretical-informed guide for researchers learning how to interview in the social sciences. Serves as guide through the practicalities of designing and conducting an interview study. Includes advice and perspectives from experienced researchers.

12384 ■ Research Methods in Practice: Strategies for Description and Causation
SAGE Publications
2455 Teller Rd.
Thousand Oaks, CA 91320
Fax: 800-583-2665

Fr: 800-818-7243
URL: http://www.sagepub.com

Dahlia K. Remler and Gregg G. Van Ryzin. 2011. $71.00 (paperback). 616 pages. Emphasizes the critical interpretation and practical application of research findings by focusing on causation and real-life data. Reflects current methodological techniques used in interdisciplinary research. Covers strategies for both description and causal estimation.

12385 ■ The SAGE Handbook of Interview Research
SAGE Publications
2455 Teller Rd.
Thousand Oaks, CA 91320
Fax: 800-583-2665
Fr: 800-818-7243
URL: http://www.sagepub.com

Jaber F. Gubrium, James A. Holstein, Amir B. Marvasti and Karyn D. McKinney. 2012. 624 pages. Emphasizes the dynamic, interactional and reflexive dimensions of the research interview. Encourages readers to learn the frameworks and technologies of interviewing.

12386 ■ Strategic Market Research: A Guide to Conducting Research that Drives Businesses
iUniverse
1663 Liberty Dr.
Bloomington, IN 47403
Ph: 800-288-4677
Fax: (812)355-4085
URL: http://www.iuniverse.com

Anne E. Beall. 2010. $9.95 (softcover). 96 pages. Addresses both qualitative and quantitative research, and illustrates real-life examples in conducting strategic market research applicable to businesses and non-profit organizations.

12387 ■ Survey Methodology
John Wiley & Sons, Inc.
111 River St.
Hoboken, NJ 07030-5774
Ph: (201)748-6000
Fax: (201)748-6088
E-mail: info@wiley.com
URL: http://www.wiley.com

Robert M. Groves, Floyd J. Fowler, Jr., Mick P. Couper, James M. Lepkowski, Eleanor Singer and Roger Tourangeau. 2009. $84.95 (paper). 488 pages. Serves as a reference for practicing survey methodologists and any professional who employs survey research methods. Presents new emerging approaches to survey research and provides comprehensive coverage of the major considerations in designing and conducting a sample review.

12388 ■ Survey and Research in the United States
Transaction Publishers Rutgers
35 Berrue Cir.
Piscataway, NJ 08854
Ph: (732)445-2280
Fax: (732)445-3138
E-mail: trans@transactionpub.com
URL: http://www.transactionpub.com

Jean M. Converse. 2009. $49.95 (paperback). 599 pages. Emphasizes the importance of survey research.

12389 ■ Surveys That Work
Rosenfeld Media, LLC
457 Third St., No. 4R
Brooklyn, NY 11215
Ph: (718)568-9756
Fax: (734)661-1655
URL: http://www.rosenfeldmedia.com

Caroline Jarrett. 2012. Provides information on what one needs to know about conducting surveys and acquiring useful data.

ONLINE JOB SOURCES AND SERVICES

12390 ■ Marketing Research Association - Career Center
URL: http://www.marketingresearch.org/career

Description: Offers current job openings and career guide in the field of marketing research. Allows employers to view resumes and post jobs.

12391 ■ Phone Survey Jobs
URL: http://www.phonesurveyjobs.com

Description: Serves as a niche job board that provides listings on telephone survey and other related jobs.

TRADESHOWS

12392 ■ American Association for Public Opinion Annual Conference
American Association for Public Opinion
111 Deer Lake Rd., Ste. 100
Deerfield, IL 60015
Ph: (847)205-2651
Fax: (847)480-9282
URL: http://www.aapor.org

Annual. Features cutting-edge educational sessions, in-depth short courses, informal access to leaders in the field and an informative exhibit hall with representatives from key service and product providers. 2013 May 3-7; Boston, MA; Seaport Boston Hotel and World Trade Center.

12393 ■ Council of American Survey Research Organizations Annual Conference
Council of American Survey Research Organizations
170 N Country Rd., Ste. 4
Port Jefferson, NY 11777
Ph: (631)928-6954
Fax: (631)928-6041
E-mail: casro@casro.org
URL: http://www.casro.org

Annual. Provides an opportunity for chief executives from companies to discuss key industry and business management issues. 2012 October 9-7; Scottsdale, AZ; Four Seasons Resort.

OTHER SOURCES

12394 ■ American Association for Public Opinion
111 Deer Lake Rd., Ste. 100
Deerfield, IL 60015
Ph: (847)205-2651
Fax: (847)480-9282
URL: http://www.aapor.org

Description: Represents the interests of public opinion and survey research professionals. Advances the science and practice of survey and opinion research. Maintains high standards of scientific competence and integrity in conducting, analyzing and interpreting survey data.

12395 ■ Amplitude Research, Inc.
2255 Glades Rd., Ste. 324A
Boca Raton, FL 33431
Ph: (561)948-2142
Fr: 877-225-7950
E-mail: careers@amplituderesearch.net
URL: http://www.amplituderesearch.com

Description: Seeks individuals who possess the skills to join the team of survey and business development professionals.

12396 ■ Council of American Survey Research Organizations
170 N Country Rd., Ste. 4
Port Jefferson, NY 11777
Ph: (631)928-6954

Fax: (631)928-6041
E-mail: casro@casro.org
URL: http://www.casro.org

Description: Represents companies and market research operations in the United States and abroad. Serves as the voice and values of the survey research industry. Promotes a rigorous code of conduct that enhances the image of survey research and protects the public's rights and privacy.

12397 ■ DataDirect
Association to Advance Collegiate Schools of Business
777 S Harbour Island Blvd., Ste. 750
Tampa, FL 33602
Ph: (813)769-6500
Fax: (813)769-6559
URL: http://www.aacsb.edu

Description: Helps conduct annual and need-based surveys to produce reports on a variety of topics. Provides benchmarking tools and research trends within management education.

12398 ■ Market Trends Research, Inc.
PO Box 115
Matheson, CO 80830
Ph: (727)421-6214
E-mail: info@markettrendsresearch.com
URL: http://www.markettrendsresearch.com

Description: Serves as an international market research company that conduct focus groups, surveys, online research, strategic analysis and consulting businesses and not-for-profit organizations.

12399 ■ Mobile Compass
Discovery Research Group
6975 Union Park Ctr., Ste. 450
Midvale, UT 84047
Fr: 800-678-3748
URL: http://www.discoveryresearchgroup.com

Description: Serves as research tool that helps to effectively reach market research respondents who are increasingly difficult to identify.

12400 ■ OMF System
Clayton Wallis Company
19050 Bay St., No. 310
El Verano, CA 95433
URL: http://www.ictcw.com

Description: Serves as a job and competency analysis questionaire that provides a solid framework for position classification, performance management and competency-based programs.

12401 ■ Readex Research
2251 Tower Dr., W
Stillwater, MN 55082
Ph: (651)439-1554
Fax: (651)439-1564
Fr: 800-873-2339
URL: http://www.readexresearch.com

Description: Designs, administers and interprets survey research for publications and associations.

12402 ■ StatPac Survey Software
StatPac Inc.
8609 Lyndale Ave. S, No. 209A
Bloomington, MN 55420
Ph: (715)442-2261
Fax: (715)442-2262
E-mail: admin@statpac.com
URL: http://www.statpac.com

Description: Guides survey researchers in designing and conducting online surveys, telephone interviews, or traditional paper questionnaires.

12403 ■ Streamline Surveys Inc.
1527 Kalaniwai Pl.
Honolulu, HI 96821
Ph: (808)377-9746
E-mail: survey@pixi.com
URL: http://www.streamlinesurveys.com

Description: Serves as an online survey and marketing research firm with paid surveys for respondents. Provides online research services for research design, probability sampling, online survey data collection and quantitative multiviriate statistical data analysis.

12404 ■ Survey Analytics
Survey Analytics, LLC
3518 Fremont Ave. N, Ste. 598
Seattle, WA 98103
Ph: (206)260-3243
Fax: (206)299-9930
Fr: 800-326-5570
URL: http://www.surveyanalytics.com

Description: Offers an enterprise grade research platform for collecting feedback to enable business, governments and consumers to participate and learn from each other.

12405 ■ Survey Console
Survey Analytics, LLC
3518 Fremont Ave. N, Ste. 598
Seattle, WA 98103
Ph: (206)260-3243
Fr: 800-326-5570
URL: http://www.surveyconsole.com

Description: Helps conduct online research to produce meaningful and actionable results.

12406 ■ Survey Sampling International
6 Research Dr.
Shelton, CT 06484
Ph: (203)567-7200
E-mail: info@surveysampling.com
URL: http://www.surveysampling.com

Description: Provides sampling, data collection and data analytic solutions for survey research.

12407 ■ Survey System
Creative Research Systems
411 B St., Ste. 2
Petaluma, CA 94952
Ph: (707)765-1001
URL: http://www.surveysystem.com

Description: Serves as a tool for market researchers, political pollsters, human resource professionals, social scientists, and others who utilize questionnaires. Features sample tables, charts and other reports.

12408 ■ SurveyGizmo Survey Software
SurveyGizmo
4888 Pearl East Cir., Ste. 300W
Boulder, CO 80301
Ph: (720)496-2990
Fr: 800-609-6480
E-mail: support@surveygizmo.com
URL: http://www.surveygizmo.com

Description: Serves as a web-based tool that helps researchers in creating online surveys, questionnaires and forms.

Sources of Help-Wanted Ads

12409 ■ American City and County
Penton Media Inc.
9800 Metcalf Ave.
Overland Park, KS 66212
Ph: (913)341-1300
Fax: (913)967-1898
URL: http://americancityandcounty.com

Monthly. Municipal and county administration magazine.

12410 ■ The American Surveyor
Spatial Media LLC
905 W 7th St., No. 331
Frederick, MD 21701
Ph: (301)620-0784
Fax: (301)695-1538
E-mail: subs@theamericansurveyor.com
URL: http://www.amerisurv.com

Monthly. $29.95/year in U.S.; $36/year in Canada; $72/year for international. Resource for land surveying, measurement and positioning technology.

12411 ■ Architectural Record
McGraw-Hill Inc.
PO Box 182604
Columbus, OH 43218
Ph: (614)430-4000
Fax: (614)759-3749
Fr: 877-833-5524
URL: http://archrecord.construction.com

Monthly. $49.00/year for individuals; $59.00/year for Canada; $109.00/year for other countries. Magazine focusing on architecture.

12412 ■ Builder
Hanley-Wood L.L.C.
1 Thomas Cir. NW, Ste. 600
Washington, DC 20005-5803
Ph: (202)452-0800
Fax: (202)785-1974
E-mail: builder@omeda.com
URL: http://www.hanleywood.com/
    default.aspx?page=magazines

$29.95/year for U.S. and Canada; $54.95/year for U.S. and Canada, 2 years; $192.00/year for other countries. Magazine covering housing and construction industry.

12413 ■ The Municipality
League of Wisconsin Municipalities
122 W Washington Ave., Ste. 300
Madison, WI 53703-2715
Ph: (608)267-2380
Fax: (608)267-0645
Fr: 800-991-5502
URL: http://www.lwm-info.org/

Monthly. Magazine for officials of Wisconsin's local municipal governments.

12414 ■ NAHRO Monitor
National Association of Housing and Redevelopment Officials
630 Eye St. NW
Washington, DC 20001
Ph: (202)289-3500
Fax: (202)289-8181
Fr: 877-866-2476
E-mail: nahro@nahro.org
URL: http://www.nahro.org/nahro_monitor

Description: Biweekly. Disseminates news on low-income housing and community development issues. Intended for member professionals and government officials.

12415 ■ PE & RS Photogrammetric Engineering & Remote Sensing
The Imaging and Geospatial Information Society
5410 Grosvenor Ln., Ste. 210
Bethesda, MD 20814-2160
Ph: (301)493-0290
Fax: (301)493-0208
URL: http://www.asprs.org/PE-RS-Journal/

Monthly. $410.00/year for individuals, first class mail; $426.00/year for Canada, airmail; $420.00/year for other countries, air standard. Peer-reviewed journal covering photogrammetry, remote sensing, geographic information systems, cartography, and surveying, global positioning systems, digital photogrammetry.

12416 ■ Western City
League of California Cities
1400 K St., 4th Fl.
Sacramento, CA 95814
Ph: (916)658-8200
Fax: (916)658-8240
Fr: 800-262-1801
URL: http://www.westerncity.com

Monthly. $39.00/year for individuals; $63.00/year for two years; $52.00/year for other countries; $26.50/year for students. Municipal interest magazine.

Employer Directories and Networking Lists

12417 ■ ABC Today—Associated Builders and Contractors National Membership Directory Issue
Associated Builders and Contractors Inc.
4250 N Fairfax Dr., 9th Fl.
Arlington, VA 22203-1607
Ph: (703)812-2000
Fax: (703)812-8235
URL: http://www.abc.org

Annual, December. $150.00. Publication includes: List of approximately 19,000 member construction contractors and suppliers.

12418 ■ Indiana Society of Professional Engineers—Directory
Indiana Society of Professional Engineers
PO Box 20806
Indianapolis, IN 46220
Ph: (317)255-2267
Fax: (317)255-2530
URL: http://www.indspe.org

Annual, fall. Covers: Member registered engineers, land surveyors, engineering students, and engineers in training. Entries include: Member name, address, phone, type of membership, business information, specialty. Arrangement: Alpha by chapter area.

Handbooks and Manuals

12419 ■ Engineering, Mechanics, and Architecture
Ferguson Publishing
132 W 31st St., 17th Fl.
New York, NY 10001
Fax: 800-678-3633
Fr: 800-322-8755
E-mail: custserv@factsonfile.com
URL: http://www.infobasepublishing.com

Kelly Wiles. 2010. $39.95. 160 pages (hardcover). Serves as a guide for readers interested in switching jobs. Contains useful advice, career tips, interviews and self-asessment questions.

Employment Agencies and Search Firms

12420 ■ CSI Executive Search LLC
9600 Great Hills Trl., Ste. 150W
Austin, TX 78759
Ph: (512)301-1119
Fax: (512)301-5559
Fr: 877-329-1828
E-mail: info@csi-executivesearch.com
URL: http://www.csi-executivesearch.com

Executive search firm that specializes in the following arenas: accounting, engineering, healthcare, information technology, and legal. Utilizes behavioral, performance, retention variable, social intelligence, and cultural assessments to ensure the best candidate/client fit. Works on a retained, retingency, and contingency search basis.

12421 ■ Precision Executive Search
977 E Schuylkill Rd., Ste. 201
Pottstown, PA 19465
Ph: (610)704-4942
E-mail: mbarcus@precision-recruiters.com
URL: http://precision-recruiters.com

Executive search firm specializing in the civil engineering, surveying, planning, and landscape architecture industries.

ONLINE JOB SOURCES AND SERVICES

12422 ■ SurveyorJobs.org
URL: http://www.surveyorjobs.org

Description: Serves as a job board that focuses on surveyor employment opportunities and recruiting.

TRADESHOWS

12423 ■ California Land Surveyors Association Conference
California Land Surveyors Association
526 South E St.
Santa Rosa, CA 95404-5138
Ph: (707)578-6016
Fax: (707)578-4406
E-mail: clsa@californiasurveyors.org
URL: http://www.californiasurveyors.org

Annual. Primary Exhibits: Land surveying equipment, computers, vehicles, software, and two-way communication systems.

OTHER SOURCES

12424 ■ American Congress on Surveying and Mapping (ACSM)
6 Montgomery Village Ave., Ste. 403
Gaithersburg, MD 20879
Ph: (240)632-9716
Fax: (240)632-1321
E-mail: curtis.sumner@acsm.net
URL: http://www.acsm.net

Description: Professionals, technicians, and students in the field of surveying and mapping including surveying of all disciplines, land and geographic information systems, cartography, geodesy, photogrammetry, engineering, geophysics, geography, and computer graphics; American Association for Geodetic Surveying, American Cartographic Association, and National Society of Professional Surveyors. Objectives are to: advance the sciences of surveying and mapping; promote public understanding and use of surveying and mapping; speak on the national level as the collective voice of the profession; provide publications to serve the surveying and mapping community. Member organizations encourage improvement of university and college curricula for surveying and mapping.

12425 ■ ASPRS - The Imaging and Geospatial Information Society
5410 Grosvenor Ln., Ste. 210
Bethesda, MD 20814-2160
Ph: (301)493-0290
Fax: (301)493-0208
E-mail: asprs@asprs.org
URL: http://www.asprs.org

Description: Firms, individuals, government employees and academicians engaged in photogrammetry, photointerpretation, remote sensing, and geographic information systems and their application to such fields as archaeology, geographic information systems, military reconnaissance, urban planning, engineering, traffic surveys, meteorological observations, medicine, geology, forestry, agriculture, construction and topographic mapping. Seeks to advance knowledge and improve understanding of these sciences and promote responsible applications. Offers voluntary certification program open to persons associated with one or more functional area of photogrammetry, remote sensing and GIS. Surveys the profession of private firms in photogrammetry and remote sensing in the areas of products and services.

12426 ■ Associated Builders and Contractors (ABC)
4250 N Fairfax Dr., 9th Fl.
Arlington, VA 22203-1607
Ph: (703)812-2000
Fax: (703)812-8201
E-mail: gotquestions@abc.org
URL: http://www.abc.org

Description: Construction contractors, subcontractors, suppliers and associates. Aims to foster and perpetuate the principles of rewarding construction workers and management on the basis of merit. Sponsors management education programs and craft training; also sponsors apprenticeship and skill training programs. Disseminates technological and labor relations information.

12427 ■ Associated General Contractors of America (AGC)
2300 Wilson Blvd., Ste. 400
Arlington, VA 22201
Ph: (703)548-3118
Fax: (703)548-3119
Fr: 800-242-1767
E-mail: info@agc.org
URL: http://www.agc.org

Description: General construction contractors; subcontractors; industry suppliers; service firms. Provides market services through its divisions. Conducts special conferences and seminars designed specifically for construction firms. Compiles statistics on job accidents reported by member firms. Maintains 65 committees, including joint cooperative committees with other associations and liaison committees with federal agencies.

12428 ■ National Association of Home Builders (NAHB)
1201 15th St. NW
Washington, DC 20005
Ph: (202)266-8200
Fax: (202)266-8400
Fr: 800-368-5242
E-mail: jhoward@nahb.com
URL: http://www.nahb.org

Description: Single and multifamily home builders, commercial builders, and others associated with the building industry. Lobbies on behalf of the housing industry and conducts public affairs activities to increase public understanding of housing and the economy. Collects and disseminates data on current developments in home building and home builders' plans through its Economics Department and nation-wide Metropolitan Housing Forecast. Maintains NAHB Research Center, which functions as the research arm of the home building industry. Sponsors seminars and workshops on construction, mortgage credit, labor relations, cost reduction, land use, remodeling, and business management. Compiles statistics; offers charitable program, spokesman training, and placement service; maintains speakers' bureau, and Hall of Fame. Subsidiaries include the National Council of the Housing Industry. Maintains over 50 committees in many areas of construction; operates National Commercial Builders Council, National Council of the Multifamily Housing Industry, National Remodelers Council, and National Sales and Marketing Council.

12429 ■ National Association of Women in Construction (NAWIC)
327 S Adams St.
Fort Worth, TX 76104
Ph: (817)877-5551
Fax: (817)877-0324
Fr: 800-552-3506
E-mail: nawic@nawic.org
URL: http://www.nawic.org

Description: Seeks to enhance the success of women in the construction industry.

12430 ■ National Center for Construction Education and Research (NCCER)
3600 NW 43rd St., Bldg. G
Gainesville, FL 32606
Ph: (352)334-0911
Fax: (352)334-0932
Fr: 888-622-3720
E-mail: marketing@nccer.org
URL: http://www.nccer.org

Description: Education foundation committed to the development and publication of Contren(TM) Learning Series, the source of craft training, management education and safety resources for the construction industry.

12431 ■ Professional Women in Construction (PWC)
315 E 56th St.
New York, NY 10022-3730
Ph: (212)486-4712
Fax: (212)486-0228
E-mail: pwc@pwcusa.org
URL: http://www.pwcusa.org

Description: Management-level women and men in construction and allied industries; owners, suppliers, architects, engineers, field personnel, office personnel and bonding/surety personnel. Provides a forum for exchange of ideas and promotion of political and legislative action, education and job opportunities for women in construction and related fields; forms liaisons with other trade and professional groups; develops research programs. Strives to reform abuses and to assure justice and equity within the construction industry. Sponsors mini-workshops. Maintains Action Line, which provides members with current information on pertinent legislation and on the association's activities and job referrals.

EMPLOYER DIRECTORIES AND NETWORKING LISTS

12432 ■ Billboard's International Talent and Touring Guide
Crown Publishing Group
1745 Broadway
New York, NY 10019
Ph: (212)782-9000
URL: http://www.billboard.biz/bbbiz/directories/index.jsp
Annual, Latest edition 2010. $149.00 for individuals. Covers: Over 30,000 artists, managers and agents from 69 countries worldwide, including the USA. and Canada; tour facilities and services; venues; entertainers, booking agents, hotels, and others in the entertainment industry; international coverage. Entries include: Company name, address, phone, fax, names and titles of key personnel. Arrangement: Classified by line of business; venues are then geographical. Indexes: Product/service.

12433 ■ Model & Talent Directory
Peter Glenn Publications
235 SE 5th Ave., Ste. R
Delray Beach, FL 33483
Ph: (561)404-4685
Fax: (561)279-4672
Fr: 888-332-6700
URL: http://www.pgdirect.com
Annual, Latest edition 26th. $22.95 for individuals. Covers: Over 1,954 listings of model and talent agencies worldwide. Arrangement: Geographical.

HANDBOOKS AND MANUALS

12434 ■ So You Want to Be a Talent Agent?: Everything You Need to Know to Start Your Own Local Talent Booking Agency
iUniverse, Inc.
1663 Liberty Dr.
Bloomington, IN 47403
Fax: (812)355-4085
Fr: 800-288-4677
URL: http://www.iuniverse.com
Tom Elliott. 2010. $21.95 (paper). 164 pages. Provides a detailed guide to every aspect of establishing and running a small, local talent booking agency. Includes tips on how to find the talent, how to build up a clientele and how to promote yourself in the industry.

OTHER SOURCES

12435 ■ Association of Talent Agents (ATA)
9255 Sunset Blvd., Ste. 930
Los Angeles, CA 90069
Ph: (310)274-0628
Fax: (310)274-5063
E-mail: shellie@agentassociation.com
URL: http://www.agentassociation.com

Description: Talent agencies that have clients in the Screen Actors Guild, American Federation of Television and Radio Artists, Directors Guild of America, Writers Guild of America, East, and Writers Guild of America, West. Negotiates terms of franchise agreements with these guilds and maintains liaison with their representatives. Assists members with contract problems, interpretations, rulings, residual matters, and arbitrations. Employs legal counsel to prepare opinions upon request and to file briefs in arbitrations and labor commission hearings. Maintains liaison with labor commission representatives in San Francisco and Los Angeles, CA, and intervenes on behalf of individual members having special problems. Conducts seminars and symposia.

SOURCES OF HELP-WANTED ADS

12436 ■ *Corporate Business Transactions Monthly*
CCH Inc.
PO Box 4307
Chicago, IL 60680
Fr: 800-248-3248
URL: http://www.cch.com

Monthly. Journal that publishes articles that contribute to professional practice in the area of corporate tax planning and related administration and compliance issues.

12437 ■ *Tax Adviser*
American Institute of Certified Public Accountants
1211 Avenue of the Americas
New York, NY 10036
Ph: (212)596-6200
Fax: (212)596-6213
Fr: 800-362-5066
URL: http://www.aicpa.org

Online magazine.

EMPLOYER DIRECTORIES AND NETWORKING LISTS

12438 ■ *Directory of State Tax Administrators*
Federation of Tax Administrators
442 N Capitol St. NW, Ste. 348
Washington, DC 20001
Ph: (202)624-5890
URL: http://www.taxadmin.org

April 2011. Provides reference and identification of key tax administrators in each jurisdiction. $10.00 for members; $50.00 for non-members.

EMPLOYMENT AGENCIES AND SEARCH FIRMS

12439 ■ Boyce Cunnane Inc.
PO Box 19064
Baltimore, MD 21284-9064
Ph: (410)583-5511
Fax: (410)583-5518
E-mail: bc@cunnane.com
URL: http://www.cunnane.com

Executive search firm.

12440 ■ ET Search Inc.
PO Box 2389
La Jolla, CA 92038
Ph: (858)459-3443

Fax: (858)459-4147
E-mail: ets@etsearch.com
URL: http://www.etsearch.com

Executive search firm focused on the tax industry.

12441 ■ Hasselbach & Company
125 Willow Oak Crt.
Double Oak, TX 75077
Ph: (817)430-4344
Fr: 800-909-8369
E-mail: peter@hasselbach.com
URL: http://www.hasselbach.com

Description: Serves as a full service tax recruiting firm placing individuals at all levels within tax departments.

12442 ■ Pro Advantage Executive Search
381 Park Ave. S, Ste. 1112
New York, NY 10016
Ph: (212)944-0222
Fax: (212)944-2666
E-mail: info@proadvantagejobs.com
URL: http://www.proadvantagejobs.com

Description: Executive recruiting and research firm specializes in financial services industries. Offers career opportunities in the field of accounting, internal auditing, finance, compliance, tax, operations, and marketing.

12443 ■ Raymond Alexander Associates
97 Lackawanna Ave., Ste. 102
Totowa, NJ 07512-2332
Ph: (973)256-1000
Fax: (973)256-5871
E-mail: raa@raymondalexander.com
URL: http://www.raymondalexander.com

Personnel consulting firm conducts executive search services in the specific areas of accounting, tax and finance. Industries served: manufacturing, financial services, and public accounting.

12444 ■ RSR Partners
8 Sound Shore Dr.
Greenwich, CT 06830
Ph: (203)861-7000
Fax: (203)618-7011
URL: http://www.rsrpartners.com

Executive search firm with a second office in New York.

12445 ■ TaxSearch, Inc.
c/o Tony Santiago, Pres.
1459 Stuart Engals Blvd., Ste. 302
Mount Pleasant, SC 29464
Ph: (843)216-7888
Fax: (843)216-7799
E-mail: tony@taxsearchinc.com
URL: http://www.taxsearchinc.com

Description: Serves as an executive search firm specializing in the field of tax professional recruitment. Provides a proprietary database of tax professionals.

ONLINE JOB SOURCES AND SERVICES

12446 ■ FinancialJobBank.com
URL: http://www.financialjobbank.com

Description: Works as a job engine that helps individual to find job openings in the areas of accounting, finance, taxation, banking, and mortgage.

12447 ■ TaxSites.com
URL: http://www.taxsites.com

Description: Provides listings of associations, companies, job opportunities, news, publications, career search and other resources in the fields of tax, accounting and payroll/HR.

12448 ■ TaxTalent.com
URL: http://www.taxtalent.com

Description: Provides career management information and access to other career enhancing tools.

TRADESHOWS

12449 ■ ACFE Fraud Conference & Exhibition
Association of Certified Fraud Examiners
716 West Ave.
Austin, TX 78701
Ph: (512)478-9000
Fax: (512)478-9297
Fr: 800-245-3321
E-mail: info@acfe.com
URL: http://www.fraudconference.com

Annual. Features the latest development in detecting and preventing fraud in organizations.

OTHER SOURCES

12450 ■ Accreditation Council for Accountancy and Taxation (ACAT)
1010 N Fairfax St.
Alexandria, VA 22314-1574
Fax: (703)549-2512
Fr: 888-289-7763
E-mail: info@acatcredentials.org

Description: Strives to raise professional standards and improve the practices of accountancy and taxation. Identifies persons with demonstrated knowledge of the principles and practices of accountancy and taxation. Ensures the continued professional growth of accredited individuals by setting stringent continuing education requirements. Fosters increased recognition for the profession in the public, private, and educational sectors.

12451 ■ Association of Certified Fraud Examiners
716 West Ave.
Austin, TX 78701-2727

Ph: (512)478-9000
Fax: (512)478-9297
Fr: 800-245-3321
E-mail: memberservices@acfe.com
URL: http://www.cfenet.com

Description: Association web site contains Career Center with job databank, giving the user the ability to post jobs and career resources and links. Must be a member of organization in order to access databank.

12452 ■ Council on State Taxation
122 C St. NW, Ste. 330
Washington, DC 20001-2109
Ph: (202)484-5222
Fax: (202)484-5229
E-mail: dlindholm@statetax.org
URL: http://www.cost.org

Description: Seeks to preserve equitable local taxation practices.

12453 ■ Federation of Tax Administrators
442 N Capitol St. NW, Ste. 348
Washington, DC 20001
Ph: (202)624-5890
URL: http://www.taxadmin.org

Description: Represents the interests of state tax administrators. Strives for improvement in the state tax administration field. Provides research and information exchange, training, as well as intergovernmental and interstate coordination.

12454 ■ Institute for Professionals in Taxation
600 Northpark Town Center
1200 Abernathy Rd. NE, Ste. L-2
Atlanta, GA 30328-1040
Ph: (404)240-2300

Fax: (404)240-2315
E-mail: bcook@ipt.org
URL: http://www.ipt.org

Description: Offers networking and other job opportunities.

12455 ■ National Association of Enrolled Agents
1120 Connecticut Ave. NW, Ste. 460
Washington, DC 20036-3953
Ph: (202)822-6232
Fax: (202)822-6270
E-mail: info@naea.org
URL: http://www.naea.org

Description: Professional society. Offers a career center.

12456 ■ National Association of Tax Professionals (NATP)
PO Box 8002
Appleton, WI 54914-8002
Fr: 800-558-3402
E-mail: natp@natptax.com
URL: http://www.natptax.com

Description: Serves professionals who work in all areas of tax practice, including individual practitioners, enrolled agents, certified public accountants, accountants, attorneys and certified financial planners.

12457 ■ National Society of Tax Professionals
910 NE Minnehaha St., Ste. 6
Vancouver, WA 98662
Ph: (360)695-8309
Fax: (360)695-7115
Fr: 800-367-8130
E-mail: taxes@nstp.org
URL: http://nstp.org/index.php

Description: Strives to help tax professionals develop, grow, and enhance their services.

12458 ■ National Tax Association
725 15th St. NW, No. 600
Washington, DC 20005-2109
Ph: (202)737-3325
Fax: (202)737-7308
E-mail: natltax@aol.com
URL: http://www.ntanet.org

Description: Serves as a group of government, corporate, academic, and independent tax professionals. Fosters study and discussion of complex and controversial issues in tax theory, practice and policy, and other aspects of public finance.

12459 ■ Society of Financial Examiners
12100 Sunset Hills Rd., Ste. 130
Reston, VA 20190-3221
Ph: (703)234-4140
Fax: 888-436-8686
Fr: 800-787-7633
URL: http://www.sofe.org

Description: Association web site contains classified advertisements for financial examiner positions as well as links to resources about the profession and an opportunity to enroll in an annual career development seminar. Visitors do not have to be members of the association to view job postings.

12460 ■ Tax Executives Institute
1200 G St. NW, Ste. 300
Washington, DC 20005
Ph: (202)638-5601
Fax: (202)638-5607
E-mail: asktei@tei.org
URL: http://www.tei.org/Pages/default.aspx

Description: Promotes understanding and administration of the federal, state, and local tax laws. Maintains high standards of competence, professionalism, and performance in business tax management and government tax administration. Facilitates interaction and assistance among members and between government tax officials.

Sources of Help-Wanted Ads

12461 ■ About Campus
John Wiley & Sons Inc.
111 River St.
Hoboken, NJ 07030-5773
Ph: (201)748-6000
Fax: (201)748-6088
Fr: 800-825-7550
URL: http://onlinelibrary.wiley.com/journal/10.1002/
(ISSN)1536-06

Bimonthly. $207.00/year for institutions, print only; $267.00/year for institutions, Canada and Mexico, print only; $318.00/year for institutions, other countries, print only; $60.00/year for U.S., Canada, and Mexico, print only; $96.00/year for other countries, print only. Journal focused on the critical issues faced by both student affairs and academic affairs staff as they work on helping students learn.

12462 ■ American Academic
American Federation of Teachers
555 New Jersey Ave. NW
Washington, DC 20001
Ph: (202)879-4400
URL: http://www.aft.org/pubs-reports/american_
academic/index.htm

Higher education policy journal.

12463 ■ Annals of Medicine
Informa Healthcare
52 Vanderbilt Ave., 7th Fl.
New York, NY 10017-3846
Ph: (212)520-2777
URL: http://informahealthcare.com/ann

$595.00/year for institutions; $980.00/year for institutions; $780.00/year for institutions. Journal covering health science and medical education.

12464 ■ Assessment & Evaluation in Higher Education
Routledge Journals
270 Madison Ave.
New York, NY 10016-0601
Ph: (212)216-7800
Fax: (212)563-2269
URL: http://www.tandf.co.uk/journals/titles/
02602938.asp

Bimonthly. $1,316.00/year for institutions, online only; $2,547.00/year for institutions, print + online; $1,462.00/year for individuals, print + online; $2,292.00/year for institutions, online only; $578.00/year for individuals, print only; $314.00/year for individuals, print only. Peer-reviewed journal focusing on publishing papers and reports on all aspects of assessment and evaluation within higher education.

12465 ■ Better
The Johns Hopkins University Press
2715 N Charles St.
Baltimore, MD 21218-4319
Ph: (410)516-6900
Fax: (410)516-6968
URL: http://www.press.jhu.edu/journals/better_
evidence_based_educ

$29.50/year for individuals, print and electronic; $80.00/year for institutions, print and electronic. Magazine for educators and policy makers interested in evidence-based education reform.

12466 ■ Brookings Papers on Education Policy
Brookings Institution Press
1775 Massachusetts Ave. NW
Washington, DC 20036
Ph: (202)797-6000
URL: http://www.brookings.edu/press/Journals/2007/
brookingspapers

$36.00/year for individuals. Journal dealing with all aspects of American education.

12467 ■ Creative Education
Scientific Research Publishing
PO Box 54821
Irvine, CA 92619-4821
E-mail: ce@scirp.org
URL: http://www.scirp.org/journal/ce/

$195.00/year for individuals. Peer-reviewed journal publishing articles on the latest advancements in creative education.

12468 ■ Education & Treatment of Children
West Virginia University Press
139 Stansbury Hall
PO Box 6295
Morgantown, WV 26506
Ph: (304)293-8400
Fax: (304)293-6585
URL: http://www.educationandtreatmentofchildren.net

Quarterly. $85.00/year for institutions; $45.00/year for individuals; $100.00/year for institutions, elsewhere; $60.00/year for individuals, elsewhere. Periodical featuring information concerning the development of services for children and youth. Includes reports written for educators and other child care and mental health providers focused on teaching, training, and treatment effectiveness.

12469 ■ Education Week
Editorial Projects in Education Inc.
6935 Arlington Rd., Ste. 100
Bethesda, MD 20814-5287
Ph: (301)280-3100
Fax: (301)280-3200
Fr: 800-346-1834
E-mail: ew@epe.org
URL: http://www.edweek.org/ew

$90.00/year for individuals, print plus online. Professional newspaper for elementary and secondary school educators.

12470 ■ Educational Research and Evaluation
Routledge Journals
270 Madison Ave.
New York, NY 10016-0601
Ph: (212)216-7800
Fax: (212)563-2269
URL: http://www.tandf.co.uk/journals/titles/
13803611.asp

Bimonthly. $428.00/year for institutions, print + online; $385.00/year for institutions, online only; $165.00/year for individuals, print only; $731.00/year for institutions, print + online; $658.00/year for institutions, online only; $275.00/year for individuals, print only. Peer-reviewed journal on theory and practice.

12471 ■ Environmental Education Research
Routledge Journals
270 Madison Ave.
New York, NY 10016-0601
Ph: (212)216-7800
Fax: (212)563-2269
URL: http://www.tandf.co.uk/journals/titles/
13504622.asp

Bimonthly. $1,373.00/year for institutions, print + online; $1,236.00/year for institutions, online only; $364.00/year for individuals, print only. Journal covering all aspects of environmental education.

12472 ■ Essays in Education
University of South Carolina
471 University Pky.
Aiken, SC 29801
Ph: (803)648-6851
URL: http://www.usca.edu/essays/

Monthly. Journal covering issues that impact and influence education.

12473 ■ Hematology
American Society of Hematology
2021 L St. NW, Ste. 900
Washington, DC 20036
Ph: (202)776-0544
Fax: (202)776-0545
URL: http://asheducationbook.hematologylibrary.org

Annual. $75.00/year for members; $125.00/year for nonmembers. Journal providing continuing medical education for physicians.

12474 ■ Interdisciplinary Journal of Teaching and Learning
Southern University at Baton Rouge
PO Box 9942
Baton Rouge, LA 70813
Ph: (225)711-4500
Fax: (225)771-4400
URL: http://www.subr.edu/CollegeofEducation/
COE%20ONLINE%20Journa

Online academic journal that publishes research and scholarly articles in the field of education and learning.

12475 ■ The International Electronic Journal of Health Education
American Alliance for Health, Physical Education, Recreation & Dance
1900 Association Dr.
Reston, VA 20191-1598
Ph: (703)476-3400
Fax: (703)476-9527
Fr: 800-213-7193
URL: http://www.aahperd.org/aahe/publications/iejhe/
Annual. Free, health education professionals and students. Journal promoting health through education and other systematic strategies.

12476 ■ International Journal of Early Years Education
Routledge Journals
270 Madison Ave.
New York, NY 10016-0601
Ph: (212)216-7800
Fax: (212)563-2269
URL: http://www.tandf.co.uk/journals/titles/09669760.asp
$705.00/year for institutions, online only; $783.00/year for institutions, print + online; $271.00/year for individuals, print only. Journal focusing on education world-wide.

12477 ■ International Journal of Inclusive Education
Routledge Journals
270 Madison Ave.
New York, NY 10016-0601
Ph: (212)216-7800
Fax: (212)563-2269
URL: http://www.tandf.co.uk/journals/titles/13603116.asp
$589.00/year for individuals, print only; $1,135.00/year for institutions, online only; $1,261.00/year for individuals, print + online; $355.00/year for individuals, print only; $694.00/year for institutions, online only; $771.00/year for institutions, print + online. Journal providing information on the nature of schools, universities and technical colleges for the educators and educational policy-makers.

12478 ■ International Journal of Leadership in Education
Routledge
711 3 Ave., 8 Fl.
New York, NY 10016
Ph: (212)216-7800
Fax: (212)563-2269
Fr: 800-634-7064
E-mail: ijle@txstate.edu
URL: http://www.tandf.co.uk/journals/tf/13603124.html
Quarterly. $240.00/year for individuals, print only; $612.00/year for institutions, online only; $680.00/year for institutions, print and online; $408.00/year for institutions, print and online; $367.00/year for institutions, online only; $142.00/year for individuals, print only. Journal dealing with leadership in education.

12479 ■ International Journal of Progressive Education
International Journal of Progressive Education
c/o Alex Jean-Charles, PhD, Asst. Mng. Ed.
320 Fitzelle Hall, Ravine Pky.
Oneonta, NY 13820
URL: http://www.inased.org/ijpe.htm
$35.00/year for members; $45.00/year for individuals; $140.00/year for institutions, library; $35.00/year for students; $25.00/year for single issue; $50.00/year for students, other countries. Peer-reviewed online journal that aims to create an open and continuing dialogue about current educational issues and future conceptions of educational theory.

12480 ■ International Journal of Whole Schooling
Whole Schooling Press
Wayne State University
217 Education
Detroit, MI 48202
URL: http://www.wholeschooling.net/Journal_of_Whole_Schooling/IJW

Free. International, refereed academic journal dedicated to exploring ways to improve learning and schooling for all children.

12481 ■ Journal of Academic Leadership
Academic Leadership
600 Park St.
Rarick Hall 219
Hays, KS 67601-4099
Ph: (785)628-4547
URL: http://www.academicleadership.org/
Journal focusing on the leadership issues in the academic world.

12482 ■ Journal of Cases in Educational Leadership
Sage Publications Inc.
2455 Teller Rd.
Thousand Oaks, CA 91320-2218
Ph: (805)499-9774
Fax: (805)583-2665
Fr: 800-818-7243
URL: http://jel.sagepub.com
Quarterly. $411.00/year for institutions, e-access; $94.00/year for individuals, e-access. Journal covering cases appropriate for use in programs that prepare educational leaders.

12483 ■ Journal of Curriculum and Supervision
Association for Supervision and Curriculum Development
1703 N Beauregard St.
Alexandria, VA 22311-1714
Ph: (703)578-9600
Fax: (703)575-5400
Fr: 800-933-2723
URL: http://www.ascd.org/publications/jcs/fall2002/On_Community.a
Scholarly journal focusing on curriculum and supervision.

12484 ■ Journal of Direct Instruction
Association for Direct Instruction
PO Box 10252
Eugene, OR 97440
Ph: (541)485-1293
Fax: (541)868-1397
Fr: 800-995-2464
URL: http://www.adihome.org/index.php?option=com_content&view=art
Quarterly. Included in membership. Journal covering education.

12485 ■ Journal of Language, Identity, and Education
Routledge Journals
270 Madison Ave.
New York, NY 10016-0601
Ph: (212)216-7800
Fax: (212)563-2269
URL: http://www.tandf.co.uk/journals/titles/15348458.asp
$316.00/year for institutions, print + online; $284.00/year for institutions, online; $43.00/year for individuals, print + online; $527.00/year for institutions, print + online; $474.00/year for institutions, online; $71.00/year for individuals, print + online; $421.00/year for institutions, print + online; $379.00/year for institutions, online; $57.00/year for individuals, print + online. Scholarly, interdisciplinary journal covering issues in language, identity and education worldwide for academics, educators and policy specialists in a variety of disciplines, and others.

12486 ■ Journal of Latinos and Education
Routledge Journals
270 Madison Ave.
New York, NY 10016-0601
Ph: (212)216-7800
Fax: (212)563-2269
URL: http://www.tandf.co.uk/journals/titles/15348431.asp

Quarterly. $286.00/year for institutions, print + online; $257.00/year for institutions, online; $38.00/year for individuals, print + online; $480.00/year for institutions, print + online; $432.00/year for institutions, online; $63.00/year for individuals, print + online; $331.00/year for institutions, print + online; $343.00/year for institutions, online; $51.00/year for individuals, print + online. Scholarly, multidisciplinary journal covering educational issues that impact Latinos for researchers, teaching professionals, academics, scholars, institutions, and others.

12487 ■ Journal of Learning Disabilities
Sage Publications Inc.
2455 Teller Rd.
Thousand Oaks, CA 91320-2218
Ph: (805)499-9774
Fax: (805)583-2665
Fr: 800-818-7243
URL: http://www.sagepub.com/journalsProdDesc.nav?ct_p=boardsΠ
Bimonthly. $77.00/year for individuals, print & e-access; $260.00/year for institutions, print & e-access; $255.00/year for institutions, print only; $234.00/year for institutions, e-access. Special education journal.

12488 ■ Journal of STEM Education
Auburn University
9088 Haley Ctr.
Auburn, AL 36849
Ph: (334)844-9088
Fax: (334)844-9027
URL: http://ojs.jstem.org/index.php?journal=JSTEM
Semiannual. Journal for educators in Science, Technology, Engineering, and Mathematics (STEM) education.

12489 ■ Leadership and Policy in Schools
Routledge Journals
270 Madison Ave.
New York, NY 10016-0601
Ph: (212)216-7800
Fax: (212)563-2269
URL: http://www.tandf.co.uk/journals/titles/15700763.asp
Quarterly. $567.00/year for institutions, print and online; $260.00/year for individuals, print only; $510.00/year for institutions, online only. Journal providing information about leadership and policy in primary and secondary education.

12490 ■ NJEA Review
New Jersey Education Association
180 W State St.
PO Box 1211
Trenton, NJ 08607-1211
Ph: (609)599-4561
Fax: (609)392-6321
E-mail: njeareview@njea.org
URL: http://www.njea.org/page.aspx?z=1094&pz=8
Monthly. $250.00/year for nonmembers. Educational journal for public school employees.

12491 ■ Oxford Review of Education
Routledge Journals
270 Madison Ave.
New York, NY 10016-0601
Ph: (212)216-7800
Fax: (212)563-2269
URL: http://www.tandf.co.uk/journals/titles/03054985.asp
$709.00/year for institutions, print + online; $1,224.00/year for institutions, print + online; $249.00/year for individuals, print only; $454.00/year for individuals, print only. Journal covering advance study of education.

12492 ■ School Effectiveness and School Improvement
Routledge
711 3 Ave., 8 Fl.
New York, NY 10016

Ph: (212)216-7800
Fax: (212)563-2269
Fr: 800-634-7064
URL: http://www.tandf.co.uk/journals/titles/
    09243453.asp

Quarterly. $387.00/year for institutions, print and on-line; $348.00/year for institutions, online only; $186.00/year for individuals, print only; $660.00/year for institutions, print and online; $594.00/year for institutions, online only; $312.00/year for individuals, print only. Journal focusing on educational progress of all students.

12493 ■ Strategies
American Alliance for Health, Physical Education,
Recreation & Dance
1900 Association Dr.
Reston, VA 20191-1598
Ph: (703)476-3400
Fax: (703)476-9527
Fr: 800-213-7193
E-mail: strategies@aahperd.org
URL: http://www.aahperd.org/naspe/publications/
    journals/strategie

Bimonthly. $130.00/year for U.S. and Canada, institutions, schools & libraries; print & online; $50.00/year for U.S. and Canada, add $5 GST; $62.00/year for other countries, schools & libraries, print & online; $130.00/year for institutions, other countries, schools & libraries, online; $142.00/year for institutions, other countries, schools & libraries, print; $162.00/year for institutions, other countries, schools & libraries, print & online. Peer-reviewed journal providing practical, hands-on information to physical educators and coaches.

12494 ■ Teaching Exceptional Children
Council for Exceptional Children
2900 Crystal Dr., Ste. 1000
Arlington, VA 22202
Ph: (703)620-3660
Fax: (703)264-9494
Fr: 888-232-7733
URL: http://www.cec.sped.org/Content/
    NavigationMenu/Publications2

$90.00/year for individuals, print; $152.00/year for two years, print; $101.00/year for Canada, print; $169.00/year for two years, Canada; $197.00/year for institutions, print; $332.00/year for two years, print; $208.00/year for institutions, Canada, print; $236.00/year for institutions, other countries, print; $399.00/year for two years, institutional (print); $225.00/year for institutions, Canada, print and online. Peer-reviewed journal exploring practical methods for teaching students who have exceptionalities and those who are gifted and talented.

12495 ■ Teaching/K-8
Teaching/K-8
40 Richards Ave.
Norwalk, CT 06854
Ph: (203)855-2650
Fr: 800-249-9363
URL: http://www.essentiallearningproducts.com

$16.00/year for individuals; $4.50/year for single issue. Magazine for elementary teachers.

12496 ■ Teaching and Learning in Nursing
Elsevier Science Inc.
360 Park Ave. S
New York, NY 10010-1710
Ph: (212)989-5800
Fax: (212)633-3990
Fr: 888-437-4636
URL: http://www.elsevier.com/wps/find/
    journaldescription.cws_home

Quarterly. $232.00/year for institutions, other countries; $134.00/year for other countries; $160.00/year for institutions; $91.00/year for individuals. Journal devoted to associate degree nursing education and practice.

12497 ■ Tech Directions
Prakken Publications Inc.
832 Phoenix Dr.
Ann Arbor, MI 48108
Ph: (734)975-2800
Fax: (734)975-2787
Fr: 800-530-9673
E-mail: tdedit@techdirections.com
URL: http://www.techdirections.com

Monthly. $30.00/year for individuals, U.S.; $47.00/year for institutions; $50.00/year for other countries; $100.00/year for individuals, domestic. Magazine covering issues, programs, and projects in industrial education, technology education, trade and industry, and vocational-technical career education. Articles are geared for teacher and administrator use and reference from elementary school through postsecondary levels.

12498 ■ Theory and Research in Education
Sage Publications Inc.
2455 Teller Rd.
Thousand Oaks, CA 91320-2218
Ph: (805)499-9774
Fax: (805)583-2665
Fr: 800-818-7243
URL: http://www.sagepub.com/
    journalsProdDesc.nav?prodId=Journal20

$546.00/year for institutions, print and e-access; $491.00/year for institutions, e-access; $535.00/year for institutions, print; $85.00/year for individuals, print; $196.00/year for single issue, institutional; $37.00/year for single issue, individual. Interdisciplinary journal covering normative and theoretical issues concerning education including multi-faceted philosophical analysis of moral, social, political and epistemological problems and issues arising from educational practice.

EMPLOYER DIRECTORIES AND NETWORKING LISTS

12499 ■ Christian Schools International—Directory
Christian Schools International
3350 E Paris Ave. SE
Grand Rapids, MI 49512-2907
Ph: (616)957-1070
Fax: (616)957-5022
Fr: 800-635-8288
URL: http://www.store.csionline.org/index.php?main_
    page=index&cPath=

Annual, Latest edition 2007-2008. $15.00 for members. Covers: Nearly 450 Reformed Christian elementary and secondary schools; related associations; societies without schools. Entries include: For schools—School name, address, phone; name, title, and address of officers; names of faculty members. Arrangement: Geographical.

12500 ■ Directory of Public School Systems in the U.S.
American Association for Employment in Education
3040 Riverside Dr., Ste. 117
Columbus, OH 43221
Ph: (614)485-1111
Fax: (360)244-7802
E-mail: office@aaee.org
URL: http://www.aaee.org/

Annual, Winter; latest edition 2004-2005 edition. $55.00 for members; $80.00 for nonmembers. Covers: About 14,000 public school systems in the United States and their administrative personnel. Entries include: System name, address, phone, website address, name and title of personnel administrator, levels taught and approx. Student population. Arrangement: Geographical by state.

12501 ■ Ganley's Catholic Schools in America—Elementary/Secondary/College & University
Fisher Publishing Co.
PO Box 5729
Sun City West, AZ 85376

Ph: (623)328-8326
URL: http://www.ganleyscatholicschools.com

Annual, summer; Latest edition 38th, 2010. $67.00 for individuals. Covers: over 8,400 Catholic K-12 Schools. Arrangement: Geographical by state, then alphabetical by Diocese name.

12502 ■ Handbook of Private Schools
Porter Sargent Publishers Inc.
11 Beacon St., Ste. 1400
Boston, MA 02108-3099
Ph: (617)523-1670
Fax: (617)523-1021
Fr: 800-342-7470
URL: http://www.portersargent.com

Annual, latest edition 92nd, 2011-2012. $99.00 for individuals. Covers: More than 1,700 elementary and secondary boarding and day schools in the United States. Entries include: School name, address, phone, fax, E-mail, URL, type of school (boarding or day), sex and age range, names and titles of administrators, grades offered, academic orientation, curriculum, new admissions yearly, tests required for admission, enrollment and faculty, graduate record, number of alumni, tuition and scholarship figures, summer session, plant evaluation and endowment, date of establishment, calendar, association membership, description of school's offerings and history, test score averages, uniform requirements, geographical, and demographic date. Arrangement: Geographical. Indexes: Alphabetical by school name, cross indexed by state, region, grade range, sexes accepted, school features and enrollment.

12503 ■ Independent Schools Association of the Southwest—Membership List
Independent Schools Association of the Southwest
Energy Sq., 505 N Big Spring St., Ste. 406
Midland, TX 79701
Ph: (432)684-9550
Fax: (432)684-9401
Fr: 800-688-5007
URL: http://www.isasw.org

Annual, August. Covers: Over 84 schools located in Arizona, Kansas, Louisiana, Mexico, New Mexico, Oklahoma, and Texas enrolling over 38,000 students. Entries include: School name, address, phone, chief administrative officer, structure, and enrollment. Arrangement: Geographical. Indexes: Alphabetical.

12504 ■ MDR's School Directories
Market Data Retrieval
6 Armstrong Rd., Ste. 301
Shelton, CT 06484-4722
Ph: (203)926-4800
Fax: (203)926-1826
Fr: 800-333-8802
URL: http://www.schooldata.com/mdrdir.asp

Annual, Latest edition 2008-2009. Covers: Over 90,000 public, 8,000 Catholic, and 15,000 other private schools (grades K-12) in the United States; over 15,000 school district offices, 76,000 school librarians; and 27,000 media specialists, 33,000 technology coordinators. Includes names of over 165,000 school district administrators and staff members in county and state education administration. Entries include: District name and address; telephone and fax number; number of schools; number of teachers in the district; district enrollment; special Ed students; limited-English proficient students; minority percentage by race, college bound students; expenditures per student for instructional materials; poverty level; title 1 dollars; site-based management; district open/close dates; construction indicator; technologies and quantities; district-level administrators, *new superintendents shaded*; school name and address—new public shaded; telephone and fax number; principal new principal shaded; librarian, media specialist and technology coordinator; grade span; special programs and school type; student enrollment; technologies and quantities (instructional computer brand noting predominant brand); Multi-Media Computers; Internet connection or access; Tech Sophistication Index. Arrangement:

Geographical. Indexes: District County; District Personnel; Principal; New Public Schools and Key Personnel; District and School Telephone; District URLs.

12505 ■ National Directory for Employment in Education
American Association for Employment in Education
3040 Riverside Dr., Ste. 117
Columbus, OH 43221
Ph: (614)485-1111
Fax: (360)244-7802
URL: http://www.aaee.org/

Annual, winter; latest edition 2008-2009. $20.00 for nonmembers; $10.00 for members. Covers: about 600 placement offices maintained by teacher-training institutions and 300 school district personnel officers and/or superintendents responsible for hiring professional staff. Entries include: Institution name, address, phone, contact name, email address, and website. Arrangement: Geographical. Indexes: Personal name, subject-field of teacher training, institutions which provide vacancy bulletins and placement services to non-enrolled students.

12506 ■ Private Independent Schools
Bunting and Lyon Inc.
615 Broad Swamp Rd.
Cheshire, CT 06410
Ph: (203)668-1897
Fax: (203)269-8908
URL: http://www.buntingandlyon.com

Annual, Latest edition 2010. $115.00 for individuals. Covers: 1,200 English-speaking elementary and secondary private schools and summer programs in North America and abroad. Entries include: School name, address, phone, fax, e-mail, website, enrollment, tuition and other fees, financial aid information, administrator's name and educational background, director of admission, regional accreditation, description of programs, curriculum, activities, learning differences grid. Arrangement: Geographical. Indexes: School name; geographical. Summer programs, general classification grid, learning differences reference grid.

HANDBOOKS AND MANUALS

12507 ■ Opportunities in Child Care Careers
The McGraw-Hill Companies
PO Box 182604
Columbus, OH 43272
Fax: (614)759-3749
Fr: 877-883-5524
E-mail: customer.service@mcgraw-hill.com
URL: http://www.mhprofessional.com/
    product.php?isbn=0071467661

Renee Wittenberg. 2006. $13.95 (paper). 160 pages. Discusses various job opportunities and how to secure a position. Illustrated.

12508 ■ Opportunities in Teaching Careers
The McGraw-Hill Companies
PO Box 182604
Columbus, OH 43272
Fax: (614)759-3749
Fr: 877-883-5524
E-mail: customer.service@mcgraw-hill.com
URL: http://www.mhprofessional.com/
    product.php?isbn=0071438173

Janet Fine. 2005. $13.95 (paper). 160 pages. Discusses licensing and accreditation programs, sources of placement information, job-seeking correspondence, selection procedures, and paths to advancement. Also covers professional associations, non-traditional teaching opportunities, and jobs abroad.

12509 ■ Teaching for Intellectual and Emotional Learning (TIEL): A Model for Creating Powerful Curriculum
Rowman & Littlefield Education
c/o Rowman & Littlefield Publishing Group
4501 Forbes Blvd., Ste. 200
Lanham, MD 20706
Ph: (301)459-3366
Fax: (301)429-5748
E-mail: customercare@rowman.com
URL: http://rowman.com

Christy Folsom. 2009. $90.00 (hardback); $36.95 (paperback). 310 pages. Educates teachers in developing standards-based curriculum that includes social-emotional learning.

ONLINE JOB SOURCES AND SERVICES

12510 ■ Teacher Aide Jobs
URL: http://www.teacheraidejobs.com

Description: Focuses on teacher aide employment opportunities and candidate recruiting.

12511 ■ WantToTeach.com
URL: http://www.wanttoteach.com

Description: Serves as an education website to search for administrative, instructional and support openings throughout the United States. Features job openings and job fairs and allows access to various education resources.

OTHER SOURCES

12512 ■ American Montessori Society (AMS)
281 Park Ave. S
New York, NY 10010-6102
Ph: (212)358-1250
Fax: (212)358-1256
E-mail: ams@amshq.org
URL: http://www.amshq.org

Description: School affiliates and teacher training affiliates; heads of schools, teachers, parents, non-Montessori educators, and other interested individuals dedicated to stimulating the use of the Montessori teaching approach and promoting better education for all children. Seeks to meet demands of growing interest in the Montessori approach to early learning. Assists in establishing schools; supplies information and limited services to member schools in other countries. Maintains school consultation and accreditation service; provides information service; assists research and gathers statistical data; offers placement service. Maintains Montessori and related materials exhibit.

12513 ■ National Association of Independent Schools (NAIS)
1620 L St. NW, Ste. 1100
Washington, DC 20036-5695
Ph: (202)973-9700
Fax: (202)973-9790
Fr: 800-793-6701
E-mail: bassett@nais.org
URL: http://www.nais.org

Description: Independent elementary and secondary school members; regional associations of independent schools and related associations. Provides curricular and administrative research and services. Conducts educational programs; compiles statistics.

12514 ■ National Community Education Association (NCEA)
3929 Old Lee Hwy., No. 91-A
Fairfax, VA 22030-2401
Ph: (703)359-8973
Fax: (703)359-0972
E-mail: ncea@ncea.com
URL: http://www.ncea.com

Description: Community school directors, principals, superintendents, professors, teachers, students, and laypeople. Promotes and establishes community schools as an integral part of the educational plan of every community. Emphasizes community and parent involvement in the schools, lifelong learning, and enrichment of K-12 and adult education. Serves as a clearinghouse for the exchange of ideas and information, and the sharing of efforts. Offers leadership training.

12515 ■ Overseas Employment Opportunities for Educators: Department of Defense Dependents Schools
DIANE Publishing Co.
PO Box 617
Darby, PA 19023-0617
Fr: 800-782-3833
URL: http://www.dianepublishing.net

Barry Leonard, editor. $20.00. 52 pages. An introduction to teachings positions in the Dept. of Defense Dependents Schools (DoDDS), a worldwide school system, operated by the DoD in 14 countries.

SOURCES OF HELP-WANTED ADS

12516 ■ Customer Interaction Solutions
Technology Marketing Corp.
800 Connecticut Ave, 1st Fl. E.
Norwalk, CT 06854
Ph: (203)852-6800
Fax: (203)866-3326
Fr: 800-243-6002
URL: http://www.tmcnet.com/call-center/
Monthly. Publication covering issues in the telecommunications industry.

12517 ■ IEEE Transactions on Communications
IEEE Electron Devices Society
445 Hoes Ln.
Piscataway, NJ 08854-4141
Ph: (732)562-3926
Fax: (732)235-1626
URL: http://ieeexplore.ieee.org/xpl/RecentIssue.jsp?punumber=26
Monthly. Journal relating to telecommunications.

12518 ■ Journal of Municipal Telecommunications Policy
National Association of Telecommunications Officers and Advisors
3213 Duke St., Ste. 695
Alexandria, VA 22314
Ph: (703)519-8035
Fax: (703)997-7080
URL: http://www.natoa.org/about/history.html
Quarterly. $10.00/year for members; $15.00/year for nonmembers. Professional journal covering issues for the telecommunications industry.

EMPLOYER DIRECTORIES AND NETWORKING LISTS

12519 ■ American Teleservices Association—Membership Directory and Resource Guide
American Teleservices Association
3815 River Crossing Pkwy., Ste. 20
Indianapolis, IN 46240
Ph: (317)816-9336
Fax: (317)218-0323
URL: http://www.ataconnect.org/public/resourcecenter/resourceguid
Annual, Latest edition 2010. $300.00 for nonmembers; free for members. Covers: Member companies in the teleservice industry; in-house call centers, services agencies, consultants and suppliers. Entries include: Company name, address, phone, name and title of contact, product or service provided, branch office location. Arrangement: Alphabetical, geographical, by business type. Indexes: Company, international/state member users of TM services, including agencies, consultants, and suppliers.

12520 ■ Quirk's Marketing Research Review—Telephone Interviewing Facilities Directory Issue
Quirk Enterprises Inc.
4662 Slater Rd.
Eagan, MN 55122
Ph: (651)379-6200
URL: http://www.quirks.com
Annual, April. Publication includes: List of more than 800 telephone interviewing facilities that conduct marketing research projects. Entries include: Company name, address, phone, fax, description of interviewing stations. Arrangement: Geographical. Indexes: Geographical.

HANDBOOKS AND MANUALS

12521 ■ Careers in Marketing
The McGraw-Hill Companies
PO Box 182604
Columbus, OH 43272
Fax: (614)759-3749
Fr: 877-883-5524
E-mail: customer.service@mcgraw-hill.com
URL: http://www.mhprofessional.com/product.php?isbn=0071493123
Leslie Stair. 2008. $16.95 (paper). 192 pages. Surveys career opportunities in marketing and related areas such as marketing research, product development, and sales promotion. Includes a description of the work, places of employment, employment outlook, trends, and salaries. Offers job hunting advice.

12522 ■ Opportunities in Direct Marketing
The McGraw-Hill Companies
PO Box 182604
Columbus, OH 43272
Fax: (614)759-3749
Fr: 877-883-5524
E-mail: customer.service@mcgraw-hill.com
URL: http://www.mhprofessional.com/product.php?isbn=0071493085
Anne Basye. 2008. $14.95 (paper). 160 pages. Examines opportunities with direct marketers, catalog companies, direct marketing agencies, telemarketing firms, mailing list brokers, and database marketing companies. Describes how to prepare for a career in direct marketing and how to break into the field. Includes sources of short-term professional training.

EMPLOYMENT AGENCIES AND SEARCH FIRMS

12523 ■ Career Development Services
150 State St.
Rochester, NY 14614
Ph: (585)244-0765
Fr: 800-736-6710
E-mail: info@careerdev.org
URL: http://www.careerdev.org
Employment agency.

12524 ■ The Esquire Staffing Group Ltd.
1 S Wacker Dr., Ste. 1616
Chicago, IL 60606-4616
Ph: (312)795-4300
URL: http://www.esquirestaffing.com
Employment agency. Fills permanent as well as temporary openings.

ONLINE JOB SOURCES AND SERVICES

12525 ■ Marketing Research Association - Career Center
URL: http://www.marketingresearch.org/career
Description: Offers current job openings and career guide in the field of marketing research. Allows employers to view resumes and post jobs.

12526 ■ Spherion
2050 Spectrum Blvd.
Fort Lauderdale, FL 33309
Ph: (954)308-7600
Fr: 800-774-3746
E-mail: help@spherion.com
URL: http://www.spherion.com
Description: Recruitment firm specializing in accounting and finance, sales and marketing, interim executives, technology, engineering, retail and human resources.

OTHER SOURCES

12527 ■ International Customer Service Association (ICSA)
1110 South Ave., Ste. No. 50
Staten Island, NY 10314
Ph: (374)273-1303
E-mail: info@icsatoday.org
URL: http://www.icsa.com
Description: Customer service professionals in public and private sectors united to develop the theory and understanding of customer service and management. Goals are to: promote professional development; standardize terminology and phrases; provide career counseling and placement services; establish hiring guidelines, performance standards and job descriptions. Provides a forum for shared problems and solutions. Compiles statistics.

SOURCES OF HELP-WANTED ADS

12528 ■ AIE Perspectives Newsmagazine
American Institute of Engineers
4630 Appian Way, Ste. 206
El Sobrante, CA 94803-1875
Ph: (510)758-6240
Fax: (510)758-6240
URL: http://www.members-aie.org

Monthly. Professional magazine covering engineering.

12529 ■ Engineering
Scientific Research Publishing
PO Box 54821
Irvine, CA 92619-4821
E-mail: eng@scirp.org
URL: http://www.scirp.org/journal/eng/

Monthly. $708.00/year for individuals. Peer-reviewed journal publishing articles on the latest advancements in engineering.

12530 ■ Engineering Conferences International Symposium Series
Berkeley Electronic Press
2809 Telegraph Ave., Ste. 202
Berkeley, CA 94705-1167
Ph: (510)665-1200
Fax: (510)665-1201
URL: http://services.bepress.com/eci/

Journal focusing on advance engineering science.

12531 ■ ENR: Engineering News-Record
McGraw-Hill Inc.
PO Box 182604
Columbus, OH 43218
Ph: (614)430-4000
Fax: (614)759-3749
Fr: 877-833-5524
URL: http://enr.construction.com/Default.asp

Weekly. $49.00/year for individuals, print; $89.00/year for Canada, print; $125.00/year for other countries, print. Magazine focusing on engineering and construction.

12532 ■ High Technology Careers Magazine
HTC
4701 Patrick Henry Dr., No. 1901
Santa Clara, CA 95054
Fax: (408)567-0242
URL: http://www.hightechcareers.com

Bimonthly. $29.00/year; $35.00/year for Canada; $85.00/year for out of country. Magazine (tabloid) containing employment opportunity information for the engineering and technical community.

12533 ■ InterJournal
New England Complex Systems Institute
283 Main St., Ste. 319
Cambridge, MA 02142

Ph: (617)547-4100
Fax: (617)661-7711
URL: http://www.interjournal.org/

Journal covering the fields of science and engineering.

12534 ■ Journal of Women and Minorities in Science and Engineering
Begell House Inc.
50 Cross Hwy.
Redding, CT 06896
Ph: (203)938-1300
Fax: (203)938-1304
URL: http://www.begellhouse.com/journals/
00551c876cc2f027

$248.00/year for institutions. Peer-reviewed journal featuring innovative ideas and programs for classroom teachers, scientific studies, and formulation of concepts related to the education, recruitment, and retention of under-represented groups in science and engineering.

12535 ■ NSBE Magazine
NSBE Publications
205 Daingerfield Rd.
Alexandria, VA 22314
Ph: (703)549-2207
Fax: (703)683-5312
URL: http://www.nsbe.org/News-Media/Magazines/
About-NSBE-Magazine

$20.00/year for individuals; $35.00/year for other countries; $15.00/year for students. Journal providing information on engineering careers, self-development, and cultural issues for recent graduates with technical majors.

12536 ■ Oral & Craniofacial Tissue Engineering
Quintessence Publishing Company Inc.
4350 Chandler Dr.
Hanover Park, IL 60133-6763
Ph: (630)736-3600
Fax: (630)736-3633
Fr: 800-621-0387
URL: http://www.quintpub.com/journals/octe/
gp.php?journal_name=OC

Quarterly. Journal covering multiple disciplinary lines involving specialties of both dentistry and medicine.

12537 ■ PE
National Society of Professional Engineers
1420 King St.
Alexandria, VA 22314
Ph: (703)684-2800
Fax: (703)684-4875
URL: http://www.nspe.org/PEmagazine/index.html

Monthly. Magazine (tabloid) covering professional, legislative, and techology issues for an engineering audience.

12538 ■ SWE, Magazine of the Society of Women Engineers
Society of Women Engineers
120 S La Salle St., Ste. 1515
Chicago, IL 60603
Ph: (312)596-5223
Fr: 877-793-4636
URL: http://societyofwomenengineers.swe.org/
index.php

Quarterly. $30.00/year for nonmembers. Magazine for engineering students and for women and men working in the engineering and technology fields. Covers career guidance, continuing development and topical issues.

12539 ■ Tissue Engineering
Mary Ann Liebert Inc. Publishers
140 Huguenot St., 3rd Fl.
New Rochelle, NY 10801-5215
Ph: (914)740-2100
Fax: (914)740-2101
Fr: 800-654-3237
E-mail: info@liebertpub.com
URL: http://www.liebertpub.com

Monthly. Peer-reviewed journal that focuses on the engineering of new biologic tissues. The official journal of the Tissue Engineering and Regenerative Medicine International Society.

12540 ■ WEPANEWS
Women in Engineering Programs & Advocates Network
1901 E Asbury Ave., Ste. 220
Denver, CO 80208
Ph: (303)871-4643
Fax: (303)871-4628
E-mail: dmatt@wepan.org
URL: http://www.wepan.org

Description: 2/year. Seeks to provide greater access for women to careers in engineering. Includes news of graduate, undergraduate, freshmen, pre-college, and re-entry engineering programs for women. Recurring features include job listings, faculty, grant, and conference news, international engineering program news, action group news, notices of publications available, and a column titled Kudos.

12541 ■ Woman Engineer
Equal Opportunity Publications, Inc.
445 Broadhollow Rd., Ste. 425
Melville, NY 11747
Ph: (631)421-9421
Fax: (631)421-1352
E-mail: info@eop.com
URL: http://www.eop.com

Annual. Magazine that is offered at no charge to qualified female engineering, computer-science, and information-technology students and professionals seeking to find employment and advancement in their careers.

Employer Directories and Networking Lists

12542 ■ Careers in Focus—Engineering
Facts On File Inc.
132 W 31st St., 17th Fl.
New York, NY 10001
Ph: (212)967-8800
Fax: 800-678-3633
Fr: 800-322-8755
URL: http://www.infobasepublishing.com

Latest edition 3rd; Published July, 2007. $32.95 for individuals. Covers: An overview of engineering, followed by a selection of jobs profiled in detail, including the nature of the job, earnings, prospects for employment, what kind of training and skills it requires, and sources for further information.

12543 ■ Indiana Society of Professional Engineers—Directory
Indiana Society of Professional Engineers
PO Box 20806
Indianapolis, IN 46220
Ph: (317)255-2267
Fax: (317)255-2530
URL: http://www.indspe.org

Annual, fall. Covers: Member registered engineers, land surveyors, engineering students, and engineers in training. Entries include: Member name, address, phone, type of membership, business information, specialty. Arrangement: Alpha by chapter area.

Handbooks and Manuals

12544 ■ Functional Tissue Engineering
Springer-Verlag New York, Inc.
233 Spring St.
New York, NY 10013
Ph: (212)460-1500
Fax: (212)460-1575
E-mail: service-ny@springer.com
URL: http://www.springer.com/life+sciences/
   cell+biology/book/978-0-387-95553-7

Farshid Guilak, David Butler, Steven Goldstein, and David Mooney. July 2004. $89.95. 426 pages.

12545 ■ Great Jobs for Engineering Majors
The McGraw-Hill Companies
PO Box 182604
Columbus, OH 43272
Fax: (614)759-3749
Fr: 877-883-5524
E-mail: customer.service@mcgraw-hill.com
URL: http://www.mhprofessional.com/
   product.php?isbn=0071641963

Geraldine O. Garner. Second edition, 2008. $16.95. 192 pages. Covers all the career options open to students majoring in engineering.

12546 ■ Orthopedic Tissue Engineering: Basic Science and Practice
Marcel Dekker Inc.
270 Madison Ave., 4th Fl.
New York, NY 10016
URL: http://www.dekker.com

Victor Goldbert and Arnold Caplan. January 2004. $249.95. 425 pages. Explores the basic science and clinical concepts impacting bone tissue engineering.

12547 ■ Tissue Engineering: Engineering Principles for the Design of Replacement Organs and Tissues
Oxford University Press Inc.
198 Madison Ave.
New York, NY 10016
Ph: (212)726-6000
Fax: (919)677-1303

Fr: 800-445-9714
E-mail: custserv.us@oup.com
URL: http://www.oup.com/us
W. Mark Saltzman. $119.99. 544 pages.

12548 ■ Tissue Engineering in Musculoskeletal Clinical Practice
American Academy of Orthopaedic Surgeons
6300 N River Rd.
Rosemont, IL 60018
Ph: (847)823-7186
Fax: (847)823-8125
E-mail: orthoinfo@aaos.org
URL: http://www4.aaos.org

Linda J. Sandell and Alan J. Grodzinsky. 2004. 415 pages. $120.00.

Employment Agencies and Search Firms

12549 ■ Aureus Group
C&A Plz., 13609 California St., Ste. 100
Omaha, NE 68154-3503
Ph: (402)891-6900
Fax: (402)891-1290
Fr: 888-239-5993
E-mail: omaha@aureusgroup.com
URL: http://www.aureusgroup.com

Provides human capital management services in a wide variety of industries. Executive search and recruiting consultants specializing in six areas: accounting and finance, data processing, aerospace, engineering, manufacturing and medical professionals. Industries served: hospitals, all mainframe computer shops and all areas of accounting.

Tradeshows

12550 ■ American Society for Engineering Education Annual Conference and Exposition
American Society for Engineering Education
1818 N. St. N.W., Ste. 600
Washington, DC 20036-2479
Ph: (202)331-3500
Fax: (202)265-8504
E-mail: conferences@asee.org
URL: http://www.asee.org

Annual. Primary Exhibits: Publications, engineering supplies and equipment, computers, software, and research companies all products and services related to engineering education. Dates and Locations: 2012 Jun 10-13; San Antonio, TX.

Other Sources

12551 ■ American Association of Engineering Societies (AAES)
1801 Alexander Bell Dr.
Reston, VA 20191
Ph: (202)296-2237
Fax: (202)296-1151
Fr: 888-400-2237
E-mail: dbateson@aaes.org
URL: http://www.aaes.org

Description: Coordinates the efforts of the member societies in the provision of reliable and objective information to the general public concerning issues which affect the engineering profession and the field of engineering as a whole; collects, analyzes, documents, and disseminates data which will inform the general public of the relationship between engineering and the national welfare; provides a forum for the engineering societies to exchange and discuss their views on matters of common interest; and represents the U.S. engineering community abroad through representation in WFEO and UPADI.

12552 ■ American Engineering Association (AEA)
533 Waterside Blvd.
Monroe Township, NJ 08831
Ph: (201)664-6954
E-mail: aea@aea.org
URL: http://www.aea.org

Description: Members consist of Engineers and engineering professionals. Purpose to advance the engineering profession and U.S. engineering capabilities. Issues of concern include age discrimination, immigration laws, displacement of U.S. Engineers by foreign workers, trade agreements, off shoring of U.S. Engineering and manufacturing jobs, loss of U.S. manufacturing and engineering capability, and recruitment of foreign students. Testifies before Congress. Holds local Chapter meetings.

12553 ■ American Institute of Engineers (AIE)
4630 Appian Way, Ste. 206
El Sobrante, CA 94803-1875
Ph: (510)758-6240
Fax: (510)758-6240
E-mail: aie@aieonline.org
URL: http://www.members-aie.org

Description: Professional association for engineers, scientists, and mathematicians. Multi-disciplined, non-technical association who aims to improve the stature and image of engineers, scientists, and mathematicians. Provides endorsements, awards and opportunities for small business start-ups within the AIE Councils. Sponsors "LA Engineer", a comedy-drama television series; produces annual "Academy Hall of FAME (TV)".

12554 ■ American Society for Cell Biology (ASCB)
8120 Woodmont Ave., Ste. 750
Bethesda, MD 20814-2762
Ph: (301)347-9300
Fax: (301)347-9310
E-mail: ascbinfo@ascb.org
URL: http://www.ascb.org

Description: Represents scientists with educational or research experience in cell biology or an allied field. Offers placement service.

12555 ■ Engineering Society of Detroit (ESD)
20700 Civic Center Dr., Ste. 450
Southfield, MI 48076
Ph: (248)353-0735
Fax: (248)353-0736
E-mail: esd@esd.org
URL: http://ww2.esd.org/home.htm

Description: Engineers from all disciplines; scientists and technologists. Conducts technical programs and engineering refresher courses; sponsors conferences and expositions. Maintains speakers' bureau; offers placement services; although based in Detroit, MI, society membership is international.

12556 ■ Engineering Workforce Commission (EWC)
1801 Alexander Bell Dr.
Reston, VA 20191
Ph: (202)296-2237
Fax: (202)296-1151
Fr: 888-400-2237
E-mail: dbateson@aaes.org
URL: http://www.ewc-online.org

Description: Represents commissioners appointed by member societies of the American Association of Engineering Societies to engage in studies and analyses of the supply, demand, use and remuneration of engineering and technical personnel. Provides representation to government groups dealing with professional manpower policy; consults with industry. Gathers and disseminates information on the engineering profession. Conducts surveys of engineering school enrollments, degrees, and salaries; monitors federal labor statistics.

12557 ■ International Federation of Professional and Technical Engineers (IFPTE)
501 3rd St. NW, Ste. 701
Washington, DC 20001
Ph: (202)239-4880
Fax: (202)239-4881
E-mail: generalinfo@ifpte.org
URL: http://www.ifpte.org

Description: Represents engineers, scientists, architects and technicians.

12558 ■ National Action Council for Minorities in Engineering (NACME)
440 Hamilton Ave., Ste. 302
White Plains, NY 10601-1813
Ph: (914)539-4010
Fax: (914)539-4032
E-mail: info@nacme.org
URL: http://www.nacme.org

Description: Leads the national effort to increase access to careers in engineering and other science-based disciplines. Conducts research and public policy analysis, develops and operates national demonstration programs at precollege and university levels, and disseminates information through publications, conferences and electronic media. Serves as a privately funded source of scholarships for minority students in engineering.

12559 ■ National Society of Professional Engineers (NSPE)
1420 King St.
Alexandria, VA 22314-2794
Ph: (703)684-2800
Fax: (703)836-4875
Fr: 888-285-6773
E-mail: memserv@nspe.org
URL: http://www.nspe.org

Description: Represents professional engineers and engineers-in-training in all fields registered in accordance with the laws of states or territories of the U.S. or provinces of Canada; qualified graduate engineers, student members, and registered land surveyors. Is concerned with social, professional, ethical, and economic considerations of engineering as a profession; encompasses programs in public relations, employment practices, ethical considerations, education, and career guidance. Monitors legislative and regulatory actions of interest to the engineering profession.

12560 ■ Society of Engineering Science (SES)
University of Illinois at Urbana-Champaign
Beckman Institute for Advanced Science and Technology
405 N Mathews Ave., Rm. 3361
Urbana, IL 61801
E-mail: swhite@uiuc.edu
URL: http://www.sesinc.org

Description: Individuals with at least a baccalaureate degree who are engaged in any aspect of engineering science or in other pursuits that contribute to the advancement of engineering science. Fosters and promotes the interchange of ideas and information among the various fields of engineering science and among engineering science and the fields of theoretical and applied physics, chemistry, and mathematics. Is dedicated to the advancement of interdisciplinary research and to the establishment of a bridge between science and engineering.

12561 ■ Society of Hispanic Professional Engineers (SHPE)
13181 Crossroads Pkwy. N, Ste. 450
City of Industry, CA 91746-3496
Ph: (323)725-3970

Fax: (323)725-0316
E-mail: shpenational@shpe.org
URL: http://oneshpe.shpe.org/wps/portal/national

Description: Represents engineers, student engineers, and scientists. Aims to increase the number of Hispanic engineers by providing motivation and support to students. Sponsors competitions and educational programs. Maintains placement service and speakers' bureau; compiles statistics.

12562 ■ Society of Women Engineers (SWE)
203 N La Salle St., Ste. 1675
Chicago, IL 60601
Ph: (312)596-5223
Fax: (312)596-5252
Fr: 877-SWE-INFO
E-mail: hq@swe.org
URL: http://societyofwomenengineers.swe.org

Description: Educational and service organization representing both students and professional women in engineering and technical fields.

12563 ■ United Engineering Foundation (UEF)
PO Box 70
Mount Vernon, VA 22121-0070
Ph: (973)244-2328
Fax: (973)882-5155
E-mail: engfnd@aol.com
URL: http://www.uefoundation.org

Description: Federation of 5 major national engineering societies: American Institute of Chemical Engineers; American Institute of Mining, Metallurgical and Petroleum Engineers; American Society of Civil Engineers; American Society of Mechanical Engineers; Institute of Electrical and Electronics Engineers. Supports research in engineering and advances the engineering arts and sciences through its conference program.

SOURCES OF HELP-WANTED ADS

12564 ■ American Machinist
Penton Media Inc.
249 W 17th St.
New York, NY 10011
Ph: (212)204-4200
URL: http://www.americanmachinist.com/

Monthly. Magazine serving the metalworking market-place, consisting of plants in industries primarily engaged in manufacturing durable goods and other metal products.

12565 ■ Tooling & Production
Nelson Publishing Inc.
2500 Tamiami Trl. N
Nokomis, FL 34275
Ph: (941)966-9521
Fax: (941)966-2590
URL: http://www.manufacturingcenter.com

Monthly. Free. Magazine concerning metalworking.

EMPLOYMENT AGENCIES AND SEARCH FIRMS

12566 ■ KForce
Fr: 877-4KF-ORCE
URL: http://www.kforce.com

Executive search firm. More than 41 locations throughout the United States and two in the Philippines.

12567 ■ Mfg/Search, Inc.
205 W Jefferson Blvd., Ste. 601
South Bend, IN 46601
Ph: (574)282-2547
Fax: (574)232-0982
E-mail: hmueller@mfgsearch.com
URL: http://www.mfgsearch.com

Executive search firm. Offices in GA, IL, MI, NY.

TRADESHOWS

12568 ■ METALFORM Mexico
Precision Metalforming Association
6363 Oak Tree Blvd.
Independence, OH 44131-2500
Ph: (216)901-8800

Fax: (216)901-9190
E-mail: pma@pma.org
URL: http://www.metalforming.com

Annual. Primary Exhibits: Presses and stamping equipment, tooling and fabricating machines, man-agement aids, and related materials. Dates and Loca-tions: 2012 May 02-04; Monterrey, NL, Mexico; Cintermex.

12569 ■ Pacific Coast Industrial and Machine Tool Show
Cygnus Expositions
3167 Skyway Ct.
Fremont, CA 94538
Ph: (510)354-3131
Fax: (510)354-3159
Fr: 800-548-1407
E-mail: john.wright@cygnusexpos.com
URL: http://www.proshows.com

Annual. Primary Exhibits: Industrial equipment, machine tools, business services, hand tools, and related equipment, supplies, and services.

12570 ■ WESTEC - Advanced Productivity Exposition
Society of Manufacturing Engineers SME
Expositions Division
1 SME Dr.
PO Box 930
Dearborn, MI 48121
Ph: (313)271-1500
Fax: (313)425-3400
Fr: 800-733-3976
E-mail: service@sme.org
URL: http://www.sme.org

Biennial. Primary Exhibits: Equipment, supplies, and services for the tool and manufacturing engineering industries. Dates and Locations: 2012 Mar 27-29; Los Angeles, CA; Los Angeles Convention Center.

OTHER SOURCES

12571 ■ American Indian Science and Engineering Society (AISES)
PO Box 9828
Albuquerque, NM 87119-9828
Ph: (505)765-1052
Fax: (505)765-5608
E-mail: info@aises.org
URL: http://www.aises.org

Description: Represents American Indian and non-Indian students and professionals in science, technol-ogy, and engineering fields; corporations represent-ing energy, mining, aerospace, electronic, and

computer fields. Seeks to motivate and encourage students to pursue undergraduate and graduate stud-ies in science, engineering, and technology. Spon-sors science fairs in grade schools, teacher training workshops, summer math/science sessions for 8th-12th graders, professional chapters, and student chapters in colleges. Offers scholarships. Adult members serve as role models, advisers, and men-tors for students. Operates placement service.

12572 ■ Composites Manufacturing Tech Group
Society of Manufacturing Engineers
One SME Dr.
Dearborn, MI 48128
Ph: (313)425-3000
Fax: (313)425-3400
Fr: 800-733-4763
E-mail: leadership@sme.org
URL: http://www.sme.org/compositesmfg

Description: A division of the Society of Manufactur-ing Engineers. Composites manufacturing profes-sionals and students in 21 countries. Addresses design, tooling, assembly, producibility, supportability, and future trends of composites materials and hardware; promotes advanced composites technology. Analyzes industry trends; evaluates composites usage. Conducts educational programs; facilitates exchange of information among members; operates placement service.

12573 ■ Precision Machined Products Association (PMPA)
6700 W Snowville Rd.
Brecksville, OH 44141
Ph: (440)526-0300
Fax: (440)526-5803
URL: http://www.pmpa.org

Description: Addresses the information, training, and technical needs of manufacturers of component parts to customers' order, machined from rod, bar, or tube stock, of metal, fiber, plastic, or other material, using automatic or hand screw machines, automatic bar machines, and CNC machines.

12574 ■ Special Interest Group on Accessible Computing (SIGACCESS)
2 Penn Plz., Ste. 701
New York, NY 10121-0701
Ph: (212)626-0500
Fax: (212)944-1318
Fr: 800-342-6626
E-mail: chair_sigaccess@acm.org
URL: http://www.sigaccess.org

Description: Promotes the professional interests of computing personnel with physical disabilities and the application of computing and information technol-ogy in solving relevant disability problems. Works to educate the public to support careers for the disabled.

SOURCES OF HELP-WANTED ADS

12575 ■ *Meeting News*
Nielsen Business Media
770 Broadway
New York, NY 10003-9595
URL: http://www.mimegasite.com/mimegasite/
index.jsp

$89.00/year for individuals; $99.00/year for Canada; $205.00/year for other countries, by airmail. The newspaper for conventions, meetings, incentive travel and trade show professionals.

12576 ■ *Tourism, Culture & Communication*
Cognizant Communications Corp.
3 Hartsdale Rd.
Elmsford, NY 10523-3701
Ph: (914)592-7720
Fax: (914)592-8981
URL: http://www.cognizantcommunication.com/
journal-titles/touris

$360.00/year for institutions, online only; $390.00/year for institutions, online & hard copy; $55.00/year for individuals, professional; $45.00/year for single issue. Journal covering tourism, culture, and communication.

12577 ■ *Travel Trade*
Travel Trade
122 E 42nd St.
New York, NY 10168
Ph: (212)730-6600
Fax: (212)730-7020
URL: http://www.traveltrade.com/

Weekly. $20.00/year for individuals; $30.00/year for two years; $40.00/year for individuals, 3 years. Travel industry magazine.

12578 ■ *Travel Weekly*
Northstar Travel Media
100 Lighting Way, 2nd Fl.
Secaucus, NJ 07094
Ph: (201)902-2000
Fax: (201)902-2045
E-mail: tweditorial@ntmllc.com
URL: http://www.travelweekly.com

Weekly (Mon.). Free to qualified subscribers. Travel industry magazine.

12579 ■ *TravelAge West*
Northstar Travel Media
100 Lighting Way, 2nd Fl.
Secaucus, NJ 07094
Ph: (201)902-2000
Fax: (201)902-2045
E-mail: letters@travelagewest.com
URL: http://www.travelagewest.com

Biweekly. Magazine for retail travel agents in western U.S. and western Canada.

EMPLOYER DIRECTORIES AND NETWORKING LISTS

12580 ■ *Survey of State Tourism Offices*
Travel Industry Association of America
1100 New York Ave. NW, Ste. 450
Washington, DC 20005-3934
Ph: (202)408-8422
Fax: (202)408-1255
URL: http://www.tia.org

Annual, Latest edition 2007. $300.00 for members; $495.00 for nonmembers. Covers: state and territorial government agencies responsible for travel and travel promotion in their states. Entries include: Agency name, address, phone, number of full- and part-time staff, number of professional staff directly involved in travel; name and title of state travel director, and length of service as director, length of service in agency, and whether employed under the Civil Service program; advertising director and agency and public relations director in separate sections. Extensive additional data is provided by a series of tables covering state activities in advertising, package tours, general promotion press and public relations, research, the establishment of welcome centers, and the department budget. Although addresses are not given, some listings do include name, title, and department of contact. Arrangement: By function (administration, advertising, etc.), then geographical.

HANDBOOKS AND MANUALS

12581 ■ *Careers in Travel, Tourism, and Hospitality*
The McGraw-Hill Companies
PO Box 182604
Columbus, OH 43272
Fax: (614)759-3749
Fr: 877-883-5524
E-mail: customer.service@mcgraw-hill.com
URL: http://www.mhprofessional.com

Marjorie Eberts, Linda Brothers, and Ann Gisler. Second edition, 2005. $15.95 (paper). 224 pages.

12582 ■ *Jobs for Travel Lovers: Opportunities at Home and Abroad*
Impact Publications
9104 Manassas Dr., Ste. N
Manassas Park, VA 20111-5211
Ph: (703)361-7300
Fax: (703)335-9486
URL: http://www.impactpublications.com

2006. $19.95. 320 pages. Covers job search strategies, with hundreds of jobs in business, government, and education, including the travel and hospital industry, non-profit organizations, international organizations, education institutions, and consulting. Includes opportunities involving airlines and cruise lines, international jobs, travel agencies and tour operators, internships and volunteering, hotels and resorts, military and merchant marine, teaching abroad, travel writing, and short-term work experiences. Provides names, addresses, telephone/fax numbers, e-mails, and websites for contacting potential employers.

12583 ■ *Travel the World Free as an International Tour Director: How to Be an International Tour Director*
BookSurge Publishing
7290 B Investment Dr.
Charleston, SC 29418
Ph: (206)266-4064
Fax: (206)266-7010
URL: http://www.booksurge.com

Gerald E. Mitchell. 2007. $26.99. 366 pages. Kit includes 250-page manual, 189-page site-inspection journal and resource start up kit with video.

ONLINE JOB SOURCES AND SERVICES

12584 ■ Tour Guide Jobs
URL: http://www.tourguidejobs.org

Description: Focuses on tour guide employment opportunities and candidate recruiting.

TRADESHOWS

12585 ■ DMAI Annual Convention
Destination Marketing Association International
2025 M St. NW, Ste. 500
Washington, DC 20036
Ph: (202)296-7888
Fax: (202)296-7889
E-mail: info@destinationmarketing.org
URL: http://www.destinationmarketing.org

Annual. Includes exhibits of products and services by destination marketing organization suppliers. Provides networking opportunities to destination marketing professionals.

12586 ■ Luxury Travel Expo
Advanstar Communications
641 Lexington Ave., 8th Fl.
New York, NY 10022
Ph: (212)951-6600
Fax: (212)951-6793
E-mail: info@advanstar.com
URL: http://www.advanstar.com

Semiannual. Primary Exhibits: Tours and tour packages sales agents.

12587 ■ World Travel Market
Reed Exhibitions North American Headquarters
383 Main Ave.
Norwalk, CT 06851

Ph: (203)840-4800
Fax: (203)840-5805
E-mail: inquiry@reedexpo.com
URL: http://www.reedexpo.com

Annual. Primary Exhibits: Goods and services related to tourism and travel.

OTHER SOURCES

12588 ■ Connected International Meeting Professionals Association (CIMPA)
9200 Bayard Pl.
Fairfax, VA 22032
Ph: (512)684-0889
Fax: (267)390-5193
E-mail: susan@cimpa.org
URL: http://www.cimpa.org

Description: Meeting planners, incentive organizers, travel agents, tour operators, and seminar organizers in 42 countries. Works to improve the skills of professional conference and convention planners. Serves as a clearinghouse of information on new travel destinations and planning technologies, techniques, and strategies. Facilitates exchange of information among Internet professionals. Produces a television program on travel and meetings. Conducts educational courses and awards Certified Internet Meeting Professional designation. Conducts research programs and placement service. Sponsors training courses on the Internet.

12589 ■ Destination Marketing Association International
2025 M St. NW, Ste. 500
Washington, DC 20036
Ph: (202)296-7888
Fax: (202)296-7889
E-mail: info@destinationmarketing.org
URL: http://www.destinationmarketing.org
Description: Represents professionals, industry partners, students, and educators. Provides educational resources, networking opportunities, and marketing benefits for members. Enhances the professionalism, effectiveness and image of destination marketing organizations worldwide.

12590 ■ United States Tour Operators Association (USTOA)
275 Madison Ave., Ste. 2014
New York, NY 10016-1101
Ph: (212)599-6599
Fax: (212)599-6744
E-mail: information@ustoa.com
URL: http://www.ustoa.com

Description: Represents wholesale tour operators, common carriers, associations, government agencies, suppliers, purveyors of travel services, trade press, communications media, and public relations and advertising representatives. Encourages and supports professional and financial integrity in tourism. Protects the legitimate interests of the consumer and the retail agent from financial loss from business conducted with members. Provides tour operators with an opportunity to formulate and express an independent industry voice on matters of common interest and self-regulation. Strives to facilitate and develop travel on a worldwide basis.

Sources of Help-Wanted Ads

12591 ■ Advanced Transportation Technology News
BCC Research
49 Walnut St., Bldg. 2
Wellesley, MA 02481
Ph: (781)489-7301
Fax: (781)253-3933
Fr: (866)285-7215
URL: http://www.bccresearch.com

Monthly. $2,250.00/year for individuals, hard copy mail delivery. Publication covering technology and related news for the transportation industry.

12592 ■ Journal of Transportation Technologies
Scientific Research Publishing
PO Box 54821
Irvine, CA 92619-4821
E-mail: jtts@scirp.org
URL: http://www.scirp.org/journal/jtts/

Quarterly. $156.00/year for individuals. Peer-reviewed journal publishing articles on the latest advancement of transportation technologies.

12593 ■ Maine Trails
Maine Better Transportation Association
146 State St.
Augusta, ME 04330
Ph: (207)622-0526
Fax: (207)623-2928
URL: http://www.mbtaonline.org/Newsroom/
MaineTrailsMagazine/tabid

Bimonthly. Magazine informing association members and the business community about Maine transportation issues.

Employer Directories and Networking Lists

12594 ■ Careers in Focus—Transportation
Facts On File Inc.
132 W 31st St., 17th Fl.
New York, NY 10001
Ph: (212)967-8800
Fax: 800-678-3633
Fr: 800-322-8755
URL: http://www.infobasepublishing.com

Latest edition 3rd; Published August, 2007. $32.95 for individuals. Covers: An overview of transportation, followed by a selection of jobs profiled in detail, including the nature of the job, earnings, prospects for employment, what kind of training and skills it requires, and sources for further information.

Online Job Sources and Services

12595 ■ Civil Engineering Jobs
URL: http://www.civilengineeringjobs.com

Description: Job postings for all civil engineering disciplines including positions in traffic/transportation.

Tradeshows

12596 ■ ATSSA Annual Convention and Traffic Expo
American Traffic Safety Services Association
15 Riverside Pkwy., Ste. 100
Fredericksburg, VA 22406-1022
Ph: (540)368-1701
Fax: (540)368-1717
Fr: 800-272-8772
E-mail: meetings@atssa.com
URL: http://www.atssa.com

Annual. Primary Exhibits: Manufacturers or service-oriented companies that provide traffic control, ITS, pavement marking, signing and various other roadway safety devices. Dates and Locations: 2012 Feb 12-16; Tampa, FL; Tampa Convention Center.

12597 ■ International Municipal Signal Association Conference
International Municipal Signal Association
165 E. Union St.
PO Box 539
Newark, NY 14513-0539
Ph: (315)331-2182
Fax: (315)331-8205
Fr: 800-723-4672
E-mail: info@imsasafety.org
URL: http://www.imsasafety.org

Annual. Primary Exhibits: Public Safety equipment, supplies, and services, including: traffic signals, street signs, alarms, roadway lighting, and communications equipment.

Other Sources

12598 ■ American Association of State Highway and Transportation Officials
444 N Capitol St. NW, Ste. 249
Washington, DC 20001
Ph: (202)624-5800
Fax: (202)624-5806
E-mail: info@aashto.org
URL: http://www.transportation.org

Description: Strives to advocate transportation policies, provide technical services, and demonstrate the contributions of transportation and facilitate change.

12599 ■ American Highway Users Alliance
1101 14th St. NW, Ste. 750
Washington, DC 20005
Ph: (202)857-1200
Fax: (202)857-1220
E-mail: info@highways.org
URL: http://www.highways.org

Description: Serves as the voice of the transportation community promoting safe highways and the enhanced freedom of mobility.

12600 ■ American Planning Association (APA)
122 S Michigan Ave., Ste. 1600
Chicago, IL 60603-6107
Ph: (312)431-9100
Fax: (312)431-9985
E-mail: customerservice@planning.org
URL: http://www.planning.org

Description: Public and private planning agency officials, professional planners, planning educators, elected and appointed officials, and other persons involved in urban and rural development. Works to foster the best techniques and decisions for the planned development of communities and regions. Provides extensive professional services and publications to professionals and laypeople in planning and related fields; serves as a clearinghouse for information. Through Planning Advisory Service, a research and inquiry-answering service, provides, on an annual subscription basis, advice on specific inquiries and a series of research reports on planning, zoning, and environmental regulations. Supplies information on job openings and makes definitive studies on salaries and recruitment of professional planners. Conducts research; collaborates in joint projects with local, national, and international organizations.

12601 ■ American Traffic Safety Services Association
15 Riverside Pkwy., Ste. 100
Fredericksburg, VA 22406-1022
Ph: (540)368-1701
Fax: (540)368-1717
Fr: 800-272-8772
URL: http://www.atssa.com

Description: Represents individuals and companies in the traffic control and roadway safety industry.

12602 ■ Association for Commuter Transportation
1341 G St. NW, 10th Fl.
Washington, DC 20005
Ph: (202)719-5331
Fr: 888-719-5772
E-mail: info@actweb.org
URL: http://www.actweb.org

Description: Professionals who specialize in commuter options and solutions.

12603 ■ Association of Metropolitan
Planning Organizations
1029 Vermont Ave., Ste. 710
Washington, DC 20005
Ph: (202)296-7051
Fax: (202)296-7054
URL: http://www.ampo.org

Description: Offers a forum for transportation policy development, conferences and workshops, and research.

12604 ■ Institute of Transportation
Engineers
1627 Eye St. NW, Ste. 600
Washington, DC 20006
Ph: (202)785-0060
Fax: (202)785-0609
E-mail: ite_staff@ite.org
URL: http://www.ite.org

Description: Traffic engineers, transportation planners, and other related professionals.

12605 ■ National Committee on Uniform
Traffic Laws and Ordinances (NCUTLO)
107 S West St., No. 110
Alexandria, VA 22314-2824
Fax: (540)465-5383

Fr: 800-807-5290
E-mail: twogen2@yahoo.com
URL: http://www.ncutlo.org

Description: Federal, state, and local highway, police, motor vehicle, and other officials; legislators; educational institutions; manufacturers of vehicles and equipment; insurance companies, motor clubs, and safety councils; other persons and organizations interested in uniform motor vehicle laws. Maintains small library on traffic law. Keeps the Uniform Vehicle Code, Collection of model laws.

12606 ■ National Highway Traffic Safety
Administration
1200 New Jersey Ave. SE, West Bldg.
Washington, DC 20590
Ph: (202)366-9550
Fr: 888-327-4236
URL: http://www.nhtsa.gov

Description: Works to save lives, prevent injuries and reduce traffic-related health care.

12607 ■ Roadway Safety Foundation
1101 14th St. NW, Ste. 750
Washington, DC 20005
Ph: (202)857-1228
Fax: (202)857-1220
URL: http://www.roadwaysafety.org

Description: Dedicated to reducing highway deaths and injuries by improving the physical characteristics of roadways.

12608 ■ The Traffic Group, Inc.
9900 Franklin Square Dr., Ste. H
Baltimore, MD 21236
Ph: (410)931-6600
Fax: (410)931-6601
Fr: 800-583-8411
E-mail: wguckert@trafficgroup.com
URL: http://www.trafficgroup.com

Description: Consists of professionals in the Traffic Engineering and Transportation Planning fields.

12609 ■ Transportation Research Board
500 5th St., NW
Washington, DC 20001
Ph: (202)334-2934
E-mail: trbsales@nas.edu
URL: http://www.trb.org

Description: Engineers, Scientists, and other transportation researchers and practitioners from the public and private sectors. Facilitates the sharing of information, promotes innovation and progress, and stimulates research.

Translators and Interpreters

SOURCES OF HELP-WANTED ADS

12610 ■ LSA Bulletin
Linguistic Society of America
1325 18th St. NW, Ste. 211
Archibald A. Hill Ste.
Washington, DC 20036-6501
Ph: (202)835-1714
Fax: (202)835-1717
E-mail: lsa@lsadc.org
URL: http://www.lsadc.org

Description: Quarterly. Covers activities of the linguistic community. Recurring features include a grants calendar, conference and job announcements, a calendar of events, reports of meetings, and job listings.

EMPLOYER DIRECTORIES AND NETWORKING LISTS

12611 ■ American Translators Association—Membership Directory
American Translators Association
225 Reinekers Ln., Ste. 590
Alexandria, VA 22314
Ph: (703)683-6100
Fax: (703)683-6122
URL: http://atanet.org/local_bin/login.pl?redirect=/membership/me

Annual, summer. Includes more than 9,000 member translators, interpreters, and linguists in the United States and over 60 countries. Entries include: Name, address, phone, languages in which member has ATA certification. Arrangement: Alphabetical.

12612 ■ ATA Directory of Translators and Interpreters
American Translators Association
225 Reinekers Ln., Ste. 590
Alexandria, VA 22314
Ph: (703)683-6100
Fax: (703)683-6122
URL: http://www.atanet.org

Covers: over 5,800 member translators and interpreters. Entries include: Name, address, languages in which proficient, subject competencies, professional background. Arrangement: Alphabetical, area of specialization, language. Indexes: Language-subject competency (with state).

12613 ■ International Literary Market Place
Information Today Inc.
143 Old Marlton Pike
Medford, NJ 08055-8750
Ph: (609)654-6266
Fax: (609)654-4309
Fr: 800-300-9868
URL: http://www.literarymarketplace.com

Annual, Latest edition 2012. $289.00 for individuals; $260.10 for individuals. Covers: Over 10,500 publishers in over 180 countries outside the United States and Canada, and about 1,499 trade and professional organizations related to publishing abroad; includes major printers, binders, typesetters, book manufacturers, book dealers, libraries, literary agencies, translators, book clubs, reference books and journals, periodicals, prizes, and international reference section. Entries include: For publishers—Name, address, phone, fax, telex, names and titles of key personnel, branches, type of publications, subjects, ISBN prefix. Listings for others include similar information but less detail. Arrangement: Classified by business activities, then geographical. Indexes: Company name, subject, type of publication.

12614 ■ Literary Market Place
Information Today Inc.
143 Old Marlton Pike
Medford, NJ 08055-8750
Ph: (609)654-6266
Fax: (609)654-4309
Fr: 800-300-9868
URL: http://books.infotoday.com

Annual, Latest edition 2012. $339.00 for individuals; $305.10 for individuals. Covers: Over 12,500 firms or organizations offering services related to the publishing industry, including book publishers in the United States and Canada who issued three or more books during the preceding year, plus a small press section of publishers who publish less than three titles per year or those who are self-published. Also included: book printers and binders; book clubs; book trade and literary associations; selected syndicates, newspapers, periodicals, and radio and TV programs that use book reviews or book publishing news; translators and literary agents. Entries include: For publishers—Company name, address, phone, address for orders, principal executives, editorial directors, and managers, date founded, number of titles in previous year, number of backlist titles in print, types of books published, ISBN prefixes, representatives, imprints, and affiliations. For suppliers, etc.—Listings usually show firm name, address, phone, executives, services, etc. Arrangement: Classified by line of business. Indexes: Principal index is 35,000-item combined index of publishers, publications, and personnel; several sections have geographical and/or subject indexes; translators are indexed by source and target language.

HANDBOOKS AND MANUALS

12615 ■ Careers in International Affairs
Georgetown University Press
3240 Prospect St., NW
Washington, DC 20007
Ph: (202)687-5889
Fax: (202)687-6340
Fr: 800-537-5487
E-mail: gupress@georgetown.edu
URL: http://www.press.georgetown.edu

Maria Carland and Candace Faber (editors). Eighth edition, 2008. $24.95 (paper). 432 pages. Includes index and bibliography.

12616 ■ Great Jobs for Foreign Language Majors
The McGraw-Hill Companies
PO Box 182604
Columbus, OH 43272
Fax: (614)759-3749
Fr: 877-883-5524
E-mail: customer.service@mcgraw-hill.com
URL: http://www.mhprofessional.com/product.php?isbn=0071476148

Julie DeGalan and Stephen Lambert. Third edition, 2007. $15.95 (paper). 192 pages. Part of "Great Jobs for...Majors" series.

12617 ■ Opportunities in Foreign Language Careers
The McGraw-Hill Companies
PO Box 182604
Columbus, OH 43272
Fax: (614)759-3749
Fr: 877-883-5524
E-mail: customer.service@mcgraw-hill.com
URL: http://www.mhprofessional.com/product.php?isbn=0071454799

Wilga Rivers. 2004. $13.95 (paper). 196 pages. Explores a variety of foreign language careers and discusses how to pursue them. Contains bibliography and illustrations.

12618 ■ A Practical Guide for Translators
Multilingual Matters Ltd.
325 Chestnut St.
Philadelphia, PA 19106
Ph: (215)625-8900
Fax: (215)625-2940
Fr: 800-634-7064
E-mail: info@multilingual-matters.com
URL: http://www.multilingual-matters.com

Geoffrey Samuelsson-Brown. Fifth edition, 2010. 224 pages. $87.96. Part of Topics in Translation series. Provides information on becoming a translator.

ONLINE JOB SOURCES AND SERVICES

12619 ■ BilingualCareer.com
URL: http://www.bilingualcareer.com

Description: Provides a resume tool to help job seekers. Offers online job postings.

12620 ■ BilingualCrossing.com
URL: http://www.bilingualcrossing.com

Description: Offers job opportunities for professionals seeking bilingual openings. Features all types of bilingual jobs, details on career advancement opportunities, and employment information for the bilingual industry.

12621 ■ LinguistList.org
E-mail: linguist@linguistlist.org
URL: http://linguistlist.org
Description: Provides an online resource for the academic field of linguistics. Includes professional and academic jobs for linguists.

12622 ■ Proz.com
URL: http://www.proz.com
Description: Provides job postings and translation tools. A community forum is available for discussions.

12623 ■ Trally.com
URL: http://www.trally.com
Description: Offers job postings for translation services.

12624 ■ TranslationDirectory.com
E-mail: ceo@translationdirectory.com
URL: http://www.translationdirectory.com

Description: Offers a directory of a wide variety of resources, including groups and mailing lists for translators, tools for language professionals, glossaries and dictionaries, translation organizations, payment collection agencies, translation blogs, freelance translators and translation agencies, language education companies and other related resources.

12625 ■ TranslatorsCafe.com
URL: http://www.translatorscafe.com
Description: Provides recent news articles and glossaries. Also offers job postings, community forums and tips for setting translation fees.

OTHER SOURCES

12626 ■ African Studies Association (ASA)
Rutgers University, Livingston Campus
54 Joyce Kilmer Ave.
Piscataway, NJ 08854-8045

Ph: (848)445-8173
Fax: (732)445-1366
E-mail: karen.jenkins@africanstudies.org
URL: http://www.africanstudies.org

Description: Persons specializing in teaching, writing, or research on Africa including political scientists, historians, geographers, anthropologists, economists, librarians, linguists, and government officials; persons who are studying African subjects; institutional members are universities, libraries, government agencies, and others interested in receiving information about Africa. Seeks to foster communication and to stimulate research among scholars on Africa. Sponsors placement service; conducts panels and discussion groups; presents exhibits and films.

SOURCES OF HELP-WANTED ADS

12627 ■ ARTA E-News
Association of Retail Travel Agents
c/o Travel Destination Inc.
4320 N Miller Rd.
Scottsdale, AZ 85251
Fr: (866)369-8969
URL: http://www.arta.travel

Description: Daily. Reviews developments in the travel industry for retail travel agents. Covers topics such as ethics, tour operations, transportation services, educational opportunities, commissions, and political action in pertinent issues. Includes chapter and Association news.

12628 ■ Business Travel News
Nielsen Business Media
770 Broadway
New York, NY 10003-9595
E-mail: nbtn@omeda.com
URL: http://www.btnmag.com/businesstravelnews/
index.jsp

Weekly. Free. Tabloid newspaper covering business travel.

12629 ■ Meeting News
Nielsen Business Media
770 Broadway
New York, NY 10003-9595
URL: http://www.mimegasite.com/mimegasite/
index.jsp

$89.00/year for individuals; $99.00/year for Canada; $205.00/year for other countries, by airmail. The newspaper for conventions, meetings, incentive travel and trade show professionals.

12630 ■ Tourism, Culture & Communication
Cognizant Communications Corp.
3 Hartsdale Rd.
Elmsford, NY 10523-3701
Ph: (914)592-7720
Fax: (914)592-8981
URL: http://www.cognizantcommunication.com/
journal-titles/touris

$360.00/year for institutions, online only; $390.00/year for institutions, online & hard copy; $55.00/year for individuals, professional; $45.00/year for single issue. Journal covering tourism, culture, and communication.

12631 ■ Travel E-Newsletter
Minnesota Office of Tourism
Metro Sq., Ste. 100
121 7th Pl., E
St. Paul, MN 55101
Ph: (651)296-5029
Fr: 888-868-7476
E-mail: explore@state.mn.us
URL: http://www.exploreminnesota.com

Description: Monthly. Reports news, research, advertising and marketing opportunities, meetings, workshops, and seminars for the travel industry. Recurring features include news of research, a calendar of events, reports of meetings, news of educational opportunities, and notices of publications available.

12632 ■ Travel Trade
Travel Trade
122 E 42nd St.
New York, NY 10168
Ph: (212)730-6600
Fax: (212)730-7020
URL: http://www.traveltrade.com/

Weekly. $20.00/year for individuals; $30.00/year for two years; $40.00/year for individuals, 3 years. Travel industry magazine.

12633 ■ Travel Weekly
Northstar Travel Media
100 Lighting Way, 2nd Fl.
Secaucus, NJ 07094
Ph: (201)902-2000
Fax: (201)902-2045
E-mail: tweditorial@ntmllc.com
URL: http://www.travelweekly.com

Weekly (Mon.). Free to qualified subscribers. Travel industry magazine.

12634 ■ TravelAge West
Northstar Travel Media
100 Lighting Way, 2nd Fl.
Secaucus, NJ 07094
Ph: (201)902-2000
Fax: (201)902-2045
E-mail: letters@travelagewest.com
URL: http://www.travelagewest.com

Biweekly. Magazine for retail travel agents in western U.S. and western Canada.

EMPLOYER DIRECTORIES AND NETWORKING LISTS

12635 ■ American Society of Travel Agents—Membership Directory
American Society of Travel Agents
1101 King St., Ste. 200
Alexandria, VA 22314
Fax: (703)739-2782
URL: http://www.asta.org/BusinessServices/
memberdirect.cfm?navlte

Annual. Covers: About 13,500 travel agents representing over 25,600 members in 130 countries. Entries include: Company name, address, phone, fax, telex, name of principal executive and other officials, services. Arrangement: Classified by membership category, then geographical. Indexes: Personal name, company name.

12636 ■ Career Opportunities in the Travel Industry
Facts On File Inc.
132 W 31st St., 17th Fl.
New York, NY 10001
Ph: (212)967-8800
Fax: 800-678-3633
Fr: 800-322-8755
URL: http://factsonfile.infobasepublishing.com

Published 2004. $18.95 for individuals. Covers: More than 75 professional and hourly jobs available in both the private and public sectors, from travel agent to tour guide and hotel general manager to flight navigator.

12637 ■ Careers in Focus—Travel & Hospitality
Facts On File Inc.
132 W 31st St., 17th Fl.
New York, NY 10001
Ph: (212)967-8800
Fax: 800-678-3633
Fr: 800-322-8755
URL: http://www.infobasepublishing.com

Latest edition 3rd; Published September, 2006. Covers: An overview of travel and hospitality, followed by a selection of jobs profiled in detail, including the nature of the job, earnings, prospects for employment, what kind of training and skills it requires, and sources for further information.

12638 ■ Global Business Travel Association—Membership Directory
Global Business Travel Association
110 N Royal St., 4th Fl.
Alexandria, VA 22314
Ph: (703)684-0836
Fax: (703)684-0263
E-mail: membership@nbta.org
URL: http://www.gbta.org/Pages/default.aspx

Annual. Covers: Over 1,900 corporate travel managers and supplier members in the United States. Entries include: Individual name, corporate name, type of membership, office address, phone, fax, e-mail, URL address. Arrangement: Alphabetical by individual/company name. Indexes: Geographical, member type, advertiser, company category listing.

12639 ■ Survey of State Tourism Offices
Travel Industry Association of America
1100 New York Ave. NW, Ste. 450
Washington, DC 20005-3934
Ph: (202)408-8422
Fax: (202)408-1255
URL: http://www.tia.org

Annual. Latest edition 2007. $300.00 for members; $495.00 for nonmembers. Covers: state and territorial government agencies responsible for travel and travel promotion in their states. Entries include: Agency name, address, phone, number of full- and part-time staff, number of professional staff directly involved in travel; name and title of state travel director, and length of service as director, length of service in agency, and whether employed under the Civil Service program; advertising director and agency and public relations director in separate sections. Extensive additional data is provided by a series of tables covering state activities in advertising, package tours, general promotion press and public relations, research, the establishment of welcome centers, and the department budget. Although addresses are not given, some listings do include name, title, and department of contact. Arrangement: By function (administration, advertising, etc.), then geographical.

HANDBOOKS AND MANUALS

12640 ■ *Careers in Travel, Tourism, and Hospitality*
The McGraw-Hill Companies
PO Box 182604
Columbus, OH 43272
Fax: (614)759-3749
Fr: 877-883-5524
E-mail: customer.service@mcgraw-hill.com
URL: http://www.mhprofessional.com

Marjorie Eberts, Linda Brothers, and Ann Gisler. Second edition, 2005. $15.95 (paper). 224 pages.

12641 ■ *Jobs for Travel Lovers: Opportunities at Home and Abroad*
Impact Publications
9104 Manassas Dr., Ste. N
Manassas Park, VA 20111-5211
Ph: (703)361-7300
Fax: (703)335-9486
URL: http://www.impactpublications.com

2006. $19.95. 320 pages. Covers job search strategies, with hundreds of jobs in business, government, and education, including the travel and hospital industry, non-profit organizations, international organizations, education institutions, and consulting. Includes opportunities involving airlines and cruise lines, international jobs, travel agencies and tour operators, internships and volunteering, hotels and resorts, military and merchant marine, teaching abroad, travel writing, and short-term work experiences. Provides names, addresses, telephone/fax numbers, e-mails, and websites for contacting potential employers.

12642 ■ *Travel the World Free as an International Tour Director: How to Be an International Tour Director*
BookSurge Publishing
7290 B Investment Dr.
Charleston, SC 29418
Ph: (206)266-4064
Fax: (206)266-7010
URL: http://www.booksurge.com

Gerald E. Mitchell. 2007. $26.99. 366 pages. Kit includes 250-page manual, 189-page site-inspection journal and resource start up kit with video.

EMPLOYMENT AGENCIES AND SEARCH FIRMS

12643 ■ ChaseAmerica Inc.
300 Park Ave.
New York, NY 10022
Ph: (215)338-1952
Fr: 800-491-4980
E-mail: info@chaseamericainc.com
URL: http://www.chaseamericainc.com

Executive search firm.

12644 ■ The Elliot Group LLC
505 White Plains Rd., Ste. 228
Tarrytown, NY 10591
Ph: (914)631-4904

Fax: (914)631-6481
URL: http://www.theelliotgroup.com

Executive search firm. Six locations throughout the United States.

12645 ■ Travel People Personnel
1199 Park Ave., Ste. 3E
New York, NY 10128-1762
Ph: (212)348-6942
Fax: (212)348-6958
E-mail: sue@travelpeople.com
URL: http://www.travelpeople.com

Provides temporary and regular placement services to travel related companies. Industries served: travel and hospitality.

ONLINE JOB SOURCES AND SERVICES

12646 ■ HCareers.com
E-mail: hospitalitydivision@hcareers.com
URL: http://www.hcareers.com

Description: Connects employers and candidates within the hospitality industry. Enables candidates to search for jobs within a specific industry or location.

12647 ■ Travel Agent Jobs
URL: http://www.jobstravelagent.com

Description: Serves as a niche job board for travel agent employment opportunities.

12648 ■ TravelingCrossing.com
URL: http://www.travelingcrossing.com

Description: Provides collection of travel job listings. Offers travel industry insights, including travel news briefs, articles, and e-resources to keep members up to date on the latest happenings in the travel world.

TRADESHOWS

12649 ■ World Travel Market
Reed Exhibitions North American Headquarters
383 Main Ave.
Norwalk, CT 06851
Ph: (203)840-4800
Fax: (203)840-5805
E-mail: inquiry@reedexpo.com
URL: http://www.reedexpo.com

Annual. Primary Exhibits: Goods and services related to tourism and travel.

OTHER SOURCES

12650 ■ American Society of Travel Agents (ASTA)
1101 King St., Ste. 200
Alexandria, VA 22314
E-mail: askasta@asta.org
URL: http://www.astanet.com

Description: Travel agents; allied members are representatives of carriers, hotels, resorts, sightseeing and car rental companies, official tourist organizations, and other travel interests. Aims to: promote and encourage travel among people of all nations and the use of professional travel agents worldwide; serve as an information resource for the travel industry worldwide; promote and represent the views and interests of travel agents to all levels of government and industry; promote professional and ethical conduct in the travel agency industry worldwide; facilitate consumer protection and safety for the traveling public. Maintains biographical archives and travel hall of fame. Conducts research and education programs.

12651 ■ Association of Corporate Travel Executives
515 King St., Ste. 440
Alexandria, VA 22314

Ph: (703)683-5322
E-mail: info1@acte.org
URL: http://www.acte.org

Description: Provides a forum for the discussion of ideas and information related to the travel industry. Offers executive-level global education and peer-to-peer networking opportunities.

12652 ■ Association of Travel Marketing Executives
PO Box 3176
West Tisbury, MA 02575
Ph: (508)693-0550
Fax: (508)693-0115
E-mail: admin@atme.org
URL: http://www.atme.org

Description: Serves the travel industry marketers representing all segments of the industry. Provides a forum for creative ideas and marketing solutions within the travel industry.

12653 ■ Connected International Meeting Professionals Association (CIMPA)
9200 Bayard Pl.
Fairfax, VA 22032
Ph: (512)684-0889
Fax: (267)390-5193
E-mail: susan@cimpa.org
URL: http://www.cimpa.org

Description: Meeting planners, incentive organizers, travel agents, tour operators, and seminar organizers in 42 countries. Works to improve the skills of professional conference and convention planners. Serves as a clearinghouse of information on new travel destinations and planning technologies, techniques, and strategies. Facilitates exchange of information among Internet professionals. Produces a television program on travel and meetings. Conducts educational courses and awards Certified Internet Meeting Professional designation. Conducts research programs and placement service. Sponsors training courses on the Internet.

12654 ■ Society of Incentive and Travel Executives (SITE)
401 N Michigan Ave.
Chicago, IL 60611
Ph: (312)321-5148
Fax: (312)527-6783
E-mail: site@siteglobal.com
URL: http://www.siteglobal.com

Description: Represents individuals responsible for the administration or sale of incentive programs including corporate users, incentive marketing companies, cruise lines, hotel chains, resort operators, airlines, and tourist boards. Unites individuals in the incentive industry and facilitates information exchange and problem solving on a personal and professional basis. Supports expansion of incentive programs through public relations, promotion, and speakers' bureau activities. Contributes to the continuing professional education of members through meetings, publications, and research services. Helps upgrade standards through educational services to nonmembers. Compiles statistics; provides placement service.

12655 ■ The Travel Institute
148 Linden St., Ste. 305
Wellesley, MA 02482
Ph: (781)237-0280
Fax: (781)237-3860
Fr: 800-542-4282
E-mail: info@thetravelinstitute.com
URL: http://www.thetravelinstitute.com

Description: Individuals who have been accredited as Certified Travel Counselors (CTC) or Certified Travel Associates (CTA) must meet the institute's testing and experience requirements. Seeks to increase the level of competence in the travel industry. Provides continuing education and examination and certification programs; conducts workshops and professional management seminars. Operates Travel Career Development Program to increase professional skills and Destination Specialist Programs to enhance the geographical knowledge of sales agents. Organizes study groups of instruction with enrolled student bodies in most major cities.

12656 ■ U.S. Travel Data Center (USTDC)
1100 New York Ave. NW, Ste. 450
Washington, DC 20005-3934

Ph: (202)408-8422
Fax: (202)408-1255
E-mail: feedback@ustravel.org
URL: http://www.tia.org
Description: Conducts statistical, economic, and market research concerning travel; encourages standardized travel research terminology and techniques. Monitors trends in travel activity and the travel industry. Measures the economic impact of travel on geographic areas and the cost of travel in the U.S. Evaluates the effect of government programs on travel and the travel industry. Forecasts travel activity and expenditures.

12657 ■ American Printer
Penton Media Inc.
9800 Metcalf Ave.
Overland Park, KS 66212
Ph: (913)341-1300
Fax: (913)967-1898
E-mail: apeditor@penton.com
URL: http://www.americanprinter.com
Monthly. Magazine covering the printing and publishing market.

12658 ■ Printing Impressions
North American Publishing Co.
1500 Spring Garden St., Ste. 1200
Philadelphia, PA 19130-4069
Ph: (215)238-5300
Fax: (215)238-5412
Fr: 800-777-8074
URL: http://www.napco.com
Monthly. Free. Trade magazine.

12659 ■ International Literary Market Place
Information Today Inc.
143 Old Marlton Pike
Medford, NJ 08055-8750
Ph: (609)654-6266
Fax: (609)654-4309
Fr: 800-300-9868
URL: http://www.literarymarketplace.com
Annual, Latest edition 2012. $289.00 for individuals; $260.10 for individuals. Covers: Over 10,500 publishers in over 180 countries outside the United States and Canada, and about 1,499 trade and professional organizations related to publishing abroad; includes major printers, binders, typesetters, book manufacturers, book dealers, libraries, literary agencies, translators, book clubs, reference books and journals, periodicals, prizes, and international reference section. Entries include: For publishers—Name, address, phone, fax, telex, names and titles of key personnel, branches, type of publications, subjects, ISBN prefix. Listings for others include similar information but less detail. Arrangement: Classified by business activities, then geographical. Indexes: Company name, subject, type of publication.

12660 ■ Literary Market Place
Information Today Inc.
143 Old Marlton Pike
Medford, NJ 08055-8750
Ph: (609)654-6266
Fax: (609)654-4309
Fr: 800-300-9868
URL: http://books.infotoday.com

Annual, Latest edition 2012. $339.00 for individuals; $305.10 for individuals. Covers: Over 12,500 firms or organizations offering services related to the publishing industry, including book publishers in the United States and Canada who issued three or more books during the preceding year, plus a small press section of publishers who publish less than three titles per year or those who are self-published. Also included: book printers and binders; book clubs; book trade and literary associations; selected syndicates, newspapers, periodicals, and radio and TV programs that use book reviews or book publishing news; translators and literary agents. Entries include: For publishers—Company name, address, phone, address for orders, principal executives, editorial directors, and managers, date founded, number of titles in previous year, number of backlist titles in print, types of books published, ISBN prefixes, representatives, imprints, and affiliations. For suppliers, etc.—Listings usually show firm name, address, phone, executives, services, etc. Arrangement: Classified by line of business. Indexes: Principal index is 35,000-item combined index of publishers, publications, and personnel; several sections have geographical and/or subject indexes; translators are indexed by source and target language.

12661 ■ Publishers Directory
Gale
PO Box 6904
Florence, KY 41022-6904
Fr: 800-354-9706
URL: http://www.gale.cengage.com
Annual, Latest edition 36th; April, 2011. $720.00 for individuals. Covers: Over 20,000 new and established, commercial and nonprofit, private and alternative, corporate and association, government and institution publishing programs and their distributors; includes producers of books, classroom materials, prints, reports, and databases. Entries include: Firm name, address, phone, fax, company e-mail address, URL, year founded, ISBN prefix, Standard Address Number, whether firm participates in the Cataloging in Publication program of the Library of Congress, names of principal executives, personal e-mail addresses, number of titles in print, description of firm and its main subject interests, discount and returns policies, affiliated and parent companies, mergers and amalgamations, principal markets, imprints and divisions, alternate formats products are offered; distributors also list firms for which they distribute, special services, terms to publishers and regional offices. Arrangement: Alphabetical; distributors listed separately. Indexes: Subject, geographical, publisher, imprints, and distributor.

12662 ■ The Workbook
Scott & Daughters Publishing Inc.
6762 Lexington Ave.
Los Angeles, CA 90038
Ph: (323)856-0008
Fax: (323)856-4368
Fr: 800-547-2688
URL: http://www.workbook.com

Annual, Latest edition 2011. $60.00 for individuals; $30.00 for individuals; $35.00 for individuals. Covers: 55,000 advertising agencies, art directors, photographers, freelance illustrators and designers, artists' representatives, interactive designers, pre-press services, and other graphic arts services in the U.S. Entries include: Company or individual name, address, phone, specialty. National in scope. Arrangement: Classified by product or service.

12663 ■ Graphic Arts Employment Specialists, Inc.
409 Pacific Coast Hwy., Ste. 455
Redondo Beach, CA 90277
Fax: (310)937-3760
Fr: 888-499-9722
E-mail: info@gaes.com
URL: http://www.gaes.com
Employment agency specializing in the publishing and packaging industries.

12664 ■ Printemps
18 Avery Pl.
Westport, CT 06880
Ph: (203)226-6869
Fax: (203)226-1594
E-mail: printemps7@aol.com
Specializes in providing temporary support for graphic design, document management and the electronic printing industry. Provides permanent placement for professionals and production personnel. Consults with printers and in-house print shops for greater production efficiency. Handles personnel management and policy programs as well. Industries served: printing, advertising, manufacturing, insurance, banking, and government agencies.

12665 ■ Zachary & Sanders Inc.
24 Linden Ln.
PO Box 32
East Norwich, NY 11732
Ph: (516)922-5500
Fax: (516)922-2286
Fr: 800-540-7919
E-mail: zacharyserch@earthlink.net
Serves the printing, packaging, publishing, advertising, direct marketing industries.

12666 ■ American Institute of Graphic Arts (AIGA)
164 5th Ave.
New York, NY 10010-5901
Ph: (212)807-1990

Fax: (212)807-1799
E-mail: grefe@aiga.org
URL: http://www.aiga.org

Description: Graphic designers, art directors, illustrators and packaging designers. Sponsors exhibits and projects in the public interest. Sponsors traveling exhibitions. Operates gallery. Maintains library of design books and periodicals; offers slide archives.

12667 ■ National Association for Printing Leadership (NAPL)
75 W Century Rd., Ste. 100
Paramus, NJ 07652-1408
Ph: (201)634-9600
Fax: (201)634-0324
Fr: 800-642-6275
E-mail: jtruncale@napl.org
URL: http://www.napl.org

Description: Represents commercial printers and suppliers to the commercial printing industry. Enables those in the industry to operate their businesses for maximum profitability. Offers following management products and services: sales and marketing, customer service, financial, human resources, operations and economic. Maintains Management Institute, which conducts Executive Certification Program. Compiles extensive economic statistics.

12668 ■ Printing Brokerage/Buyers Association (PB/BA)
PO Box 744
Palm Beach, FL 33480
Ph: (215)821-6581

Fax: (561)845-7130
Fr: 877-585-7141
URL: http://www.pbba.org

Description: Printing buyers/brokers/distributors, printers, typographers, binders, envelope and book manufacturers, packagers, color separation houses, pre-press service organizations, and related companies in the graphic arts industry. Promotes understanding, cooperation, and interaction among members while obtaining the highest standard of professionalism in the graphic arts industry. Gathers information on current technology in the graphic communications industry. Sponsors seminars for members to learn how to work with buyers, brokers and printers; also conducts technical and management seminars. Maintains referral service; compiles statistics. Conducts charitable programs.

12669 ■ Printing Industries of America (PIA)
200 Deer Run Rd.
Sewickley, PA 15143
Ph: (412)741-6860
Fax: (412)741-2311
Fr: 800-910-4283
E-mail: printing@printing.org
URL: http://www.printing.org

Description: Commercial printing firms (lithography, letterpress, gravure, platemakers, typographic houses); allied firms in the graphic arts. Provides extensive management services for member companies, including government relations, industry research and statistical information, technology information and assistance, and management education and

publications. Compiles statistical and economic data, including annual ratio study that provides a benchmark for printers to compare profits as a basis for improving individual member company and industry profits. Provides reporting system on provisions, rates, and other matters relating to union contracts in effect throughout the industry. Sponsors annual Premier Print Awards Competition.

12670 ■ Type Directors Club (TDC)
347 W 36th St., Ste. 603
New York, NY 10018
Ph: (212)633-8943
Fax: (212)633-8944
E-mail: director@tdc.org
URL: http://tdc.org

Description: Serves as a professional society of typographic designers, type directors, and teachers of typography; sustaining members are individuals with interests in typographic education. Seeks to stimulate research and disseminate information. Provides speakers, classes and offers presentations on history and new developments in typography.

12671 ■ Typophiles
15 Gramercy Park S, No. 6C
New York, NY 10003
E-mail: info@typophiles.org
URL: http://www.typophiles.org

Description: Represents designers, printers, book collectors, artists, calligraphers, private press owners, wood engravers, librarians and others interested in graphic arts. Promotes the love and appreciation of fine graphic design and printing. Conducts quarterly meeting-luncheons and maintains publications.

12672 ■ *OfficePRO*
Stratton Publishing and Marketing Inc.
5285 Shawnee Rd., Ste. 510
Alexandria, VA 22312-2334
Ph: (703)914-9200
Fax: (703)914-6777
URL: http://www.iaap-hq.org/publications/officepro

$25.00/year for individuals; $40.00/year for individuals, two years; $57.00/year for individuals, three years; $59.00/year for individuals, international; $109.00/year for individuals, international, two years. Magazine for administrative assistants, office managers, and secretaries featuring information on trends in business, technology, career development, and management.

EMPLOYMENT AGENCIES AND SEARCH FIRMS

12673 ■ Apple One Employment Services
18538 Hawthorne Blvd.
Torrance, CA 90504
Ph: (310)370-0708
Fr: 800-564-5644
E-mail: torrance-ca@appleone.com
URL: http://www.appleone.com

Employment agency. Additional offices in Anaheim, Oakland, Cerritos, San Francisco, Manhattan Beach, and Glendale.

12674 ■ The Aspire Group
711 Boylston St.
Boston, MA 02116-2616
Fax: (617)500-7284
Fr: 800-487-2967
URL: http://www.bmanet.com/Aspire/index.html

Employment agency.

12675 ■ Beverly Hills Bar Association Personnel Service
300 S Beverly Dr., Ste. 201
Beverly Hills, CA 90212-4805
Ph: (310)601-2422
Fax: (310)601-2423
URL: http://www.bhba.org

Employment agency.

12676 ■ Davis-Smith, Inc.
27656 Franklin Rd.
Southfield, MI 48034
Ph: (248)354-4100
Fax: (248)354-6702
E-mail: info@davissmith.com
URL: http://www.davissmith.com

Healthcare staffing agency. Executive search firm.

12677 ■ The Esquire Staffing Group Ltd.
1 S Wacker Dr., Ste. 1616
Chicago, IL 60606-4616
Ph: (312)795-4300
URL: http://www.esquirestaffing.com

Employment agency. Fills permanent as well as temporary openings.

12678 ■ Hallmark Services
603 Stewart St., Ste. 1021
Seattle, WA 98101
Ph: (206)587-5360
Fax: (206)587-5319
E-mail: hallmark@hallmarkservices.com
URL: http://www.hallmarkservices.com

Employment agency. Fills openings for permanent employment.

12679 ■ OfficeTeam.com
2884 Sand Hill Rd.
Menlo Park, CA 94025
Fr: 800-804-8367
URL: http://www.officeteam.com

Serves as a specialized temporary staffing service for administrative professionals including executive assistant, administrative assistant, office manager, project coordinator, receptionist, human resource assistant, marketing assistant, customer service representative, and data entry specialist.

12680 ■ Pathfinders, Inc.
229 Peachtree St. NE
International Tower, Ste. 1500
Atlanta, GA 30303
Ph: (404)688-5940
URL: http://www.pathfindersinc.com

Permanent employment agency focusing on the secretarial field.

ONLINE JOB SOURCES AND SERVICES

12681 ■ DataEntryJobs101.com
URL: http://www.dataentryjobs101.com

Description: Aims to help recently laid-off people in the secretarial, administrative and communications sectors find hourly or project-based data entry jobs that they can do from home.

OTHER SOURCES

12682 ■ American Academy of Professional Coders
2480 S 3850 W, Ste. B
Salt Lake City, UT 84120
Ph: (801)236-2200
Fax: (801)236-2258

Fr: 800-626-2633
E-mail: info@aapc.com
URL: http://www.aapc.com

Description: Represents physician-based medical coders. Aims to provide education and professional certification to physician-based medical coders and to elevate the standards of medical coding. Provides student training, certification, ongoing education, networking, and job opportunities.

12683 ■ Association of Information Technology Professionals (AITP)
401 N Michigan Ave., Ste. 2400
Chicago, IL 60611-4267
Ph: (312)245-1070
Fax: (312)673-6659
Fr: 800-224-9371
E-mail: aitp_hq@aitp.org
URL: http://www.aitp.org

Description: Managerial personnel, staff, educators, and individuals interested in the management of information resources. Founder of the Certificate in Data Processing examination program, now administered by an intersociety organization. Maintains Legislative Communications Network. Professional education programs include EDP-oriented business and management principles self-study courses and a series of videotaped management development seminars. Sponsors student organizations around the country interested in information technology and encourages members to serve as counselors for the Scout computer merit badge. Conducts research projects, including a business information systems curriculum for two- and four-year colleges.

12684 ■ Black Data Processing Associates (BDPA)
9500 Arena Dr., Ste. 350
Largo, MD 20774
Ph: (301)584-3135
Fax: (301)560-8300
Fr: 800-727-BDPA
E-mail: office@bdpa.org
URL: http://www.bdpa.org

Description: Represents persons employed in the information processing industry, including electronic data processing, electronic word processing and data communications; others interested in information processing. Seeks to accumulate and share information processing knowledge and business expertise to increase the career and business potential of minorities in the information processing field. Conducts professional seminars, workshops, tutoring services and community introductions to data processing. Makes annual donation to the United Negro College Fund.

12685 ■ NaSPA
7044 S 13th St.
Oak Creek, WI 53154
Ph: (414)908-4945
E-mail: customercare@naspa.com
URL: http://www.naspa.com

Description: Technicians and technical management personnel in 90 countries who work in corporate data processing. Works to enhance the level of technical education among members through publications, public domain software, electronic information sharing, job and career assistance, and scholarships and grants. Conducts charitable and educational programs; maintains speakers' bureau and placement service; compiles statistics.

Sources of Help-Wanted Ads

12686 ■ Best's Review
A.M. Best Company, Inc.
Ambest Rd.
Oldwick, NJ 08858
Ph: (908)439-2200
URL: http://www.ambest.com/sales/
newsoverview.asp#br

Monthly. $50.00/year for individuals. Magazine covering issues and trends for the management personnel of life/health insurers, the agents, and brokers who market their products.

12687 ■ Business Insurance
Crain Communications Inc.
1155 Gratiot Ave.
Detroit, MI 48207-2997
Ph: (313)446-6000
URL: http://www.businessinsurance.com

Weekly. $399.00/year for individuals, print; $149.00/year for individuals, print & digital; $69.00/year for individuals, digital edition. International newsweekly reporting on corporate risk and employee benefit management news.

12688 ■ National Underwriter Property and Casualty/Risk and Benefits Management
National Underwriter Co.
5081 Olympic Blvd.
PO Box 14367
Erlanger, KY 41018
Ph: (859)692-2100
Fax: (859)692-2175
Fr: 800-543-0874
URL: http://www.propertycasualty360.com/National-Underwriter-Prop

Weekly. $94.00/year for individuals, 2nd class; $133.00/year for Canada, air mail; $178.00/year for U.S. and Canada, air mail; $211.00/year for other countries, air mail. Newsweekly for agents, brokers, executives, and managers in risk and benefit insurance.

12689 ■ The Standard
Standard Publishing Corp.
155 Federal St., 13th Fl.
Boston, MA 02110
Ph: (617)457-0600
Fax: (617)457-0608
E-mail: stnd@earthlink.net
URL: http://www.spcpub.com

Weekly (Fri.). $95.00/year for individuals, U.S.; $165.00/year for two years. Trade newspaper covering insurance events, legislation, regulatory hearings, and court sessions for independent insurance agents in New England.

Employer Directories and Networking Lists

12690 ■ Best's Insurance Reports
A.M. Best Co.
Ambest Rd.
Oldwick, NJ 08858
Ph: (908)439-2200
URL: http://www.ambest.com

Annual, Latest edition 2011. Published in three editions—Life-health insurance, covering about 1,750 companies, property-casualty insurance, covering over 3,200 companies; and international, covering more than 1,200 insurers. Each edition lists state insurance commissioners and related companies and agencies (mutual funds, worker compensation funds, underwriting agencies, etc.). Entries include: For each company—Company name, address, phone; history; states in which licensed; names of officers and directors; financial data; financial analysis and Best's rating. Arrangement: Alphabetical.

12691 ■ Business Insurance—Agent/Broker Profiles Issue
Business Insurance
360 N Michigan Ave.
Chicago, IL 60601-3806
Ph: (312)649-5200
Fax: (312)280-3174
Fr: 888-446-1422
URL: http://www.businessinsurance.com

Annual, Latest edition 2008. Publication includes: List of top 10 insurance agents/brokers worldwide specializing in commercial insurance. Entries include: Firm name, address, phone, fax, branch office locations, year established, names of subsidiaries, gross revenues, premium volume, number of employees, principal officers, percent of revenue generated by commercial retail brokerage, acquisitions. Arrangement: Alphabetical by company. Indexes: Geographical.

12692 ■ Insurance Phone Book
Briefings Media Group
2807 N Parham Rd., Ste. 200
Richmond, VA 23294
Ph: (570)567-1982
Fr: 800-791-8699
URL: http://www.douglaspublications.com

Annual, latest edition 2009-2010. $195.00; $389.00. Covers: About 3,700 life, accident and health, worker's compensation, auto, fire and casualty, marine, surety, and other insurance companies; 2,300 executive contacts from presidents and CEOs to claims and customer service managers. Entries include: Company name, address, phone, fax, toll-free number, type of insurance provided. Arrangement: Alphabetical.

12693 ■ Kirschner's Insurance Directories
National Underwriter Co.
5081 Olympic Blvd.
PO Box 14367
Erlanger, KY 41018
Ph: (859)692-2100
Fax: (859)692-2175
Fr: 800-543-0874
URL: http://www.nationalunderwriter.com

Annual, Latest edition 2007. Covers: Insurance agents and agencies in all 50 states and the District of Columbia. Published in 24 separate editions for Southern California, Northern California, Pacific Northwest (AK, ID, HI, OR, WA, MT), Michigan, Illinois, New England states (CT, ME, MA, NH, RI, VT), Ohio, Rocky Mountain states (AZ, CO, NV, NM, UT, WY), South Central states (GA, AL, MS), Indiana, Texas, Kentucky/Tennessee, East Central states (VA, WV, NC, SC), South Central West states (AR, OK, LA), Wisconsin, Central states (KS, MO, NE), North Central states (IA, MN, ND, SD), Mid-Atlantic states (DE, MD, NJ, DC), Pennsylvania, Florida. Entries include: For companies—Name, address, key personnel (with addresses and phone numbers). Arrangement: Separate alphabetical sections for insurance companies, wholesalers, field agents, and agencies. Indexes: Type of insurance.

Handbooks and Manuals

12694 ■ Opportunities in Insurance Careers
The McGraw-Hill Companies
PO Box 182604
Columbus, OH 43272
Fax: (614)759-3749
Fr: 877-883-5524
E-mail: customer.service@mcgraw-hill.com
URL: http://www.mhprofessional.com/
product.php?isbn=0071482075

Robert M. Schrayer. Revised, 2007. $14.95 (paper). 160 pages. A guide to planning for and seeking opportunities in the field. Contains bibliography and illustrations.

Employment Agencies and Search Firms

12695 ■ International Insurance Personnel, Inc.
300 W Wieuca Rd., Bldg. 2, Ste. 101
Atlanta, GA 30342
Ph: (404)255-9710
Fax: (404)255-9864
E-mail: iipjulie@bellsouth.net
URL: http://realpages.com/sites/intlinspersonnel/
index.html

Employment agency specializing in the area of insurance.

12696 ■ J. R. Peterman Associates, Inc.
PO Box 3083
Stowe, VT 05672
Ph: (802)253-6304
Fax: (802)253-6314
E-mail: peterman@jrpeterman.com
URL: http://www.jrpeterman.com

Description: Recruit professionals in permanent and contract positions for the life and health insurance industry and employee benefits consulting.

12697 ■ Lear & Associates, Inc.
1235 N Orange Ave.
Orlando, FL 32804
Ph: (407)645-4611
Fax: (407)645-5735
E-mail: info@learsearch.com
URL: http://www.learsearch.com

Serves as recruitment firm specializing in the insurance industry.

12698 ■ Questor Consultants, Inc.
2515 N Broad St.
Colmar, PA 18915
Ph: (215)997-9262
Fax: (215)997-9226
E-mail: sbevivino@questorconsultants.com
URL: http://www.questorconsultants.com

Executive search firm specializing in the insurance and legal fields.

12699 ■ Todd Mitchell Associates
3333 New Hyde Park Rd.
New Hyde Park, NY 11042
Fax: (516)365-2460
Fr: 800-886-1562
E-mail: todd.mitchell@toddmitchell.com
URL: http://www.toddmitchell.com

Executive search firm for the insurance industry. Specializes in the recruitment and placement of executive and technical personnel whose expertise is within the disciplines of underwriting, marketing, claims, and loss control.

ONLINE JOB SOURCES AND SERVICES

12700 ■ Insurance Underwriting Jobs
URL: http://www.insuranceunderwritingjobs.org

Description: Features listings for insurance underwriting jobs. Connects job seekers with hiring managers and employers.

12701 ■ InsuranceUnderwritingWeb.com
E-mail: info@insuranceunderwritingweb.com
URL: http://www.insuranceunderwritingweb.com

Description: Assists underwriters in finding employment and job postings.

12702 ■ UltimateInsuranceJobs.com
URL: http://www.ultimateinsurancejobs.com/index.asp

Description: Provides insurance job listings, recruiter directory, and resources. Offers job seekers the opportunity to post and edit their resumes, and employers the opportunity to search through insurance resumes.

12703 ■ UnderwriterJobs.com
URL: http://www.underwriterjobs.com

Description: Provides new job openings for underwriters. Includes insightful research into the insurance employment market and an informative career articles section, written and frequented by industry professionals.

12704 ■ UnderwritingCrossing.com
URL: http://www.underwritingcrossing.com

Description: Provides a collection of top underwriting job openings. Includes Fortune 500 and Fortune 1,000 companies.

12705 ■ UnderwritingJobs.com
Ph: (972)679-4542
E-mail: admin@underwritingjobs.com
URL: http://www.underwritingjobs.com

Description: Job search website for underwriters. Seekers may search databank by field of interest or geography, post their resume or visit career-related links.

12706 ■ USAInsuranceJobs.com
URL: http://usainsurancejobs.com

Description: Specializes in helping job seekers find insurance jobs at insurance companies and state insurance departments nationwide.

TRADESHOWS

12707 ■ CPCU Conferment Ceremony
American Institute for CPCU
720 Providence Rd.
Ste. 100
Malvern, PA 19355-3433
Fax: (610)640-9576
Fr: 800-644-2101
E-mail: cserv@cpcuiia.org
URL: http://www.aicpcu.org

Annual. Primary Exhibits: Exhibits for insurance personnel and Chartered Property Casualty Underwriters (CPCUs).

12708 ■ Financial Services Forum
Society of Financial Service Professionals
19 Campus Blvd., Ste. 100
Newtown Square, PA 19073-3239
Ph: (610)526-2500
Fax: (610)527-1499
URL: http://www.financialpro.org

Annual. Primary Exhibits: Exhibitors who offer products and services for the leaders in the insurance and financial services industry.

12709 ■ National Association of Review Appraisers and Mortgage Underwriters Convention - National Conference & Expo
National Association of Review Appraisers and Mortgage Underwriters
1224 N Nokomis NE
Alexandria, MN 56308-5072
Ph: (320)763-6870
Fax: (320)763-9290
URL: http://iami.org/nara

Annual. Primary Exhibits: Real estate-related information and services.

12710 ■ Public Agency Risk Managers Association Convention
Public Agency Risk Managers Association
PO Box 6810
San Jose, CA 95150
Ph: 888-907-2762
Fax: 888-907-2762
Fr: 888-90P-ARMA
E-mail: brenda.reisinger@parma.com
URL: http://www.parma.com

Annual. Primary Exhibits: Risk management equipment, supplies, and services.

OTHER SOURCES

12711 ■ American Council of Life Insurers (ACLI)
101 Constitution Ave. NW, Ste. 700
Washington, DC 20001-2133
Ph: (202)624-2000
Fr: 877-674-4659
E-mail: webadmin@acli.com
URL: http://www.acli.com

Description: Represents the interests of legal reserve life insurance companies in legislative, regulatory and judicial matters at the federal, state and municipal levels of government and at the NAIC. Member companies hold majority of the life insurance in force in the United States.

12712 ■ American Institute for CPCU (AICPCU)
720 Providence Rd., Ste. 100
Malvern, PA 19355-3433
Fax: (610)640-9576
Fr: 800-644-2101
E-mail: customerservice@cpcuiia.org
URL: http://www.aicpcu.org

Description: Purpose: Determines qualifications for professional certification of insurance personnel; conducts examinations and awards designation of Chartered Property Casualty Underwriter (CPCU).

12713 ■ Association of Home Office Underwriters
2300 Windy Ridge Pkwy., Ste. 600
Atlanta, GA 30339
Ph: (770)984-3715
Fax: (770)984-3758
E-mail: president@ahou.org
URL: http://ahou.org

Description: Serves as an organization of insurance professionals responsible for risk assessment in the life, health and disability insurance industries. Strives to meet the career development needs of its members through educational meetings and seminars as well as special projects and studies.

12714 ■ Association of Real Estate Women
1201 Wakarusa Dr., Ste. C3
Lawrence, KS 66049
Ph: (212)599-6181
Fax: (785)832-1551
Fr: 888-329-2739
E-mail: info@arew.org
URL: http://www.arew.org

Description: Provides programs and networking opportunities that can contribute to the career growth of both men and women in all segments and all levels of the real estate industry. Helps members find new employment opportunities.

12715 ■ Chartered Property Casualty Underwriters Society
720 Providence Rd.
Malvern, PA 19355
Fax: (610)251-2780
Fr: 800-932-CPCU
E-mail: membercenter@cpcusociety.org
URL: http://www.cpcusociety.org

Description: Consists of property and casualty insurance professionals. Strives to meet the career development needs of its members while promoting excellence through ethical behavior and continuing education.

12716 ■ CPCU Society
720 Providence Rd.
Malvern, PA 19355-3402
Ph: (610)251-2727
Fax: (610)251-2780
Fr: 800-932-2728
E-mail: membercenter@cpcusociety.org
URL: http://www.cpcusociety.org

Description: Serves as a professional society of individuals who have passed national examinations of the American Institute for Chartered Property Casualty Underwriters, have 3 years of work experience, have agreed to be bound by a code of ethics, and have been awarded CPCU designation. Promotes education, research, social responsibility, and professionalism in the field. Holds seminars, symposia, and workshops.

12717 ■ Group Underwriters Association of America
PO Box 118
Weatogue, CT 06089
E-mail: jpollar1@maine.rr.com
URL: http://www.guaa.com

Description: Promotes the study, analysis, and discussion pertaining to all matters of mutual interest in underwriting group products. Provides its members the opportunities for professional development, networking and information gathering.

12718 ■ Insurance Information Institute (III)
110 William St.
New York, NY 10038
Ph: (212)346-5500
E-mail: members@iii.org
URL: http://www.iii.org
Description: Property and casualty insurance companies. Provides information and educational services to mass media, educational institutions, trade associations, businesses, government agencies, and the public.

12719 ■ LOMA
2300 Windy Ridge Pkwy., Ste. 600
Atlanta, GA 30339-8443
Ph: (770)951-1770
Fax: (770)984-0441
Fr: 800-275-5662
E-mail: askloma@loma.org
URL: http://www.loma.org
Description: Life and health insurance companies and financial services in the U.S. and Canada; and overseas in 45 countries; affiliate members are firms that provide professional support to member companies. Provides research, information, training, and educational activities in areas of operations and systems, human resources, financial planning and employee development. Administers FLMI Insurance Education Program, which awards FLMI (Fellow, Life Management Institute) designation to those who complete the ten-examination program.

12720 ■ National Association of Health Underwriters (NAHU)
2000 N 14th St., Ste. 450
Arlington, VA 22201
Ph: (703)276-0220

Fax: (703)841-7797
E-mail: info@nahu.org
URL: http://www.nahu.org
Description: Insurance agents and brokers engaged in the promotion, sale, and administration of disability income and health insurance. Sponsors advanced health insurance underwriting and research seminars. Testifies before federal and state committees on pending health insurance legislation. Sponsors Leading Producers Roundtable Awards for leading salesmen. Maintains a speakers' bureau and a political action committee.

12721 ■ National Association of Insurance Women International (NAIW)
9343 E 95th Ct. S
Tulsa, OK 74133
Ph: (918)294-3700
Fax: (918)294-3711
Fr: 800-766-6249
E-mail: joinnaiw@naiw.org
URL: http://www.naiw.org
Description: Insurance industry professionals. Promotes continuing education and networking for the professional advancement of its members. Offers education programs, meetings, services, and leadership opportunities. Provides a forum to learn about other disciplines in the insurance industry.

12722 ■ National Association of Review Appraisers and Mortgage Underwriters (NARA/MU)
810 N Farrell Dr.
Palm Springs, CA 92262
Ph: (760)327-5284
Fax: (760)327-5631
E-mail: support@assoc-hdqts.org
URL: http://www.naramu.org
Description: Real estate professionals and mortgage

underwriters who aid in determining value of property. Acts as umbrella group for real estate appraisers. Conducts educational seminars; maintains speakers' bureau; operates placement service.

12723 ■ Professional Liability Underwriting Society
5353 Wayzata Blvd., Ste. 600
Minneapolis, MN 55416
Ph: (952)746-2580
Fax: (952)746-2599
Fr: 800-845-0778
E-mail: info@plusweb.org
URL: http://plusweb.org

Description: Serves individuals interested in the promotion and development of the professional liability industry. Commits to enhancing the professionalism of its members through education and other activities and to addressing issues related to professional liability insurance.

12724 ■ Society of Financial Service Professionals (SFSP)
19 Campus Blvd., Ste. 100
Newtown Square, PA 19073-3239
Ph: (610)526-2500
Fax: (610)527-1499
Fr: 800-392-6900
E-mail: info@financialpro.org
URL: http://www.financialpro.org

Description: Represents the interests of financial advisers. Fosters the development of professional responsibility. Assists clients to achieve personal and business-related financial goals. Offers educational programs, online professional resources and networking opportunities.

Urban and Regional Planners

SOURCES OF HELP-WANTED ADS

12725 ■ American City and County
Penton Media Inc.
9800 Metcalf Ave.
Overland Park, KS 66212
Ph: (913)341-1300
Fax: (913)967-1898
URL: http://americancityandcounty.com

Monthly. Municipal and county administration magazine.

12726 ■ Architectural Record
McGraw-Hill Inc.
PO Box 182604
Columbus, OH 43218
Ph: (614)430-4000
Fax: (614)759-3749
Fr: 877-833-5524
URL: http://archrecord.construction.com

Monthly. $49.00/year for individuals; $59.00/year for Canada; $109.00/year for other countries. Magazine focusing on architecture.

12727 ■ Better Roads
James Informational Media Inc.
2720 S River Rd.
Des Plaines, IL 60018-5142
Ph: (847)391-9070
Fax: (847)391-9058
Fr: 800-957-9305
URL: http://www.betterroads.com

Monthly. Free. Magazine serving federal, state, county, city, and township officials involved in road, street, bridge, and airport construction, maintenance and safety.

12728 ■ Builder
Hanley-Wood L.L.C.
1 Thomas Cir. NW, Ste. 600
Washington, DC 20005-5803
Ph: (202)452-0800
Fax: (202)785-1974
E-mail: builder@omeda.com
URL: http://www.hanleywood.com/
default.aspx?page=magazines

$29.95/year for U.S. and Canada; $54.95/year for U.S. and Canada, 2 years; $192.00/year for other countries. Magazine covering housing and construction industry.

12729 ■ IDA
International Downtown Association
1025 Thomas Jefferson St., NW, Ste. 500W
Washington, DC 20007
Ph: (202)393-6801
Fax: (202)393-6869
E-mail: question@ida-downtown.org
URL: http://www.ida-downtown.org

Description: Quarterly. Covers issues of downtown revitalization, management districts, planning, development, promotion, marketing, financing, and related legislation. Recurring features include news of organization and "member cities"' activities.

12730 ■ ITE Journal
Institute of Transportation Engineers
1099 14th St. NW, Ste. 300 W
Washington, DC 20005-3419
Ph: (202)289-0222
Fax: (202)289-7722
URL: http://www.ite.org/itejournal/

Monthly. $65.00/year for U.S., Canada, and Mexico; $85.00/year for other countries; $160.00/year for U.S., Canada, and Mexico, 3 years; $200.00/year for other countries, 3 years; $5.00/year for single issue, back issue. Technical magazine focusing on the plan, design, and operation of surface transportation systems.

12731 ■ Jobs Online
American Planning Association
205 N Michigan Ave., Ste. 1200
Chicago, IL 60603-6107
Ph: (312)431-9100
Fax: (312)786-6700
E-mail: customerservice@planning.org
URL: http://www.planning.org

Description: Semimonthly. Reports on jobs in the planning field, covering urban and regional opportunities and related jobs in community development and transportation. Recurring features include educational opportunities and internships.

12732 ■ Land Use Law Report
Business Publishers Inc.
2222 Sedwick Dr., Ste. 101
Durham, NC 27713
Fr: 800-874-9180
E-mail: custserv@bpinews.com
URL: http://www.bpinews.com/

Monthly. $417/year. Provides up-to-date information on court decisions, legislation, and regulations that impact today's most pressing land-use policy, planning, and legal issues. Readers receive in-depth coverage on zoning and planning policies, regulatory takings, undesirable land uses, environmental legislation, and much more. Also available via e-mail.

12733 ■ MAPC News
Metropolitan Area Planning Council
60 Temple Pl.
Boston, MA 02111
Ph: (617)451-2270
Fax: (617)482-7185
URL: http://www.mapc.org

Description: Monthly. Reports on regional planning news on issues concerning economic developers. Topics include housing, transportation, environment, and open space protection. Recurring features include a calendar of events, reports of meetings, and news of educational opportunities.

12734 ■ Municipal Art Society Newsletter
Municipal Art Society
111 W 57th St.
New York, NY 10019
Ph: (212)935-3960
Fax: (212)753-1816
E-mail: info@mas.org
URL: http://mas.org

Description: Six issues/year. Provides updates on advocacy efforts, exhibitions, and programming on urban issues. Recurring features include a calendar of events and tour schedule.

12735 ■ The Municipality
League of Wisconsin Municipalities
122 W Washington Ave., Ste. 300
Madison, WI 53703-2715
Ph: (608)267-2380
Fax: (608)267-0645
Fr: 800-991-5502
URL: http://www.lwm-info.org/

Monthly. Magazine for officials of Wisconsin's local municipal governments.

12736 ■ NAHRO Monitor
National Association of Housing and Redevelopment Officials
630 Eye St. NW
Washington, DC 20001
Ph: (202)289-3500
Fax: (202)289-8181
Fr: 877-866-2476
E-mail: nahro@nahro.org
URL: http://www.nahro.org/nahro_monitor

Description: Biweekly. Disseminates news on low-income housing and community development issues. Intended for member professionals and government officials.

12737 ■ New Urban News
New Urban Publications Inc.
PO Box 6515
Ithaca, NY 14851
Ph: (607)275-3087
Fax: (607)272-2685
E-mail: mail@newurbannews.com
URL: http://newurbannetwork.com

Description: Eight issues/year. $79/year. Devoted to new urbanism and news and analysis of new and additional development in urban planning. Recurring features include letters to the editor, interviews, news of research, calendar of events, book reviews, job listings, notices of publications available, and columns from guest contributors.

12738 ■ PAS Memo
American Planning Association
122 S Michigan Ave., Ste. 1600
Chicago, IL 60603-6107
Ph: (312)431-9100

Fax: (312)431-9985
E-mail: customerservice@planning.org
URL: http://www.planning.org/pas/memo/index.htm

Description: Bimonthly. Focuses on subjects related to urban planning, zoning, and renewal. Provides advice and commentary on topics such as economic development, land use planning, growth management, and suburbanization.

12739 ■ *PE & RS Photogrammetric Engineering & Remote Sensing*
The Imaging and Geospatial Information Society
5410 Grosvenor Ln., Ste. 210
Bethesda, MD 20814-2160
Ph: (301)493-0290
Fax: (301)493-0208
URL: http://www.asprs.org/PE-RS-Journal/

Monthly. $410.00/year for individuals, first class mail; $426.00/year for Canada, airmail; $420.00/year for other countries, air standard. Peer-reviewed journal covering photogrammetry, remote sensing, geographic information systems, cartography, and surveying, global positioning systems, digital photogrammetry.

12740 ■ *Progressive Planning*
Planners Network
106 W Sibley Hall
Cornell University
Ithaca, NY 14853
Ph: (607)254-8890
Fax: (607)255-1971
E-mail: info@plannersnetwork.org
URL: http://www.plannersnetwork.org

Description: Quarterly. Covers news of the Planners Network. Recurring features include letters to the editor, a calendar of events, job listings, and notices of publications available.

12741 ■ *Roads & Bridges Magazine*
Scranton Gillette Communications Inc.
3030 W Salt Creek Ln., Ste. 201
Arlington Heights, IL 60005-5025
Ph: (847)391-1000
Fax: (847)390-0408
URL: http://www.roadsbridges.com

Monthly. Free to qualified subscribers. Magazine containing information on highway, road, and bridge design, construction, and maintenance for government agencies, contractors, and consulting engineers.

12742 ■ *RPA Blueprint*
Regional Plan Association
4 Irving Pl., 7th Fl.
New York, NY 10003
Ph: (212)253-2727
Fax: (212)253-5666
E-mail: npranger@rpa.org
URL: http://www.rpa.org

Description: Quarterly. Focuses on regional planning, forums, and economic development.

12743 ■ *The Times*
Council on Tall Buildings & Urban Habitat
Illinois Institute of Technology
S.R. Crown Hall
3360 S State St.
Chicago, IL 60616-3796
Ph: (312)567-3487
Fax: (312)567-3820
E-mail: info@ctbuh.org
URL: http://www.ctbuh.org

Description: 3-4 issues/year. Concerned with all aspects of the planning, design, construction, and operation of tall buildings. Examines the role of tall buildings in the urban environment and acts as a forum for exchange of information among engineering, architectural, and planning professionals. Recurring features include news of research, book reviews, notices of publications available, reports on the committees of the Council, a calendar of events, and a column titled On My Mind.

12744 ■ *The Urban Open Space Manager*
Urban Wildlife Resources
5130 W Running Brook Rd.
Columbia, MD 21044
Ph: (410)997-7161
Fax: (410)997-6849
URL: http://users.erols.com/urbanwildlife

Description: Quarterly. Contains substantive articles involving research, planning, design, education, and management relative to urban open spaces.

12745 ■ *Western City*
League of California Cities
1400 K St., 4th Fl.
Sacramento, CA 95814
Ph: (916)658-8200
Fax: (916)658-8240
Fr: 800-262-1801
URL: http://www.westerncity.com

Monthly. $39.00/year for individuals; $63.00/year for two years; $52.00/year for other countries; $26.50/year for students. Municipal interest magazine.

12746 ■ *Zoning and Planning Law Report*
Thomson West
610 Opperman Dr.
PO Box 64833
Eagan, MN 55123
Ph: (651)687-7000
Fr: 800-850-9378
URL: http://store.westlaw.com

Description: Monthly. Features articles on land use law, zoning by initiative and referendum, impact fees, affordable housing laws, wetlands regulations, First Amendment land use cases, due process and taking clause claims, and choice of forum in land use litigation. Recurring features include descriptions of recent cases and notices of upcoming conferences.

EMPLOYER DIRECTORIES AND NETWORKING LISTS

12747 ■ *ENR—Top 500 Design Firms Issue*
McGraw-Hill Inc.
PO Box 182604
Columbus, OH 43218
Ph: (614)430-4000
Fax: (614)759-3749
Fr: 877-833-5524
URL: http://enr.construction.com/toplists/
    sourcebooks/2010/design

Annual, latest edition 2010. $82.00 for individuals. Publication includes: List of 500 leading architectural, engineering, and specialty design firms selected on basis of annual billings. Entries include: Company name, headquarters location, type of firm, current and prior year rank in billings, types of services, countries in which operated in preceding year. Arrangement: Ranked by billings.

HANDBOOKS AND MANUALS

12748 ■ *Opportunities in Social Science Careers*
The McGraw-Hill Companies
PO Box 182604
Columbus, OH 43272
Fax: (614)759-3749
Fr: 877-883-5524
E-mail: customer.service@mcgraw-hill.com
URL: http://www.mcgraw-hill.com

Rosanne J. Marek. 2004. $13.95. 160 Pages. VGM Opportunities Series.

ONLINE JOB SOURCES AND SERVICES

12749 ■ *UrbanPlanningCareers.com*
URL: http://www.urbanplanningcareers.com
Description: Provides resources for urban planners

and other related professionals. Offers job listings and career opportunities.

12750 ■ UrbanPlanningNow.com
URL: http://www.urbanplanningnow.com

Description: Provides employment services in urban planning. Offers a general search service, a private list of job openings found throughout the internet and a location for employers to post their jobs.

TRADESHOWS

12751 ■ National Community Development Association Annual Conference
National Community Development Association
522 21st St. NW, No. 120
Washington, DC 20006
Ph: (202)293-7587
Fax: (202)887-5546
E-mail: ncda@ncdaonline.org
URL: http://www.ncdaonline.org

Annual. Provides forums to discuss and develop relevant legislative and administrative initiatives for the membership. Provides members an opportunity to network, exchange experiences and ideas, and engage in public policy discussions.

OTHER SOURCES

12752 ■ American Institute of Certified Planners (AICP)
American Planning Association
1030 15th St. NW, Ste. 750 W
Washington, DC 20005-1503
Ph: (202)872-0611
Fax: (202)872-0643
E-mail: aicp@planning.org
URL: http://www.planning.org/aicp

Description: Serves as the professional institute of the American Planning Association. Consists of members of the APA who have met the requirements of education, practice, and examination established for the professional practice of public planning. Provides continuing education and a written professional examination. Maintains code of ethics; conducts research.

12753 ■ American Planning Association (APA)
122 S Michigan Ave., Ste. 1600
Chicago, IL 60603-6107
Ph: (312)431-9100
Fax: (312)431-9985
E-mail: customerservice@planning.org
URL: http://www.planning.org

Description: Public and private planning agency officials, professional planners, planning educators, elected and appointed officials, and other persons involved in urban and rural development. Works to foster the best techniques and decisions for the planned development of communities and regions. Provides extensive professional services and publications to professionals and laypeople in planning and related fields; serves as a clearinghouse for information. Through Planning Advisory Service, a research and inquiry-answering service, provides, on an annual subscription basis, advice on specific inquiries and a series of research reports on planning, zoning, and environmental regulations. Supplies information on job openings and makes definitive studies on salaries and recruitment of professional planners. Conducts research; collaborates in joint projects with local, national, and international organizations.

12754 ■ ASPRS - The Imaging and Geospatial Information Society
5410 Grosvenor Ln., Ste. 210
Bethesda, MD 20814-2160
Ph: (301)493-0290

Fax: (301)493-0208
E-mail: asprs@asprs.org
URL: http://www.asprs.org

Description: Firms, individuals, government employees and academicians engaged in photogrammetry, photointerpretation, remote sensing, and geographic information systems and their application to such fields as archaeology, geographic information systems, military reconnaissance, urban planning, engineering, traffic surveys, meteorological observations, medicine, geology, forestry, agriculture, construction and topographic mapping. Seeks to advance knowledge and improve understanding of these sciences and promote responsible applications. Offers voluntary certification program open to persons associated with one or more functional area of photogrammetry, remote sensing and GIS. Surveys the profession of private firms in photogrammetry and remote sensing in the areas of products and services.

12755 ■ Fusion Architecture

PO Box 66853
Phoenix, AZ 85082-6853
E-mail: info@fusionarchitecture.org
URL: http://www.fusionarchitecture.org

Description: Represents the interests of architecture, urban design, graphic design, engineering and cultural practitioners. Encourages young designers to create design solutions to socio-cultural issues. Promotes the use of graphic and information design tools to reach out and produce projects that have influence on the economics, politics, cultural and social structure facing urban communities.

12756 ■ National Association of Regional Councils

1666 Connecticut Ave. NW, Ste. 300
Washington, DC 20009
Ph: (202)986-1032

Fax: (202)986-1038
URL: http://narc.org

Description: Promotes the advancement of regional cooperation through interaction and advocacy with congress, federal officials, and other related agencies. Addresses community planning, development opportunities, and issues. Provides members with information and research on key national policy issues, federal policy developments, and best practices. Conducts training sessions, conferences, workshops, and satellite telecasts.

12757 ■ National Community Development Association

522 21st St. NW, No. 120
Washington, DC 20006
Ph: (202)293-7587
Fax: (202)887-5546
E-mail: ncda@ncdaonline.org
URL: http://ncdaonline.org

Description: Represents local government administrators of housing and community development programs. Provides information and technical support to its members on federal housing and community development programs. Serves as a national clearinghouse of ideas for local government officials and federal policy-makers on pertinent national issues affecting America's communities.

12758 ■ National Urban Fellows (NUF)

102 W 38th St., Ste. 700
New York, NY 10018
Ph: (212)730-1700
Fax: (212)730-1823
E-mail: info@nuf.org
URL: http://www.nuf.org

Description: Aims to meet the need for competent urban and rural administrators, particularly minority group members and women, by combining a nine-month, on-the-job assignment as special assistant to an experienced practitioner with several kinds of academic work.

12759 ■ Society of Iranian Architects and Planners (SIAP)

PO Box 643066
Los Angeles, CA 90064
E-mail: abdiziai@gmail.com
URL: http://siap.org

Description: Represents Iranian graduates in the field of architecture, planning, interior design and landscape architecture. Promotes cultural, scientific and professional aspects in the field architecture and encourages members to develop and advance their skills and abilities in the profession. Provides members with a means of communication for coordination of mutual professional and cultural relationships with similar Iranian organizations around the globe.

12760 ■ Urbanists International

134 The Uplands
Berkeley, CA 94705
Ph: (510)547-5500
Fax: (510)654-5807
E-mail: info@urbanists.org
URL: http://urbanists.org

Description: Offers urban design, planning and economic development assistance to developing countries. Promotes global awareness about the critical role that good urban planning can play in a country's development.

SOURCES OF HELP-WANTED ADS

12761 ■ American Journal of Animal and Veterinary Sciences
Science Publications
Vails Gate Heights Dr.
PO Box 879
Vails Gate, NY 12584-0879
URL: http://thescipub.com/ajavs.toc

Quarterly. $1,100.00/year for individuals; $300.00/year for single issue. Peer-reviewd scholarly journal covering animal husbandry and veterinary medicine.

12762 ■ American Journal of Veterinary Research
American Veterinary Medical Association
1931 N Meacham Rd., Ste. 100
Schaumburg, IL 60173-4360
Ph: (847)925-8070
Fax: (847)925-1329
Fr: 800-248-2862
URL: http://www.avma.org/journals/ajvr/ajvr_about.asp

Monthly. $245.00/year for individuals; $255.00/year for other countries; $35.00/year for single issue; $40.00/year for single issue, other Country. Veterinary research on nutrition and diseases of domestic, wild, and furbearing animals.

12763 ■ Animal Keepers' Forum
American Association of Zoo Keepers Inc.
3601 SW 29th St., Ste. 133
Topeka, KS 66614-2054
Ph: (785)273-9149
Fax: (785)273-1980
URL: http://aazk.org/category/akf/toc/

Monthly. $10.00/year for members; $20.00/year for Canada, members. Professional journal of the American Association of Zoo Keepers, Inc.

12764 ■ The Chronicle of the Horse
The Chronicle of the Horse Inc.
PO Box 46
108 De Plains
Middleburg, VA 20118
Ph: (540)687-6341
Fax: (540)687-3937
E-mail: staff@chronofhorse.com
URL: http://www.chronofhorse.com/index.php?cat=40311032977488

Weekly. $2.95/year; $2.95/year for single issue; $159.00/year for other countries, print only; $60.00/year for individuals, print & digital; $160.00/year for other countries, print & digital; $109.00/year for two years, print & digital; $35.00/year for individuals, digital only; $59.00/year for individuals, print only; $108.00/year for two years, print only. Magazine covering English riding and horse sports.

12765 ■ CME Supplement to Veterinary Clinics of North America
Elsevier Science Inc.
360 Park Ave. S
New York, NY 10010-1710
Ph: (212)989-5800
Fax: (212)633-3990
Fr: 888-437-4636
URL: http://www.elsevier.com/wps/find/journaldescription.cws_home

$55.00/year for individuals. Journal covering veterinary medicine, surgical treatment of animals.

12766 ■ Dog World
Bowtie, Inc.
PO Box 6050
Mission Viejo, CA 92690-6040
Ph: (949)855-8822
Fax: (949)855-3045
E-mail: letters@dogworld.com
URL: http://www.dogchannel.com/dog-magazines/dogworld/default.asp

Monthly. $15.00/year for individuals; $27.00/year for other countries. Magazine serving breeders, exhibitors, hobbyists and professionals in kennel operations, groomers, veterinarians, animal hospitals/clinics and pet suppliers.

12767 ■ DVM Newsmagazine
Advanstar Communications
Veterinary Group
8033 Flint
Lenexa, KS 66214
Fr: 800-255-6864

Monthly. Magazine for veterinarians in private practices in the U.S.

12768 ■ Equus
Primedia Equine Network
656 Quince Orchard Rd., Ste. 600
Gaithersburg, MD 20878
Ph: (301)977-3900
Fax: (301)990-9015
E-mail: eqletters@equinetwork.com
URL: http://www.equisearch.com/equus

Monthly. $29.95/year for two years; $14.97/year for individuals; $26.97/year for Canada; $53.95/year for Canada, two years. Magazine featuring health, care, and understanding of horses.

12769 ■ Journal of the American Veterinary Medical Association
American Veterinary Medical Association
1931 N Meacham Rd., Ste. 100
Schaumburg, IL 60173-4360
Ph: (847)925-8070
Fax: (847)925-1329
Fr: 800-248-2862
URL: http://www.avma.org/journals/javma/javma_about.asp

Semimonthly. $210.00/year for nonmembers; $230.00/year for other countries; $25.00/year for

single issue; $30.00/year for single issue, foreign. Trade journal for veterinary medical professionals.

12770 ■ Journal of Animal Science
American Society of Animal Science
2441 Village Green Pl.
Champaign, IL 61822
Ph: (217)356-9050
Fax: (217)398-4119
URL: http://jas.fass.org/

Monthly. $135.00/year for members, U.S. online; $135.00/year for Canada and Mexico, members online; $135.00/year for other countries, members online; $210.00/year for members, U.S. print + online; $210.00/year for Canada and Mexico, members print + online; $235.00/year for other countries, members print + online; $575.00/year for institutions, U.S. print + online; $575.00/year for Canada and Mexico, print + online; $600.00/year for other countries, print + online. Professional journal covering animal science.

12771 ■ Journal of Avian Medicine and Surgery
Allen Press Inc.
810 E 10th St.
PO Box 368
Lawrence, KS 66044-0368
Ph: (785)843-1234
Fax: (785)843-1226
URL: http://www.aav.org/jams/index.php

Quarterly. $155.00/year for individuals; $160.00/year for Canada. Medical journal for veterinarians treating birds, students and technicians with an interest in the field.

12772 ■ The Journal of Equine Veterinary Science
Mosby Inc.
11830 Westline Industrial Dr.
St. Louis, MO 63146-3326
Ph: (314)872-8370
Fax: (314)432-1380
Fr: 800-325-4177
URL: http://www.elsevier.com/wps/find/journaldescription.cws_home

Monthly. $515.00/year for institutions; $331.00/year for individuals; $83.00/year for students, U.S.; $404.00/year for institutions, U.S.; $267.00/year for individuals, U.S.; $168.00/year for students. Journal publishing articles for equine veterinarians and other equine health care specialists.

12773 ■ Journal of Herpetological Medicine and Surgery
Association of Reptilian and Amphibian Veterinarians
810 E 10th
PO Box 1897
Lawrence, KS 66044
Fax: (785)843-6153
Fr: 800-627-0326
URL: http://www.arav.org/ECOMARAV//timssnet/publications/tnt_publ

Quarterly. $170.00/year for institutions, North America; $155.00/year for U.S., Canada, and Mexico. Journal covering issues for reptile and amphibian veterinarians.

12774 ■ Journal of Veterinary Behavior
Elsevier Science Inc.
360 Park Ave. S
New York, NY 10010-1710
Ph: (212)989-5800
Fax: (212)633-3990
Fr: 888-437-4636
URL: http://www.elsevier.com/wps/find/
   journaldescription.cws_home

$314.00/year for institutions, other countries; $194.00/year for other countries; $111.00/year for students, other countries; $284.00/year for institutions; $169.00/year for individuals; $85.00/year for students. Journal focused on veterinary behavioral medicine.

12775 ■ Lab Animal
Nature Publishing Group
75 Varick St., 9th Fl.
New York, NY 10013-1917
Ph: (212)726-9200
Fax: (212)696-9006
Fr: 888-331-6288
E-mail: editors@labanimal.com
URL: http://www.labanimal.com/laban/index.html

Monthly. $250.00/year for individuals; $1,932.00/year for institutions; $139.00/year for individuals; $1,160.00/year for institutions; $270.60/year for individuals; $2,091.19/year for institutions; $215.00/year for individuals; $1,798.00/year for institutions; $20,000.00/year for individuals; $238,280.00/year for institutions. Life science magazine.

12776 ■ The Morgan Horse
American Morgan Horse Association
4066 Shelburne Rd., Ste. 5
Shelburne, VT 05482
Ph: (802)985-4944
Fax: (802)985-8897
URL: http://www.morganhorse.com/

Monthly. $31.50/year for individuals, 2nd class; $70.50/year for individuals, 1st class; $53.50/year for Canada and Mexico; $61.50/year for other countries, surface; $130.50/year for other countries, mail. Magazine for Morgan horse enthusiasts.

12777 ■ Newsletter-Animal Behavior Society
Animal Behavior Society
ABS Central Office
402 N Park St.
Bloomington, IN 47408
Ph: (812)856-5541
Fax: (812)856-5542
E-mail: aboffice@indiana.edu
URL: http://animalbehaviorsociety.org/central-office/
   abs-newsletters

Description: Quarterly. Informs members of the Society of activities, events, meetings, announcements and opportunities in the field of animal behavior. Recurring features include news of educational opportunities, job listings, and notices of publications available.

12778 ■ Preventive Veterinary Medicine
Mosby Inc.
11830 Westline Industrial Dr.
St. Louis, MO 63146-3326
Ph: (314)872-8370
Fax: (314)432-1380
Fr: 800-325-4177
URL: http://www.elsevier.com/wps/find/
   journaldescription.cws_home

$2,669.00/year for institutions, all countries except Europe, Japan and Iran; $316,800.00/year for institutions; $2,386.00/year for institutions, for European countries and Iran. Journal focusing on the epidemiology of domestic and wild animals, costs of epidemic and endemic diseases of animals, the latest methods in veterinary epidemiology, disease control or eradication by public veterinary services, relationships

between veterinary medicine and animal production, and development of new techniques in diagnosing, recording, evaluating and controlling diseases in animal populations.

12779 ■ Research in Veterinary Science
Mountain Association for Community Economic Development
433 Chestnut St.
Berea, KY 40403-1510
Ph: (859)986-2373
Fax: (859)986-1299
URL: http://www.elsevier.com/wps/find/
   journaldescription.cws_home

Bimonthly. $437.00/year for individuals, for European countries; $47,000.00/year for individuals; $407.00/year for individuals, for all countries except Europe and Japan; $671.00/year for institutions, for all countries except Europe and Japan; $81,600.00/year for institutions; $756.00/year for institutions, for European countries. Journal publishing original articles, reviews and short communications of a high scientific and ethical standard in the veterinary sciences.

12780 ■ Topics in Companion Animal Medicine
Mosby Inc.
11830 Westline Industrial Dr.
St. Louis, MO 63146-3326
Ph: (314)872-8370
Fax: (314)432-1380
Fr: 800-325-4177
URL: http://www.journals.elsevierhealth.com/
   periodicals/tcam

Quarterly. $191.00/year for individuals; $98.00/year for students; $245.00/year for other countries; $125.00/year for students, other countries. Peer-reviewed journal providing practitioners with a convenient, comprehensive resource to enhance their office practice of veterinary medicine.

12781 ■ TRENDS Magazine
American Animal Hospital Association
12575 W Bayaud Ave.
Lakewood, CO 80228
Ph: (303)986-2800
Fax: (303)986-1700
Fr: 800-883-6301
URL: http://www.aahanet.org/publications/
   trendsmagazine.aspx

$60.00/year for U.S. and Canada; $70.00/year for other countries; $20.00/year for single issue. Professional magazine covering the management of small animal veterinary practices.

12782 ■ Veterinary Practice News
Bowtie Inc.
477 Butterfield, Ste. 200
Lombard, IL 60148
Ph: (630)515-9493
Fax: (630)515-9784
URL: http://www.veterinarypracticenews.com/

Monthly. $42.00/year for U.S. and Canada, digital; $48.00/year for individuals, print. Magazine covering veterinary practice in the United States featuring developments and trends affecting companion animals and livestock.

12783 ■ Veterinary Research Communications
Springer Publishing Co.
11 W 42nd St., 15th Fl.
New York, NY 10036
Ph: (212)431-4370
Fax: (212)941-7842
Fr: 877-687-7476
URL: http://www.springerlink.com/content/103009/

$1,182.00/year for institutions, print & online; $1,418.00/year for institutions, print & enhanced access. Journal focusing on the current developments in the entire field of veterinary science.

12784 ■ Vetz Magazine
Vetz Magazine
608 Hampton Dr.
Venice, CA 90291
Ph: (310)452-3900
URL: http://www.vetzmagazine.com/

Quarterly. $55.60/year for individuals. Lifestyle magazine for veterinarians that address personal, financial, health, and business issues unique to those in veterinary practice.

12785 ■ Western Horseman
Western Horseman
2112 Montgomery St.
Fort Worth, TX 76107
Ph: (817)737-6397
Fax: (817)737-9266
E-mail: edit@westernhorseman.com
URL: http://www.westernhorseman.com/

Monthly. $18.00/year for individuals; $58.00/year for other countries; $38.00/year for Canada; $1.50/year for single issue. Magazine covering forms of horsemanship and all breeds of horses; emphasizing western stock horses and western lifestyle.

EMPLOYER DIRECTORIES AND NETWORKING LISTS

12786 ■ American College of Veterinary Pathologists—Membership Directory
American College of Veterinary Pathologists
2810 Crossroads Dr., Ste. 3800
Madison, WI 53718
Ph: (608)443-2466
Fax: (608)443-2474
URL: http://www.acvp.org

Annual, March. Covers: 1,200 veterinary anatomic pathologists and veterinary clinical pathologists. Entries include: Name, office address, phone, e-mail. Arrangement: Alphabetical.

12787 ■ American Society of Veterinary Ophthalmology—Directory
American Society of Veterinary Ophthalmology
1416 W Liberty Ave.
Stillwater, OK 74075
URL: http://www.asvo.org

Bimonthly, December. Covers: 250 member veterinarians interested in animal ophthalmology. Entries include: Name, address, office and home phone numbers, and year of graduation. Arrangement: Geographical. Indexes: Alphabetical, chronological.

12788 ■ American Veterinary Medical Association—Directory and Resource Manual
American Veterinary Medical Association
1931 N Meacham Rd., Ste. 100
Schaumburg, IL 60173-4360
Ph: (847)925-8070
Fax: (847)925-1329
Fr: 800-248-2862
E-mail: avmainfo@avma.org
URL: http://www.avma.org

Annual, January; Latest edition 2008-2009. $150.00 for nonmembers; $175.00 for nonmembers. Covers: AVMA members; code of ethics, AVMA bylaws. Entries include: Name, spouse's name, address, email, phones and codes for practice activity, type of employer, institution granting degree, and year received. Arrangement: Geographical and alphabetical. Indexes: Alphabetical.

12789 ■ Association of Veterinary Practice Management Membership Directory
Association of Veterinary Practice Management
PO Box 121625
Clermont, FL 34712-1625
Ph: (352)243-2014
Fax: (352)243-2013
URL: http://www.avpmca.org

Quarterly. Covers: complete listing of members and their contact information based on expertise areas.

12790 ■ *Careers in Focus—Animal Care*

Facts On File Inc.
132 W 31st St., 17th Fl.
New York, NY 10001
Ph: (212)967-8800
Fax: 800-678-3633
Fr: 800-322-8755
URL: http://www.infobasepublishing.com

Latest edition 4th. $32.95 for individuals. Covers: An overview of animal care, followed by a selection of jobs profiled in detail, including the nature of the job, earnings, prospects for employment, what kind of training and skills it requires, and sources for further information.

12791 ■ *Discovering Careers for Your Future—Animals*

Facts On File Inc.
132 W 31st St., 17th Fl.
New York, NY 10001
Ph: (212)967-8800
Fax: 800-678-3633
Fr: 800-322-8755
URL: http://factsonfile.infobasepublishing.com

Latest edition 2nd, 2005. $21.95 for individuals; $19.75 for libraries. Covers: Animal shelter workers, aquarists, farmers, naturalists, veterinarians, wildlife photographers, and zoo and aquarium curators; links career education to curriculum, helping children investigate the subjects they are interested in, and the careers those subjects might lead to.

HANDBOOKS AND MANUALS

12792 ■ *Career Choices for Veterinarians: Private Practice and Beyond*

Smith Veterinary Consulting and Publishing
PO Box 698
Peshastin, WA 98847
Ph: (509)548-2010
E-mail: info@smithvet.com
URL: http://smithvet.com

Carin A. Smith. 2011. $57.95 (paper). 280 pages. Offers practical advice, including self-assessments, web links to hundreds of resources and real-life examples of veterinarians working in unique career paths all over the world.

12793 ■ *Career Choices for Veterinary Technicians: Opportunities for Animal Lovers*

American Animal Hospital Association
12575 W Bayaud Ave.
Lakewood, CO 80228
Ph: (303)986-2800
Fax: (303)986-1700
Fr: 800-883-6301
E-mail: info@aahanet.org
URL: http://www.aahanet.org

Rebecca Rose, Carina A. Smith. 2009. $24.95 for member; $29.95 for non-member (paper). 144 pages. Covers multiple career options within the field of veterinary technology, including careers within general practice, specialty practice, industry, higher education, government and more.

12794 ■ *Career Opportunities Working with Animals*

Ferguson Publishing
132 W 31st St., 17th Fl.
New York, NY 10001
Fax: 800-678-3633
Fr: 800-322-8755
URL: http://www.infobasepublishing.com

Shelly Field. 2011. $49.50 (hardcover). 308 pages. Describes more than 80 occupations in animal-related fields such as veterinary medicine; shelters, sanctuaries, and refuges; veterinary offices/hospitals/clinics; animal advocacy organizations; care and conservation of wildlife; zoos and aquariums; creative careers; pet care, training, and grooming; pet food, pet supply, and pet merchandise stores; and horses.

12795 ■ *Expert Resumes for Health Care Careers*

Jist Works
875 Montreal Way
St. Paul, MN 55102
Fr: 800-648-5478
E-mail: educate@emcp.com
URL: http://www.jist.com

Wendy S. Enelow and Louise M. Kursmark. 2010. $16.95. 288 pages.

12796 ■ *Health Careers Today*

Elsevier
11830 Westline Industrial Dr.
St. Louis, MO 63146
Ph: (314)453-7010
Fax: (314)453-7095
Fr: 800-545-2522
E-mail: usbkinfo@elsevier.com
URL: http://www.elsevier.com

Gerdin, Judith. Fourth edition. 2007. $74.95. 496 pages. Covers more than 45 health careers. Discusses the roles and responsibilities of various occupations and provides a solid foundation in the skills needed for all health careers.

12797 ■ *Large Animal Clinical Procedures for Veterinary Technicians*

Elsevier
1600 John F. Kennedy Blvd., Ste. 1800
Philadelphia, PA 19103
Ph: (215)239-3900
Fax: (215)239-3990
Fr: 800-523-1649
URL: http://us.elsevierhealth.com

Kristin J. Holtgrew-Bohling. 2012. $43.46. 584 pages. Large animal medical and surgical techniques are described. The book is divided into four parts: equine, bovine, small ruminant (sheep and goats), and swine.

12798 ■ *Opportunities in Health and Medical Careers*

The McGraw-Hill Companies
PO Box 182604
Columbus, OH 43272
Fax: (614)759-3749
Fr: 877-883-5524
E-mail: customer.service@mcgraw-hill.com
URL: http://www.mhprofessional.com/
  product.php?isbn=0071437274

I. Donald Snook, Jr. and Leo D'Orazio. 2004. $14.95 (paper). 157 pages. Covers the full range of medical and health occupations. Illustrated.

EMPLOYMENT AGENCIES AND SEARCH FIRMS

12799 ■ *Continental Search and Outplacement, Inc.*

PO Box 43873
Baltimore, MD 21236
Fr: 888-276-6789
URL: http://www.consearch.com

Recruiting firm specializes in animal jobs including animal science jobs, beef jobs, dairy jobs, swine careers, poultry jobs, animal health and integrated food companies.

12800 ■ *Veterinary Staffing Solutions*

1400 Woodloch Forest Dr., Ste. 300-8
The Woodlands, TX 77380
Ph: (866)981-4473
Fax: (281)754-4518
E-mail: admin@vetss.org
URL: http://www.vetss.org

Description: Serves as a staffing agency that works with the veterinary field. Offers permanent or tempo-rary positions to veterinarians, registered veterinary assistants, managers, front office staff and kennel assistants with veterinary facilities and other related businesses.

ONLINE JOB SOURCES AND SERVICES

12801 ■ *AnimalJobs.com*

URL: http://www.animaljobs.com

Description: Functions as a niche job board for people who work with animals including veterinarians, pet stores, groomers, farmers, horse breeders, rescuers, and shelters.

12802 ■ *HEALTHeCAREERS Network*

Fr: 888-884-8242
E-mail: info@healthecareers.com
URL: http://www.healthecareers.com

Description: Career search site for jobs in all health care specialties; educational resources; visa and licensing information for relocation; interesting articles; relocation tools; links to professional organizations and general resources.

12803 ■ *ProHealthJobs.com*

Ph: (484)443-8545
Fax: (484)443-8549
E-mail: info@prohealthjobs.com
URL: http://prohealthjobs.com/jobboard

Description: Career resources site for the medical and health care field. Lists professional opportunities, product information, continuing education and open positions.

12804 ■ *VeterinaryCrossing.com*

URL: http://www.veterinarycrossing.com

Description: Offers employment opportunities for veterinarians and veterinary technicians. Includes lists of employer career pages, job websites, newspaper classifieds and recruitment sites.

12805 ■ *VeterinaryLife.com*

URL: http://www.veterinarylife.com

Description: Posts classified ads for veterinarian and clinic jobs available worldwide.

12806 ■ *Vetquest Classifieds*

URL: http://www.vetquest.com

Description: Serves as an online resource for veterinary classified advertisements. Includes job opportunities for veterinarians.

12807 ■ *VetRelief.com*

URL: http://www.vetrelief.com

Description: Serves as a career network that caters to the needs of individuals searching for work as a veterinarian as well as for individuals seeking to hire a veterinarian.

TRADESHOWS

12808 ■ *ACVS Veterinary Symposium*

American College of Veterinary Surgeons
19785 Crystal Rock Dr., Ste. 305
Germantown, MD 20874
Ph: (301)916-0200
Fax: (301)916-2287
Fr: 877-217-2287
E-mail: acvs@acvs.org
URL: http://www.acvs.org

Annual. Primary Exhibits: Veterinary surgery equipment, supplies, and services. Dates and Locations: 2012 Nov 01-03; Washington, DC; 2013 Oct 23-26; San Antonio, TX.

12809 ■ American Animal Hospital Association Annual Conference
American Animal Hospital Association
12575 W Bayaud Ave.
Lakewood, CO 80228
Ph: (303)986-2800
Fax: (303)986-1700
Fr: 800-883-6301
E-mail: info@aahanet.org
URL: http://www.aahanet.org
Annual. Provides a forum for sharing of both scientific and management knowledge in the veterinary profession. Offers opportunities to view new technology, products and procedures. 2013 March 14-17; Phoenix, AZ.

12810 ■ American Association of Bovine Practitioners Annual Conference
American Association of Bovine Practitioners
PO Box 3610
Auburn, AL 36831-3610
Ph: (334)821-0442
Fax: (334)821-9532
Fr: 800-269-2227
E-mail: aabphq@aabp.org
URL: http://www.aabp.org/
Annual. Primary Exhibits: Pharmaceutical and biological manufacturers, equipment companies, agricultural-related companies, and computer programs and supplies.

12811 ■ American Association of Swine Veterinarians Meeting
American Association of Swine Veterinarians
830 26th St.
Perry, IA 50220
Ph: (515)465-5255
Fax: (515)465-3832
E-mail: aasv@aasv.org
URL: http://www.aasv.org
Annual. Offers an opportunity for commercial technical representatives to exchange information and interact with swine veterinarians from around the world and provides continuing education to swine veterinarians.

12812 ■ American College of Veterinary Pathologists Annual Meeting
American College of Veterinary Pathologists
2424 American Ln.
Madison, WI 53704
Ph: (608)433-2466
Fax: (608)443-2474
URL: http://www.acvp.org
Annual. Primary Exhibits: Veterinary pathology (origin, nature, and course of diseases in animals) equipment, supplies, and services. Dates and Locations: 2012 Dec 01-05; Seattle, WA; Washington Trade and Convention Center and Sheraton Seattle; 2013 Nov 16-20; Montreal, QC, Canada; Montreal Convention Center and the LeWestin Montreal Hotel.

12813 ■ American Veterinary Medical Association Annual Convention
American Veterinary Medical Association
1931 N. Meacham Rd., Ste. 100
Schaumburg, IL 60173-4360
Ph: 800-248-2862
Fax: (847)925-1329
E-mail: avmainfo@avma.org
URL: http://www.avma.org
Annual. Primary Exhibits: Products, materials, equipment, data, and services for veterinary medicine. Dates and Locations: 2012 Aug 04-07; San Diego, CA; 2013 Jul 20-23; Chicago, IL; 2014 Jul 26-29; Denver, CO; 2015 Jul 11-14; Boston, MA; 2016 Aug 05-08; San Antonio, TX.

12814 ■ Arkansas Veterinary Medical Association's Winter Meeting
Arkansas Veterinary Medical Association
PO Box 17687
Little Rock, AR 72222-7687
Ph: (501)868-3036
Fax: (501)868-3034
E-mail: info@arkvetmed.org
URL: http://www.arkvetmed.org/
Annual. Primary Exhibits: Exhibits relating to the veterinary profession. Dates and Locations: 2012 Feb 02-05; Hot Springs, AR.

12815 ■ Association of Avian Veterinarians Conference and Expo
Association of Avian Veterinarians
90 Madison St., Ste. 403
Denver, CO 80206
Ph: (303)756-8380
Fax: (303)759-8861
E-mail: aav@conferenceoffice.com
URL: http://www.aav.org
Annual. Offers lectures, practical laboratory sessions, and features discussions on the latest developments in veterinary medicine. 2012 August 15; Louisville, KY; Louisville Marriott.

12816 ■ International Congress on Veterinary Acupuncture
International Veterinary Acupuncture Society IVAS
1730 S College Ave., Ste. 301
Fort Collins, CO 80525
Ph: (970)266-0666
Fax: (970)266-0777
E-mail: office@ivas.org
URL: http://www.ivas.org
Annual. Primary Exhibits: Veterinary acupuncture equipment, supplies, and services. Dates and Locations: 2012 Aug 31 - Sep 01; Galway, Ireland; Radisson Blu Hotel.

12817 ■ International Wildlife Rehabilitation Council Conference
International Wildlife Rehabilitation Council
PO Box 8187
San Jose, CA 95155
Ph: (408)271-2685
Fax: (408)271-9285
E-mail: office@iwrc-online.org
URL: http://iwrc-online.org
Annual. Primary Exhibits: Equipment, supplies, and services for the rehabilitation of wildlife, including the handling and care of sick and injured wild animals. T-shirts, books, jewelry, artwork, etc.

12818 ■ Joint Annual Meeting of the American Dairy Science Association and the American Society of Animal Science
Federation of Animal Science Societies
2441 Village Green Pl.
Champaign, IL 61822
Ph: (217)356-3182
Fax: (217)398-4119
E-mail: fass@assochq.org
URL: http://www.fass.org
Annual. Primary Exhibits: Exhibits related to the investigation, instruction, or extension in animal sciences and in the production, processing, and dissemination of livestock and livestock products. Dates and Locations: 2012 Jul 15-20; Phoenix, AZ; 2013 Jul 08-12; Indianapolis, IN.

12819 ■ The North American Veterinary Conference
The North American Veterinary Conference NAVC
5003 S.W. 41st Blvd.
Gainesville, FL 32608
Ph: 800-756-3446
Fax: (352)375-4145
URL: http://www.tnavc.org
Annual. Primary Exhibits: Exhibits relating to the education of veterinary healthcare.

12820 ■ Therio/ACT Conference & Symposium
Society for Theriogenology
PO Box 3007
Montgomery, AL 36109-3007
Ph: (334)395-4666
Fax: (334)270-3399
URL: http://www.therio.org
Annual. Features theriogenology business meetings, student case presentations, breeders session, exhibits, and other discussions relevant to theriogenology.

12821 ■ VHMA Annual Meeting and Conference
Veterinary Hospital Managers Association
PO Box 2280
Alachua, FL 32616
Ph: (518)433-8911
Fax: 888-795-4520
Fr: 877-599-2707
E-mail: admin@vhma.org
URL: http://www.vhma.org
Annual. Provides opportunities for veterinary management practitioners to learn and network. Includes exhibits.

12822 ■ Western Veterinary Conference
Western Veterinary Conference
2425 E Oquendo Rd.
Las Vegas, NV 89120-2406
Ph: (702)739-6698
Fax: (702)739-6420
Fr: (866)800-7326
E-mail: info@westernveterinary.org
URL: http://www.wvc.org
Annual. Primary Exhibits: Veterinary equipment, supplies, and services, including drugs. Dates and Locations: 2012 Feb 19-23; Las Vegas, NV; Mandalay Bay Resort & Casino.

12823 ■ Wisconsin Veterinary Medical Association Annual Convention
Wisconsin Veterinary Medical Association
2801 Crossroads Dr., Ste. 1200
Madison, WI 53718
Ph: (608)257-3665
Fax: (608)257-8989
E-mail: wvma@wvma.org
URL: http://www.wvma.org
Annual. Primary Exhibits: Veterinary supplies, pharmaceuticals, pet food, business systems, and record-keeping equipment.

OTHER SOURCES

12824 ■ Academy of Veterinary Consultants
PO Box 24305
Overland Park, KS 66283
Ph: (913)766-4373
Fax: (913)766-0474
E-mail: paula@avc-beef.org
URL: http://www.avc-beef.org
Description: Comprised of veterinarians involved in beef cattle medicine, herd health programs and consultation. Provides continuing education, member support and leadership among various entities of the beef cattle industry. Strives for productivity of a safe, high-quality product.

12825 ■ American Academy of Clinical Toxicology (AACT)
110 W Lancaster Ave., Ste. 230
Wayne, PA 19087
Ph: (703)556-9222
Fax: (703)556-8729
E-mail: admin@clintox.org
URL: http://www.clintox.org
Description: Physicians, veterinarians, pharmacists, nurses research scientists, and analytical chemists. Seeks to unite medical scientists and facilitate the exchange of information. Encourages the development of therapeutic methods and technology. Conducts professional training in poison information and emergency service personnel.

12826 ■ American Animal Hospital Association
12575 W Bayaud Ave.
Lakewood, CO 80228
Ph: (303)986-2800
Fax: (303)986-1700
Fr: 800-883-6301
E-mail: info@aahanet.org
URL: http://www.aahanet.org

Description: Represents and promotes the interests of veterinarians. Enhances the abilities of veterinarians to provide quality medical care to companion animals. Enables veterinarians to successfully conduct their practices and maintain their facilities with high standards of excellence.

12827 ■ American Association of Equine Practitioners
4075 Iron Works Pkwy.
Lexington, KY 40511
Ph: (859)233-0147
Fax: (859)233-1968
E-mail: aaepoffice@aaep.org
URL: http://www.aaep.org

Description: Represents individuals who are actively involved in ethics issues, practice management, research and continuing education in the equine veterinary profession and horse industry. Works to improve the health and welfare of horses. Strives to further the professional development of its members and to provide resources and leadership for the benefit of the equine industry.

12828 ■ American Association of Swine Veterinarians
830 26th St.
Perry, IA 50220-1703
Ph: (515)465-5255
Fax: (515)465-3832
E-mail: aasv@aasv.org
URL: http://www.aasv.org

Description: Comprised of veterinarians and veterinary students. Commits to increase the knowledge of swine veterinarians by promoting the development and availability of the resources which enhance the effectiveness of professional activities. Works to create opportunities that inspire personal and professional growth.

12829 ■ American Association of Veterinary Laboratory Diagnosticians
PO Box 1770
Davis, CA 95617
Ph: (530)754-9719
Fax: (530)752-5680
E-mail: secretary-treasurer@aavld.org
URL: http://www.aavld.org

Description: Holds a membership that is open to any individual interested in animal disease laboratory diagnosis. Seeks to disseminate information relating to the diagnosis of animal diseases. Offers a web-based career center that connects job seekers with prospective employers in the veterinary diagnostics industry.

12830 ■ American Association of Wildlife Veterinarians
c/o Dr. Mark Drew, Treas.
Idaho Department of Fish and Game
16569 S 10th Ave.
Caldwell, ID 83607
E-mail: mdrew@idfg.idaho.gov
URL: http://www.aawv.net

Description: Consists of veterinary practitioners, pathologists, researchers and policy makers. Seeks to enhance the contribution of veterinary medicine to the welfare of wildlife resources. Promotes and encourages the utilization of veterinarians in the fields of wildlife management, conservation and research.

12831 ■ American Association of Zoo Veterinarians (AAZV)
581705 White Oak Rd.
Yulee, FL 32097
Ph: (904)225-3275
Fax: (904)225-3289
E-mail: aazvorg@aol.com
URL: http://www.aazv.org

Description: Veterinarians actively engaged in the practice of zoo and wildlife medicine for at least four years; veterinarians who do not qualify for active membership; persons interested in diseases of wildlife; students of veterinary medicine in any accredited veterinary school. Purposes are to: advance programs for preventive medicine, husbandry, and scientific research dealing with captive and free-ranging wild animals; provide a forum for the presentation and discussion of problems related to the field; enhance and uphold the professional ethics of veterinary medicine.

12832 ■ American Veterinary Medical Association (AVMA)
1931 N Meacham Rd., Ste. 100
Schaumburg, IL 60173-4340
Fax: (847)925-1329
Fr: 800-248-2862
E-mail: avmainfo@avma.org
URL: http://www.avma.org

Description: Professional society of veterinarians. Conducts educational and research programs. Provides placement service. Sponsors American Veterinary Medical Association Foundation and Educational Commission for Foreign Veterinary Graduates. Compiles statistics. Accredits veterinary medical education programs and veterinary technician education programs.

12833 ■ Association of Avian Veterinarians
90 Madison St., Ste. 403
Denver, CO 80206
Ph: (303)756-8380
Fax: (303)759-8861
E-mail: office@aav.org
URL: http://www.aav.org

Description: Represents veterinarians from private practice, zoos, universities, and industry. Promotes and advances avian medicine, stewardship, and conservation. Provides members with educational programs and networking opportunities.

12834 ■ Association for Women Veterinarians Foundation (AWVF)
Northern Illinois University
Lowden Hall 301
DeKalb, IL 60115
Ph: (815)753-1883
Fax: (815)753-1631
E-mail: lfreeman1@niu.edu
URL: http://www.womenveterinarians.org

Description: Works to support veterinary medicine by providing leadership in women's issues.

12835 ■ Association of Zoos and Aquariums
8403 Colesville Rd., Ste. 710
Silver Spring, MD 20910
Ph: (301)562-0777
Fax: (301)562-0888
URL: http://www.aza.org

Description: 218 accredited members. Promotes the welfare of animals and encourages the advancement of education, animal care, conservation and sciences.

12836 ■ International Veterinary Acupuncture Society
1730 S College Ave., Ste. 301
Fort Collins, CO 80525
Ph: (970)266-0666
Fax: (970)266-0777
E-mail: office@ivas.org
URL: http://www.ivas.org

Description: Veterinarians and veterinary students. Encourages knowledge and research of the philosophy, technique, and practice of veterinary acupuncture. Fosters high standards in the field; promotes scientific investigation. Accumulates resources for scientific research and education; collects data concerning clinical and research cases where animals have been treated with acupuncture; disseminates information to veterinary students, practitioners, other scientific groups, and the public. Offers 120-contact hour basic veterinary acupuncture course; administers certification examination; also offers advanced traditional Chinese herbal veterinary medicine.

12837 ■ National Association of Federal Veterinarians (NAFV)
1910 Sunderland Pl. NW
Washington, DC 20036-1608
Ph: (202)223-4878
Fax: (202)223-4877
E-mail: mgilsdorf@nafv.org
URL: http://www.nafv.net

Description: Professional society of veterinarians employed by the U.S. Government. Maintains speakers' bureau.

12838 ■ National Association of Veterinary Technicians in America
1666 K St. NW, Ste. 260
Washington, DC 20006
Ph: (703)740-8737
Fax: (202)449-8560
E-mail: info@navta.net
URL: http://www.navta.net

Description: Represents and promotes the profession of veterinary technology through education, advocacy and promotion within the industry and to the general public. Provides direction, education, support, and coordination for its members. Works to foster high standard of veterinary care while influencing the future of its members' professional goals.

12839 ■ Society for Theriogenology
PO Box 3007
Montgomery, AL 36109-3007
Ph: (334)395-4666
Fax: (334)270-3399
E-mail: roberta@franzmgt.com
URL: http://www.therio.org

Description: Licensed veterinarians and veterinary students who have interest in the area of reproduction of domestic species. Provides forums to disseminate emerging information to veterinarians and students. Fosters awareness and encourages a network for collegial exchange.

12840 ■ Veterinary Emergency and Critical Care Society
6335 Camp Bullis Rd., Ste. 12
San Antonio, TX 78257
Ph: (210)698-5575
Fax: (210)698-7138
E-mail: info@veccs.org
URL: http://veccs.org

Description: Consists of veterinarians, veterinary technicians, veterinary students, and other individuals engaged in the practice of veterinary emergency and critical patient care. Promotes the advancement of knowledge and high standards of practice in veterinary emergency medicine and critical patient care. Fosters and encourages education, research, and scientific progress among members.

12841 ■ Veterinary Hospital Managers Association
PO Box 2280
Alachua, FL 32616
Ph: (518)433-8911
Fax: 888-795-4520
Fr: 877-599-2707
E-mail: admin@vhma.org
URL: http://www.vhma.org

Description: Serves professionals in veterinary management through education, certification, and networking. Advances the study, teaching, and practice of veterinary practice management. Provides a forum for the exchange of information among members.

12842 ■ VeterinaryVentures
2613 NW Raleigh St., No. 25
Portland, OR 97210
E-mail: vetventures@gmail.com
URL: http://www.veterinaryventures.com

Description: Represents skilled animal care professionals and enthusiasts. Provides quality veterinary
care and humane population control to the world's
underserved animal populations. Addresses issues
concerning humane methods of animal population
control.

SOURCES OF HELP-WANTED ADS

12843 ■ Edge
Future Network USA
4000 Shoreline Ct., Ste. 400
South San Francisco, CA 94080
Ph: (650)872-1642
URL: http://www.futureplc.com/contact/

$69.99/year for U.S.; $147.64/year for two years, in United States; $34.99/year for individuals; $58.49/year for individuals, 2 years; $74.99/year for individuals, European and rest of world; $147.64/year for two years, European and rest of world. Consumer magazine covering computers and games.

12844 ■ Game Developer Magazine
United Business Media LLC
600 Community Dr.
Manhasset, NY 11030
Ph: (516)562-5000
URL: http://www.jointhegamenetwork.com/print/gdmag/index.html

Monthly. Valuable reference for those looking to begin a career in the video game industry as well as professionals already in the field which includes strategies for creating successful and successful video games as well as resources for getting a job.

12845 ■ Game Informer Magazine
Sunrise Publications Inc.
724 N First St., 4th Fl.
Minneapolis, MN 55401
Ph: (612)486-6100
Fax: (612)486-6101
URL: http://www.gameinformer.com/default.htm

Monthly. $19.98/year for individuals; $24.98/year for two years. Consumer magazine covering video and computer game information and reviews.

12846 ■ Game Revolution
Game Revolution
732 Gilman St.
Berkeley, CA 94710
E-mail: info@game-revolution.com
URL: http://www.gamerevolution.com/

Monthly. Consumer magazine covering gaming news, reviews, and information.

12847 ■ International Journal of Computer Games Technology
Hindawi Publishing Corp.
410 Park Ave., 15th Fl.
287 PMB
New York, NY 10022-4407
Fax: (215)893-4392
E-mail: ijcgt@hindawi.com
URL: http://www.hindawi.com/journals/ijcgt/

$195.00/year for individuals. Journal covering research and development aspects of games technology.

12848 ■ PC Gamer
Future Network USA
4000 Shoreline Ct., Ste. 400
South San Francisco, CA 94080
Ph: (650)872-1642
URL: http://www.futureus.com/what-we-do/portfolios/games/pc-gamer

Monthly. $19.95/year for individuals, cd-rom, 12 issues; $34.95/year for individuals, cd-rom, 24 issues. Consumer magazine covering computer games.

EMPLOYER DIRECTORIES AND NETWORKING LISTS

12849 ■ Casino Vendors Guide
Casino City Press
95 Wells Ave.
Newton, MA 02459
Ph: (617)332-2850
Fax: (617)964-2280
Fr: 800-490-1715
URL: http://www.casinocitypress.com

Annual, Latest edition 2011. $49.95. Covers: 10,000 industry suppliers, manufacturers, and distributors, 1,000 gaming products and services, 1,500 gaming properties around the world, gaming associations, analysts, attorneys, trade shows, and trade publications. Entries include: Company name, address, branch office locations, phone and fax numbers, email and website addresses, executive contacts and company description.

12850 ■ International Game Developers Association Membership Directory
19 Mantua Rd.
Mount Royal, NJ 08061
Ph: (856)423-2990
Fax: (856)423-3420
E-mail: info@igda.org
URL: http://www.igda.org

Directory of the 15,021 members of the International Game Developers Association. Information consists of a listing of all members with a public member profile, including member country, job type, company type and more.

12851 ■ Play Meter—Directory Issue
Play Meter Magazine
6600 Fleur de Lis Dr.
PO Box 337
New Orleans, LA 70124
Ph: (504)488-7003
Fax: (504)488-7083
Fr: 888-473-2376
URL: http://www.playmeter.com

Annual, January. Covers: About 500 firms that manufacture and distribute coin-operated video and electronic games and other amusement machines; 300 firms that supply the industry; state and national trade associations; exporters and importers; foreign

manufacturers and distributors. Entries include: Company name, address, phone, cable address, telex, names and titles of key personnel, product line. Arrangement: Alphabetical.

HANDBOOKS AND MANUALS

12852 ■ 21st Century Game Design
Charles River Media
20 Channel Center St.
Boston, MA 02210
Ph: (617)289-7700
Fax: (617)289-7844
Fr: 800-354-9706
E-mail: crminfo@cengage.com
URL: http://www.courseptr.com

Chris Bateman and Richard Boon. 2005. $39.95. 332 pages. Discusses the importance of the audience model when designing video games in an attempt to create better video game designers who will create interesting and innovative games for the public.

12853 ■ Becoming a Digital Designer: A Guide to Careers in Web, Video, Broadcast, Game and Animation Design
Wiley Publishing
10475 Crosspoint Blvd.
Indianapolis, IN 46256
Ph: (317)572-3000
Fax: (317)572-4000
E-mail: info@wiley.com
URL: http://www.wiley.com

Steven Heller and David Womack. 2007. $34.95. 336 pages. Provides an ideal starting point for anyone considering a career in the video game design industry and includes information concerning the preparation of an effective portfolio and resources for finding a job within the field.

12854 ■ Business and Legal Primer for Game Development
Charles River Media
20 Channel Center St.
Boston, MA 02210
Ph: (617)289-7700
Fax: (617)289-7844
Fr: 800-354-9706
E-mail: crminfo@cengage.com
URL: http://www.courseptr.com

S. Gregory Boyd and Brian Green, editors. 2006. $49.95. 450 pages. Explores the major business and legal issues involved in game development and design. Also provides an excellent reference of information from issues as diverse as contract negotiation, employment law, taxation, licensing, and basic business operations.

12855 ■ Career Opportunities in the Internet, Video Games, and Multimedia
Ferguson Publishing Company
132 W 31st St., 17th Fl.
New York, NY 10001

Fax: 800-678-3633
Fr: 800-322-8755
E-mail: custserv@factsonfile.com
URL: http://ferguson.infobasepublishing.com
Allan Taylor, James Robert Parish and Dan Fiden. 2007. $49.50. 384 pages.

12856 ■ Creating Casual Games for Profit and Fun
Course Technology PTR
20 Channel Center St.
Boston, MA 02210
Ph: (617)289-7700
Fax: (617)289-7844
Fr: 800-354-9706
URL: http://www.courseptr.com
Allen Partridge. 2007. $35.99. 320 pages. Covers the video game industry's standards and expectations.

12857 ■ Designing a Digital Portfolio
Peachpit Press
1249 8th St.
Berkeley, CA 94710
Fr: 800-283-9444
E-mail: press@peachpit.com
URL: http://www.peachpit.com/store/product.aspx?isbn=0321637518
Cynthia Baron. 2010. $35.99. 360 pages. Gives the reader inspiring examples of digital portfolios for those looking for a job as a digital artist, particularly video game designers. Also provides step-by-step instructions for creating a portfolio that will stand out in this competitive industry as well as important insights from the professionals who evaluate designer portfolios.

12858 ■ Emergence in Games
Course Technology PTR
20 Channel Center St.
Boston, MA 02210
Ph: (617)289-7700
Fax: (617)289-7844
Fr: 800-354-9706
URL: http://www.courseptr.com
Penny Sweetser. 2007. $49.99. 312 pages. Discusses the future direction of video game design and development and shows those looking for a job in the field how to use emergence to make video games more lifelike and interactive which will set them apart from the competition.

12859 ■ FabJob Guide to Become a Video Game Designer
FabJob.com
4616 25th Ave. NE, No. 224
Seattle, WA 98105
Ph: (403)873-1018
URL: http://www.fabjob.com/video.asp
Phil Marley. $9.97. 177 pages. Provides information about how the video game industry works, the best ways to find out about and apply for jobs, how to ace the interview process, how to get a job through an agency, as well as a list of companies who are hiring, including their contact information.

12860 ■ Fundamentals of Game Design
Prentice Hall PTR
One Lake St.
Upper Saddle River, NJ 07458
Ph: (201)236-7000
Fr: 800-922-0579
URL: http://prenticehall.com
Ernest Adams. 2009. $95.00. 700 pages. Focuses on designing for the commercial entertainment market and provides readers with resources in which to break into the video game industry or further develop their skills as a professional video game designer.

12861 ■ The Game Asset Pipeline
Charles River Media
20 Channel Center St.
Boston, MA 02210
Ph: (617)289-7700

Fax: (617)289-7844
Fr: 800-354-9706
E-mail: crminfo@cengage.com
URL: http://www.courseptr.com
Ben Carter. 2004. $39.95. 302 pages. Overview of what it takes to get a video game into the marketplace.

12862 ■ Game Career Guide
CMP Media LLC
600 Community Dr.
Manhasset, NY 11030
Ph: (516)562-5000
URL: http://www.gamecareerguide.com
Annual. Important resource that gives students, recent graduates, and experienced professionals resources on ways to update their skillsets and take control of their careers.

12863 ■ Game Design: A Practical Approach
Course Technology PTR
20 Channel Center St.
Boston, MA 02210
Ph: (617)289-7700
Fax: (617)289-7844
Fr: 800-354-9706
E-mail: esales@cengage.com
URL: http://www.courseptr.com
Paul Schuytema. 2006. $44.95. 375 pages. Provides a complete and practical examination of the craft of game design for new video game designers as well as practicing designers. Also includes invaluable insights and tips from the industry's top game designers about working in the field successfully.

12864 ■ Game Design: From Blue Sky to Green Light
A K Peters, Ltd.
888 Worcester St., Ste. 230
Wellesley, MA 02482
Ph: (781)416-2888
Fax: (781)416-2889
E-mail: editorial@akpeters.com
URL: http://www.crcpress.com/ecommerce_product/product_detail.jsf?isbn=9781568813189
Deborah Todd. 2007. $49.00. 304 pages. Covers the world of video game design and is an invaluable resource for those looking to start a career in the industry as well as for established professionals already working as video game designers.

12865 ■ Game Design: Principles, Practice, and Techniques: The Ultimate Guide for the Aspiring Game Designer
Wiley Publishing
10475 Crosspoint Blvd.
Indianapolis, IN 46256
Ph: (317)572-3000
Fax: (317)572-4000
E-mail: info@wiley.com
URL: http://as.wiley.com/WileyCDA/WileyTitle/productCd-0471968943.html
Jim Thompson, Barnaby Berbank-Green and Nic Cusworth. 2007. $50.00. 192 pages. Provides advice for those wanting to break into the video game design industry as well as a host of resources.

12866 ■ Game Design, Second Edition
Course Technology PTR
20 Channel Center St.
Boston, MA 02210
Ph: (617)289-7700
Fax: (617)289-7844
Fr: 800-354-9706
URL: http://www.courseptr.com
Bob Bates. Second edition, 2004. $35.99. 450 pages. Offers a behind-the-scenes look at how a video game gets designed and developed with interviews, document templates and the latest techniques and development models. Also includes various video game industry resources.

12867 ■ Game Design: The Art and Business of Creating Games
Course Technology
20 Channel Center St.
Boston, MA 02210
Ph: (617)289-7700
Fax: (617)289-7844
Fr: 800-354-9706
URL: http://academic.cengage.com
Bob Bates. 2005. $39.99. 450 pages. Comprehensive guide provides insight on how to turn video game design into a career.

12868 ■ The Game Developer's Dictionary: A Multidisciplinary Lexicon for Professionals and Students
Cengage Learning
PO Box 6904
Florence, KY 41022-6904
Fax: 800-487-8488
Fr: 800-354-9706
URL: http://www.cengage.com
Dan Carreker. 2012. $44.99 (hardcover). 352 pages. Features collection of current game development terminology and its definitions for gaming professionals. Includes survey of game industry job titles and their descriptions.

12869 ■ Game Development Essentials: Game Interface Design
Delmar, Cengage Learning
5 Maxwell Dr.
Clifton Park, NY 12065
Fax: 800-430-4445
Fr: 800-648-7450
E-mail: esales@cengage.com
URL: http://www.delmarlearning.com
Kevin Saunders and Jeannie Novak. 2007. $85.95. 296 pages. Gives advice from a host of professionals in the video game design industry about the topic of user interface design. Also includes resources for the aspiring video game designer.

12870 ■ Game Development Essentials: Game Project Management
Delmar, Cengage Learning
5 Maxwell Dr.
Clifton Park, NY 12065
Fax: 800-430-4445
Fr: 800-648-7450
E-mail: esales@cengage.com
URL: http://www.cengage.com
John Hight and Jeannie Novak. 2008. $66.95. 320 pages. Offers a comprehensive look at the video game project management process including: roles and responsibilities of team members, concept development, roles and responsibilities of team members, scheduling, marketing and budgeting.

12871 ■ Game Interface Design
Course Technology PTR
20 Channel Center St.
Boston, MA 02210
Ph: (617)289-7700
Fax: (617)289-7844
Fr: 800-354-9706
URL: http://www.courseptr.com
Brent Fox. 2004. $39.99. 232 pages. Outlines each step of the video game interface and defines goals in creating that interface. Also gives an overview of the video game industry with a look into developer and publisher relationships, budget constraints, scheduling, and the politics of the industry.

12872 ■ The Game Localization Handbook
Course Technology PTR
20 Channel Center St.
Boston, MA 02210
Ph: (617)289-7700
Fax: (617)289-7844
Fr: 800-354-9706
URL: http://www.courseptr.com
Heather Chandler. 2004. $40.46. 338 pages. Compre-

hensive guide to producing localized games for any platform discusses the importance for video game designers to start thinking in a global mindset. Manual provides an overview of each phase of the localization process including staffing needs, determining budgets, scheduling, working with third-party vendors and console submission process.

12873 ■ Game Testing All in One
Course Technology PTR
20 Channel Center St.
Boston, MA 02210
Ph: (617)289-7700
Fax: (617)289-7844
Fr: 800-354-9706
E-mail: esales@cengage.com
URL: http://www.courseptr.com

Charles Schultz, Robert Bryant and Tim Langdell. 2005. $44.99. 416 pages. Describes how to apply software test engineer methodologies to the video game industry in order to test a new video game. Also includes tips for finding employment in the field.

12874 ■ In the Mind of a Game
Course Technology PTR
20 Channel Center St.
Boston, MA 02210
Ph: (617)289-7700
Fax: (617)289-7844
Fr: 800-354-9706
E-mail: esales@cengage.com
URL: http://www.courseptr.com

John Flynt, PhD. 2005. $35.99. 384 pages. Valuable resource for both professional video game designers and those looking to break into the field; covers video game development, use, marketing, financing, criticism and consumption of computer games as well as a personalized account of the author's direct experience developing a video game.

12875 ■ Introduction to Game Development, Second Edition
Course Technology PTR
20 Channel Center St.
Boston, MA 02210
Ph: (617)289-7700
Fax: (617)289-7844
Fr: 800-354-9706
URL: http://www.courseptr.com

Steve Rabin. 2009. $69.99. 1,016 pages. Comprehensive guide based on the curriculum guidelines of the IGDA surveys all aspects of the theory and practice of video game development, design and production. Also includes resources

12876 ■ Introduction to the Game Industry
Prentice Hall PTR
One Lake St.
Upper Saddle River, NJ 07458
Ph: (201)236-7000
Fr: 800-328-6172
URL: http://prenticehall.com

Michael E. Moore and Jennifer Sward. 2006. $98.33. 500 pages. Provides an overview of how the video game industry works and describes how games are designed and built for those looking to break into the field.

12877 ■ Mobile 3D Game Development: From Start to Market
Course Technology PTR
20 Channel Center St.
Boston, MA 02210
Ph: (617)289-7700
Fax: (617)289-7844
Fr: 800-354-9706
URL: http://www.courseptr.com

Carlos Morales and David Nelson. 2007. $49.99. 496 pages. Provides an overview of the burgeoning mobile video game industry as well as instruction for developing commercial-quality 3D games for Java enabled mobile phones. Also includes resources for breaking into the 3D game market.

12878 ■ The Official Guide to 3D GameStudio
Course Technology PTR
20 Channel Center St.
Boston, MA 02210
Ph: (617)289-7700
Fax: (617)289-7844
Fr: 800-354-9706
URL: http://www.courseptr.com

Mike Duggan. 2007. $39.99. 480 pages. Provides information about video game design and gives readers tips regarding the game industry as a whole, including how video games are made, what job opportunities exist and how to break into the field.

12879 ■ Paid to Play: An Insider's Guide to Video Game Careers
Prima Games
3000 Lava Ridge Ct., Ste. 100
Roseville, CA 95661
Fr: 800-733-3000
URL: http://www.primagames.com

Alice Rush, David Hodgson and Bryan Stratton. 2006. $12.99. 272 pages. Overview of the video game industry gives readers a career guide which outlines the differences in jobs available in the field and interviews over 100 professionals currently working in the industry.

12880 ■ Patterns in Game Design
Course Technology PTR
20 Channel Center St.
Boston, MA 02210
Ph: (617)289-7700
Fax: (617)289-7844
Fr: 800-354-9706
URL: http://www.courseptr.com

Staffan Bjork and Jussi Holopainen. 2004. $44.96. 423 pages. Resource provides professional and aspiring video game designers a practical collection of game design patterns that facilitate the design of a successful game and defines a common language video game designers can use to speak concisely about the essence of video games.

12881 ■ Secrets of the Game Business
Charles River Media
20 Channel Center St.
Boston, MA 02210
Ph: (617)289-7700
Fax: (617)289-7844
Fr: 800-354-9706
E-mail: crminfo@cengage.com
URL: http://www.courseptr.com

Francois Dominic Laramee. 2005. $35.96. 432 pages. Provides an in-depth look into the video game industry for those seeking to begin a career in the field as well as those seeking to advance their careers.

12882 ■ Serious Games: Games That Educate, Train and Inform
Course Technology PTR
20 Channel Center St.
Boston, MA 02210
Ph: (617)289-7700
Fax: (617)289-7844
Fr: 800-354-9706
URL: http://www.courseptr.com

David Michael and Sandra Chen. 2005. $34.99. 352 pages. Provides information about the growing market of games used for education, training, healing and more. Also includes a detailed overview of all of the major markets for serious games and the goals of each of those markets as well as the types of games on which they focus and market-specific issues the video game designer must consider. Aims to show aspiring video game designers ways in which to successfully apply their skills to this growing area in order to stand out from the competition.

12883 ■ Ultimate Guide to Video Game Writing and Design
Lone Eagle
1745 Broadway
New York, NY 10019
E-mail: info@watsonguptill.com
URL: http://www.randomhouse.com/catalog/
    display.pperl?isbn=9781580650663

Flint Dille and John Zuur Platten. 2008. $19.95. 272 pages. Provides an in-depth look into the video game industry for those looking to start a career in the field as well as those looking to advance their job position.

12884 ■ Video Game Design Revealed
Course Technology PTR
20 Channel Center St.
Boston, MA 02210
Ph: (617)289-7700
Fax: (617)289-7844
Fr: 800-354-9706
URL: http://www.courseptr.com

Guy Lecky-Thompson. 2007. $35.99. 336 pages. Provides an overview of the steps and processes involved in bringing a video game from concept to completion. Also includes tips and information on how to find and contact game studios and publishers.

12885 ■ The Virtual Handshake: Opening Doors and Closing Deals Online
AMACOM
1601 Broadway
New York, NY 10019
Fax: (518)891-2372
Fr: 800-250-5308
E-mail: pubs_cust_serv@amanet.org
URL: http://www.amacombooks.org

David Teten and Scott Allen. 2005. $19.95 (paper). 272 pages. Covers such topics as finding a dream job in the video game design industry, how to meet more relevant senior employees, creating a powerful presence online, and building strong relationships within the industry.

EMPLOYMENT AGENCIES AND SEARCH FIRMS

12886 ■ GameRecruiter.com
401 E Las Olas Blvd., No. 130-112
Fort Lauderdale, FL 33301
Fax: (866)345-0265
Fr: (866)358-4263
E-mail: info@gamerecruiter.com
URL: http://www.gamerecruiter.com

Employment agency.

12887 ■ JobMonkey, Inc.
PO Box 3956
Seattle, WA 98124
Fr: 800-230-1095
E-mail: adminstaff2@jobmonkey.com
URL: http://www.jobmonkey.com/videogamejobs/
    video_game_developer_jobs.html

Recruitment firm specializing in jobs in the technology fields, particularly video game designers.

12888 ■ Showbizjobs.com, LLC
3579 E Foothill Blvd.
Pasadena, CA 91107
Ph: (626)798-4533
Fax: (626)798-4533
URL: http://www.showbizjobs.com

Employment agency includes listings for jobs in the video gaming industry.

12889 ■ Studio Search, LLC
7667 NE Park Ln.
Otis, OR 97368
Ph: (541)994-4441

Fax: (541)994-4473
E-mail: resumes@studio-search.com
URL: http://www.studio-search.com

Employment agency for the video gaming industry.

12890 ■ TSC Management Services Group
PO Box 384
Barrington, IL 60010
Ph: (847)381-0167
E-mail: grant@tscsearch.com
URL: http://www.tscsearch.com

Employment agency.

12891 ■ Wired Talent
2355 Northside Dr., Ste. 100
San Diego, CA 92108
Fr: (866)579-4733
E-mail: info@wiredtalent.com
URL: http://www.wiredtalent.com

Description: Provides staffing solutions for the game community.

ONLINE JOB SOURCES AND SERVICES

12892 ■ Gamasutra
CMP Media LLC
600 Harrison St., 5th Fl.
San Francisco, CA 94107
Ph: (516)562-5000
E-mail: help@gamasutra.com
URL: http://www.gamasutra.com

Online resource provides up-to-date information about the video game industry as well as job listings, resumes, and featured companies.

12893 ■ GameJobs.com
URL: http://www.gamejobs.com

Description: Provides jobs in the video and computer gaming industry.

12894 ■ Get Video Game Designer Jobs
URL: http://www.getvideogamedesignerjobs.com

Description: Provides a searchable database of job opportunities for video game designers.

12895 ■ WomenGamers.com
URL: http://www.womengamers.com

Description: Provides employment and networking opportunities for women in the gaming industry.

TRADESHOWS

12896 ■ Austin Game Developers Conference
UBM TechWeb
South Tower, Ste. 900
303 2nd St.
San Francisco, CA 94107
Ph: (415)947-6925
Fax: (415)947-6011
URL: http://www.gdconline.com

Annual. Primary Exhibits: Three days of conference content, two days of exhibits, the Game Career Seminar, and industry-defining keynote speakers.

12897 ■ E3 Media & Business Summit
Entertainment Software Association
575 7th St. NW, Ste. 300
Washington, DC 20004
E-mail: dhewitt@theesa.com
URL: http://www.e3expo.com

Annual. Primary Exhibits: Suite-based meetings for those in the video gaming industry, as well as video game demonstrations and panel discussions.

12898 ■ Game Careers Seminar
UBM TechWeb
South Tower, Ste. 900
303 2nd St.
San Francisco, CA 94107
Ph: (415)947-6925
Fax: (415)947-6011
URL: http://www.jointhegamenetwork.com/event/gcs/index.html

Annual. Primary Exhibits: Several mini-conferences for those who are interested in getting a job in the video game industry; includes networking opportunities, lessons in how to get a jumpstart in the field and keynote speakers willing to share their insights as professionals working in the industry.

12899 ■ Game Developers Choice Awards
UBM TechWeb
South Tower, Ste. 900
303 2nd St.
San Francisco, CA 94107
Ph: (415)947-6925
Fax: (415)947-6011
URL: http://www.gamechoiceawards.com

Annual. Primary Exhibits: Networking event seeks to recognize those in the video game design industry who are driving innovation; provides a forum in which video game designers can share information.

12900 ■ Game Developers Conference
UBM Tech Web
South Tower, Ste. 900
303 2nd St.
San Francisco, CA 94107
Ph: (415)947-6926
Fax: (415)947-6011
URL: http://www.gdconf.com

Annual. Primary Exhibits: Keynote speakers highlight the most up-to-date topics facing game industry professionals.

12901 ■ Game Developers Conference Mobile
UBM Tech Web
South Tower, Ste. 900
303 2nd St.
San Francisco, CA 94107
Ph: (415)947-6926
Fax: (415)947-6011
URL: http://www.jointhegamenetwork.com/event/index.html

Annual. Primary Exhibits: Networking opportunity for the next generation of mobile video game designers includes keynote speakers and demonstrations.

12902 ■ Game Developers Conference Prime
UBM TechWeb
South Tower, Ste. 900
303 2nd St.
San Francisco, CA 94107
Ph: (415)947-6856
Fax: (415)947-6011
URL: http://www.gdconf.com

Annual. Primary Exhibits: Exclusive networking event for executives in the video game industry which seeks to identify solutions on how to improve the industry and drive innovations.

12903 ■ Independent Games Festival
UBM TechWeb
South Tower, Ste. 900
303 2nd St.
San Francisco, CA 94107
Ph: (415)947-6925
Fax: (415)947-6011
URL: http://www.igf.com

Annual. Primary Exhibits: Networking opportunity for video game industry professionals that recognizes leaders within the field and serves as a forum in which to bring fresh new talent and groundbreaking material into the industry.

12904 ■ The Interactive Achievement Awards
The Academy of Interactive Arts and Sciences
23622 Calabasas Rd., Ste. 220
Calabasas, CA 91302
Ph: (818)876-0826
Fax: (818)876-0850
URL: http://www.interactive.org

Annual. Primary Exhibits: Networking event aims to honor those video game developers and publishers who continue to move the industry forward with their talent and passion.

OTHER SOURCES

12905 ■ Entertainment Software Association
575 7th St. NW, Ste. 300
Washington, DC 20004
E-mail: esa@theesa.com
URL: http://www.theesa.com

Dedicated to serving the needs of video game designers and developers through business and consumer research, government relations, an anti-piracy program, and a number of other resources provided to members.

12906 ■ Georgia Game Developers Association
PO Box 2528
Suwanee, GA 30024
Ph: (678)546-5107
Fax: (678)546-5158
E-mail: info@ggda.org
URL: http://www.ggda.org

Seeks to elevate the local video game industry by fostering relationships, providing vital resources to video game designers and other industry figures, representing concerns of the industry on issues appearing before Georgia lawmakers, and promoting awareness of the region's talented game developers to foster further economic growth and development within the region. Membership levels range in price.

12907 ■ International Game Developers Association
19 Mantua Rd.
Mount Royal, NJ 08061
Ph: (856)423-2990
Fax: (856)423-3420
E-mail: info@igda.org
URL: http://www.igda.org

Seeks to advance the careers and enhance the lives of game developers through peer networking, promoting professional development, and advocating on issues affecting the developer community. Membership of 15,021 individuals includes programmers, designers, artists, producers and other development professions in the gaming industry.

12908 ■ North American Simulation and Gaming Association (NASAGA)
PO Box 78636
Indianapolis, IN 46278
Ph: (317)387-1424
Fax: (317)387-1921
Fr: 888-432-GAME
E-mail: info@nasaga.org
URL: http://www.nasaga.org

Description: Teachers, trainers, media specialists, faculty, and researchers in various disciplines. Seeks to promote training of specialists in the field of simulation and gaming; facilitate communication between these specialists, policymakers, students, and others; promote the development of better techniques in the field of simulation and gaming. Provides referrals to simulation-gaming consultants; maintains speakers' bureau and gaming archives. (Gaming is the application of experimental techniques to simulated conditions, especially for training or testing purposes.)

12909 ■ Think Services Game Group
600 Community Dr.
Manhasset, NY 11030

Ph: (415)947-6365
Fax: (415)947-6090
E-mail: asimms@think-services.com
URL: http://www.jointhegamenetwork.com/education/
    index.html

Provides a definitive source for reaching game industry professionals through a host of resources.

SOURCES OF HELP-WANTED ADS

12910 ■ Agricultural Technology Information Network
2910 E Barstow Ave., MS 115
Fresno, CA 93740
Ph: (559)278-4872
E-mail: jnorton@csufresno.edu
URL: http://www.atinet.org

Listing of agricultural jobs for students and professionals, particularly those in the wine industry.

12911 ■ American Wine Society Journal
American Wine Society
113 S Perry St.
PO Box 279
Lawrenceville, GA 30045
Fax: (678)377-7005
Fr: 888-297-9070
URL: http://www.americanwinesociety.org/

Quarterly. $4.00/year for single issue, add 2 for shipping. Wine magazine.

12912 ■ Court of Master Sommeliers
PO Box 6170
Napa, CA 94581
Ph: (707)255-5056
Fax: (707)255-2868
E-mail: klewis@mastersommeliers.org
URL: http://www.mastersommeliers.org

Educational program offers The Master Sommelier diploma, the highest distinction a professional can attain in fine wine and beverage service; also includes a list of job postings for professionals in the wine industry.

12913 ■ Grape Times
Florida Grape Growers Association
111 Yelvington Rd., Ste. 1
East Palatka, FL 32131
Ph: (386)329-0318
Fax: (386)329-1262
URL: http://www.fgga.org/

Bimonthly. Magazine for wine enthusiasts and those working in wineyards and wineries.

12914 ■ Restaurant Wine
TasteTour Publications
306 Randolph St.
PO Box 222
Napa, CA 94559
Ph: (707)224-4777
Fax: (707)224-6740
E-mail: ronn.wiegand@gmail.com
URL: http://www.tastetour.com

Bimonthly. $109.00/per year for individuals. Magazine covers wine trends, winery profiles, tips for training wine staff, reviews, and other resources concerning the wine industry; also includes annual issues such

as the Smart Business Issue and The USA Wine Market On-Premise Issue.

12915 ■ Wine Business Insider
Wine Communications Group
110 W Napa St.
Sonoma, CA 95476
Ph: (707)939-0822
Fax: (707)939-0833
Fr: 800-895-9463
E-mail: info@winebusiness.com
URL: http://www.winebusiness.com

Weekly. $295.00/year for individuals. Analyzes the week's top stories pertaining to the winemaking industry including key personnel changes, mergers and acquisitions, production and harvest reports, retail numbers and bulk wine and grape prices.

12916 ■ Wine Business Monthly
Wine Communications Group
110 W Napa St.
Sonoma, CA 95476
Ph: (707)939-0822
Fax: (707)939-0833
Fr: 800-895-9463
E-mail: info@winebusiness.com
URL: http://www.winebusiness.com

Monthly. $39.00/year for individuals; $49.00/year for Canadian subscriptions; $89.00 for other countries. Magazine provides up-to-date information to growers, wineries, suppliers and distributors about the latest trends and developments in the global business of making wine; also covers the best practices and new products as they pertain to grape growing, winemaking, marketing, sales, finance and business administration.

12917 ■ Wine Enthusiast Magazine
Wine Enthusiast Co.
333 N Bedford Rd.
Mount Kisco, NY 10549
Ph: (914)345-8463
Fax: (914)218-9186
Fr: 800-356-8466
URL: http://www.winemag.com

$29.95/year for individuals; $49.95/year for two years; $69.95/year for individuals, 3 years; $49.95/year for Canada; $79.95/year for other countries. Magazine reporting news on wines and spirits; includes profiles of industry leaders from around the world as well as a consumer wine report.

12918 ■ Wine Spectator
M. Shanken Communications Inc.
387 Park Ave. S
New York, NY 10016
Ph: (212)684-4224
Fax: (212)481-1540
URL: http://www.winespectator.com

$49.95/year for individuals, online; $79.95/year for two years; $80.00/year for Canada; $135.00/year for Canada, 2 years; $145.00/year for other countries;

$250.00/year for other countries, two years. Lifestyle Magazine for the wine consumer.

12919 ■ Wine & Spirits Magazine
Wine & Spirits Magazine Inc.
2 W 32nd St., Ste. 601
New York, NY 10001
Ph: (212)695-4660
URL: http://www.wineandspiritsmagazine.com

Monthly. $29.95/year for individuals; $51.95/year for two years; $15.00/year for individuals, first class mail; $10.00/year for Canada and Mexico. Magazine containing consumer buying information on wine and spirits with in-depth articles on regions and trends in food and wine.

12920 ■ Wines & Vines
Hiaring Co.
1800 Lincoln Ave.
San Rafael, CA 94901-1298
Ph: (415)453-9700
Fax: (415)453-2517
Fr: (866)453-9701
URL: http://www.winesandvines.com

Monthly. $38.00/year for individuals; $48.00/year for Canada and Mexico; $85.00/year for other countries; $59.00/year for two years, USA. Periodical on wine industry.

EMPLOYER DIRECTORIES AND NETWORKING LISTS

12921 ■ All American Wineries
PO Box 189
Pinnacle, NC 27043
E-mail: bobh@allamericanwineries.com
URL: http://www.allamericanwineries.com/

Directory of wineries, vineyards, events and guides associated with the wine industry. Also includes information concerning wineries and the law, feedback about wineries featured in the directory and other resources.

12922 ■ American Society for Enology and Viticulture—Membership Directory Issue
American Society for Enology and Viticulture
PO Box 1855
Davis, CA 95617-1855
Ph: (530)753-3142
Fax: (530)753-3318
URL: http://www.asev.org

Approximately annual. for members. Publication includes: List of 2,500 member vineyard and winery owners, technicians, academicians interested in enology and viticulture, and agricultural advisors. Entries include: Name, membership classification, address. Arrangement: Alphabetical.

12923 ■ The California Directory of Fine Wineries

Ten Speed Press
PO Box 7123
Berkeley, CA 94707
Ph: (510)559-1600
Fax: (510)559-1629
Fr: 800-841-2665
E-mail: sales@tenspeed.com
URL: http://www.randomhouse.com

Marty Olmstead, Tom Silberkleit and Robert Holmes. 2009. $19.95. 160 pages. Directory includes Northern California wineries.

12924 ■ The Complete Handbook of Winemaking

American Wine Society
113 S Perry St.
PO Box 279
Lawrenceville, GA 30045
Fax: (678)377-7005
Fr: 888-297-9070
URL: http://www.americanwinesociety.org

Annual, September. $17.50 for individuals. Covers: Suppliers of juice, other products, equipment, and services for wine and beer making; publishers who have books, pamphlets, and textbooks on the process; colleges and universities offering courses in viticulture and enology. Entries include: For suppliers and publishers—Name, address, phone; product, service, or title of publication. For colleges and universities—Name, address, and phone.

12925 ■ East Coast Wineries

Rutgers University Press
100 Joyce Kilmer Ave.
Piscataway, NJ 08854-8099
Ph: (732)445-7762
Fax: (732)445-7039
Fr: 800-446-9323
URL: http://rutgerspress.rutgers.edu/acatalog/__
  East_Coast_Wineri

Latest edition 2004. $21.95 for individuals. Covers: Nearly 300 wineries in the northeast coastal states of the United States (Connecticut, Delaware, Maine, Maryland, Massachusetts, New Hampshire, New Jersey, New York, Pennsylvania, Rhode Island, Vermont, Virginia, West Virginia). Entries include: Name, address, phone, brief history, list of wines offered with recommended buys, directions, and hours of operation. Also includes list of annual wine festivals and other special events.

12926 ■ LocalWineEvents.com

2042 Gen. Alexander Dr.
Malvern, PA 19355
Ph: (610)647-4888
E-mail: info@localwineevents.com
URL: http://www.localwineevents.com

Online directory and events calendar for the wine industry.

12927 ■ The Oxford Companion to the Wines of North America

Facts On File Inc.
132 W 31st St., 17th Fl.
New York, NY 10001
Ph: (212)967-8800
Fax: 800-678-3633
Fr: 800-322-8755
URL: http://factsonfile.infobasepublishing.com

Publication includes: Organizations and people associated with wineries in North America. Principal content of publication is encyclopedic information about wine. Indexes: Comprehensive index listing U.S. wine licensees, American Viticultural Areas, people, and techniques mentioned in the text.

12928 ■ Pocket Encyclopedia of American Wine East of the Rockies

Wine Appreciation Guild Ltd.
360 Swift Ave., Unit 30-40
South San Francisco, CA 94080

Ph: (650)866-3020
Fax: (650)866-3513
Fr: 800-231-9463
E-mail: shannon@wineappreciation.com
URL: http://www.wineappreciation.com

Biennial, Latest edition 2002. $13.95. Covers: more than 300 wineries in 24 states east of the continental divide. Entries include: Name of winery, address, phone, key personnel, wines produced, history. Arrangement: Alphabetical. Indexes: By state and by winery names.

12929 ■ Sonoma

Chronicle Books L.L.C.
680 2nd St.
San Francisco, CA 94107
Ph: (415)537-4200
Fax: (415)537-4460
Fr: 800-759-0190
URL: http://www.chroniclebooks.com

Latest edition 2nd; Published February, 2005. $19.95 for individuals. Covers: 25 wineries throughout Sonoma county, California. Entries include: In-depth descriptions.

12930 ■ Uncork New York

New York Wine and Grape Foundation
800 S Main St., Ste. 200
Canandaigua, NY 14424
Ph: (585)394-3620
Fax: (585)394-3649
E-mail: uncork@nywine.com
URL: http://www.newyorkwines.org

Annual, May. Covers: Over 120 wineries in New York state. Entries include: Winery name, address, phone. Arrangement: Geographical.

12931 ■ Vineyard & Winery Management—Directory Product Guide Issue

Vineyard & Winery Management
PO Box 14459
Santa Rosa, CA 95402-6459
Ph: (707)577-7700
Fax: (707)577-7705
Fr: 800-535-5670
URL: http://www.vwm-online.com

Annual, Latest edition 2009. $95.00 for individuals; $20.00 for other countries. Publication includes: List of about 21,000 grape growers and wine producers and processors in the U.S. and Canada; suppliers of equipment, products, and services to the wine and grapegrowing industry; wine competitions in the U.S. and Europe. Entries include: For growers and wine producers and processors—Name, address, phone, fax, names and titles of key personnel, description of products or services. For suppliers—Name, address, phone, fax, telex, name and title of contact, products and services. For competitions—Company name, address, phone, fax, names and titles of key personnel, geographical area served. Incorporates information from "Vineyard & Winery Management—Industry Directory Issue" and "Goldwyn's Directory of Wine Judgings," which have been discontinued. Arrangement: Geographical.

12932 ■ Wine Industry Index

Vineyards & Winery Management, Inc.
PO Box 14459
Santa Rosa, CA 95402-6459
Ph: (707)577-7700
Fax: (707)577-7705
Fr: 800-535-5670
URL: http://www.vwm-online.com

$95.00. Reference guide includes: wineries in the United States and Canada; vineyard and winery suppliers, products and services; North American Winery and Grower Associations; viticultural areas within the United States and Canada; wine competitions; regulatory office listings; wine industry universities, research centers and faculty and listings of trade shows, seminars and workshops.

12933 ■ The Wine Tours Project

PO Box 625
Troy, NY 12180
E-mail: sales@wine-tours.com
URL: http://www.wine-tours.com/winemain.html

Covers more than 7,300 wine-related businesses. Entries include: business name, address, available Web and email address as well as phone and fax numbers.

HANDBOOKS AND MANUALS

12934 ■ Introduction to Wine Laboratory Practices and Procedures

Springer Publishing Company
11 W 42nd St., 15th Fl.
New York, NY 10036
Fr: 877-687-7476
E-mail: cs@springerpub.com
URL: http://www.springer.com/food+science/book/
  978-0-387-24377-1

Jean L. Jacobson. 2006. $74.95. 382 pages. Provides a step-by-step guide on performing routine and essential winemaking duties for small and large wineries, entry level chemists and enologists, students and professionals in the wine industry.

12935 ■ The Science of Wine: From Vine to Glass

University of California Press
2120 Berkeley Way
Berkeley, CA 94704
Ph: (510)642-4247
Fax: (510)643-7127
E-mail: askucp@ucpress.edu
URL: http://www.ucpress.edu/books/pages/
  10619.php

Jamie Goode. 2006. $37.95. 216 pages. Provides a comprehensive overview of current scientific and technological innovations that are now influencing how grapes are grown and how wine is made. Students, winemakers, wine professionals and those looking to get into the industry will find this a valuable reference book.

12936 ■ Spinning the Bottle

Wine Appreciation Guild
360 Swift Ave., Unit 30-40
South San Francisco, CA 94080
Ph: (650)866-3020
Fr: 800-231-9463
E-mail: info@wineappreciation.com
URL: http://www.wineappreciation.com

Harvey Posert. 2004. $39.95. 224 pages. Collection of guidelines and case studies for promoting wine, wine companies and wine-related issues is as relevant to the student of wine and marketing as it is to the seasoned executive or winery owner.

12937 ■ Wine & Winemaking

World Fine Art
PO Box 5365
Scottsdale, AZ 85261
URL: http://www.quips.com/wine-links.htm

$9.00. Provides notes, quotes and anecdotes about the business of wine and winemaking.

12938 ■ Women of Wine

University of California Press
2120 Berkeley Way
Berkeley, CA 94704
Ph: (510)642-4247
Fax: (510)643-7127
E-mail: askucp@ucpress.edu
URL: http://www.ucpress.edu

Ann B. Matasar. 2006. $50. 270 pages. Discusses the role of women in the wine industry and covers such issues of importance for women looking to work in the field such as mentorship, networking, education, corporate life and risk taking.

EMPLOYMENT AGENCIES AND SEARCH FIRMS

12939 ■ Produce Careers Inc.
122 LePoint St., Ste. 202
Arroyo Grande, CA 93420
Ph: (805)481-3200
Fax: (805)481-3545
E-mail: support@producecareers.com
URL: http://www.producecareers.com

Employment agency and executive search firm.

12940 ■ WineTalent
PO Box 19861
Sacramento, CA 95819
Ph: (916)802-1280
E-mail: amy@winetalent.net
URL: http://www.winetalent.net

Executive search firm that focuses on the wine industry. Provides searches for professionals in all areas of the wine business.

ONLINE JOB SOURCES AND SERVICES

12941 ■ ENews Monitor
E-mail: editor@bensonmarketing.com
URL: http://bensonmarketing.com/services/enews-monitor-signup

Email news clipping service about the wine industry delivers specific category subscriptions for the wine lover, retailer, restaurateur, wholesaler, winery, grape grower and media.

12942 ■ Hospitality Link
URL: http://www.hospitalitylink.com

Online job site for the wine and hospitality industry.

12943 ■ Juju Job Search Engine
URL: http://www.job-search-engine.com/jobs?k=winemaking

Online listing of jobs, particularly those in the wine industry.

12944 ■ Michigan Wines
E-mail: mda-michigan-wines@michigan.gov
URL: http://www.michiganwines.com

Online resource provides a directory of Michigan wineries, listings of meetings and events, articles, newsletters, and additional resources concerning the wine industry in Michigan.

12945 ■ OregonWines.com
URL: http://www.oregonwines.com

Online resource provides job postings, a directory of Oregon wineries, an events calendar, news concerning the wine industry and editorials.

12946 ■ Professional Friends of Wine
E-mail: jimlamar@winepros.org
URL: http://winepros.org

Online resource providing wine education, wine information and wine training as well as a directory of wineries and an events calendar.

12947 ■ Squire Partners LLC: WineSquire.com
URL: http://www.winesquire.com/users/scott-miller

Online resource provides job listings for the wine industry as well as directories, links, event listings and articles.

12948 ■ Vault Inc.
URL: http://www.vault.com

Online resource provides job listings, particularly for the food and wine industry.

12949 ■ Voice of the Vine
E-mail: schwenso@wsu.edu
URL: http://wine.wsu.edu/vinevoice

Biweekly. Free. Provides current news concerning Washington's wine industry as well as profiles of researchers, students and alumni working in the field.

12950 ■ Wine Business Daily News
E-mail: info@winebusiness.com
URL: http://www.winebusiness.com/news

Daily. Free. Emailed newsletter covers the top stories concerning the winemaking industry.

12951 ■ Wine Events Calendar
E-mail: events@wineevents-calendar.com
URL: http://www.wineevents-calendar.com

Online directory of regional wine events, classes, wine tastings, and other networking opportunities and resources also includes ratings, reviews and editorials concerning the wine industry.

12952 ■ Wine and Spirits Jobs
PO Box 22
Mokena, IL 60448
Fr: (866)975-4473
E-mail: info@wineandspiritsjobs.com
URL: http://www.wineandspiritsjobs.com

Online resource lists jobs in the wine industry. Also encourages job seekers to post their resumes.

12953 ■ WineAndHospitalityJobs.com
URL: http://www.wineandhospitalityjobs.com

Online resource for both job seekers looking for work in the wine industry and employers from the wine industry in need of help. Website also includes articles, industry news, forums and other information concerning the industry and encourages job seekers to post their resumes.

12954 ■ WineBusiness.com
E-mail: info@winebusiness.com
URL: http://www.winebusiness.com

Resource includes information about the business and technology of winemaking as well as classified ads and listings of jobs in the wine industry.

12955 ■ WineCountry.com
URL: http://www.winecountry.com

Online resource provides interviews and profiles of leading winemakers and wine professionals across the country as well as information about the business of wine; also includes message boards, an event calendar and a directory of wineries throughout the country.

12956 ■ WineJobs.com
E-mail: info@winebusiness.com
URL: http://www.winebusiness.com/classifieds/winejobs

Online resource for the wine industry includes classified ads for used equipment, real estate, grapes and bulk wine.

12957 ■ WineJobs.com Daily Email Alert
E-mail: info@winebusiness.com
URL: http://www.winebusiness.com/classifieds/winejobs/?go=emailalerts

Provides the latest job listings for all sectors of the winemaking industry including finance, winemaking and production, vineyards, sales and marketing, information systems, hospitality and retail, human resources and general administration.

TRADESHOWS

12958 ■ Boston Wine Expo
Resource Plus Shows and Events
200 Seaport Blvd., Ste. 309
Boston, MA 02210
Ph: (617)385-5088

Fax: (617)385-5166
E-mail: info@resource-plus.com
URL: http://www.resource-plus.com

Annual. Primary Exhibits: Wineries, fine foods, and wine-related products. Dates and Locations: 2012 Jan 21-22; Boston, MA; Seaport World Trade Center.

12959 ■ Direct to Consumer Symposium
Coalition for Free Trade
2700 Napa Valley Corporate Dr., Ste. H
Napa, CA 94558
Ph: (707)254-1115
Fax: (707)254-0433
URL: http://www.dtcwinesymposium.com/index2.html

Annual. Primary Exhibits: Sessions about direct marketing and sales which include: consumer research findings about who is buying; starting a winning direct marketing program; food and wine marketing to increase sales; direct to consumer legislation and enforcement; lessons from those in the winery industry; telemarketing; tactics to increase mailing lists; shipping updates for various states; tips on building a successful wine club.

12960 ■ Managing the Winery Laboratory Seminar
Vineyards & Winery Management, Inc.
421 E St.
Santa Rosa, CA 95404
Ph: (707)577-7700
Fax: (707)577-7705
Fr: 800-535-5670
E-mail: adproduction@vwm-online.com
URL: http://www.vwm-online.com

Annual. Primary Exhibits: Networking and educational opportunity presents new technologies vital to running a successful lab as well as information pertaining to such issues as obtaining TTB certification or ISO accreditation.

12961 ■ Sixth Annual Walk-Around Wine Tasting
Association of African American Vintners
101 W American Canyon Rd.
American Canyon, CA 94503
Ph: (707)334-6048
E-mail: info@aaavintners.org
URL: http://aaavintners.org

Annual. Primary Exhibits: Networking opportunity aims to celebrate sommeliers, African American women in wine, winemakers and winery owners. Sessions include advice from California's leading African American vintners, growers and winemakers.

12962 ■ Telluride Wine Festival
Commission for Community Assistance, Arts & Special Events
238 E Colorado, Ste. 9
Telluride, CO 81435
Fax: (212)766-2068
E-mail: telluridewinefest@akawinegeek.com
URL: http://www.telluridewinefestival.com

Annual. Primary Exhibits: Educational programs to increase awareness, interest and understanding of the new and developing aspects of wine and food production, preparation and consumption.

12963 ■ Wine Club Summit
Vineyards & Winery Management, Inc.
421 E St.
Santa Rosa, CA 95404
Ph: (707)577-7700
Fax: (707)577-7705
Fr: 800-535-5670
URL: http://www.vwm-online.com

Annual. Primary Exhibits: Networking opportunity for wine industry professionals.

12964 ■ Wineries Unlimited
Vineyards & Winery Management, Inc.
421 E St.
Santa Rosa, CA 95404
Ph: (707)577-7700

Fax: (707)577-7705
Fr: 800-535-5670
E-mail: adproduction@vwm-online.com
URL: http://www.vwm-online.com

Annual. Primary Exhibits: Networking opportunity includes expanded sessions on enology, viticulture, finance, management and marketing.

OTHER SOURCES

12965 ■ American Institute of Wine and Food
26384 Carmel Rancho Ln., Ste. 200E
Carmel, CA 93923
Fax: (831)250-7641
Fr: 800-274-2493
E-mail: info@aiwf.org
URL: http://www.aiwf.org

National organization with 25 chapters in major cities across the United States which is made up of wine and food professionals and enthusiasts; seeks to provide a networking opportunity in which industry professionals are able to meet with enthusiasts so they will then know and understand their core consumers. Offers scholarships and additional resources.

12966 ■ American Society for Enology and Viticulture (ASEV)
PO Box 1855
Davis, CA 95617-1855
Ph: (530)753-3142
Fax: (530)753-3318
E-mail: society@asev.org
URL: http://asev.org

Description: Persons concerned with the management and technical aspects of the wine and grape industry including owners, technicians, academic personnel, and farm advisors. Promotes technical advancement in enology and viticulture through integrated research by science and industry; provides a medium for the free exchange of technical information and information on problems of interest to the wine and grape industries.

12967 ■ American Sommelier Association
580 Broadway, Ste. 716
New York, NY 10012
Ph: (212)226-6805
Fax: (212)226-6407
E-mail: office@americansommelier.org
URL: http://www.americansommelier.org

Provides certification courses and support to members as well as the American sommelier industry; also includes a list of job postings for professionals in the wine industry.

12968 ■ American Vineyard Foundation (AVF)
PO Box 5779
Napa, CA 94581-0779
Ph: (707)252-6911
Fax: (707)252-7672
E-mail: scott@avf.org
URL: http://www.avf.org

Description: Collects funds for research on grape growing and wine making.

12969 ■ American Wine Society (AWS)
PO Box 279
Englewood, OH 45322
Ph: (937)529-7800
Fax: (937)529-7888
E-mail: executivedirector@americanwinesociety.org
URL: http://www.americanwinesociety.org

Description: Represents amateur and professional winemakers, wine enthusiasts, wine merchants, and anyone who enjoys wine and wants to learn more about it. Seeks to further the knowledge, appreciation and enjoyment of wine. Sponsors educational programs. Conducts wine tastings and trips to vineyards and wineries.

12970 ■ Atlantic Seaboard Wine Association (ASWA)
PO Box 11332
Burke, VA 22009
Ph: (703)323-6873
Fax: (703)323-1271
E-mail: fairfax@earthlink.net
URL: http://www.vwga.org

Description: Promotes public appreciation and understanding of wine and its production. Supports state and national wine educational forums and research. Provides technical, cultural, and historical wine information. Promotes wine enjoyment and responsible consumption as part of a healthy lifestyle. Supports quality production and sales of all grape wines. Lobbies on behalf of state and federal legislation favorable to the growth and economic viability of the U.S. wine industry. Strengthens cooperation with other wine organizations in addressing wine issues of common concern.

12971 ■ Brotherhood of the Knights of the Vine (KOV)
3343 Industrial Dr., Ste. 2
Santa Rosa, CA 95403
Ph: (707)579-3781
Fax: (707)579-3996
E-mail: info@kov.org
URL: http://www.kov.org

Description: Vintners, grape growers, wine wholesalers and retailers, professors of enology (the study of wine and wine-making), wine lovers with an interest in American grapes and wine. Seeks to promote wine as a healthy, hygienic beverage. Bestows titles of Supreme Knight, Master Knight, Knight or Gentle Lady, and Supreme Lady for services rendered to the cause of vines and wines of America. Sponsors Knights of the Vine Scholarship Fund at the University of California-Davis, Washington State University, Fresno State University, and Texas A&M University. National chapters conduct educational programs on wine.

12972 ■ California Association of Winegrape Growers (CAWG)
1325 J St., Ste. 1560
Sacramento, CA 95814
Ph: (916)379-8995
Fax: (916)379-8999
Fr: 800-241-1800
E-mail: info@cawg.org
URL: http://www.cawg.org

Description: Corporations, associations, and individuals who grow grapes in California for wine and related products. Serves as a unified voice to address issues aimed at improving the domestic and foreign market for California wines and wine grapes. Lobbies state and federal legislatures and regulatory agencies. Holds annual reception for the California Legislature and annual Wines of America Reception for Congress; co-sponsors the annual Unified Wine and Grape Symposium.

12973 ■ Department of Viticulture & Enology, University of California
1 Shields Ave.
Davis, CA 95616
Ph: (530)752-0380
Fax: (530)752-0382
URL: http://wineserver.ucdavis.edu

Website includes a listing of jobs in the grape growing and winemaking industries.

12974 ■ Free the Grapes
2700 Napa Valley Corporate Dr., Ste. H
Napa, CA 94558
Ph: (707)254-1107
Fax: (707)254-0433
E-mail: shackles@freethegrapes.org
URL: http://www.freethegrapes.org

Seeks to augment the three-tier system currently in place by many states which "creates monopolies in wine distribution and prevents consumers from purchasing wine directly from the winemakers despite

the consumer demand to buy wine products that are not always available by the wholesaler middlemen."

12975 ■ International Wine Guild
1600 Wynkoop St., Ste. 300
Denver, CO 80202
Ph: (303)296-3966
Fax: (303)904-3245
E-mail: info@internationalwineguild.com
URL: http://www.internationalwineguild.com

Seeks to encourage study to develop professional and technical understanding and increased knowledge of wine throughout all areas of the food and wine service industry. Offers programs for certification as well as an advanced program path leading to a Guild Wine Master Educator.

12976 ■ Long Island Wine Council
PO Box 600
Riverhead, NY 11901
Ph: (631)722-2220
Fax: (631)722-2221
E-mail: info@liwines.com
URL: http://www.liwines.com

Seeks to promote and develop the region's wine industry; offers educational programs for those looking to work in the field; sponsors wine events for networking and promotion.

12977 ■ Monterey County Vintners and Growers Association (MCVGA)
PO Box 1793
Monterey, CA 93942-1793
Ph: (831)375-9400
Fax: (831)375-1116
E-mail: info@montereywines.org
URL: http://montereywines.org

Description: Represents grape growers and wine producers of Monterey County, CA. Seeks to develop awareness and promote the image of Monterey wines.

12978 ■ Napa Valley Grapegrowers (NVG)
1795 3rd St.
Napa, CA 94559-2803
Ph: (707)944-8311
Fax: (707)224-8644
E-mail: info@napagrowers.org
URL: http://www.napagrowers.org

Description: Grape growers, wineries, businesses that work with growers, and others interested in the wine grape growing industry with particular emphasis on the Napa Valley. Provides marketing assistance to growers; promotes legislation at the local and state levels that will benefit growers. Has established a Napa Valley viticultural area designation, and is involved in the technical aspects of grape growing. Cosponsors marketing and promotional programs. Compiles statistical data on Napa Valley grapes and local markets.

12979 ■ Napa Valley Vintners Association (NVV)
PO Box 141
St. Helena, CA 94574
Ph: (707)963-3388
Fax: (707)963-3488
E-mail: nvv@napavintners.com
URL: http://www.napavintners.com

Description: Promotes Napa Valley, CA, wines and wineries; disseminates information about Napa Valley wines to the public.

12980 ■ Napa Valley Wine Library Association (NVWLA)
PO Box 328
St. Helena, CA 94574-0328
Ph: (707)963-5145
E-mail: info@napawinelibrary.org
URL: http://www.napawinelibrary.org

Description: Represents persons interested in wines, particularly those of the Napa Valley. Collects, preserves, and makes available books, publications, periodicals, and ephemera concerning Napa Valley wine. Conducts wine tasting courses.

12981 ■ New York Wine/Grape Foundation (NYWGF)

800 S Main St., Ste. 200
Canandaigua, NY 14424-2213
Ph: (585)394-3620
Fax: (585)394-3649
E-mail: bonitahampton@nywgf.org
URL: http://www.newyorkwines.org

Description: Grape growers from New York State; wineries and juice processors, suppliers, financiers, insurance representatives, consultants to growers, restaurateurs, and consumers. Promotes the demand for and sale of grapes and grape products through advertising and promotional work; assist members by performing services relative to the production, harvesting, and marketing of wine grapes, and any related research; provide members with production and marketing information; promote mutual understanding and goodwill between growers and processors of grapes. Seeks to educate consumers on the variety and quality of grapes grown and grape products made in New York State. Sponsors Women for New York State Wines, consisting of women supporting the New York State wine industry; WNYSW promotes wine salesand holds wine tasting to teach people how to read wine labels and distinguish between wines made from various types of wine grapes

12982 ■ Paso Robles Wine Country Alliance

530 10th St.
Paso Robles, CA 93446
Ph: (805)239-8463
Fax: (805)237-6439
Fr: 800-549-9463
E-mail: info@pasowine.com
URL: http://www.pasowine.com

Seeks to enhance the status of Paso Robles as a world-class wine region by marketing and promoting the unique attributes of the region; offers educational resources that can help the membership to optimize business opportunities as well as their products; monitors local governments to protect member property rights, water rights and rights to farm. Website provides winery and vineyard profiles, event calendar, a wine directory and classified ads which offer job listings.

12983 ■ Santa Cruz Mountains Winegrowers Association (SCMWA)

7605-A Old Dominion Ct.
Aptos, CA 95003
Ph: (831)685-8463
Fax: (831)688-6961
E-mail: info@scmwa.com
URL: http://www.scmwa.com

Description: Wineries in the Santa Cruz Mountains area. Facilitates exchange of information among members. Promotes wines of the Santa Cruz Mountains appellation. Holds grape growing and winemaking seminars.

12984 ■ SF Sommelier Consulting

PO Box 318002
San Francisco, CA 94131-8002

Ph: (415)779-2397
E-mail: sfsommelier@sbcglobal.net
URL: http://www.sfsommelier.com

Provides educational programs and organizes wine events for the wine industry.

12985 ■ Society of Wine Educators (SWE)

1319 F St. NW, Ste. 303
Washington, DC 20004
Ph: (202)408-8777
Fax: (202)408-8677
E-mail: info@societyofwineeducators.org
URL: http://www.societyofwineeducators.org

Description: Represents individuals who teach or write about wine for the trade or academic communities; those associated with wineries, restaurants, or the wine retail, wholesale, or import industry; consumers with an interest in wine and wine education. Facilitates the flow of information among wine producers, marketers, retailers, and consumers.

12986 ■ Sonoma County Vintners (SCV)

420 Aviation Blvd., Ste. 106
Santa Rosa, CA 95403-1039
Ph: (707)522-5840
Fax: (707)573-3942
Fr: 800-939-7666
E-mail: info@sonomawine.com
URL: http://www.sonomawine.com

Description: Wineries that produce and label at least one wine made in Sonoma County. Promotes the wines of Sonoma County. Conducts events designed to educate the public about wine, wine tasting, and wine-producing regions. Sponsors annual national wine tasting tour in March and April, and Canadian tour in October and November.

12987 ■ Sonoma County Wine Library

139 Piper St.
Healdsburg, CA 95448-3899
Ph: (707)433-3772
Fax: (707)433-7946
E-mail: bo@sonoma.lib.ca.us
URL: http://www.sonomalibrary.org/wine/

Four stated collections include: the science and technology of growing grapes and making wine; the history of wine worldwide; the history of wine in Sonoma County; the business and economics of the wine industry; also includes videos, 16mm films, photographs, and books about careers in the wine industry.

12988 ■ Sonoma County Winegrape Commission

PO Box 1959
Sebastopol, CA 95473
Ph: (707)829-3963
E-mail: info@scgga.org
URL: http://www.sonomawinegrape.org

Description: Growers of wine grapes for commercial sale to wineries. Promotes the wines of Sonoma County, CA; addresses agricultural issues that affect grape growers. Provides information on Sonoma County food and wine. Maintains speakers' bureau.

12989 ■ United States Sommelier Association (USSA)

1111 Lincoln Rd., Ste. 400-9
Miami Beach, FL 33139

Ph: (954)437-0449
E-mail: info@ussommelier.com
URL: http://www.ussommelier.com

Description: Represents individuals dedicated to the promotion and teaching of the wine culture to wine lovers and industry professionals. Promotes the enjoyment of wine. Educates and shares information about wines and spirits. Offers training and certification programs.

12990 ■ Wine Appreciation Guild (WAG)

360 Swift Ave., Unit 30-40
South San Francisco, CA 94080-6228
Ph: (650)866-3020
Fax: (650)866-3513
Fr: 800-231-9463
E-mail: info@wineappreciation.com
URL: http://www.wineappreciation.com

Description: Represents winery owners and distributors. Disseminates information on wine, with emphasis on American wines. Conducts wine evaluations and research programs on wine and health, cooking with wine, and consumer wine. Offers wine study courses and compiles statistics. Sponsors competitions.

12991 ■ Wine Business Program, Sonoma State University

1801 E Catati Ave.
Rohnert Park, CA 94928
Ph: (707)664-2377
E-mail: winebiz@sonoma.edu
URL: http://www.sonoma.edu/sbe/wine-business-institute

Located within the university's School of Business & Economics, Sonoma State's Wine Business Program is the first and only in the United States to focus exclusively on the business aspects of the wine industry. Website includes listing of internships and industry employment.

12992 ■ The Wine Institute

425 Market St., Ste. 1000
San Francisco, CA 94105
Ph: (415)512-0151
Fax: (415)356-7569
URL: http://www.wineinstitute.org

Advocacy and public policy association concerning California wineries brings together the resources of 1,000 wineries and affiliated businesses to support legislation and regulation, international market development, scientific research, media relations and educational programs that benefit the entire California wine industry.

12993 ■ WineAmerica

1015 18th St. NW, Ste. 500
Washington, DC 20036
Ph: (202)783-2756
E-mail: info@wineamerica.org
URL: http://www.wineamerica.org

Seeks to encourage the dynamic development and growth of American wineries and winegrowing through the advancement and advocacy of sound public policy; also provides membership services to assist wineries with a variety of business operations including job referral services.

12994 ■ Adweek
Nielsen Business Media
770 Broadway
New York, NY 10003-9595
URL: http://www.adweek.com/

Weekly. $299.00/year for individuals, print & online; $24.95/year for individuals, print & online per month; $19.95/year for individuals, online per month; $149.95/year for individuals, digital edition access. Advertising news magazine.

12995 ■ Afterimage
Visual Studies Workshop
31 Prince St.
Rochester, NY 14607
Ph: (585)442-8676
Fax: (585)442-1992
E-mail: afterimage@vsw.org
URL: http://www.vsw.org/ai

Bimonthly. $33.00/year for individuals; $20.00/year for students; $100.00/year for institutions, library; $90.00/year for other countries; $165.00/year for institutions, other countries, libraries. Publication providing independent critical commentary on issues in media arts, including scholarly research, in-depth reviews, investigative journalism, interviews, and the largest list of exhibitions, festivals, position announcements and calls for work of its kind.

12996 ■ American Artist
Interweave Press L.L.C.
201 E 4th St.
Loveland, CO 80537
Ph: (970)669-7672
Fax: (970)613-8317
Fr: 800-272-2193
URL: http://www.artistdaily.com

$29.95/year for individuals; $52.95/year for two years. Art and educational journal.

12997 ■ Art in America
Brant Publications Inc.
575 Broadway, 5th Fl.
New York, NY 10012-3230
Ph: (212)941-2800
URL: http://www.artinamericamagazine.com

Monthly. $34.95/year for individuals; $79.95/year for Canada; $95.00/year for out of country. Art magazine.

12998 ■ Art and Living
Art and Living
8306 Wilshire Blvd., Ste. 2029
Beverly Hills, CA 90211
Ph: (310)313-3171
Fax: (310)313-2125
URL: http://www.artandliving.com/jm/
    index.php?lang=en-US

$76.00/year for other countries; $36.00/year for U.S.

and Canada; $12.00/year for single issue. Magazine covering art and art topics.

12999 ■ The Artist's Magazine
F+W Media Inc.
4700 E Galbraith Rd.
Cincinnati, OH 45236
Ph: (513)531-2690
Fax: (513)531-0798
Fr: 800-289-0963
E-mail: tamedit@fwmedia.com
URL: http://www.artistsnetwork.com/the-artists-
    magazine

$20.96/year for individuals; $30.96/year for Canada, including GST/HST; $30.96/year for other countries, surface delivery. Magazine by artists for artists. Covers artwork, working methods, tools, and materials.

13000 ■ ARTnews Magazine
Art News L.L.C.
48 W 38th St.
New York, NY 10018
Ph: (212)398-1690
Fax: (212)819-0394
Fr: 800-284-4625
URL: http://artnews.com

Monthly. $39.95/year for Canada; $99.95/year for other countries; $19.95/year for individuals. News magazine reporting on art, personalities, issues, trends, and events that shape the international art world.

13001 ■ Current Jobs in Art
Foster Opportunities, Inc.
1834 Olmstead Dr.
Falls Church, VA 22043
Ph: (703)506-4400
Fax: 888-870-3069
E-mail: admin@graduatejobs.com
URL: http://www.graduatejobs.com/art.htm

Monthly. $49.50/year. Covers vacancies in all visual arts fields, including applied arts, art education and art history.

13002 ■ Dirty Goat
Host Publications, Inc.
277 Broadway, Ste. 210
New York, NY 10007
Ph: (212)905-2365
Fax: (212)905-2369
URL: http://www.thedirtygoat.com/index.html

Semiannual. $20.00/year for individuals. Journal covering poetry, prose, drama, literature and visual art.

13003 ■ DM News
DM News
114 W 26th St., 4th Fl.
New York, NY 10001
Ph: (646)638-6000

Fax: (646)638-6159
E-mail: inquiry@dmnews.com
URL: http://www.dmnews.com/

Weekly. $148.00/year for individuals; $198.00/year for Canada; $228.00/year for other countries; $265.00/year for two years; $355.00/year for Canada, 2 years; $395.00/year for other countries, 2 years. Tabloid newspaper for publishers, fund raisers, financial marketers, catalogers, package goods advertisers and their agencies, and other marketers who use direct mail, mail order advertising, catalogs, or other direct response media to sell their products or services.

13004 ■ Editor & Publisher
Editor & Publisher Magazine
17782 Cowan, Ste. A
Irvine, CA 92614
Ph: (949)660-6150
Fax: (949)660-6172
URL: http://www.editorandpublisher.com/

Weekly (Mon.). $65.00/year for individuals, print and online; $125.00/year for two years, print and online; $85.00/year for other countries; $49.00/year for individuals, digital only. Magazine focusing on newspaper journalism, advertising, printing equipment and interactive services.

13005 ■ Film History
Indiana University Press
601 N Morton St.
Bloomington, IN 47404-3778
Ph: (812)855-8817
Fax: (812)855-8507
Fr: 800-842-6796
E-mail: filmhist@aol.com
URL: http://inscribe.iupress.org/loi/fil

Quarterly. $82.50/year for individuals, print and online; $75.00/year for individuals, print only; $67.50/year for individuals, online only; $273.50/year for institutions, print and online; $199.50/year for institutions, print only; $179.50/year for institutions, online only. Journal tracing the history of the motion picture with reference to social, technological, and economic aspects, covering various aspects of motion pictures such as production, distribution, exhibition, and reception.

13006 ■ GNSI Newsletter
Guild of Natural Science Illustrators Inc.
PO Box 652
Ben Franklin Sta.
Washington, DC 20044-0652
Ph: (301)309-1514
Fax: (301)309-1514
URL: http://www.gnsi.org/resources/publications/gnsi-
    newsletter

Description: Ten issues/year. Serves as a forum for member professional scientific illustrators and technical artists. Provides information on supplies, techniques, methods, and materials for production of highly-rendered and accurate illustrations of natural science subjects. Also discusses business practices of interest to professional as well as aspiring illustrators. Recurring features include announcements of Guild activities, examples of members' work, book reviews and notices of publications available, and job listings.

13007 ■ Jobline News
Graphic Artists Guild
32 Broadway, Ste. 1114
New York, NY 10004
Ph: (212)791-3400
Fax: (212)791-0333
E-mail: jobline@gag.org
URL: http://www.graphicartistsguild.org

Description: Weekly. Lists jobs for freelance and staff artists in areas such as graphic design, illustration, and art education. Lists jobs from across the country; quantity and locales vary weekly.

13008 ■ Me
Me Magazine
185 W Houston St., No. 4K
New York, NY 10014
URL: http://www.memagazinenyc.com

Quarterly. $35.00/year for Canada and Mexico; $50.00/year for other countries; $30.00/year for individuals; $10.00/year for Canada and Mexico, single issue; $15.00/year for other countries, single issue. Magazine devoted to people in creative professions. Provides biographical insight into the personal lives of people in the creative community.

13009 ■ NSS News Bulletin
National Sculpture Society
75 Varick St., 11th Fl.
New York, NY 10013
Ph: (212)764-5645
Fax: (212)764-5651
E-mail: info@nationalsculpture.org
URL: http://www.nationalsculpture.org/Newsbulletin

Description: Bimonthly. Covers sculpture competitions, awards, grants, exhibitions, and commissions. Reports members' works and activities. Recurring features include news of research, a calendar of events, reports of meetings, news of educational opportunities, job listings, notices of publications available, and Seeking and Offering.

13010 ■ Producers Masterguide
Producers Masterguide
60 E 8th St., 34th Fl.
New York, NY 10003-6514
Ph: (212)777-4002
Fax: (212)777-4101
URL: http://www.producers.masterguide.com/cover.html

Annual. $185.00/year for U.S.; $175.00/year for Canada; $205.00/year for other countries. An international film and TV production directory and guide for the professional motion picture, broadcast television, feature film, TV commercial, cable/satellite, digital and videotape industries in the U.S., Canada, the UK, the Caribbean Islands, Mexico, Australia, New Zealand, Europe, Israel, Morocco, the Far East, and South America.

13011 ■ Professional Artist Magazine
1500 Park Center Dr.
Orlando, FL 32835
Ph: (407)563-7000
Fax: (407)563-7099
E-mail: khall@artcalendar.com
URL: http://www.artcalendar.com

Description: Monthly, except August. Lists art grants, shows, and commissions. Features articles on the psychology of creativity. Recurring features include interviews, a calendar of events, news of educational opportunities, job listings, book reviews, notices of publications available, and columns titled Marketing Strategies, Art Law, Perspective, and Federal Updates.

13012 ■ Publishers Weekly
Publishers Weekly
71 W 23 St., No. 1608
New York, NY 10010
Ph: (212)377-5500
URL: http://www.publishersweekly.com

Weekly. $249.99/year for individuals; $299.99/year for Canada; $399.99/year for other countries, air delivery. Magazine for publishers.

13013 ■ The Salmagundi Stew
Salmagundi Club
47 5th Ave.
New York, NY 10003
Ph: (212)255-7740
E-mail: info@salmagundi.org
URL: http://www.salmagundi.org

Description: 2/year. Highlights activities of the Club, a fellowship and exhibition organization for painters, sculptors, writers, and artists. Profiles artists and their work. Recurring features include notes on members, coverage of Clubhouse activities.

13014 ■ SignCraft
Signcraft Publishing Company Inc.
10271 Deer Run Farms Rd.
PO Box 60031
Fort Myers, FL 33966
Ph: (239)939-4644
Fax: (239)939-0607
Fr: 800-204-0204
URL: http://www.signcraft.com

$39.00/year for individuals; $69.00/year for two years; $49.00/year for other countries; $91.00/year for other countries, 2 years. Trade magazine.

13015 ■ Stained Glass Quarterly
Stained Glass Association of America
9313 E 63rd St.
Raytown, MO 64133
Ph: (816)737-2090
Fax: (816)737-2801
Fr: 800-438-9581
E-mail: quarterly@sgaonline.org
URL: http://stainedglassquarterly.com/

Quarterly. $29.00/year for individuals; $47.00/year for Canada and Mexico; $59.00/year for other countries. Magazine on architectural stained and decorative art glass.

13016 ■ State of the Arts
Montana Arts Council
830 N Warren St., 1st Fl.
PO Box 202201
Helena, MT 59601
Ph: (406)444-6430
Fax: (406)444-6548
E-mail: mac@mt.gov
URL: http://art.mt.gov

Description: Bimonthly. $15/year for out-of-state residents. Contains artists' profiles; news of educational opportunities; updates of legislation and government support programs, especially the National Endowment for the Arts; news of conferences and Council activities; grant announcements; calls for exhibit entries; notices of publications available; a calendar of events; and job listings.

EMPLOYER DIRECTORIES AND NETWORKING LISTS

13017 ■ Black Book Photography
Black Book Marketing Group
740 Broadway, Ste. 202
New York, NY 10003
Ph: (212)979-6700
Fax: (212)673-4321
Fr: 800-841-1246
URL: http://www.BlackBook.com

Annual, Latest edition 2008. $60.00 for individuals. Publication includes: Over 19,000 art directors,

creative directors, photographers and photographic services, design firms, advertising agencies, and other firms whose products or services are used in advertising.

13018 ■ Career Ideas for Teens in the Arts and Communications
Facts On File Inc.
132 W 31st St., 17th Fl.
New York, NY 10001
Ph: (212)967-8800
Fax: 800-678-3633
Fr: 800-322-8755
URL: http://factsonfile.infobasepublishing.com

Published 2005. $40.00 for individuals. Covers: A multitude of career possibilities based on a teenager's specific interests and skills and links his/her talents to a wide variety of actual professions.

13019 ■ Careers in Focus—Art
Facts On File Inc.
132 W 31st St., 17th Fl.
New York, NY 10001
Ph: (212)967-8800
Fax: 800-678-3633
Fr: 800-322-8755
URL: http://www.infobasepublishing.com

Latest edition 2nd; Published July, 2008. $32.95 for individuals. Covers: An overview of art, followed by a selection of jobs profiled in detail, including the nature of the job, earnings, prospects for employment, what kind of training and skills it requires, and sources for further information.

13020 ■ Discovering Careers for Your Future—Art
Facts On File Inc.
132 W 31st St., 17th Fl.
New York, NY 10001
Ph: (212)967-8800
Fax: 800-678-3633
Fr: 800-322-8755
URL: http://factsonfile.infobasepublishing.com

Latest edition 2nd, 2008. $21.95 for individuals. Covers: Artists, cartoonists, graphic designers, illustrators, and photographers; links career education to curriculum, helping children investigate the subjects they are interested in, and the careers those subjects might lead to.

13021 ■ National Directory of Arts Internships
National Network for Artist Placement
935 West Ave. 37
Los Angeles, CA 90065
Ph: (323)222-4035
E-mail: info@artistplacement.com
URL: http://www.artistplacement.com

Biennial, odd years; latest edition 11th. $95.00 for individuals. Covers: Over 5,000 internship opportunities in dance, music, theater, art, design, film, and video & over 1,250 host organizations Entries include: Name of sponsoring organization, address, name of contact; description of positions available, eligibility requirements, stipend or salary (if any), application procedures. Arrangement: Classified by discipline, then geographical.

13022 ■ National Directory of Magazines
Oxbridge Communications Inc.
186 5th Ave.
New York, NY 10010-5202
Ph: (212)741-0231
Fax: (212)633-2938
Fr: 800-955-0231
URL: http://www.oxbridge.com

latest edition 2011. $995.00 for individuals; $1,195.00 for individuals; $1,995.00 for individuals. Covers: Over 20,000 magazines; coverage includes Canada. Entries include: Title, publisher name, address, phone, fax number, names and titles of contact and key personnel, financial data, editorial and advertising information, circulation. Arrangement: Classified by subject. Indexes: Title, geographical, publisher.

13023 ■ *Printworld Directory of Contemporary Prints and Prices*
Printworld International Inc.
937 Jefferson Way
PO Box 1957
West Chester, PA 19380
Ph: (610)431-6654
Fax: (610)431-6653
Fr: 800-788-9101
URL: http://www.printworlddirectory.com

Irregular, Latest edition 13th; April 2010. $359.00 for individuals; $259.00 for individuals. Publication includes: Biographical data on 5,000 international artists in contemporary printmaking; thousands of galleries who handle prints and hundreds of print publishers, and 600,000 print/price listings.

13024 ■ *Society of Illustrators—Annual of American Illustration*
Society of Illustrators
128 E 63rd St.
New York, NY 10065-7303
Ph: (212)838-2560
Fax: (212)838-2561
URL: http://societyillustrators.org/shop/index.cms

Annual, January; Latest edition 49th. $45.00 for individuals. Covers: 800 illustrators and art directors. Entries include: Personal or firm name, address, clients. Arrangement: Alphabetical.

13025 ■ *Top Careers for Art Graduates*
Facts On File Inc.
132 W 31st St., 17th Fl.
New York, NY 10001
Ph: (212)967-8800
Fax: 800-678-3633
Fr: 800-322-8755
URL: http://www.infobasepublishing.com

Published March, 2004. Covers: Several of the best career opportunities for art graduates in a number of industries.

13026 ■ *The Workbook*
Scott & Daughters Publishing Inc.
6762 Lexington Ave.
Los Angeles, CA 90038
Ph: (323)856-0008
Fax: (323)856-4368
Fr: 800-547-2688
URL: http://www.workbook.com

Annual, Latest edition 2011. $60.00 for individuals; $30.00 for individuals; $35.00 for individuals. Covers: 55,000 advertising agencies, art directors, photographers, freelance illustrators and designers, artists' representatives, interactive designers, pre-press services, and other graphic arts services in the U.S. Entries include: Company or individual name, address, phone, specialty. National in scope. Arrangement: Classified by product or service.

Handbooks and Manuals

13027 ■ *Career Opportunities in the Visual Arts*
Facts On File Inc.
132 W 31st St., 17th Fl.
New York, NY 10001
Fax: 800-678-3633
Fr: 800-322-8755
E-mail: custserv@factsonfile.com
URL: http://factsonfile.infobasepublishing.com

2006. $49.50. Covers over 65 profiles such as art teacher, book designer, financial officer, framer, gallery director, graphic designer, medical illustrator, storyboard artists. Includes comprehensive descriptions of certification, education, special skills, and trainings required.

13028 ■ *Careers for Color Connoisseurs and Other Visual Types*
The McGraw-Hill Companies
PO Box 182604
Columbus, OH 43272
Fax: (614)759-3749
Fr: 877-883-5524
E-mail: customer.service@mcgraw-hill.com
URL: http://www.mhprofessional.com/
product.php?isbn=0071465197

Jan Goldberg. Second edition, 2005. $19.95 (paper). 176 pages.

13029 ■ *Careers for Crafty People and Other Dexterous Types*
The McGraw-Hill Companies
PO Box 182604
Columbus, OH 43272
Fax: (614)759-3749
Fr: 877-883-5524
E-mail: customer.service@mcgraw-hill.com
URL: http://www.mhprofessional.com/
product.php?isbn=0071487263

Mark Rowh. Third edition, 2006. $13.95 (paper). 160 pages.

13030 ■ *Careers in Health Care*
The McGraw-Hill Companies
PO Box 182604
Columbus, OH 43272
Fax: (614)759-3749
Fr: 877-883-5524
E-mail: customer.service@mcgraw-hill.com
URL: http://www.mhprofessional.com/
product.php?isbn=0071466533

Barbara M. Swanson. Fifth edition, 2005. $19.95 (paper). 192 pages. Describes job duties, work settings, salaries, licensing and certification requirements, educational preparation, and future outlook. Gives ideas on how to secure a job.

13031 ■ *Creative Careers: Paths for Aspiring Actors, Artists, Dancers, Musicians and Writers*
SuperCollege, LLC
3286 Oak Ct.
Belmont, CA 94002
Ph: (650)618-2221
URL: http://www.supercollege.com

Elaina Loveland. 2009. $17.95. 352 pages. Provides tips and advice for job seekers aiming for a career in the field of arts. Includes details on salaries, job descriptions, job outlook, training and education requirements for each artistic career.

13032 ■ *The Fine Artist's Career Guide*
Allworth Press
307 W 36th St., 11th Fl.
New York, NY 10018
Ph: (212)643-6816
Fax: (212)643-6819
URL: http://www.allworth.com/book/
?GCOI=58115100439540

Daniel Grant. Second edition, 2004. $29.95 (paper). 320 pages. Covers the fine and applied arts.

13033 ■ *How to Survive and Prosper as an Artist: Selling Yourself Without Selling Your Soul*
Holt Paperbacks
175 Fifth Ave.
New York, NY 10010
Ph: (646)307-5095
Fax: (212)633-0748
Fr: 800-672-2054
URL: http://us.macmillan.com

Caroll Michels. 6 edition, 2009. $21.99. 400 pages. Includes index and bibliographical references.

13034 ■ *Opportunities in Arts and Crafts Careers*
The McGraw-Hill Companies
PO Box 182604
Columbus, OH 43272
Fax: (614)759-3749
Fr: 877-883-5524
E-mail: customer.service@mcgraw-hill.com
URL: http://www.mhprofessional.com/
product.php?isbn=0071448497

Elizabeth Gardner. 2005. $13.95 (paper). 211 pages.

13035 ■ *Opportunities in Visual Arts Careers*
The McGraw-Hill Companies
PO Box 182604
Columbus, OH 43272
Fax: (614)759-3749
Fr: 877-883-5524
E-mail: customer.service@mcgraw-hill.com
URL: http://www.mhprofessional.com/
product.php?isbn=0071545298

Mark Salmon. 2008. $14.95 (paper). 160 pages. Points the way to a career in the visual arts, examining opportunities for designers, painters, sculptors, illustrators, animators, photographers, art therapists, educators, and others. Offers a view of the pros and cons of working for an art or design company or on your own.

13036 ■ *Starting Your Career as an Artist: A Guide for Painters, Sculptors, Photographers, and Other Visual Artists*
Allworth Press
307 W 36th St., 11th Fl.
New York, NY 10018
Ph: (212)643-6816
Fax: (212)643-6819
URL: http://www.allworth.com

Angie Wojak and Stacy Miller. 2011. $19.95 (paper). 256 pages. Guides artists seeking professional careers. Covers topics essential to emerging artists such as networking, finding a mentor, setting up a studio, writing the best resume, and refining career aspirations.

13037 ■ *Taking the Leap: Building a Career as a Visual Artist*
Chronicle Books LLC
680 Second St.
San Francisco, CA 94107
Ph: (415)537-4200
Fax: (415)537-4460
Fr: 800-722-6657
E-mail: frontdesk@chroniclebooks.com
URL: http://www.chroniclebooks.com

Cay Lang. 2006. $19.95. 256 pages.

Employment Agencies and Search Firms

13038 ■ Claremont-Branan, Inc.
1298 Rockbridge Rd., Ste. B
Stone Mountain, GA 30087
Fr: 800-875-1292
URL: http://cbisearch.com

Employment agency. Executive search firm.

13039 ■ Graphic Arts Employment Specialists, Inc.
409 Pacific Coast Hwy., Ste. 455
Redondo Beach, CA 90277
Fax: (310)937-3760
Fr: 888-499-9722
E-mail: info@gaes.com
URL: http://www.gaes.com

Employment agency specializing in the publishing and packaging industries.

13040 ■ Randolph Associates, Inc.
950 Massachusetts Ave., Ste. 105
Cambridge, MA 02139-3174

Ph: (617)441-8777
Fax: (617)441-8778
E-mail: jobs@greatjobs.com
URL: http://www.greatjobs.com
Employment agency. Provides regular or temporary placement of staff.

ONLINE JOB SOURCES AND SERVICES

13041 ■ ArtBistro.com
URL: http://artbistro.monster.com

Description: Serves as a social network for artists and designers allowing them to advance their careers, share portfolios, make new connections, and read the latest art and design news.

13042 ■ ArtJob Online
E-mail: artjob@westaf.org
URL: http://www.artjob.org

Description: Contains up-to-date national and international listings of arts employment and related opportunities in the arts: full- and part-time employment, internships, grants, public art projects, and residencies. User can search by region, art discipline, type of organization. Fee: Subscribers pay $25 for 3 months, $40 for six months and $75 for one year.

13043 ■ AWN Career Connection
E-mail: jobs@awn.com
URL: http://jobs.awn.com

Description: Exists to provide the professional and enthusiast communities an assembly of animation resources. Allows job seekers to anonymously seek or investigate new career opportunities, while providing recruiters, HR personnel and other employment personnel a set of tools to find, assess and discretely contact those job seekers.

13044 ■ Graphic Artists Guild
32 Broadway, Ste. 1114
New York, NY 10004
Ph: (212)791-3400
Fax: (212)791-0333
E-mail: membership@gag.org
URL: http://www.graphicartistsguild.org

Description: JOBLine News section of Guild Resources page contains weekly e-mail newsletter of job listings. Fee: Must subscribe to e-mail newsletter non-member six-month rates start at $80. Visitors may download a free sample.

TRADESHOWS

13045 ■ Art Libraries Society of North America Conference
Art Libraries Society of North America
7044 S 13th St.
Oak Creek, WI 53154
Ph: (414)768-8000
Fax: (414)768-8001
Fr: 800-817-0621
URL: http://www.arlisna.org

Annual. 2013 April 25-29; Pasadena, CA. Provides networking opportunities for attendees.

OTHER SOURCES

13046 ■ Aid to Artisans (ATA)
1030 New Britain Ave., Ste. 102
West Hartford, CT 06110
Ph: (860)756-5550
Fax: (860)756-7558
E-mail: info@aidtoartisans.org
URL: http://www.aidtoartisans.org

Description: Offers practical assistance worldwide to artisans. Fosters artistic traditions and cultural vitality to improve livelihood and keep communities healthy, strong and growing. Works with its artisan partners to develop products with the appeal to compete successfully in new markets around the world and to improve their business skills so that the changes achieved are enduring.

13047 ■ American Institute of Graphic Arts (AIGA)
164 5th Ave.
New York, NY 10010-5901
Ph: (212)807-1990
Fax: (212)807-1799
E-mail: grefe@aiga.org
URL: http://www.aiga.org

Description: Graphic designers, art directors, illustrators and packaging designers. Sponsors exhibits and projects in the public interest. Sponsors traveling exhibitions. Operates gallery. Maintains library of design books and periodicals; offers slide archives.

13048 ■ American Society of Artists (ASA)
PO Box 1326
Palatine, IL 60078
Ph: (312)751-2500
E-mail: asoa@webtv.net
URL: http://community-2.webtv.net/ASOA/ASA

Description: Professional artists and craftspeople. Maintains art referral service and information exchange service. Sponsors art and craft festivals and a Lecture and Demonstration Service; the Special Arts Services Division aids disabled individuals to either practice or enjoy the visual arts. Presents demonstrations in visual arts to better acquaint the public with various processes in different media.

13049 ■ Art Directors Club (ADC)
106 W 29th St.
New York, NY 10001
Ph: (212)643-1440
Fax: (212)643-4266
E-mail: info@adcglobal.org
URL: http://www.adcglobal.org

Description: Art directors of advertising magazines and agencies, visual information specialists, and graphic designers; associate members are artists, cinematographers, photographers, copywriters, educators, journalists, and critics. Promotes and stimulates interest in the practice of art direction. Sponsors Annual Exhibition of Advertising, Editorial and Television Art and Design; International Traveling Exhibition. Provides educational, professional, and entertainment programs; on-premise art exhibitions; portfolio review program. Conducts panels for students and faculty.

13050 ■ Art Libraries Society of North America
7044 S 13th St.
Oak Creek, WI 53154
Ph: (414)768-8000
Fax: (414)768-8001
Fr: 800-817-0621
URL: http://www.arlisna.org

Description: Consists of architecture and art librarians, visual resources professionals, artists, curators, educators, publishers, students, and others interested in visual arts information. Promotes the advancement of art library and information professionals. Collaborates with other professional and educational organizations through participation in international forums.

13051 ■ Association of Medical Illustrators (AMI)
201 E Main St., Ste. 1405
Lexington, KY 40507
Fax: (859)514-9166
Fr: (866)393-4264
E-mail: hq@ami.org
URL: http://www.ami.org

Description: Represents medical illustrators and individuals engaged in related pursuits. Promotes the study and encourages the advancement of medical illustration and allied fields of visual education. Works to advance medical education and to promote understanding and cooperation with medical and related professions; accredits six postgraduate medical illustration programs. Offers continuing education program; provides professional certification; compiles statistics.

13052 ■ Cartoonists Northwest (CNW)
PO Box 31122
Seattle, WA 98103
E-mail: cartoonistsnw@gmail.com
URL: http://sites.google.com/site/cartoonistnw/home

Description: Cartoonists, writers, publishers, illustrators, agents, and others interested in cartooning. Members are accepted nationwide and internationally. Provides information on all aspects of the cartooning profession to amateur, aspiring, and practicing cartoonists. Promotes cartooning as an art form. Provides networking opportunities and referral services. Conducts educational programs.

13053 ■ College Art Association (CAA)
275 7th Ave., 18th Fl.
New York, NY 10001
Ph: (212)691-1051
Fax: (212)627-2381
E-mail: nyoffice@collegeart.org
URL: http://www.collegeart.org

Description: Professional organization of artists, art historians and fine art educators, museum directors, and curators. Seeks to raise the standards of scholarship and of the teaching of art and art history throughout the country.

13054 ■ Health Science Communications Association (HeSCA)
39 Wedgewood Dr., Ste. A
Jewett City, CT 06351-2420
Ph: (860)376-5915
Fax: (860)376-6621
E-mail: hescaone@sbcglobal.net
URL: http://www.hesca.org

Description: Represents media managers, graphic artists, biomedical librarians, producers, faculty members of health science and veterinary medicine schools, health professional organizations, and industry representatives. Acts as a clearinghouse for information used by professionals engaged in health science communications. Coordinates Media Festivals Program that recognizes outstanding media productions in the health sciences. Offers placement service.

13055 ■ Illustrators' Partnership of America (IPA)
845 Moraine St.
Marshfield, MA 02050
Ph: (781)837-9152
E-mail: info@illustratorspartnership.org
URL: http://www.illustratorspartnership.org

Description: Acts as an advocate for the protection of intellectual property rights of members. Educates artists on how to protect and manage their intellectual property rights. Conducts research on electronic licensing and publication of the works of illustrators, and the development of authentic, secondary markets for the artists' works.

13056 ■ Institute of American Indian Arts (IAIA)
83 Avan Nu Po Rd.
Santa Fe, NM 87508
Ph: (505)424-2300
Fax: (505)424-3900
Fr: 800-804-6423
E-mail: setzel@iaia.edu
URL: http://www.iaia.edu

Description: Federally chartered private institution. Offers 4-year degrees in Creative Writing, New Media Arts, Museum Studies, Indigenous Studies and Studio arts primarily to Native American and Alaska Natives (but school is open enrollment). Emphasis is placed upon Indian traditions as the basis for creative expression in fine arts including painting, sculpture, museum studies, creative writing, printmaking, photography, communications, design, and dance, as well as training in metal crafts, jewelry, ceramics, textiles, and various traditional crafts. Students are encouraged to identify with their heritage and to be aware of themselves as members of a culture rich in architecture, the fine arts, music, pageantry, and the humanities. All programs are based on elements of the Native American cultural heritage that emphasizes differences between Native American and non-Native American cultures. Sponsors Indian arts-oriented junior college offering Associate of Fine Arts degrees in various fields as well as seminars, an exhibition program, and traveling exhibits. Maintains extensive library, museum, and biographical archives. Provides placement service. Conventions/Meetings: varies.

13057 ■ International Polymer Clay Association (IPCA)
1350 Beverly Rd., Ste. 115-345
McLean, VA 22101
URL: http://www.npcg.org

Description: Seeks to educate the public about polymer clay and to study and promote interest in the use of polymer clay as an artistic medium. Promotes polymer clay work to galleries and museums as well as to the public. Develops opportunities for artists to show their work to the public and engage in public-service activities.

13058 ■ Society of Illustrators (SI)
128 E 63rd St.
New York, NY 10021-7303
Ph: (212)838-2560

Fax: (212)838-2561
E-mail: info@societyillustrators.org
URL: http://www.societyillustrators.org

Description: Professional society of illustrators and art directors. Maintains Museum of American Illustration which sponsors continuous exhibits; holds annual exhibit (February-April) of best illustrations of the year; conducts benefit and sale in gallery in December. Participates in annual U.S. Air Force exhibits. Maintains hall of fame; traveling exhibition.

13059 ■ Southeastern Theatre Conference (SETC)
1175 Revolution Mill Dr., Ste. 14
Greensboro, NC 27405
Ph: (336)272-3645
Fax: (336)272-8810
E-mail: info@setc.org
URL: http://www.setc.org

Description: Serves the needs of individuals and theatre organizations involved in professional, university/college, community, children/youth, and secondary school theatres. Brings together people interested in theatre and theatre artists and craftsmen from 10 southeastern states of the U.S., across the nation and internationally in order to promote high standards and to stimulate creativity in all phases of theatrical endeavor. Services include: job contact service for technical hiring and job listings, resume service, etc.; playwriting projects for new plays; scholarships for a variety of theatre interests; and annual auditions (spring and fall) for professional,

dinner, repertory, summer indoor and outdoor theatres, cruise lines and entertainment venues.

13060 ■ United States Artists (USA)
5757 Wilshire Blvd., Ste. 580
Los Angeles, CA 90036
Ph: (323)857-5857
Fax: (323)857-5867
URL: http://www.unitedstatesartists.org

Description: Promotes the value and work of artists. Provides financial support to artists living in the United States. Advocates for the role of artists in the social, economic, and political capital development.

13061 ■ Women's Caucus for Art (WCA)
Canal St. Sta.
PO Box 1498
New York, NY 10013
Ph: (212)634-0007
E-mail: president@nationalwca.org
URL: http://www.nationalwca.org

Description: Professional women in visual art fields: artists, critics, art historians, museum and gallery professionals, arts administrators, educators and students, and collectors of art. Aims to increase recognition for contemporary and historical achievements of women in art. Ensures equal opportunity for employment, art commissions, and research grants. Encourages professionalism and shared information among women in art. Stimulates and publicizes research and publications on women in the visual arts. Conducts workshops, periodic affirmative action research, and statistical surveys.

Website Designers

SOURCES OF HELP-WANTED ADS

13062 ■ *Computer Graphics World*
PennWell Corp.
98 Spit Brook Rd.
Nashua, NH 03062-5737
Ph: (603)891-0123
Fax: (603)891-9294
Fr: 800-225-0556
URL: http://www.cgw.com

Monthly. $68.00/year for individuals; $90.00/year for Canada; $105.00/year for other countries; $126.00/year for two years; $178.00/year for Canada, 2 years; $205.00/year for other countries, 2 years; $12.00/year for single issue. Publication reporting on the use of modeling, animation, and multimedia in the areas of science and engineering, art and entertainment, and presentation and training.

13063 ■ *IEEE Computer Graphics and Applications*
IEEE Computer Society
10662 Los Vaqueros Cir.
PO Box 3014
Los Alamitos, CA 90720-1314
Ph: (714)821-8380
Fax: (714)821-4010
Fr: 800-272-6657
E-mail: cga-ma@computer.org
URL: http://www.computer.org/portal/web/cga

Bimonthly. $1,020.00/year for individuals, online; $1,065.00/year for individuals, print; $1,330.00/year for individuals, print and online. Magazine addressing the interests and needs of professional designers and users of computer graphics hardware, software, and systems.

13064 ■ *PC WORLD*
101 Communications
9121 Oakdale Ave., Ste. 101
Chatsworth, CA 91311
Ph: (818)814-5200
Fax: (818)734-1522
E-mail: pcwletters@pcworld.com
URL: http://www.pcworld.com

Quarterly. $19.97/year for individuals; $29.97/year for two years. Technology or business magazine meeting the informational needs of tech-savvy managers, both at work and at home.

EMPLOYER DIRECTORIES AND NETWORKING LISTS

13065 ■ *Career Opportunities in Computers and Cyberspace*
Facts On File Inc.
132 W 31st St., 17th Fl.
New York, NY 10001
Ph: (212)967-8800
Fax: 800-678-3633
Fr: 800-322-8755
URL: http://www.infobasepublishing.com

Published March, 2004. Covers: Nearly 200 professions, clustering them by skill, objectives, and work conditions. Entries include: Education, salaries, employment prospects.

13066 ■ *Careers in Focus—Internet*
Facts On File Inc.
132 W 31st St., 17th Fl.
New York, NY 10001
Ph: (212)967-8800
Fax: 800-678-3633
Fr: 800-322-8755
URL: http://www.infobasepublishing.com

Latest edition 3rd; Published September, 2006. $32.95 for individuals. Covers: An overview of the Internet, followed by a selection of jobs profiled in detail, including the nature of the job, earnings, prospects for employment, what kind of training and skills it requires, and sources for further information.

13067 ■ *Computer Directory*
Computer Directories Inc.
23815 Nichols Sawmill Rd.
Hockley, TX 77447
Ph: (281)259-5959
Fax: (281)259-5959
Fr: 800-234-4353
URL: http://www.compdirinc.com

Annual, fall. Covers: Approximately 130,000 computer installations; 19 separate volumes for Alaska/Hawaii, Connecticut/New Jersey, Dallas/Ft. Worth, Eastern Seaboard, Far Midwest, Houston, Illinois, Midatlantic, Midcentral, Mideast, Minnesota/Wisconsin, North Central, New England, New York Metro, Northwest, Ohio, Pennsylvania/West Virginia, Southeast, and Southwest Texas. Entries include: Company name, address, phone, fax, email, name and title of contact, hardware used, software application, operating system, programming language, computer graphics, networking system. Arrangement: Geographical. Indexes: Alphabetical, industry, hardware.

HANDBOOKS AND MANUALS

13068 ■ *Careers for Color Connoisseurs and Other Visual Types*
The McGraw-Hill Companies
PO Box 182604
Columbus, OH 43272
Fax: (614)759-3749
Fr: 877-883-5524
E-mail: customer.service@mcgraw-hill.com
URL: http://www.mhprofessional.com/
product.php?isbn=0071465197

Jan Goldberg. Second edition, 2005. $19.95 (paper). 176 pages.

13069 ■ *Careers for Computer Buffs and Other Technological Types*
The McGraw-Hill Companies
PO Box 182604
Columbus, OH 43272
Fax: (614)759-3749
Fr: 877-883-5524
E-mail: customer.service@mcgraw-hill.com
URL: http://www.mhprofessional.com/
product.php?isbn=0071458778

Marjorie Eberts and Margaret Gisler. Third edition, 2006. $13.95 (paper). 160 pages. Suggested jobs in a wide range of settings, from the office to the outdoors.

13070 ■ *Expert Resumes for Computer and Web Jobs*
Jist Publishing
875 Montreal Way
St. Paul, MN 55102
Fr: 800-648-5478
E-mail: info@jist.com
URL: http://www.jist.com

Wendy Enelow and Louise Kursmark. Third edition, 2011. $17.95 (paper). 304 pages.

13071 ■ *Ferguson Career Coach: Managing Your Career in the Computer Industry*
Facts On File
132 W 31st St., 17th Fl.
New York, NY 10001
Fax: 800-678-3633
Fr: 800-322-8755
E-mail: custserv@factsonfile.com
URL: http://factsonfile.infobasepublishing.com

Shelly Field. 2008. $39.95 (hardcover). 280 pages. Provides tips for students who dream of pursuing a career as a software engineer or a web designer. Contains advice from professionals, career strategies, insider secrets, and more.

13072 ■ *Starting Your Career as a Freelance Web Designer*
Allworth Press
307 W 36th St., 11th Fl.
New York, NY 10018
Ph: (212)643-6816
Fax: (212)643-6819
URL: http://www.allworth.com

Neil Tortorella. 2011. $19.95 (paper). 256 pages. Serves as a guide for those who want to pursue a freelance career in web design. Contains topics on drafting a solid business plan, negotiating contracts, managing time and money, and creating winning proposals.

EMPLOYMENT AGENCIES AND SEARCH FIRMS

13073 ■ *Creative Placement*
13 N Main St.
Norwalk, CT 06854-2702

Ph: (203)838-7772
Fr: 800-521-4616
E-mail: kheine@creativeplacement.com
URL: http://www.creativeplacement.com

Description: Serves as an executive search firm for the creative industry. Provides placement for web, design, branding, packaging, advertising, and promotion.

13074 ■ Creative Talent Source
10 S. Riverside Plz., Ste. 1800
Chicago, IL 60606
Ph: (312)238-9004
Fax: (866)536-4719
Fr: 888-843-4864
E-mail: info@creativetalentsource.com
URL: http://creativetalentsource.com

Description: Provides professionals for design, writing and creative project management whether for print, web or multimedia. Specializes in freelance and full time placement of Chicago-area creative talent.

13075 ■ DillonGray
1796 Equestrian Dr.
Pleasanton, CA 94588
Ph: (925)846-9396
E-mail: info@dillongray.com
URL: http://www.dillongray.com

Executive search firm focused on technology related companies.

13076 ■ Graphic Arts Employment Specialists, Inc.
409 Pacific Coast Hwy., Ste. 455
Redondo Beach, CA 90277
Fax: (310)937-3760
Fr: 888-499-9722
E-mail: info@gaes.com
URL: http://www.gaes.com

Employment agency specializing in the publishing and packaging industries.

13077 ■ MicroStaff Corporation
1275 Nightfire Cir.
Castle Rock, CO 80104
Ph: (303)663-5441
E-mail: recruiting@microstaff.com
URL: http://www.microstaff.com

Description: Matches contract, contract-to-hire or permanent placement professionals who can fulfill computer-based technologies, web, interactive media and marketing project requirements.

13078 ■ Profiles
217 N Charles St., 4th Fl.
Baltimore, MD 21201
Ph: (410)244-6400
Fax: (410)244-6406
URL: http://careerprofiles.com

Recruits professionals for freelance, temporary, and direct hire opportunities specializing in marketing, advertising, creative, web design, graphic design and communications.

13079 ■ Right Brain Resource, LLC
1101 SE Salmon St.
Portland, OR 97214
Ph: (503)232-8418
Fax: (503)233-8105
Fr: 877-727-8401
E-mail: info@rightbrainresource.com
URL: http://www.rightbrainresource.com

Description: Exists as a professional staffing agency which specializes in creative, graphic design, web design, advertising, digital media, and marketing jobs.

13080 ■ Semper, LLC
607 Bolyston St., 3rd Fl.
Boston, MA 02116
Fax: 888-836-9703
Fr: 800-954-4993
E-mail: dhresumes1@semperllc.com
URL: http://www.semperllc.com

Description: Serves as a placement firm in the graphic arts and printing industry. Specializes in the print, copy and digital industries. Offers several staffing options such as flexible, permanent, flex-to-hire and direct. Offers outplacement service that provides professional career management assistance and counseling to employees who are facing a career change.

13081 ■ TECHEAD
111 N 17th St.
Richmond, VA 23219
Ph: (804)782-6971
Fax: (804)782-2033
Fr: 877-TEC-HEAD
E-mail: info@techead.com
URL: http://www.techead.com

Description: Offers creative and IT staffing services for both job seekers and employers. Provides graphics support and desktop publishing services to local clients. Provides creative talent and information technology staffing services, ADOBE product software training, and creative web development solutions to clients.

ONLINE JOB SOURCES AND SERVICES

13082 ■ AllWebJobs.com
E-mail: info@allwebjobs.com
URL: http://www.allwebjobs.com

Description: Serves as a job board for website professionals. Lists only internet related jobs across the U.S. Features jobs for webmasters, web designers, web producers, web developers, web marketers, web editors, information architect jobs, search engine specialist jobs and other web jobs.

13083 ■ Aquent.com
711 Boylston St.
Boston, MA 02116
Ph: (617)535-6000
Fax: (617)535-6001
E-mail: questions@aquent.com
URL: http://aquent.us

Description: Aquent finds contract, project-based, and permanent work for a broad range of creative and information technology professionals. Applicants submit their applications, which are reviewed by an Aquent agent and, if qualifications match job opportunities, they will be called in for an interview and skills assessment. If skills and experience are appropriate, then will then be assigned an Aquent agent who will get to work finding contract or permanent jobs. Also offers free career resources.

13084 ■ AuthenticJobs.com
URL: http://www.authenticjobs.com

Description: Provides information for web and creative professionals and the companies seeking to hire them. Provides full-time and freelance job opportunities for designers and developers.

13085 ■ ComputerWork.com
Fr: 800-691-8413
URL: http://www.computerwork.com

Description: Job search and resume submission service for professionals in information technology.

13086 ■ Computerworld Careers
URL: http://www.computerworld.com/careertopics/careers

Description: Offers career opportunities for IT (information technology) professionals. Job seekers may search the jobs database, register at the site, and read about job surveys and employment trends. Employers may post jobs.

13087 ■ Computing Research Association Job Announcements
1828 L St. NW, Ste. 800
Washington, DC 20036-4632

Ph: (202)234-2111
Fax: (202)667-1066
E-mail: info@cra.org
URL: http://www.cra.org/ads

Description: Contains dated links to national college and university computer technology positions.

13088 ■ Creative Hotlist
E-mail: contact@creativehotlist.com
URL: http://www.creativehotlist.com

Description: Career site for professionals in the web design and graphic design fields. Enables individuals and companies to find resources for any aspect of the creative marketplace including job openings, creative services, artists, designers, programmers, printers, service bureaus, schools and clubs.

13089 ■ CreativePublic.com
URL: http://www.creativepublic.com

Description: Offers graphic designers and web designers resources and information. Shows designers what to do and what not to do in the graphic design business world. Gives graphic designers resources for starting their own business or expanding into a freelance role.

13090 ■ Dice.com
URL: http://www.dice.com

Description: Job search database for computer consultants and high-tech professionals, listing thousands of high tech permanent contract and consulting jobs for programmers, software engineers, systems administrators, web developers, and hardware engineers. Also free career advice e-mail newsletter and job posting e-alerts.

13091 ■ FreshWebJobs.com
URL: http://www.freshwebjobs.com

Description: Serves as job board for web professionals providing freelance and full-time jobs.

13092 ■ GetGigs.com
URL: http://www.getgigs.com

Description: Seeks to provide an on-line experience for creative types, performing artists, and musicians around the world by integrating internet technologies into a one-stop information resource. Also functions as a creative directory and talent network.

13093 ■ Guru.com
5001 Baum Blvd., Ste. 760
Pittsburgh, PA 15213
Fax: (412)687-4466
Fr: 888-687-1316
URL: http://www.guru.com

Description: Job board specializing in contract jobs for creative and information technology professionals. Also provides online incorporation and educational opportunities for independent contractors along with articles and advice.

13094 ■ ItJobs.com
E-mail: comments@itjobsllc.com
URL: http://www.itjobs.com

Description: Provides information technology employment opportunities for the following categories: internet/intranet/extranet, network systems, open systems, client/server, software engineering and development, software QA and testing, ERP applications and management consulting, and legacy systems.

13095 ■ JustTechJobs.com
E-mail: support@justtechjobs.com
URL: http://www.justtechjobs.com

Description: Serves as a jobsite that provides employers with a technology specific focus and provides job seekers with job postings aimed at those specific tech jobs. Offers a community of 15 million tech professionals and also supports several technology websites.

13096 ■ Tech-Engine.com
URL: http://techengine.com
Description: Features employment listings concerning the IT and engineering fields. Features employers and recruiters information, resume posting and career resources.

13097 ■ ZDNet Tech Jobs
URL: http://www.zdnet.com
Description: Site houses a listing of national employment opportunities for professionals in high tech fields. Also contains resume building tips and relocation resources.

TRADESHOWS

13098 ■ Society for News Design Annual Workshop & Exhibition
Society for News Design
424 E Central Blvd., Ste. 406
Orlando, FL 32801

Ph: (407)420-7748
Fax: (407)420-7697
E-mail: snd@snd.org
URL: http://www.snd.org

Annual. Gathers visual journalists from around the world for workshops and general sessions. 2012 October 11-13; Cleveland, OH; The Plain Dealer.

OTHER SOURCES

13099 ■ Society for News Design
424 E Central Blvd., Ste. 406
Orlando, FL 32801
Ph: (407)420-7748
Fax: (407)420-7697
E-mail: snd@snd.org
URL: http://www.snd.org

Description: Comprised of editors, designers, graphic artists, publishers, illustrators, art directors, photographers, advertising artists, website designers, students and faculty. Encourages high standards of journalism through design. Serves as a forum and resource for all those interested in news design.

13100 ■ World Organization of Webmasters
PO Box 1743
Folsom, CA 95763
Ph: (916)989-2933
Fax: (916)987-3022
E-mail: info@joinwow.org
URL: http://webprofessionals.org

Description: Supports individuals and organizations that create, manage, or market websites. Provides education, certification, technical, and employment opportunities to aspiring and practicing web professionals worldwide.

SOURCES OF HELP-WANTED ADS

13101 ■ Special Events
Penton Media
249 W 17th St.
New York, NY 10011-5390
Ph: (212)204-4200
URL: http://specialevents.com

Monthly. $59.00/year, for free to qualified subscribers; $110.00/year for Canada; $106.00/year for other countries; $200.00/year for Canada, two years; $200.00/year for other countries, two years. Magazine for special event professionals.

HANDBOOKS AND MANUALS

13102 ■ How to Start a Home-Based Event Planning Business
Globe Pequot Press
246 Goose Ln.
Guilford, CT 06437
Ph: (203)458-4500
Fr: 800-820-2329
E-mail: info@globepequot.com
URL: http://www.globepequot.com

Jill Moran. 2010. $18.95. 240 pages. This insider's handbook reveals how to start a successful business planning a wide variety of events from home.

ONLINE JOB SOURCES AND SERVICES

13103 ■ American Academy - Wedding Professionals
URL: http://www.aa-wp.com

Description: Provides training course for wedding planners. Web site also includes career assistance and certification.

13104 ■ Coordinators' Corner
E-mail: nancy@coordinatorscorner.com
URL: http://www.coordinatorscorner.com

Description: Offers access to articles on managing a wedding consultant business. Provides information from the industry's top experts.

13105 ■ National Bridal Service
URL: http://www.nationalbridal.com/index.htm

Description: Provides training and certification in wedding consulting, independent bridal store sales, and gift registry sales.

13106 ■ The Wedding Consultant Certification Institute
URL: http://
www.weddingconsultantcertificationinstitute.com

Description: Provides a workshop for wedding consultant certification. Educational materials are provided upon enrollment.

13107 ■ weddingplannerjobs.us
URL: http://weddingplannerjobs.us

Description: Serves as a niche job board that focuses exclusively on wedding planner employment opportunities and candidate recruiting.

13108 ■ Weddings Beautiful
E-mail: info@weddingsbeautiful.com
URL: http://www.weddingsbeautiful.com

Description: Provides a training course for starting a wedding consultancy business.

TRADESHOWS

13109 ■ The Great Bridal Expo
The Great Bridal Expo Group, Inc.
1510 S.E. 17th St., Ste. 200
Fort Lauderdale, FL 33316
Ph: (954)522-7001
Fax: (954)522-7337
Fr: 800-422-3976
E-mail: info@greatbridalexpo.com
URL: http://www.greatbridalexpo.com/

Periodic. Primary Exhibits: Wedding accessories, bakeries, bridal gowns and wedding dresses, cakes, catering, dance lessons, DJs, florists, hotels, insurance, honeymoons, invitations, music, party rentals, photography, rehearsal dinner, transportation, travel, tuxedos, video, wedding gift registry, and more.

OTHER SOURCES

13110 ■ Association of Bridal Consultants (ABC)
56 Danbury Rd., Ste. 11
New Milford, CT 06776
Ph: (860)355-7000
Fax: (860)354-1404
E-mail: info@bridalassn.com
URL: http://www.bridalassn.com

Description: Represents independent bridal and wedding consultants; persons employed by companies in wedding-related businesses and novices looking to get into the business. Strives to improve professionalism and recognition of bridal and wedding consultants. Offers professional development program, startup manual and seminars. Provides advertising, publicity, referrals and information services. Operates speakers' bureau; compiles statistics.

13111 ■ Association of Certified Professional Wedding Consultants (ACPWC)
122 Destry Ct.
San Jose, CA 95136
Ph: (408)227-2792

Fax: (408)226-0697
E-mail: dmoody@acpwc.com
URL: http://www.acpwc.com

Description: Aims to uphold the standards of professionalism and integrity among its members. Raises the level of education, ensures uniformity, and promotes career success in the wedding and special event industry. Offers training courses, extended weekend classes, seminars, and home study program for wedding planners/consultants, and church and facility coordinators.

13112 ■ Association of Wedding Professionals
PO Box 743005
Dallas, TX 75374-3005
E-mail: awpdallas@sbcglobal.net
URL: http://www.awpdallas.com

Description: Dedicated to helping its members grow through networking opportunities, education programs, and special event showcases.

13113 ■ Association for Wedding Professionals International
6700 Freeport Blvd., Ste. 202
Sacramento, CA 95822
Ph: (916)392-5000
Fax: (916)392-5222
Fr: 800-242-4461
E-mail: richard@afwpi.com
URL: http://afwpi.com

Description: Acts as a central source of information and referrals.

13114 ■ Bridal Association of America
531 H St.
Bakersfield, CA 93304
Ph: (661)633-1949
Fax: (661)633-9199
Fr: 800-200-9935
E-mail: kyle@bridalassociationofamerica.com
URL: http://www.bridalassociationofamerica.com

Description: Acts as a forum for wedding professionals.

13115 ■ June Wedding, Inc.
19375 Pine Glade
Guerneville, CA 95446
Ph: (707)865-9894
URL: http://www.junewedding.com

Description: Offers beginning and advanced courses in wedding planning. Certification is available.

13116 ■ Wedding and Portrait Photographers International (WPPI)
6059 Bristol Pkwy., Ste. 100
Culver City, CA 90230
Ph: (310)846-4770
Fax: (310)846-5995
URL: http://www.wppionline.com

Description: Represents wedding portrait and digital

photographers and photographers employed at general photography studios. Promotes high artistic and technical standards in wedding photography. Serves as a forum for the exchange of technical knowledge and experience; makes available the expertise of top professionals in the field of photographic arts and technology, advertising, sales promotion, marketing, public relations, accounting, business management, tax, and profit planning. Members are offered the opportunity to purchase special products and services.

SOURCES OF HELP-WANTED ADS

13117 ■ Becoming a Life Coach: A Complete Workbook for Therapists
New Harbinger Publications
5674 Shattuck Ave.
Oakland, CA 94609
Fax: (510)652-5472
Fr: 800-748-6273
URL: http://www.newharbinger.com

David Skibbins. 2007. $24.95. 160 pages. Includes information about necessary skills, tips on integrating coaching and therapy, business models and marketing advice. Offers a strategy that professionals can use to incorporate life coaching into their practices.

13118 ■ Life Coach News
Life Coach Marketing
PO Box 540
Dahlonega, GA 30533
Ph: (706)864-5025
Fr: 800-841-8776
E-mail: info@lifecoachmarketing.com
URL: http://www.lifecoachnews.com

Monthly. Available in print and online. Covers various information on life coaching such as personal growth information, self-improvement strategies, and self-help tips. Includes interviews, news, articles, quotes and stories that promote personal development. Features opportunities for business and career development.

HANDBOOKS AND MANUALS

13119 ■ Becoming a Professional Life Coach: Lessons from the Institute for Life Coach Training
W.W. Norton & Company, Inc.
500 Fifth Ave.
New York, NY 10110
Ph: (212)354-5500
Fax: (212)869-0856
E-mail: ksilvasy-neale@wwnorton.com
URL: http://books.wwnorton.com/books/
   detail.aspx?ID=9397

Diane S. Menendez, Patrick Williams. 2007. $40 (hardcover). 384 pages. Provides career advice to therapists and psychologists who wish to add life coaching to their current business.

13120 ■ Business and Practice of Coaching: Finding Your Niche, Making Money, and Attracting Ideal Clients
W. W. Norton & Company, Inc.
500 Fifth Ave.
New York, NY 10110
Ph: (212)354-5500

Fax: (212)869-0856
URL: http://books.wwnorton.com/books/
   detail.aspx?ID=9346

Wendy Allen, Lynn Grodzki. 2005. $33.95 (hardcover). 320 pages. Focuses on basic business principles and strategies on coaching. Provides explanations on the current state of the coaching profession and offers advice and strategies.

13121 ■ Career Counseling: A Holistic Approach
Brooks Cole
PO Box 6904
Florence, KY 41022-6904
Fr: 800-354-9706
URL: http://www.cengage.com

Vernon G. Zunker. 2006. $140.95 (hardcover). 688 pages. Covers career theories as well as practical techniques and examples. Features case examples, tables and exercises that help students develop an understanding of the theoretical models of career counseling.

13122 ■ Co-Active Coaching, 2nd Edition: New Skills for Coaching People Toward Success in Work and Life
Davies-Black Publishing
20 Park Plaza, Ste. 1115A
Boston, MA 02116
Ph: (617)523-3801
Fax: (617)523-3708
Fr: 888-273-2539
URL: http://www.nicholasbrealey.com/na/store/pc/
   viewPrd.asp?idcategory=0&idproduct=222

Laura Whitworth. 2007. $39.95 (paper). 336 pages. Helps define the coaching profession. Discusses what it takes to design and maintain coaching relationships. Contains a description of model-placing the client's agenda at the heart of the coaching partnership, defines the skills required for success and provides sample coaching conversations. Includes a coach's toolkit of exercises, questionnaires, checklists and forms to make a proven principle and technique.

13123 ■ Coach U Personal and Corporate Coach Training Handbook
Wiley
111 River St.
Hoboken, NJ 07030-5774
Ph: (201)748-6000
Fax: (201)748-6088
E-mail: info@wiley.com
URL: http://as.wiley.com/WileyCDA/WileyTitle/
   productCd-047171173X.html

Coach U Inc. 2005. $209.95 (hardcover). 400 pages. Provides step by step training for individuals seeking preparation and certification as a personal and/or corporate coach. Draws an approach and presents a guide to the practice and business of personal and corporate coaching.

13124 ■ The Coach U Personal Development Workbook and Guide
Wiley
111 River St.
Hoboken, NJ 07030-5774
Ph: (201)748-6000
Fax: (201)748-6088
E-mail: info@wiley.com
URL: http://as.wiley.com/WileyCDA/WileyTitle/
   productCd-0471711756.html

Coach U, Inc. 2005. $104.95 (paper). 228 pages. Provides tools to build a coach's personal foundation and prepare to coach others. Features self-assessment lesson plans that allow the user to set his/her own pace while engaging in a continuous process of self-awareness and self-improvement to become an effective and successful coach.

13125 ■ The Coaching Manual: The Definitive Guide to the Process, Principles and Skills of Personal Coaching
FT Press
1 Lake St.
Upper Saddle River, NJ 07458
URL: http://www.ftpress.com/store/
   product.aspx?isbn=9780273713524

Julie Starr. 2009. 368 pages. Includes information on principles, values and beliefs of a good coach, key questions and considerations to help take a coaching career forward, how to plan a coaching assignment, the barriers to a good coaching conversation and how coaches can avoid them.

13126 ■ Excellence in Coaching: The Industry Guide
Kogan Page Ltd.
1518 Walnut St., No. 1100
Philadelphia, PA 19102
Ph: (215)928-9112
Fax: (215)928-9113
E-mail: info@koganpage.com
URL: http://www.koganpageusa.com

Jonathan Passmore. 2010. $39.95 (paper). 288 pages. Covers the different coaching models, coaching ethics and information for running a coaching practice.

13127 ■ FabJob Guide to Become a Life Coach
FabJob Inc.
4616-25th Ave. NE, No. 224
Seattle, WA 98105
Ph: (403)949-4980
Fr: 888-322-5621
URL: http://www.fabjob.com/LifeCoach.asp#

$39.95. Includes a bonus CD-ROM. Discusses how to get started and how to succeed as a life coach. Covers topics of vital importance to anyone who wants to become a life coach including: getting ready to coach, how to do life coaching and starting your own coaching business.

13128 ■ Life Coaching Skills: How to Develop Skilled Clients
Sage Publications Ltd.
2455 Teller Rd.
Thousand Oaks, CA 91320
Ph: 800-818-7243
E-mail: info@sagepub.com
URL: http://www.sagepub.com/textbooksProdDesc.nav?prodId=Book230602&

Richard Nelson-Jones. $46 (paper). 240 pages. Provides an introduction to the skills needed to be an effective life coach and incorporates practical activities for coaches to use to help clients develop self-coaching skills.

13129 ■ Lifestyle Fitness Coaching
Human Kinetics
PO Box 5076
Champaign, IL 61825-5076
Fax: (217)351-1549
Fr: 800-747-4457
E-mail: info@hkusa.com
URL: http://www.humankinetics.com

James Gavin. 2005. 296 pages. Provides information on coaching dialogues between the health fitness professional and the client, addressing issues such as the types of questions to ask, how to provide feedback effectively, and how to make referrals.

13130 ■ Philosophy and Practice of Coaching: Insights and Issues for a New Era
John Wiley & Sons, Inc.
111 River St.
Hoboken, NJ 07030-5774
Ph: (201)748-6000
Fax: (201)748-6088
E-mail: info@wiley.com
URL: http://as.wiley.com/WileyCDA/WileyTitle/productCd-0470987219.html

David B. Drake. 2008. $49.95 (hardcover). 378 pages. Features three key sections: foundations for coaching, applications of coaching and organizations and coaching that focuses on enabling the reader to link theory and practice.

13131 ■ Promising Outcomes: The Impact of Positive Psychology on Health and Wellness Coaching
Healthcare Intelligence Network
PO Box 1442
Wall Township, NJ 07719
Fax: (732)449-4463
Fr: 888-446-3530
E-mail: info@hin.com
URL: http://store.hin.com/Health-Coach-Collection_p_3577.html

Dr. Neal Mayerson. 2007. $157 (spiral-bound). 55 pages. Explores theories and coaching models, research linking physical and mental health, and coaching skills and outcomes that help bring about lasting behavioral change.

13132 ■ The Successful Coach: Insider Secrets to Becoming a Top Coach
Wiley
111 River St.
Hoboken, NJ 07030-5774
Ph: (201)748-6000
Fax: (201)748-6088
E-mail: info@wiley.com
URL: http://as.wiley.com/WileyCDA/WileyTitle/productCd-0471789968.html

Terri Levine, Larina Kase, Joe Vitale. 2006. $37.95 (paper). 240 pages. Provides readers with everyday action steps to fill their practice, generate more referrals and find more clients by taking positive actions.

13133 ■ Transformational Life Coaching: Creating Limitless Opportunities for Yourself and Others
Health Communications Inc.
3201 SW 15th St.
Deerfield Beach, FL 33442

Ph: (954)360-0909
Fax: (954)360-0034
Fr: 800-441-5569
URL: http://www.hcibooks.com/p-3639-transformational-life-coaching.aspx

Dr. Cherie Carter-Scott. 2007. $14.95 (paper). 256 pages. Provides strategies of transformational life coaching including checklists for a session, importance of acknowledging, integrating and honoring feelings, listening to messages to guide the process, transforming old negative patterns into positive imprints, marketing and building the coaching practice and steps to living the process of transformational life coaching.

13134 ■ Wellness Coaching for Lasting Lifestyle Change
Whole Person Associates, Inc.
210 W Michigan St.
Duluth, MN 55802-1908
Ph: (218)727-0500
Fax: (218)727-0505
Fr: 800-247-6789
E-mail: books@wholeperson.com
URL: http://www.wholeperson.com/x-trainer/coach.html

Michael Arloski. 2009 $29.95 (paper). 280 pages. Provides principles of wellness promotion and personal life coaching.

ONLINE JOB SOURCES AND SERVICES

13135 ■ HPCareer.Net
URL: http://www.hpcareer.net/index.jsp

Description: Serves professionals in the health promotion related fields including health education, wellness, health, and fitness. Provides industry-specific career services for members/subscribers.

13136 ■ Life Coach Directory
URL: http://www.life-coach-directory.com

Description: Serves as a directory of life coaching resources for individuals interested in life coaching. Covers a variety of topics regarding life coaching such as certifications, strategies, courses and careers.

13137 ■ Lifecoaching.com
URL: http://www.lifecoaching.com

Description: Serves as an information resource for both life coaches and clients. Provides life coaching resources, life coaching quizzes and other vital tools for any individual intending to becoming a life coach.

13138 ■ Medical Fitness Association
1905 Huguenot Rd.
Richmond, VA 23235-8026
Ph: (804)897-5701
E-mail: info@medicalfitness.org
URL: http://medicalfitness.org

Description: Serves as a resource to the medical fitness industry as it informs, promotes, and provides networking and educational opportunities to expand knowledge about the industry. Fosters professional development by sponsoring conferences, seminars, and educational programs. Provides career listings and internships while pursuing growth and success for the medical fitness industry.

13139 ■ Plus50Lifestyles.com
URL: http://plus50lifestyles.com

Description: Serves as a resource of information and materials that are intended to encourage boomers and seniors to live an inspiring life. Provides listings and other resources for individuals involved in coaching such as retirement coaching, life coaching, wellness coaching and others.

13140 ■ Premier Health and Fitness Resources
URL: http://phfr.com

Description: Health and fitness professionals. Offers a broad spectrum of health promotion services, networking opportunities, and resource sharing materials. Features resources for finding quality fitness jobs, health promotion job postings, corporate wellness employment opportunities, or other fitness staff positions.

13141 ■ WellnessCoachCareers.com
URL: http://www.exercisecareers.com/index.cfm?page=wellnesscoachcareers

Description: Serves as a job board for wellness coaches. Also features a resume writing tool for coaches seeking employment.

TRADESHOWS

13142 ■ Healthy Life Expo
MediaMax Events and Expos Inc.
6106 Excelsior Blvd., Ste. No. 10
Minneapolis, MN 55416
Ph: (952)238-1700
E-mail: info@mediamaxevents.com
URL: http://www.mediamaxevents.com

Biannual. Offers an exhibit venue for companies that cater to holistic health conscious consumers.

13143 ■ International Coach Federation Annual International Conference
International Coach Federation
2365 Harrodsburg Rd., Ste. A325
Lexington, KY 40504
Ph: (859)219-3580
Fax: (859)226-4411
Fr: 888-423-3131
E-mail: icfheadquarters@coachfederation.org
URL: http://www.coachfederation.org

Annual. Provides coaches with new techniques and concepts through programming and opportunities to network with other coaches.

13144 ■ National Wellness Conference
National Wellness Institute
PO Box 827
Stevens Point, WI 54481
Ph: (715)342-2969
Fax: (715)342-2979
E-mail: nwi@nationalwellness.org
URL: http://www.nationalwellness.org

Annual. Explores the current issues facing wellness and health promotion professionals. 2012 July 16-19; Stevens Point, WI.

OTHER SOURCES

13145 ■ Care Continuum Alliance
701 Pennsylvania Ave. NW, Ste. 700
Washington, DC 20004-2694
Ph: (202)737-5980
Fax: (202)478-5113
E-mail: info@carecontinuum.org
URL: http://www.carecontinuum.org

Description: Stakeholders who provide services along the care continuum toward the goal of population health improvement. Promotes the role of population health improvement in raising the quality of care, improving health outcomes, and reducing preventable health care costs for individuals with chronic conditions and those at risk of developing chronic conditions. Supports advocacies, research, and the promotion of best practices in care management.

13146 ■ The Coach Connection, LLC
15861 Dorth Cr.
Fort Myers, FL 33908
Ph: (239)415-1777
Fax: (239)415-1782

Fr: 800-887-7214
E-mail: coaches@findyourcoach.com
URL: http://findyourcoach.com

Description: Life coaches, business coaches, career coaches, personal coaches, mentor coaches, and various other coaches. Helps clients to discover and achieve their unique life, business and career improvement goals. Provides a personal matching service to discover the client's true needs and match it with the ideal coaches. Provides resources and links for job opportunities.

13147 ■ International Society for Performance Improvement
1400 Spring St., Ste. 400
Silver Spring, MD 20910-2753
Ph: (301)587-8570
Fax: (301)587-8573
E-mail: info@ispi.org
URL: http://www.jobtarget.com/home/index.cfm?site_id=2637

Description: Represents performance technologists, training directors, human resources managers, instructional technologists, human factors practitioners and organization consultants. Seeks to improve performance and productivity in the workplace.

13148 ■ Wellness Coaches USA
725 Skippack Pike, Ste. 300
Blue Bell, PA 19422
Fax: (215)628-3262
Fr: (866)894-1300
E-mail: mhowe@wellnesscoachesusa.com
URL: http://www.wellnesscoachesusa.com

Description: Professional wellness coaches. Provides an effective onsite wellness coaching model. Deploys highly trained wellness coaches directly to the workplace to personally engage employees in unique and proprietary onsite, coach powered, wellness processes.

Wholesale and Retail Buyers

Sources of Help-Wanted Ads

13149 ■ Aftermarket Business
Advanstar Communications, Inc.
6200 Canoga Ave., 2nd Fl.
Woodland Hills, CA 91367
Ph: (818)593-5000
Fax: (818)593-5020
URL: http://aftermarketbusiness.search-autoparts.com/

Monthly. Free to qualified subscribers. Magazine (tabloid) for purchasing professionals in the retail automotive aftermarket.

13150 ■ Benchmarking Purchasing
American Purchasing Society
8 E Galena Blvd., Ste. 203
Aurora, IL 60506
Ph: (630)859-0250
Fax: (630)859-0270
URL: http://www.american-purchasing.com

Annual. Professional journal covering issues in purchasing.

13151 ■ Chain Store Age
Lebhar-Friedman, Inc.
425 Park Ave.
New York, NY 10022
Ph: (212)756-5000
URL: http://www.chainstoreage.com

Monthly. Magazine for management of retail chain headquarters. Reports on marketing, merchandising, strategic planning, physical supports, and shopping center developments, retail technology credit and communications.

13152 ■ DNR
Fairchild Publications Inc.
750 Third Ave., 8th Fl.
New York, NY 10017
Ph: (212)630-4600
Fax: (212)630-4015
URL: http://www.dnrnews.com/

Daily (morn.). $129.00/year for individuals; $99.00/year for individuals, online; $169.00/year for individuals, online + print; $895.00/year for individuals, online archive. Daily newspaper reporting on men's and boys' clothing, retailing, and textiles.

13153 ■ Electronic Business
Reed Business Information
360 Park Ave. S
New York, NY 10010-1710
Ph: (646)746-6400
URL: http://www.edn.com/index.asp?layout=businessCenter

Monthly. Magazine for purchasing managers and buyers of electronic components and materials used in end product manufacture.

13154 ■ Gifts & Decorative Accessories
Sandow Media Corp.
3731 NW 8th Ave.
Boca Raton, FL 33431
Ph: (561)750-0151
Fax: (561)750-0152
URL: http://www.giftsanddec.com/

Monthly. $36.00/year for individuals; $39.00/year for Canada; $135.00/year for other countries. International magazine for retailers of gifts, greeting cards, decorative accessories, and stationery-related merchandise.

13155 ■ Home Channel News
Lebhar-Friedman, Inc.
425 Park Ave.
New York, NY 10022
Ph: (212)756-5000
URL: http://www.homechannelnews.com

$189.00/year for individuals. Business tabloid serving home center/building material retailers.

13156 ■ LDB Interior Textiles
E.W. Williams Publications Co.
2125 Center Ave., Ste. 305
Fort Lee, NJ 07024-5898
Ph: (201)592-7007
Fax: (201)592-7171
URL: http://www.ldbinteriortextiles.com

Monthly. $72.00/year for individuals; $125.00/year for Canada; $150.00/year for elsewhere, airmail; $100.00/year for two years; $7.00/year for single issue; $12.00/year for single issue, Canada; $18.00/year for single issue, elsewhere. Magazine for buyers of home fashions, including bed, bath and table linens, hard and soft window treatments, home fragrances, decorative pillows and home accessories, accent rugs, and decorative fabrics.

13157 ■ Music Inc.
Maher Publications Inc.
102 N Haven Rd.
Elmhurst, IL 60126
Ph: (630)941-2030
Fr: 800-554-7470
E-mail: editor@musicincmag.com
URL: http://www.musicincmag.com/magazine.html

$17.00/year for individuals. Magazine serving retailers of music and sound products.

13158 ■ Music Trades
Music Trades Corp.
80 West St.
Englewood, NJ 07631
Ph: (201)871-1965
Fax: (201)871-0455
Fr: 800-423-6530
URL: http://www.musictrades.com/

Monthly. $45.00/year for individuals, foreign; $23.00/year for two years, domestic; $16.00/year for individuals, domestic. Music trade magazine.

13159 ■ National Jeweler
Nielsen Business Media
770 Broadway
New York, NY 10003-9595
URL: http://www.nationaljewelernetwork.com/njn/index.jsp

Semimonthly. $10.00/year for single issue, cover; $89.00/year for U.S.; $104.00/year for Canada; $330.00/year for other countries, airmail only. Jewelry industry magazine.

13160 ■ Purchasing Magazine
Reed Business Information
360 Park Ave. S
New York, NY 10010-1710
Ph: (646)746-6400
E-mail: info.purchasing@reedbusiness.com
URL: http://www.purchasing.com

Monthly. Free. Magazine for buying professionals.

13161 ■ Retailing Today
Lebhar-Friedman, Inc.
425 Park Ave.
New York, NY 10022
Ph: (212)756-5000
URL: http://www.retailingtoday.com/

Semimonthly. $119.00/year for individuals; $228.00/year for two years. Retailing business industry news and information.

13162 ■ Sporting Goods Dealer
Bill Communications Inc.
1115 Northmeadow Pkwy.
Roswell, GA 30076
Ph: (770)569-1540
Fax: (770)569-5105
Fr: 800-241-9034
URL: http://www.sgdealer.com/sportinggoodsdealer/index.jsp

Bimonthly. Magazine which offers expert reporting on trends affecting team dealers and retailers who service schools, colleges, pro and local teams.

13163 ■ Tire Business
Crain Communications Inc.
77 Franklin St., Ste. 809
Boston, MA 02110-1510
Ph: (617)292-3385
URL: http://www.tirebusiness.com

Semimonthly. $79.00/year for individuals; $148.00/year for two years; $107.00/year for individuals, Canada; $194.00/year for two years, Canada; $119.00/year for other countries; $208.00/year for two years, all other countries; $99.00/year for individuals, web only. Newspaper (tabloid) serving independent tire dealers, retreaders, tire wholesalers and others allied to the tire industry.

13164 ■ Tire Review
Babcox
3550 Embassy Pky.
Akron, OH 44333

Ph: (330)670-1234
URL: http://www.tirereview.com/

Monthly. Free to qualified subscribers. Magazine containing news and business information about the tire, custom wheel, automotive service, and retreading industries.

13165 ■ *TWICE*
NewBay Media, LLC
28 E 28th St., 12th Fl.
New York, NY 10016
Ph: (212)378-0400
Fax: (917)281-4704
URL: http://www.twice.com

Free. Trade tabloid covering consumer electronics, appliance, and camera industries for retailers, manufacturers, and distributors.

EMPLOYER DIRECTORIES AND NETWORKING LISTS

13166 ■ *Directory of Department Stores*
Chain Store Guide
3922 Coconut Palm Dr.
Tampa, FL 33619
Ph: (813)627-6800
Fax: (813)627-6888
Fr: 800-927-9292
URL: http://www.chainstoreguide.com

Annual, Latest edition 2011. $395.00 for individuals; $445.00 for individuals; $1,075.00 for individuals; $1,375.00 for individuals. Covers: 6,000 department store companies, 1,600 shoe store companies, jewelry store companies, 95 optical store companies, and 70 leather and luggage store companies in the United States and Canada, with annual sales of $160 billion. Entries include: Company name; physical and mailing addresses; phone and fax numbers, company e-mail and web addresses; listing type; total sales; industry sales; total selling square footage; store prototype sizes; total units; units by trade name; trading areas; projected openings and remodeling; self-distributing indicator; distribution center locations; resident buyers' name and location; leased departments area, name, and location; mail order catalog indicator; Internet order processing indicator; private label softlines, hardlines, and credit card indicators; furniture styles and price lines; average number of checkouts; year founded; public company indicator; parent company name and location; subsidiaries' names and locations; regional and divisional office locations; key personnel with titles; store locations, with address, phone number, and manager name (department stores only); 3,000 personnel email addresses. Arrangement: Geographical. Indexes: Alphabetical, product lines, exclusions.

13167 ■ *Directory of Drug Store & HBC Chains*
Chain Store Guide
3922 Coconut Palm Dr.
Tampa, FL 33619
Ph: (813)627-6800
Fax: (813)627-6888
Fr: 800-927-9292
URL: http://www.chainstoreguide.com/

Annual, latest edition 2010. $395.00 for individuals;

$445.00 for individuals; $1,375.00 for individuals; $1,075.00 for individuals. Covers: More than 1,200 drug store chains operation two or more units, including mass merchants and grocers with pharmacies; 215 wholesale drug companies in the United States and Canada. Entries include: For retailers—company name; phone and fax numbers; physical and mailing addresses; company e-mail and web addresses; listing type; number of stores; product lines; percentage of sales by product line; total sales; prescription drug sales; percentage of prescriptions filled with generic drugs; number of prescriptions filled daily; percentage of prescriptions filled with private third party, cash, and Medicaid; number of stores by type; mail order pharmacy indicator; managed care division indicator; projected openings and remodeling; store prototype sizes; total selling square footage; trading area; franchise group headquarters' name and location; distribution center and primary wholesaler names and locations; number of specialty departments; packaged liquor indicators; private label indicators; computerized pharmacy indicator; average number of checkouts; year founded; public company indicator; parent company name and location; regional and divisional office locations; headquarters personnel with titles. For wholesalers—company name, address, phone, and fax; e-mail and web addresses; listing type; product lines; percentage of sales by product line; total sales; percentage of sales by customer type; total stores served; number of member and non-member stores served; trading area; group store trading names; wholesaler type; distribution center locations; private label indicator; year founded; public company indicator; headquarters personnel with titles. Arrangement: Separate geographical sections for retailers and wholesalers. Indexes: Alphabetical, exclusions.

13168 ■ *STORES—Top 100 Retailers Issue*
National Retail Federation
325 7th St. NW, Ste. 1100
Washington, DC 20004
Ph: (202)783-7971
Fax: (202)737-2849
Fr: 800-673-4692
URL: http://www.stores.org

Annual, Latest edition 2011. $75.00. Publication includes: 100 U.S. retail companies having largest estimated sales during preceding year.

13169 ■ *The Wholesaler—'The Wholesaling 100' Issue*
TMB Publishing Inc.
1838 Techny Ct.
Northbrook, IL 60062
Ph: (847)564-1127
URL: http://www.plumbingengineer.com

Annual, July. $50.00 for individuals. Publication includes: Ranks 100 leading wholesalers of plumbing, heating, air conditioning, refrigeration equipment, and industrial pipe, valves and fittings. Entries include: Company name, address, phone, fax, names and titles of key personnel, number of employees, business breakdown (percentage). Arrangement: Ranked by sales.

EMPLOYMENT AGENCIES AND SEARCH FIRMS

13170 ■ The Aspire Group
711 Boylston St.
Boston, MA 02116-2616
Fax: (617)500-7284

Fr: 800-487-2967
URL: http://www.bmanet.com/Aspire/index.html
Employment agency.

OTHER SOURCES

13171 ■ Black Retail Action Group
PO Box 1192
New York, NY 10185
Ph: (212)234-3050
Fax: (212)234-3053
E-mail: bragorgusa@yahoo.com
URL: http://www.bragusa.org

Description: Represents minorities dedicated to the inclusion of all groups in the mainstream of the American economy. Promotes the acceptance and participation of people of color at all levels of retail and related industries.

13172 ■ National Association of College Stores (NACS)
500 E Lorain St.
Oberlin, OH 44074
Fax: (440)775-4769
Fr: 800-622-7498
E-mail: webteam@nacs.org
URL: http://www.nacs.org

Description: Institutional, private, leased, and cooperative college stores selling books, supplies, and other merchandise to college students, faculty, and staff; associate members include publishers and suppliers. Seeks to effectively serve higher education by providing educational research, advocacy and other to college stores and their suppliers. Maintains NACSCORP, Inc., a wholly owned subsidiary corporation, which distributes trade and mass market books and educational software. Sponsors seminars. Conducts manager certification, specialized education, and research programs. Maintains College Stores Research and Educational Foundation which provides grants for educational programs and conducts research.

13173 ■ National Retail Federation (NRF)
325 7th St. NW, Ste. 1100
Washington, DC 20004
Ph: (202)783-7971
Fax: (202)737-2849
Fr: 800-673-4692
E-mail: shaym@nrf.com
URL: http://www.nrf.com

Description: Represents state retail associations, several dozen national retail associations, as well as large and small corporate members representing the breadth and diversity of the retail industry's establishment and employees. Conducts informational and educational conferences related to all phases of retailing including financial planning and cash management, taxation, economic forecasting, expense planning, shortage control, credit, electronic data processing, telecommunications, merchandise management, buying, traffic, security, supply, materials handling, store planning and construction, personnel administration, recruitment and training, and advertising and display.

SOURCES OF HELP-WANTED ADS

13174 ■ Adweek
Nielsen Business Media
770 Broadway
New York, NY 10003-9595
URL: http://www.adweek.com/

Weekly. $299.00/year for individuals, print & online; $24.95/year for individuals, print & online per month; $19.95/year for individuals, online per month; $149.95/year for individuals, digital edition access. Advertising news magazine.

13175 ■ Amherst Writers and Artists Newsletter
Amherst Writers & Artists Press Inc.
PO Box 1076
Amherst, MA 01004
Ph: (413)253-3307
E-mail: amherstwriters@gmail.com
URL: http://www.amherstwriters.com

Description: Semiannual, February and September. Newsletter of the Amherst Writers and Artists Press. Recurring features include a calendar of events, news of members, notices of publications available, and news of educational opportunities.

13176 ■ ASJA Members' Newsletter
American Society of Journalists and Authors
1501 Broadway, Ste. 403
New York, NY 10036
Ph: (212)997-0947
Fax: (212)937-2315
URL: http://www.asja.org/newspub/newspub.php

Description: Monthly. Includes confidential market information.

13177 ■ Authors Guild-Bulletin
Authors Guild
31 E 32nd St., 7th Fl.
New York, NY 10016
Ph: (212)563-5904
Fax: (212)564-5363
E-mail: staff@authorsguild.org
URL: http://www.authorsguild.org

Description: Quarterly. Concerned with the business interests of professional authors, including copyright protection, contract problems, freedom of expression, taxation, and relevant legislation. Recurring features include listings of books by members, news of members and publishers, editorial job changes, job openings, surveys, symposia transcripts, and legal updates.

13178 ■ Authors' Newsletter
Arizona Authors' Association
6145 W Echo Ln.
Glendale, AZ 85302

Ph: (623)847-9343
E-mail: info@azauthors.com
URL: http://www.azauthors.com

Description: Bimonthly. Serves as a information and referral service of the Association.

13179 ■ AWP Job List
Association of Writers & Writing Programs
Mailstop 1E3
George Mason Univ.
Fairfax, VA 22030-4444
Ph: (703)993-4301
Fax: (703)993-4302
E-mail: services@awpwriter.org
URL: http://www.awpwriter.org/careers/joblist.htm

Description: Monthly. Lists job opportunities for writers, both in academia and in the business sector.

13180 ■ Children's Book Insider
901 Columbia Rd.
Fort Collins, CO 80525
Ph: (970)495-0056
Fax: (815)572-9207
E-mail: mail@write4kids.com
URL: http://www.write4kids.com

Description: Monthly. Discusses writing and selling books and stories for children. Recurring features include interviews, news of educational opportunities, job listings, and columns titled Writing Workshop, Market News, and Trends.

13181 ■ Columbia Journalism Review
Columbia Journalism Review
2950 Broadway, Journalism Bldg.
Columbia University
New York, NY 10027
Ph: (212)854-1881
Fax: (212)854-8367
URL: http://www.cjr.org/

Bimonthly. $19.95/year for individuals; $27.95/year for other countries. Magazine focusing on journalism.

13182 ■ Creativity Connection
University of Wisconsin
21 N Park St., 7th Fl.
Madison, WI 53715
Ph: (608)263-6960
Fax: (608)265-2901
E-mail: info@dcs.wisc.edu
URL: http://www.dcs.wisc.edu/LSA/writing/creativity-connection.htm

Description: Quarterly. $18/year. 20 pages. Features profiles and how-to articles for writers. Recurring features include letters to the editor, interviews, news of research, collection, book reviews, notices of publications available, and columns titled What Every Writer Should Know, Pub Tour, All Questions Considered, and Carson's Corner.

13183 ■ Current Jobs in Writing, Editing & Communications
Foster Opportunities, Inc.
1834 Olmstead Dr.
Falls Church, VA 22043-0494
Ph: (703)506-4400
Fr: 888-870-3069
E-mail: admin@graduatejobs.com
URL: http://www.graduatejobs.com/wec.htm

Monthly. $49.50/year. Focuses on vacancies in writing, editing, publishing, media, and all communications fields.

13184 ■ Daily Variety
Reed Business Information
360 Park Ave. S
New York, NY 10010-1710
Ph: (646)746-7764
Fax: (646)746-7583
URL: http://www.reedbusiness.com/index.asp?layout=theListProfile&

Daily. $329.99/year for individuals. Global entertainment newspaper (tabloid).

13185 ■ Dirty Goat
Host Publications, Inc.
277 Broadway, Ste. 210
New York, NY 10007
Ph: (212)905-2365
Fax: (212)905-2369
URL: http://www.thedirtygoat.com/index.html

Semiannual. $20.00/year for individuals. Journal covering poetry, prose, drama, literature and visual art.

13186 ■ Editor & Publisher
Editor & Publisher Magazine
17782 Cowan, Ste. A
Irvine, CA 92614
Ph: (949)660-6150
Fax: (949)660-6172
URL: http://www.editorandpublisher.com/

Weekly (Mon.). $65.00/year for individuals, print and online; $125.00/year for two years, print and online; $85.00/year for other countries; $49.00/year for individuals, digital only. Magazine focusing on newspaper journalism, advertising, printing equipment and interactive services.

13187 ■ Fiction Writer's Guideline
Fiction Writer's Connection
PO Box 72300
Albuquerque, NM 87195
Ph: (505)352-9490
E-mail: bcamenson@aol.com
URL: http://www.fictionwriters.com

Description: Bimonthly. Offers practical advice and support on writing and getting published. Recurring features include interviews, book reviews, and advice from agents and editors.

13188 ■ Freelance Daily Newsletter
Freelance Daily
c/o Suzanne Franco, Contact
1143 Heimer Lange Rd.
Spring Branch, TX 78070
Ph: (210)867-9781
Fax: (210)568-4561
E-mail: contact@freelancedaily.net
URL: http://www.freelancedaily.net
Daily. Specializes in finding writing jobs and opportunities for freelance writing professionals. Includes features such as freelance writing leads, publishers notes, freelance job of the day, and quote of the day.

13189 ■ History News
American Association for State and Local History
1717 Church St.
Nashville, TN 37203-2991
Ph: (615)320-3203
Fax: (615)327-9013
URL: http://www.aaslh.org/historynews.htm
Quarterly. Magazine for employees of historic sites, museums, and public history agencies. Coverage includes museum education programs and techniques for working with volunteers.

13190 ■ Independent Publisher Online
Jenkins group Inc.
1129 Woodmere Ave., Ste. B
Traverse City, MI 49686
Ph: (231)933-0445
Fax: (231)933-0448
Fr: 800-706-4636
URL: http://www.independentpublisher.com/
Monthly. Free. Online magazine containing book reviews and articles about independent publishing.

13191 ■ Metro Magazine
Bobit Business Media
3520 Challenger St.
Torrance, CA 90503
Ph: (310)533-2400
E-mail: info@metro-magazine.com
URL: http://www.metro-magazine.com
Free. Magazine on public transportation.

13192 ■ Muse: A Quarterly Journal of The Lit
Cleveland's Literary Center
2570 Superior Ave., Ste. 203
Cleveland, OH 44114
Ph: (216)694-0000
E-mail: judith@the-lit.org
URL: http://www.the-lit.org
Quarterly. $35/year. Contains book reviews, announcements, calendars, interviews, and articles of interest to writers living in Ohio.

13193 ■ The New Republic
The New Republic L.L.C.
1331 H St. NW, Ste. 700
Washington, DC 20005
Ph: (202)508-4444
Fax: (202)628-9380
Fr: 800-827-1289
E-mail: tnrcustserv@cdsfulfillment.com
URL: http://www.tnr.com
Weekly. $44.97/year for individuals, print; $29.97/year for individuals, digital. Journal featuring current events comments and reviews.

13194 ■ Novelists, Inc.
PO Box 2037
Manhattan, KS 66505
Fax: (785)537-1877
E-mail: ninc@varney.com
URL: http://www.ninc.com
Description: Monthly. Covers activities of Novelists, Inc. Reports on activities of Novelists, Inc, an association dedicated to serving the needs of multi-published writers of popular fiction. Offers advice and wisdom from other writers.

13195 ■ Producers Masterguide
Producers Masterguide
60 E 8th St., 34th Fl.
New York, NY 10003-6514
Ph: (212)777-4002
Fax: (212)777-4101
URL: http://www.producers.masterguide.com/cover.html
Annual. $185.00/year for U.S.; $175.00/year for Canada; $205.00/year for other countries. An international film and TV production directory and guide for the professional motion picture, broadcast television, feature film, TV commercial, cable/satellite, digital and videotape industries in the U.S., Canada, the UK, the Caribbean Islands, Mexico, Australia, New Zealand, Europe, Israel, Morocco, the Far East, and South America.

13196 ■ Publishers Weekly
Publishers Weekly
71 W 23 St., No. 1608
New York, NY 10010
Ph: (212)377-5500
URL: http://www.publishersweekly.com
Weekly. $249.99/year for individuals; $299.99/year for Canada; $399.99/year for other countries, air delivery. Magazine for publishers.

13197 ■ The Quarterly of the National Writing Project
National Writing Project
School of Education
University of California
2105 Bancroft Way, No. 1042
Berkeley, CA 94720-1042
Ph: (510)642-0963
Fax: (510)642-4545
E-mail: nwp@nwp.org
URL: http://www.nwp.org/
Description: Four issues/year. Explores the teaching and learning of writing and the connections between research and practice. Recurring features include book reviews.

13198 ■ Romance Writers Report
Romance Writers of America Inc.
14615 Benfer Rd.
Houston, TX 77069
Ph: (832)717-5200
Fax: (832)717-5201
E-mail: info@rwanational.org
URL: http://www.rwanational.org
Description: Monthly. Provides romance writers with information, assistance, knowledge, and support by publishing agents' special reports, author profiles, and how-to articles. Recurring features include editorials, news of members' activities, letters to the editor, interviews, reports of meetings, book reviews, and a calendar of events. Includes columns titled Market News, President's Column, Conferences and Contests, and Sparks 'N' Spice.

13199 ■ The Salmagundi Stew
Salmagundi Club
47 5th Ave.
New York, NY 10003
Ph: (212)255-7740
E-mail: info@salmagundi.org
URL: http://www.salmagundi.org
Description: 2/year. Highlights activities of the Club, a fellowship and exhibition organization for painters, sculptors, writers, and artists. Profiles artists and their work. Recurring features include notes on members, coverage of Clubhouse activities.

13200 ■ Sojourners
Sojourners
3333 14th St., NW Ste. 200
Washington, DC 20010
Ph: (202)328-8842
Fax: (202)328-8757
Fr: 800-714-7474
URL: http://www.sojo.net/

Monthly. $39.95/year for individuals; $49.95/year for Canada; $59.95/year for other countries. Independent, ecumenical Christian magazine which analyzes faith, politics, and culture from a progressive, justice-oriented perspective.

13201 ■ Techcomments
Society for Technical Communication, Southeastern Michigan Chapter
PO Box 1289
Ann Arbor, MI 48106
E-mail: newsletter@stc-sm.org
URL: http://www.stc-sm.org/
Description: Quarterly. Keeps chapter members informed of events and shares information about the work of technical communicators. Recurring features include letters to the editor, a calendar of events, reports of meetings, news of educational opportunities, job listings, book reviews, notices of publications available, and messages from chapter president and regional director.

13202 ■ A View from the Loft
Open Book, Ste. 200
1011 Washington Ave., S
Minneapolis, MN 55415
Ph: (612)215-2575
Fax: (612)215-2576
E-mail: loft@loft.org
URL: http://www.loft.org
Description: Bimonthly, except for July. Acts as a "forum for the exchange of information and opinions of writers." Presents articles on writing and publishing.

13203 ■ The Writer Magazine
Kalmbach Publishing Co.
21027 Crossroads Cir.
PO Box 1612
Waukesha, WI 53187-1612
Ph: (262)796-8776
Fax: (262)796-1615
Fr: 800-533-6644
URL: http://www.writermag.com
Monthly. $32.95/year for individuals; $42.95/year for Canada; $61.00/year for two years; $44.95/year for other countries. Magazine for free-lance writers. Publishing practical information and advice on how to write publishable material and where to sell it.

13204 ■ Writers Ask
Glimmer Train Press Inc.
4763 SW Maplewood
PO Box 80430
Portland, OR 97280-1430
E-mail: kgillen@fulcoinc.com
URL: http://www.glimmertrain.com/writersask.html
Description: Quarterly. $22/year. Disseminates information of interest to writers.

13205 ■ Writer's Digest
F+W Media Inc.
4700 E Galbraith Rd.
Cincinnati, OH 45236
Ph: (513)531-2690
Fax: (513)531-0798
Fr: 800-289-0963
E-mail: writersdigest@fwmedia.com
URL: http://www.writersdigest.com
$19.96/year for individuals; $29.96/year for Canada, including GST/HST; $31.96/year for other countries, surface delivery. Professional magazine for writers.

13206 ■ Writing That Works
Communications Concepts Inc.
7481 Huntsman Blvd., No. 720
Springfield, VA 22153-1648
Ph: (703)643-2200
Fax: (703)643-2329
URL: http://www.writingthatworks.com
Description: Bimonthly. Advises corporate, nonprofit, agency and independent communicators on business writing and publishing. Also covers writing techniques, style matters, publication management, and online

publishing. Publisher also sponsors annual APEX Awards for Publication Excellence.

EMPLOYER DIRECTORIES AND NETWORKING LISTS

13207 ■ American Society of Journalists and Authors—Directory
American Society of Journalists & Authors
1501 Broadway, Ste. 302
New York, NY 10036
Ph: (212)997-0947
Fax: (212)937-2315
URL: http://www.asja.org

Annual, January. $98.00 for individuals. Covers: 1,000 member freelance nonfiction writers. Entries include: Writer's name, home and office addresses and phone numbers, specialties, areas of expertise; name, address and phone of agent; memberships; books; periodicals to which contributed; awards. Arrangement: Alphabetical. Indexes: Subject specialty, type of material written, geographical.

13208 ■ ANR National Directory of Community Newspapers
American Newspaper Representatives Inc.
2075 W Big Beaver Rd., Ste. 310
Troy, MI 48084
Ph: (248)643-9910
Fax: (248)643-9914
Fr: 800-550-7557
URL: http://gotoanr.com/directory/

Weekly (Mon.), Latest edition 2010. $125.00 for individuals; $75.00 for individuals. Number of listings: 9,000. Entries include: Name of weekly newspaper, address, county, type of area, circulation, day published, name of publisher, and information on advertising rates and production specifications. Arrangement: Geographical.

13209 ■ Association of American University Presses—Directory
Association of American University Presses
28 W 36th St., Ste. 602
New York, NY 10018
Ph: (212)989-1010
Fax: (212)989-0975
URL: http://www.aaupnet.org

Annual, Latest edition 2011. $30.00 for individuals. Covers: 124 presses and affiliates worldwide. Entries include: Press name, address, phone, e-mail, URL; titles and names of complete editorial and managerial staffs; editorial program; mailing, warehouse, printing, and/or customer service addresses; other details. Arrangement: Classified by press affiliation, alphabetical by press name. Indexes: Personal name.

13210 ■ Association of Professional Communication Consultants—Membership Directory
Association of Professional Communication Consultants
104 Trace Ridge
Clinton, MS 39056-6153
Ph: (601)924-2173
Fax: (601)924-0522
E-mail: revadaniel@aol.com
URL: http://www.consultingsuccess.org/

Annual. Covers: 200 members. Entries include: Company or individual name, address, phone, areas of consulting expertise, services. Arrangement: Geographical and alphabetical.

13211 ■ Bowker's News Media Directory
R.R. Bowker L.L.C.
630 Central Ave.
New Providence, NJ 07974
Ph: (908)286-1090
Fr: 888-269-5372
E-mail: wpn@bowker.com
URL: http://www.bowker.com

Annual, Latest edition 2009. $668.00 for individuals. Covers: In three separate volumes, syndicates and over 8,500 daily and weekly newspapers; 1,750 newsletters; over 16,800 radio and television stations; 5,500 magazines; 1,000 internal publications. Entries include: Name of publication or station, address, phone, fax, e-mail and URL; names of executives, editors, writers, etc., as appropriate. Broadcasting and magazine volumes include data on kinds of material accepted. Technical and mechanical requirements for publications are given. Arrangement: Magazines are classified by subject; newspapers and broadcasting stations geographical. Indexes: Newspaper department/editor by interest, metro area, feature syndicate subject; magazine subject, publication title; television director/personnel by subject, radio personnel and director by subject.

13212 ■ Career Opportunities in the Publishing Industry
Facts On File Inc.
132 W 31st St., 17th Fl.
New York, NY 10001
Ph: (212)967-8800
Fax: 800-678-3633
Fr: 800-322-8755
URL: http://www.infobasepublishing.com

Latest edition 2nd; Published December, 2009. $49.50 for individuals. Covers: More than 90 jobs, such as writing, editing, design, printing, selling, publicity, advertising, marketing, and distribution.

13213 ■ Careers in Focus—Publishing
Facts On File Inc.
132 W 31st St., 17th Fl.
New York, NY 10001
Ph: (212)967-8800
Fax: 800-678-3633
Fr: 800-322-8755
URL: http://www.infobasepublishing.com

Latest edition 3rd; Published July, 2007. $32.95 for individuals. Covers: An overview of publishing, followed by a selection of jobs profiled in detail, including the nature of the job, earnings, prospects for employment, what kind of training and skills it requires, and sources for further information.

13214 ■ Children's Writer's & Illustrator's Market
Writer's Digest Books
4700 E Galbraith Rd.
Cincinnati, OH 45236
Ph: (715)445-4612
Fr: 800-258-0929
URL: http://www.writersdigest.com

Annual, Latest edition 2011. $13.99 for individuals. Covers: About 700 book and magazine publishers that publish works by authors and illustrators for young audiences; sponsors of writing and illustrating contests and awards; writers' organizations; and workshops. Entries include: For Publishers—Name, address, phone, name and title of contact, type of business, type and number of books published annually, average length of material bought, list of recently published material, reporting times, terms of payment to authors. Arrangement: Separate sections for book and magazine publishers. Indexes: Age level for books, general, magazine.

13215 ■ Contemporary Theatre, Film, and Television
Gale
PO Box 6904
Florence, KY 41022-6904
Fr: 800-354-9706
URL: http://www.gale.cengage.com

Bimonthly, Latest edition December, 2011. $293.00 for individuals. Covers: 116 volumes, more than 20,000 leading and up-and-coming performers, directors, writers, producers, designers, managers, choreographers, technicians, composers, executives, and dancers in the United States, Canada, Great Britain and the world. Each volume includes updated biographies for people listed in previous volumes and

in "Who's Who in the Theatre," which this series has superseded. Entries include: Name, agent and/or office addresses, personal and career data; stage, film, and television credits; writings, awards, other information. Arrangement: Alphabetical. Indexes: Cumulative name index also covers entries in "Who's Who in the Theatre" editions 1-17 and in "Who Was Who in the Theatre.".

13216 ■ Directory of Poetry Publishers
Dustbooks
PO Box 100
Paradise, CA 95967
Ph: (530)877-6110
Fax: (530)877-0222
Fr: 800-477-6110
URL: http://www.dustbooks.com/dp.htm

Annual, Latest edition 27th; 2011-2012. $49.95 for individuals; $21.00 for individuals. Covers: About 1,800 magazines, small presses, commercial presses, and university presses that accept poetry for publication. Entries include: Publisher name and address, number of submissions accepted, percentage of submissions published, deadlines, reporting time, list of recent contributors, rights purchased, and method of payment. Arrangement: Alphabetical. Indexes: Subject, Geographical.

13217 ■ Directory of Small Press—Magazine Editors and Publishers
Dustbooks
PO Box 100
Paradise, CA 95967
Ph: (530)877-6110
Fax: (530)877-0222
Fr: 800-477-6110
URL: http://www.dustbooks.com/de.htm

Annual, Latest edition 42nd; 2011-2012. $49.95 for individuals; $21.00 for individuals. Covers: About 7,500 publishers and editors. Entries include: Individual name, title of press or magazine, address and phone number. Arrangement: Alphabetical.

13218 ■ Discovering Careers for Your Future—English
Facts On File Inc.
132 W 31st St., 17th Fl.
New York, NY 10001
Ph: (212)967-8800
Fax: 800-678-3633
Fr: 800-322-8755
URL: http://factsonfile.infobasepublishing.com

Latest edition 2nd, 2005. $21.95 for individuals. Covers: Editors, education directors and museum teachers, interpreters and translators, literary agents, public relations specialists, screenwriters, teachers, and more; links career education to curriculum, helping children investigate the subjects they are interested in, and the careers those subjects might lead to.

13219 ■ The Dramatists Guild Resource Directory
The Dramatists Guild of America Inc.
1501 Broadway, Ste. 701
New York, NY 10036-3988
Ph: (212)398-9366
Fax: (212)944-0420
URL: http://www.dramatistsguild.com/pub_directory.aspx

Annual, Latest edition 2009. Publication includes: Lists of Broadway and off-Broadway producers; theater and producing organizations; agents; regional theaters; sources of grants, fellowships, residencies; conferences and festivals; playwriting contests; and sources of financial assistance. Entries include: For producers—Name, address, credits, types of plays accepted for consideration. For groups—Name, address, contact name, type of material accepted for consideration, future commitment, hiring criteria, response time. For agents—Name, address. For theaters—Theater name, address, contact name, submission procedure, types of plays accepted for consideration, maximum cast, limitations, equity contract, opportunities, response time. For grants, fellowships, residencies, financial assistance, conferences, and festivals—Name, address, contact name, description, eligibility and application requirements, deadline. For play contests—Name, address, prize, deadline, description. Arrangement: Contests are by deadline; others are classified.

13220 ■ Editor & Publisher International Year Book

Editor & Publisher Magazine
17782 Cowan, Ste. A
Irvine, CA 92614
Ph: (949)660-6150
Fax: (949)660-6172
URL: http://www.editorandpublisher.com

Annual, Latest edition 2009. $150.00 for individuals; $135.00 for individuals; $75.00 for individuals; $239.00 for individuals; $180.00 for individuals. Covers: Daily and Sunday newspapers in the United States and Canada; weekly newspapers; foreign daily newspapers; special service newspapers; newspaper syndicates; news services; journalism schools; foreign language and Black newspapers in the United States; news, picture, and press services; feature and news syndicates; comic and magazine services; advertising clubs; trade associations; clipping bureaus; house organs; journalism awards; also lists manufacturers of equipment and supplies. Entries include: For daily papers—Publication name, address, phone, fax, e-mail, web site URL, names of executives and departmental editors (business, financial, book, food, etc.), circulation and advertising data, production information including format of paper and equipment used. Similar but less detailed information for other publications. Arrangement: Publications and schools are geographical; most other lists are alphabetical.

13221 ■ Editorial Freelancers Association—Membership Directory

Editorial Freelancers Association Inc.
71 W 23rd St., 4th Fl.
New York, NY 10010-4181
Ph: (212)929-5400
URL: http://www.the-efa.org

Annual, spring. Covers: 1,100 member editorial freelancers. Entries include: Personal name, address, phone, services provided, specialties. Arrangement: Alphabetical. Indexes: Product/service, special interest, geographical, computer skills.

13222 ■ The Guide to Writers Conferences & Workshops

ShawGuides Inc., Educational Publishers
1499 NW 79th Ave.
Miami, FL 33126
Ph: (305)532-9775
URL: http://writing.shawguides.com

Continuously updated. Free. Covers: Listings for more than 1,500 conferences and workshops for writers in the U.S. and abroad, searchable by date, state or country, or by type. Entries include: Name of workshop or program, description of programs, fees, locations, contact name, address, phone, fax, e-mail, web site.

13223 ■ International Directory of Little Magazines and Small Presses

Dustbooks
PO Box 100
Paradise, CA 95967
Ph: (530)877-6110
Fax: (530)877-0222
Fr: 800-477-6110
URL: http://www.dustbooks.com/d.htm

Annual, Latest edition 47th; 2011-2012. $65.00 for individuals; $49.95 for individuals; $30.00 for individuals. Covers: Over 4,000 small, independent magazines, presses, and papers. Entries include: Name, address, size, circulation, frequency, price, type of material used, number of issues or books published annually, and other pertinent data. Arrangement: Alphabetical. Indexes: Subject, regional.

13224 ■ International Literary Market Place

Information Today Inc.
143 Old Marlton Pike
Medford, NJ 08055-8750
Ph: (609)654-6266
Fax: (609)654-4309
Fr: 800-300-9868
URL: http://www.literarymarketplace.com

Annual, Latest edition 2012. $289.00 for individuals; $260.10 for individuals. Covers: Over 10,500 publishers in over 180 countries outside the United States and Canada, and about 1,499 trade and professional organizations related to publishing abroad; includes major printers, binders, typesetters, book manufacturers, book dealers, libraries, literary agencies, translators, book clubs, reference books and journals, periodicals, prizes, and international reference section. Entries include: For publishers—Name, address, phone, fax, telex, names and titles of key personnel, branches, type of publications, subjects, ISBN prefix. Listings for others include similar information but less detail. Arrangement: Classified by business activities, then geographical. Indexes: Company name, subject, type of publication.

13225 ■ Literary Market Place

Information Today Inc.
143 Old Marlton Pike
Medford, NJ 08055-8750
Ph: (609)654-6266
Fax: (609)654-4309
Fr: 800-300-9868
URL: http://books.infotoday.com

Annual, Latest edition 2012. $339.00 for individuals; $305.10 for individuals. Covers: Over 12,500 firms or organizations offering services related to the publishing industry, including book publishers in the United States and Canada who issued three or more books during the preceding year, plus a small press section of publishers who publish less than three titles per year or those who are self-published. Also included: book printers and binders; book clubs; book trade and literary associations; selected syndicates, newspapers, periodicals, and radio and TV programs that use book reviews or book publishing news; translators and literary agents. Entries include: For publishers—Company name, address, phone, address for orders, principal executives, editorial directors, and managers, date founded, number of titles in previous year, number of backlist titles in print, types of books published, ISBN prefixes, representatives, imprints, and affiliations. For suppliers, etc.—Listings usually show firm name, address, phone, executives, services, etc. Arrangement: Classified by line of business. Indexes: Principal index is 35,000-item combined index of publishers, publications, and personnel; several sections have geographical and/or subject indexes; translators are indexed by source and target language.

13226 ■ Midwest Travel Writers Association—Membership Directory

Midwest Travel Writers Association
PO Box 83542
Lincoln, NE 68501-3542
Ph: (402)438-2253
Fax: (866)365-4851
URL: http://www.mtwa.org

Annual, February. $50.00; $65.00. Covers: Over 100 travel writers, editors, and representatives of the travel and tourism industry, located in 13 Midwestern states. Entries include: Name, spouse's name, address, phone; title, year membership began, publications, professional affiliations, writing specialties. Arrangement: Alphabetical. Indexes: Geographical.

13227 ■ National Directory of Arts Internships

National Network for Artist Placement
935 West Ave. 37
Los Angeles, CA 90065
Ph: (323)222-4035
E-mail: info@artistplacement.com
URL: http://www.artistplacement.com

Biennial, odd years; latest edition 11th. $95.00 for individuals. Covers: Over 5,000 internship opportunities in dance, music, theater, art, design, film, and video & over 1,250 host organizations Entries include: Name of sponsoring organization, address, name of contact; description of positions available, eligibility requirements, stipend or salary (if any), application procedures. Arrangement: Classified by discipline, then geographical.

13228 ■ National Directory of Magazines

Oxbridge Communications Inc.
186 5th Ave.
New York, NY 10010-5202
Ph: (212)741-0231
Fax: (212)633-2938
Fr: 800-955-0231
URL: http://www.oxbridge.com

latest edition 2011. $995.00 for individuals; $1,195.00 for individuals; $1,995.00 for individuals. Covers: Over 20,000 magazines; coverage includes Canada. Entries include: Title, publisher name, address, phone, fax number, names and titles of contact and key personnel, financial data, editorial and advertising information, circulation. Arrangement: Classified by subject. Indexes: Title, geographical, publisher.

13229 ■ Novel & Short Story Writer's Market

Writer's Digest Books
4700 E Galbraith Rd.
Cincinnati, OH 45236
Ph: (715)445-4612
Fr: 800-258-0929
URL: http://www.writersdigest.com

Annual, Latest edition 2011. $19.79 for individuals. Publication includes: List of 1,100 literary magazines, general periodicals, small presses, book publishers, and authors' agents; contests awards; and writers' organizations. Entries include: For markets—Publication name (if a periodical), publisher name and address, phone, name of editor or other contact; description of periodical or type of work published; frequency and circulation for periodicals, number of titles published for others; needs, method of contact, terms, payment, advice, comments, or tips given by firm. For contests and awards—Name, sponsoring organization name and address, name and title of contact, frequency; purpose, requirements, other information. Arrangement: Contests and awards are alphabetical; markets are classified by type of publisher or type of periodical. Indexes: Market category.

13230 ■ Poet's Market

Writer's Digest Books
4700 E Galbraith Rd.
Cincinnati, OH 45236
Ph: (715)445-4612
Fr: 800-258-0929
E-mail: poetsmarket@fwpubs.com
URL: http://www.poetsmarket.com

Annual, Latest edition 2009. $13.99 for individuals. Covers: 1,800 publishers, periodicals, and other markets accepting poetry for publication. Entries include: Name, address, phone, name and title of contact, types of poetry accepted, submission requirements. Arrangement: Alphabetical. Indexes: Subject, geographical, chapbook publishers.

13231 ■ Professional Freelance Writers Directory

The National Writers Association
10940 S Parker Rd., No. 508
Parker, CO 80134
Ph: (303)841-0246
Fax: (303)841-2607
URL: http://www.nationalwriters.com

Annual. Free. Database covers: About 200 professional members selected from the club's membership on the basis of significant articles or books, or production of plays or movies. Entries include: Name, address, phone (home and business numbers), special fields of writing competence, titles of books published by royalty firms, mention of contributions to specific magazines, journals, newspapers or anthologies, recent awards received, relevant activities and skills (photography, etc.). Arrangement: Alphabetical. Indexes: By author alphabetical, by state, by subject.

13232 ■ Publishers Directory
Gale
PO Box 6904
Florence, KY 41022-6904
Fr: 800-354-9706
URL: http://www.gale.cengage.com

Annual, Latest edition 36th; April, 2011. $720.00 for individuals. Covers: Over 20,000 new and established, commercial and nonprofit, private and alternative, corporate and association, government and institution publishing programs and their distributors; includes producers of books, classroom materials, prints, reports, and databases. Entries include: Firm name, address, phone, fax, company e-mail address, URL, year founded, ISBN prefix, Standard Address Number, whether firm participates in the Cataloging in Publication program of the Library of Congress, names of principal executives, personal e-mail addresses, number of titles in print, description of firm and its main subject interests, discount and returns policies, affiliated and parent companies, mergers and amalgamations, principal markets, imprints and divisions, alternate formats products are offered; distributors also list firms for which they distribute, special services, terms to publishers and regional offices. Arrangement: Alphabetical; distributors listed separately. Indexes: Subject, geographical, publisher, imprints, and distributor.

13233 ■ Publishers, Distributors, and Wholesalers of the United States
R.R. Bowker L.L.C.
630 Central Ave.
New Providence, NJ 07974
Ph: (908)286-1090
Fr: 888-269-5372
URL: http://www.bowker.com

Annual, latest edition 2010. $500.00 for individuals. Covers: Over 196,066 publishers, distributors, and wholesalers; includes associations, museums, software producers and manufacturers, and others not included in 'Books in Print'. Entries include: Publisher name, editorial and ordering addresses, e-mail, websites, phone, Standard Address Numbers (SANs), International Standard Book Number prefix. Arrangement: Alphabetical; distributors and wholesalers are listed separately. Indexes: ISBN prefix, abbreviation, type of business, imprint name, geographical, inactive and out of business company name, toll-free phone and fax, wholesaler and distributor.

13234 ■ PubWest Membership Directory
Publishers Association of the West
17501 Hill Way
Lake Oswego, OR 97035
Ph: (503)635-0056
Fax: (602)234-3062
URL: http://www.pubwest.org

Annual, Latest edition 2011-2012. Free; $10.00 for nonmembers. Covers: Publishers, printers, designers, binderies, and publishing freelancers. Entries include: Company name, address, phone, fax, e-mail and website address.

13235 ■ Self-Publishing Manual
Para Publishing
530 Ellwood Ridge Rd.
Santa Barbara, CA 93117-1047
Ph: (805)968-7277
Fax: (805)968-1379
Fr: 800-727-2782
URL: http://www.parapublishing.com

Biennial, odd years. $19.95 for individuals. Publication includes: Lists of wholesalers, reviewers, exporters, suppliers, direct mailing list sources, publishing organizations, and others of assistance in publishing. Entries include: Organization or company name, address, email addresses and web address. Arrange-

ment: Classified by ZIP code. Indexes: General subject.

13236 ■ Society of American Travel Writers—Membership Directory
Society of American Travel Writers
11950 W Lake Park Dr., Ste. 320
Milwaukee, WI 53224-3049
Ph: (414)908-4949
Fax: (414)768-8001
URL: http://www.satw.org/index.php/membership/ directory

Annual, Latest edition 2011. $250.00 for individuals. Covers: About 1,200 newspaper and magazine travel editors, writers, columnists, photo journalists, and broadcasters in the United States and Canada. Also covers separately 400 executives in public relations who handle tourist attractions and travel industry accounts. Entries include: For regular members—Name, business address, phone, year joined; awards, publications, specialties, publications contributed to; spouse's name. For public relations executives—Name, address, phone, year joined, clients. Arrangement: Classified by type of membership. Indexes: Geographical, travel editor affiliation, free lance travel writers, public relations executive affiliation.

13237 ■ Space Coast Writers Guild—Membership Information/Directory
Space Coast Writers Guild Inc.
PO Box 262
Melbourne, FL 32902-0262
Ph: (321)723-7345
URL: http://www.scwg.org

Annual. Free. Covers: About 350 professional and aspiring writers in Florida. Entries include: Name, address, phone, area and form of specialty. Arrangement: Alphabetical. Indexes: By genre.

13238 ■ SRDS International Media Guides
SRDS
1700 Higgins Rd.
Des Plaines, IL 60018-5605
Ph: (847)375-5000
Fax: (847)375-5001
Fr: 800-851-7737
URL: http://www.srds.com

Annual. $455.00 for individuals. Covers: approximately 19,000 newspapers and color newspaper magazines/supplements from 200 countries, including the United States. Entries include: Publication name; publisher name, address, phone, fax, e-mail, URL, names of editor, advertising manager, and representatives in the United States and worldwide; advertising rates in U.S. dollars and/or local currency, circulation, mechanical data, ad closing, readership description, etc. Arrangement: Geographical.

13239 ■ Ulrich's Periodicals Directory
R.R. Bowker L.L.C.
630 Central Ave.
New Providence, NJ 07974
Ph: (908)286-1090
Fr: 888-269-5372
E-mail: ulrichs@bowker.com
URL: http://www.bowker.com

Annual, Latest edition 2010. $1,260.00 for individuals. Covers: Nearly 200,000 current periodicals and newspapers published worldwide. Entries include: In main listing—Publication title; Dewey Decimal Classification number, Library of Congress Classification Number (where applicable), CODEN designation (for sci-tech serials), British Library Document Supply Centre shelfmark number, country code, ISSN; subtitle, language(s) of text, year first published, frequency, subscription prices, sponsoring organization, publishing company name, address, phone, fax, e-mail and website addresses, editor and publisher names; regular features (reviews, advertising, abstracts, bibliographies, trade literature, etc.), indexes, circulation, format, brief description of content; availability of microforms and reprints; whether refereed; CD-ROM availability with vendor name; online availability with service name; services that index or

abstract the periodical, with years covered; advertising rates and contact; right and permissions contact name and phone; availability through document deliver Arrangement: Main listing is classified by subject; U.S. general daily and weekly newspapers are listed in a separate volume; lists of cessations, online services, and CD-ROM vendors are alphabetical. Indexes: Cessations, subjects, title (including variant, former, and ceased titles), ISSN, periodicals available on CD-ROM, online periodical title, refereed serial, and international organization publication title.

13240 ■ Washington Independent Writers—Directory
Washington Independent Writers
1001 Connecticut Ave. NW, Ste. 701
Washington, DC 20036
Ph: (202)775-5150
Fax: (202)775-5810
URL: http://www.washwriter.org/

Biennial. Covers: About 2,500 member freelance writers in the Washington, D.C. area. Entries include: Name, address, home and office phone, area of specialization; personal and career data usually included. Arrangement: Alphabetical. Indexes: Specialty.

13241 ■ Writer's Market
Writer's Digest Books
4700 E Galbraith Rd.
Cincinnati, OH 45236
Ph: (715)445-4612
Fr: 800-258-0929
E-mail: writersmarker@fwpubs.com
URL: http://www.writersdigest.com

Annual, Latest edition 2010. $19.79 for individuals. Covers: Over 3,500 buyers of books, articles, short stories, plays, gags, verse, fillers, and other original written material. Includes book and periodical publishers, greeting card publishers, play producers and publishers, audiovisual material producers, syndicates, and contests and awards. Entries include: Name and address of buyer, phone, payment rates, editorial requirements, reporting time, how to break in. Arrangement: Classified by type of publication. Indexes: Subject, alphabetical.

HANDBOOKS AND MANUALS

13242 ■ Career Opportunities in Journalism
Ferguson Publishing Company
132 W 31st St., 17th Fl.
New York, NY 10001
Fax: 800-678-3633
Fr: 800-322-8755
E-mail: custserv@factsonfile.com
URL: http://ferguson.infobasepublishing.com/ Bookdetail.aspx?ISBN=0816064199&eBooks=0

Jennifer Bobrow Burns. 2007. $49.50 (hardcover). 336 pages. Covers journalism careers in a variety of contexts, from newspapers and broadcasting to education and new media. Contains appendixes of related educational programs, professional associations and publications, companies, and internship and scholarship resources.

13243 ■ Careers in Communications
The McGraw-Hill Companies
PO Box 182604
Columbus, OH 43272
Fax: (614)759-3749
Fr: 877-883-5524
E-mail: customer.service@mcgraw-hill.com
URL: http://www.mhprofessional.com/ product.php?isbn=0071454764

Shonan Noronha. Fourth edition, 2004. $15.95 (paper). 192 pages. Examines the fields of journalism, photography, radio, television, film, public relations, and advertising. Gives concrete details on job locations and how to secure a job. Suggests many resources for job hunting.

13244 ■ Careers in Health Care
The McGraw-Hill Companies
PO Box 182604
Columbus, OH 43272
Fax: (614)759-3749
Fr: 877-883-5524
E-mail: customer.service@mcgraw-hill.com
URL: http://www.mhprofessional.com/
  product.php?isbn=0071466533
Barbara M. Swanson. Fifth edition, 2005. $19.95 (paper). 192 pages. Describes job duties, work settings, salaries, licensing and certification requirements, educational preparation, and future outlook. Gives ideas on how to secure a job.

13245 ■ Careers for Health Nuts and Others Who Like to Stay Fit
The McGraw-Hill Companies
PO Box 182604
Columbus, OH 43272
Fax: (614)759-3749
Fr: 877-883-5524
E-mail: customer.service@mcgraw-hill.com
URL: http://www.mhprofessional.com
Blythe Camenson. Second edition. $13.95 (paper). 208 pages.

13246 ■ Careers in Journalism
The McGraw-Hill Companies
PO Box 182604
Columbus, OH 43272
Fax: (614)759-3749
Fr: 877-883-5524
E-mail: customer.service@mcgraw-hill.com
URL: http://www.mhprofessional.com/
  product.php?isbn=0071466371
Jan Goldberg. Third edition, 2005. $15.95 (paper). 192 pages.

13247 ■ Careers for Mystery Buffs and Other Snoops and Sleuths
The McGraw-Hill Companies
PO Box 182604
Columbus, OH 43272
Fax: (614)759-3749
Fr: 877-883-5524
E-mail: customer.service@mcgraw-hill.com
URL: http://www.mhprofessional.com
Blythe Camenson. Second edition. $14.95 (hardback). 160 pages.

13248 ■ The Complete Help Book for Authors and Publishers
Hannacroix Creek Books, Incorporated
1127 High Ridge Rd., No. 110B
Stamford, CT 06905-1203
Ph: (203)321-8674
Fax: (203)968-0193
E-mail: hannacroix@aol.com
URL: http://www.hannacroixcreekbooks.com/
Jan Yeager. 2007. $29.95. Explores self-publishing for authors.

13249 ■ Creative Careers: Paths for Aspiring Actors, Artists, Dancers, Musicians and Writers
SuperCollege, LLC
3286 Oak Ct.
Belmont, CA 94002
Ph: (650)618-2221
URL: http://www.supercollege.com
Elaina Loveland. 2009. $17.95. 352 pages. Provides tips and advice for job seekers aiming for a career in the field of arts. Includes details on salaries, job descriptions, job outlook, training and education requirements for each artistic career.

13250 ■ The Everything Guide to Getting Published
Adams Media
57 Littlefield St.
Avon, MA 02322
Ph: (508)427-7100

Fax: (508)427-6790
URL: http://www.adamsmedia.com
Randy Ladenheim-Gil. 2012. $16.95. 304 pages. Guides beginners and experienced writers in building a successful writing career. Includes tips and advice on submitting manuscripts, writing a query, and navigating the uncertain waters of self-publishing and e-books. Also features guide on crafting a career plan and negotiating contracts.

13251 ■ FabJob Guide to Become an Advertising Copywriter
FabJob Inc.
4616 - 25th Ave. NE, No. 224
Seattle, WA 98105
Ph: (403)949-4980
Fr: 888-322-5621
URL: http://www.fabjob.com
Brooke J. Claussen. $14.97. 140 pages. Discusses key points on how to get started and how to succeed in the advertising industry.

13252 ■ Great Jobs for English Majors
The McGraw-Hill Companies
PO Box 182604
Columbus, OH 43272
Fax: (614)759-3749
Fr: 877-883-5524
E-mail: customer.service@mcgraw-hill.com
URL: http://www.mhprofessional.com
Julie DeGalan and Stephen Lambert. Third edition, 2006. $15.95 (paper). 192 pages.

13253 ■ Great Jobs for Liberal Arts Majors
The McGraw-Hill Companies
PO Box 182604
Columbus, OH 43272
Fax: (614)759-3749
Fr: 877-883-5524
E-mail: customer.service@mcgraw-hill.com
URL: http://www.mhprofessional.com/
  product.php?isbn=0071482148
Blythe Camenson. Second edition, 2007. $16.95 (paper). 192 pages.

13254 ■ Opportunities in Writing Careers
The McGraw-Hill Companies
PO Box 182604
Columbus, OH 43272
Fax: (614)759-3749
Fr: 877-883-5524
E-mail: customer.service@mcgraw-hill.com
URL: http://www.mhprofessional.com/
  product.php?isbn=0071458727
Elizabeth Foote-Smith. 2006. $13.95 (paper). 160 pages. Discusses opportunities in the print media, broadcasting, advertising or publishing. Business writing, public relations, and technical writing are among the careers covered. Contains bibliography and illustrations.

13255 ■ Starting Your Career as a Freelance Editor
Allworth Press
307 W 36th St., 11th Fl.
New York, NY 10018
Ph: (212)643-6816
Fax: (212)643-6819
URL: http://www.allworth.com
Mary Embree. 2011. $19.95 (paper). 256 pages. Provides guidelines on how to pursue a career as a freelance editor. Includes tips on how to manage the business side of being a freelance editor.

13256 ■ Starting Your Career as a Freelance Writer
Allworth Press
307 W 36th St., 11th Fl.
New York, NY 10018
Ph: (212)643-6816
Fax: (212)643-6819
URL: http://www.allworth.com
Moira Anderson Allen. 2011. $24.95 (paper). 304

pages. Serves as a guide for those who want to pursue a career in freelance writing.

13257 ■ Write Your Way into Animation and Games
Focal Press
225 Wyman St.
Waltham, MA 02451
Fr: 800-545-2522
E-mail: usbkinfo@elsevier.com
URL: http://www.focalpress.com
Christy Marx. 2010. $39.95 (paperback). 424 pages. Provides jobseekers with tips and tricks for launching a writing career in the games and animation industry. Shows how to: generate ideas and create storylines with featured advice from professional writers and game developers; navigate the business aspects of the profession; gain skills and develop the craft of writing specifically for animation and games.

13258 ■ Writing (Discovering Careers)
Ferguson
c/o Infobase Publishing
132 W 31st St., 17th Fl.
New York, NY 10001
Fax: (600)678-3633
Fr: 800-322-8755
E-mail: custserv@factsonfile.com
URL: http://www.infobasepublishing.com
Facts on File, Inc. 2012. $24.95 (hardcover). Covers 20 writing careers for jobseekers interested in having their work appear in print, broadcast and online media.

EMPLOYMENT AGENCIES AND SEARCH FIRMS

13259 ■ Amtec Human Capital
2749 Saturn St.
Brea, CA 92821
Ph: (714)993-1900
Fax: (714)993-2419
E-mail: info@amtechc.com
URL: http://www.amtechc.com
Employment agency.

13260 ■ Bert Davis Publishing Placement Consultants
425 Madison Ave.
New York, NY 10017
Ph: (212)838-4000
Fax: (212)935-3291
E-mail: info@bertdavis.com
URL: http://www.bertdavis.com
Executive search firm.

13261 ■ Brattle Temps
50 Congress St., Ste. 935
Boston, MA 02109-4008
Ph: (617)523-4600
Fax: (617)523-3939
E-mail: temps@brattletemps.com
Personnel consulting firm specializes in providing temporary consultants. Skill areas available include: computer operators, secretaries, editors, librarians, graphic artists, and marketing professionals. Industries served: universities, publishing, engineering, manufacturing, and government agencies.

13262 ■ Career Development Services
150 State St.
Rochester, NY 14614
Ph: (585)244-0765
Fr: 800-736-6710
E-mail: info@careerdev.org
URL: http://www.careerdev.org
Employment agency.

13263 ■ Chaloner Associates
36 Milford St.
Boston, MA 02118

Ph: (617)451-5170
Fax: (617)451-8160
E-mail: info@chaloner.com
URL: http://www.chaloner.com
Executive search firm.

13264 ■ The Esquire Staffing Group Ltd.
1 S Wacker Dr., Ste. 1616
Chicago, IL 60606-4616
Ph: (312)795-4300
URL: http://www.esquirestaffing.com
Employment agency. Fills permanent as well as temporary openings.

13265 ■ The Howard-Sloan-Koller Group
300 E 42nd St., 15th Fl.
New York, NY 10017
Ph: (212)661-5250
Fax: (212)557-9178
E-mail: hsk@hsksearch.com
URL: http://www.hsksearch.com
Provides professional search and recruitment services for a wide range of sectors within online and print media, advertising, entertainment, information, events and public relations, nationally and internationally. Also consults with organizations regarding staffing, development, and growth strategies.

13266 ■ Howard-Sloan Professional Search Inc.
261 Madison Ave.
New York, NY 10016
Ph: (212)704-0444
Fr: 800-221-1326
E-mail: info@howardsloan.com
URL: http://www.howardsloan.com
Executive search firm.

13267 ■ LandaJob Advertising Staffing Specialists
222 W Gregory Blvd., Ste. 304
Kansas City, MO 64114
Ph: (816)523-1881
Fax: (816)523-1876
Fr: 800-931-8806
E-mail: adstaff@landajobnow.com
URL: http://www.landajobnow.com
Personnel consultants and recruiters for advertising, marketing, and communications positions. Industries served: advertising, communications, marketing, graphic arts, printing and publishing.

13268 ■ Max Brown
3208 Q St. NW
Washington, DC 20007
Ph: (202)338-2727
Fax: (202)338-3131
E-mail: maxbrown65@hotmail.com
Executive recruiter to the magazine and book publishing industries. Employment placements in all publishing disciplines, including operation and financial management, new product development, marketing, advertising sales, editorial, graphic design, production, manufacturing, circulation, distribution, corporate communications, promotion and administration. Secondary concentrations include management advising for publishers, providing the following services: marketing and product positioning for new and existing publications, market research and development, business planning and financial projections, publishing models, launch strategies and start-up operations and acquisitions and mergers counsel.

13269 ■ Recruiting Partners
3494 Camino Tassajara Rd., No. 404
Danville, CA 94506
Ph: (925)964-0249
E-mail: info@recruitingpartners.com
URL: http://www.recruitingpartners.com
Description: Serves as an executive and technical recruiting firm that specializes in accounting, legal,

information technology, engineering, executive management and technical writing.

13270 ■ SHS Careers Front Page
711 DeLasalle Ct.
Naperville, IL 60565
Ph: (630)718-1704
Fax: (630)718-1709
URL: http://www.shsinc.com
Executive search firm for pharmaceutical advertising, medical communications and education, healthcare public relations, and biotechnology industries.

13271 ■ Technical Talent Locators Ltd.
5570 Sterrett Pl., Ste. 208
Columbia, MD 21044
Ph: (410)740-0091
E-mail: steve@ttlgroup.com
URL: http://www.ttlgroup.com
Permanent employment agency working within the following fields: software and database engineering; computer, communication, and telecommunication system engineering; and other computer-related disciplines.

13272 ■ Zachary & Sanders Inc.
24 Linden Ln.
PO Box 32
East Norwich, NY 11732
Ph: (516)922-5500
Fax: (516)922-2286
Fr: 800-540-7919
E-mail: zacharyserch@earthlink.net
Serves the printing, packaging, publishing, advertising, direct marketing industries.

ONLINE JOB SOURCES AND SERVICES

13273 ■ EditingCrossing.com
URL: http://www.editingcrossing.com
Description: Shows jobs from employer career pages, job websites, association websites, newspaper classified ads and recruiter sites. Includes editing jobs from all Fortune 500 and Fortune 1,000 companies.

13274 ■ FreelanceWriting.com
URL: http://www.freelancewriting.com
Description: Career resource for freelance writing professionals. Includes listings of freelance writing jobs, articles, writing contests, writing events, and more.

13275 ■ GetGigs.com
URL: http://www.getgigs.com
Description: Seeks to provide an on-line experience for creative types, performing artists, and musicians around the world by integrating internet technologies into a one-stop information resource. Also functions as a creative directory and talent network.

13276 ■ Guru.com
5001 Baum Blvd., Ste. 760
Pittsburgh, PA 15213
Fax: (412)687-4466
Fr: 888-687-1316
URL: http://www.guru.com
Description: Job board specializing in contract jobs for creative and information technology professionals. Also provides online incorporation and educational opportunities for independent contractors along with articles and advice.

13277 ■ JournalismJobs.com
Ph: (510)653-1521
E-mail: info@journalismjobs.com
URL: http://www.journalismjobs.com
Description: Career-related site for journalists and other media professionals. Seekers can search for jobs, post a resume online, and manage the search

online with the Job Seeker Folder feature. They also can receive free job announcements by e-mail.

13278 ■ JournalismNext.com
E-mail: info@journalismnext.com
URL: http://www.journalismnext.com
Description: Exists as a community website for minority journalists and media professionals. Allows employers to post job openings while also allowing job seekers to search through job listings.

13279 ■ JournalismNow.com
URL: http://www.journalismnow.com
Description: Assists journalism job candidates in securing employment. Lists job opportunities with newspapers, online media, TV, radio, and magazines. Includes articles that relate to the field of journalism and current events.

13280 ■ MediaBistro.com
URL: http://www.mediabistro.com
Description: Serves as a career resource for anyone who creates or works with content, or who is a non-creative professional working in a content/creative industry (including editors, writers, producers, graphic designers, book publishers, and others in industries including magazines, television, film, radio, newspapers, book publishing, online media, advertising, PR, and design). Provides opportunities to meet, share resources, become informed of job opportunities and interesting projects and news, improve career skills, and showcase one's work.

13281 ■ Sunoasis Jobs
E-mail: sunoasisjobs@earthlink.net
URL: http://www.sunoasis.com
Description: Provides job leads for individuals intending to work in the writing, editing and copyediting industry while also providing a resource base for individuals looking for writers, editors, and copywriters.

13282 ■ TechWritingJobs.com
URL: http://www.techwritingjobs.com
Description: Offers up-to-the-minute job listings and job advice for tech writers. Includes other vital career information for tech writers such as writing a tech writing resume, jobs with tech writing agencies, marketing oneself as a freelance technical writer, training for tech writers and more.

13283 ■ WriteJobs.com
URL: http://www.writejobs.com
Description: Provides job listings, career resources and information for journalism, media and publishing professionals.

13284 ■ WritingCareer.com
URL: http://www.writingcareer.com
Description: Offers valuable advice on career training, career education, and changing careers aimed at writers and freelance writers. Includes site features such as career guides, free writing career articles, podcasts, writing career help, writing career jobs and writing events.

13285 ■ WritingCrossing.com
URL: http://www.writingcrossing.com
Description: Features listings of writing jobs worldwide. Offers job listings for writers, freelancers, technical writers, associate writers, marketing writers, copywriters, business writers, web writers, and editors.

TRADESHOWS

13286 ■ Association of Alternative Newsmedia Annual Convention
Association of Alternative Newsmedia
1156 15th St. NW, Ste. 905
Washington, DC 20005

Ph: (202)289-8484
Fax: (202)289-2004
E-mail: web@aan.org
URL: http://www.altweeklies.com

Annual. Brings together individuals involved in all aspects of alternative newsweeklies. Organizes roundtables and other networking opportunities for attendees and participants.

13287 ■ Association of Alternative Newsmedia Web Publishing Conference

Association of Alternative Newsmedia
1156 15th St. NW, Ste. 905
Washington, DC 20005
Ph: (202)289-8484
Fax: (202)289-2004
E-mail: web@aan.org
URL: http://www.altweeklies.com/aan/web-publishing-conference/Page

Biennial. Provides assistance to AAN publishers and editors in strategizing online presence and adapting new electronic-publishing formats and technologies.

13288 ■ Association of Writers & Writing Programs Annual Conference

Association of Writers & Writing Programs
George Mason University
MS 1E3
Fairfax, VA 22030-4444
Ph: (703)993-4301
Fax: (703)993-4302
E-mail: conference@awpwriter.org
URL: http://www.awpwriter.org

Annual. Features presentations, readings, lectures, panel discussions, and forums plus hundreds of book signings, receptions, dances, and informal gatherings. 2013 March 6-9; Boston, MA; Sheraton Hotel and Hynes Convention Center; 2014 February 26-March 1; Seattle, WA; Sheraton Seattle and Washington State Convention Center; 2015 April 8-11; Minneapolis, MN; Hilton Minneapolis and Minneapolis Convention Center; 2016 March 30-April 2; Los Angeles, CA; JW Marriott L.A. and Los Angeles Convention Center.

13289 ■ Black Writers Reunion & Conference

National Black Writers Foundation
PO Box 542711
Grand Prairie, TX 75054-2711
E-mail: conference@blackwriters.org
URL: http://www.blackwriters.org

Annual. Aims to educate, support, and motivate aspiring, emerging, and published writers.

13290 ■ National Federation of Press Women Conference

National Federation of Press Women
PO Box 5556
Arlington, VA 22205
Fax: (703)237-9808
Fr: 800-780-2715
E-mail: presswomen@aol.com
URL: http://www.nfpw.org

Annual. Features speakers as well as other activities, workshops, resources, and networking opportunities.

13291 ■ National Society of Newspaper Columnists Conference

National Society of Newspaper Columnists
PO Box 411532
San Francisco, CA 94141
Ph: (415)488-6762
Fax: (484)297-0336
E-mail: director@columnists.com
URL: http://www.columnists.com

Annual. Brings together newspaper columnists (general interest, humor, op-ed, online, etc.) for resource sharing, learning opportunities and other similar activities intending to help promote professionalism, career development, and camaraderie among newspaper columnists.

13292 ■ Online News Association Annual Conference

Online News Association
c/o Jane McDonnell, Exec. Dir.
PO Box 65741
Washington, DC 20035
Ph: (646)290-7900
E-mail: director@journalists.org
URL: http://journalists.org

Annual. Includes activities such as pre-conference workshops, job fair, online journalism awards banquet and more. 2012 September 20-22; San Francisco, CA; Hyatt Regency San Francisco.

13293 ■ Society for News Design Annual Workshop & Exhibition

Society for News Design
424 E Central Blvd., Ste. 406
Orlando, FL 32801
Ph: (407)420-7748
Fax: (407)420-7697
E-mail: snd@snd.org
URL: http://www.snd.org

Annual. Gathers visual journalists from around the world for workshops and general sessions. 2012 October 11-13; Cleveland, OH; The Plain Dealer.

13294 ■ Spring Real Estate Journalism Conference

National Association of Real Estate Editors
1003 NW 6th Terrace
Boca Raton, FL 33486
Ph: (561)391-3599
Fax: (561)391-0099
URL: http://www.naree.org

Annual. Offers professional development sessions and/or area tours.

OTHER SOURCES

13295 ■ American Medical Writers Association

30 W Gude Dr., Ste. 525
Rockville, MD 20850
Ph: (301)294-5303
Fax: (301)924-9006
E-mail: amwa@amwa.org
URL: http://www.amwa.org

Description: Consists of over 5,600 professional organization members involved in the medical communication industry. Promotes excellence in medical communication. Encourages extension of members' professional expertise through distance learning, networking opportunities (through an annual conference and chapter activities), web site services, job listings, freelance directory and the AMWA Journal.

13296 ■ American Society of Business Publication Editors (ASBPE)

214 N Hale St.
Wheaton, IL 60187
Ph: (630)510-4588
Fax: (630)510-4501
E-mail: info@asbpe.org
URL: http://www.asbpe.org

Description: Represents editors and writers working for business, trade, association, professional, technical print magazines and newsletters and Internet publications. Serves to enhance editorial standards and quality and raise the level of publication management skills of its members.

13297 ■ American Society of Magazine Editors (ASME)

810 7th Ave., 24th Fl.
New York, NY 10019
Ph: (212)872-3700
Fax: (212)906-0128
E-mail: asme@magazine.org
URL: http://www.magazine.org/asme

Description: Represents magazine editors. Spon-

sors annual editorial internship program for college juniors and the National Magazine Awards.

13298 ■ American Society of News Editors (ASNE)

11690B Sunrise Valley Dr.
Reston, VA 20191-1436
Ph: (703)453-1122
Fax: (703)453-1133
E-mail: asne@asne.org
URL: http://asne.org

Description: Consists of leaders of multimedia news organizations, deans and endowed chairs at accredited journalism schools. Focuses on open government and the First Amendment, journalism education, leadership and diversity.

13299 ■ Art Directors Club (ADC)

106 W 29th St.
New York, NY 10001
Ph: (212)643-1440
Fax: (212)643-4266
E-mail: info@adcglobal.org
URL: http://www.adcglobal.org

Description: Art directors of advertising magazines and agencies, visual information specialists, and graphic designers; associate members are artists, cinematographers, photographers, copywriters, educators, journalists, and critics. Promotes and stimulates interest in the practice of art direction. Sponsors Annual Exhibition of Advertising, Editorial and Television Art and Design; International Traveling Exhibition. Provides educational, professional, and entertainment programs; on-premise art exhibitions; portfolio review program. Conducts panels for students and faculty.

13300 ■ Asian American Journalists Association (AAJA)

5 Third St., Ste. 1108
San Francisco, CA 94103
Ph: (415)346-2051
Fax: (415)346-6343
E-mail: national@aaja.org
URL: http://www.aaja.org

Description: Serves Asian Americans and Pacific Islanders by encouraging young people to consider journalism as a career, developing managers in the media industry, and promoting fair and accurate news coverage. Serves as an alliance partner in UNITY Journalists of Color, along with the Native American Journalists Association, National Association of Hispanic Journalists, and National Association of Black Journalists.

13301 ■ Associated Press Managing Editors (APME)

450 W 33rd St.
New York, NY 10001
Ph: (212)621-1838
Fax: (212)506-6102
E-mail: apme@ap.org
URL: http://www.apme.com

Description: Represents managing editors or executives on the news or editorial staff of The Associated Press newspapers. Aims to: advance the journalism profession; examine the news and other services of the Associated Press in order to provide member newspapers with services that best suit their needs; provide a means of cooperation between the management and the editorial representatives of the members of the Associated Press. Maintains committees dealing with newspapers and news services.

13302 ■ Association of Alternative Newsmedia

1156 15th St. NW, Ste. 905
Washington, DC 20005
Ph: (202)289-8484
Fax: (202)289-2004
E-mail: web@aan.org
URL: http://www.altweeklies.com

Description: Serves as a diverse group of alt-weekly news organizations covering every major metropolitan area and other less-populated regions of North America. Encourages high-quality journalism among its members. Brings together publications that offer a valuable alternative to the mainstream media.

13303 ■ Association for Business Communication (ABC)
PO Box 6143
Nacogdoches, TX 75962-0001
Ph: (936)468-6280
Fax: (936)468-6281
E-mail: abcjohnson@sfasu.edu
URL: http://www.businesscommunication.org

Description: College teachers of business communication; management consultants in business communications; training directors and correspondence supervisors of business firms, direct mail copywriters, public relations writers, and others interested in communication for business.

13304 ■ Association of Earth Science Editors (AESE)
554 Chess St.
Pittsburgh, PA 15205-3212
E-mail: llindsay@sunbeltpub.com
URL: http://www.aese.org

Description: Editors, managing editors, and others in editorial management positions in the field of earth science publications; interested individuals. Seeks to provide efficient means for cooperation among earth science editors and to promote effective publishing of journals, reviews, monograph series, maps, abstract journals and services, indexes, micro cards, and other publications that disseminate information on the earth sciences.

13305 ■ Association of Health Care Journalists
Missouri School of Journalism
10 Neff Hall
Columbia, MO 65211
Ph: (573)884-5606
Fax: (573)884-5609
E-mail: info@healthjournalism.org
URL: http://www.healthjournalism.org

Description: Represents and supports journalists who cover health, medicine, and health care. Advances the public understanding of health care issues. Works to improve the quality, accuracy and visibility of health care reporting, writing and editing. Advocates the professional development opportunities of journalists who cover any aspect of health and health care.

13306 ■ Association of Legal Writing Directors (ALWD)
DePaul University College of Law
25 E Jackson Blvd.
Chicago, IL 60604
E-mail: sthrower@depaul.edu
URL: http://www.alwd.org

Description: Seeks to enhance the leadership skills and professional development of legal writing professionals. Supports the administration of legal writing programs. Encourages research and scholarship in, and development of, the discipline of legal writing.

13307 ■ Association Media and Publishing
1760 Old Meadow Rd., Ste. 500
McLean, VA 22102
Ph: (703)506-3285
Fax: (703)506-3266
E-mail: info@associationmediaandpublishing.org
URL: http://associationmediaandpublishing.org

Description: Assists association publishers and communications professionals. Fosters effective relationships among publishers, communications professionals, and industry providers. Develops and maintains editorial and advertising standards through excel awards and publications review program, provides members with the latest industry movements, and connects professionals with career opportunities in association publishing through its career center.

13308 ■ Association for Women in Communications (AWC)
3337 Duke St.
Alexandria, VA 22314
Ph: (703)370-7436
Fax: (703)342-4311
E-mail: info@womcom.org
URL: http://www.womcom.org

Description: Professional association of journalism and communications.

13309 ■ Association for Women in Sports Media
161 W Sylvania Ave.
Neptune City, NJ 07753
URL: http://www.awsmonline.org

Description: Comprised of women sportswriters, editors, broadcasters and media relations directors and others who are interested in sports media career. Supports and fosters advancement of women involved in sports media. Works to promote and increase diversity in sports media through its internship/scholarship programs.

13310 ■ Association of Writers and Writing Programs (AWP)
George Mason University
Mail Stop 1E3
Fairfax, VA 22030-4444
Ph: (703)993-4301
Fax: (703)993-4302
E-mail: awp@awpwriter.org
URL: http://www.awpwriter.org

Description: Writers; students and teachers in creative writing programs in university departments of English; editors, publishers, and freelance creative and professional writers. Fosters literary talent and achievement; advocates the craft of writing as primary to a liberal and humane education; provides publications and services to the makers and readers of contemporary literature. Operates career services and job listings; sponsors literary competitions.

13311 ■ Authors Guild (AG)
31 E 32nd St., 7th Fl.
New York, NY 10016
Ph: (212)563-5904
Fax: (212)564-5363
E-mail: staff@authorsguild.org
URL: http://www.authorsguild.org

Description: Professional book and magazine writers. Maintains legal staff to provide book and magazine contract reviews for members. Group health insurance available. Members of the guild are also members of the Authors League of America.

13312 ■ Authors League of America (ALA)
31 E 32nd St., 7th Fl.
New York, NY 10016
Ph: (212)563-5904
Fax: (212)564-5363
E-mail: staff@authorsguild.org
URL: http://www.authorsguild.org

Description: Serves as a professional organization of authors of books, magazine material, and plays.

13313 ■ Catholic Press Association (CPA)
205 W Monroe St., Ste. 470
Chicago, IL 60606
Ph: (312)380-6789
Fax: (312)361-0256
E-mail: cathjourn@catholicpress.org
URL: http://www.catholicpress.org

Description: Consists of Catholic writers and publishers of Catholic newspapers, magazines, newsletters and books. Maintains 25 committees, including Freedom of Information, Fair Publishing Practices Code, Catholic News Service Liaison.

13314 ■ Construction Writers Association (CWA)
PO Box 14784
Chicago, IL 60614-0784

Ph: (773)687-8726
Fax: (773)687-8627
E-mail: info@constructionwriters.org
URL: http://www.constructionwriters.org

Description: Writers and editors for media, public relations, and marketing in the construction field.

13315 ■ Council for the Advancement of Science Writing (CASW)
PO Box 910
Hedgesville, WV 25427
Ph: (304)754-6786
E-mail: diane@nasw.org
URL: http://www.casw.org

Description: Operated by a council of 19 science writers, editors, television executives, scientists, and physicians. Works to increase public understanding of science by upgrading the quality and quantity of science writing and improving the relationship between scientists and the press. Conducts seminars, workshops, and conferences; sponsors programs to train minority journalists in science and medical writing.

13316 ■ Council of Science Editors (CSE)
10200 W 44th Ave., Ste. 304
Wheat Ridge, CO 80033
Ph: (720)881-6046
E-mail: cse@councilscienceeditors.org
URL: http://www.councilscienceeditors.org

Description: Active and former editors of primary and secondary journals in the life sciences and those in scientific publishing and editing. Through study and discussion groups, panels, and committees, considers all aspects of communication in the life sciences with emphasis on publication, especially in primary journals and retrieval in secondary media.

13317 ■ Dow Jones Newspaper Fund (DJNF)
PO Box 300
Princeton, NJ 08543-0300
Ph: (609)452-2820
Fax: (609)520-5804
E-mail: djnf@dowjones.com
URL: http://www.newsfund.org

Description: Established by Dow Jones and Company, publisher of *The Wall Street Journal*, to encourage careers in journalism. Operates newspaper's editing, and Sports Copy Editing Internship Programs for all junior, senior, and graduate level college students interested in journalism. Also offers Business Reporting Intern Program for minority college sophomores and juniors to complete summer internships on daily newspapers as business reporters. Students receive monetary scholarships to return to school in the fall. Offers information on careers in journalism.

13318 ■ Editorial Freelancers Association (EFA)
71 W 23rd St., 4th Fl.
New York, NY 10010
Ph: (212)929-5400
Fax: (212)929-5439
Fr: (866)929-5439
E-mail: office@the-efa.org
URL: http://www.the-efa.org

Description: Represents persons who work full or part-time as freelance writers or editorial freelancers. Promotes professionalism and facilitates the exchange of information and support. Conducts professional training seminars; and offers job listings.

13319 ■ Education Writers Association (EWA)
2122 P St. NW, Ste. 201
Washington, DC 20037
Ph: (202)452-9830
Fax: (202)452-9837
E-mail: ewa@ewa.org
URL: http://www.ewa.org

Description: Education writers and reporters of daily and weekly newspapers, national magazines of general circulation, and radio and television stations; associate members are school and college public relations personnel and others with a serious interest in education writing. Improves the quality of education reporting and interpretation; encourages the development of education coverage by the press; to help attract top-notch writers and reporters to the education field. Sponsors regional and special workshops. Provides job referral/bank services.

13320 ■ Evangelical Press Association (EPA)
PO Box 28129
Crystal, MN 55428
Ph: (763)535-4793
Fax: (763)535-4794
E-mail: director@epassoc.org
URL: http://www.epassoc.org

Description: Editors and publishers of Christian periodicals. Maintains placement service.

13321 ■ Garden Writers Association
10210 Leatherleaf Ct.
Manassas, VA 20111
Ph: (703)257-1032
Fax: (703)257-0213
E-mail: info@gardenwriters.org
URL: http://www.gardenwriters.org

Description: Serves as a forum for professional communicators in the lawn and garden industry. Provides opportunities for education, recognition, career development and a forum for diverse interactions for professionals in the field of garden communication. Promotes respect, love and stewardship of gardening, the environment and the industry.

13322 ■ Health Science Communications Association (HeSCA)
39 Wedgewood Dr., Ste. A
Jewett City, CT 06351-2420
Ph: (860)376-5915
Fax: (860)376-6621
E-mail: hescaone@sbcglobal.net
URL: http://www.hesca.org

Description: Represents media managers, graphic artists, biomedical librarians, producers, faculty members of health science and veterinary medicine schools, health professional organizations, and industry representatives. Acts as a clearinghouse for information used by professionals engaged in health science communications. Coordinates Media Festivals Program that recognizes outstanding media productions in the health sciences. Offers placement service.

13323 ■ Horror Writers Association (HWA)
244 5th Ave., Ste. 2767
New York, NY 10001-7604
E-mail: hwa@horror.org
URL: http://www.horror.org

Description: Horror writers, including creators of comic strips, screenplays, and role-playing games, who have sold at least one work at professional rates are active members; horror writers who have sold something but not at professional rates are affiliate members. Non-writing professionals are associate members. Seeks to assist aspiring and accomplished horror writers in advancing their art and careers. Facilitates networking among members; gathers and disseminates information on horror fiction markets; serves as liaison between members and writers' agents and publishers.

13324 ■ Intercultural Alliance of Artists and Scholars (IAAS)
PO Box 4378
New York, NY 10163-4378
E-mail: maragon@theiaas.org
URL: http://theiaas.org/online

Description: Fosters understanding of, and respect for, cultural diversity through literature and media literacy. Collaborates with artists, scholars and community organizations to advance the art of writing. Promotes literary talent and achievement among artists and scholars.

13325 ■ International Association of Media Tie-in Writers (IAMTW)
PO Box 8212
Calabasas, CA 91372
E-mail: info@iamtw.org
URL: http://www.iamtw.org

Description: Enhances the professional and public image of tie-in writers. Works with the media to review tie-in novels and publicize their authors. Raises public awareness of media tie-in writers. Provides a forum for tie-in writers to share information and discuss issues related to the field of tie-in writing.

13326 ■ International Black Writers and Authors (IBWA)
PO Box 43576
Los Angeles, CA 90043
Ph: (213)964-3721
E-mail: ibwa_la@yahoo.com
URL: http://ibwa.tripod.com

Description: Seeks to discover and support new black writers. Conducts research and monthly seminars in poetry, fiction, nonfiction, music, and jazz. Provides writing services and children's services. Maintains speakers' bureau. Offers referral service. Plans to establish hall of fame, biographical archives, and museum.

13327 ■ International Society of Weekly Newspaper Editors (ISWNE)
Missouri Southern State University
Institute of International Studies
3950 E Newman Rd.
Joplin, MO 64801-1595
Ph: (417)659-4442
Fax: (417)659-4445
E-mail: stebbins-c@mssu.edu
URL: http://www.mssu.edu/iswne

Description: Represents editors and writers of editorial comment in weekly newspapers. Promotes wise and independent editorial comments, news content and leadership in community newspapers throughout the world. Facilitates the exchange of ideas and viewpoints of community editors. Helps in the development of the community newspaper press as an instrument of mutual understanding and world peace and fosters freedom of the press in all nations.

13328 ■ International Thriller Writers (ITW)
PO Box 311
Eureka, CA 95502
E-mail: membership@internationalthrillerwriters.com
URL: http://www.thrillerwriters.org

Description: Promotes suspense or thriller novels. Enhances the prestige and raises the profile of thriller writers. Provides opportunities for collegiality among authors and other industry professionals.

13329 ■ International Women's Writing Guild (IWWG)
PO Box 810
Gracie Sta.
New York, NY 10028-0082
Ph: (212)737-7536
Fax: (212)737-9469
E-mail: elizabethjulia88@aol.com
URL: http://www.iwwg.org

Description: Women writers in 24 countries interested in expressing themselves through the written word professionally and for personal growth regardless of portfolio. Seeks to empower women personally and professionally through writing. Facilitates manuscript submissions to literary agents and independent presses. Participates in international network. Maintains dental and vision program at group rates.

13330 ■ Investigative Reporters and Editors
Missouri School of Journalism
141 Neff Annex
Columbia, MO 65211
Ph: (573)882-2042

Fax: (573)882-5431
E-mail: info@ire.org
URL: http://www.ire.org

Description: Fosters excellence in investigative journalism. Provides training, resources and a community of support to investigative journalists.

13331 ■ Islamic Writers Alliance (IWA)
PO Box 27503
Tempe, AZ 85285
E-mail: director@islamicwritersalliance.net
URL: http://www.islamicwritersalliance.net

Description: Represents Muslims involved in the literary arts, including published and aspiring authors, novelists, poets, essayists, publishers, editors, illustrators, journalists, spoken word artists, and playwrights. Promotes alliance members' works to the public, both Muslim and non-Muslim, and to book distributors and retailers. Supports unpublished authors in their efforts to seek publication, and promotes their work to Islamic publishers. Promotes reading and writing of creative Islamic fiction among Muslim children.

13332 ■ Journalism & Women Symposium
3701 Drakeshire Dr.
Modesto, CA 95356
Ph: (510)764-1877
Fax: (510)764-1122
E-mail: info@jaws.org
URL: http://www.jaws.org

Description: Consists of journalists who are employed by newspapers, news services, syndicates, magazines, television or radio stations or other electronic disseminators of news and information programming, college-level teachers of journalism, and freelancers. Supports the professional empowerment and personal growth of women in journalism. Conducts camps and workshops for its members.

13333 ■ Media Alliance (MA)
1904 Franklin St., Ste. 500
Oakland, CA 94612
Ph: (510)832-9000
Fax: (510)238-8557
E-mail: information@media-alliance.org
URL: http://www.media-alliance.org

Description: Writers, photographers, editors, broadcast workers, public relations practitioners, videographers, filmmakers, commercial artists and other media workers and aspiring media workers. Supports free press and independent, alternative journalism that services progressive politics and social justice.

13334 ■ Military Writers Society of America (MWSA)
PO Box 264
Bridgeville, PA 15017
E-mail: mwsapresident@gmail.com
URL: http://www.militarywriters.com

Description: Represents authors, poets and artists who are active duty military, retirees, military veterans or non-military personnel whose works include strong military themes. Seeks to educate members on marketing and publishing their works. Facilitates exchange of information and ideas among members.

13335 ■ Mystery Writers of America (MWA)
1140 Broadway, Ste. 1507
New York, NY 10001
Ph: (212)888-8171
Fax: (212)888-8107
E-mail: mwa@mysterywriters.org
URL: http://www.mysterywriters.org

Description: Professional writers in the mystery-crime field; publishers and agents are associate members; affiliate members are writers of crime/mystery/suspense fiction who are not yet professionally published, and others with an interest in the genre.

13336 ■ National Association of Hispanic Journalists (NAHJ)
1050 Connecticut Ave. NW, 10th Fl.
Washington, DC 20036-5334
Ph: (202)662-7145
Fax: (202)662-7144
E-mail: nahj@nahj.org
URL: http://www.nahj.org

Description: Aims to organize and support Hispanics involved in news gathering and dissemination. Encourages journalism and communications study and practice by Hispanics. Seeks recognition for Hispanic members of the profession regarding their skills and achievements. Promotes fair and accurate media treatment of Hispanics; opposes job discrimination and demeaning stereotypes. Works to increase educational and career opportunities and development for Hispanics in the field. Seeks to foster greater awareness of members' cultural identity, interests, and concerns. Provides a united voice for Hispanic journalists with the aim of achieving national visibility. Offers placement services to Hispanic students. Activities include: a census of Hispanic media professionals nationwide; writing contest for Hispanic students. Offers scholarships, seminars, and training workshops.

13337 ■ National Association of Home and Workshop Writers (NAHWW)
PO Box 12
Baker, NV 89311
Fr: (866)457-2582
E-mail: geary775@mwpower.net
URL: http://www.nahww.org

Description: Writers and illustrators of materials on home maintenance and improvement projects, manual skills, woodworking, and do-it-yourself projects and techniques. Aims to promote communication among colleagues by sharing information on publishers, marketing conditions, and mutual problems.

13338 ■ National Association of Real Estate Editors
1003 NW 6th Terrace
Boca Raton, FL 33486
Ph: (561)391-3599
Fax: (561)391-0099
URL: http://www.naree.org

Description: Consists of real estate journalists. Offers opportunities for networking among its members. Provides meetings and conferences where freelance writers, columnists, and publicists visit with up to a dozen of the nation's leading real estate journalists and gather under one roof for a mini press tour.

13339 ■ National Association of Science Writers (NASW)
PO Box 7905
Berkeley, CA 94707
Ph: (510)647-9500
E-mail: director@nasw.org
URL: http://www.nasw.org

Description: Writers and editors engaged in the preparation and interpretation of science news for the public.

13340 ■ National Conference of Editorial Writers
3899 N Front St.
Harrisburg, PA 17110
Ph: (717)703-3015
Fax: (717)703-3014
E-mail: ncew@pa-news.org
URL: http://www.ncew.org

Description: Consists of professional editorial writers for newspapers or magazines of general circulation or radio or television stations, or online outlets, columnists, teachers of journalism, college students who profess a serious interest in editorial writing, and others who play an active role in editorial operations. Exists to improve the quality of editorial pages and broadcast editorials and to promote high standards among opinion writers and editors. Supports the advancement of craft of opinion journalism through education, professional development, exploration of issues of public importance and vigorous advocacy within journalism organizations.

13341 ■ National Federation of Press Women
PO Box 5556
Arlington, VA 22205
Fax: (703)237-9808
Fr: 800-780-2715
E-mail: presswomen@aol.com
URL: http://www.nfpw.org

Description: Serves as a group of professional women and men pursuing careers across the communications spectrum.

13342 ■ National Newspaper Association
PO Box 7540
Columbia, MO 65205-7540
Ph: (573)777-4980
Fax: (573)777-4985
Fr: 800-829-4662
URL: http://www.nnaweb.org

Description: Holds a membership of owners, publishers and editors of America's community newspapers. Creates a legal and regulatory environment conducive to the growth of community newspapers. Provides business and educational programs and services to improve the quality, reach, and relevance of community newspapers throughout the country.

13343 ■ National Press Club (NPC)
National Press Bldg.
529 14th St. NW, 13th Fl.
Washington, DC 20045
Ph: (202)662-7500
Fax: (202)662-7512
URL: http://www.press.org

Description: Reporters, writers and news people employed by newspapers, wire services, magazines, radio and television stations and other forms of news media. Sponsors sports, travel and cultural events, rap sessions with news figures and authors and newsmaker breakfasts and luncheons. Offers monthly training.

13344 ■ National Resume Writers' Association (NRWA)
1050 E Ray Rd., No. A5, 195
Chandler, AZ 85225
Ph: (602)788-3121
Fr: 877-843-6792
URL: http://www.nrwaweb.com

Description: Promotes high standards of excellence in resume writing through mentoring, education and support services. Represents the interests of writers, recruiters, counselors and other employment and career-related professionals.

13345 ■ National Sportscasters and Sportswriters Association (NSSA)
PO Box 1545
Salisbury, NC 28145
Ph: (704)633-4275
E-mail: dgoren@nssafame.com
URL: http://www.nssahalloffame.com

Description: Sportscasters and sportswriters. Pursues matters of common interest to members. Elects charter members to U.S. Olympic Hall of Fame.

13346 ■ National Writers Association (NWA)
10940 S Parker Rd., No. 508
Parker, CO 80134
Ph: (303)841-0246
Fax: (303)841-2607
E-mail: natlwritersassn@hotmail.com
URL: http://www.nationalwriters.com

Description: Professional full- or part-time freelance writers who specialize in business writing. Aims to serve as a marketplace whereby business editors can easily locate competent writing talent. Establishes communication among editors and writers.

13347 ■ National Writers Union (NWU)
256 W 38th St., Ste. 703
New York, NY 10018
Ph: (212)254-0279
Fax: (212)254-0673
E-mail: nwu@nwu.org
URL: http://www.nwu.org

Description: Freelance writers; journalists, authors, poets, and technical and public relations writers who are not represented by any existing union. Engages in collective bargaining and provides other services for members such as grievance handling and health insurance. Works to raise rates and improve treatment of freelance writers by magazine and book publishers. Holds conferences on legal, economic, trade, and craft issues affecting writers.

13348 ■ New York Financial Writers' Association (NYFWA)
PO Box 338
Ridgewood, NJ 07451-0338
Ph: (201)612-0100
Fax: (201)612-9915
E-mail: nyfwa@aol.com
URL: http://www.nyfwa.org

Description: Financial and business editors and reporters whose publications are located in metropolitan New York.

13349 ■ Online News Association
c/o Jane McDonnell, Exec. Dir.
PO Box 65741
Washington, DC 20035
Ph: (646)290-7900
E-mail: director@journalists.org
URL: http://journalists.org

Description: Consists of news writers, producers, designers, editors, photographers, technologists and others who produce news for the Internet or other digital delivery systems, as well as academic members and others interested in the development of online journalism. Acts as a resource for journalists seeking guidance and growth. Provides conferences, training, awards and community outreach.

13350 ■ Outdoor Writers Association of America (OWAA)
615 Oak St., Ste. 201
Missoula, MT 59801
Ph: (406)728-7434
Fax: (406)728-7445
E-mail: info@owaa.org
URL: http://www.owaa.org

Description: Professional organization of newspaper, magazine, radio, television and motion picture writers and photographers (both staff and free-lance) concerned with outdoor recreation and conservation. Conducts surveys for educational and industrial organizations; compiles market data for writer members and offers liaison aid in writer assignments.

13351 ■ Poets & Writers
90 Broad St., Ste. 2100
New York, NY 10004
Ph: (212)226-3586
Fax: (212)226-3963
E-mail: poets&writers@emailcustomerservice.com
URL: http://www.pw.org

Represents poets, fiction writers, and creative nonfiction writers. Serves as a source of information, support, and guidance for creative writers.

13352 ■ Romance Writers of America (RWA)
14615 Benfer Rd.
Houston, TX 77069
Ph: (832)717-5200
Fax: (832)717-5201
E-mail: info@rwa.org
URL: http://www.rwanational.org

Description: Writers, editors, and publishers of romance novels. Aims to support beginning, intermediate, and advanced romance writers; promotes recognition of the genre of romance writing as a serious literary form. Conducts workshops.

13353 ■ Science Fiction and Fantasy Writers of America (SFWA)
PO Box 155
Kenosha, WI 53141
E-mail: jeanr@sff.net
URL: http://www.sfwa.org

Description: Professional writers of science fiction stories, novels, radio plays, teleplays, or screenplays. Works to achieve the best working conditions possible for writers. Maintains legal fund and emergency medical fund to help members in time of need. Helps mediate between writers and publishers. Encourages public interest in science fiction literature through use of school and public library facilities; produces and disseminates science fiction literature of high quality. Conducts discussions, lectures, and seminars. Maintains speakers' bureau.

13354 ■ Smart Women's Institute of Entrepreneurial Learning
24165 IH-10 W, Ste. 217-637
San Antonio, TX 78257
Fax: (866)821-5829
Fr: (866)821-5829
E-mail: info@smartwomeninstitute.com
URL: http://www.smartwomeninstitute.com

Description: Works to empower women to achieve financial independence by learning how to leverage their time, money, and expertise exponentially.

13355 ■ Society of American Business Editors and Writers (SABEW)
555 N Central Ave., Ste. 416
Phoenix, AZ 85004-1248
Ph: (602)496-7862
Fax: (602)496-7041
E-mail: sabew@sabew.org
URL: http://sabew.org

Description: Active business, economic, and financial news writers and editors for newspapers, magazines, and other publications; broadcasters of business news; teachers of business or journalism at colleges and universities. Plans periodic seminars on problems and techniques in business news coverage and occasional special meetings with business, financial, government and labor leaders, and other experts. Maintains the Resume Bank, a service that keeps resumes of members on file; editors looking for job candidates can request the resumes of candidates that meet their requirements.

13356 ■ Society of Features Journalism
University of Maryland
1100 Knight Hall
College Park, MD 20742
Ph: (301)314-2631
E-mail: merrileesfj@gmail.com
URL: http://featuresjournalism.org

Description: Represents Sunday and Feature editors from United States and Canada dedicated to the quality of features in newspapers and the craft of feature writing.

13357 ■ Society for News Design
424 E Central Blvd., Ste. 406
Orlando, FL 32801
Ph: (407)420-7748
Fax: (407)420-7697
E-mail: snd@snd.org
URL: http://www.snd.org

Description: Comprised of editors, designers, graphic artists, publishers, illustrators, art directors, photographers, advertising artists, website designers, students and faculty. Encourages high standards of journalism through design. Serves as a forum and resource for all those interested in news design.

13358 ■ Society of Professional Journalists (SPJ)
Eugene S. Pulliam National Journalism Center
3909 N Meridian St.
Indianapolis, IN 46208
Ph: (317)927-8000
Fax: (317)920-4789
E-mail: hlimor@wcpo.com
URL: http://www.spj.org

Description: Professional society - journalism.

Promotes a free and unfettered press; high professional standards and ethical behavior; journalism as a career. Conducts lobbying activities; maintains legal defense fund. Sponsors Pulliam/Kilgore Freedom of Information Internships in Washington, DC, and Indianapolis, IN. Holds forums on the free press.

13359 ■ Society for Technical Communication (STC)
9401 Lee Hwy., Ste. 300
Fairfax, VA 22031
Ph: (703)522-4114
Fax: (703)522-2075
E-mail: stc@stc.org
URL: http://www.stc.org

Description: Writers, editors, educators, scientists, engineers, artists, publishers, and others professionally engaged in or interested in the field of technical communication; companies, corporations, organizations and agencies interested in the aims of the society. Seeks to advance the theory and practice of technical communication in all media. Sponsors high school writing contests.

13360 ■ Western Writers of America (WWA)
1665 E Julio St.
Sandy, UT 84093
Ph: (505)277-5234
E-mail: wwa@unm.edu
URL: http://www.westernwriters.org

Description: Represents freelance writers of Western fiction and nonfiction, editors, literary agents, historians, romance writers, screenplay and scriptwriters, and journalists. Sponsors competitions; maintains speakers' bureau, hall of fame, and library.

13361 ■ Women's National Book Association (WNBA)
PO Box 237
New York, NY 10150-0231
Ph: (212)208-4629
Fax: (212)208-4629
E-mail: publicity@bookbuzz.com
URL: http://www.wnba-books.org

Description: Women and men who work with and value books. Exists to promote reading and to support the role of women in the book community.

CPSIA information can be obtained
at www.ICGtesting.com
Printed in the USA
FFOW032140310113
803FF